S0-BBX-964

THE NEW COLLEGE PHYSICS
A Spiral Approach

THE NEW

A SERIES OF BOOKS IN PHYSICS

Editors: Henry M. Foley, Malvin A. Ruderman

COLLEGE PHYSICS
A Spiral Approach

ALBERT V. BAEZ

W. H. FREEMAN AND COMPANY   *San Francisco and London*

© Copyright 1967 by W. H. Freeman and Company

The publisher reserves all rights to reproduce this book,
in whole or in part, with the exception of the right
to use short quotations for review of the book.

Library of Congress Catalog Card Number: 67-12180

Printed in the United States of America

3 4 5 6 7 8 9 10

To my wife, JOAN

and to my daughters, PAULINE, JOAN, and MIMI

Preface

The main feature of this book is its *spiral approach*, which I have described in some detail in the Foreword to the Student. The method is to take up the important concepts of physics repeatedly, treating them in greater depth, or in broader scope, at each successive encounter. This procedure is, of course, not new in teaching, for all teachers use it; but no other physics textbook that I know of is written in this way.

An understanding of concepts requires, however, much more than the ability to recite the associated words and their dictionary definitions. It is necessary to study, and preferably to experience, the *operations* that give meaning to the words. My method is to start with a word ("energy," let us say) as it is used in everyday speech and then, with illustrations, experiments, and problems, to reinforce those aspects of its meaning that accord with the correct physical meaning. Numerous examples—and even some non-examples—clarify each concept and test the student's ability to distinguish between subtle shades of meaning. The formal mathematical definition comes last, after its significance has already been sensed intuitively.

A corollary advantage of the spiral approach is that it permits us to begin with some simple experiments—experiments involving topics (wave motion and light, for example) that do not seem so forbidding as the subtle—and, for many students, elusive—topic of dynamics. Practice in the setting up and solving of problems, in measurement, and in the manipulation of laboratory apparatus can thus precede the study of dynamics. The spirit of inquiry can be aroused and the sense of discovery can be achieved, after all, by optics and elementary electricity.

This book was designed for a full-year course meeting three times a week at lectures and once a week in the laboratory. I intended to keep each chapter short enough to make a reading assignment for one lecture, but I did not succeed with every chapter. Still, the total number of chapters, fifty-nine, gives only two per week for two semesters of fifteen weeks each. In my own lectures I used a great deal of demonstration material. I found, therefore, that I needed two lectures per week for demonstrations and exposition and one for theory and problem-solving. I counted on the weekly laboratory work to enhance the operational significance of the theoretical concepts.

The book was written for non-specialists, for college students who do not intend to major in physics or engineering. This group includes pre-medical students and those who will major in biological sciences or the liberal arts. The book was written, in short, for the professional men and women of the future—physicians, lawyers, writers, teachers, businessmen, politicians, and statesmen, for whom a course based on this book would be their first, and perhaps their last, college course in physics. It should also be useful to serious persons who are not enrolled in any physics course but who seek at least a partial answer to the question "What is physics all about?"

I once facetiously referred to the contents of the book (and to Part I in particular) as "the physics every senator should know." Since our fate is, and will be, to a certain extent, under the control of non-scientists holding high political office and making decisions about such serious matters as the proper use of nuclear energy, in controlled or explosive form, we must hope that they will come to understand the basic physical principles, the historical setting in which those principles evolved, the liberating effect of scientific knowledge in general, and the great power and beauty of physics in particular.

High-school algebra and geometry are prerequisites for a course based on this book. High-school physics, however, is not; nor are trigonometry, analytic geometry, and vectors, for these are developed as they are needed. Students who have already taken a course equivalent to that of the PSSC should be able to go through Part I very quickly; this is preferable to omitting it completely, for the treatment in subsequent parts depends upon the terminology of Part I and upon the concepts treated descriptively and carefully there.

Most books at this level avoid the differential and integral calculus, and this book is no exception. Through the use of the difference quotient, however, I lead the student to the brink of the calculus. Although I use some of the basic ideas, such as "limit" and "exact rate of change," I avoid the notation and terminology of the calculus, for some students are frightened by them. The student who decides later to study the calculus will find that he has a good introduction to its fundamentals. These are presented in a philosophical and historical setting that will enable liberal-arts students to appreciate the calculus as an intellectual achievement. I found it challenging to lead such students to a share in the excitement of the calculus without demanding extensive practice in its manipulations.

A knowledge of mathematics would help considerably in the manipulations required for the quantitative results needed by the physicist and engineer, and I do not hide that fact. I strive, however, to make the physical idea come alive without leaning on mathematical formalism. One example is the treatment of the interdependence of the electric and magnetic fields associated with Maxwell's equations. Though I treat those equations only in an approximate way, I am able to show, by an argument that is almost completely physical, that all electromagnetic waves travel at the speed of light.

In choosing topics for this book I have used as broad guidelines, in addition to the unifying picture of the Bohr atom, the principles of the conservation of energy and momentum, the nature of waves and their ultimate importance in atomic physics, and the electrical nature of matter and light. Much of the subject matter included in the traditional compartments—mechanics, heat, light, sound, electricity—is included here; but the emphasis is different: the material is weighted so that it favors an understanding of the ideas needed in Bohr's theory of the hydrogen atom. Strong emphasis is given, for example, to particle dynamics, vibrations and waves, and the electromagnetic character of light, but a very light treatment is given to such topics as statics, calorimetry, thermodynamics, and the theory of electric circuits.

Logically, kinematics and dynamics should be treated first, but anyone who has tried to teach Newton's laws of motion early in the course knows how difficult it is to keep them interesting. The reason is obvious: the laws of motion are abstractions. They must, therefore, be abundantly illustrated. The student must have a certain maturity, moreover, if he is to assimilate them. To the beginner they often seem trivial, uninteresting, and unimportant, for their deeper meanings and implications reveal themselves slowly.

Part I: Throughout this part (although the chapter titles do not suggest it) the mathematical tools needed for the rest of the book are developed gradually. The instructor using the spiral approach for the first time should remember that *Part I must move along at a rather brisk pace* even if the student gets the feeling that the treatment is sketchy. The student must be assured, however, that at least a few of the topics will be taken up for detailed study later. For the time being he is on the top of a mountain, looking down at the woods and streams in the valleys and deciding which he will explore. Meanwhile he must cover two chapters a week in order to stay on schedule.

Part II: Vibrations and waves, whether those of sound, light, or other wave phenomena, are here treated more or less on an equal footing. The book has no separate section on sound.

Part III, on dynamics: The relations among force, mass, and motion are studied quantitatively. The highlights here are Newton's laws of motion and gravitation.

Part IV: As Newton is the hero of Part III, so Maxwell is the hero here. The classical concepts of electricity are evolved with a view to linking electricity and magnetism with light. The high point is the association of light with Maxwell's electromagnetic waves. Electric current in wires is treated, from the first, as a flow of electrons.

Part V: Bohr is now the hero. The high point of this part is also the high point of the book: Bohr's theory of the hydrogen atom. A great deal of what has preceded is shown to play a role in Bohr's theory. Although, according to modern wave mechanics, Bohr's picture is incorrect, the student can learn so much good physics by trying to understand what Bohr did, and the resulting picture is so vivid and fruitful, that it seems doubtful if Bohr's theory will ever cease to be taught.

Part VI: In this introduction to nuclear physics the ideas that were successful in explaining the atom are applied to the nucleus itself. This part will probably be considered optional by some instructors, and it may be omitted without serious loss. It is the only part in which very modern developments are discussed, however, and the instructor may therefore wish to choose at least a few topics from it. It is also the only part in which the social and economic implications of nuclear technology are discussed and in which the social responsibility of scientists, and the scientific responsibility of laymen, are stressed. It should probably not be omitted if the instructor feels some concern about communicating these ideas along with the facts and principles of physics. Believing that physics, in the middle of the twentieth century, should be a part of every liberal education, I have not hesitated to consider—briefly—some topics of mainly philosophical or historical interest.

A natural question to put to the author of such a book as this is: "What that a student was not able to do before studying the book should he be able to do afterward?" Since the development of the ideas that lead to Bohr's theory of the hydrogen atom is the core of the book, it is fairly easy to state my expectations.

The student should certainly be able, at the end of the course, to derive Bohr's formula for the energy levels of the hydrogen spectrum. That alone is fairly simple, for the derivation takes only a couple of pages. I also expect the student to prove that he understands all the physical concepts that enter into the derivation. That is asking a good deal more, but it is still not enough. I expect him also to be able to perform—or at least to describe—experiments that illustrate *operationally* the meaning of each of those concepts. Even that ability, however, does not demonstrate a complete understanding of Bohr's theory; I therefore expect the student to know why Bohr's theory is now considered wrong and yet be able to defend its presentation in an elementary course.

So far my expectations. My hopes go higher: I want the student to see the development of physics in historical perspective, to sense the human qualities of some of the great physicists, and to recognize the social responsibility that is borne, today, by all scientists.

If I am demanding too much, I should take less for a mere pass. If a student has read the whole book, has done about half of the problems, and is able to derive the formula for Bohr's hydrogen atom, I should give him a passing grade.

Even of such a student I should hope that I had fired his imagination and curiosity enough to ensure that he would always be interested in the world that is real and stimulating to the physicist. Some of my students, in the past, were so greatly excited by the calculus—or relativity theory or quantum mechanics—that they continued later, with or without formal guidance, to pursue the study of the subject that had aroused them. A number of such students, moreover, became friends of mine. The development of such personal relations has always been important to me. I have felt a special responsibility when I considered that for many students this was not only the first but the last physics course they would ever take, and that I was the only physicist with whom they would ever have close contact. Some of the humanistic and philosophical overtones of the book had their origin in this personal intercourse.

I am deeply indebted to Professor Paul Kirkpatrick of Stanford University for many years of guidance and inspiration in both research and teaching and for the encouragement he gave me while I was writing this book. He read the entire manuscript, caught many errors, and suggested many improvements. To Professor Robert Ward I am indebted for testing a preliminary version by teaching from it at Scripps College. The clarity of many passages and the order of presentation of topics have been improved with his help. Ray Helmke of Harvey Mudd College spent a summer helping me invent the problems that follow the chapters. To Professor Jack Goldstein of Brandeis University I am indebted for his help on all of Part VI and in particular for extensive modifications of the last chapter, which deals with the particles and fields of modern physics—a topic on which I needed much help. I am pleased to thank President Joseph Platt of Harvey Mudd College for reducing my teaching load while I worked on the book. My writing benefited from contacts with the stream of knowledgeable enthusiasts whom I met in the early days of the PSSC. My wife, Joan, helped transcribe the first set of lectures tape-recorded at Stanford. So many faithful secretaries all the way from California to Paris have helped me that I must refrain from naming them all as I thank them, or this paragraph would become unbelievably long.

Paris, January 1967   ALBERT V. BAEZ

Foreword to the Student

The order in which physical concepts are presented in this book is quite unusual. You may visualize it as a spiral. Imagine the important concepts of physics—such as space, time, matter, motion, energy, electricity, wave, particle, light, atom—as occupying the sectors between the spokes of a wheel. Your progress through the concepts will follow a spiral—starting in one sector, moving into the next and then the next, and, after completing the first round, returning to each sector again and again in an ever broadening spiral.

Take the concept of matter as an example. I can't say all there is to say about it when I introduce it; its many subtle implications can be learned only gradually. By following the spiral approach you will encounter the concept again and again, and each time with greater understanding; at each successive encounter you may explore it more thoroughly and, if necessary, with more refined mathematical tools.

It is not important in which sector you start, but it is important to tackle certain concepts again and again. Occasionally, perhaps, you may leave the spiral for a direct route.

You may go through Part I rather rapidly; it takes you round the first turn of the spiral. The treatment may strike you as light, even inadequate. Rest assured, however, that you are laying a good foundation for a more concise and mathematical treatment in the following chapters.

Contents

III. FORCE AND MOTION

VI. ELEMENTARY CONCEPTS OF NUCLEAR PHYSICS

APPENDIXES

INDEX

SYMBOLS AND ABBREVIATIONS

Latin Alphabet

a	acceleration
A	angstrom
A	amplitude
	area
	mass number
	Wien displacement constant
amp	ampere
atm	atmosphere
B	magnetic induction
Bev	billion electron volts
Btu	British thermal unit
c	speed of light
C	Celsius [°C = degree(s) Celsius]
C	capacitance
cal	calorie
CGS	centimeter-gram-second
cm	centimeter
coul	coulomb
d	displacement
D	deviation
e	electronic charge
	2.718 (base of the natural logarithms)
E	energy
E	electric field intensity
ε	electromotive force
ev	electron volt
f	focal length
F	Fahrenheit [°F = degree(s) Fahrenheit]
F	force
FR	frame of reference
ft	foot
g	acceleration due to gravity
G	gravitational constant
gal	gallon
gm	gram
h	hour
h	height
	Planck constant
hp	horsepower
i	electric current (electrons)
	image distance
I	electric current (positive)
	rotational inertia
in.	inch

j	electric-current density
J	joule
J	mechanical equivalent of heat
k	Boltzmann constant
	a constant
	radioactive-decay constant
K	Kelvin (absolute) temperature [°K = degree(s) Kelvin]
K	constant of proportionality in Coulomb's law
	kinetic energy
KE	kinetic energy
kg	kilogram
km	kilometer
kt	kiloton
kWh	kilowatt hour
l	angular-momentum quantum number
	length
L	inductance
	length
lb	pound
m	meter
m	magnetic quantum number
	mass
M	atomic mass
Mev	million electron volts
mi	mile
min	minute
MKS	meter-kilogram-second
mm	millimeter
mph	miles per hour
n	index of refraction
	integer
	neutron
	principal quantum number
N	number of molecules in an arbitrary sample
N_A	Avogadro constant
nt	newton
o	object distance
p	pressure
	proton
p	electric dipole moment
	linear momentum
P	power
	pressure

PE	potential energy		T	period
q	electric charge			temperature
Q	disintegration energy		u	unified atomic mass unit
	electric charge		U	internal energy
	heat energy			potential energy
r	radius		v	speed
r	displacement		**v**	velocity
R	resistance		V	volt
	Rydberg constant		V	electric potential, voltage
rad	radian			volume
rev	revolution		W	watt
rms	root-mean-square		W	work, energy
s	distance		x	distance
	specific heat			variable
	spin quantum number		yd	yard
sec	second		yr	year
t	temperature		z	valence
	time		Z	atomic number

Greek Alphabet
(in alphabetical order of English names of letters)

alpha	α	alpha particle			angular speed
	α	angular acceleration		ω	angular velocity
beta	β	beta particle	phi	ϕ	angle
delta	Δ	change in, small part of		Φ	flux
epsilon	ϵ	small quantity	pi	π	3.1416, the ratio of a circle's circumference
gamma	γ	gamma ray			to its diameter
		photon	rho	ρ	mass density
	γ	gravitational field intensity			resistivity
lambda	λ	wavelength	sigma	σ	conductivity
mu	μ	1/1,000,000 of			Stefan-Boltzmann constant
	μ	magnetic dipole moment		Σ	sum of
nu	ν	frequency	tau	τ	torque
omega	ω	angular frequency	theta	θ	angle

I

THE CONCEPTS
AND LANGUAGE
OF PHYSICS

Le Château des Pyrénées
From a painting by René Magritte, who wrote to the author of this book in 1963: "I seek to paint only images that evoke the mystery of the world." (Photograph from the Collection Harry Torczyner, New York.)

There is something arresting about a rock hovering in midair. It almost forces you to ask, "Why doesn't it fall?" But did you ever ask yourself a more obvious question: "Why *does* a rock fall?" Great physicists from Newton to Einstein have been curious about commonplace events. Their theories of space, time, and matter, for example, began with such simple questions as "Why does an apple fall?" and "Why does a magnet pull?" and "What makes a wave move on and on?" A sense of *wonder* has been characteristic of many artists and scientists. A mood of wonder is a proper one in which to begin the study of physics.

Introduction

IT IS customary to begin a textbook in physics by telling what physics is about. Very well, let us begin in that way. *Physics is a study of space, time, matter, motion, and energy.* Now what can you learn from a statement like that? You have certainly heard the words before, for they are ordinary English words and are used all the time by people who are not physicists; but do they have precise meanings for you? Not unless you have learned to use them in a special way, in the way that physicists call *operational*. Those words, and all the other words used by physicists, take on meaning only as we operate with them—that is, as we do something with them or do something about them. By the time we reach Chapter 12 you will have had some operational experience in the laboratory, and then I shall try to answer directly, in a few words, the question "What is physics?" For the present I shall try in other ways to show what physics is about.

It's like trying to explain what baseball is all about to a girl who has never seen a game. She has no doubt heard terms like "home run," "steal a base," and "triple play," but she has only vague notions of their meaning. Verbal explanations alone, we soon find, are inadequate. We therefore decide to take her to a ball game, where she can *see* and *hear* what "bases loaded," "hit," and other terms mean. The one game is not, of course, enough; it leaves her with a few new words in her vocabulary, a clear notion of what a bat and a ball look like, but very fuzzy notions about the subleties of the game.

A third method—perhaps the best—is to take her out to a sandlot where some boys are playing ball and ask them to let you both join the game. Your apprentice can now handle a bat, hit (or miss) a ball, and (maybe) run for a base. This comes closest to being the *operational approach.* After many experiences of this sort she may even be able to answer for herself the deeper question "Why does one play baseball?"

Now some people have argued that this is what we have to do with physics too. They say: "Never mind wordy definitions of what physics is; *physics is what physicists do.* If you want to know what physics is, you'd better see what some physicists are doing." This may be analogous to watching a ball game without taking part in it; still, it is a way of getting started. Let's see what some physicists are doing. Let's go on an imaginary visit to three real laboratories.

1.1. What Physicists Do

We visit first the W. W. Hansen Laboratories at Stanford University. Near them a tunnel two miles long is nearing completion. The public-relations officer is holding a press conference, and we listen to that instead of trying to find one of the scientists to answer our questions.

QUESTION: What are you going to do in this tunnel?
ANSWER: We're building a linear accelerator.
Q: What are you going to accelerate?
A: Electrons.
Q: What are electrons?
A: They are the basic particles of electricity.

Q: How are you going to accelerate them?

A: We'll use a combination of magnetic and electric fields to push them along. They'll wind up at the other end doing better than 99 percent of the speed of light.

Q: Why do you want to accelerate them?

A: We want to bombard things with them at the other end.

Q: What for?

A: This will help us learn something about the properties of atoms and about their innermost parts, called nuclei.

Q: Why does anyone want to know about atoms and nuclei?

But that last, you see, is not a fair question to ask a public-relations officer. It's a difficult question like "Why does anybody play baseball?" We are not yet in a position to consider such questions. We observe, however, that playing baseball and building linear accelerators are both human activities: both seem to evoke the intense interest of people—certain kinds of people.

Let's try another visit. This time we are at the Space Technology Laboratories in Los Angeles (California). A young physicist takes us into the room where he is doing his experiments. We see a huge bank of large black boxes.

Q: What's that?

A: It's a large condenser bank.

Q: What do you condense?

A: Well, "condense" is probably not the right word. They store electrical charges.

Q: You mean electrons?

A: Yes.

Q: You mean you can dump electrons into something like a big box the way you pour water into a pail?

A: Yes, something like that. It is more like storing air molecules in a tank under pressure.

Q: In the last lab I visited they were trying to push electrons along very fast, and here you seem to want to store them.

A: Yes, but only to release them at the right time with a great push.

Q: What will you do with them then?

A: We'll send them through a conductor and produce a momentary but strong magnetic field.

Q: You mean like the magnetic field of the earth?

A: Yes, something like it, only about 10 million times stronger.

Q: What will that do?

A: It will produce what we call a *pinch effect*. It will cause charged particles to suddenly get close to one another, very close to one another.

Q: And what will that do?

A: It will raise their temperature to about 5 million degrees.

Q: How can you hold anything that hot? Won't everything melt?

A: That's the problem. You can't contain particles at such high temperatures except by magnetic fields.

Q: And why are you doing all this?

A: Well, we want to see if we can produce the nuclear process called fusion.

Q: I don't know what that is, but why are you interested in doing that?

A: Because, among other things, we think it is fusion that is responsible for the tremendous amount of energy that comes from the sun, and we would like to understand it.

Q: Is this space research?

A: Yes, you could call it that.

Let's try one more. The first was a university research center, the second an organization that gets most of its funds from the Air Force. Our inquisitive visitor might have asked why the Air Force is sponsoring this kind of research, but I said we were going to leave the difficult questions until later. Let's take one more sample, remembering that this could go on for months without our ever really getting a true picture of all the kinds of things that physicists do.

We are at the RCA Research Center at Princeton (New Jersey). It is very near an active university, and our questioner might well begin by asking whether there is any relation between the university and the industrial laboratories. A large group of people is standing in front of a tremendous bank of electronic gear—huge rectangular boxes with lots of dials, oscilloscopes, and radio receiving equipment. Periodically a signal appears on an oscilloscope, and a corresponding noise comes out of a loudspeaker.

Q: What's going on?

A: The weather satellite TIROS is about to make a pass.

Q: At whom or what? What kind of pass?

A: It is about to pass over a nearby receiving station that feeds us the electrical signals coming from it.

Q: What does TIROS stand for?

A: Television Infra-Red Observational Satellite.

Q: Are you a physicist?

A: No, I am an electrical engineer.

Q: But you know quite a bit about physics?

A: I know a little about electricity.

Q: Are physicists involved in this project?

A: Oh, yes. There are ten physics Ph.D.'s in this laboratory. They guide and direct a great deal of the work that is going on.

Q: What does the satellite do?

A: It is about a hundred miles above the surface of the earth and looks down with TV cameras. The pictures are stored electrically on special tape recorders in the satellite, and the recorders send the signals down to earth by command from us when they are about to make a pass over our receiving station.

Q: And what do you do with those signals?

A: We store them here on another tape recorder.

Q: Is that all? What good are they there?

A: They're no good until we take them off this tape recorder at our leisure and translate them into a picture, like this one.

Q: What is that funny, wiggly pattern in the pictures?

A: It is the Nile River [Fig. 1.1], and this other is a huge cloud formation over an area about 2,000 miles in diameter.

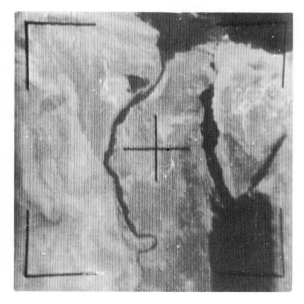

FIG. 1.1. *The Red Sea, the Nile River and Delta, the Suez Canal, and part of the Mediterranean Sea, as recorded by the TIROS V satellite during its sixteenth orbit round the earth and received at the TIROS Ground Station (Point Mugu, California) of the National Aeronautics and Space Administration (NASA).*

Q: Is this what you are after?

A: It's part of what the Weather Bureau is after.

These imaginary interviews give us some glimpses of what physicists do. We could learn many of the words that they use, some of them over and over again, like "electron," "field," and "energy," but it should be obvious by now that this is not the way we are going to learn what physics is. At least it is not the only way. We are going to have to get actively involved, *operationally* involved, before long.

I said earlier that, to learn to play baseball, or even to understand why people play baseball, you have to handle a baseball and a bat. In a similar way, to learn about physics, you will have to get into the laboratory and handle some of the physicist's tools. But physics is so broad and so deep, and it includes and involves so many things, that it is possible to spend many years taking many courses and doing many experiments, and still fail to find the time to ask, "Why do we do this?" or "What is it all about?" or "What are we after?" This book is a very elementary introduction to the concepts of physics, but we shall pause occasionally to question—to examine our methods and even the purpose behind what we are doing. Many of the activities of the physicist differ from the normal activities of men only in degree, and to the extent that we question and observe and experiment and test and correlate and theorize about anything, especially about any physical event, we are behaving like physicists.

1.2. Particles and Waves

Suppose, for example, that you are at the edge of a well on a dark and moonless night. You want to know whether there is any water in the well, and, if so, how deep that water is, and how far down its surface is. You have no training in physics. How do you get started?

Let us suppose that you are lucky enough to have brought along a string that you can tie round a stone. You let the stone down until you hear it touch the water, and then you let it down still farther until the string slackens and you feel pretty certain that the stone is resting on the ground beneath the water. You tie a knot in your string and then pull it up, measuring against the length of your arm, counting the number of arm's lengths until you reach the wet part of the string, and you continue doing this to measure the wet part. Now you know that there is water in the well, and you also know the answer to your other questions, at least roughly: you know how far down it is to the water and how deep the water is. This is a simple physical problem involving a measurement of length, and you got an approximate answer to your question rather quickly.

Suppose, however, that you have no string. What will you do? You may try dropping a pebble and listening for the splash. Remember now, you can't see a thing, but you drop the pebble, and you do hear a splash. If you do this several times, you may even estimate the length of time it takes for you to hear the splash. This can give you a rough idea of the distance to the water, and perhaps you sense intuitively that someone with more training in physics could measure the time accurately and deduce an accurate measure of the depth. You don't know how deep the water is, but you got a rough answer to one of your questions. And you did intuitively something that even the most sophisticated physicists are doing with their accelerating machines: you threw a particle at something, and from the interaction of the two you drew a conclusion. I am using the word "particle" rather loosely for the pebble.

If you have no pebble or other particle to throw down the well, you may try simply yelling into it, and from the echo received you may deduce that the water surface is very near or very far. And, of course, if you have a flashlight, you can turn it on and look down. You may see the reflection of your flashlight in the water and thus get an answer to one of your questions.

Is this a problem in physics? It is indeed. It is a simple one, and I have shown how to get approximate answers, but you can see very well how each answer could be refined if necessary. The problem involved the concepts of space, time, matter, and motion, and it exemplified two methods of probing nature that are commonly applied in problems from the simplest to the most sophisticated: the use of *particles* and *waves* as probes. The pebble

was an example of the particle, and the sound and the light were examples of waves. It is because we can use them to extract information from nature, and, indeed, because they are part of nature themselves, that particles and waves are important. Let's see how these ideas apply to some of the problems of modern physics.

Some physicists, along with the astronomers, are curious about the origin of the energy that comes to us from the sun and also about the physical make-up of the planets and other heavenly bodies. What we now call science evolved— in part, at least—from questions about the planets—questions asked by early investigators like Galileo and Newton: How do the planets move? What holds them in their courses? How far away are they? How did they come into existence? What are they made of? These questions of astronomy were alive when science was young, and today they are again of great importance. For centuries the light of the sun, coming to us directly or bouncing off the moon and the planets, has acted as the wave that carried information to us through our telescopes. But today man himself can generate waves (radar and laser) on the earth, send them out into space, and bounce them not only off the moon but even, with radar, off the corona of the sun, 93 million miles away, We are, indeed, tossing out waves and getting information from the way they bounce off matter. How about particles? The missiles and rockets that have been shot from the surface of the earth are, by comparison with the size of the earth, certainly particles. They are being sent out to sample the electric, magnetic, and gravitational fields that lie round the earth, in the planetary system, and, it may be, far out in interstellar space. The word "particle" is going to have a pretty flexible meaning, for in some cases even the moon will be treated as a particle when we consider its motion round the earth.

Usually, however, we reserve the word "particle" for something very, very small. Among the smallest particles are the atoms, and smaller still are the atomic constituents called nuclei. One way to study the properties of matter is to bombard it with particles. The huge accelerating machines— cyclotrons, bevatrons, linear accelerators—accel-

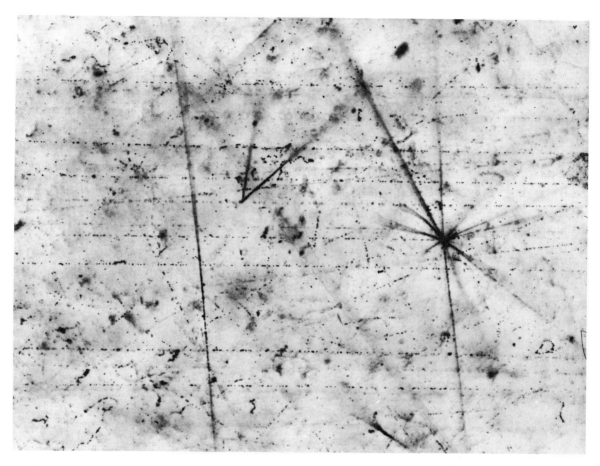

FIG. 1.2. *Photographic emulsion exposed to billion-volt protons: The dotted lines, horizontal and parallel, were made by protons. The radial cluster of heavy lines at the right was produced when an incoming proton knocked ten or more particles out of the nucleus of an atom (such as bromine or silver). The heavy* **V** *to the left was produced when an incoming proton knocked two heavy particles out of a nucleus. (From the Brookhaven National Laboratory.)*

erate particles to such high speeds that their collision with the nucleus of an atom can yield new fragments and perhaps new information. Such collisions are pictured in Figure 1.2. The particles involved here have dimensions measured in millionths of a millionth of an inch. Within the greater atomic distances (hundredths of a millionth of an inch) waves also are extremely useful in giving us information. When x-rays (so called even though they are waves) are allowed to hit a crystal, they bounce off in a symmetrical way, producing pictures like Figure 1.3; and from pictures of this sort one can get information about the arrangement of atoms within a crystal. Our hypothetical problem of the well, we see, has introduced us to the two kind of probes, particles and waves, that are used at both extremes of the universe, the astronomical and the nuclear.

Observation is the first important step in any kind of scientific investigation, but only if we measure and count and can express the results of our observations in numbers do they have the precision that we usually associate with scientific knowledge. We want to answer such questions as "How far away is the planet Pluto?" and "What is the mass of the sun?" and "How fast does light travel?" and "How many fundamental particles are there in a pound of lead?" In order to answer such *quantitative* questions, we shall, of course, need to use mathematics. Let us examine four mathematical concepts—constant, variable, function, and sequence—as illustrations of the natural relationship between mathematics and physics.

1.3. Constants

If the temperature in a room does not change, we say that it is constant. If it does change, we say that it is variable. Since physical quantities like temperature can be associated with a number on a scale and with a symbol, such as t, the mathematical definition of "constant" or "variable" is

FIG. 1.3. *Interaction between waves and particles: The waves in this case are x-rays. The particles are the atoms of a single ice crystal. A single beam of x-rays is spread out into this symmetrical pattern by the orderly array of atoms in the crystal. (Photograph by I. Fankuchen of the Polytechnic Institute of Brooklyn.)*

usually expressed in terms of the symbol rather than of the physical quantity.

In a mathematics book, for example, you may find a definition like the following: A **constant** is a symbol that may assume only one numerical value during the given discussion. The symbols 1, 2, 3, 4, etc., are constants, for each represents a fixed whole number. The first letters of the alphabet, a, b, c, etc., are often used as symbols for constants. The Greek letter π is a constant with a special geometrical meaning. It stands for the ratio of circumference to diameter in a circle. In elementary school you learned that $\pi = 22/7$, but this is only approximately true. In high school you learned that $\pi = 3.1416$; this is also an approximation but is better than 22/7. The fact that π is a constant regardless of the size of the circle may be proved mathematically, but let us consider the problem physically.

Given a waste-paper basket with a circular base, we might seek an experimental value of π by measuring its circumference and its diameter and taking their ratio. Here are the values obtained with a crude cloth tape-measure whose smallest subdivision was a quarter of an inch:

$$C = 32 \text{ inches}$$
$$D = 10\tfrac{1}{4} \text{ inches}$$

This yields

$$\frac{C}{D} = \frac{32 \text{ in.}}{10\tfrac{1}{4} \text{ in.}} = \frac{128}{41} = 3.12$$

The ratio is said to be a pure number because the unit of length, being the same in both numerator (C) and denominator (D), canceled out. Notice that units cancel out like numbers.

This answer raises a lot of questions: Have we hereby shown experimentally that π is equal to 3.12? Why did we round off the answer (which was 3.1219 . . .) to three figures? Could errors have crept into our measurements? Could we have minimized our errors even with the same measuring tape? How? Could you ever prove experimentally that $C/D = 3.1416$ . . . (the accepted value)? How can the mathematician compute π to 100 decimal places? Can you prove experimentally that C/D is a constant for all circles?

I have raised many more questions than I can answer at present, but I have already shown how the concept of a constant may arise in physics. For the time being I assert that the ratio of circumference to diameter *is* a constant for all circles but that experiment can only suggest this, not prove it. Many geometrical truths were probably first suggested by physical measurements.

As an example of another kind of constant consider *g*. Physicists often speak of the acceleration due to gravity as a constant with the numerical value 9.80 m/sec²; but, if we press them, we discover that they mean that over a small region of space (for example, within the bounds of a certain laboratory) all freely falling bodies will pick up an increment of speed equal to 9.80 m/sec every second. If you went to a laboratory at the North Pole, however, the value of *g* would be more nearly 9.83 m/sec²; and, if you measured *g* at the equator, the experimental value would come closer to 9.78 m/sec². There are also variations in *g* with height above sea level. What does all this mean? Is *g* a constant? In the strict mathematical sense, obviously not. Yet for many experiments and *to a certain degree of accuracy* it is not far wrong to say that the acceleration of gravity is a constant. Does this mean that the physicist will tolerate sloppier statements than the mathematician? You might say that he does so with tongue in cheek. If he is a good physicist, he will write his numerical results in ways that indicate to other physicists that he knows the limits outside which his experimental error lies. This is the important point: not that the physicist cannot ever make a perfect measurement, but that in stating the numerical results of his measurements he can indicate the limits within which his results are correct.

Among the important constants of physics are the speed of light, *c*; the Avogadro constant, N_A; and the charge on the electron, *e*:

$$c = (2.997925 \pm 0.000003) \times 10^8 \text{ m/sec}$$
$$N_A = (6.02252 \pm 0.00028) \times 10^{23} \text{ per gram-mole}$$
$$e = (1.60210 \pm 0.00007) \times 10^{-19} \text{ coul}$$

The notation implies in the case of *c*, for example, that the uncertainty is 0.000003×10^8 meters per second (written as m/sec). The other units will be introduced later as needed. (The use of powers of ten to express large and small numbers is explained in Appendix A.)

The letter *e* is also used for the base of the so-called natural system of logarithms: $e = 2.71828183$. (The context usually makes it clear which *e* is being considered.) This number, like $\pi = 3.14159265$, and unlike the charge on the electron or the speed of light, is a mathematical constant and not one obtained by physical measurements. The errors in *e* and π are omitted here, not because they are not known (π and *e* can be computed to any degree of accuracy desired), but because those constants are expressed here to a greater degree of accuracy than is usually needed.

Physical quantities that remain constant are of interest to physicists. Some of them (like the speed of light) are so important that improved techniques for measuring them experimentally are always being sought. Mathematical constants, such as π and *e*, are also frequently used by physicists in their computations.

1.4. Variables

A **variable** is a symbol, such as *x*, that may assume any one of a set of numerical values throughout the given discussion. This is a mathematical definition of the word "variable." The set of numbers that it may take on is called its **range.** The set may contain a finite or an infinite number of values. The temperature in a room is a physical quantity measurable on a scale. The symbol *t* may represent the temperature, in which case *t* is a variable, and we speak of the temperature itself as a variable. If, during a 24-hour period, the lowest temperature was 65°F and the highest was 89°F, we feel certain that the variable *t* assumed not only the values 65 and 89 but all numerical values in between. (That is, the range was $65 \leq t \leq 89$; read this as "*t* is equal to or greater than 65 and equal to or less than 89.") There is an infinite number of numbers between 65 and 89 (as we shall see), and *t* assumes all of them at some time during the 24-hour period in question. This is typical of the behavior of many variables in physics. But sometimes a variable may assume only a finite set of discrete numerical values. This also happens in many physical applications. The following example suggests experiments for you to make.

TABLE 1.1

Lengths of Twenty-one Leaves Picked at Random (left) and Arranged (right) in the Order of Increase

Length, l, in Centimeters	
13.5	8.1
11.9	9.6
14.1	10.4
13.4	10.8
12.0	11.1
12.2	11.4
12.6	11.8
12.5	11.9
10.8	11.9
15.2	12.0
11.4	12.2
10.4	12.4
12.9	12.5
11.1	12.6
8.1	12.9
12.4	13.2
11.9	13.4
11.8	13.5
14.4	14.1
9.6	14.4
13.2	15.2
255.4	255.4

TABLE 1.2

Frequency with which Leaves Are Found in the Several Intervals

Interval	Frequency (number of leaves in interval)
8–9	1
9–10	1
10–11	2
11–12	5
12–13	6
13–14	3
14–15	2
15–16	1

EXAMPLE 1.1. We pick twenty-one leaves at random from a laurel bush. They have an elongated shape. The length of each is measured with a metric ruler and recorded in the left column of Table 1.1. If l stands for the length of the leaves in this sample, it is apparent that l is a variable. But it is a variable that may assume only twenty-one discrete values in this discussion.

In another column we arrange the numbers in the order of increase. We make a frequency tabulation by considering first how many leaves have lengths equal to or greater than 8.0 but less than 9.0 cm, then how many have lengths equal to or greater than 9.0 but less than 10.0 cm, etc. We tabulate this information (Table 1.2) and plot it (Fig. 1.4). Such a plot, called a **frequency distribution,** is a useful way of displaying certain kinds of numerical data. Next we observe that the leaf with a length of 12.2 cm lies exactly in the middle of the column at the right of Table 1.1. This number is called the **median** of this set of values. If we add the numbers in either column, the sum is 255.4. If we divide this by the total number (21) of leaves, we get 12.1619. This number is called the **mean** of the set of numbers (more precisely, the arithmetic mean, or average). Rounding off to three figures (for reasons that will be explained in more detail elsewhere), we get 12.2. We say that the set of leaves has a mean length of 12.2 cm.

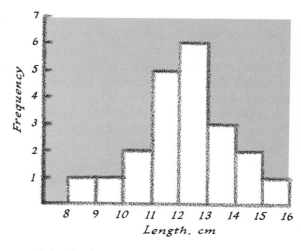

FIG. 1.4. *The frequency of occurrence of a numerical value within each interval may be plotted in this way. The figure indicates, for example, that six leaves had lengths equal to or greater than 12 cm but less than 13 cm.*

This example illustrates a few of the ways in which numbers (and hence mathematics) creep into physics in a natural way. In this book we shall go rather slowly in developing the mathematical concepts needed for an understanding of physics. Often we shall stress the non-numerical, or qualitative, aspects of physical ideas at length before considering the related quantitative treatment, but it will be quite evident throughout that the ideal in much of physical science is to reach a point where the results can be stated in a quantitative and mathematical form.

1.5. Functions

If a value of the variable y is associated with each value of the variable x in its range, we say that y is a **function** of x.

The letters used to denote a variable are not important. In a physical application a letter suggesting the physical variable is often chosen—for example, l for the *length* of a simple pendulum and T for its period (the *time* required for one complete vibration). There are good historical reasons for choosing the simple pendulum as an example. Galileo learned a great deal from his study of it, and a pendulum involves us quickly with *mass*, *length*, and *time*, which are basic physical concepts. (Mass is a measure of the inertia of a body, but, until we define inertia quantitatively, we shall have to be satisfied with an intuitive notion of mass. A heavy body has more mass than a light one, but mass and weight are not the same thing.)

Suppose that you make a simple pendulum by taking a key (or an iron washer or a heavy machine nut) and tying it to a length of string. Even without a watch it is apparent that the period, T, becomes shorter as the length, l, of the string is decreased. To each value of l there corresponds a definite value of T; hence T is a function of l.

Is T also a function of m, the mass of the object tied to the string? Does T depend on the pull of gravity at the given place, and does it depend on the width of the swing? These apparently simple questions, mulled over in the mind of Galileo, produced a revolution in man's thinking. For the present I shall simply assert that mass, length, and time play fundamental roles in physics. By doing a simple pendulum experiment (see Prob. 1.2) you can learn how these terms take on operational meaning. The basic unit of mass we shall use is the kilogram, that of length the meter, and that of time the second. Each will be treated in more detail later. Of the three, you are best acquainted with the second, for mechanical clocks are designed to tick off seconds. A meter is a little longer than a yard, and a kilogram is the mass possessed by a bag of sugar (or potatoes or sand; mass is a property of matter of every kind or form) weighing about 2.2 pounds. The **MKS system** is based on the meter (m), the kilogram (kg), and the second (sec). (When the coulomb, symbolized by q, is added as a unit of electric charge, the system is called the MKSQ system. I shall continue to use the common shorter form MKS.)

Most physical quantities have a magnitude and a unit. If the length of a string is 0.25 meter, it is incorrect to say simply that the length is 0.25. With certain exceptions the answer to a physical problem is wrong if it does not give both a number and its unit.

The functional relation between period T and length l might be expressed as

$$T = f(l)$$

This is read as "T is a function of l." This statement does not exhibit the explicit form of the function. (The pendulum function is $T = 2\pi\sqrt{l/g}$, but I shall not be able to prove this until Chap. 25.) Nevertheless, expressions of the form

$$y = f(x)$$

(read "y is a function of x") will be found useful in our work.

1.6. Sequence

The concepts of function and variable presuppose an acquaintance with numbers. Let's backtrack a bit to consider the simplest set of numbers, the positive integers: 1, 2, 3, 4, ... It is obvious that this set has a first member but no last. If you think at first that you have the last one, you can always add one to it and get another, and our decimal system is so simply and wonderfully constructed (compare with Roman numerals!) that it is always obvious how to write the next number.

The set of positive integers is also called the set of natural numbers. These alone do not serve all the numerical needs of physics, but we can better understand other numbers, such as fractions and decimals, if we start with the integers. Leopold Kronecker, a German mathematician (1823–1891), once said: "God created the integers; all the rest is the work of man." (Which has always made me wonder whether he was praising God or man!)

Any other set of numbers that has a first member, no last member, and a law of formation whereby the different members can be generated, is called an **infinite sequence.** For example,

$$2, 4, 6, 8, \ldots$$

is such a sequence. The three dots indicate that it goes on without end. The nth term in this case is $2n$. (The first was 2×1; the second, 2×2; the third, 2×3; and so on.)

There are various reasons for starting with se-quences. One is that in nature the values of the variables often form infinite sequences. The frequencies of a vibrating string, for example, form a sequence. It can be an interesting game to find the secret of a sequence—an expression for the nth term as a function of n. (See Prob. 1.4.) The wavelengths of the light given off by hydrogen atoms form a sequence (Balmer series, Lyman series, etc.). It took some time to discover the law of formation of the sequence; this then led to the formulation by Niels Bohr of a physical theory that could explain the sequence on physical principles.

You will have to take my word for it that sequences can help us understand some of the mysteries presented to us by nature as we study space, time, matter, motion, and energy. Fortunately, they are also fun to play with, as a game or a puzzle. Each problem you solve is like a battle won, giving you strength and courage for the next. That's how we shall pursue the study of physics—with a graduated series of challenging problems, some apparently trivial, but in their entirety helping us to understand the physical world.

Problems

This chapter and all the others in Part I are meant to be read rapidly. You are not expected to understand everything you read. Comprehension will often come *after* you have done some of the problems at the ends of the chapters.

1.1. Many of the words of physics were used in this chapter. Look up the following words in a dictionary: space, time, matter, motion, field, energy, particle, wave, electron. Select three definitions that tell how the words are used in physics, and write them down for future reference.

1.2. To illustrate the meaning of the word "operational," do the following experiment. Tie a small heavy object, such as a ring or a key, to a light thread, and use it as a pendulum.

1. Measure the period (the time for one whole swing) by timing ten full swings and dividing by 10 when the string is about a meter (close to 40

inches) long. Record both the period in seconds and the length in whatever units your ruler has. Keeping the length the same, repeat, allowing the total arc of the swing to be about 60°. Keeping the length the same, repeat, allowing the total arc of the swing to be about 10°. Compare the results of the three measurements. Is the period a constant?

2. Repeat for lengths about 1/2, 1/4, and 1/8 of the original length. Record all periods and lengths.

3. Plot the periods (vertically) against the lengths (horizontally) on a piece of graph paper. Are the plots straight lines?

4. So far you have operated with rulers and clocks and measured lengths and times. Though I have not defined time or length, you have given them some operational meaning by the very act of doing the experiment. Now predict, from the graph, what the period should be for some length other than those used above. Test the prediction by an experiment.

Observe that the graph gives a value for T when l is chosen arbitrarily. The fact that T is a function of l is therefore implicit in the graph.

1.3. Take six identical coins, shake them, and throw them out on a table. Count and record the number of heads. Repeat this twenty times, recording, in a column, the number of heads at each throw. Plot the frequency distribution of your results. Calculate the mean of these numbers. Is it what you think it should be? If not, why not?

1.4. Find an expression for the nth term of each of the following sequences:

A. 0, 1, 2, 3, . . .   Answer: $n - 1$.
B. 1, 3, 5, 7, . . .
C. 1/2, 1/4, 1/8, 1/16, . . .
D. 1, 4, 27, 256, . . .
E. 1, 4, 9, 16, . . .
F. 1, 2, 6, 24, 120, . . .

1.5. Write the first five terms of each sequence whose nth term is given below. Write each term in decimal form—that is, for example, 0.5 instead of 1/2.

A. $n + 1$ Answer: 2, 3, 4, 5, 6, . . .

B. $\dfrac{n^2}{n + 1}$

C. $\dfrac{n - 1}{n + 1}$

D. $1 - \dfrac{1}{n}$

E. $\dfrac{n(-1)^n}{n + 1}$

F. $\sqrt{n^2}$

G. $\dfrac{1}{2^2} - \dfrac{1}{(n + 2)^2}$ This sequence is related to the energy levels in a hydrogen atom.

1.6. 1. You are given the equation

$$f(x) = x^2 - 2x + 1$$

(Read this as "f of x equals x squared minus two x plus one.") Find f(−1), f(0), and f(+1). Example: Suppose that you are to find f(2). You put a 2 in place of each x and evaluate. Thus

$$f(2) = 2^2 - 2 \times 2 + 1 = 4 - 4 + 1 = 1$$

2. You are given the equation

$$g(x) = \frac{x}{x + 1}$$

(The "g" stands for another function; we need not always use the letter "f.") Find g(0), g(1), and g(2). What can you say about g(−1)?

3. You are given the equation

$$T(l) = 2\pi\sqrt{l/g}$$

Using the values $g = 9.8$ and $\pi = 3.14$, find $T(1)$, $T(1/2)$, $T(1/4)$, and $T(1/8)$. [When l is the length in meters and g is the acceleration due to gravity (9.8 meters per second per second), this function gives the period of a pendulum. How do your results here compare with your results in Prob. 1.2?]

The following problems may be regarded as supplementary.

1.7. The ratio of the circumference of a circle to its diameter is a pure number. Is the ratio of the area of a sphere to its diameter a pure number? What about the ratio of the volume of a sphere to its surface area? What about the ratio of this surface area to the area of the largest circle that we can make by cutting the sphere with a plane? Explain, using units.

1.8. The ratio of the thickness to the diameter of red blood cells is a physical constant that is a pure number. From your own experience list some other physical constants that are pure numbers. They need not, like π or the integers, be perfectly constant.

1.9. In § 1.3 we computed π by dividing 32 by $10\frac{1}{4}$. When this arithmetic operation is carried out to four digits, the result is 3.122. We are told that $C = 32$ inches. Presumably this means that the circumference is closer to 32 inches than to 31 or 33 inches. On this assumption the actual value could have been 32.4 inches or 31.6 inches or something in between. Using 32.4 and 31.6 as limits on the value of the circumference, and assuming that $10\frac{1}{4}$ is exact, calculate to four digits the ratio of circumference to diameter. Explain why it would have been incorrect to write the experimental value of π as 3.122. (Consult Appendix A for a discussion of significant figures.)

1.10. Consider this set of numbers: . . . , −8, −6, −4, −2, 0, 0, 2, 4, 6, 8, . . . (three dots indicate the omission of an infinite set of numbers). Does this set have a first number? If so, what is it? If not, is the set a sequence? Now consider this set: 0, 0, 2, −2, 4, −4, 6, −6, ... Is it a sequence? Does this set have the same numbers as the first set?

Space

"It has been said that the chemists won World War I, and that the physicists won World War II. Now, perhaps, it is the lot of the astronomers not to win but to prevent World War III by utilizing space in the dignity of human exploration rather than in the indignity of war."

J. ALLAN HYNEK, quoted in the *Christian Science Monitor*, May 17, 1961

WHEN it is not called the atomic age or something else, our age is called the age of space. Space —and in this chapter we are, of course, considering extraterrestrial space—has caught the popular imagination. The launching of the first successful earth satellite had an electrifying effect. To some, who had never conceived the possibility of exploring space, and certainly not of traveling through it, the event seemed to usher in an age fraught with new mysteries and fears. To others it seemed to promise unprecedented opportunities for adventure and military advantage. To all of us the word "space" is no longer new. We ask, however, "Is space of serious interest to physicists?"

At the moment, space seems to be linked with political and military activities. Every missile or rocket that is fired, for whatever reason, seems to have propaganda overtones. No ordinary ship was ever launched with such precision in timing to coincide with major political events as are the missiles and rockets of the great and aspiring powers. But does this interest in space really arise from scientific curiosity? Is interest in space really something new from the point of view of the physicist? No, indeed; for the first explorers of space were the astronomers of earlier ages.

2.1. Exploration of Space

At first those astronomers were not so much concerned with the regions of space near the earth as with the heavens. They focused their attention on the distant objects in the sky, the moon and the stars and the planets, speculated about their trajectories, plotted their positions and courses, and theorized about the laws that governed their motions. Eventually, returning to the earth as a member of the solar system, they considered such of its properties as density, size, and age. The geologists, on the other hand, who first focused their attention on the earth, have today, as geophysicists, been forced to move farther away from the earth, measuring its gravitational and magnetic fields in space and pushing farther out to discover uncharted radiation belts far from their orbiting platform called the earth. So astronomers became geophysicists, and geophysicists had to become astronomers. No, interest in space is not new, but its exploration was first pursued by a small and dedicated band of scholars.

By 1670 they had made great strides. The names of Nicolaus Copernicus, Tycho Brahe, Johannes Kepler, Galileo Galilei, and Isaac Newton will forever merit a high place on the scrolls of history for their contributions to man's knowledge about the universe. They patiently observed and recorded the workings of this huge celestial machine, evolved the basic principles governing its motions, and waited, often for years, until events in space confirmed their predictions. Eventually, confirmation piled upon confirmation, and it was realized that a major triumph of understanding had been effected. Man knew what made the universe tick—or so he thought.

How about the modern exploration of space? With all its expenditure of millions of dollars, has it yet resulted in a major breakthrough of understanding comparable to Newton's laws, which govern all motions and make the prediction of such things as eclipses possible? At the moment we must answer "no." Rockets are fired in strict conformity with the laws of motion first stated by Newton (see Part III, especially Chap. 34); and even Kepler, who preceded Newton, could have calculated the orbits of our earth satellites by using the laws, now named after him, that the planets obey (see Chap. 33).

What, then, *is* new in space? First and foremost, the intricate technology developed over the last three hundred years, which has produced rocket fuels, engines with great thrust, alloys that can withstand high temperatures, and the electronics used for guidance and communication over the vast expanse of uncharted space. Perhaps the really new fact of basic importance is that astronomy has changed from a contemplative to an *experimental* science. For the first time in history man has been able to launch satellites of his own making. He has learned empirically that the laws that govern celestial bodies govern, in the same way, his man-made bullets or particles. Never, since scientific thinking began, has he doubted this, but now he knows. He has sent up his own probes to sample gravity and magnetism and radiation out in space. So far as the laws of motion are concerned, each experiment thus far says: "Newton was right. His laws are universal." But now, of course, the door is open to an exploration of a magnitude hitherto undreamed of.

2.2. The Meanings of "Space"

The concept of space has been of interest to at least three distinct groups: philosophers, mathematicians, and physicists. Astronomers might be grouped with the physicists, and I suppose theologians could be put in with the philosophers, though not without some objections all round.

Men have asked: Is space finite or infinite? Does it have an existence apart from time and matter? Is it only a mental concept? Has it always existed? Will it last forever? These are philosophical questions. One may argue about their meaning or importance, but one cannot deny that they have been considered by thinking men for a long time.

In geometry the concept of space is linked with the basic elements called points, lines, and planes and with the concept of distance. The Pythagorean theorem, for example, which states that the square of the hypotenuse is equal to the sum of the squares of the other two sides of a right triangle, is a mathematical statement about space, as are the many other statements that arise in Euclidean geometry. The axiom that parallel lines will never meet, no matter how far extended, is also a mathematical statement about space. Modern geometry regards the axioms that the older geometricians called "self-evident truths" as mere assumptions that can be neither proved nor disproved. Other basic assumptions lead to other geometries, which are true only in the sense that they follow logically from their basic assumptions. The exercise in logic that has produced these other geometries has not been in vain. It has opened our eyes to several new mathematical interpretations of space. It has caused us to examine in great detail the foundations of mathematics and has suggested new interpretations of space to the physicist.

Physics is the third realm in which the term "space" is used. When we seek to learn what space means in physics, we discover that questions of philosophy and mathematics have often motivated physicists, and that the significant breakthroughs in physical knowledge have often been approached through a reappraisal of philosophical concepts. (Physics used to be called "natural philosophy.") Albert Einstein, for example, was willing to propose drastic new assumptions that contradicted previous philosophical ideas about space, time, and matter; and Max Planck put forth revolutionary ideas about the granularity of energy.

Is there a concept of space belonging only to physics? Since physics attempts to describe the real and measurable world around us, it demands of space an objectivity greater than that required by philosophy or mathematics. The physicist wants to know the length of a particular steel rod, or the distance between the earth and the moon, or the volume of water contained in all the seas. If he cannot define space, he describes operationally how to measure the distance between two points. If you insist that he define "point" (which the mathematician was unable to do), he will describe means of measuring the distance from one rock to another, or from one pebble to another, in this way arriving at an idealization of the concept "particle" (which is an extrapolation, to be carried to its limit as a mental exercise) —the concept of a real object that gets smaller and smaller. The word "point," to a physicist, might mean, then, the abstract localization of his already ideal "particle." In other words, the physicist localizes his points with rectangular coordinates (numbers); though he *uses* mathematics, he approaches the idea of a point by way of things like moons or rocks or sand grains, which have "objective reality" to him. I have put "objective reality" in quotation marks because at this point the philosopher could ask us what the phrase means.

Let us take a simple-minded approach: we assert that one way to get started is to show what we mean by length and area and volume with instruments like rulers, which can be used to measure length, and to show how different observers must use the instruments if they are to get the same results with them. Before we do that, however, let us reconsider, from the physicist's point of view, what we have said about space. All we have really said is that in physics real objects made of matter seem to have an objective reality that we can grasp more readily than the abstract concepts of space and time; that we can give instructions about how to use a ruler to measure the distance between two objects; that, if the objects are made smaller and smaller, we are led to the idealization called a point. All of this seems only dimly related to the ideas about space exploration with which we started.

Notice, however, that the physicist is really interested in *events*, and that to describe them he must first describe how to measure distance and time. One physical event is an eclipse of the sun. To describe it, we must answer questions like

"what?" and "where?" and "when?" A physicist's answers to these questions inevitably involve space, time, and matter all together, not considered abstractly and separately. We consider it a major triumph that physics stated the laws of mechanics in such a precise way that we can predict the time and the place of the next eclipse of the sun by the moon.

To the physicist, space is a theater where events take place. It was interesting to observe and record celestial events (early astronomy), but it was even more interesting to discover their regularities and state them in the language of mathematics (Brahe, Copernicus, Kepler). Newton's achievement was to discover and formulate the laws (of gravitation and motion) from which such events could be *predicted*. Today the new vistas in astronomy and space exploration present the possibility of actual "experimentation with the universe" (explorer satellites and eventually exploration by men).

But periods of accumulation of new knowledge must always be followed by periods of digestion— when the new facts are interpreted and put into their proper places, making philosophy and mathematics adjust themselves to the new discoveries. With the International Geophysical Year (1959–1960) we entered such an active era of data-collection. We must not lose sight of the fact that the new discoveries may produce further adjustments in philosophy.

2.3. The Operational Meaning of "Length"

"What is the length of this table?" This is the kind of question about space that a physicist answers by performing the simple operation of *counting* the number of times some rigid rod (used as a scale) fits along the edge of the table. (In the following illustration the rigid rod is ₋n ordinary meter stick.) If he finds that seven lengths are too short but eight lengths are too long, it is easy to decide that the table is longer than seven units but not as long as eight. In some cases the decision is not so easy to make. Suppose, for example, that the table, the first time it is measured, seems to be exactly seven times as long as the rod, that the second time it seems to be a little more than seven times as long, and that the third time it seems to be a little less than seven times as long. The correctness of the decision as to the length depends, in part, on the observer's experience and on his ability to reduce the causes of error; but *counting* and *decision-making* are the essential processes involved.

The name of the unit of measurement is not important, but its stability is. The standard meter, until October 1960, was the distance between two marks on a rigid bar of platinum-iridium alloy kept in a laboratory at Sèvres, on the outskirts of Paris.† Notice that length, the basic measure of space, was defined in terms of matter (the platinum-iridium bar) and a certain property of matter, rigidity. What *is* a rigid body? We know that metals expand when their temperature is raised. How do we know that they return to the same length when they return to the original temperature? We don't, really. At first, however, we must proceed on the assumption that, within certain limits of temperature, the length of our standard meter bar is constant enough to permit us to use it as a standard of length.

The metric system evolved out of the French Revolution. In the "age of reason" that the revolutionists fostered, the French decided to discard all old standards and start with a fresh set based on logic. The original meter was intended to be one ten-millionth of the distance from the equator to either pole. It turned out that the prototype meter did not have its intended length, but it was kept as a standard nevertheless. Observe that the French authorities went to what they considered the most stable solid object, the earth itself, and used it in defining the unit of length. The multiples and subdivisions of the meter are decimal; the centimeter, for example, is $1/100$ (10^{-2}) meter, and the kilometer is 1,000 (10^3) meters. The metric system is accepted in scientific work throughout the world today.‡ A summary of other prefixes and their meanings is given in Table 2.1.

Returning to the problem of measuring our table, we see that the process of counting seems to lead only to the integers (1, 2, 3, . . .). Observe, however, that the length of the table can be stated more precisely. We take our arbitrary unit (I said earlier that our rod happens to be a meter stick) and divide it into ten equal parts (by a procedure described in Euclidean geometry). The interval between 7 meters and 8 meters has now been divided into subintervals with ends at 7.1, 7.2, 7.3, . . . 7.9, 8.0 meters. Again counting the number of times our ruler can be laid along the table, we find that the length of the table, beyond the 7 meters we had counted before, lies between the fourth and fifth of these new intervals (called decimeters, but not commonly used); that is, we decide, upon observation, that the length is greater than 7.4 m and less than 7.5 m. By repeating this process and dividing the decimeter into centimeters, we may conclude that the length of the table is greater than 7.42 m and less than 7.43 m. Notice that 7.4 is really a fraction, expressible as the ratio of two whole numbers, 74/10, and that 7.43 may be written as 743/100. One of the advantages of the decimal notation is that it makes it just as simple to multiply two fractions as two integers. Since $743 \times 278 = 205,554$, we know from the rules of arithmetic that $7.43 \times 2.78 = 20.5554$.

The point of all this is simply that length, as

† The new standard, accepted at the Eleventh International Conference on Weights and Measures (1960), is defined as 1,650,763.73 wavelengths of the orange-red light given off by electrically excited krypton 86. The U.S. inch is 41,929,399 wavelengths. A master standard must be at least ten times as accurate as the practical measuring systems derived from it. An error of a millionth of an inch (about the smallest measurement that could be made with the platinum-iridium bar as a standard) in the borehole of a guidance gyroscope could cause a shot to the moon to miss by a thousand miles. Error as low as about one part in a hundred million is possible with the new standard.

‡ In engineering practice, however, the British system of length, based on the foot (and its subdivisions called inches: 12 inches = 1 foot), the yard (1 yard = 3 feet), and the mile (5,280 feet = 1 mile), has been adhered to tenaciously

in the English-speaking world—so much so that we cannot ignore it in a physics text. We shall use the metric system most of the time, but factors for converting to the British system are given in tabular form on the front flyleaf.

In some matters we associate the Latin temperament of the French with a willingness to be moved by emotion rather than reason; yet in scientific matters the French chose a most rational system of units while the British adhered to a system that seems to have no rhyme or reason. The unit called the foot was probably based on the length of some monarch's foot.

Since neither the present standard meter nor the present foot has any great claim to representing accurately any perfect model, we must concede that both are really arbitrary. The wavelength of light serves today as a better and more reproducible standard of length.

TABLE 2.1

Some Multiples and Submultiples of Metric Quantities

Common quantities	10	100	1,000	1,000,000	1,000,000,000	1,000,000,000,000
meter gram second	deca-	hekto-	kilo-	mega-	giga-	tera-
$1 = 10^0$	10^1	10^2	10^3	10^6	10^9	10^{12}

Common quantities	$\dfrac{1}{10}$	$\dfrac{1}{100}$	$\dfrac{1}{1,000}$	$\dfrac{1}{1,000,000}$	$\dfrac{1}{1,000,000,000}$	$\dfrac{1}{1,000,000,000,000}$
meter gram second	deci-	centi-	milli-	micro-	nano-	pico-
$1 = 10^0$	10^{-1}	10^{-2}	10^{-3}	10^{-6}	10^{-9}	10^{-12}

measured in physics, depends on setting up a correspondence between the points on a scale and a set of numbers on that scale, and that in practice our ability to measure accurately is limited by the closeness with which marks can be put on that scale. In practice the physicist does not ask what the *true* length is; he is content with the numbers he gets from scales provided he can specify the bounds within which he is sure to be right. He may have to look through a microscope to estimate the lengths of very small objects or through a telescope to estimate the lengths of large and distant objects, but eventually he has to get back to the marks on some scale if he wants to state his results in meters.

The length of large and distant objects can be found by triangulation from a base line measured with a calibrated ruler—that is, by the measurement of angles and trigonometric computation. The surveyor uses a transit to sight points on his distant object. (He assumes that light travels in straight lines.) The distance from the earth to other astronomical bodies may be determined by this method, but the base line has to be very long if we want to measure very great distances. We can use the computed diameter of the earth's orbit as a base line by sighting at intervals six months apart, but even with this line the greatest distance

that can be measured by this method is about 65 trillion (65×10^{12}) miles. This is indeed a great distance, but astronomers know that there are billions of stars still farther away. An isosceles triangle with a base line 186 million miles long and a vertex angle of 0.00016 degree has an altitude of about 65 trillion miles (Fig. 2.1). In measuring the distance to the star 61 Cygni, the Prussian astronomer F. W. Bessel (1784–1846) used the diameter of the earth's orbit, 186 million miles, as a base line, but he had to *measure* the angle of approximately 0.00016 degree on an instrument with a scale on it. It is this *parallax* measurement that sets the upper limit to the distances that can be computed by triangulation.

Two other properties of light (besides rectilinear propagation) can be used in the measurement of great distances. One is its speed. In a vacuum, light travels about 186,000 miles in one second. In one year it therefore travels $186,000 \times 60 \times 60 \times 24 \times 365$ miles. To three significant figures this comes out as 5.87×10^{12} miles. In astronomical work this unit, called the **light-year,** is useful. Since, as we have seen, radar waves, which travel at the same speed as light, have been sent from the earth and bounced off the moon (mean distance 3.84×10^7 m) and even off the sun's corona (mean distance 1.50×10^{10} m), the method of measuring great distances by measuring transit time is already in use with man-made sources of radiation and sensitive electronic equipment.

Still another measure of distance depends on the intensity of light. Light gets dimmer as its source gets farther away. If you stand one meter from a point source of light and take a reading with a photographer's photoelectric exposure meter, you may record a unit intensity, 1. At two meters the intensity will be 1/4 unit; at three meters it will be 1/9 unit. We generalize by saying that the intensity falls off as the inverse square of the distance. The distances to stars that are many millions of light-years away have been estimated by use of this **inverse-square law,** but several complicating factors make it inadvisable to describe the method here.

Let us return to lengths that are encountered in the laboratory. Suppose that you put a pencil mark at random on the south wall of a room and another at random on the east wall. No matter how small you make the pencil marks, they will not be mathematical points. (They are, in fact, sizable chunks of graphite when looked at under a microscope.) How do you measure the distance between the two points of which these marks are imperfect indicators? You could use the techniques involving light, but it would require a fair amount of equipment to get a numerical result. What would a housewife do? She would probably get a seamstress's tape measure, stretch it between the two points with the aid of an assistant, and read off the answer. (It would be a good exercise to criticize this technique and tell how to improve it.) The housewife's intuition was correct. A *short* rigid ruler alone would not be of use. (Two rulers that overlapped might be.) She approximated a straight line by stretching the tape, thus removing the sag—but we don't want a measure that can be lengthened by stretching.

It is one thing, we see, to assert that a straight line is the shortest distance between two points, but it is another to provide the tools and give precise directions so that someone else can measure a distance and get the same result that we do (within the limits of allowable error).

Still more interesting problems develop when we try to measure the smallest distances dis-

cernible with a microscope (about 10^{-6} m) or atomic distances (about 10^{-10} m) or the diameters of nuclei (about 10^{-14} m). Since we have stated these minute distances in terms of the meter, there must be ways of comparing even them with the standard meter. The details will have to wait.

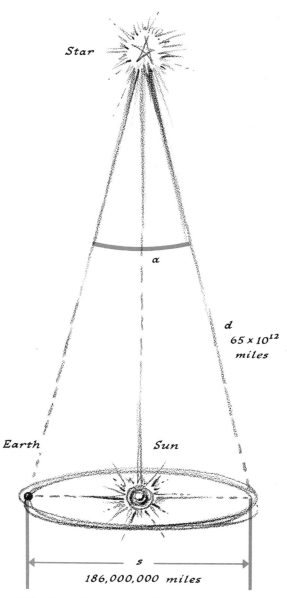

FIG. 2.1. *The relation among* d, α, *and* s *is expressed approximately by the equation* s = dα *if* α *is in radians. For 61 Cygni,* α *is measured as 0.00016 degree. The distance* d *is 65,000,000,000,000 miles.*

In the metric system areas are measured in square meters (m²) and volumes in cubic meters (m³). We say that a length has a *dimensionality* expressible as L, an area one expressible as L^2, and a volume one expressible as L^3.

The area of a sphere, for example, is $4\pi r^2$; the radius, r, being a length, has L for a physical dimension, and $4\pi r^2$ has the dimensions of L^2. The volume of a sphere, $(4/3)\pi r^3$, has the dimensions of L^3. We shall return to this idea of physical dimensions very often as a check on our work. We can often detect an error in a formula by treating the dimensionality as an algebraic quantity.

EXAMPLE 2.1. We wish to check the statement: "The area of a cone with height h and with a base of radius r is $\pi r^2 h/2$." We write

$$A = \pi r^2 h/2$$

The dimensionality of an area is L^2. Since both r and h are lengths, the right side has the dimension of L^3. Our formula *must* be wrong.

2.4. The Parts of Space

It will be convenient to designate very small, ordinary, and very great distances as *atomic*, *molar*, and *extragalactic*.

The term **atomic** refers to distances of atomic size (about 10^{-10} m). No light microscope can distinguish objects separated by much less than about 4×10^{-7} m. In a so-called atomic region of space we encounter only a few of nature's fundamental particles at a time, and the physical laws that apply there may or may not be the same as the laws that apply to the larger regions of space encountered in our daily lives.

The term **molar** comes from the chemical term "mole" (a mole contains 6.02×10^{23} molecules). A grain of sand is about 10^{-4} m in diameter and contains about 10^{16} molecules. The sun is about 1.4×10^9 m in diameter, has a mass of 2.0×10^{30} kg, and contains perhaps 10^{55} atomic particles of one kind or another. Since both the grain of sand and the sun are called molar, it is obvious that all objects of terrestrial and laboratory size are classed as molar.

Our sun is only about 15×10^{-6} light-year away. Beyond our solar system are the fixed stars, the nearest of which, α-Centauri, is 4.3 light-years away. All the stars we can see with the unaided eye, and many millions more, visible with telescopes, belong to a great system sometimes called the Galaxy, the diameter of which is estimated at about 300,000 light-years. Outside this Galaxy of ours are hundreds of millions of other galaxies, or **extragalactic** nebulas, such as the Crab Nebula (Fig. 2.2) and the Great Nebula in Andromeda, which is about 3×10^6 light-years away. Evidence seems to reveal galaxies that are even farther away. With radio telescopes (Fig. 2.3) galaxies have been seen as far away as 7×10^9 light-years. We can only conjecture about the physical nature of regions whose light signals take more than a million years to reach us.

What kind of geometry holds for such great distances? Is the geometry of Euclid, which serves us well for our ordinary purposes, valid here? What is the operational means of measuring such distances? What assumptions about the properties of light are we making if we try to use light to confirm such a theorem as "the square on the hypotenuse of a right triangle is equal to the sum of the squares on the other two sides" for extragalactic distances? These are interesting questions to think about; but, fortunately, any diagram that we may draw on paper, any line no longer than the distance from the earth to the sun, obeys the geometry of Euclid so closely that no deviation has ever been observed.

Geometries that contradict the basic assumptions of Euclid have been invented, and some of them have been found useful in the interpretation of data from the extragalactic realm. In the rest of this book, however, we shall be concerned primarily with physics in the atomic and molar realms, and there the geometry of Euclid is obeyed so closely that we can pursue our elementary investigations with little concern for the special geometry that may be needed for extragalactic distances.

Today space is being explored at both extremes, the atomic and the extragalactic (Fig. 2.4), by the nuclear physicists at one end and by the astrophysicists at the other—and in between as well.

The laws of physics were first discovered in the molar realm. Even the moon-orbiting and sun-orbiting satellites move within this region, which, by comparison with extragalactic space, is tiny indeed. Yet it is apparent that the region of space into which man can send his own instruments on exploration has expanded in a fantastic way. The exploration will continue in both directions, atomic and extragalactic. It may seem odd that man, in order to explore the larger regions of molar space, first had to develop atomic and nuclear physics and the powerful tools of elec-

tronics. Now, armed with those new tools and that new knowledge, he ventures forth with great resources of hitherto untapped power to propel his instruments and eventually himself into the distant regions of space. It seems certain, nevertheless, that, for a long time to come, information from extragalactic space must still be gleaned from the particles and the waves generated by nature, not by man—by events that, though they occurred before the birth of our solar system, are just now being seen through telescopes and otherwise felt by extremely sensitive detectors of atomic

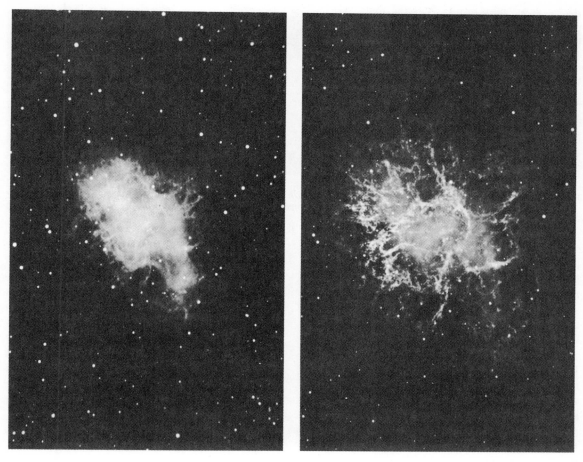

FIG. 2.2. *Two photographs of the same object, the Crab Nebula, taken with the 200-inch Hale reflector. The one on the left was taken on photographic plates sensitive to invisible light of the infrared range (see also Figs. 22.2 and 22.3). The one on the right was taken with crimson light; it shows the glowing hydrogen that surrounds the central mass. The nebula is now thought to be the debris of a cataclysmic thermonuclear explosion that was observed by Chinese astronomers in 1054. (Photographs from the Mount Wilson and Palomar Observatories.)*

FIG. 2.3. *Radio telescope at Jodrell Bank, England. It can receive natural radio signals from points in space as far away as 1,000 million light-years and can sense events that took place millions of years ago. (British Crown Copyright.)*

particles. Man cannot yet do experiments in extragalactic space. He must continue to receive and record nature's signals.

2.5. Motion: Successive Events in Space

An event is localized when you answer the questions "where" and "when" about it. The first involves space; the second, time. Suppose that a car running along a road (Fig. 2.5) passes a tree at A at time t_1. Later it passes another tree, at B, at time t_2. If the distance from an arbitrary post at O to A is s_1 and the distance from O to B is s_2, the distance traveled in the time interval $t_2 - t_1$ is $s_2 - s_1$. The average speed of the car in the interval is defined by the equation

$$\bar{v} = \frac{s_2 - s_1}{t_2 - t_1} \qquad [2.1$$

The bar over the v denotes *average* value. A mathematician would say that we have made the assumption that to the set of geometrical points from O to B there corresponds a set of numbers and, conversely, that to every number there corresponds a point. Though all this seems fairly obvious intuitively, it actually took many people thinking for many years to clarify all the notions involved. Out of all this was born the calculus, both differential and integral. We shall not need the calculus in this course but shall go to the brink of it by easy stages. The concept of sequence, introduced in Chapter 1, plays a role here.

We have worked with some sequences consisting of whole numbers and with others consisting of fractions with integral numerators and denominators, and we have seen how the decimal

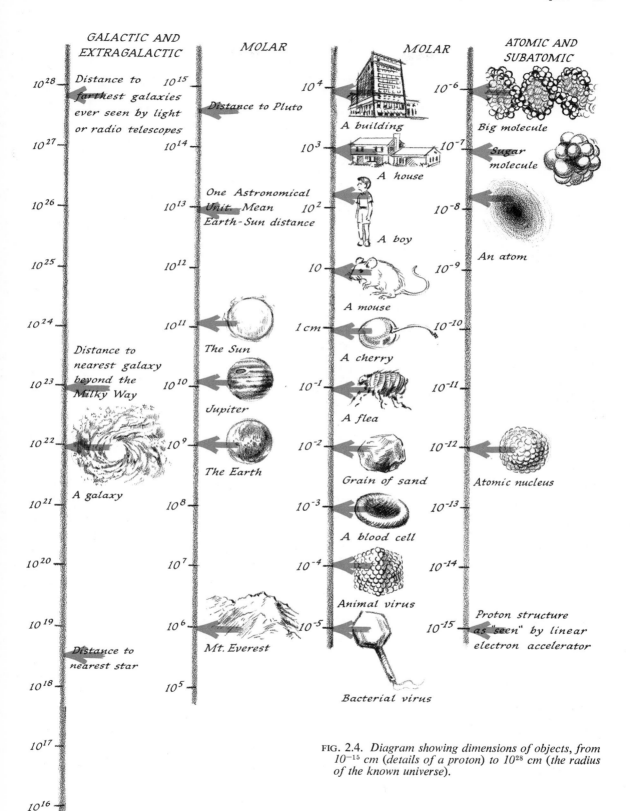

GALACTIC AND EXTRAGALACTIC

10^{28} — Distance to farthest galaxies ever seen by light or radio telescopes

10^{27} —

10^{26} —

10^{25} —

10^{24} —

10^{23} — Distance to nearest galaxy beyond the Milky Way

10^{22} —

10^{21} — A galaxy

10^{20} —

10^{19} —

10^{18} — Distance to nearest star

10^{17} —

10^{16} —

MOLAR

10^{15} — Distance to Pluto

10^{14} —

10^{13} — One Astronomical Unit. Mean Earth-Sun distance

10^{12} —

10^{11} — The Sun

10^{10} — Jupiter

10^{9} — The Earth

10^{8} —

10^{7} —

10^{6} — Mt. Everest

10^{5} —

MOLAR

10^{4} — A building

10^{3} — A house

10^{2} — A boy

10 — A mouse

$1 \; cm$ — A cherry

10^{-1} — A flea

10^{-2} — Grain of sand

10^{-3} — A blood cell

10^{-4} — Animal virus

10^{-5} — Bacterial virus

ATOMIC AND SUBATOMIC

10^{-6} — Big molecule

10^{-7} — Sugar molecule

10^{-8} — An atom

10^{-9} —

10^{-10} —

10^{-11} —

10^{-12} — Atomic nucleus

10^{-13} —

10^{-14} —

10^{-15} — Proton structure as "seen" by linear electron accelerator

FIG. 2.4. *Diagram showing dimensions of objects, from 10^{-15} cm (details of a proton) to 10^{28} cm (the radius of the known universe).*

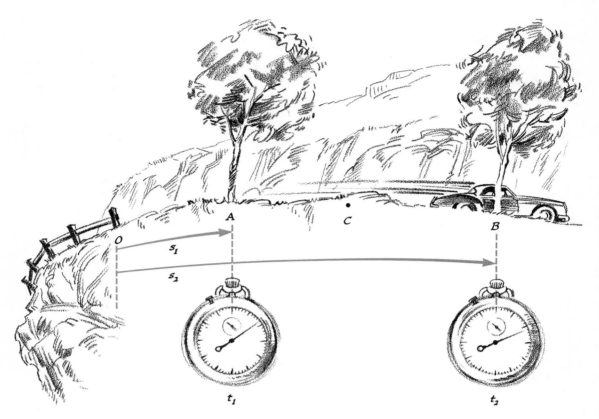

FIG. 2.5. *To find the average speed of the car, we need the distance* AB *and the time it took to cover that distance.*

notation makes it possible to manipulate even fractions in a simple way; but we have certainly not examined completely the nature of this one-to-one correspondence between numbers and points—this marriage of arithmetic and geometry that made possible Descartes' analytic geometry. For the time being let us assume that this correspondence exists and try to clarify our notions about it when new problems arise.

Another notation for $s_2 - s_1$ is Δs (read "delta s"). Similarly, for $t_2 - t_1$ we may write Δt (delta t). The average speed may then be written as

$$\bar{v} = \frac{\Delta s}{\Delta t} \qquad [2.2$$

The average speed, $\bar{v}$, is not necessarily what the speed was when the car passed the first tree nor when it passed any other randomly chosen point between A and B. If C is such a point, we may ask how we can find the *exact* speed as the car

passes C. We imagine a *sequence* of intervals,

$$(\Delta s)_1, (\Delta s)_2, (\Delta s)_3, \ldots \qquad [2.3$$

each containing C and each smaller than the previous one. To each of these there corresponds a time interval, Δt. For example, $(\Delta t)_1$ is the time it takes to travel $(\Delta s)_1$; $(\Delta t)_2$ is the time it takes to travel $(\Delta s)_2$; and so on. So there is a new sequence,

$$(\Delta t)_1, (\Delta t)_2, (\Delta t)_3, \ldots \qquad [2.4$$

corresponding to the first.

Now consider a third sequence:

$$\frac{(\Delta s)_1}{(\Delta t)_1}, \frac{(\Delta s)_2}{(\Delta t)_2}, \frac{(\Delta s)_3}{(\Delta t)_3}, \ldots \qquad [2.5$$

It has a first member but no last member, and we may be able to state a law of formation for it. (See Prob. 2.8.) Let us take an example contrived to illustrate what I mean. Suppose these numbers had turned out to be

$$0.30000, 0.33000, 0.33300, 0.33330, \ldots \qquad [2.6$$

Our acquaintance with the decimal system permits us to say that, though no member of this sequence is equal to 1/3, no member exceeds it. The members of the sequence are, in fact, getting progressively "closer" to 1/3 (borrowing the natural word from the language of space, or geometry).

If the law of formation of the sequence guarantees that the first zero in a term is replaced by a three in the next term, we say that 1/3 is the **limit** of this sequence even though no member of it is equal to 1/3. In that case the exact speed at C is 1/3 (in some particular unit).

The idea of the limit of a sequence, which I have illustrated here with a rather artificial-looking numerical example, lies at the heart of a proper understanding of motion. We shall pursue the study of limits slowly throughout Part I and especially in the chapters on kinematics, my immediate objective being to introduce the delta notation and to give some simple illustrations of sequences that have limits. What you learn here will have application beyond the elementary study of motion.

2.6. Summary

The modern exploration of space by the use of rockets and satellites has given new impetus to work that was begun long ago by astronomers. The concepts of space have been of interest in philosophy, in mathematics, in physics, and in astronomy.

The simplest operation related to space is the measurement of the length of an object. This involves counting the number of times a standard of length fits along some line in the object. Since this number is seldom exactly a whole number, a decision based on the judgment of the observer is required. The measurement of very great and very small distances requires special techniques, but it always involves counting and decision-making. The basic unit of length in the metric system is the meter.

In physics we are seldom concerned with space alone as an abstract concept; we usually observe events that involve space, time, matter, and motion inextricably interwoven.

Problems

Some useful terrestrial and solar data may be found in Appendix C and Appendix D.

2.1. Using a ruler with a metric scale, measure the length of an index card as follows. Suppose the scale is divided into centimeter and millimeter divisions. Make one edge of the card coincident with a certain mark on the scale. Record the length of the card, *estimating to the nearest tenth of a millimeter* (for example, 10.43 cm). The last figure is only an estimate, but it is the best estimate you can make under the circumstances. (You may use a magnifier for it.) Repeat this procedure ten times at different positions on the card and always starting at a different initial mark on the scale. Find the median of the length readings. Find the arithmetic mean (the average) of all the readings, and call this value L. Find the deviation of each reading from the mean (the difference between the mean value and the reading), considering only the magnitude of the deviations—that is, ignoring positive and negative

signs. Find the average of the deviations, and call this value D. Write your result as $L \pm D$ (for example, 10.42 ± 0.031 cm).

2.2. 1. Which of the following area formulas are incorrect when judged by a dimensional test? All the letter symbols (except π) represent lengths.
A. The area of a triangle is $hb/2$.
B. The area of a triangle is

$$\sqrt{s^2(s-a)(s-b)(s-c)}$$

C. The area of the ring between two circles of radii r_1 and r_2 is

$$\pi(r_1 + r_2)(r_1 - r_2)$$

2. Which of the following volume formulas are incorrect?
A. The volume of a cylinder is $\pi r^2 h^2$.
B. The volume of a cone is $\pi r^2 h/3$.
C. The volume of a spheroid is $4\pi a^2 b^2/3$.

2.3. When the product of two variables is a constant, they are said to be inversely proportional to each other. The statement that $xy = 1$ implies that $y = 1/x$, and we say that y is inversely proportional to x. Make a table of values of y corresponding to the following values of x: 0.1, 0.4, 0.8, 1.0, 2, 4, and 8. Plot the results with y as the ordinate (on a vertical axis) and x as the abscissa (on a horizontal axis); use graph paper and a pencil with a fine point, and connect the points with as smooth a curve as you can make.

2.4. On the sheet used for Prob. 2.3, plot $y = 1/x^2$. In this case y is said to be inversely proportional to the square of x. We also say that it illustrates an inverse-square variation.

2.5. Following the instructions of Appendix B, convert (1) one light-year into miles; (2) the speed of light from 3.0×10^8 m/sec into mi/h; (3) the distance between the earth and the sun (93 million miles) into centimeters.

2.6. Suppose that, in the case illustrated by Fig. 2.5, $s_2 = 25.43$ m, $s_1 = 22.27$ m, $t_2 = 10.98$ sec, and $t_1 = 10.42$ sec. Find the average speed (1) in m/sec; (2) in mi/h.

2.7. Choose, from the problems of Chap. 1, sequences that have limits, and state the limit of each. (A sequence with a general term, a_n, has a limit, L, if the difference $L - a_n$ becomes and remains as small in magnitude as we please for some value of n and all subsequent values of n.) The sequence

$$\frac{1}{2}, \frac{2}{3}, \frac{3}{4}, \frac{5}{6}, \cdots \frac{n}{n+1}$$

has 1 as a limit because the quantity

$$1 - \frac{n}{n+1} = \frac{1}{n+1}$$

becomes as small as we please. For example, let us choose 1/16 as a small number. For all values of n equal to or greater than 16,

$$\frac{1}{n+1}$$

is less than 1/16.)

2.8. 1. The sequence

$$(\Delta s)_1, (\Delta s)_2, (\Delta s)_3, \ldots$$

has an nth term expressible as

$$\frac{1/n}{1 + 1/n}$$

Prove that the limit of this sequence is 0.
2. The sequence

$$(\Delta t)_1, (\Delta t)_2, (\Delta t)_3, \ldots$$

has an nth term expressible as $1/n$. Prove that the limit of this sequence is 0.
3. Form the sequence

$$\frac{(\Delta s)_1}{(\Delta t)_1}, \frac{(\Delta s)_2}{(\Delta t)_2}, \frac{(\Delta s)_3}{(\Delta t)_3}, \cdots$$

Express its terms decimally; for example,

$$\frac{(\Delta s)_1}{(\Delta t)_1} = 2.0, \quad \frac{(\Delta s)_2}{(\Delta t)_2} = 1.5$$

Prove that the limit of this sequence is 1.

3

Forces

LIKE "space," the word "force," though we use it in our daily speech, needs precise definition to get the meaning it has in physics. A good place to begin is with the words "push" and "pull." We know from experience (Fig. 3.1) what it means to push an automobile that has run out of gasoline or to pull on a line that has a fighting fish on the end. Experiences of this sort give us our intuitive notion of force. We are on the right track if we begin by saying that a force is a push or a pull.

3.1. A Force is a Push or a Pull

Every human life begins with the exertion of a force. We are almost literally extruded into individual life, and even our earliest attempts to reach for food or to walk involve pushes and pulls. So we have a backlog of experience that can help us to say more precisely what "force" really means. We observe, for example, that it takes a pull on a cord to keep a weight at the other end swinging in a circle (Fig. 3.2.A). Then, when we observe the planets moving in circles (the planets' orbits are elliptic, but some are very nearly circular) round the sun (Fig. 3.2.B), we naturally ask, "Does the planet also feel a pull that keeps it from flying off in a straight line?" If it does, a connection between space and force is apparent. It turns out that it does indeed take a force to keep a planet in its orbit.

We must be able to measure forces before we can use them scientifically. Our first qualitative guide is muscular sensation: we can distinguish roughly between a weak push and a strong one by

FIG. 3.1. *Experiences with pushes (A) and pulls (B) give us our intuitive notions of force.*

the effect we feel in our muscles. But this anthropomorphic measure is too crude. Let us observe what forces can do; then let us try to devise, from their effects, a suitable means of measuring them. What *can* forces do? They can deform or accelerate matter. Let us consider first their ability to deform.

3.2. Forces Can Deform Matter

You can dent a football by treading heavily on it (Fig. 3.3.A). You can stretch a steel spring by pulling on both ends (Fig. 3.3.B). In general, pairs of forces can stretch, compress, twist, and otherwise deform bodies. (I shall call any sample of matter—solid, liquid, or gaseous—a body.) A body may return to its original shape when the forces are removed: a diving board springs back to normal after the diver has jumped off; a rubber band springs back to its original shape when it is no longer stretched; the gas in a cylinder shrinks when pressed by a piston but springs back to its original volume when the piston returns to its original position. But forces can change the shapes of some bodies permanently: the clay molded by the sculptor's hands retains its new shape (Fig. 3.4); taffy is made by pulling and changes shape as long as it is pulled; a steel wire stretched beyond a certain limit does not return to its original length; a steel automobile body is pressed into permanent shape. Finally, by cutting or shearing,

cloth, paper, and even metal can be torn apart. Forces, then, can stretch, compress, deform, break, or tear bodies.

How can we use the change in the shape of a body as a measure of the force on it?

Let us use the properties of an **elastic body.** A body is said to be elastic if it returns to its original shape after the forces changing its shape are removed. A steel wire of length l and cross-sectional area A will experience an elongation, Δl, if subjected to a stretching force, F, along its length, the force being due to the weight of the objects suspended from the wire (Fig. 3.5). It is found that the ratio $(F/A) \div (\Delta l/l)$ remains constant; we therefore write

$$\frac{F/A}{\Delta l/l} = Y \qquad [3.1$$

the constant Y being called Young's modulus. For steel Y is 2.8×10^7 lb/in.^{2}; for aluminum it is 9.0×10^6 lb/in.^{2}. If we lump the constants, l, Y, and A, together and solve for Δl, we can write

$$\Delta l = \left(\frac{l}{AY}\right) F \qquad [3.2$$

Equation 3.2 states that the elongation, Δl, is *directly proportional* to the stretching force, F. This is characteristic of bodies that behave elastically. The change in shape (Δl in this case) is directly proportional to the force that produces the change, at least within limits.

A helical steel spring behaves in a similar way

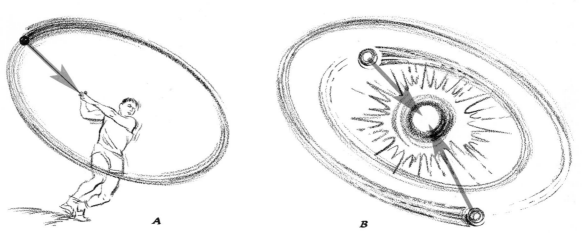

A   B

FIG. 3.2. *It takes a force to keep an object moving in a circle whether it be a ball at the end of a cord (A) or a planet in orbit (B).*

and can be designed so that small forces will produce sizable stretches. Suspended vertically from
a spring (Fig. 3.6), a weight-holder, *H*, reaches
level *A*. With a one-pound weight on it, it stretches
the spring by length *x* and reaches level *B*. The
same spring will stretch by length 2*x* with a two-
pound weight on it, by 3*x* with a three-pound
weight, and so on. In other words, the equation
relating the weight, *F*, to the stretch is of the form

The plot of such an equation is a straight line
(Fig. 3.7). The constant of proportionality, *k*
(often called the **force constant** of the spring),
depends upon the units we use for force and distance; it might, for example, be in pounds per
inch. We have used the pound as a measure of
force because it is well known to us in everyday
usage, but we shall presently see that in physics
another unit, called the newton, will be used more
often.

Observing that the weight had an effect, we assumed that it exerted a force. It changed the shape
of the spring, and we know that we could have
done the same by pulling on the spring by hand.
But now we pass the burden of responsibility from
our muscle (which might get tired and deceive us)
to a steel spring, which will give reproducible
numerical results when forces are applied to it.
According to equation 3.3, the amount of stretch
in inches is a direct measure of the force in pounds.
Properly calibrated, the spring is called a spring
balance (Fig. 3.8).

Rubber bands are often called elastic bands. To
test whether they are elastic in the sense that they
return to their original shape when the stretching
forces are removed and to see if they obey equa-

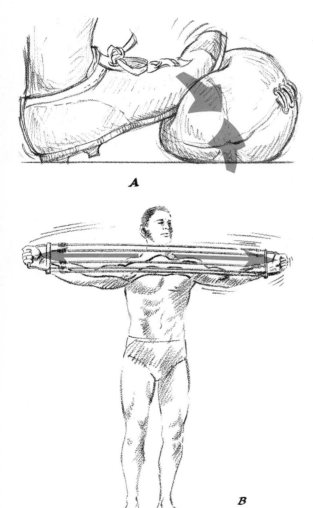

FIG. 3.3. *Pairs of forces are required to deform bodies:
(A) the shoe pushes down on the ball, and the floor
pushes up; (B) the hands exert forces on the spring
in opposite directions.*

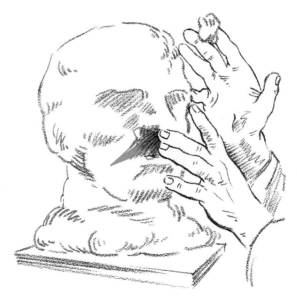

FIG. 3.4. *Modeling clay does not return to its original
shape when the distorting forces are removed.*

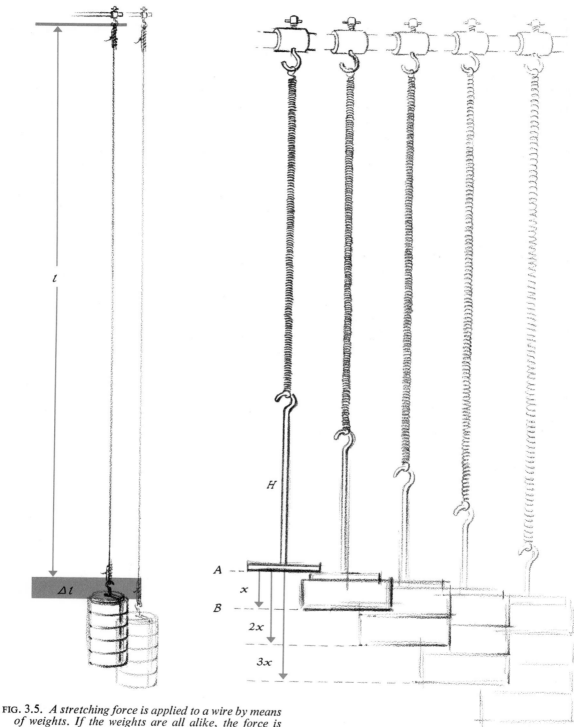

FIG. 3.5. *A stretching force is applied to a wire by means of weights. If the weights are all alike, the force is proportional to the number of weights. The elongation may be slight enough to require special optical devices for observing and measuring it.*

FIG. 3.6. *The elongation, x, of a spring is proportional to the stretching force.*

tion 3.3, a set of exercises is suggested in Problem 3.3. Because they are readily available, rubber bands can be useful in experimental work.

Recall that the standard meter was originally defined arbitrarily as the distance between two marks on a platinum-iridium bar. Couldn't we have defined an arbitrary unit of force by taking a certain steel spring and saying, "A unit of force is the force that will stretch this particular spring by one inch"? This standard spring could be kept in some national or international laboratory, and against it secondary standards could be calibrated. Yes, such an arbitrary standard of force, based on the ability of forces to deform a body, could have been chosen. But it was not; another property of forces, their ability to accelerate matter, was used to define the unit of force. It is too bad, in a way, that there is not a standard spring in Sèvres just as there is a standard meter; if there were, it would be conceptually easier to think of the unit of force. But then doubts about the permanence of the spring's properties, and about the reproducibility of the results obtained with it, would always haunt us. Whether we like it or not, history took a different turn—one that led to dynamics, the science of matter and motion. Let us see how the ability of forces to accelerate matter can be used to define a unit of force.

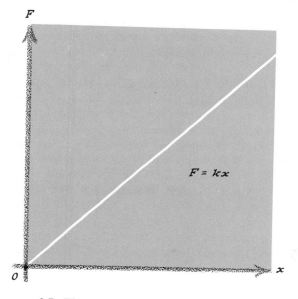

FIG. 3.7. *The equation* F = kx *describes the direct proportionality between the force and the elongation.*

3.3. Forces Can Accelerate Matter

In Figure 3.9 a block of iron, B, sits in a block of solid carbon dioxide, D (Dry Ice, obtainable from an ice-cream dealer), which rests on a horizontal glass surface, G. The block of solid carbon dioxide actually "floats" on a layer of gaseous carbon dioxide; so there is very little friction between G and D. A stretched steel spring (or a

FIG. 3.8. *Properly calibrated, a spring can be used as a spring balance to measure forces.*

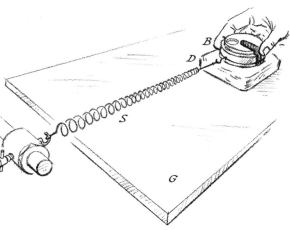

FIG. 3.9. *When weight* B, *resting on a slab of solid carbon dioxide,* D, *is released, it accelerates; that is, it picks up speed.*

chain of rubber bands), S, pulls on B, which is kept from moving by the hand. When B is released, D and B together start moving rapidly toward the fixed end of the spring. The speed increases under the action of a force. This speeding up is called **acceleration.** An unbalanced force can accelerate a body.

But a force can also slow down a body, and such slowing down is also called acceleration. The force of the wind on the sail of an iceboat can speed it up. But a skater racing into the wind finds that he is brought to rest soon after he stops pushing. On a calm day he may coast for a hundred feet or so; but, moving into the wind, he is brought to rest much sooner. The retarding force of the wind produces a negative acceleration. That, of course, is what brakes do to an automobile; utilizing the force of friction, they *decrease* the speed by producing a negative acceleration.

The ability of a force to produce an acceleration is the basic property that is chosen in physics to define the fundamental unit of force. We are going to defer a detailed study of the accelerating effect of forces until Part III of this book, for we want to become fully acquainted with motion first; but we need to use the basic unit of force called the *newton* (abbreviated as "nt"), and we must describe at least tentatively how it is defined.

Let us approach the problem experimentally. We have a metronome, a meter stick, and several identical metal blocks each labeled 1 kg. We also have several long, strong rubber bands that can exert forces. The metronome will measure time intervals, the meter stick distances. We have already discussed the meter as the basic unit of length in the MKS system, and we know that a metronome can be set to tick off seconds. Notice that we don't say we know what time *is;* we simply assert that with a metronome we can measure time intervals. Similarly, we make no claim to an understanding of what *mass* is (we shall devote the whole of Chap. 5 to its properties), but we proceed on the assumption that, if the metal blocks all have the same volume and are all made of the same material (iron), they all have the same mass, in this case 1 kg.

We have now introduced the three basic quantities of physics: mass, length, and time. It was not a very formal introduction, to be sure, but acquaintance through experiment is the only way we can begin to give these terms operational meaning. For the time being, then, we must trust our tools. We trust our meter stick because the manufacturer says he checked it against a metal prototype, stored in Washington, that was once checked against the standard meter in Sèvres. We trust our metronome because we observe that sixty of its ticks correspond to one minute by the electric clock on the wall; we repeat the test several times to convince ourselves that the readings are reproducible. We trust the identity of the metal blocks simply because the manufacturer says that they are all identical and also that they have been checked (for the time being we don't ask how) against nationally and internationally accepted standards of mass.

Our experiment is the following: We slip one end of a long rubber band over a hook attached to one of the blocks, slip the other end of the band over a hook attached to one end of the meter stick, and stretch the band to length L as shown in Figure 3.10. The 1-kg block rests on a thin block of carbon dioxide. We start the metronome ticking and begin counting: $-3, -2, -1, 0$. At 0 we release the block and pull on the stick to keep the rubber band stretched to a length as close to L as possible. As the metronome ticks off the seconds, 1, 2, 3, the block picks up speed. An assistant makes marks on the table indicating where the forward end of the block was at the end of each second. We repeat this several times to be sure that the results are at least approximately reproducible. Since the block was at rest when we counted 0 and moving when we counted 3, it has increased its speed. We shall call the increase Δv.

Next we want to investigate the effect of doubling the force; so we use two identical rubber bands instead of one, both slipped over the two hooks. We repeat the experiment and find that the block, in three seconds, covers about twice as much distance with two rubber bands as it did with one.

We do the experiment again with three identical rubber bands, and we find that the total distance covered in three seconds is now about three times what it was with one band.

It seems that the increase in speed, Δv, is proportional to the number of rubber bands and hence to the force acting on the 1-kg block. We write

$$\Delta v \propto F \qquad [3.4$$

Now we begin a new series of experiments, keeping the force constant (using only one rubber band) but increasing the mass by using first two and then three 1-kg blocks. We discover that, if the distance covered in three seconds by an object with a mass of one kilogram is d, the distance covered in three seconds by an object with a mass of two kilograms is about $d/2$ and by an object with a mass of three kilograms is about $d/3$. This lends *plausibility* (we are not *proving* anything rigorously) to the idea that, when F is constant,

$$\Delta v \propto \frac{1}{m} \qquad [3.5$$

if m is the mass in kilograms. Finally, leaving F and m fixed, but increasing the time, t, to six seconds and then to nine seconds, we make plausible the idea that

$$\Delta v \propto \Delta t \qquad [3.6$$

A single expression that encompasses all three results is

$$\Delta v \propto \frac{F(\Delta t)}{m} \qquad [3.7$$

We read this as "The increase in speed is directly proportional to the force and the time but inversely proportional to the mass." The proportionality sign can be replaced by an equality sign provided we insert a constant of proportionality. Quite arbitrarily—for we have not yet defined the

unit of force—we are going to use 1 as the constant of proportionality. We write, accordingly,

$$\Delta v = \frac{F(\Delta t)}{m} \qquad [3.8$$

which can obviously be rewritten as

$$F = m\frac{\Delta v}{\Delta t} \qquad [3.9$$

We are now ready to define the basic unit of force, the **newton**. *A newton is the unbalanced force that will produce in a mass of one kilogram a change in velocity of one meter per second in one second.*†

How do we get all that from looking at equation 3.9? It's quite simple. Using the units of our MKS system, let us substitute 1 kg for m, 1 m/sec for Δv, and 1 sec for Δt in the right-hand side of the equation. The product thereby becomes

$$\frac{1 \text{ kg} \times 1 \text{ m/sec}}{1 \text{ sec}} = 1 \text{ kg}\frac{m}{sec^2}$$

One unit of force—that is, one newton—is therefore the same as one kilogram-meter per second squared.

Note that we have not rigorously proved equation 3.9; we have only made it plausible. So many

† The product mv is called **momentum**. We introduce it here for future reference. The equation

$$\mathbf{F} = m\left(\frac{\Delta \mathbf{v}}{\Delta t}\right)$$

may be written as

$$\mathbf{F} = \frac{\Delta(m\mathbf{v})}{\Delta t}$$

if m is constant. This may be read as "Force is equal to the rate of change of momentum." This statement is true even if m is variable (see § 24.2).

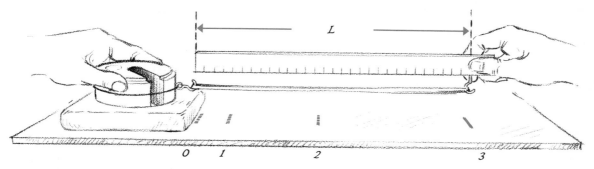

FIG. 3.10. *If the rubber band is kept stretched to the same length,* L, *a constant force will act upon the block and cause it to move with constant acceleration when released.*

FIG. 3.11. *Two forces acting in a line add algebraically. If one points in one direction and the other in exactly the opposite direction, one may be considered positive and the other negative. The result may be zero.*

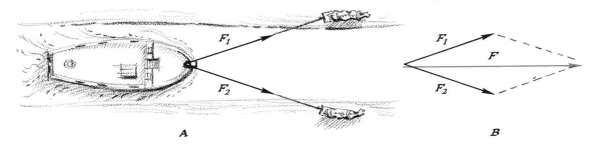

FIG. 3.12. *The barge moves (A) under the action of the resultant of the two forces $\mathbf{F}_1$ and $\mathbf{F}_2$. Its direction in this example is that of neither one, but it points somewhere between the two. The vector diagram (B) shows how to add the vector quantities $\mathbf{F}_1$ and $\mathbf{F}_2$. The resultant, $\mathbf{F}$, is the diagonal of the parallelogram of which $\mathbf{F}_1$ and $\mathbf{F}_2$ are sides.*

accurate experiments have confirmed it, however, that it stands as one of the basic laws of all mechanics. Since the quantity $\Delta v / \Delta t$ is the acceleration, equation 3.9 is also written as $F = ma$.

Although it has taken us some time to define the newton, we are not going to study the implications of the equation $F = ma$ seriously until Part III; yet, since the newton is the accepted unit of force in the MKS system, we had to introduce it here for several reasons. One is that, in checking equations dimensionally, we need to know that force defined dynamically (that is, from equation 3.9) has the dimensions of MLT^{-2}—a result we get directly from the equations

$$\left[m \frac{\Delta v}{\Delta t} \right] = [m] \frac{[\Delta v]}{[\Delta t]} = MLT^{-1}T^{-1} = MLT^{-2}$$

This will come in handy in checking equations. (The square brackets around a quantity indicate that we are considering the physical dimensions of that quantity; for example, $[\pi r^2] = L$. The italic capitals M, L, and T will be used to denote the physical dimensions of mass, length, and time respectively.)

For practical reasons it is good to know that a newton is approximately equal to the pull of the earth on a mass of 0.102 kg. We say "approximately" because the pull of the earth varies slightly from place to place. A newton is also equivalent to a force of 0.2248 pound; a child weighing 100 newtons weighs 22.48 pounds. Here we see a discrepancy between our daily experience, in which bathroom scales are calibrated in pounds, and our physics laboratory experiences, in which, even though few scales are actually labeled in newtons, most of the theoretical calculations involving force are based on the newton (or on some other unit defined in terms of acceleration). We can now drop the matter of units for a while to discuss some other aspects of forces. How, for example, do forces combine with one another?

3.4. Forces Are Vector Quantities

A force has a direction as well as a magnitude. To a man in a sailboat it makes a difference whether the wind is blowing from the east or from the north. When two or more forces combine, the directions as well as the magnitudes play a role.

In describing the effect of the force of the rubber bands on the block (Fig. 3.10), we postulated (and it can be proved) that two forces acting in the same direction have effects that can be added to each other: 2 newtons plus 2 newtons are equivalent to 4 newtons if they act in the same direction. Forces can also be added algebraically when they act in exactly opposite directions if we consider those going one way positive and those going the opposite way negative; 2 newtons + (−2 newtons) = 0 newtons (Fig. 3.11). But how about two forces acting in different directions (not at 0° or 180° to each other)? A barge can be pulled by two horses as shown in Figure 3.12.A. One rope exerts a pull, F_1, in one direction and the other a pull, F_2, in a different direction. We see that the combined effect may be equivalent to that of a single force pulling the barge parallel to the banks. It can be shown, in fact, that, if the forces are represented by arrows whose lengths are proportional to the magnitudes of the forces and whose directions run parallel to the ropes, the diagonal of a parallelogram (Fig. 3.12.B) whose sides are F_1 and F_2 will have the proper magnitude and direction. The parallelogram construction, in other words, provides us with a means of *adding* forces graphically.

EXAMPLE 3.1. One rope pulls a small barge toward the east with a force of 100 nt. Another rope pulls it toward the exact northeast with a force of 200 nt. We wish to know the single force that would have

the effect of both these forces acting simultaneously. We seek a graphical solution (Fig. 3.13.A). Draw an arrow pointing east, and make it 1 in. long to represent 100 nt; this represents the first force, F_1. Starting at the initial point of F_1, draw an arrow pointing northeast, and make it 2 in. long to represent 200 nt; this represents the second force, F_2. Now draw the other sides of the parallelogram, AC and BC, and the diagonal, OC, and draw an arrowhead at the end of OC. The diagonal represents the *resultant* of the two forces F_1 and F_2. We can obtain its magnitude graphically by measuring it carefully with a scale. Since it is 2.80 in. long, it represents a force of 280 nt. Just as important is its direction. With a protractor we can measure the angle, θ, between OC and OA. It is 30°. A complete description of the resultant force, therefore, specifies a magnitude of 280 nt and a direction 30° north of east.

Quantities that have both direction and magnitude and combine according to the parallelogram rule are called **vector quantities.** The fact that forces combine in this way is an *experimental* fact. Whenever we discover physical quantities having both direction and magnitude, we must check experimentally to see if they combine according to the parallelogram rule before we can call them vector quantities.

Let us now describe a construction that is equivalent to the parallelogram rule but more generally applicable. In Figure 3.13.B we redraw the two force vectors F_1 and F_2 of Example 3.1. In Figure

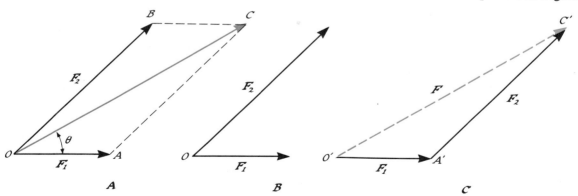

FIG. 3.13. (A) *The parallelogram rule for the addition of vectors: the resultant is the diagonal of the parallelogram of which F_1 and F_2 are sides, whose initial points are coincident at O. (B) In preparation for an alternative construction we begin again with the two vectors, giving them a common initial point at O. (C) The polygon method of adding vectors (in this case the polygon is a triangle): The initial point of F_2 has been shifted to the terminal point of F_1; the resultant has its initial point at O' and its terminal point at C', which is the terminal point of F_2.*

3.13.C we redraw OA with its proper direction and magnitude as $O'A'$, representing vector $\mathbf{F}_1$. Using the terminal point A' as a new initial point, we draw vector $\mathbf{F}_2$ with its proper direction and magnitude ($A'C'$)—that is, parallel to OB and equal to it in length. The vector whose initial point is O' and whose terminal point is C'—the vector $\mathbf{F}$—is the resultant of $\mathbf{F}_1$ and $\mathbf{F}_2$. We can see that this is correct by comparing Figure 3.13.C with the lower half of the parallelogram of Figure 3.13.A. We say that $\mathbf{F}$ is the **vector sum** of $\mathbf{F}_1$ and $\mathbf{F}_2$, and we write

$$\mathbf{F} = \mathbf{F}_1 + \mathbf{F}_2 \qquad [3.10$$

In this book vectors will always be printed in boldface type. Equation 3.10 uses the symbols $=$ and $+$, which so far have had meaning only when the quantities used were algebraic. What we are really doing is inventing an *algebra of vectors*, and equation 3.10 simply summarizes the meaning of Figure 3.13. Observe that the equation $\mathbf{a} = \mathbf{b}$ no longer means that number a equals number b. It means more than that. It means that the vector $\mathbf{a}$ has the same direction and magnitude as the vector $\mathbf{b}$.

A quantity that is even simpler than a force to conceive as a vector is **displacement.** Suppose that a helicopter taxis on the ground for 100 yards in an easterly direction and then taxis 200 yards in a northeasterly direction. Each of these movements is a displacement. What single displacement would have taken us from the starting point to the terminal point? We can visualize the two displacements as vectors and draw them as $\mathbf{d}_1$ and $\mathbf{d}_2$ (according to the triangle rule rather than the parallelogram rule) in Figure 3.14. This vector diagram is a graphical description of how the helicopter actually moved. Since it went 100 yards to the east, we draw OP, or $\mathbf{d}_1$, 1 inch long in an easterly direction. Since it then went 200 yards to the northeast from P to Q, we draw PQ, or $\mathbf{d}_2$, 2 inches long. This time it is obvious that the single displacement, $\mathbf{d}$, from O to Q is the equivalent of the two successive displacements $\mathbf{d}_1$ and $\mathbf{d}_2$. Its magnitude is 280 yards. Its direction is 30° north of east.

For displacements, the rule that says, "Connect the initial point of the second vector to the terminal point of the first vector, and draw the second

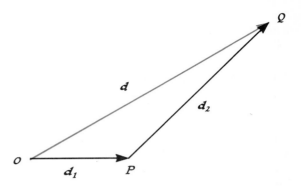

FIG. 3.14. *Displacements combine according to the same rules as forces; in other words, displacement is a vector quantity. The initial point of $\mathbf{d}_2$ is placed at the terminal point of $\mathbf{d}_1$, and the resultant displacement, $\mathbf{d}$, goes from the initial point of $\mathbf{d}_1$ to the terminal point of $\mathbf{d}_2$.*

vector with its proper direction and magnitude," seems obvious indeed. For this reason the displacement vector can be thought of as the most primitive, or "primordial," vector.

Now I can summarize. To be a vector, a quantity must (a) have direction; (b) have magnitude; (c) obey the rule of combination that applies to displacements.

That rule of combination is not limited to two dimensions or to two vectors. A helicopter, for example, moves east 100 yards ($\mathbf{d}_1$), then northeast 200 yards ($\mathbf{d}_2$), then vertically upward 100 yards ($\mathbf{d}_3$). What single displacement, $\mathbf{d}$, would have achieved the same result? It is apparent that the vector OR (Fig. 3.15) is the right answer. It represents the resultant, $\mathbf{d}$, of the three consecutive displacements. We therefore write

$$\mathbf{d} = \mathbf{d}_1 + \mathbf{d}_2 + \mathbf{d}_3 \qquad [3.11$$

What I have said about displacements in three dimensions holds for forces and other vectors as well. We can obtain the sum, or resultant, graphically by attaching the vectors successively "tip to tail." The sum is the vector that goes from the first initial point to the final terminal point.

3.5. The Scalar Called Speed and the Related Vector Called Velocity

A vector has both magnitude and direction. The magnitude is a **scalar,** a quantity whose measure involves only one number. The reader may experience the same surprise and delight at learning that he has used scalars all his life (without calling them by that name) as Molière's Monsieur Jourdain at learning that he had been using prose all his life without knowing it. Temperature is a scalar quantity, and so is mass; but displacement, velocity, acceleration, and force are vector quantities. The *magnitude* of a vector is a scalar. Velocity, as we have seen, is a vector, but its magnitude alone—a scalar—is called **speed**. The speedometer of a car indicates speed only. A compass would be needed to give direction as well. It is not sufficient to know that a car is going fifty miles an hour. You have to know in what direction it is moving if you want to predict where it will be later.

An automobile moving distance s along a path has an average speed defined by the equation

$$\bar{v} = \frac{\Delta s}{\Delta t}$$

The bar over the v indicates the average. This quantity is a scalar. The velocity vector will be denoted by a boldface **v**. Its magnitude, which is the speed, will appear as an italic v. Consider now (Fig. 3.16) the location of a point, A, on the path of a car, given by a displacement vector, $\mathbf{r}_1$, drawn from O. At time Δt later the car is at point B, localized by displacement vector $\mathbf{r}_2$. We have drawn vector AB and labeled it $\Delta \mathbf{r}$. Observe that

$$\mathbf{r}_1 + \Delta \mathbf{r} = \mathbf{r}_2 \qquad [3.12$$

This follows from the rules for vector addition. The initial point of $\Delta \mathbf{r}$ is at the terminal point of $\mathbf{r}_1$; $\mathbf{r}_2$ goes from the first initial point to the last terminal point.

Let us handle equation 3.12 as if it were ordinary algebra:

$$\Delta \mathbf{r} = \mathbf{r}_2 - \mathbf{r}_1 \qquad [3.13$$

We are justified in doing this if we consider $\Delta \mathbf{r}$ the vector that we must add to $\mathbf{r}_1$ in order to get $\mathbf{r}_2$ as

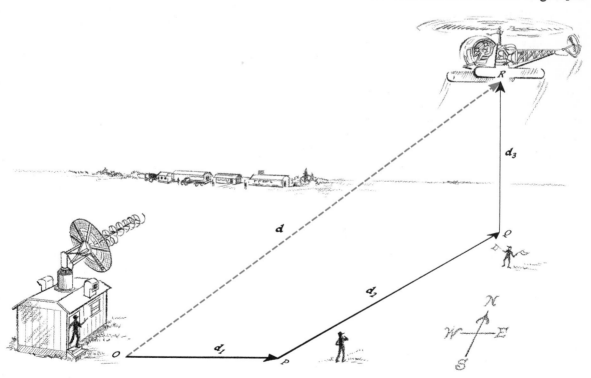

FIG. 3.15. *The polygon rule for combining vectors applies to more than two vectors, and they need not all be in the same plane. The resultant displacement,* **d**, *of a helicopter is the vector that starts at the first initial point,* O, *and ends at the last terminal point,* R, *as a result of the three displacement vectors* **d**₁, **d**₂, *and* **d**₃, *connected end to end as shown.*

a resultant. We are defining the *difference* between two vectors in terms of the sum of two others, just as we do in algebra: the equation $a = b - c$ implies that c added to a will yield b. Now consider the equation

$$\bar{\mathbf{v}} = \frac{\Delta \mathbf{r}}{\Delta t} \qquad [3.14$$

The right-hand side tells us that the dimensions are LT^{-1}, the same as those of speed. But $\bar{\mathbf{v}}$ is a vector. It has the direction of $\Delta \mathbf{r}$. How about its magnitude?

To answer this, we must first explain what $k\mathbf{a}$ means if $\mathbf{a}$ is a vector and k is a scalar. Consider the equation

$$\mathbf{a} + \mathbf{a} = 2\mathbf{a} \qquad [3.15$$

The vector diagram Figure 3.17.A shows that $\mathbf{a} + \mathbf{a}$ is a vector whose direction is that of $\mathbf{a}$ and whose magnitude is 2 times that of $\mathbf{a}$. Figure 3.17.B shows that $3\mathbf{a}$ is a vector whose direction is that of $\mathbf{a}$ and whose magnitude is 3 times that of $\mathbf{a}$. In general, then, $k\mathbf{a}$ is a vector whose direction is that of $\mathbf{a}$ and whose magnitude is k times that of $\mathbf{a}$. Now k is just a number (hence it can represent a scalar quantity); it can be less than one and even negative. For example, $(1/2)\mathbf{a}$ is a vector whose direction is that of $\mathbf{a}$ and whose magnitude is $1/2$ that of $\mathbf{a}$, and $-\mathbf{a}$ is a vector whose magnitude is that of $\mathbf{a}$ and whose direction is exactly opposite to that of $\mathbf{a}$. The various vectors shown in Figure

3.18 were obtained as the result of multiplying a vector, $\mathbf{a}$, by a scalar, k, which took on the values $1, -1, -2, -1/2, 1.4, 3,$ and 4.

Now back to $\Delta \mathbf{r}/\Delta t$. What is its magnitude? Since it can be written as $(1/\Delta t)\Delta \mathbf{r}$, we see that it is a vector whose direction is that of $\Delta \mathbf{r}$ and whose magnitude is $1/\Delta t$ times that of $\Delta \mathbf{r}$. We call $\Delta \mathbf{r}/\Delta t$ the *average-velocity vector*. The limit of this quantity,

$$\lim_{\Delta t \to 0} \frac{\Delta \mathbf{r}}{\Delta t}$$

is the exact velocity, $\mathbf{v}$, of the moving body at a point. It has direction and magnitude. It is apparent that $\bar{\mathbf{v}}$ can also be written as

$$\bar{\mathbf{v}} = \frac{\mathbf{r}_2 - \mathbf{r}_1}{t_2 - t_1} \qquad [3.16$$

3.6. The Three Basic Forces in Nature

We digressed to consider the language of vectors because it is admirably suited to the problems of velocity, acceleration, and forces. Now let us concentrate on a basic question of physics rather than mathematics. How many different kinds of forces are there? Wherever you see things speeding up or slowing down in nature you can be sure that forces are at work. Flowers grow, sap rises in trees, leaves drop, rain falls, the moon orbits round the sun, water falls at Niagara, winds blow, waves roll.

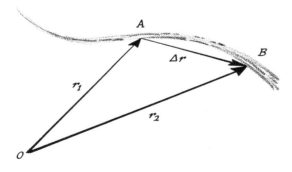

FIG. 3.16. *A body moves in a curved path, two points of which are A and B. Point A may be localized by a vector, $\mathbf{r}_1$, and B by another vector, $\mathbf{r}_2$, having the same origin, O. Because the vector $\Delta \mathbf{r}$, going from A to B, obviously obeys the formula $\mathbf{r}_1 + \Delta \mathbf{r} = \mathbf{r}_2$, we write that $\Delta \mathbf{r} = \mathbf{r}_2 - \mathbf{r}_1$. If it takes time Δt to go from A to B, the average velocity (a vector) is defined as $\Delta \mathbf{r}/\Delta t$.*

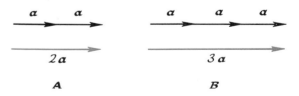

FIG. 3.17. *Addition of vectors illustrated.*

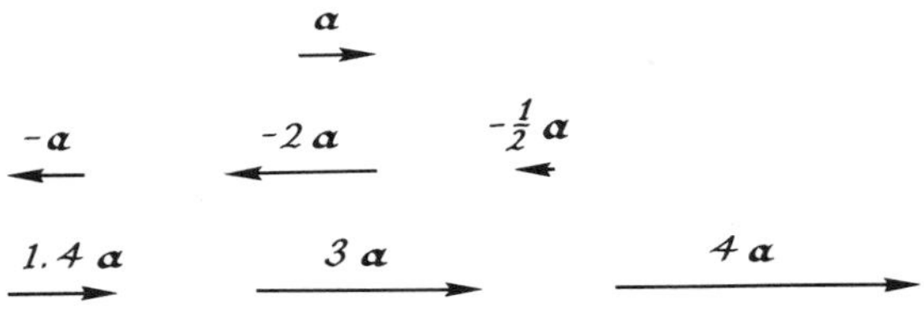

FIG. 3.18. *Vectors representing the effect of multiplying vector $\mathbf{a}$ by the scalars $+1, -1, -2, -1/2, +1.4, +3,$ and $+4$.*

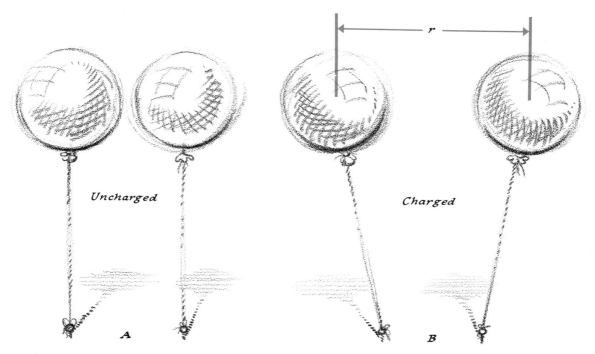

FIG. 3.19. *Two helium-filled balloons, uncharged (A) do not attract or repel each other; the same two balloons, after being rubbed with wool, are electrically charged (B) and repel each other strongly.*

Even in static structures we know that forces of tension exist; the cables of the Golden Gate Bridge exert great force, and a skyscraper must push down very hard on the ground. There seem to be a multitude of forces.

Nevertheless, I assert here that there are basically three kinds of force: electrical, gravitational, and nuclear forces.

We can illustrate electrical forces by an experiment. An inflated toy balloon rubbed with wool will repel another, similarly treated balloon (Fig. 3.19). We attribute this action to their state of electric charge. We shall see later that the force of repulsion obeys the equation

$$F = \frac{KQ_1Q_2}{r^2} \qquad [3.17$$

Strictly speaking, this equation holds if one small object bearing charge Q_1 is separated by distance r from another small object bearing charge Q_2. (We shall see later that, if the charges are measured in a unit called the coulomb, the force will be in newtons if $K = 9 \times 10^9$ nt-m²/coul². We shall not use equation 3.17 much until we reach Part IV, but I do want to point out that the electrical force varies inversely as the square of the distance between the charged bodies.)

Many ordinary objects, such as combs and phonograph records, can be charged by rubbing with a cloth. A pencil, a knife, or even a meter stick, supported in a home-made stirrup such as that shown in Figure 3.20, will exhibit electrical attraction to or repulsion from a suitably charged plastic rod or other charged object. The point of these experiments is to demonstrate that practically anything will exhibit electrical forces under the proper circumstances.

The gravitational attraction between the earth and all objects near it is well known to us. All objects fall under the force of this attraction unless some other force interferes. The gravitational force between an apple, of mass m_1, and the earth, of mass m_2, is

$$F = \frac{Gm_1m_2}{r^2} \qquad [3.18$$

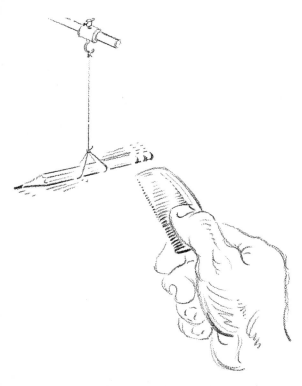

FIG. 3.20. *A simple stirrup made of string can support many household objects in a way that will exhibit electric attractions and repulsions due to charged objects.*

If the masses are in kilograms and the distance, r, between the center of the earth and the center of the apple is in meters, the force, F, will be in newtons if

$$G = 6.670 \times 10^{-11} \text{ nt-m}^2/\text{kg}^2$$

We notice immediately one similarity and one difference between equations 3.17 and 3.18: they both contain the expression $1/r^2$; but equation 3.17 contains the factor 10^9, and 3.18 contains 10^{-11}. The ratio of these two numbers is $10^9/10^{-11} = 10^{20}$. This is a large number! You can name it if you care to. In figures it is 1 followed by twenty zeros:

$$10^{20} = 100,000,000,000,000,000,000$$

This gives us our first clue to the relative strength of electrical and gravitational forces. Equation 3.18 expresses not only the gravitational force that the earth exerts on the apple but also the force that the *apple exerts on the earth!* It holds, in fact, for any small mass m_1 separated by distance r from any mass m_2 in the universe. It holds

even for large spherical objects if r is the distance between their centers. The important points to observe are (a) that all masses attract one another, and (b) that the force of attraction is inversely proportional to the square of the distance between them.

The third basic force is the one that operates at the nuclear level. The force produced by the atomic bomb is essentially due to the release of nuclear forces. They can be enormous, as everyone today knows. They will be discussed in Part VI.

All other forces in nature are in some way or another related to these three: the electrical, the gravitational, and the nuclear. The connection between the forces of our daily experience and these three basic forces is not always obvious. What, for example, about the forces of tension produced in the cables that support the Golden Gate Bridge? What kind are they? We shall eventually see that they are electrical, but for now I simply assert that this can be proved.

We have traveled a long way from the simple push-pull concept to the point where we boil all existing forces in the universe down to three. There are many gaps for us to fill in before it all becomes clear, but it may help to know at the outset that some order can be brought into the apparent chaos of diversity. The basic nature of these three forces underlies our modern concept of forces.

3.7. The Concept of Contact

The three forces, gravitational, electrical, and nuclear, have some things in common. They get stronger as bodies get closer. They can act at a distance, and they can act through a vacuum: the gravitational pull of the sun 93 million miles away holds the earth in its orbit even though the intervening space is practically empty (by earthbound standards).

Yet, in the laboratory, we see that one steel ball can push another only by touching it (Fig. 3.21). When one ball is allowed to hit the other, we can see that both experience forces. One slows down, and the other speeds up. We hear them click. We say that they collide.

Now consider another experiment. Two magnets, oriented to repel each other, are hung as shown in Figure 3.22. (In Chap. 39 I shall show that the force between magnets is due to electric charges in motion.) When we pull back one magnet, then release it and let it swing toward the other, we find that it repels the other without touching it. Both experience forces: one slows down, and one speeds up. This is a collision, but there is no *contact* in the usual sense. That raises a basic question: What *is* contact after all? Is it conceivable that at the atomic level even the collision of two steel balls involves very strong forces acting across very small distances? We leave this interesting question unanswered for the time being. What do you think?

3.8. Summary

Our intuitive notion of force begins with a push or a pull. Forces can deform bodies, accelerate them, or do both. Bodies that return to their original shape when the distorting forces are removed are called elastic. The unit of force in the MKS system is the newton. One newton can change the speed of a body with a mass of one kilogram by one meter per second in one second. Forces are vector quantities. They combine according to the law that governs the addition of displacements. The vector equation $\bar{\mathbf{v}} = \Delta\mathbf{r}/\Delta t$ defines average velocity. Despite the apparent diversity of the forces found in nature, they all fall into one of the following categories: gravitational, electrical, and nuclear. These forces can act at a distance, and they diminish as the distance increases.

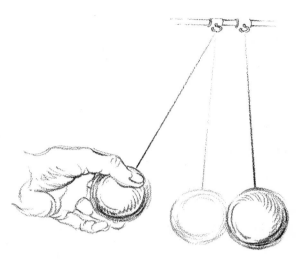

FIG. 3.21. *When the two steel balls shown here collide, we hear a click and observe that one slows down as the other speeds up. We say that they come in contact with each other.*

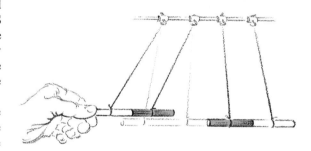

FIG. 3.22. *Magnets can collide with each other without touching if they are oriented to repel each other. Here is a collision without contact.*

Problems

3.1. List some common experiences in which forces produce deformations.

3.2. List some forces producing accelerations.

3.3. 1. Make a chain with three links, using thin rubber bands. Hang the chain on a paper clip that has been Scotch-taped to the wall, and suspend from it a wire coat-hanger; from that hanger suspend four identical hangers, each hooked on the one above. Record on the wall the position of the lower end of the chain. Remove the hangers one at a time, recording each time the lower end of the chain. Graph the elongation against the stretching force (measured by the weight of the hangers). Plot force (f) vertically and elongation (x) horizontally. In order to take the kinks out of the chain, leave one hanger on for the zero reading. An elastic steel spring obeys the relation $F = kx$, in which k is a constant. Does the rubber chain obey a similar relation?

2. An elastic body returns to its original shape when the distorting forces are removed. Find out experimentally if the rubber-band chain is an elastic body.

3.4. The constant k of equation 3.3 is called the stiffness constant. To an already stretched spring an additional force of 100 nt is added. This produces an elongation of 5 cm. What is the value of the stiffness constant? What are its units?

3.5. In arithmetic we know that $3 + 4 = 7$. With vectors, however, a force of 3 lb combined with one of 4 lb might yield a resultant force of 5 lb. Illustrate this with a vector diagram. Could they also add up (vectorially) to 1 lb?

3.6. 1. Using meter sticks and strings, do an experiment to compute the magnitude of the resultant of the following displacements: north 2 miles, east 4 miles, and straight up 5 miles.

2. Compute the magnitude of the resultant of the following forces: one pointing north (200 nt), one pointing east (400 nt), and one pointing straight up (500 nt). Refer to part 1 for a hint.

3.7. Some vector equations have a simple interpretation—for example, $\mathbf{r} = \mathbf{v}_0 t$. Suppose that $\mathbf{v}_0$ points east and has a magnitude of 25 m/sec. Draw, with a common origin, the vectors corresponding to $t = 1$, 2, 3, 4, 5 sec. How would you describe in words the motion of the tip of the arrow? Begin your sentence with "It moves with . . .".

3.8. A bicycle is turned upside down so that the wheels turn freely. A wheel rotates at a constant speed: once in 4 sec. What is the magnitude of the average velocity of a point on the rim (radius 0.5 m) during a quarter rotation? Use the ideas leading to equation 3.14.

3.9. Try some experiments suggested by Figs. 3.19 and 3.20. Try deflecting a very fine stream of water by bringing an electrically charged plastic or glass rod near it. (A comb works.)

3.10. Try an experiment such as that shown in Fig. 3.21. Steel balls for this purpose are available from laboratory supply houses, but large marbles should work if you can glue the string to them. As you observe the behavior, try to analyze the forces that act on the balls. What are their directions, their relative magnitudes, and their mutual effects?

4

Fields

IN THE last chapter I pointed out that the three basic forces—gravitational, electrical, and nuclear—can act at a distance through empty space. We now focus our attention on that space.

4.1. The Field Concept

Newton conceived of space as virtually empty except for such concentrations of mass as stars and planets. Yet it was he who first stated the universal law of gravitation—that an object attracts any other object in the universe with a force that is proportional to the product of the masses and inversely proportional to the square of the dis-

tance between them. According to this, an earth satellite in orbit (Fig. 4.1) is being pulled not only by the earth but also by the sun and the moon and to a lesser degree by the other planets and even by the stars. An object released from rest in space would accelerate in the direction of the resultant of all the forces acting upon it. If you released it at point A (Fig. 4.1), near the earth, it would fall toward the earth. If you released it at point B, near the moon, it would gravitate to the moon. The behavior at A and B would be different, and this gives rise to the idea that space itself is endowed with a property at A that is different from the property at B. We say that the gravitational field at A is different from the gravitational field

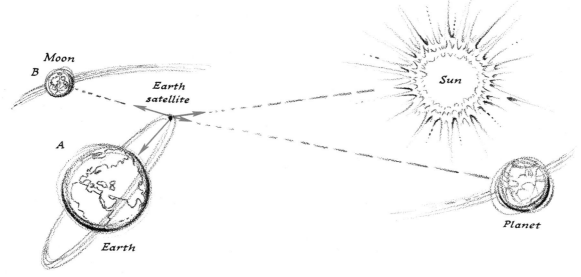

FIG. 4.1. *An earth satellite moves in a gravitational field that is due to the other bodies in space.*

at *B*. At each point of space there is a unique value of the gravitational field.

What does this mean, operationally? Observe that I do not ask, "Does a field really exist?" If we can give instructions on how to define "field" in an operational way, and if different investigators, following these instructions, all get the same answer, within acceptable limits, we shall endow the word "field" with an operational meaning. This is what I propose to do.

4.2. Scalar Fields

We see that a field is a region of space where something measurable can happen at each point. Before considering electric, magnetic, and gravitational fields, all of which are vector fields, let us first explore, with a few examples, the simpler concept of a scalar field.

EXAMPLE 4.1 (a two-dimensional scalar field). Imagine a rectangular flat plate made of steel. Beneath its center is a gas flame (Fig. 4.2). With a special thermometer, a small thermistor, we can take the temperature at different points of the surface. After letting the gas flame burn for a while we find that a *steady state* is achieved—that the temperature at any one point remains constant. The plate is, of course, hotter near the flame and cooler near the edges, but a definite temperature is associated with each point of its surface. Temperature is a scalar quantity; we therefore have here a two-dimensional (*x-y*) scalar field.

EXAMPLE 4.2 (a three-dimensional scalar field). An air-raid siren at the top of a high post is blasting away. A microphone in the vicinity picks up a signal that can be measured on a meter or displayed on an oscilloscope. The thing measured is the amplitude of the air-pressure wave at the point where the microphone is. At every point in the vicinity of the air-raid siren there is a definite reading. This illustrates a three-dimensional (*x-y-z*) scalar field.

The criterion is simple: Choose a two-dimensional or three-dimensional region; if a scalar quantity (such as temperature, pressure, or density) can be measured at all points of the region, a scalar field exists there.

4.3. Vector Fields

One difference between a vector and a scalar, we know, is that a vector has direction as well as magnitude. It takes only one number (for example, 78°F) to describe a scalar quantity. It takes several numbers to describe a vector quantity. The velocity of a car moving in a plane requires two numbers, one for speed and the other for orientation (39° east of north, for example). The velocity of a helicopter moving in the air requires three: one for speed and two for orientation.

We see at once that a vector field is more complicated than a scalar field. The basic ideas, however, are very similar.

EXAMPLE 4.3. Imagine the wind velocity at a point in the vicinity of a tornado (Fig. 4.3). It has direction as well as magnitude. At every point a definite vector represents the wind velocity. Here we have a three-dimensional vector field. (Incidentally, the wind-velocity vector field, unlike the temperature of the steel plate, never reaches a steady state.)

The essential thing about a field is that there is a measurable quantity at every point. If the quantity is a scalar, we have a scalar field; if the quantity is a vector, we have a vector field. Let us now examine the vector fields due to the fundamental forces mentioned in the last chapter.

4.4. Electric Fields

As our first example (Fig. 4.4), consider the region around the metal sphere, *B*, of a charged Van de Graaff generator.† Let us assume that the charge is negative—that is, it is due to an excess of electrons. We explore the region around the sphere as follows. We tie a piece of pith (or a Rice Krispy), at *A*, to a very light silk thread, the other end of which is tied to an insulating handle, *C* (glass, plastic, or hard rubber, for example).

---

† I shall not describe here how the generator works except to say that it deposits electric charges on the outer surface of the sphere by means of an internal mechanism. See § 36.5.

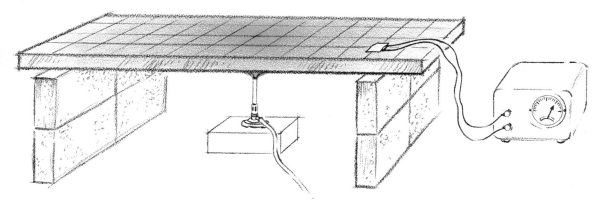

FIG. 4.2. *Temperature as a two-dimensional scalar field.*

We find that the thread points toward the center of the sphere because of the electrical attraction of the sphere for the pith.† The direction of the force at A is clearly indicated by the direction, CA, of the thread. If we move the handle to a new position, the thread still points toward the center of the sphere ($C'A'$, $C''A''$, $C'''A'''$). At each point of space we can imagine a vector pointing to the center of the sphere.

How about the magnitude of such a vector? It is not possible to get good numerical data from such a crude demonstration, but we can definitely show that the field gets weaker as we move away from the sphere. If we move C too far away, the thread falls downward, indicating that the gravitational pull of the earth on the pith is now greater than the electrical attraction of the sphere.

Let us imagine another experiment. Suppose we use a very weak and very light rubber-band chain instead of the thread. Its stretch would measure the magnitude of the pull. We have good reason to believe that it would register a force that varied inversely with the square of the distance between A and the center of the sphere. (This is true, strictly speaking, only if the charge is uniformly distributed on the sphere, and it might not be if the pith ball approached too closely.)

† It does so even if we do not make the pith a conductor by coating it with graphite or aluminum. In the subsequent argument we assume that the pith has a positive charge.

FIG. 4.3. *Only two vectors, v_1 and v_2, are shown here but there is a wind-velocity vector at every point in the space affected by a tornado.*

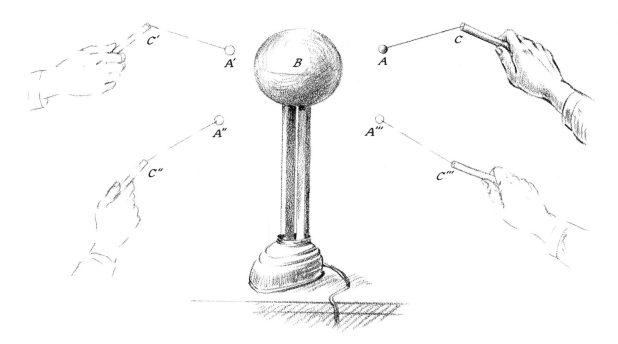

FIG. 4.4. *A classroom Van de Graaff generator can produce a sizable electric charge on its metal sphere.*

The vector field in this case is due to what we call the **electric field intensity, E,** which is defined as follows:

$$\mathbf{E} = \mathbf{F}/q \qquad [4.1$$

In this equation **F** is the force, in newtons, felt by a charged body (such as the pith) at A, and q is the electric charge, in coulombs, carried by it (one coulomb is the charge on about 6×10^{18} electrons). The direction of the vector **E** is that of **F**, and the magnitude is $1/q$ times the magnitude of **F**. The symbol **E** stands for the force per unit charge at a point. Now q does not have to be a whole coulomb in order for us to measure the force per unit charge any more than you have to run a whole mile in order to measure your speed in miles per hour. An hour is too long an interval, and a coulomb happens to be much too large an electric charge to rest on something like a rice kernel.

We can now imagine another experiment that may clarify some of the advantages of the field concept. Suppose you are in a room that has absolutely nothing else in it. You bring into it the pith ball, A, on which you know there is a charge of magnitude q, tied to a very light rubber band whose stretch can serve as a measure of force. The band is also tied to an insulating handle, C. You discover that the charged pith ball is pulled toward one of the upper corners of the room (Fig. 4.5). You move about the room and observe that the rubber band does not always point precisely to the corner but does point in approximately the same

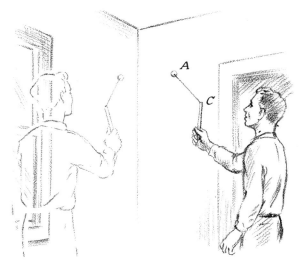

FIG. 4.5. *The point of this illustration is that we can measure a field without knowing its cause.*

direction no matter where you hold C. By measuring the stretch of the rubber band, you know the force, $\mathbf{F}$, that is acting on A. You know everything you need for computation of the field intensity, $\mathbf{E}$. At each point you simply compute $\mathbf{E} = \mathbf{F}/q$. The totality of these vectors, each associated with one position of A in the room, *is* the electric-intensity vector field.

Notice that what we have done is to give an operational set of instructions on how to measure that field. We may, of course, be curious about *why* the rubber band points the way it does, and we may surmise that there is a strong Van de Graaff generator outside the room; but we don't really need to know what the *cause* is. We have operational proof that an electric-intensity vector field exists within the room; we have recognized its existence and measured it.

4.5. The Graphical Representation of Vector Fields

One way to map a field is to draw many vectors in it with their proper directions and magnitudes. The electric field around an electrically charged sphere would require large vectors near the sphere

and progressively smaller ones as we moved away from it, but all would point toward its center (Fig. 4.6.A). Theoretically, we could treat each point in space as the initial point of a vector, but many vectors would then overlap on any radial line. We therefore draw only a representative sample of vectors. The advantage of the vector representation is that it shows graphically the direction and the relative magnitude of the electric field at many points.

Suppose now that we draw only the radial lines, with only one arrowhead on each (Fig. 4.6.B). The direction of the field is clear enough. At any point in space a radial line points to the center of the sphere. Now observe that, even if we draw only a finite number of radial lines to points equally spaced along the sphere, they are close together near the sphere and less close farther away. The *density of lines* is therefore an indication of field strength.† Hence both the direction and the rela-

---

† If n radial lines cross a sphere of radius r_1, the same n lines will cross a larger concentric sphere of radius r_2. The number of lines per square centimeter crossing the spheres is $n/4\pi r_1^2$ and $n/4\pi r_2^2$, respectively, since $4\pi r^2$ is the formula for the surface area of a sphere. Hence the line density falls off as the inverse square of r, just as we should wish for an electric field.

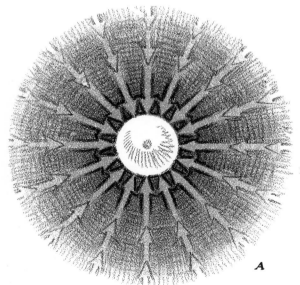

A

B

FIG. 4.6. *Two ways of mapping a field.*

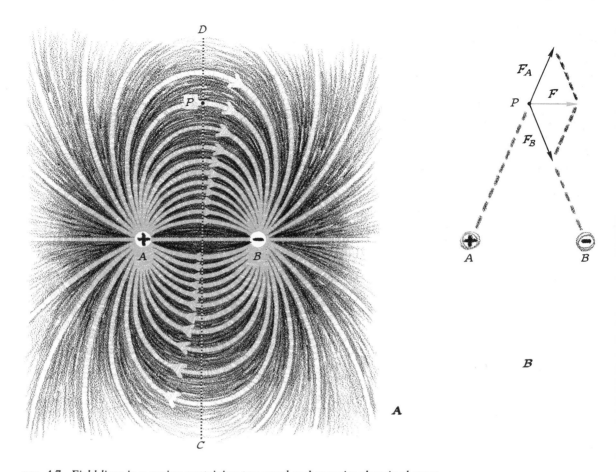

FIG. 4.7. *Field lines in a region containing two equal and opposite electric charges.*

tive magnitude of an electric field can be indicated by the field lines alone. They represent the vector nature of **E** without the drawing of many vectors.

The field lines in a region containing two equal and opposite electric charges are shown in Figure 4.7.A. A conducting sphere at A has charge $+Q$, and a similar sphere at B has charge $-Q$. The electric field intensity can be represented by the curved field lines shown. First let us see if the pattern looks plausible. In the space near one of the spheres we expect the effects of that sphere to predominate; so the pattern should resemble the radial pattern of Figure 4.6.B, and it does. If we move away from the charges along the line CD, which is the perpendicular bisector of AB, we expect the field to get weaker. Hence we expect the line density to diminish, and it does. Finally, how do we account for the fact that all the field

lines crossing CD run parallel to AB? To answer this question, we return to an analysis by means of vectors.

In Figure 4.7.B we redraw A and B and the point P, but not the lines of Figure 4.7.A. We then ask, "What force would a unit positive charge (this is the arbitrary convention) at P experience because of charge $+Q$ on A?" It would experience a repulsion, $\mathbf{F}_A$, in the direction AP, as shown. Next we ask, "What force would the unit positive charge at P experience because of charge $-Q$ on B?" It would experience an attraction, $\mathbf{F}_B$, in the direction PB, as shown. The resultant of the two vectors $\mathbf{F}_A$ and $\mathbf{F}_B$ is $\mathbf{F}$, the diagonal of the parallelogram whose sides are $\mathbf{F}_A$ and $\mathbf{F}_B$. Because the charges on A and B are numerically equal and P is equidistant from A and B, $\mathbf{F}_A$ and $\mathbf{F}_B$ are equal in magnitude. The resultant, $\mathbf{F} = \mathbf{F}_A + \mathbf{F}_B$, must

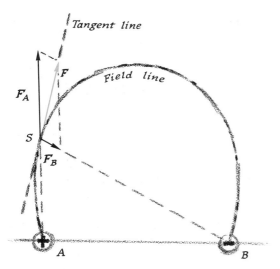

FIG. 4.8. *Direction of a field vector when the field line is curved.*

any point of a field line has the direction of the field vector at the point. At point S of Figure 4.8, for example, the separate vectors $\mathbf{F}_A$ and $\mathbf{F}_B$ are drawn, along with their resultant, $\mathbf{F}$. We observe that $\mathbf{F}$, the field vector at S, *is* tangent to the field line there. The field lines do, therefore, provide an adequate representation of both the direction and the relative magnitude of the electric-intensity vector at each point. The density of lines shows the relative magnitude, and the direction of the line (the direction of its tangent) shows the direction, of the vector.

Figure 4.9 illustrates three electric-field patterns produced between charged electrodes (electrically conducting bodies). Observe that the field lines always meet the surface of an electrode normally. Look for regions where the field is strong and for others where it is weak.

therefore be parallel to AB. Since this argument applies to any point on the perpendicular bisector, the field lines should all be perpendicular to CD; and Figure 4.7.A shows that they are. We have come a long way in reconciling the field-line diagram with the concept of vectors.

It can be shown that a tangent line drawn at

4.6. The Direction of a Curve: a Mathematical Concept

We know what the direction of a straight line is, but the direction of a curve deserves a little analysis. Imagine an automobile moving on a circular

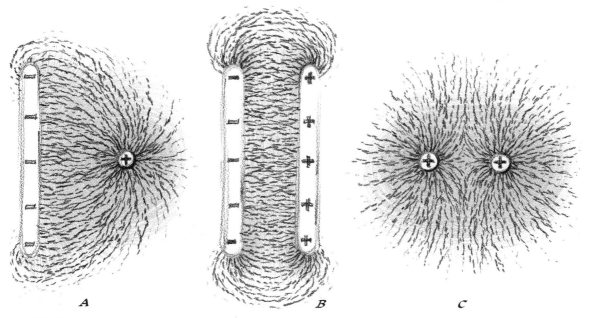

FIG. 4.9. *Electric-field patterns produced between charged conductors of different shapes, as shown by grass seeds floating on oil.*

track (Fig. 4.10). Looking down on it from above, we see it traveling clockwise in a circle (A). We say that it is traveling east at A, south at B, west at C, and north at D. In other words, we *do* associate direction with a point moving in a curved path. Let us analyze carefully what this means.

In part B of the figure we have taken the top of part A and enlarged it. We have drawn three secant lines, AB', AB'', and AB'''. Imagine an infinite set of secant lines, each going through A and through one of a sequence of points, B', B'', B''', . . . , each progressively closer to A. The *sequence of lines* AB', AB'', AB''', . . . has as its limit the line T, tangent at A. Now T is not a secant line, but it *is* the limit of a sequence of secant lines. We *define* the direction of the curve at A as the direction of the tangent line at A.

The direction of any curve—it doesn't have to be a circle—at a point is simply the direction of its tangent line at that point. For electric and gravitational fields, in particular, the direction of a field line at a point is simply the direction of a tangent line at that point. Although this is no doubt intuitively evident, I shall go into the matter mathematically to illustrate how the limit concept is used.

A mathematical way of dealing with the direction of a curve is to give the *slope* of the curve. Let's see what this means. Let the function $y = f(x)$ be plotted on a set of rectangular x-y coordinates (Fig. 4.11). We know what the slope of a straight line is. The slope of the secant line AB, for example, is (by definition) $\Delta y/\Delta x$. (The engineer would say it is the *rise* divided by the *run*.) The slope of the tangent line at A is, by a repetition of the previous argument, the limit of the sequence of the slopes of the secant lines through the point A. Therefore

$$\text{slope of tangent line at } A = \lim_{\Delta x \to 0} \frac{\Delta y}{\Delta x} \qquad [4.2$$

The slope of the curve at A, being defined as the slope of the tangent line at A, is therefore also

$$\lim_{\Delta x \to 0} \frac{\Delta y}{\Delta x}$$

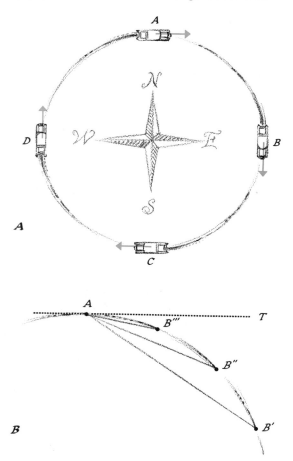

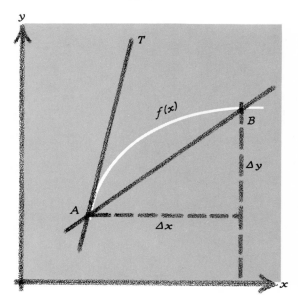

FIG. 4.10. *Analysis of the direction of a curve.*

FIG. 4.11. *Slope of a curve.*

The evaluation of this limit for many special functions lies at the heart of the differential calculus. In order to give you some practice with the Δ-notation, I shall exhibit a few examples here.

EXAMPLE 4.4. We wish to plot the curve $y = x^2$ from $x = 0$ to $x = 3$ and evaluate the slope of the curve at $x = 2$ (Fig. 4.12). First observe that, at $x = 2$, $y = 4$, and that, at $x = 3$, $y = 9$. The secant line S between these two points therefore has the slope $\Delta y/\Delta x = (9 - 4)/(3 - 2) = 5/1 = 5$. We see from the diagram that the slope of the line T, tangent at A, must be less than 5. Let us write (x, y) for the coordinates of A and $(x + \Delta x, y + \Delta y)$ for the coordinates of B. Now $y = f(x) = x^2$. Therefore

$$y + \Delta y = f(x + \Delta x) = (x + \Delta x)^2$$
$$= x^2 + 2x(\Delta x)^2 + (\Delta x)^2 \qquad [4.3$$

But

$$y = x^2 \qquad [4.4$$

Subtracting equation 4.4 from 4.3, we get

$$\Delta y = 2(x)(\Delta x) + (\Delta x)^2 \qquad [4.5$$

Now we begin to consider our special case. We let x equal 2; then

$$\Delta y = 4(\Delta x) + (\Delta x)^2 \qquad [4.6$$

To consider the secant line AB, we also let Δx equal 1. Then

$$\Delta y = 4(1) + 1 = 5$$

and

$$\Delta y/\Delta x = 5/1 = 5$$

as we expected. But that is still only the slope of a certain secant line. Let us go back to equation 4.6 and divide through by Δx:

$$\frac{\Delta y}{\Delta x} = \frac{4(\Delta x) + (\Delta x)^2}{\Delta x} \qquad [4.7$$

$$= 4 + (\Delta x) \qquad [4.8$$

Now we can sense *intuitively* that, as Δx approaches 0, $\Delta y/\Delta x$ approaches 4. Therefore

$$\left(\lim_{\Delta x \to 0} \frac{\Delta y}{\Delta x} \right)_{\text{at } x = 2} = 4$$

The slope of the curve at A is therefore precisely 4.

Another point deserves mention here. We have been dealing with x and y as pure numbers. In physical problems they would also have physical dimensions. We have used a large unit of distance on the x axis and a small one on the y axis simply

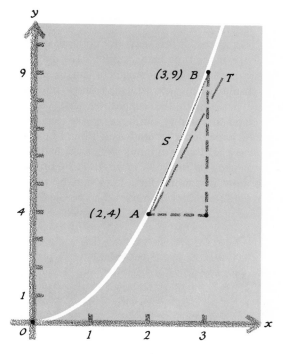

FIG. 4.12. *Plot of the function* $y = x^2$ *from* $x = 0$ *to* $x = 3$.

to make the plotting of points easier. The angle between the tangent line and the x axis is affected, obviously, by this choice. The mathematical computation of the slope, however, is not affected.

4.7. Magnetic Fields

We can get the best intuitive grasp of what "field" means physically by handling a magnet and feeling how an iron object, such as a nail, is pulled to it. With a modern Alnico magnet a force of several newtons can be felt while the magnet and the nail are still a few millimeters apart. The magnetic field feels very real.

You may have wondered why I did not mention magnetic fields earlier, along with the basic electric, gravitational, and nuclear fields. The reason is a bit complicated. It has to do with the fact that all magnetic effects are due to moving electric charges. The electric field is therefore still the basic one. We believe electric charges, even in a so-called permanent magnet, to be responsible for the magnetic effect.

The details of all this need not concern us until Part IV. For the time being, because the magnetic fields around permanent magnets can be graphically displayed by iron filings, I show one such display here—with the suggestion that you try your hand at making similar ones. A magnet, a sheet of paper over it, and iron filings in a salt shaker are all the equipment you need to obtain patterns such as that of Figure 4.13. Figure 4.14 shows how individual field lines can be plotted with a small magnetic compass. The needle orients itself along the tangent to a line (approximately).

Moving the compass through its own diameter in the direction last pointed by the needle then puts it approximately on the continuation of the field line. In its new position it will have a new orientation. The process can be repeated as you follow a line completely from one pole of the magnet to the other.

The pattern shown in Figure 4.15 was produced by iron filings arranging themselves on a plastic sheet while electric charges flowed through a coil of copper wire. This is our first experimental clue to the fact that magnetic fields are related to electric charges in motion (electric current). I shall say more of this later.

4.8. Gravitational Fields

At every point of space in the vicinity of a large object such as the earth a small object of mass m experiences a gravitational force, **F**. Therefore, by definition, a gravitational field exists. It is a vector field. The direction at any point is that of the force **F** felt by the mass m. If we consider the earth as a perfect sphere, all the gravitational field vectors should point toward its center. The field lines,

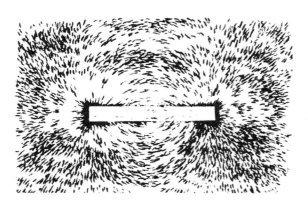

FIG. 4.13. *Iron filings in a magnetic field.*

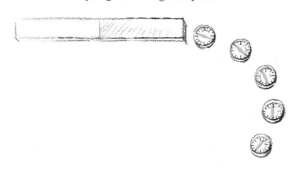

FIG. 4.14. *An individual field line may be plotted with a small compass. Mark two points on the paper indicating the ends of the needle after it has come to rest under the action of the field. Move the compass through a distance equal to its diameter along the line joining the two points. The needle will now assume a new position. Repeat the operation. The series of dots will be an approximate representation of a field line. (See Prob. 4.2.)*

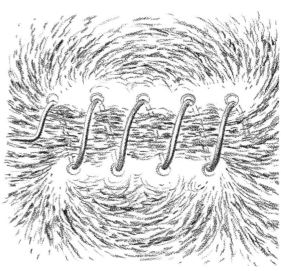

FIG. 4.15. *Field lines produced by a coil of wire carrying an electric current.*

therefore, are again radial lines emanating from the center of the sphere. The precise definition of this gravitational field vector, **γ**, is

$$\mathbf{\gamma} = \mathbf{F}/m \qquad [4.9$$

The vector is, in other words, the force per unit of mass. The MKS units are newtons per kilogram, written as nt/kg. The physical dimensions are $MLT^{-2}/M = LT^{-2}$. Gravitational fields around objects of ordinary laboratory size are difficult to measure, but the field around a massive object like the earth is strong enough to exert the sizable pulls we experience daily. On the surface of the earth, the magnitude of the gravitational field vector is close to 9.8 nt/kg; it gets weaker with distance, following an inverse-square relation.

The present interest in space exploration demands accurate knowledge of such fields and of those extending much farther away from the earth as well. The sun is the most massive body in our planetary system. Its effects are felt even farther

away than the planet Pluto, which is more than 3,666,000,000 miles away, completing one revolution in its orbit every 284 years.

The exploration of the fields in the vicinity of the earth is intensely active today. A great deal of this activity was stimulated by the IGY, the International Geophysical Year, beginning in July 1957, during which many aspects of geophysics, including the magnetic, electric, and gravitational fields around the earth, were intensively investigated.

It is interesting to conceive of the earth as the seat of powerful fields. The curved green lines in Figure 4.16 represent the magnetic field lines; the straight white lines represent the gravitational field lines. Not shown are the electric field lines, which are due to the earth's being a charged sphere (with a charge density of about 1.2×10^{-3} coul/km²), nor the varying fields—those associated with transient electrical storms, for example. The exploration of these fields requires the most advanced technological tools of rocketry and **telemetry** (the transmission of data by radio waves). One of the least expected results of rocket exploration during the IGY was the discovery of the huge belts of radioactivity now called the Van Allen belts, plotted in cross-section in Figure 4.17.

4.9. Why is the Study of Fields Important?

One of the motives of such study is to know more and more about the universe. This is simply the modern counterpart of the ancient quest of astronomers and philosophers. If there are magnetic, electric, gravitational, and other fields out in space, we want to know about them.

I have said nothing about nuclear fields because they are extremely short-range fields and because experimental confirmation of their existence must wait until we have learned more about the basic tools of physics.

We know theoretically and experimentally that, though the electric and gravitational fields diminish with distance, their intensity never goes to zero. The expressions $\mathbf{E} = \mathbf{F}/q$ (force per unit charge) for electric field intensity and $\mathbf{\gamma} = \mathbf{F}/m$ (force per

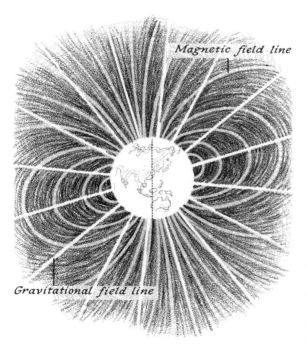

Magnetic field line

Gravitational field line

FIG. 4.16. *The earth as the seat of magnetic and gravitational fields extending far out into space.*

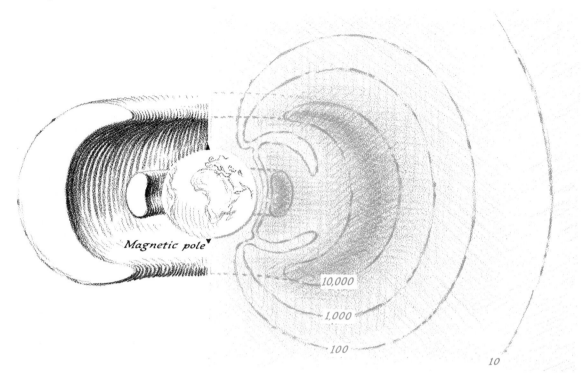

FIG. 4.17. *The Van Allen belts in cross-section. The figures express relative intensities of radiation.*

unit mass) for gravitational field intensity turn out to be inversely proportional to the square of the distance. The magnitude of **E** due to charge Q is proportional to Q/r^2. The magnitude of **γ** due to mass M is proportional to M/r^2. The constants that will convert these proportionalities into equalities are not important here. The important idea is that neither **E** nor **γ** actually vanishes anywhere. They may get too small for us to measure with our present instruments, but we have good theoretical reasons for believing that they do not really vanish.

Our interest in fields will finally extend all the way from the extragalactic realms of space down to the microscopic, atomic, and nuclear realms. The atom turns out to be held together by electric fields, and the nucleus by even more powerful nuclear fields. There may be philosophical argument about their reality; but the physicist today

lives with operational knowledge of nuclear, electric, and gravitational fields.

4.10. Summary

If a vector quantity can be measured at all points of a region, a vector field exists there. The vector at each point has a definite direction and magnitude. Electric, magnetic, and gravitational fields are vector fields. Electric intensity is defined as the force per unit charge at a point: $\mathbf{E} = \mathbf{F}/q$. Similarly, the force per unit mass at a point defines the gravitational field: $\mathbf{γ} = \mathbf{F}/m$.

The direction of a field at any point is that of the tangent to a field line at that point, and the magnitude of the field vector there is indicated by the density of field lines. Scalar fields have a magnitude, but no direction, at each point.

Problems

4.1. Fig. 4.18 represents an overhead view of a room with a fireplace in it. When a fire is burning, it draws air from the room into the fireplace. First assume that all windows and doors are closed but slightly leaky.

1. Assuming that the window at *B* is closed, draw a set of lines representing the field lines of the air-velocity vector field near the floor. The two characteristics to remember are: (a) The direction of a curve at a point is the direction of the velocity of the air at the point. (b) The velocity is higher where the lines are crowded than where they are far apart.

2. Repeat, assuming that the window at *B* is open.

4.2. A very instructive project for home or laboratory is to plot many field lines surrounding a flat bar magnet by using a small compass needle as described in connection with Fig. 4.14. First find the north-south direction in the room by using the compass far from magnets and other disturbing influences.

Then place the magnet, with its long axis parallel to the north-south line, on a large sheet of paper in such a way that, when the compass is placed on the perpendicular bisector of the line segment drawn from one end of the magnet to the other, the compass points *opposite* to the way it points when the magnet is removed. Along this perpendicular bisector the field intensity due to the magnet gets weaker as you move away from the magnet, and at some point it will be equal and opposite to the magnetic field due to the earth, making the resultant field intensity zero there. Drawing several field lines that start at one pole and end at the other will help to clarify the field concept and will locate these special points where the resultant field intensity is zero.

4.3. A positive charge resides on a small sphere at *A* (Fig. 4.19). A negative charge of equal magnitude resides on a small sphere at *B*. The curve joining them is supposed to be a field line. Observe the direction of this line at *C*, which is on the perpendicular bisector of *AB*; and, after constructing the resultant of the vectors that would act on a small positive charge at *C* because of the charges at *A* and *B*, criticize the drawing.

4.4. 1. *ABC* is a right triangle whose sides, *CA*, *AB*, and *BC*, are, respectively, 3, 4, and 5 meters long. Assume equal positive charges at *A* and *B*. By a careful construction determine the direction of the electric-field-intensity vector at *C*. (The force due

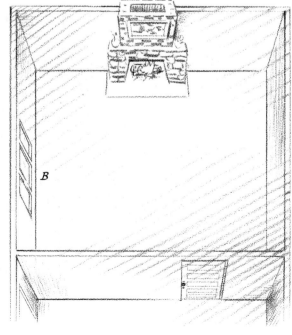

FIG. 4.18

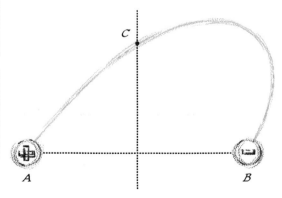

FIG. 4.19

to the charge at B on a small charge at C is proportional to $1/25$; that due to the charge at A is proportional to $1/9$.)

2. Repeat for the case in which the charges at A and B are opposite in sign.

3. Determine, from the graphs, the ratio of the two magnitudes of the resultant vectors.

The following problems are related to the field concept only as the slope of a curve is related to the direction of a field line. They appear here primarily to continue the development of the limit concept in preparation for its use in the study of motion.

4.5. The numbered exercises exhibit a pair of sequences each of which approaches zero as a limit but whose ratio does not. The answers are given but you should work out the details. Then solve the following problem.

1. Write the first few terms of the sequence whose nth term is 10^{-n}. Answer: 0.1, 0.01, 0.001, 0.0001, . . .

2. What is the limit of the sequence? Answer: zero.

3. Another sequence has the nth term

$$2(10^{-n}) + 10^{-2n}$$

Write the first few terms. Answer: 0.21, 0.0201, 0.002001, . . .

TABLE 4.1

t (sec)	y (cm)
0.00	0.00
0.50	10.0
1.00	15.0
1.25	15.7
1.50	15.0
2.00	10.0
2.50	0.00
3.00	−15.00

4. What is the limit of this sequence? Answer: zero.

5. Write the first few terms of the sequence obtained by dividing the terms of part 3 by the corresponding terms of part 1. Answer: 2.100, 2.010, 2.001, . . .

6. What is the limit of this sequence? Answer: 2.

Consider the function $y = x^2$ of Example 4.4. The analysis leads to (equation 4.5)

$$\Delta y = 2x(\Delta x) + (\Delta x)^2$$

Hence $\Delta y/\Delta x = 2x + \Delta x$. Use the values $x = 1$ and $\Delta x = 0.1$, 0.01, 0.001, 0.0001 to evaluate the corresponding set of values of $\Delta y/\Delta x$. Answer: 2.1, 2.01, 2.001, 2.0001, . . . What is the limit of this sequence?

4.6. You are given the function $y = 3x^2 + 1$.

1. Using the procedure of Example 4.4, find a general expression for $\Delta y/\Delta x$.

2. Evaluate the expression at $x = 2$ for $\Delta x = 1/2$.

3. Find

$$\lim_{\Delta x \to 0} \frac{\Delta y}{\Delta x}$$

at $x = 2$ by considering a sequence of $\Delta y/\Delta x$ when $\Delta x = 1/2$, $1/4$, $1/8$, $1/16$, etc.

4.7. The displacement y as a function of the term t has the values given in Table 4.1. We shall continue to call $\Delta y/\Delta t$ the slope of the curve even though in this problem the physical meaning of $\Delta y/\Delta t$ is speed (cm/sec).

1. Plot y as a function of t from $t = 0.00$ sec to $t = 3.00$ sec on a full-page graph ($8\frac{1}{2}'' \times 11''$). Draw the set of secant lines to the curve that start at $t = 0.50$ sec and end at $t = 2.50$ sec, 1.50 sec, 1.00 sec, 0.75 sec, 0.60 sec. Also draw the tangent to the curve at $t = 0.50$ sec. From the graph find the slope of each of the secant lines and of the tangent line.

2. The equation for this curve is $y = 25t - 10t^2$ (in which the 25 stands for cm/sec and the 10 for cm/sec²). Carry through a calculation similar to that done in § 4.6 to find an algebraic expression for the slope $\Delta y/\Delta t$. Then take the limit as Δt approaches 0, and find the value of the slope of the tangent line at $t = 0.50$ sec. Compare this with the slope of the tangent as found in part 1.

Matter

"What is matter?"
"Never mind!"
"What is mind?"
"No matter!"

THE DICTIONARY says that matter is (1) what a thing is made of; (2) whatever occupies space and is perceptible to the senses in some way. These definitions can serve as a point of departure; but, since they do not tell us how to measure matter, they are not satisfactory from an operational point of view. (The dictionary also talks about "laughing matter," "printed matter," and "matter of fact," illustrating uses of the word that are irrelevant to our present discussion.)

5.1. The Properties of Matter

In previous chapters we found it difficult to talk about space without mentioning matter, and now we see that the reverse is also true: "whatever *occupies space* and is perceptible to the senses in some way." As examples of matter we may cite *sticks* and *stones*, *men*, *moons*, and *missiles*, or *cabbages* and *kings*. Everything your eyes can see or your hands can touch, in fact, is matter; and many things you can't see (the air we breathe) are matter also.

This chapter could be called "The Properties of Matter in Bulk," for it will concentrate on *molar* samples of matter and their properties. Whether atomic and extragalactic aggregates of matter have the same properties will be considered else-

where. What does the literature of physics have to say about the properties of matter? A great deal! A 332-page book entitled *The Properties of Matter*† names, in its chapter titles, elasticity, compressibility, viscosity, capillarity, surface films, diffusion, and osmosis. These words suggest the physical properties of matter that have been of theoretical and practical interest to the physicist and the engineer, but the list is not exhaustive. Many others could have been included, such as electrical conductivity, hardness, and transparency to light. Haven't we bitten off too big a chunk for one chapter? We can't do justice to such a list, and we won't attempt it. We are going to limit ourselves to a few of the basic properties common to *all* kinds of matter. Two of them, mass and weight, which are subtle, and others, such as density, which, viewed superficially, seems obvious but hides some subtleties, we shall at least uncover.

Matter exists in three forms. We call them the *states* of matter: solid, liquid, and gas. The outward distinctions of these are well known because of the common example of water, which is known to us as ice, water, and vapor. A substance that is almost as common today is carbon dioxide, now

† F. C. Champion and N. Davy, *The Properties of Matter*, 3rd edition (Blackie & Son, London, 1959).

sold both in the gaseous form, for carbonating water, and in the solid form, called Dry Ice, for use when low temperatures are desired.†

Carbon dioxide, by the way, is a fascinating substance. For one thing, it passes directly from the solid to the gaseous state, at room temperature, without going through the liquid state; and, if it were allowed to do so in a tightly closed chamber, its pressure would rise to a value more than fifty times greater than the normal pressure of the atmosphere! We mention this primarily because a device called the "frictionless puck," which utilizes carbon dioxide, will be used a great deal in later sections. But we must forgo the discussion of these and related phenomena. An explanation of them would take us into the atomic realm of matter, and we wish to stay in the molar realm for the time being.

In many of the illustrations that follow we shall use solid matter, but the properties of weight and mass apply to all three states. Of all the properties of matter, however, perhaps the one of greatest physical importance is inertia. Let us try to clarify what this means.

† A mixture of carbon dioxide and alcohol can, under ordinary laboratory conditions, reach temperatures below −70°C. Since mercury, which is a liquid at room temperatrue, freezes at −38.87°C, we can make a mercury hammer that can drive real nails by freezing mercury in a mixture of carbon dioxide and alcohol.

5.2. Inertial Mass

Historically, a consideration of astronomical bodies preceded and motivated the detailed study of the properties of earthbound matter. To answer questions about the planets, men had to perform experiments with matter in the laboratory. Here is a description of a simple experiment that will guide our thinking (Fig. 5.1). Since solid carbon dioxide is readily available, we shall use a Dry Ice puck to illustrate almost frictionless motion. The puck, D, consists of a chamber into which pieces of solid carbon dioxide can be inserted. A rubber stopper seals the top. In the base is a tiny hole out of which carbon dioxide gas can escape. The puck rides on this invisible layer of gas. A suction cup, S, with a vertical handle, is made fast to a flat horizontal sheet of glass, G. A rubber band, R, makes visible by its stretch the tension in the strings between which it is tied. The other ends of the strings are looped round D and S. A slight tangential push on D starts it moving in a circular path. A visible stretch in the rubber band demonstrates that a force, **F**, is acting on the puck to keep it moving in a circle.

If the string is burned through when the puck is at point A, the puck travels thereafter in a straight line, ABC, along the tangent to its former circular path. This illustrates a basic and impor-

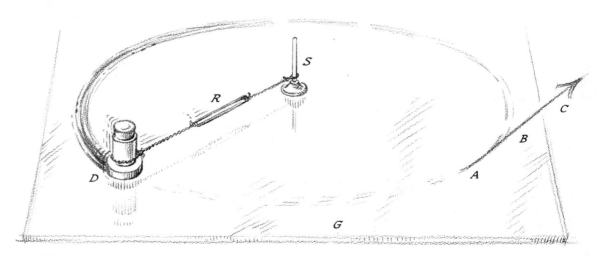

FIG. 5.1. *A Dry Ice puck moving in a circle with negligible friction under the action of a central force.*

tant property of matter. Left alone (that is, with no forces acting on it), a body in motion continues to move in a straight line at a constant speed. Countless other experiments have confirmed this statement. Neither the motion of the planets round the sun nor the motion of a man-made earth satellite can be understood unless we first grasp this elemental fact: *Matter can travel in a straight line at a constant speed without need of an applied force.* (A body at rest continues at rest unless acted upon by an external force.)

In this experiment the other forces acting *on the puck* were its weight (downward), the push of the carbon dioxide (upward), and the very slight friction between the puck and the glass. No experiment involving motion has ever been performed with absolutely no friction, but no experiment has revealed a contradiction of the idea that matter always behaves as I have said.

This behavior confirms what the equation

$$\mathbf{F} = m\frac{\Delta \mathbf{v}}{\Delta t} \qquad [5.1$$

predicts: that, if the vector sum of the forces acting on the body is zero, the change in velocity, $\Delta \mathbf{v}$, is also zero. Let us illustrate how vectors are treated algebraically. We use $\mathbf{v}_2$ for the new velocity and $\mathbf{v}_1$ for the old:

$$\mathbf{v}_2 - \mathbf{v}_1 = \Delta \mathbf{v} = \mathbf{0} \qquad [5.2$$

Then

$$\mathbf{v}_2 - \mathbf{v}_1 = \mathbf{0} \qquad [5.3$$

and

$$\mathbf{v}_2 = \mathbf{v}_1 \qquad [5.4$$

The new velocity equals the old. In other words, the velocity is constant. It does not change in direction or in magnitude.

Here is where the word "inertia" creeps in. We associate this behavior of a body with inertia; we say that the object possesses *inertial mass*, abbreviated as m_i. The symbol for mass in equation 5.1 should therefore be m_i, and the equation should be written as

$$\mathbf{F} = m_i \frac{\Delta \mathbf{v}}{\Delta t} \qquad [5.5$$

The newton, then, is, strictly speaking, defined in terms of the change in velocity experienced by a body with inertial mass under the influence of an external force.

All material bodies have inertial mass; that is, they have the ability to offer resistance to change in their motion. This is a universal property of material bodies. I have indulged in a bit of circular reasoning; what I should say is that this property *defines* "material body." I try again: A material body has an inertial mass by virtue of which it can travel in a straight line at a constant speed when the vector sum of the forces acting on it is zero.

An interesting example of motion with no net force occurs when a parachutist achieves his terminal velocity on a calm day (Fig. 5.2). Two forces are acting on him: $\mathbf{F}_1$, the pull of gravity downward, and $\mathbf{F}_2$, the pull of the parachute upward. If $\mathbf{F}_1 = -\mathbf{F}_2$, then $\mathbf{F}_1 + \mathbf{F}_2 = \mathbf{0}$, and $\Delta \mathbf{v} = \mathbf{0}$. The man falls at a constant speed.

5.3. Gravitational Mass

Another property of all material bodies is that they attract one another. This was first discovered for the planets. Measurements indicate that they

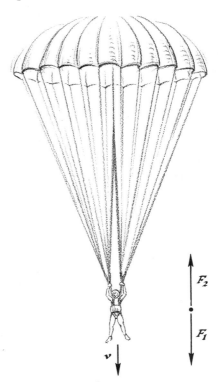

FIG. 5.2. *Parachute descent at constant velocity.*

move in almost circular elliptic orbits under the action of a gravitational force of attraction by the sun. This force is tremendous because the masses involved are tremendous. The mass of the moon, for example, is 7×10^{22} kg, that of the earth is 6×10^{24} kg, and that of the sun is 2×10^{30} kg. The ratio of the mass of the sun to that of the moon is

$$\frac{2\times10^{30}}{7\times10^{22}} = \frac{2}{7}\times10^{8}$$

It would take almost 30 million moons to equal the mass of the sun.

Remember that the force of attraction between a body of mass M_1 and a body of mass M_2 obeys the formula

$$F = \frac{GM_1M_2}{r^2}$$

in which G is approximately 6.7×10^{-11} nt-m²/kg². This implies that the force of attraction between two objects each with a mass of one kilogram at a distance of one meter between their centers is 6.7×10^{-11} newton. This is a fantastically small number! Even if the mass could be concentrated so that the distance between the centers was only one centimeter, the force of attraction would be only 6.7×10^{-7} newton. This is a very small force indeed, and it is no wonder that it requires extremely sensitive apparatus to detect it. Nevertheless, the attraction between a box full of sand and a small bottle full of water has been demonstrated with equipment that an industrious high-school student could probably get together.† The original experiment was performed by Henry Cavendish in 1798. A schematic diagram of his apparatus is shown in Figure 34.2.

I have been stressing how small the force of attraction between two masses as close to each other as one centimeter actually is. How do we reconcile that with the facts that the pull of the sun on the earth is about 4×10^{22} newtons, even though they are 93 million miles apart, and that the pull of the moon on the earth is about 2×10^{20} newtons, though they are about 240,000 miles apart? Here are the details of a calculation carried out to two significant figures:

† This is demonstrated in the motion-picture "Forces," produced by Educational Services Inc., 164 Main Street, Watertown, Massachusetts.

The mass of the sun is

$$M_1 = 2.0\times10^{30} \text{ kg}$$

The mass of the earth is

$$M_2 = 6.0\times10^{24} \text{ kg}$$

The distance between the sun and the earth is

$$r = 93\times10^{6} \text{ mi} = 1.5\times10^{11} \text{ m}$$

The universal constant of gravitation is

$$G = 6.7\times10^{-11} \text{ nt-m}^2/\text{kg}^2$$

The formula for gravitational force is

$$F = \frac{GM_1M_2}{r^2}$$

Substituting the numerical quantities, we get

$$F = \frac{6.7\times10^{-11} \text{ nt-m}^2/\text{kg}^2 \times 2\times10^{30} \text{ kg} \times 6\times10^{24} \text{ kg}}{(1.5\times10^{11})^2 \text{ m}^2}$$

$$= 3.6\times10^{22} \text{ nt}$$

The arithmetic makes it clear how the huge masses make up for the very great distance.

Now let us pause to consider the term *gravitational mass*. This is the attribute by virtue of which a body attracts other bodies. Let us distinguish it from inertial mass by using the subscript g, thus: m_g.

We have considered two different attributes of a body. One (m_i) is its inertial mass, the attribute by virtue of which it resists change in its motion. The other (m_g) is its gravitational mass, the attribute by virtue of which it attracts other bodies. These are different attributes indeed.

A ball can have several different and unrelated attributes at the same time, such as being round and being red. But it can also have attributes that are related, such as being soft and being made of rubber. In the human realm the attribute of being wealthy often goes with the attribute of being influential. With matter it turns out that being able to attract other bodies always goes along with resisting change in motion. In other words, it is an experimental fact that a body with a large inertial mass also has a large gravitational mass. We can prove experimentally that, if you double its inertial mass, you automatically double its gravitational mass.

Strictly speaking, we should always write m_i in the equation

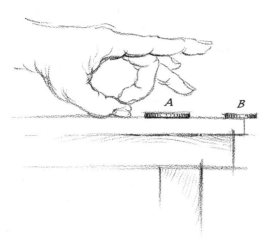

FIG. 5.3. *Demonstrating that two bodies at the same place fall at the same rate.*

$$\mathbf{F} = m_i \frac{\Delta \mathbf{v}}{\Delta t}$$

and we should always write m_g in the equation

$$F = \frac{G(m_g)_1(m_g)_2}{r^2}$$

But we don't bother to do so because experiments prove that m without a subscript will serve in most practical situations. You can prove this by an experiment with two coins. On the edge of a horizontal table (Fig. 5.3) lay a quarter, B. Near it lay a half dollar, A. With a finger flick the half dollar diagonally so that it starts the quarter falling at the same instant it begins to fall itself. What you will hear is that both coins hit the floor at the same time. In Figure 5.4 a multiple-exposure photograph shows how two balls fall in a similar experiment.

From many experiments of this sort we conclude that any two bodies fall at the same rate in the same place. These experiments have an important consequence. Let us analyze it as follows. The pull of gravity on a body near the surface of the earth is proportional to its gravitational mass, m_g. We write (after dispensing with the vector notation)

$$F = km_g \qquad [5.6$$

But a body's acceleration, $\Delta v/\Delta t$, under the action of *any* force depends on its inertial mass, m_i.

Hence from the equation $\mathbf{F} = m_i(\Delta \mathbf{v}/\Delta t)$ we get the equation

$$\frac{\Delta v}{\Delta t} = \frac{F}{m_i} \qquad [5.7$$

In particular, if the pull on the body is due to gravity, we can use the force of equation 5.6 in equation 5.7 to obtain the equation

$$\frac{\Delta v}{\Delta t} = \frac{km_g}{m_i} \qquad [5.8$$

Now the experimental facts are (a) that k is the same constant for all bodies at the same place on earth, and (b) that $\Delta v/\Delta t$ is the same for all bodies at that place. Under the circumstances, equation 5.8 asserts that gravitational mass is proportional to inertial mass; that is, there is a constant, c, for which

$$m_g = cm_i \qquad [5.9$$

Let us assume that we have defined the standard mass (for example, the standard kilogram in Sèvres) as that of an arbitrary cylinder of platinum. We use this as the standard kilogram in

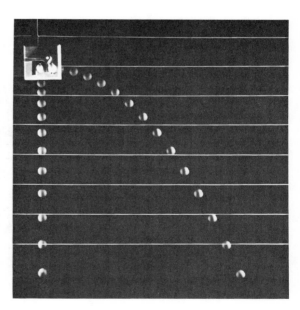

FIG. 5.4. *Multiple-exposure photograph consisting of a sequence of instantaneous exposures taken after equal intervals of time. The two balls fall at the same rate despite their difference in horizontal motion. (From Physical Science Study Committee,* Physics, *D. C. Heath & Co., Boston, 1960.)*

terms of which we define the newton; that is, we treat it as the standard of inertial mass. Now, since we have not yet defined the unit of gravitational mass, we are at liberty to use for it the *same* standard. This amounts to saying that we arbitrarily make the constant c one. We can now say that one unit of gravitational mass is numerically equivalent to one unit of inertial mass.

The practical consequence of this discussion is that we shall henceforth give mass in kilograms and not specify whether we are talking about inertial mass or about gravitational mass. We shall use the subscripts i and g only when we wish to emphasize the distinction between inertial mass and gravitational mass. Otherwise we shall simply talk about the mass of a body.

5.4. Weighing

The weight of a body on or near the earth is the gravitational force with which the earth pulls on it. (Some subtle points are discussed in § 25.3 and § 34.3.) Since it is proportional to the body's gravitational mass, let us write it in the form

$$km_g \qquad [5.10$$

We observe that, when we drop a body, the pull accelerates it. We discover experimentally that this acceleration is

$$\Delta v/\Delta t = g = \text{about } 9.8 \text{ m/sec}^2$$

If, in the equation $F = m_i a$, we substitute km_g for F (the weight) and g for a, we get the equation $km_g = m_i g$. But, according to the discussion above, $m_g = m_i$. Therefore $k = g$. The weight of a body is simply mg. If m is in kg and g is in m/sec^2, the product mg is in kg-m/sec^2, or newtons. I repeat: the mass of the body is m, in kilograms, but the weight of the body is mg, in newtons.

EXAMPLE 5.1. 1. An object with a mass of 2.5 kg has a weight of 24.5 nt. We wish to know the acceleration due to gravity in its region. Using the formula $w = mg$, we obtain

$$g = \frac{24.5 \text{ nt}}{2.5 \text{ kg}} = 9.8 \text{ m/sec}^2$$

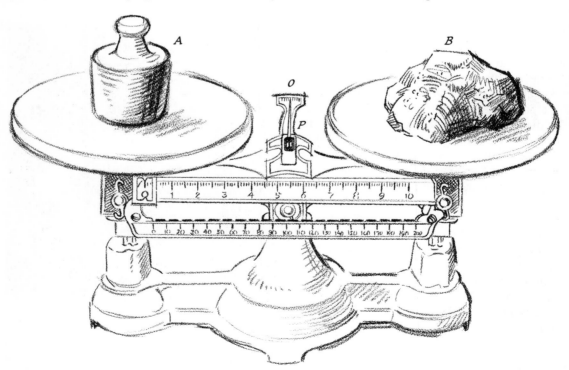

FIG. 5.5. *A common type of rugged laboratory balance.*

2. An object with a mass of 7.5 kg has a weight of 73.5 nt. We find the acceleration due to gravity in its region:

$$g = \frac{73.5 \text{ nt}}{7.5 \text{ kg}} = 9.8 \text{ m/sec}^2$$

It looks as if the two regions were one and the same; at any rate, their values of g, the acceleration due to gravity, are identical within 1 percent.

We weigh an object by comparing its weight with the weight of an accepted standard. Instruments used for this purpose are called balances or scales. A balance (Fig. 5.5) uses the pull of gravity on the standard weight,† A, and on the object of unknown weight, B. Strictly speaking, it uses the effect of the gravitational mass of the earth on the gravitational masses of A and B; that is, it compares gravitational masses. The geometry of the linkages in this platform balance is such that, when the earth pulls equally on A and on B, the pointer, P, points to zero. If A and B balance at one point on the earth, they will balance anywhere on, in, or above the earth; if, for example, you go to a place where g is stronger, gravity will still pull with equal strength on both A and B.

† For better or worse, the word "weight" is also used to mean an object of known weight that is used in the weighing of other objects.

What chemists call the analytical balance was one of the first measuring tools capable of giving results to four or five significant figures. This precise tool played a very important role in putting the science of chemistry on a firm footing; it was used by John Dalton (1766–1844) and the other early chemists. A modern balance of novel design (Fig. 5.6) is capable of weighing an object with a mass of 10^{-3} gm with a precision of 10^{-7} gm. The object of unknown weight is balanced by a force produced by the current in a coil in a magnetic field (§ 38.2).

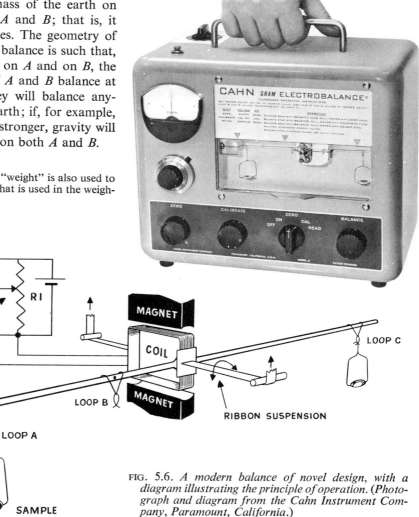

FIG. 5.6. *A modern balance of novel design, with a diagram illustrating the principle of operation. (Photograph and diagram from the Cahn Instrument Company, Paramount, California.)*

Another kind of balance (Fig. 5.7) uses the ability of a force to deform a body elastically (§ 3.2). The common laboratory example, the spring balance, has the advantages of portability and ruggedness. A model accurate enough to be read to 0.1 percent would record the weight of a body with a mass of one kilogram as 9.82 newtons in Alaska but only 9.79 newtons in Hawaii. Very delicate spring balances can therefore detect small variations in g, the acceleration due to gravity.

5.5. Massing

We have seen that the platform balance enables us to compare the gravitational masses of objects. Since the inertial masses are numerically equal to these, the obvious way to compare inertial masses is also by weighing with a balance. But is there some way of measuring the inertial mass of a body directly without depending on its gravitational mass? There is, and such a device might be called an inertial balance. The process of making such a comparison we shall call *massing*.

Suppose that we wish to mass object A. First we suspend it by a long string. In equilibrium its weight, w, is balanced by the tension in the string. We have artificially made it weightless by this means. But it is not massless. It is still reluctant to change its motion. The proof of this is that the homemade inertial balance (Fig. 5.8), consisting of two hacksaw blades and two wooden blocks, vibrates about twenty times per second when clamped alone to the table but only about two times per second when A is inserted in a hole in the movable block, B. The inertial mass of the system has been increased by the addition of A.

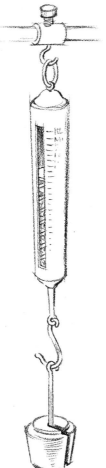

FIG. 5.7. *A typical laboratory spring balance.*

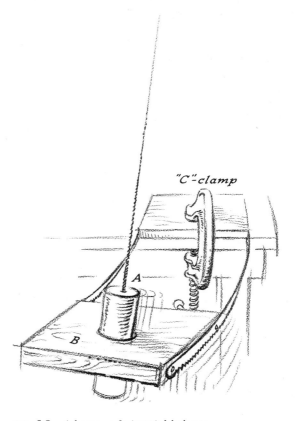

FIG. 5.8. *A homemade inertial balance.*

A certain period of vibration of the system corresponds to the mass of A; we can determine that
period by measuring the total time for one hundred swings and dividing it by 100.

Now suppose that A happens to be a standard
kilogram. If we replaced A with an object, C, of
unknown inertial mass, we could, by finding the
period of the inertial balance, determine quickly
whether the mass of C was less than, equal to, or
greater than that of A. If it was a little less, we
could add inertial mass (for example, by adding
small lead pellets to it) until the period of vibration of C was the same as that of A. The *inertial*
mass of C would then be equal to that of A. In
the laboratory you may devise a systematic procedure for finding the inertial mass of an unknown
in this way (see Prob. 5.8). It would then be instructive to put the unknown on a platform balance and find its gravitational mass independently.

5.6. Mass and Weight

If we are going to drop the distinction between
inertial mass and gravitational mass, we should at
least clarify our future use of the words "mass"
and "weight" in this book.

Let us consider a simple laboratory experiment
and a corresponding imagined experiment on the
moon. We have an iron ball. It has a mass of 50
kilograms. That makes it pretty heavy. We hang
it from the ceiling by a rope. If we try to lift it by
pushing straight upward, we have to exert a force
of about $50 \times 9.8 = 490$ newtons (approximately
110 pounds). If we do this experiment on the
moon, we find that it takes only about 80 newtons
(18 pounds) to lift the ball.

We return to earth. We tie a rubber-band chain
at B (Fig. 5.9). We find that, if we suddenly stretch
it horizontally about a meter, we get a barely perceptible horizontal acceleration of the ball. We
repeat this experiment on the moon. Although,
as we know in advance, the ball is about six times
as light on the moon as on the earth, it behaves
about the way it did on the earth: it exhibits the
same barely perceptible acceleration. Even though
its weight has changed, its inertial mass has not
changed. (Neither has its gravitational mass.) One
important difference between mass and weight is

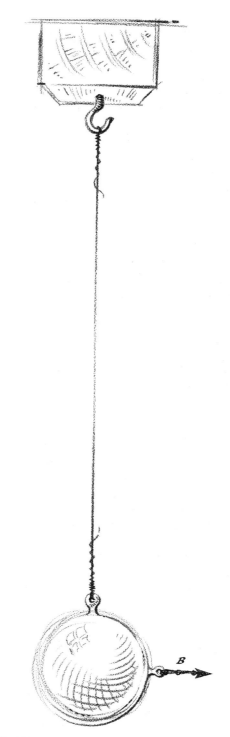

FIG. 5.9. *Illustration of the distinction between mass
and weight.*

clear: the mass of a body is a constant, but its weight is a variable that depends on its location. In certain places in the universe the ball's weight would be close to zero.

The distinction between mass and weight, which we might consider unimportant so long as we are limited to objects close to the surface of the earth, obviously becomes more and more important as space travel comes closer and closer to being realized. A rocket needs to climb only to a height equal to one earth radius to lose 75 percent of its weight (aside from what it throws away in the form of gas).

We hear expressions like "the weight of the moon" and "the weight of the earth." What do they mean? We are told that an electron has a mass of 9×10^{-31} kg. What does this mean operationally? You can't put an electron on a platform balance or on a spring. But you can deflect a beam of electrons (as you do in a television image tube). Do electrons have inertial mass? I do not propose to answer such questions now. I simply wanted to illustrate how the concepts of mass are being used both in the realm of outer space and in the microscopic world of the atom.

5.7. Density

Long before the questions of mass and weight attracted Newton (1642-1727), Archimedes (287? -212 B.C.) was involved in the measurement of density. The concept is a simple one, and we shall consider it here as a relief from other "weighty" matters.

Imagine a piece of metal in the form of a cube. We measure its mass, M, by weighing, and we get its volume, V, by measuring the length, L, of one side. Its density, D, is simply

$$D = \frac{M}{V} \qquad [5.11$$

For a cube

$$D = \frac{M}{L^3} \qquad [5.12$$

The right-hand side of the equation has quantities that are measurable in kilograms and cubic meters. The physical dimensions of density are ML^{-3}.

The densities of silver and gold were of par-

ticular interest to Archimedes because he was given a problem involving the relative quantities of these metals in a king's crown. In Table 5.1 the

TABLE 5.1
Density of Various Substances in gm/cm³

Air in a room	1.2×10^{-3}	Copper	8.9
Balsa wood	0.13	Iron	7.85
Oak wood	0.60–0.90	Lead	11.3
Ebony wood	1.11–1.33	Silver	10.5
Ice	0.917	Gold	19.3
Aluminum	2.7	Compressed gases in	
The human body	≈ 1.07	the center of the	
Beryllium	1.8	densest stars	10^6

densities of a few substances are given in gm/cm³ rather than in kg/m³ because the density of water is very close to 1 gm/cm³. (Notice that

$$1 \text{ kg/m}^3 = 1,000 \text{ gm}/(10^2)^3 \text{ cm}^3 = 10^{-3} \text{ gm/cm}^3$$

Therefore 1 gm/cm³ = 1,000 kg/m³. The density of water in the MKS system is 1,000 kg/m³.) This is easy to remember and convenient as a standard because the volume of water in cubic centimeters is practically equivalent to its mass in grams. Since the density of gold, as the table shows, is considerably greater than that of silver, cheating by the maker of the crown was detectable if Archimedes could determine its density.

But how do you determine the density of an irregular body such as a crown? Its volume is not easy to measure directly. We are indebted to Archimedes for a principle, which now goes by his name, that makes the determination of the density of an irregular body possible.

Archimedes proved that *a body immersed in a fluid experiences a buoyant force equal to the weight of the fluid displaced.* This can be proved experimentally, but let us at least make it plausible by what we call the blob proof. A vessel contains water that has come to rest. We imagine a blob (an aggregate of water of irregular shape), round which (Fig. 5.10) we have drawn a dashed line (actually a surface) as a boundary. We imagine an experiment. We ask: What forces are acting on the blob? One force, obviously, is the weight of the blob. But the blob is at rest; so the vector sum

FIG. 5.10. *Imaginary experiment illustrating Archimedes' principle.*

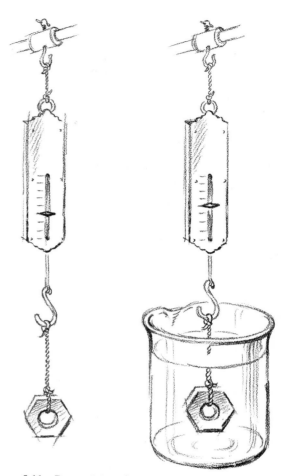

FIG. 5.11. *Determining the density of a heavy object of irregular shape.*

of all the upward forces acting on it must equal the weight of the blob. Now imagine a solid piece of matter of exactly the same shape as the blob replacing the water there. If the solid happens to have the same density as the water, its weight is the same as that of the water it replaced. But the upward force must be exactly as it was before, for we have not disturbed the shape of the rest of the water at all. We conclude that the solid will remain at rest under the action of the upward force, which is *equal to the weight of the water it displaced* and to its own weight. Now let us imagine another solid, identical in shape but denser than water. If it replaces the former solid, it cannot be in equilibrium, for the upward force on it is only equal to the weight of water displaced, but the downward force on it is its own weight, which is greater than the upward force. It will therefore sink.

Let us measure the forces involved in a similar experiment. The weight of an irregular, heavy solid suspended in air from a spring balance (Fig. 5.11) is W. When the solid is immersed in a liquid, the balance shows a lesser weight, W_1. The apparent loss of weight, $W - W_1$, must, according to Archimedes, be equal to the weight of the liquid displaced. Let us form the ratio

$$\frac{W - W_1}{W} = \frac{\text{weight of liquid displaced}}{\text{weight of solid}}$$

$$= \frac{\text{mass of liquid displaced} \times g}{\text{mass of solid} \times g}$$

$$= \frac{\text{density of liquid} \times \text{volume of solid}}{\text{density of solid} \times \text{volume of solid}}$$

$$= \frac{\text{density of liquid}}{\text{density of solid}}$$

Thus the density of the solid may be found if the density of the liquid is known.†

5.8. The Density at a Point

We have been considering the average density of a body. Suppose that the constituents of an alloy of silver and gold were not very well mixed

† When the solid hung in air, it experienced a buoyant force due to the weight of the air it displaced. We disregarded it because the density of water is about a thousand times greater than the density of air.

before it cooled. It is conceivable that, though the average density is about 12 gm/cm³, indicating that there is more silver than gold, a small sample of the metal taken from one region might have a density of 18.0 gm/cm³.

Again let us do an experiment in thought. We take a sample of volume $(\Delta v)_1$ and find its mass to be $(\Delta m)_1$.† From within it we take a smaller sample, of volume $(\Delta v)_2$ and mass $(\Delta m)_2$. Imagine repeating this procedure over and over again (Fig. 5.12), always getting closer to point P. This yields a sequence of volumes,

$$(\Delta v)_1, (\Delta v)_2, (\Delta v)_3, \ldots \qquad [5.13$$

whose limit is zero. It also yields a sequence of masses,

$$(\Delta m)_1, (\Delta m)_2, (\Delta m)_3, \ldots \qquad [5.14$$

whose limit is also zero. Now consider the sequence of ratios:

$$\frac{(\Delta m)_1}{(\Delta v)_1}, \frac{(\Delta m)_2}{(\Delta v)_2}, \frac{(\Delta m)_3}{(\Delta v)_3}, \ldots \qquad [5.15$$

Will the limit of this sequence also be zero?

If you have been thinking in terms of our im-

† The use of the delta to indicate small quantity is a little different from its former use to indicate change, but I am leading to a sequence of ratios such as those already used in slopes and velocities.

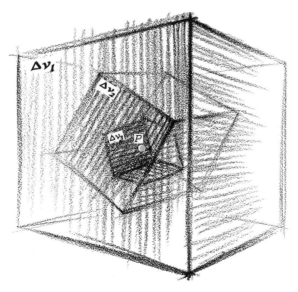

FIG. 5.12. *Imaginary experiment on the density at a point.*

perfectly mixed silver-gold alloy, and if you have physical intuition, you will probably say that the limit of this sequence should be somewhere between 10.5 and 19.3. For obvious reasons, the limit is the number that we assign to the density, d_p, at point P:

$$\lim_{\Delta v \to 0} \frac{\Delta m}{\Delta v} = d_p$$

I said at the beginning of this chapter that I should confine the discussion to the molar realm. From a strictly mathematical point of view the expression $\Delta v \to 0$ implies that we can let Δv become as small as we please. From a physical point of view, however, we may imagine that, if matter is atomic, Δv may become smaller than an atom, and I didn't mean that at all when I wrote

$$\lim_{\Delta v \to 0} \frac{\Delta m}{\Delta v}$$

Besides, if most of an atom's mass resides in its nucleus, and if Δv keeps closing in round a point, P, that happens to be the location of an atomic nucleus, Δm may finally remain the same even though Δv keeps getting smaller and smaller, because the nucleus at P contains virtually all the mass. Therefore $\Delta m/\Delta v$ would now approach a larger and larger number—in effect, the density of a nucleus! We have reason to believe that the density of an isolated nucleus of lead is about 1,000,000,000,000 times the density of lead in bulk.

5.9. Summary

The main concepts associated here with matter are inertia and gravitation. Because matter is reluctant to change its state of rest or of motion in a straight line at constant speed unless acted upon by an external force, we say it has inertial mass. Because matter attracts other matter, we say it has gravitational mass. Since inertial mass is proportional to gravitational mass, one basic unit, the kilogram, suffices for both.

The weight of an object is just the gravitational force that the earth exerts on it. Far from the earth and other bodies, an object has a constant mass but less weight than on the earth's surface.

It does not require a force to keep a body moving at a constant velocity, but our everyday experience, in which friction plays a strong part, makes this difficult to believe.

Density is mass per unit volume. Water has a density of approximately 1 gm/cm³. Very few substances, in samples of ordinary size, have densities in excess of 10 gm/cm³; an atomic nucleus, however, may have a density of 10^{14} gm/cm³.

Archimedes discovered that the buoyant force on a body immersed in a fluid is equal to the weight of the fluid displaced, and he used this principle to find the density of objects of irregular shape.

Problems

5.1. 1. A rocket is traveling at a speed of 1,000 mi/h in relation to the fixed stars. Its fuel gives out, and it finds itself in space very far from attracting bodies. Describe its probable behavior for the next few hours.

2. A very large balloon is inflated by a gas source from the rocket while it is in transit in space and then released. Describe its probable behavior for the next few hours.

5.2. The mathematical argument beginning with equation 5.1 ends with equation $v_2 = v_1$ (equation 5.4). Although this is a single vector equation, it summarizes two facts. Test your knowledge of them by answering the following questions.

1. How does the final speed compare with the initial speed?

2. How does the final direction compare with the initial direction?

3. Hence, how did the body move? Describe its motion in words.

5.3. A parachutist has a mass of 80 kg. His parachute and all his other gear add up to another 50 kg. At a place where the acceleration due to gravity is 9.78 m/sec² he has reached a constant terminal velocity. What upward force in newtons is acting on him and his parachute?

5.4. This problem requires only that you be able to "plug in" numbers into formulas and do it accurately, but it is important to be able to do so. A lead ball 1 m in diameter is placed so that its center is 0.55 m from the nearest point of an identical ball. What is the gravitational force in newtons between them? You will need to know that the volume of a sphere is $4\pi r^3/3$ (r is the radius), that mass = volume × density, and that the force of attraction obeys the formula $F = GM_1M_2/r^2$, in which $G = 6.7 \times 10^{-11}$ nt-m²/kg². The density of lead is given in Table 5.1, but watch the units! It is best to set up the problem for slide-rule computation to avoid carrying useless significant figures.

5.5. This is a problem in thought; the answer is not as important as the reasoning that produces it. An astronaut stubs his toe on a steel ball whose mass is 100 kg. The ball hardly budges. Its weight on the earth is 980 newtons. On the moon its weight is only about 130 newtons. The astronaut stubs his toe on the same ball on the moon. Does it move appreciably? (A different way of asking the question—which presupposes that you know that the ball pushes back on the toe with the same force that the toe exerts on the ball—is this: Does the astronaut's toe hurt as much on the moon?)

5.6. In a liquid whose density is 0.95 gm/cm³ a rectangular block of wood sinks so that 1/5 of its volume is above the surface of the liquid. Find the density of the wood. Here, again, the actual answer is of no real consequence. The important thing to learn is how to use Archimedes' Principle with the aid of a clear diagram and some algebra. Here is a suggested series of steps: Draw a diagram. Label the volume submerged and the volume above the liquid with different symbols. Express the total weight of the block in terms of its volume and density, *using symbols*. (Do not put in numerical values until the end. This is a procedure that you should practice in general.) Write an expression for the buoyant force, using a symbol for the density of the liquid. Equate the total downward force on the block to the total upward force on it. Solve this equation, *in symbols*, for the density of the block. Now put in numerical values, with their appropriate units, and solve to get a numerical answer and its proper units.

5↑

5.7. If all the volumes $(\Delta v)_1$, $(\Delta v)_2$, $(\Delta v)_3$, . . . of equation 5.13 are large enough to contain many thousands of atoms of the substance in question, the limit of the sequence of densities (equation 5.15) will represent the macroscopic density of the substance at a particular point.

Imagine, however, a set of cubes the lengths of whose sides in cm form the sequence 10^{-8}, 10^{-9}, 10^{-10}, 10^{-11}, . . . They are all so small that only one atomic nucleus can be contained within each. For simplicity's sake assume that this nucleus is also a cube, the length of whose side is $d = 10^{-12}$ cm (volume $= d^3$), with a mass of 1.5×10^{-24} gm. Keeping in mind that each cube contains the same nucleus or a part of it, write down numerical values for the first four terms of the sequence

$$\frac{(\Delta m)_1}{(\Delta v)_1}, \frac{(\Delta m)_2}{(\Delta v)_2}, \frac{(\Delta m)_3}{(\Delta v)_3}$$

Do you think this sequence eventually approaches a limit?

5.8. With an apparatus similar to that of Fig. 5.8 (Educational Services Inc., 164 Main Street, Watertown, Massachusetts) without cylinder A, perform the experiment suggested in § 5.5; that is, adjust the mass of a test object placed in the holder, B, by adding lead shot to it until the period of the apparatus is the same as its period when an object chosen arbitrarily to represent a standard mass is in B. Finally compare the mass of the test object with that of the standard by weighing. What are your experimental conclusions?

6

Energy

"Work is the act of producing a change of configuration in a system in opposition to a force which resists that change. Energy is the capacity of doing work. Work is the transference of energy from one system to another."

JAMES CLERK MAXWELL, *Matter and Motion*

ENERGY is a widely used word. We read about solar and nuclear energy and about the depletion of our natural resources of energy. We also use the word in connection with human activities: we say that a person is full of energy or that he expresses himself energetically. Again we are up against an abstraction like space, time, matter, and motion. It will be convenient to start with the everyday meaning of the word and sharpen it up until we understand the precise way in which it is used in physics.

6.1. The Meaning of "Energy"

Let's observe what a boy can do when he says he is full of energy. He may run up a hill or chop down a tree or mow a lawn. All of these activities, but especially the last, illustrate the concept of *work*, which we must soon define. Even before we do that, we must ask how we know that something has energy. Of all the possible clues, the most obvious one is motion. If a body is in motion, we can assert with confidence that it has energy. If one thing can put another thing into motion, the first thing has energy. A boy can put a baseball into motion, or he can clear a driveway of snow; so we say that the boy has energy. By this criterion, there is obviously energy in a thunderstorm, in the wind, in a roaring river, and in the moving clouds. These illustrations are all meteorological, and all trace their origin to the action of the sun on the surface and atmosphere of the earth. This strongly suggests that the sun must be the seat of a tremendous amount of energy, for it is 93 million miles away and delivers only a tiny fraction of its total energy to the earth.

In the launching of a missile we see something large put into motion. This suggests that rocket fuels have much energy. But other fuels also—coal, wood, gasoline, diesel oil—and even electricity, which is not fuel, can put things into motion because they have energy. The chapter headings of physics textbooks suggest different kinds of energy: mechanical energy, heat, sound, light, electricity, atomic energy, and nuclear energy. We could very well say that physics is a study of energy.

Now we must show how energy is measured. In order to do that, we must introduce the concept of work, for energy is the capacity to do work.

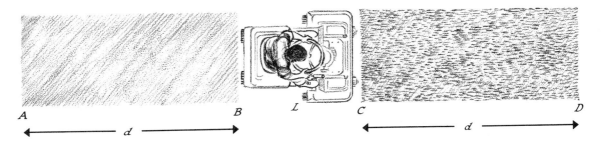

FIG. 6.1. *Work is proportional to distance.*

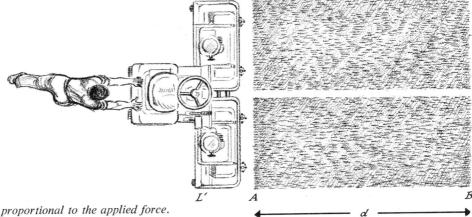

FIG. 6.2. *Work is proportional to the applied force.*

6.2. Work and Power

Energy cannot be measured with a ruler or a platform balance. But fuels, which we know have energy, also have volume and weight, which are easily measurable. In order to get started, let us say that one pint of gasoline represents an arbitrary unit of energy. If we put this pint of gasoline into a power mower, we find that it can mow an area of lawn, as shown schematically in Figure 6.1, in which L represents the mower and d represents the distance through which the mower, powered by one pint of gasoline, travels in going from A to B. One pint of gasoline can perform a definite task involving motion, in this case the mowing of a stretch of lawn as wide as the mower and as long as d. We say that work has been done in opposition to a resisting force. One unit of energy was able to perform one unit of work.

If we put another pint of gasoline into the engine, we can proceed from C to D, cutting another area of length d. Doubling the energy has

doubled the work done by doubling the distance traveled. This suggests that, if all other factors are kept constant, work is proportional to d. We may write

$$W \propto d \qquad [6.1$$

A boy holding a pile of wood without moving does no work in the physical sense. Distance is one of the factors involved. The other is force, and in the following illustration I shall try to motivate its introduction.

We can dispense with gasoline power and do a unit of work by pushing mower L by hand, with force F, from A to B. If we align and connect two mowers as in Figure 6.2, we have to push twice as hard on L' as on L; and, if we push L' through distance d, we perform two units of work. A generalization of this idea is that, if we keep the distance and other factors constant but double the force applied, we do twice as much work. Work, it seems, is proportional to the applied force when other factors are constant:

$$W \propto F \qquad [6.2$$

These two illustrations suggest how the concept of work came to be defined. A single expression that incorporates the features of both expression 6.1 and expression 6.2 is

$$W \propto Fd \qquad [6.3$$

The unit of force in the MKS system has already been stated to be the newton and the unit of distance to be the meter. Since we are at liberty to choose the unit of work as we please, we can replace the proportionality sign in expression 6.3 with an equality sign and a constant of proportionality, which we arbitrarily make one. Therefore

$$W = Fd \qquad [6.4$$

The unit of work, instead of being called the newton-meter, is called the **joule** (after the English physicist James Prescott Joule, 1818–1889), abbreviated as "J."

The rate at which work is done is called **power**. A defining equation for power is

$$P = \frac{\Delta W}{\Delta t} \qquad [6.5$$

The unit of power in the MKS system, the joule per second, is called the **watt** (after the Scottish engineer James Watt, 1736–1819); when work is performed at the rate of 1 joule per second, we say that a power of 1 watt is being expended.

The physical dimensions of work and of energy, which we define as the capacity of doing work, are ML^2T^{-2}. Any unit of force multiplied by any unit of distance yields a unit of work or of energy. In the British system, for example, in which the pound is a unit of force and the foot is a unit of distance, the foot-pound is a unit of work. In the CGS system, forces are measured in dynes and distances in centimeters, and the unit of work equivalent to the dyne-centimeter is called the **erg**.

We shall use MKS units in most of our work in this book. It is therefore important to get some feeling for the magnitude of a joule. Consider the work done by a man in lifting his own weight up one step of a flight of stairs: it is approximately 100 joules. We estimate it as follows: A man whose mass is 50 kg weighs 50×9.8 nt; if the step is 20 cm high, the work done is 50×9.8 nt $\times 0.20$ m = 98 J. The other units of energy often used, besides the joule, the erg, and the foot-pound, are the **calorie** (cal) and the **electron volt**

(ev). These units have their own interesting historical background. The calorie arises in the study of heat, and the electron volt is useful in atomic physics. For the time being all we need to know is that, just as there are simple conversion factors to get us from inches to feet or yards or miles, all of which measure the same physical quantity, length, so there are simple conversion factors to get us from calories to joules or electron volts. These all measure the same thing: energy. Table 6.1 is a conversion table, and Example 6.1 shows how to use it.

EXAMPLE 6.1. A 150-lb man climbs a vertical ladder 50 ft high in 12 sec.

1. We wish to find the work done against gravity in foot-pounds. $W = Fd = 150$ lb $\times 50$ ft = 7,500 ft-lb.

2. We wish to express the work in joules. According to Table 6.1, 1 ft-lb = 1.356 J. Since multiplying anything by

$$\frac{1.356 \text{ J}}{1 \text{ ft-lb}}$$

is like multiplying by 1 (the numerator and denominator being equal),

$$7{,}500 \text{ ft-lb} \times \frac{1.356 \text{ J}}{1 \text{ ft-lb}} \doteq 10{,}150 \text{ J}$$

TABLE 6.1
Conversion of Units

		In one	There is (are)	
Energy and work		erg	10^{-7}	joule(s) (J)
		kilowatt-hour (kWh)	3.6×10^6	
		calorie (cal)	4.184	
		foot-pound (ft-lb)	1.356	
		British thermal unit (Btu)	1,055	
		electron volt (ev)	1.602×10^{-19}	
Power		erg per second (erg sec^{-1})	10^{-7}	watt(s) (W)
		calorie per second (cal sec^{-1})	4.184	
		British thermal unit per hour (Btu h^{-1})	0.2930	
Force and weight		dyne	10^{-5}	newton(s) (nt)
		pound (lb)	4.4482	

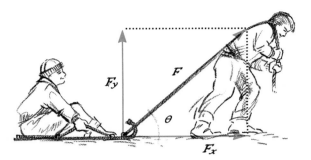

FIG. 6.3. *Rectangular components of a force.*

3. We wish to express the average power expended in watts.

$$P = \frac{\Delta W}{\Delta t} = \frac{10{,}150 \text{ J}}{12 \text{ sec}} = 845 \text{ W}$$

I shall have more to say about the conversion of one type of energy into another in a later section. Now I want to refine our definition of work, for we have not yet taken into consideration the fact that force and displacement are vectors. The simple definition we have given so far is good only if the force and the displacement are in the same direction. Let us now consider how to handle the cases in which they are not.

6.3. Work as the Scalar Product of Two Vectors

Both force and displacement are vectors. I have shown how to add vectors, but I have not discussed the multiplication of vectors.

In the illustrations given so far, we have taken into consideration, in computing the work, only the magnitude of the force and the magnitude of the displacement. That was permissible because they were both in the same direction. But now let us consider a case in which the force, **F**, and the displacement, **d**, are vectors in different directions. Imagine a sled being pulled by a rope that makes angle θ with the horizontal; if the road is horizontal, the displacement is horizontal, and **F** and **d** are obviously not in the same direction. In Figure 6.3 we show two vectors, one ($\mathbf{F}_x$) in the direction of **d** and one ($\mathbf{F}_y$) at right angles to it. The figure forms a parallelogram in which **F** is diagonal. It is apparent that $\mathbf{F}_x + \mathbf{F}_y = \mathbf{F}$; that is,

vector **F** is equivalent to the sum of its rectangular components, vectors $\mathbf{F}_x$ and $\mathbf{F}_y$. It is clear that $\mathbf{F}_x$ is the component that lies in the same direction as **d**. The way to extend our definition of work is therefore to write

$$W = F_x d \qquad [6.6$$

I have written F_x and d as scalars because they represent only the magnitudes of the vectors involved. It is apparent from the definition of the cosine function that

$$\frac{F_x}{F} = \cos \theta \qquad [6.7$$

From this equation we obtain the equation

$$W = (F \cos \theta) d \qquad [6.8$$

If work is being done against friction, F_x is the component of **F** that is doing the work. The role that F_y plays is an indirect one; it tends to lift the sled and hence to reduce the force with which the sled presses against the road, and to that extent it changes the frictional force. We shall have more to say about friction later.

Now, since force and displacement are vectors, it becomes convenient to define what we shall call the **scalar product** of two vectors. This is sometimes called the **dot product** because the dot is the sign used for this kind of multiplication. We write

$$W = \mathbf{F} \cdot \mathbf{d} \qquad [6.9$$

and the meaning of this expression is exactly the same as that of equation 6.8. To evaluate the scalar product of two vectors, you multiply the product of their magnitudes by the cosine of the angle between their directions. Once again we have seen how a physical concept has motivated the introduction of a new process in the algebra of vectors.

6.4. Rectangular Components

The sum of a pair of vectors may, we know, be equal to another vector. In Figure 6.4, for example,

$$\mathbf{a} + \mathbf{b} = \mathbf{c} \qquad [6.10$$

and

$$\mathbf{a}' + \mathbf{b}' = \mathbf{c} \qquad [6.11$$

and

$$\mathbf{a}'' + \mathbf{b}'' = \mathbf{c} \qquad [6.12$$

We say that **a** and **b** are rectangular components of **c** because they are perpendicular to each other. Similarly, **a'** and **b'** are rectangular components of **c**, for they also are mutually perpendicular. Finally, **a''** and **b''**, though they are components of **c**, are not rectangular components, for they are not mutually perpendicular.

A vector has a unique pair of rectangular components only if we specify the rectangular axes, x and y, along which we are going to resolve it. The choice of the particular pair of axes that will be useful for the solution of a problem will often be apparent from the nature of the problem. In Figure 6.3 you saw the notation often used for rectangular components: vector **F** has the component F_x in the x direction and F_y in the y direction. Observe that, when a symbol like F_x is not printed in boldface type, it stands for magnitude only. From the definitions of sine and cosine we obtain the equations

$$F_x = F \cos \theta \qquad [6.13$$

and

$$F_y = F \sin \theta \qquad [6.14$$

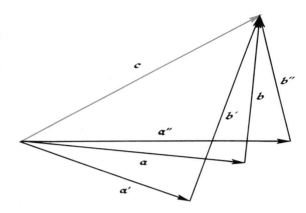

FIG. 6.4. *Vectors as components of another vector.*

6.5. The Graphical Interpretation of Work

In Figure 6.5 we see schematically a block resting on a horizontal table and being pulled to the right by a force of magnitude F. There is friction between the block and the table. If the block is being dragged along at a constant velocity, F must be equal in magnitude to the frictional force, which acts in the opposite direction. If F is a constant, the graph of F against x is a line parallel to the x axis (Fig. 6.6). As the block moves from x_1 to x_2, the work done is $F(x_2 - x_1)$. The geometrical representation of this product is the area of the rectangle whose altitude is F and whose base is $x_2 - x_1$. This association of the area under a curve with the work done by a force is going to be very useful.

Let us now consider a case (Fig. 6.7) in which the force does not remain constant in magnitude. The force, F, required to stretch a spring increases with the distance, x. The graph of F against x, as a first approximation, is a straight line (Fig. 6.8). At the point where the elongation

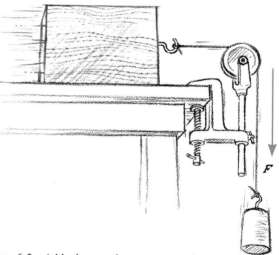

FIG. 6.5. *A block moved at constant velocity.*

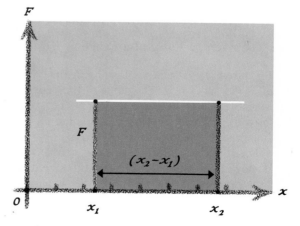

FIG. 6.6. *A graphical interpretation: the work done is $F(x_2 - x_1)$, which is also the darker green area.*

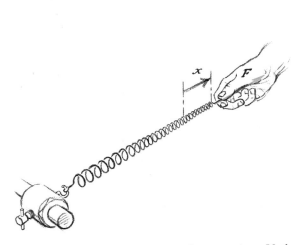

FIG. 6.7. *A variable force stretches a spring. If the average force is* $\bar{F}$, *the work done is* $(\bar{F}x_2 - x_1)$.

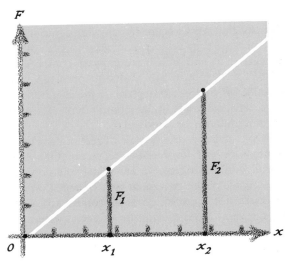

FIG. 6.8. *The graph of* F *against* x.

is x_1, the force is F_1; where the elongation is x_2, the force is F_2. The total work done is neither $F_1(x_2 - x_1)$ nor $F_2(x_2 - x_1)$: the first value is too small, and the second is too large. It is apparent that some value of F, when multiplied by $x_2 - x_1$, gives the correct value of the work done by this variable force. That value of F, in this case, is $(F_1 + F_2)/2$, which, as we shall see presently, is the average value of F in the interval $x_1 \leq x \leq x_2$ (read as "x is equal to or greater than x_1 and equal to or less than x_2"). This leads us to the concept of the average value of a function, which we shall now consider in an abstract way, without particular application to forces.

6.6. The Average Value of a Function

In Figure 6.9 you see the plot of y against x, in which $y = \mathrm{f}(x)$ (§ 1.5). The value of the dependent variable is y_1 at one end and y_2 at the other. We now ask: "What is the *average* value of y in this interval?" The definition of "average" given in advanced mathematical texts is compatible with the following simple illustration. Imagine that the area bounded by two vertical lines at x_1 and x_2, the x axis, and the curve $y = \mathrm{f}(x)$ is filled with very tiny balls. We shall use the balls as a measure of the area enclosed by these boundaries. We now contain the balls by putting a ruler at x_1, another

at x_2, and another along the x axis. We tilt the board on which they rest, and shake it, so that the balls, falling from the higher to the lower part of the curve, form the rectangle $ABCD$. The *altitude of this rectangle is the average value of* y *in this interval*. In symbols,

$$\bar{y}(x_2 - x_1) = A \qquad [6.15$$

In this equation $\bar{y}$ means the average value of y, and A means the area bounded by the curve, the two vertical lines at x_1 and x_2, and the x axis. We now derive the average value of the function:

$$\bar{y} = \frac{A}{x_2 - x_1} \qquad [6.16$$

In some cases the calculation of areas presents more sophisticated mathematical problems than we shall take up at this time, but in others only very simple mathematics is required. We shall now use this idea in considering the average value of a linear function.

Suppose that the variable, y, is a linear function of x; that is, suppose that the graph of y against x is a straight line, as shown in Figure 6.10. Let us find the average value of the function in the interval $x_1 \leq x \leq x_2$. The area under the graph in that interval can be conceived as the sum of rectangle $ABCD$ and triangle BCE. The area of the rectangle is

$$(AB)(AD) = y_1(x_2 - x_1)$$

The area of the triangle is

$$\tfrac{1}{2}(BC)(CE) = \tfrac{1}{2}(x_2 - x_1)(y_2 - y_1)$$

The total area is

$$A = y_1(x_2 - x_1) + \tfrac{1}{2}(x_2 - x_1)(y_2 - y_1) \qquad [6.17$$

Using equation 6.16 (that is, dividing the area by $x_2 - x_1$), we get

$$\bar{y} = y_1 + \tfrac{1}{2}(y_2 - y_1) \qquad [6.18$$

which simplifies to

$$\bar{y} = \frac{y_1 + y_2}{2} \qquad [6.19$$

The result of this simple derivation is worth stating in words: "If y is a linear function of x, the average value of y in the interval $x_1 \leq x \leq x_2$ is the sum of the first and last values of y divided by 2." This is easy to remember because it agrees with common sense; it is the value we should have guessed intuitively. The proof that this value of y occurs at a value of x that is halfway between x_1 and x_2 is left as a problem (Prob. 6.4).

Returning to Figure 6.8, we see that, since the force, F, in a spring is a linear function of x, the average value of the force in the interval between x_1 and x_2 is $(F_1 + F_2)/2$. If we let x_1 be 0 and x_2 be x (the maximum displacement), F_1 will be 0 and F_2 will be F (the maximum force), and the total work done, the average force multiplied by the displacement, will be $(0 + F)x/2$. In symbols,

$$W = \frac{Fx}{2} \qquad [6.20$$

F, we must remember, is the maximum force. This special equation applies only if the force varies linearly with x, starting from the point of no stretch.

EXAMPLE 6.2. It takes a force of 1.5 nt to stretch a certain spring through a distance of 0.30 m. We wish to know how much work is done in stretching this spring from its position of no stretch through 0.70 m.

A spring obeys the equation $F = kx$. Therefore

$$k = \frac{F}{x} = \frac{1.5 \text{ nt}}{0.30 \text{ m}} = 5.0 \frac{\text{nt}}{\text{m}}$$

When the spring is stretched through 0.70 m, the force is

$$F = kx = 5.0 \frac{\text{nt}}{\text{m}} \times 0.70 \text{ m} = 3.5 \text{ nt}$$

This is the maximum force. The average force is $F/2$, and the work done is $Fx/2$. Therefore

$$W = \frac{Fx}{2} = \frac{3.5 \text{ nt} \times 0.70 \text{ m}}{2} = 1.225 \text{ J}$$

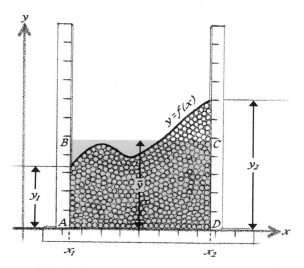

FIG. 6.9. *If the area of the rectangle ABCD is equal to the area under the curve y = f(x) between x_1 and x_2, its altitude, AB, is the average value, $\bar{y}$, of the function f(x) in the interval.*

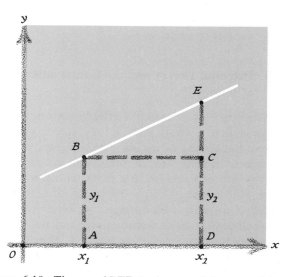

FIG. 6.10. *The area ABED is the sum of the area of the rectangle ABCD and that of the triangle BCE. The average value of y is (area ABED)/($x_2 - x_1$). It is proved in the text that $\bar{y} = (y_1 + y_2)/2$.*

6.7. Kinetic Energy

I began the discussion of energy by saying that a moving body has energy. The energy that a body has because of its motion is called **kinetic energy** (abbreviated as KE). I shall prove in Chapter 27 that a body's kinetic energy is $mv^2/2$ if m is the mass of the body and v is its speed. We can now at least check this formula for dimensional consistency: $[mv^2/2] = M(LT^{-1})^2 = ML^2T^{-2}$. We can safely assert that $mv^2/2$ is not dimensionally incorrect.

I have emphasized the fact that no force is required to keep a body moving at a constant velocity. In this state it neither gains nor loses kinetic energy. If a net unbalanced force acts on it, its speed may change and also its kinetic energy. The work done by the external force turns out to equal the gain or loss in the body's kinetic energy (see § 27.3).

EXAMPLE 6.3. A six-man re-entry vehicle is orbiting round the earth at a speed of 8,000 m/sec. Its mass is 14,000 kg. We wish to know its kinetic energy (KE) in joules.

$$\begin{aligned} \text{KE} &= mv^2/2 = 1/2 \times 14{,}000 \text{ kg} \times (8{,}000)^2 \text{ m}^2/\text{sec}^2 \\ &= 7 \times 10^3 \times 64 \times 10^6 \text{ J} \\ &= 448 \times 10^9 \text{ J} \\ &= 4.48 \times 10^{11} \text{ J} \end{aligned}$$

6.8. Potential Energy and the Conservation of Energy

When a ball is tossed vertically upward, we observe that it starts with a high speed, which keeps diminishing as it rises. At its highest point its speed is zero, and at that point its kinetic energy is therefore zero. But it started up with a high kinetic energy. What happened to that energy? If we wait a little longer, we observe that the ball returns to its starting point and that it is then going about as fast as when it started up. Its loss of kinetic energy on the way up seems to have been compensated by its gain in kinetic energy on the way down.

Now we know that, if the ball had been caught at its highest point by someone on a tower, it could have been held there indefinitely, but that, when released later, it would have picked up the same speed on the way down that it did when allowed to rise and fall untouched. This suggests that the energy it lost on the way up was somehow *stored* by its being held there, for that energy, as we observed when the ball was finally released, was still available. The energy that a body has by virtue of its relative position or configuration is called **potential energy** (abbreviated as PE). The potential energy of a body that has been lifted above the surface of the earth is called **gravitational potential energy.** It takes a force, mg, to lift a body of mass m at a place where the acceleration due to gravity is g. The work done in lifting it to height h is mgh. We say that its potential energy (in joules) was increased by mgh by its being lifted to height h.

A simple but profound observation is that a body thrown upward gains in potential energy exactly what it loses in kinetic energy. This gives rise to the concept of the **conservation of mechanical energy,** one of the most useful ideas in physics. (Kinetic energy and gravitational potential energy are examples of mechanical energy. Heat and chemical energy belong, for the time being, in another category.)

A bouncing ball exhibits interesting transformations of energy from the potential to the kinetic. Just before it is dropped to the floor it has gravitational potential energy. As it drops, it picks up speed, and hence its kinetic energy increases as its potential energy decreases. Just before it touches the floor its kinetic energy is at its greatest value. Then, for a few milliseconds, it is compressed, and it now has potential energy of a different sort: not gravitational potential energy, but potential energy due to a change in configuration or shape. Soon it starts to spring back, losing that kind of potential energy but gaining kinetic energy, and now it starts its upward trip. As it leaves the floor, it again has a high kinetic energy. The fact that it does not go back to the height from which it fell shows, however, that some energy has been lost. A steel ball landing on a very massive steel plate, however, loses very little energy and goes up and down many times before it stops.

As an example of the far-reaching consequences of the concept of conservation of mechanical energy, consider the behavior of a planet. A planet moves in an elliptical path (Fig. 6.11), with the sun, S, at one focus. When the planet is at A, it has a certain kinetic energy, $mv_1^2/2$. Later, when it is at a more distant point, B, the very fact that it is farther away from the sun means that its potential energy is greater. Its kinetic energy, $mv_2^2/2$, must therefore be less at B than at A; hence it must be going slower at B than at A.

Historically, it was learned *by observation* that the planets do move slower when they are farther away from the sun. The concept of energy was not formulated until much later, but we are taking advantage of the hindsight that our vantage point makes possible. The concept of the conservation of mechanical energy makes many phenomena fall into place quite readily, not only at the astronomical level but all the way down into the atomic level, where electrons swirl round nuclei and where the forces and hence the potential energies are electrical rather than gravitational.

Though there is one formula for kinetic energy, $mv^2/2$, there is no general formula for potential energy, for there are many forms of energy due to configuration. I have mentioned the formula mgh for gravitational potential energy, but this is only an approximation and holds only for values of h much smaller than that of the earth's radius.

No introduction to energy would be complete without the formula $E = mc^2$, which comes from Einstein's theory of relativity. It states that mass has energy and that energy has the attributes of mass. It has been confirmed in nuclear physics that, when a mass, m, is "annihilated" (and I shall have to explain in great detail what this means), mc^2 is the energy "released" ($c = 3 \times 10^8$ m/sec, the speed of light). Since $c^2 = 9 \times 10^{16}$ m^2/sec^2, 1 kg of mass is "equivalent to" 9×10^{16} J. This is a tremendous quantity of energy, and we can begin to understand how engines that utilize nuclear fuels enable a submarine to circle the globe several times without refueling.

With this brief introduction we take temporary

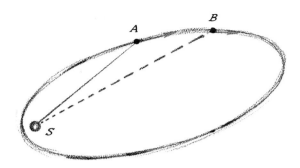

FIG. 6.11. *Since it takes work to move a planet away from the sun, its potential energy at* B *is greater than that at* A. *The kinetic energy and hence the speed of the planet are less at* B *than at* A.

leave of what are believed by some to be the most important concepts in all of physics and perhaps in all of science: the concepts of energy, its transformations, and its conservation. When we consider that life requires energy and that the energy demands of human beings on this planet are increasing, not only in total quantity but in joules per individual, the human importance of energy is inescapable. To deal with it, we must first learn to measure it, and we have taken the first step in that direction in this chapter.

6.9. Summary

Work is defined by the equation $W = \mathbf{F} \cdot \mathbf{d}$. If the force $\mathbf{F}$ is in newtons and the displacement $\mathbf{d}$ is in meters, the work is in joules. No work is done if the displacement or the force is zero or if they are mutually perpendicular.

Power is the rate of doing work: $P = \Delta w / \Delta t$.

Energy is the capacity for doing work and is measured in work units. Kinetic energy ($mv^2/2$) is due to motion, and potential energy is due to position or configuration. The energy of a system can change from the kinetic to the potential and back.

The physical dimensions of work are ML^2T^{-2}.

Mass, m, has the amount of energy, E, given by the equation $E = mc^2$, in which c is the speed of light.

Problems

If you are used to thinking of the weight of things in pounds, it may be helpful to remember that a force of 22.5 pounds is approximately the same as 100 newtons.

6.1. An athlete weighing 600 nt pulls himself up to the top of a vertical rope through a distance of 9 m.

1. How much work in joules does he do to reach the top?

2. His average upward speed is 0.5 m/sec. What power in watts does he expend?

3. What is his average kinetic energy while moving at that speed if $g = 9.8$ m/sec²?

4. What is his gravitational potential energy at the top if it is taken as zero at the bottom?

6.2. A sled is pulled along a horizontal road by a boy with a rope tied to the sled and inclined at an angle of 45° to the horizontal. The tension in the rope, a force of 95 nt, pulls the sled forward through a distance of 45 m.

1. What is the horizontal component of this force?

2. What is the vertical component of this force?

3. How much work is done by the boy?

4. Is that work converted into gravitational potential energy?

6.3. We have seen that a body of mass m, raised to height h at a place where the acceleration of gravity is g, acquires the increment of potential energy mgh, and that, if dropped from that height, it acquires kinetic energy $mv^2/2$ just before hitting the ground. Assume below that there are no energy losses so that $mv^2/2 = mgh$.

1. To what height must an automobile with a mass of 1,000 kg be raised for it, when dropped, to achieve on landing the same kinetic energy that it had when moving along the road at 27 m/sec (close to 60 mph)? Assume that $g = 9.8$ m/sec².

2. Answer the same question for an automobile with a mass of 2,000 kg.

6.4. This problem involves only the algebraic proof of an important statement made in the text (equation 6.19): that the average value of a linear function is halfway between its initial and final values. We wish to prove that the function assumes this value at the midpoint of the x interval. The result is intuitively obvious from Fig. 6.10, but that is not enough. We want an algebraic proof. Begin by writing $y = mx + b$. (This is a straight line of slope m and meeting the y axis at distance b from the origin.) The problem is this: What is the value of x when $y = (y_1 + y_2)/2$? The answer comes out as $(x_1 + x_2)/2$. You may prove it deductively or simply check the result by putting $x = (x_1 + x_2)/2$ into $y = mx + b$ and proving that y comes out as $(y_1 + y_2)/2$. (Hint: $y_1 = mx_1 + b$, $y_2 = mx_2 + b$.)

6.5. It takes a force of 3 nt to stretch a spring from zero to 5.0 cm, and a force of 4.8 nt to stretch it from zero to 8.0 cm. How much work (in joules) is done in stretching it from 5.0 to 8.0 cm? (Remember that 1 J $= 1$ nt $\times 1$ m.)

6.6. 1. Make the best possible estimate of the average value of the function $f(x) = x^2/5$ between $x = 2$ and $x = 10$. You can estimate the area under the curve by counting squares and approximating triangular areas.

2. Sketch in another function (not a straight line) whose average value is 6 in the same interval.

6.7. This problem is simply computational, but the results may be instructive.

1. Using the equation $E = mc^2$, compute the energy in joules possessed by 10 gm (0.01 kg) of matter.

2. The daily output of Hoover Dam is about 20×10^{10} watt-hours. Is this larger than the result of part 1? (Note: 1 watt-hour $= 1$ J/sec $\times 3,600$ sec $= 3,600$ J.)

7

Time

"The idea of Time in its most primitive form is probably the recognition of the order of sequence in our states of consciousness. If my memory were perfect, I might be able to refer every event within my own experience to its proper place in a chronological period. But it would be difficult, if not impossible, for me to compare the time interval between one pair of events and that between another pair."

JAMES CLERK MAXWELL, *Matter and Motion*

"Philosophers and scientists in all ages have been fascinated by the mysteries of time—its relentless, arrow-like flight in one direction, its psychological vagaries, the difficulty of measuring it with absolute precision. In our atomic age the last of these aspects affords the most intriguing speculation and exploration. Because 'the pendulum's swing is a variable thing,' and the motions of the earth and stars are inconstant, today 'the atom's vibrating has the highest rating' among chronologers."

HAROLD LYONS, "Atomic Clocks," *Scientific American*, February 1957

"Space is the abstract of all relations of co-existence; Time is the abstract of all relations of sequence."

GOTTFRIED WILHELM VON LEIBNIZ

WHAT *is* time? You will not get a good answer to that question in this book; but you will learn something about how time is measured. The quotation from Leibniz above defines both space and time, but it suffers from being too short. It packs too much thought into one sentence. We must first pick up some *operational* experience with time in order to understand it.

7.1. Measuring Time

We can measure time even if we don't know what it is. The proof of this is that most of us carry watches. Unlike primitive men, who follow the rhythm of the sun and the stars in a loose sort of way, we order the events of our daily lives by the clock, often to the nearest minute. Yet we have one thing in common with primitive man: most of us are almost as ignorant about the working of wristwatches as he was about the working of the solar system.

The relative importance that we attach to mass, length, and time is shown by the fact that, although most of us do not carry tape measures to measure length, or scales to measure mass, we do carry delicate (though often inexpensive) instruments that can measure the length of a day with an error of less than one part in a thousand or use an electric clock whose motor is driven by a distant generator with even greater accuracy.

Open the back of your watch, and peek inside, the way the jeweler does. What you see is a culmination of the art of keeping time with mechanical clocks—an art that goes back to the Middle Ages. You will probably see an oscillating system consisting of a balance and a coiled spring. Energy is converted from kinetic energy in the balance to potential energy in the spring, and vice versa, in a regular cycle. The function of the rest of the watch is to count these oscillations, and record them. Or you may see, instead of a spring, a little battery, and your watch may hum instead of ticking. If so, it probably works by counting the oscillations of an electrically driven tuning fork. Whatever kind of timepiece you have, it has something that vibrates regularly and something else that counts and records the vibrations.

The essential word is "regularity." We all expect regularity in the cycles of a clock. It is not easy, however, to state precisely what regularity is and how to check it. For the present I simply assert that, to measure time, you must have something that repeats a cycle regularly. (An exception is the radioactive clock mentioned in § 7.6.)

7.2. The Sense of Time: Events

Even without a watch we feel time go by. Alone, and in the dark, we might lose our sense of space and orientation, but some sense of the flow of time would prevail—perhaps because we continue to breathe or because our hearts continue to beat. It is a curious fact—the exact cause is not well understood—that some people can awaken at will at a predetermined hour quite accurately without an alarm clock. A certain kind of slug, even when kept for a whole year in an artificial laboratory environment, begins to lay its eggs about the first of August. Different animals have different clock-like characteristics.

Human beings seem to share one intuition and two abilities related to time: (1) we have a feeling that time flows without interruptions or breaks (I shall discuss this in § 7.4); (2) we can put past events in their proper order in our memory (just as we can quickly arrange a bunch of sticks according to length without measuring each with a

ruler, so we can arrange events according to their order of occurrence); (3) we can estimate—often only roughly—the length of time between two events. In the exercise of the latter ability our mind can play tricks on us. Our estimate of the time from the moment we begin a meal in a restaurant to the moment we pay the bill depends on many factors, physiological and psychological—among them the emotional influence of our companions, our state of weariness, and the amount and kind of stimulants consumed.

Just as we need objective measures of space and mass, so we need an objective measure of time. We need at least clocks that will give the same reading—except for the usual variations due to small, unavoidable, and insignificant errors—to different observers.

An essential word in discussions of the physical meaning of time is "event." The birth of a child is an event. Observe how it is heralded: announcement cards proclaim the time and place of the occurrence and give the weight of the baby, and some even give its size; mass, length, and time are involved in the specification of this event. An eclipse is an event. The collision of two galaxies is an event. The collision of two steel balls in the laboratory is an event. The disintegration of an atomic nucleus (Fig. 7.1) is an event. The word "event" is most useful in physical reasoning when it pertains to something assignable to a point in time. The collision of the steel balls and the disintegration of the nucleus illustrate this well, the other examples only approximately. Events are separated from one another in space and time. They usually involve matter also. We can try to deal abstractly with time as if it could be divorced from matter and space, but in the real world all three go together.

7.3. Motion Pictures and the Stroboscope

Someone has said that time is like a river. You can dip your hand into it to represent the present. The water still coming and that already gone represent the future and the past, respectively. This is more poetry than physics, but it does make graphic our feeling that time flows without interruption.

A little reflection reveals that, since all matter is now thought to be made up of atoms, it must be granular and not continuous. Since even water is made up of atoms, the continuity of a stream of water is an illusion. This suggests that continuity in time may also be an illusion.

We know how easily the eye can be fooled. We know that a motion picture consists of a sequence of still pictures that create the illusion of continuity when shown in rapid succession. A professional movie camera normally shoots twenty-four frames per second. When the projector exhibits them at the same rate, events on the screen appear natural because the intervals of time between them on the screen are the same as they were in reality. If the projector exhibits the film at six-teen frames per second, the action looks slow; if at forty-eight frames per second, the action looks fast. We can produce similar effects by running the film through the camera faster or slower and then projecting it at the normal rate. A whole football game, from the moment people first enter the stadium to the moment the last of the milling crowd leaves its portals, can be shown in two minutes. At the other extreme, certain cameras can expose 1,400,000 frames per second. Such a film, projected at normal speed, makes things seem to move at 1/58,300 of normal speed.

A projector can be run backward—a favorite trick of home movie enthusiasts; and this is the only way to "reverse time." A boy can run forward along a track and then backward, but all the time the clock is moving forward. "Time's arrow always points one way."

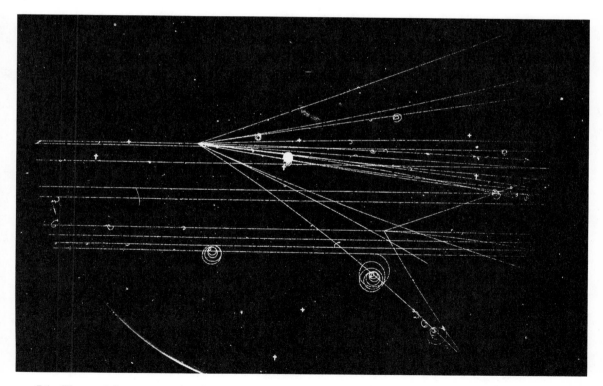

FIG. 7.1. *The particles associated with the nuclei of atoms are invisible, but in the liquid-hydrogen bubble chamber (§ 56.4) they leave visible tracks that are records of nuclear events. A careful analysis of this photograph shows, among other things, that a proton and an antiproton (see Chap. 59) can annihilate each other and produce a great variety of sub-nuclear by-products. (Photograph from CERN, the European Organization for Nuclear Research.)*

Even when the movie projector is running forward, the wheels of a cart sometimes appear to be turning backward on the screen. To understand how this happens, imagine a wheel making twenty-four revolutions per second (Fig. 7.2.A). (It would be breaking all speed laws at that rate, but I have chosen this number for convenience.) If one frame of the movie film catches a certain spoke at *a*, the next frame will also catch it at *a*, and so will the next, for the camera shoots a picture every 1/24 second. The wheel will therefore seem to stand still when the film is projected. If the wheel happens to turn twenty-three times per second (Fig. 7.2.B), the spoke completes only 23/24 revolution between frames. It will therefore appear at *b* in the second frame, at *c* in the third frame, and so on; and, when the film is projected, the wheel will seem to turn slowly backward. If the wheel turns twenty-five frames per second, the wheel on the screen will seem to turn slowly forward. This is called the **stroboscopic effect.** By means of a simple homemade stroboscope (Fig. 7.3), which is easily built, many repetitive phenomena (vibration of tuning forks, vibration of loudspeaker cones, turning of wheels) can be "stopped" for inspection. Problem 7.1 shows how a stroboscope can give quantitative information.

7.4. Continuity

Let us return to the movie camera viewing some simple non-repetitive motion—that of a running boy, for example. The frames of the film present time chopped up into little pieces. (Actually, a piece or interval of time is not an instant, but the limit of a sequence of instants of diminishing size may be. Only speaking loosely can we say that the photographic exposure on the film is instantaneous.) This idea that time can be conceived as a succession of "instants" underlies the way in which time is to be handled mathematically. It even forms the basis, in fact, of a certain philosophical interpretation of reality— the idea that real things may be regarded as a succession of impermanent things. This idea interested Bertrand Russell, who wrote in one of his essays: "When I first read [Henri] Bergson's statement that the mathematician conceives the world after the analogy of a cinematograph [motion picture], I had never seen a cinematograph, and my first visit to one was determined by the desire to verify Bergson's statement, which I found to be completely true, at least so far as I am concerned." This statement is quoted for two reasons. The first is that to those of us who were brought

FIG. 7.2. *Illustration of the stroboscopic effect.*

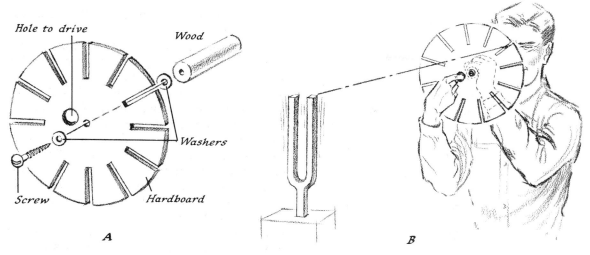

FIG. 7.3. *Experimenting with a homemade stroboscope.*

FIG. 7.4. *Illustration of one-to-one correspondence.*

up on movies, both in the theater and in the school, the thought of a mathematician and philosopher going to see his first movie for the express purpose of confirming a philosophical idea of time is novel indeed. The second reason is that it suggests what we are about to do with mathematics—that is, to use numbers on a line as representative of separate instants of time and then to use this representation in handling the continuity (real or apparent) of time.

Mathematicians worked out a theory of continuity before the atomicity of matter was confirmed. We now know that matter is granular, not continuous, but such knowledge has not stopped us from using the mathematical tools of the calculus, which assume continuity. Atoms are so small that even the growth of a crystal by the accretion of layers of atoms to its surface looks perfectly continuous even under the highest-powered light microscopes.

We may show why we can handle the concept of continuity for both space and time with the same mathematical tools by drawing a long line segment with chalk on the blackboard. If we move the chalk at a constant speed of one foot per second, we can then number marks one foot apart (Fig. 7.4) as 0, 1, 2, 3, . . . , and these numbers can stand either for distance or for time. We assert that there is a one-to-one correspondence between all the points of the line segment (not just those we numbered) and all the instants of the interval of time.

By "one-to-one correspondence" we mean that to every point there corresponds one and only one instant and to every instant there corresponds one and only one point. To illustrate: When each finger of the left hand is made to touch the corresponding finger (thumb to thumb, middle to middle, etc.) of the right hand, a one-to-one correspondence is established; at a dance for married couples, in a monogamous society, a one-to-one correspondence exists between husbands and wives. These are finite sets. The set of points on any line segment and the set of instants in any interval of time are infinite sets, but a one-to-one correspondence exists between them nevertheless.

What we need is a way of establishing a one-to-

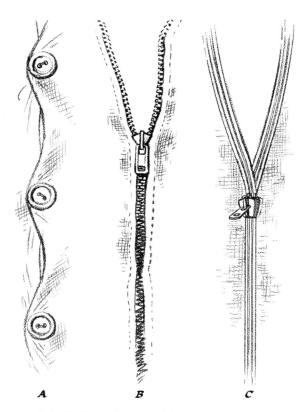

FIG. 7.5. *Different degrees of discontinuity.*

one correspondence between *numbers* and points on a line. We should then be ready to handle time numerically. We have made a start by associating the integers (whole numbers) 1, 2, 3, 4, . . . with a certain set of points on a line. But there are big gaps in between.

The integers are spaced (Fig. 7.5) like buttons on a coat (A). A zipper, with its many small teeth, does a better job of closing the gap between the two edges of the coat (B), but still there are gaps, and we still have discontinuity; if the number of teeth could be increased, and the distance between each two successive teeth decreased, without end, we should have continuity. A better example is the new fastener that joins two long grooved strips of soft plastic material in such a way that no apparent discontinuities exist at all (C); one smooth plastic track seems to fit continuously into the other. Yet we know that even here discontinuities would be disclosed by the

microscope (and in our mind's eye by the atoms themselves).

We really need a set of numbers so dense that no point on a line is left without a number. Our decimal system is admirably suited to this purpose. Taking the interval between 0 and 1, for example, we can associate the numbers 0.0, 0.1, 0.2, 0.3, 0.4, 0.5, 0.6, 0.7, 0.8, 0.9, and 1.0 with points 0.1 unit apart. But we can go on to take the interval between any two of these—for example, between 0.2 and 0.3—and write 0.20, 0.21, 0.22, 0.23, 0.24, 0.25, 0.26, 0.27, 0.28, 0.29, 0.30. We have now found number labels for nine points equally spaced between 0.2 and 0.3. By an extension of this idea we can subdivide the interval between 0 and 1 into as many intervals with as many end points as we wish.

How do we know that *all* the points between 0 and 1 can be labeled in this way? We cannot answer this question easily. Historically, it took a great deal of time and thought to give an adequate answer to it. To show that the problem is not trivial, I exhibit a set of numbers that looks quite complete but that does, as we can prove, have gaps.

Consider this set of fractions:

$$\frac{1}{1}, \frac{1}{2}, \frac{1}{3}, \frac{1}{4}, \frac{1}{5}, \frac{1}{6}, \frac{1}{7}, \ldots$$
$$\frac{2}{1}, \frac{2}{2}, \frac{2}{3}, \frac{2}{4}, \frac{2}{5}, \frac{2}{6}, \frac{2}{7}, \ldots$$
$$\frac{3}{1}, \frac{3}{2}, \frac{3}{3}, \frac{3}{4}, \frac{3}{5}, \frac{3}{6}, \frac{3}{7}, \ldots$$
$$\frac{4}{1}, \frac{4}{2}, \frac{4}{3}, \frac{4}{4}, \frac{4}{5}, \frac{4}{6}, \frac{4}{7}, \ldots$$

etc.

Observe that each row, considered as a sequence, has 0 as its limit (for example, $\frac{1}{1}$, $\frac{1}{2}$, $\frac{1}{3}$, . . . $\frac{1}{n}$, . . . approaches zero). The numbers of this subset therefore crowd thickly near 0. Next observe that subsequences such as $\frac{1}{2}$, $\frac{2}{3}$, $\frac{3}{4}$, $\frac{4}{5}$, . . . and $\frac{2}{1}$, $\frac{3}{2}$, $\frac{4}{3}$, $\frac{5}{4}$, . . . have 1 as a limit. The numbers of these subsets therefore crowd near 1. The numbers of particular subsets in this set are pretty thick, in fact, in the vicinity of *any* number, as you can see by locating points on a line for each of the numbers shown explicitly above.

Now we ask, "Is $\sqrt{2}$ to be found among these numbers?" To answer this question, space the integers 0, 1, 2, and 3 equally along the x axis (Fig. 7.6). Draw a square whose sides are of length 1 as shown. Since the diagonal, *AB*, is the hypot-

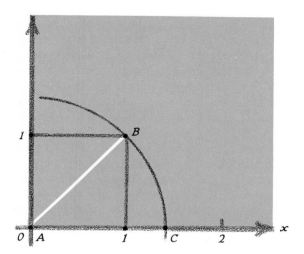

FIG. 7.6. *Determining the point whose* x *coordinate is* $\sqrt{2}$.

enuse of a right triangle, $(AB)^2 = 1^2 + 1^2 = 2$. Hence $AB = \sqrt{2}$. Draw a circle with its center at A and with radius AB. It will meet the x axis at point C. Obviously $AC = \sqrt{2}$. We now ask whether point C is represented by one of the fractions of the set shown on page 86. In other words, is $\sqrt{2}$ a rational number? (A **rational number** is one that can be expressed as the ratio of two whole numbers. The set of fractions shown above contains all the positive rational numbers.) The answer is no.† Although that set is dense everywhere on the x axis, it does not contain $\sqrt{2}$.

This illustration poses but does not solve one of the numerical problems of continuity. We want every point to have a number associated with it, and we want every number to have a unique point associated with it, but the set discussed above does not contain $\sqrt{2}$ (or $\sqrt{3}$ or π or any other irrational number).

† Assume that $\sqrt{2}$ may be written as $\sqrt{2} = p/q$ if p and q are integers with no factors in common other than 1. Write $q\sqrt{2} = p$. Squaring both sides, you get $2q^2 = p^2$. Hence p^2 is an even integer; so p must be even. Write it as $p = 2k$, in which k is an integer. Square both sides and get $p^2 = 4k^2$. Substitute this into the next equation to the last above, and obtain $4q^2 = 2q^2$. Hence q^2 is even, but this implies that q is even, and we have been led to the conclusion that both p and q are even, which is contrary to the assumption that they had no common factors other than 1. Our assumption was false.

If we look up $\sqrt{2}$ in a table, we read that it equals 1.414214, but this cannot be correct, for 1.414214 is a rational number; it is, in fact, the ratio of the two integers 1,414,214 and 1,000,000. The number 1.414214 is simply a very good approximation to $\sqrt{2}$. The sequence of *rational numbers* 1.0, 1.4, 1.41, 1.414, 1.4142, . . . (obtainable by the process taught in schools for extracting square root) has an *irrational* number ($\sqrt{2}$) as its limit! It can be shown, in fact, that every irrational number can be expressed as the limit of a set of rational numbers. This is as far as I shall go in proving that the decimal system can handle all the numbers on a line, rational or irrational. (Incidentally, the fact that a decimal number does not terminate is not enough to make it irrational. Consider 0.333333 . . . . It represents 1/3; that is, the limit of the set of *rational* numbers 0.3000, 0.3300, 0.3330, 0.3333, . . . is the *rational* number 1/3.)

The fascinating mathematical problems of continuity that I have just touched upon belong to the infinitesimal calculus. I have only suggested how they are handled. The concept of the limit of a sequence is central to their solution.

I assert without proof, therefore, that the points on a line can be put into a one-to-one correspondence with the set of real numbers, and that the decimal fractions can cope with real numbers in all practical problems of computation.

I also assert, therefore, that both the geometrical points on a line and the instants of time can be put into a one-to-one correspondence with the decimals themselves or with the limits of sequences of decimals.

7.5. Clocks and the Units of Time

The unit of time in the MKS system is the **second**. Let us define it as 1/86,400 day (86,400 sec/day = 24 h/day × 60 min/h × 60 sec/min).† Let us see, at least in principle, how to effect this subdivision. Imagine doing the following experi-

† In 1960, at the Eleventh International Conference on Weights and Measures, the second was defined as 1/31,556,925.9747 of the solar year 1900.

ment very early in the morning on May 15 (for reasons that will be clear later).

Drive a stick vertically into the ground somewhere in the northern hemisphere. At dawn it casts a long shadow to the west. As the day progresses, the shadow gets shorter and points more and more toward the north. At sunset the shadow is again long and points to the east. There was a certain instant when the shadow was at its shortest. At that instant the shadow pointed north. Let's call that instant *noon*.

Now take a simple pendulum about a meter long. Such a pendulum makes about 86,400 half-cycles from the noon of one day to the noon of the following day—noon, of course, being the instant when the shadow of the stick is shortest. Instead of describing the difficult process by which one might adjust the length of the pendulum so that it made *precisely* 86,400 half-cycles between two successive noons, let us grant that on this day we managed to do just that! Observe that we have used a periodic phenomenon, the rotation of the earth on its axis, to define the unit of time called the day, and another periodic phenomenon, the swing of a pendulum, to define the second. The pendulum we have described has a period of two seconds, and we say that it ticks off seconds.

The day I have described is called, for obvious reasons, a **solar day.** If we had a clock driven by our pendulum (designed to go on indefinitely in an environment in which the temperature, the air resistance, the input of energy, and other factors were kept constant), we should find that the number of its ticks per solar day did *not* remain constant as the weeks and months went by.

This poses a dilemma: Which clock is right? We are really asking, "Which is inconstant, the earth or the pendulum?" (Today we know that, because the earth moves in an ellipse, some of its solar days are longer than others.) The experimental way to answer the question is to find some other periodic phenomenon and to see whether its natural period maintains a constant relation to either the solar day or the swing of the pendulum. Let's try looking to the stars instead of to the sun.

At point P on the earth (Fig. 7.7) a plane is determined by P and the north (N) and the south (S) poles of the earth. A telescope is mounted at P

so that its longitudinal axis lies in the plane PNS. It is free to rotate about another axis perpendicular to the plane PNS. We observe a star crossing the vertical hairline in its eyepiece. Call this event T_1. On the next night, a little less than twenty-four hours later (by the pendulum clock that was geared to a solar day), we look through the telescope again. We see the image of the same star approaching the vertical hairline. When it crosses, we call this event T_2. The interval of time between T_1 and T_2 is called a **sidereal day** (*sidus* = star). If we build a new pendulum that ticks 86,400 times between successive transits of this star, this pendulum ticks off (to a very close approximation) **sidereal seconds.** If we observe this same star night after night for a whole year, we find that every sidereal day has the same number of pendulum ticks as any other sidereal day (to a very high degree of accuracy).†

That seems to settle the question. We ought to use the sidereal day and forget about the solar day. That is, in effect, what astronomers do. Since they are primarily concerned with celestial events, they build clocks to tick off sidereal seconds, hours, and days, and thereby they keep track of celestial motions.

All this amounts to saying that, if we measure them with a very accurate pendulum clock, the solar day is a variable and the sidereal day is a constant. This statement, though not perfectly accurate, is in the right direction.

In practice, we use the **mean solar day,** which is based on the motion of a fictitious *mean sun* that moves uniformly in the heavens at such a rate that it completes its annual apparent motion among the stars in one year, the same time that it takes the real sun to do this. Accurate clocks are adjusted to divide this mean solar day into 86,400 parts called **mean solar seconds.** (I chose May 15 for our imaginary experiment at the beginning of this section because it is one of the four times in the year when a real solar day does

---

† The actual procedure is much more involved than that suggested here. The reader is referred to Norman Feather, *An Introduction to the Physics of Mass, Length, and Time* (Edinburgh University Press, 1959), Chap. 3, "The Measurement of Time," and to "Time Measurement," *Encyclopaedia Britannica* (1960), vol. 22.

last 86,400 mean solar seconds.) If we compare sidereal and solar clocks, we find that a sidereal day is 23 hours, 56 minutes, and 4.0905 seconds of mean solar time. A year contains 365.242195 mean solar days and 366.242195 sidereal days.

This brief and not quite precise explanation ....kes it seem that the rotation of the earth, as seen from the stars, is constant, and that the only reason why the solar day varies throughout the year is that the earth has to turn more on some days than on others in order for the same point on its surface to face the sun. This is only approximately true; refined techniques have shown that the angular motion of the earth is *not* constant. For this reason a refinement of sidereal time called **ephemeris time** has been adopted. Since the difference between the two is only about one part in ten million, we shall not pursue the matter further here, but later we shall see that con-

templated experiments involving space travel may require ephemeris time. (The second as defined in 1960 corresponds to what astronomers used to call the ephemeris second.)

I have said that a pendulum one meter long has a period of about two seconds. When we study dynamics (§ 25.6), I shall prove that the formula for the period of a simple pendulum is $T = 2\pi\sqrt{l/g}$ if l is its length and g is the acceleration due to gravity. Substitute 1 m for l and 9.8 m/sec² for g in this formula in order to see that T comes out close to two seconds.

Another vibrating object that is often used in the laboratory is the loaded helical spring. I shall prove later (§ 25.6) that, if the mass (in kg) of the suspended weight is m and the stiffness constant (in nt/m) of the spring is k, the period of the system is $T = 2\pi\sqrt{m/k}$. (You are not expected

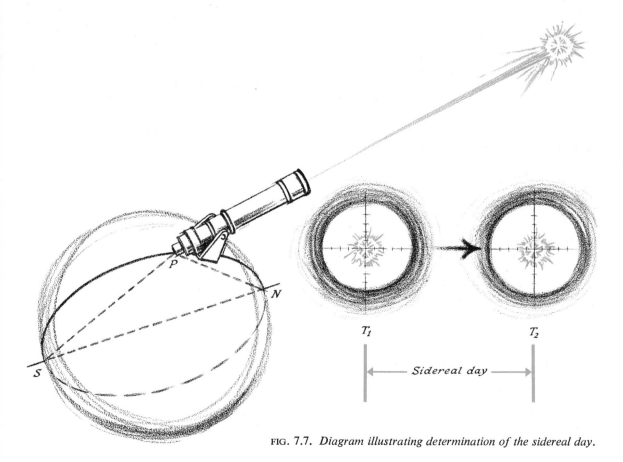

FIG. 7.7. *Diagram illustrating determination of the sidereal day.*

to understand these formulas yet, but it is not difficult to make them seem plausible. A long pendulum, for example, should, according to the formula $T = 2\pi\sqrt{l/g}$, have a long period, and experiments confirm this.)

The transition from the simple pendulum to the modern pendulum-regulated clock, and the transition from the linear vibrations of a coil spring to the angular vibrations of the spring in a modern watch, make long and interesting stories involving the contributions of many clever craftsmen and of some men famous in the history of physics, such as Galileo Galilei (1564–1642), Robert Hooke (1635–1703), and Christian Huygens (1629–1695). As we shall see later, contributions to the theory and measurement of time are still being made by modern physicists.

7.6. Special Clocks

The modern trend in time-measuring devices is away from clocks that depend on gravitational forces, such as that of the earth, toward clocks in which the other basic forces, electric and nuclear, play a more important role. The development of modern electronics has made possible several new ways of measuring time. Some of these are described here very briefly.

1. *The Quartz-crystal Oscillator*

Quartz crystals have natural periods of oscillation of about 10^{-5} sec. When deformed, a crystal produces an electric potential across its faces, and this, if incorporated into an electronic oscillator, will produce a very constant frequency. The output of this oscillator can be used to drive a clock. The day-to-day variation in period of the best quartz-crystal oscillators is about 2 parts in 10^{10}, or about 0.00002 sec/day, which is smaller than the difference between sidereal and ephemeris time. This is about a hundred times better than the best pendulum clocks. Through the use of quartz-crystal clocks it is possible to determine accurately the variations in the speed of the earth's rotation.

2. *The Cathode-ray Oscilloscope*

This device (explained in detail in § 15.1) is becoming fairly common in modern laboratories. A beam of electrons produces a light when it impinges on the fluorescent screen of a tube specially designed for this purpose. (The television picture tube uses the same idea.) The beam, controlled by electric fields, can be made to sweep across the face of the tube at a rate governed by an electronic oscillator. This motion is governed by a cyclic sweep circuit. Since the period of the cycle can be controlled very accurately by electronic circuits, short signals can be very accurately timed. If, for example, the sweep circuit causes the beam of electrons to travel from A to B on the screen (Fig. 7.8) 10,000 times per second, AB becomes a linear scale representing 1/10,000 sec. We can record events separated by 1/100,000 sec by momentarily deflecting the beam vertically at, for example, C and D. Oscilloscopes that can detect intervals shorter than 10^{-9} sec are available.

The oscilloscope is not a clock in the sense that it records long intervals of time, but it does measure short intervals with some accuracy. Light sent to a mirror 15 m away, for example, would return in 10^{-7} sec. (The speed of light is 3×10^8 m/sec.) This interval could be measured with an oscilloscope.

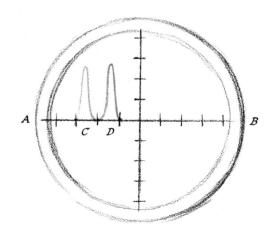

FIG. 7.8. *Diagram illustrating measurement of time with an oscilloscope.*

3. *Atomic Clocks*

The first so-called atomic clock was based on the vibrations of the nitrogen atom in the ammonia molecule. The atom's natural frequency of oscillation is about 23,870,000,000 times per second. A radio wave of this frequency sent through ammonia gas is, to a considerable extent, absorbed: ammonia seems very willing to take energy from a radio wave of this natural frequency. If a quartz-crystal oscillator is designed to operate at this frequency, the absorption by the ammonia serves as a very accurate check and can even indirectly drive the oscillator to the high precision of the natural frequency of the nitrogen atom in ammonia. The best clocks built on this principle seem to have an error of only about 3 parts in 10 billion.

The cesium clock uses cesium atoms instead of ammonia molecules. It has a natural frequency of about 9,192,000,000 cycles per second. It works a little differently from the ammonia clock, but the principle is the same: to utilize the constant natural oscillations of atoms. Error of only about 1 part in 10 billion seems possible. This corresponds to an error in time-keeping of 1 second in 300 years. But the end is not yet in sight. New ways to excite very constant vibrations in hydrogen and to produce gamma rays of very constant energy are the basis of new devices with which it is hoped to build clocks with an error of less than 1 second in 30 million years. It looks as if the very small atomic systems would be capable of much greater accuracy than the large astronomical systems.

4. *The Radioactive Clock*

For the measurement of very long time intervals the disintegration of atomic nuclei can be used. The radioactive clock is different from all the clocks we have discussed so far, for it depends, not on the great regularity of some repetitive process, but on the completely chaotic and random nature of the disintegrations. What makes the clock regular enough to be useful is the great number of disintegrations. Although the atomic nuclei are disintegrating at random (and giving off particles that can be counted), the *average* number of disintegrations per second is proportional to the number of atoms in the sample. For this reason a radioactive element exhibits what is known as **half-life** (§ 57.2). The half-life of radioactive strontium 90, for example, is 28 years. This means that a sample producing N disintegrations per minute today will produce very close to $N/2$ disintegrations per minute 28 years from now, $N/4$ disintegrations per minute 56 years from now, and so on. Because some radioactive elements have half-lives of hundreds and even thousands of years, we can apply their rates of disintegration to estimations of long time intervals. A now commonly accepted estimate of the age of the earth, for example, is 3.35×10^9 years. To get more than three significant figures in this result, we must determine the half-lives of uranium 238 and uranium 235 more precisely. Though, as we see, the percentage error is considerably greater than in the measurement of short time intervals, we shall probably soon know the age of the earth more accurately than the average person knows his own height.

7.7. Time and Relativity†

I cannot close a chapter on time without mentioning the great revolution in thinking introduced by Albert Einstein's theory of relativity. Newton's idea that there is an "absolute time," which for practical purposes is measured by sidereal (or, more precisely, by ephemeris) time, remained unchallenged until Einstein found that, in order to understand some of the phenomena of modern physics, he had to reconstruct space and time in new and unconventional ways. He assumed an operational approach and said, in effect, "Let us talk about things we can measure."

Now the speed of light is a measurable quantity; it is about 3×10^8 m/sec. Light must, obviously, play an important role in our description of events,

---

† This section may be omitted on first reading without serious loss, but it has some interesting ideas that are worth at least a quick glance.

for our awareness of events usually comes to us as a light signal. We observe the collision of two cars or an eclipse of the moon. They happen in space and in time. To describe them, we have to answer the questions "where?" and "when?" An answer to "when?" usually involves the messenger light. If two explosions in outer space were simultaneous, we should judge them to be so because we saw two flashes at the same time. But someone sitting on a star very near one explosion and very far from the other would not judge them to be simultaneous. Who would be right? What *is* simultaneity?

I cannot answer this question now, but I do want to suggest that the speed of light must play an important role in any discussion of the time at which events seem to take place. Different observers see events differently according to the **frame of reference** from which they observe. If I drop a book in the cabin of an airplane in flight, it seems to me to drop in a straight line. To an observer on the ground the path of the book would look curved (it moves forward as well as downward).

In order to handle mathematically the relation between motion as you see it on the ground and the same motion as I see it in the airplane, we have to set up equations. Let x and y (Fig. 7.9) be a system, A, in a fixed laboratory, and let x' and y' be a system, B, in a laboratory moving at speed v in relation to A. The dot P represents an event, whose x coordinate in system A is x, in system B is x'. If A and B were together at $t = 0$, $AB = vt$ if t was the time at which P took place. "Obviously,"

$$x' = x - vt \qquad [7.1$$

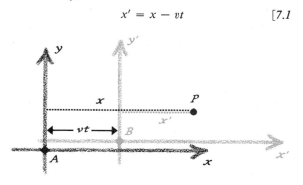

FIG. 7.9. *Two frames of reference.*

The quotation marks around *obviously* are there because most of us would admit that the statement seems obvious. To Einstein it was not obvious. He deduced, in fact, that the correct equation is

$$x' = k(x - vt)$$

Here k is very close to 1 if v is small. But k really involves the speed of light, c:

$$k = \frac{1}{\sqrt{1 - (v/c)^2}} \qquad [7.2$$

We took it for granted, of course, that identical clocks in A and B would keep identical time if they read alike at $t = 0$. Einstein suggested that though the clock in A would record P as taking place at t, the clock in B would record a *different* time, t':

$$t' = k(t - xv/c^2) \qquad [7.3$$

Identical clocks do not keep the same time if they are moving in relation to each other!

One purpose of the recent activity in building atomic clocks of great precision is to test these new laws of Einstein directly. They have already received tremendous indirect confirmation. The formula $E = mc^2$, for example, comes out of the theory. I shall discuss all this more thoroughly in Chapter 46.

7.8. Summary

Although we seem to have a built-in sense of time, it is difficult to define it. Instead, we describe how to measure intervals of time by using clocks. Most clocks work by counting the number of repetitive cycles of some mechanism, whether it be the swing of a pendulum or the vibration of a molecule.

To handle time mathematically, we set up a one-to-one correspondence between instants of time and the points on a line, which, in turn, we associate with the real numbers, usually written decimally.

The unit of time in the MKS system is the second. There are approximately 86,400 (60 × 60 × 24) seconds in a mean solar day. Since 1960 the second has been defined as a certain fraction of the solar year 1900.

In his theory of relativity, Albert Einstein pointed out that two events are not separated by an absolute interval of time, but, rather, that two different observers who are moving in relation to each other would measure different time intervals even with identical clocks. This effect becomes measurable only when the relative speed approaches that of light.

Problems

7.1. This problem will test your comprehension of the stroboscope. It will also give you some practice with fractions.

A stroboscope like the one of Fig. 7.3 is rotated so that f_s slots pass the eye per second. A tuning fork seen through it seems to vibrate f_a times per second. We call this the apparent frequency. Prove that the real frequency, f_r, of the fork may be $f_s + f_a$ or $f_s - f_a$. [Hint: Let T stand for the period (time for one complete cycle) and f for the frequency (number of cycles per second). In general, $T = 1/f$. (Observe that sec/cycle is the inverse of cycle/sec.) Let the subscripts a, s, and r stand for *apparent*, *stroboscope*, and *real*, respectively. Consider a possible case. During T_s seconds (the time required for one slot to replace the previous one) the tuning fork *really* completes $1 + x$ cycles (x being less than 1) but *apparently* completes only x cycles. Hence $f_r = (1 + x)/T_s$ but $f_a = x/T_s$. This leads to the case $f_r = f_s + f_a$.] Exhibit all the logical steps in writing, and consider other possible cases.

7.2. The objective of this problem is to prove that one sidereal day is approximately 23 hours and 56 minutes, but the numerical result is not as important as learning how to set up such a problem by using a good figure and effecting the computation with a minimum of arithmetic.

In Fig. 7.10 an observer on the earth at A sees a distant star directly overhead (position I). An observer at B simultaneously sees the sun directly overhead. The line AB is a diameter of the earth. One sidereal day later (position II) AB is parallel to its former position. The star once again appears overhead to the observer at A, but the earth must rotate through an additional angle, α, before the observer at B sees the sun overhead. In the figure, α is greatly exaggerated; it is actually about 1/365 of a complete turn. One solar day $\cong (1 + 1/365)$ sidereal day; hence one sidereal day $\cong 365/366 \times 24$ h. (We accept 1 solar day as 24 h.)

Prove that one sidereal day $\cong$ 23 h and 56 min. It is difficult, with a slide rule, to distinguish 365/366 from 1. If you write

$$365/366 = (366 - 1)/366 = 1 - 1/366$$

you can get

$$1 \text{ sidereal day} = (24 - 24/366) \text{ h}$$

The last fraction *can* be evaluated on the slide rule. Take all the steps suggested, and be sure that you understand them.

7.3. This problem requires only simple substitution into the formula $T = 2\pi\sqrt{l/g}$, but you may derive some satisfaction from it by testing your result experimentally.

1. How long must a pendulum be to have a period of 3 sec?

2. Make a pendulum out of a light thread and a small heavy object like a ring, and check the prediction of part 1 experimentally. Can you account for the observed discrepancy?

3. Would it be feasible to build a pendulum whose period was 200 sec? Defend your answer.

7.4. This problem should interest students who do well in algebra. The objective is to illustrate with a specific example how you can prove, in general, that

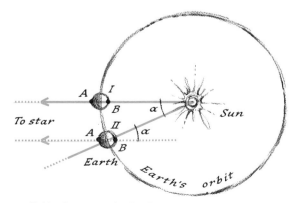

FIG. 7.10. *Diagram for Prob. 7.2.*

a repeating decimal is a rational number—that is, that it can be expressed as the ratio of two whole numbers. I asserted in the chapter that all real numbers can be expressed decimally. Here you are to show only that infinitely repeating decimal fractions are rational.

1. Consider the repeating decimal 0.343434343434 . . . Observe that it may be written as

$$0.34 + 0.34 \times 10^{-2} + 0.34$$
$$\times 10^{-4} + 0.34 \times 10^{-6} + \ldots$$

Factoring out 0.34, you get

$$0.34(1 + 10^{-2} + 10^{-4} + 10^{-6} \ldots)$$

The part within the parentheses is of the form

$$1 + r + r^2 + r^3 + r^n + \ldots$$

with $r = 10^{-2}$. In algebra books it is proved that this gets as close as we please to $1/(1 - r)$ when r is less than one. Hence this repeating decimal is said to be equal to

$$0.34 \times 1/(1 - r) = 0.34/(1 - 0.01)$$
$$= 0.34/0.99 = 34/99$$

which is a rational number.

2. Now we know that $\sqrt{2}$ is approximately 1.414214. That is as far as most tables go. Is it conceivable that $\sqrt{2}$ might be

$$1.414214414214414214 \ldots$$

—that is, that it might be a repeating decimal? Try your hand at the logic that starts: $\sqrt{2}$ is an infinitely repeating decimal; but all repeating decimals are rational numbers . . . What do you conclude?

7.5. The objective of this problem is to show how the concept of one-to-one correspondence is applicable to infinite sets. First consider a finite set. When you match the fingers of the right hand with those of the left by touching thumb to thumb, index finger to index finger, and so on, you illustrate the one-to-one correspondence between these sets. More generally, if each member of a set (A) corresponds to one and only one member of another set (B) and vice versa, we say that a one-to-one correspondence exists between sets A and B.

1. Applying these ideas to infinite sets, show that you can put the set of all positive odd integers into one-to-one correspondence with the set of all even integers by writing corresponding terms beneath one another and expressing the nth term of each as a function of n.

2. Prove that the set 1/1, 1/2, 1/3, 1/4, . . . 1/n can be put into one-to-one correspondence with the set of positive integers. On the x axis put dots corresponding to the location of these numbers.

3. Can you crowd as many numbers between 0 and 1 as there are in the whole set of positive integers? (One infinite set is said to have as many members as another infinite set if they can be put into one-to-one correspondence with each other.)

7.6. The factor $k = 1/\sqrt{1 - (v/c)^2}$ of equation 7.2 plays an important part in the theory of relativity. Compute it for $v/c = 0.1$ (v is 1/10 of the speed of light) and also for $v/c = 0.9$ (v is 9/10 of the speed of light). This should at least convince you that for low speeds k is practically 1. Incidentally, how fast (in mph) would a car have to go to satisfy the equation $v/c = 0.1$? (The speed of light is 3×10^8 m/sec.)

Motion

"My purpose is to set forth a very new science dealing with a very ancient subject. There is, in nature, perhaps nothing older than motion, concerning which the books written by philosophers are neither few nor small; nevertheless I have discovered by experiment some properties of it which are worth knowing and which have not hitherto been either observed or demonstrated. Some superficial observations have been made as, for instance, that the free motion (*naturalem motum*) of a heavy falling body is continuously accelerated; but to just what extent this acceleration occurs has not yet been announced; for so far as I know, no one has yet pointed out that the distances traversed, during equal intervals of time, by a body falling from rest, stand to one another in the same ratio as the odd numbers beginning with unity."

GALILEO GALILEI, "Mathematics of Motion: Change of Position" (*De Motu Locali*), in James R. Newman, *The World of Mathematics* (Simon & Schuster, New York, 1956), vol. 2, p. 734.

MAX BORN, in his book *The Restless Universe*,[†] says: "It is odd to think that there is a word for something which, strictly speaking, does not exist, namely, 'rest'." If an object seems to be at rest, you need only remember that it is on the spinning earth to know that it is moving. The planets—wanderers—were so called because of their motion, and many of the other objects in the sky, which seem fixed, reveal their motion under scrutiny. If you consider the atoms of which an object is composed, you realize that even its microscopic parts are all in motion.

Yet the problem of motion has troubled philosophers since the days of Zeno of Elea (about 490–420 B.C.), who denied the logical possibility of motion as earnestly as Born refutes the possibility of rest. Consider one of Zeno's paradoxes:[‡]

Before a body in motion can reach a given point, it must first traverse the half of the distance; before it can traverse the half, it must first traverse the quarter; and so on ad infinitum. Hence, for a body to pass from one point to another, it must traverse an infinite number of divisions. But an infinite distance (which the paradox does not distinguish from a finite distance infinitely divided) cannot be traversed in a finite time. Consequently, the goal can never be reached.

The apparent irrationalities of motion were not resolved until Galileo, Newton, and a host of others set their minds to the task. In this chapter we shall learn how the tools of mathematics are applied to the study of motion.

If we consider an automobile coming to a halt at a stop-light, we perceive that space, time, matter, and forces are involved in its motion. To consider all of these at once is the formidable task of **dynamics.** If we disregard matter and force

† Dover Publications, New York, 1951.
‡ "Zeno," *Encyclopaedia Britannica*, 1960, vol. 23.

at first (that is, if we study what we might call "pure motion"), we shall be dealing only with space and time. This study is called **kinematics.** It is a kind of marriage of geometry and time. This chapter deals with the simplest concepts of kinematics.

The pre-eminent position of physics today stems from the early triumphs of mechanics: the study of space, time, matter, and motion. Logically, motion belongs first in such a sequence. We have deferred it until now in order to build the mathematical and intuitive background for it. Now we must tackle it mathematically. Our treatment will not be sophisticated: that would require the calculus. It will be simple, but it will demonstrate that the study of physics would be almost impossible without mathematics.

If you are the kind of reader who dreads mathematical symbols or who automatically skips them in reading, prepare to take the plunge. You cannot avoid them any longer and still learn some physics. But be heartened by the fact that the reward, in satisfaction and understanding, can be great. Perhaps you recall the satisfaction you had in learning to ride a bicycle. It was worth the effort. You could move much faster on a bicycle than you could by walking. Mathematics is like a bicycle or even like a high-speed motorcycle: with it we can make journeys into thought that are practically impossible with verbal reasoning alone.

8.1. Particle Kinematics

I have used the word "particle" to mean something very small, but I have also said that something as large as the moon, in an approximate discussion of its motion, can be treated as a particle. This usually means that we disregard its spin. A real object can spin as it moves forward. If it is small, the effects of its spin may be negligible. In a mathematical treatment of motion, therefore, the concept of particle is idealized to mean an object with finite mass but infinitesimally small size. When I speak of particle kinematics, it is in this restricted sense that I use the word "particle." The mathematical treatment will deal abstractly with particles in motion but can be

applied to real objects having only **translational motion.**† A train moving along a track is not a particle, but particle kinematics is applicable to it.

The simplest motion is called **uniform motion.** The motion of an automobile moving along a straight road so that its speedometer reading remains constant is an example of uniform motion. Uniform motion is a natural kind of motion: it's the way a body moves if no forces act on it, but pure examples of it are hard to exhibit. A Dry Ice puck on a horizontal glass surface will move in a straight line at an almost constant speed for a long time. A parachute jumper, having achieved his terminal velocity on a still day, moves in nearly uniform motion. These two examples illustrate the principle of inertia stated earlier: in the absence of an unbalanced force, a body is not accelerated. This implies, in terms of vectors, that the *change in velocity* is zero:

$$\Delta \mathbf{v} = 0 \qquad [8.1$$

This means that

$$\mathbf{v} - \mathbf{v}_0 = 0 \qquad [8.2$$

or that

$$\mathbf{v} = \mathbf{v}_0 \qquad [8.3$$

The final velocity is the same as the initial velocity. (It agrees with common sense, of course, that direction and magnitude are unchanged. You may find these first examples so simple that you prefer to deal with them without the mathematical formalism, but you are urged to treat even these simple cases mathematically in order to learn the formalism without which the more difficult cases cannot be treated.)

The proper mathematical language for motion is that of vectors. But for motion in a straight line—along the x axis, for example—we don't need to use the vector notation. Let us see why.

Imagine a railroad train moving on one of those long flat stretches in the western part of the United States where the road is straight and the telegraph poles are equally spaced. By clocking the train we observe that it covers the intervals of space

---

† Suppose that a point, A, on a body undergoes vector displacement AA'. If every other point, B, on the body undergoes the *same* displacement (that is, if vector BB' is the same as vector AA'), the motion is pure translation without rotation.

between the poles in equal intervals of time. Its motion is uniform. It obeys the equation

$$\bar{v} = \frac{\Delta x}{\Delta t} = \text{a constant} \qquad [8.4$$

Because $\bar{v}$ is a constant, we can dispense with the bar (meaning "average") over it and write simply

$$v = \frac{x_2 - x_1}{t_2 - t_1} = \frac{\Delta x}{\Delta t} \qquad [8.5$$

We keep the letter v (meaning velocity), even though we have written a scalar equation, because the *sign* of Δx indicates direction and hence imparts a vectorial quality to Δx. This can be seen clearly in a numerical example. Suppose that a point on the train is found at 80 feet and 160 feet from a fixed point at instants of time marked $t_1 = 24$ seconds and $t_2 = 25$ seconds. Putting these numbers into equation 8.5 yields

$$v = \frac{160 - 80}{25 - 24} \text{ ft/sec} = 80 \text{ ft/sec}$$

If the train had been at 300 feet at $t_1 = 24$ seconds and at 220 feet at $t_2 = 25$ seconds, the result would have been

$$v = \frac{220 - 300}{25 - 24} \text{ ft/sec} = -80 \text{ ft/sec}$$

The negative sign clearly indicates that the velocity is in the negative x direction.

We want to extend these ideas to motion along a curved path. If our train comes to a curve, it can still keep a constant speed, but its direction will be changing. For objects like a train on a curved track or a bead sliding on a curved wire, we write the equation

$$v = \frac{s_2 - s_1}{t_2 - t_1} = \frac{\Delta s}{\Delta t} \qquad [8.6$$

in which s means a length measured *along the curve*. Motion at a constant speed along a curve is illustrated in Figure 8.1. The numbers represent successive clock readings marking off equal time intervals. From equation 8.6 we obtain the expression

$$\Delta s = v(\Delta t) \qquad [8.7$$

which may be written as

$$s - s_0 = vt \qquad [8.8$$

if s_0 is the initial distance along the curve from an arbitrary starting point where the time was 0. An equivalent way of writing it is

$$s = s_0 + vt \qquad [8.9$$

The equation obviously applies equally well to motion at a constant speed along a straight line. In both cases v is a constant.

If we start from rest and move with constant speed, the graphical representations of distance and velocity (along the curve) are those shown in Figures 8.2 and 8.3 respectively. Figure 8.2 illustrates

$$s = vt \quad \text{or} \quad \frac{\Delta s}{\Delta t} = v = \text{a constant}$$

Figure 8.3 illustrates

$$v = \text{a constant}$$

FIG. 8.1

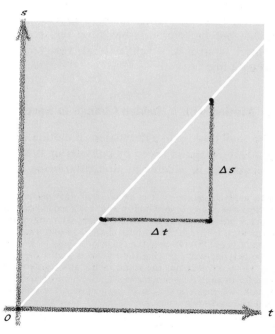

FIG. 8.2

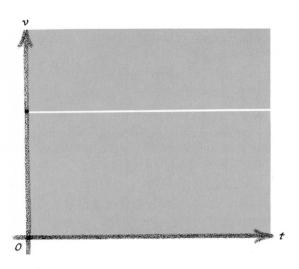

FIG. 8.3

The more general equation (8.9) is represented graphically in Figure 8.4. Figure 8.5 illustrates the meanings of s_0 and s in a hypothetical situation. Distance, s, is measured along the curved track from an arbitrary origin, O. A stopwatch is started as a train passes point A. It reads $t = 0$ there. The distance covered to that point is s_0. Later, at B, the clock reads t when the total distance traveled is s. Similar remarks apply to Figure 8.6, but the symbol s has been replaced by the more familiar x, which is usually reserved for a straight line.†

8.2. Motion with a Sudden Change in Speed

We shall lead up to a discussion of motion with a gradual change in speed by considering first an idealized case in which a motion, after being uni-

---

† In analytic geometry it is shown that an equation of the type $y = mx + b$, in which y and x are variables and m and b are constants, has as its graph, in rectangular coordinates, a straight line whose slope is m and whose y intercept is b. Observe that the equation $s = vt + s_0$ is of the same type, with v playing the role of m and s_0 the role of b. However, v is not the slope in the strict geometric sense, for in analytic geometry m is a pure number and b is a length, whereas v and s_0 have, respectively, the units of speed and distance.

I shall continue to apply the word "slope" to expressions like $\Delta s / \Delta t$ with the understanding that it does not necessarily represent the tangent of the angle of inclination of the secant line involved.

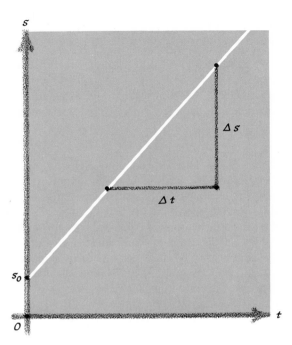

FIG. 8.4

form at one speed, changes suddenly to a motion that is uniform at another speed. Consider, for example, a car going along at 20 mph for 6 minutes (0.1 hour) and suddenly changing its speed to 50 mph. It is impossible, of course, to change the speed of anything in no time at all. "Suddenly" simply means that the change occurs in a very short time. Let us assume that the time is so short in comparison with the length of the whole experiment that we may consider it negligible. If the car continues at a constant 50 mph for the next 6 minutes, the graph of its motion will be as represented in Figure 8.7. The car covered 2.0 miles during the first 6 minutes and 5.0 miles during the second 6 minutes. The graph clearly indicates an increased steepness at 50 mph. Measured on the graph, $\Delta s / \Delta t$ is 20 mph anywhere in the first part of the trip and 50 mph anywhere in the second part.

A large $\Delta s / \Delta t$ implies a high speed and a great steepness in the curve. Three cars, A, B, and C, clocked at 20 mph, 50 mph, and 100 mph, have graphs like lines A, B, and C, respectively, in Figure 8.8. This shows clearly that a steep slope means a high speed.

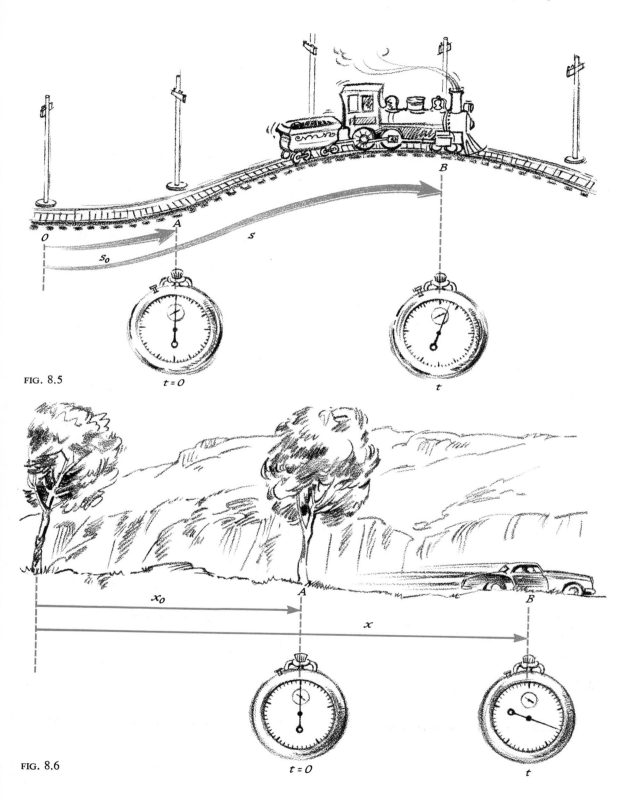

FIG. 8.5

FIG. 8.6

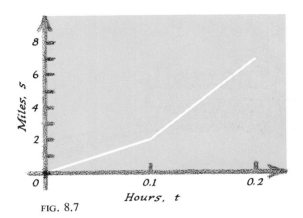

FIG. 8.7

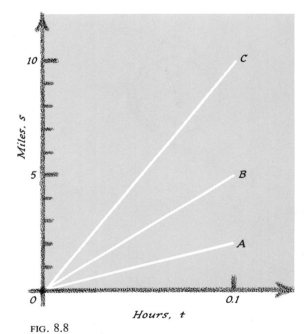

FIG. 8.8

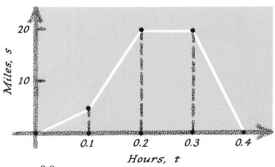

FIG. 8.9

Now let us try to interpret Figure 8.9. The motion involved may have occurred along the curved path shown in Figure 8.10. The marks along the way represent the instants of time in hours at which the vehicle passed by. It was going slowly, we see, from 0.0 to 0.1, going rapidly from 0.1 to 0.2, standing still from 0.2 to 0.3, and moving rapidly back to the starting point ($s = 0$) from 0.3 to 0.4. This shows that zero slope means zero speed and that a negative slope means going backward. In the last interval $\Delta s = 0.0 - 20$ miles; therefore, since Δt is always positive, $\Delta s/\Delta t = -20$ miles/0.1 h $= -200$ mph. You should check the details of this motion against Figure 8.10.

Figure 8.11 plots the trip, OD, of a car that ran at a constant speed. Another car ran faster from O to A, stopped while the driver had a coffee break, and continued, BC, at a high speed; it arrived later than the first car. (If a point on the time axis is to the *right* of another, it represents a *later* instant of time.) (You may test your under-

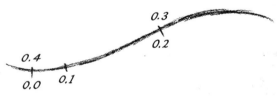

FIG. 8.10

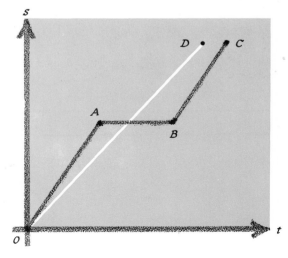

FIG. 8.11

standing of this by choosing reasonable values for units of s and t in Fig. 8.11.)

Figure 8.12 plots the motion of two cars that arrived at A at the same time. The one that traveled slowly at first (OB) had to speed up considerably (BA) in order to catch up. (See Prob. 8.5.)

8.3. Motion with a Continuous Change in Speed

In practice it is impossible to drive a car so that the speedometer reads 40 mph at one instant and 50 mph the next instant, without some time between. This consequence of the inertia of matter accounts for the dictum *Natura non saltus fecit* (Nature does not take jumps). For matter in molar sizes this is certainly true.

The graph of a real motion that changes continuously is continuous. In Figure 8.13, for example, points A and B, associated with instants t_1 and t_2, are joined by a smooth curve. The slope of secant line AB, specified by the equation

$$\frac{\Delta s}{\Delta t} = \frac{s_2 - s_1}{t_2 - t_1}$$

is the average velocity in the interval Δt. The average velocity is less than the instantaneous velocity at t_1 and greater than the instantaneous

velocity at t_2. It should be possible to find an instant between t_1 and t_2 at which the instantaneous velocity is equal to the average velocity. To find this instant (Fig. 8.14), consider a sequence of secant lines all parallel to AB and meeting the curve at $A'B'$, $A''B''$, . . . The limit of the sequence is a line tangent to the curve at a single point, P. By a limiting process we have arrived at the point (P) on the curve at which the instantaneous veloc-

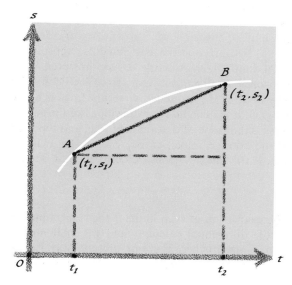

FIG. 8.13

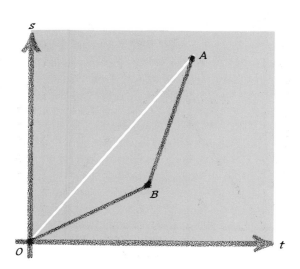

FIG. 8.12

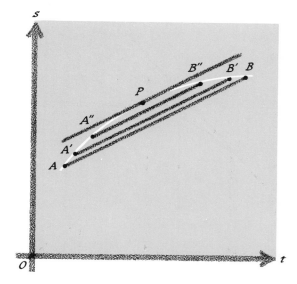

FIG. 8.14

ity is the same as the average velocity for any of the corresponding intervals Δt. (See Prob. 8.6.) In this illustration each Δt is smaller than the previous one.

We may find the instantaneous velocity (Fig. 8.15) at a point like A by taking a sequence of secant lines with A fixed. Points like B' and B'' are chosen progressively closer to A. This sequence of secant lines has as a limit the tangent line at A. The instantaneous velocity at A is therefore taken as the limit of $\Delta s/\Delta t$ as Δt approaches 0—that is, the limit of the sequence $\Delta s_1/\Delta t_1$, $\Delta s_2/\Delta t_2$, $\Delta s_3/\Delta t_3$, . . . as both Δt_n and the associated Δs_n approach 0 as a limit. The quantity $\Delta s/\Delta t$, however, may approach a value other than zero. (See Prob. 8.7.) The limit of the sequence of secant lines is a line tangent at A. The limit of the slopes of the secant lines is the slope of that tangent line, and the limit of the average velocities, $\Delta s_n/\Delta t_n$, in the Δt intervals is the instantaneous velocity, v, at A. Hence

$$v = \lim_{\Delta t \to 0} \frac{\Delta s}{\Delta t}$$

The evaluation of such limits is the subject matter of the differential calculus, and we shall not go into it any further. For our present purpose we are content to observe that the instantaneous

velocity at a point has a clear geometrical meaning. That velocity is the slope of the tangent line at that point of the graph of s against t.

EXAMPLE 8.1. Data taken from the odometer (distance meter) of an automobile are tabulated. Plotting these as a smooth curve, we obtain Fig. 8.16. Even a cursory examination shows that the slope is positive at points A, B, C, and D. Since the slope,

$$\lim_{\Delta t \to 0} \frac{\Delta s}{\Delta t}$$

at each point is numerically equal to the velocity at that point, the curve of the velocity must have the general shape of the curve labeled velocity.

If the motion can be reversed, as it can in the case of a bead sliding along a wire, the increments in s can be negative at times. In Fig. 8.17 the horizontal axis represents time. The vertical axis represents distance for the white curve and velocity for the black curve. A quick qualitative analysis is made as follows: We first observe the points where the slope is zero. These are A, B, and C. At the corresponding instants of time the velocity is zero, and the velocity curve must, therefore, cross the t axis at those points (A, B', and C'). We next observe that the positive slope from A to B implies that the velocity is positive in this region. From B to C the slope is negative,

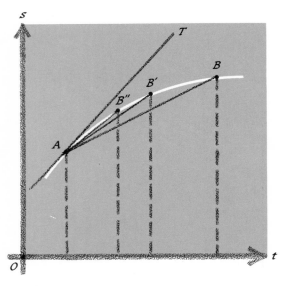

FIG. 8.15

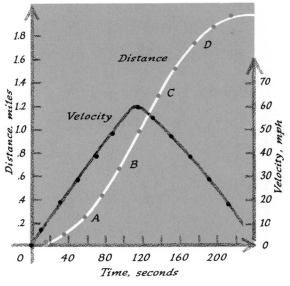

FIG. 8.16

and the greater steepness indicates a high velocity. From C to D the slope is once again positive and becoming steeper.

All that is required of you at this stage is to recognize that the steepness of an s-vs-t curve is related to velocity; that a zero slope (s curve parallel to t axis) means a zero velocity; and that a negative slope (s decreasing as t increases) means a negative velocity (body going backward along its line of motion). This knowledge will be useful in our later analysis of the motion of a pendulum, for example.

Instead of pursuing any further such complicated motions as that shown in Figure 8.17, we turn now to a simple and very important kind of motion in a straight line.

8.4. Uniformly Accelerated Motion in a Straight Line

A kind of motion in a straight line that is only a little more sophisticated than uniform motion (in which $\Delta v / \Delta t = 0$) is called uniformly accelerated motion. It occurs when $\Delta v / \Delta t$, which, by definition, is the average acceleration, is a constant. Since the average acceleration is constant,

we can omit the bar (meaning "average") over the symbol and simply write $\Delta v / \Delta t = a$. The simplest examples of this motion are that of a falling body and that of a body sliding down a frictionless inclined plane. A body pulled across a smooth horizontal plane by a spring in such a way that the stretch remains constant also has a constant acceleration.

We now assume motion along the x axis—and write v as a scalar although the sign of Δx and hence that of v indicate direction. The mathematical analysis is simple. From $\Delta v / \Delta t = a$ we get

$$\Delta v = a(\Delta t) \qquad [8.10$$

If $t_0 = 0$, $\Delta t = t$, and we may write

$$v = v_0 + at \qquad [8.11$$

We plot equation 8.11 in Figure 8.18. The v intercept is v_0, and the slope ($\Delta v / \Delta t$) is now a. The dimensions of a, as seen in equation 8.10, are LT^{-2}. The units in the MKS system are meters per second per second, or meters per second squared, abbreviated as m/sec^2.

Because the acceleration is constant, the ratio $\Delta v / \Delta t$ is the same constant regardless of the size of the Δt interval chosen and regardless of the place on the curve where it is measured. Because the curve is a straight line, the average value of v

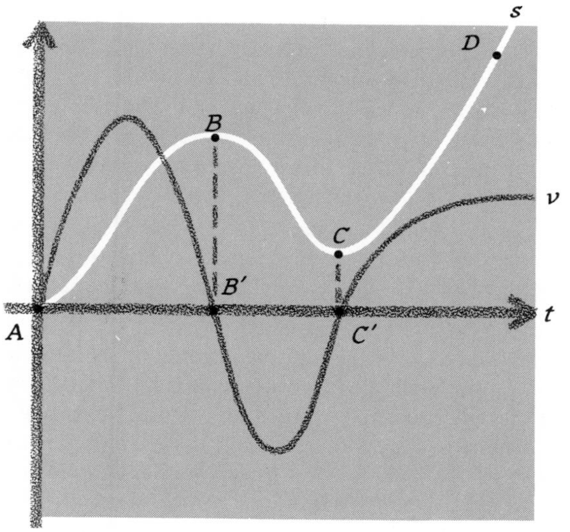

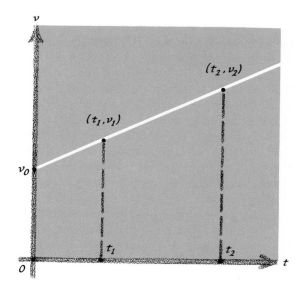

FIG. 8.17. *Distance and the corresponding velocity plotted against time on the same set of rectangular coordinates.*

FIG. 8.18

in the interval from t_1 to t_2 is simply

$$\bar{v} = \frac{v_1 + v_2}{2} \qquad [8.12$$

(Refer to § 6.6.)

The distance covered in any interval may be found from the equation

$$\Delta x = \bar{v}(\Delta t) \qquad [8.13$$

If $x = x_0$ and $v = v_0$ at $t = 0$, and if the distance is x when the time is t, we may write $\Delta t = t$. Equations 8.12 and 8.13 imply that

$$x - x_0 = \frac{v_0 + v}{2} t \qquad [8.14$$

Using the value of v from equation 8.11, we obtain the equation

$$x - x_0 = \frac{2v_0 + at}{2} t$$

which may be written as

$$x = x_0 + v_0 t + \tfrac{1}{2}at^2 \qquad [8.15$$

It is left to you as an exercise (see Prob. 8.8) to prove that

$$v^2 = v_0{}^2 + 2a(x - x_0) \qquad [8.16$$

I summarize the three results by repeating some of these equations in a block:

$$\left. \begin{array}{l} v = v_0 + at \\ x = x_0 + v_0 t + \tfrac{1}{2}at^2 \\ v^2 = v_0{}^2 + 2a(x - x_0) \end{array} \right\} \qquad [8.17$$

Though many problems can be solved by the use of these equations (8.17), it remains true that all problems dealing with uniformly accelerated motion can be solved from more basic notions: "distance equals average velocity multiplied by time" (equation 8.13) and "the average velocity equals the initial velocity plus the final velocity divided by two" (equation 8.12). The first statement holds in all cases by the definition of average, but the second statement holds only for uniformly accelerated motion. You are urged to solve problems directly from equations 8.12 and 8.13, wherever possible, as an aid to understanding of the physical principles involved. Reliance on the final forms (equations 8.17) may promote a tendency toward a blind substitution in formulas and a minimum of physical understanding. Further physical understanding of equations 8.17 comes from dimensional analysis.

EXAMPLE 8.2. On the left side of equation

$$x = x_0 + v_0 t + \tfrac{1}{2}at^2$$

we have a length. Hence $[x] = L$. Analyzing the right-hand side, we get

$$\begin{aligned}[x_0 + v_0 t + \tfrac{1}{2}at^2] &= [x_0] + [v_0 t] + [\tfrac{1}{2}at^2] \\ &= L + LT^{-1}T + LT^{-2}T^2 \\ &= L + L + L \\ &= L \end{aligned}$$

Each term of the right-hand side has the dimension of length, as it should. If any one of the terms had come out with a different dimensionality, the whole expression would have been wrong. *Dimensional consistency* is prerequisite to the correctness of any physical formula.

EXAMPLE 8.3. Another way to enhance physical understanding of these equations is to take a special case and talk about it. If, for example, $v_0 = 0$ and $x_0 = 0$ at $t = 0$, equations 8.17 become

$$\left. \begin{array}{l} v = at \\ x = \tfrac{1}{2}at^2 \\ v^2 = 2ax \end{array} \right\} \qquad [8.18$$

Going back to equations 8.17, we can now verbalize as we read. For example,

$$x = x_0 = v_0 t + \tfrac{1}{2}at^2$$

can be thought out as follows: If $v_0 = 0$ and $a = 0$, the distance traveled is simply the initial distance, x_0. If $a = 0$ and $v_0 \neq 0$, the term $v_0 t$ simply represents the distance traveled in time t at constant velocity v_0. Finally, if $v_0 = 0$ and $a \neq 0$, the term $at^2/2$ represents the distance that a body starting from rest travels in time t. It is as if the constant velocity, v_0, added the distance $v_0 t$ to the initial distance and as if the constant acceleration added its contribution, $at^2/2$, to the distance independently. The sum of these terms is $x_0 + v_0 t + at^2/2$.

It is very easy to reconstruct equations 8.17 from equations 8.18 by thinking them out in this way. Equations 8.18 follow immediately from equations 8.17, of course, if we let v_0 equal 0 and x_0 equal 0.

EXAMPLE 8.4. A falling body affords the commonest example of uniformly accelerated motion. When a body is projected upward with initial velocity v_0, it begins to "fall" immediately; that is, it begins to lose velocity. Of course it goes up, but not as far as it would if gravity were turned off. With gravity off, it would obey the equation $y = v_0 t$ and reach constantly higher points at successive instants of time. With gravity acting, it obeys the equation $y = v_0 t - gt^2/2$, which is a special case of equation 8.15, with

y replacing x, and with a equal to $-g$ because the positive direction of y is arbitrarily made upward and the acceleration is therefore considered negative ($g \cong 9.8 \text{ m/sec}^2$).

Many other examples are given in the problems. Understanding of this subject may not necessarily grow in proportion to the number of these that you solve, but it will certainly be very limited if you don't do any.

8.5. Distance from a Graph of Velocity Against Time

In § 8.3 we saw how a graph of velocity against time can be obtained from the corresponding graph of distance against time. The concept of the slope of a curve came to our aid. We now raise the inverse problem. Can a graph of distance against time be obtained from a graph of velocity against time, and, if so, by what means? If the velocity is constant, the relation between the x and v curves is simple. Starting with the fact that the velocity is constant (Fig. 8.19, v vs t), how do we obtain Fig. 8.20 (x vs t) from it by reasoning?

We observe that the area under the v-vs-t curve is simply the area of a rectangle. It is the altitude times the base, or $v_0 t$. The physical dimensions of this product are $LT^{-1}T = L$, which is obviously a distance. As t increases, the vertical line AB moves to the right, sweeping out an ever-increasing area. The area grows *linearly* with time; that is, when t

doubles, the area doubles; when t triples, the area triples; and so on. In other words, x is *proportional* to t. Hence the graph of x against t must be a straight line starting at the origin (Fig. 8.20). The equation is simply $x = v_0 t$, and the slope of its curve is the constant v_0.

This may seem like belaboring an obvious situation. Surely, if the velocity is constant, the formula for distance starting from rest is $x = v_0 t$, from which we could have obtained Figure 8.20. We went about getting the same result from a consideration of areas because that is needed in what follows.

Now consider a theoretical motion that takes place at speeds v_1, v_2, v_3, and v_4 for equal intervals of time. The graph of the motion is shown in Figure 8.21. It is obvious that

$A_1 = v_1(t_1 - t_0) = $ distance covered during interval Δt_1
$A_2 = v_2(t_2 - t_1) = $ distance covered during interval Δt_2
$A_3 = v_3(t_3 - t_2) = $ distance covered during interval Δt_3
$A_4 = v_4(t_4 - t_3) = $ distance covered during interval Δt_4

As we go from t_0 to t_1, the velocity is constant; the x curve (Fig. 8.22) must be a straight line whose slope is v_1. As we go from t_1 to t_2, the velocity has the larger value v_2; the x curve must be a straight line with the steeper slope v_2. Between t_2 and t_3 the x curve must have the slope v_3, between t_3 and t_4 the slope v_4. The relation is this: If a vertical line of length equal to the ordinate, v, moves from left to right in Figure 8.21, it sweeps

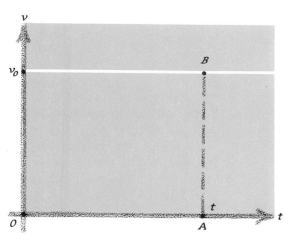

FIG. 8.19

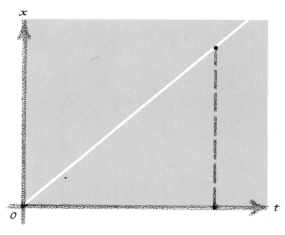

FIG. 8.20

out an area whose magnitude is equal to the total distance, x, covered since t_0. When it reaches a point like t_3, it has swept out the total area $A_1 + A_2 + A_3$, which is numerically equal to the total distance (x_3) covered from t_0 to t_3. If we go to any point t in Figure 8.22 the ordinate (x) there is numerically equal to the total distance from the starting point.

In a more general situation the v-vs-t curve is a smooth curve (Fig. 8.23). The corresponding x curve is also smooth, and at any point t the ordinate (x) on the x curve (Fig. 8.24) is numerically equal to the distance from the origin traversed in accordance with the v-vs-t curve shown in Figure 8.23 and hence is equal to the area under that curve. (See Prob. 8.9.)

We shall not consider any further the ideas that lead to the calculus. I only wanted to point out that there are processes by means of which the slope of a curve can be exactly computed—

$$\lim_{\Delta t \to 0} \frac{\Delta x}{\Delta t}$$

which is the basic problem of the differential cal-culus—and other processes, in some sense the inverse of those just mentioned, by means of which the area under a curve can be exactly cal-culated (related to the basic problem of the inte-gral calculus). You need not fear any further exploration into these topics. If your appetite has been whetted, good! If not, never mind; we shall make only qualitative application of these ideas in this book.

8.6. Summary

Kinematics is the study of motion. The simplest motion, one that takes place in a straight line at constant speed, is called uniform motion. If it takes place along the x axis, for example, it obeys equations like $v = \Delta x/\Delta t$ and $x = x_0 + vt$, in which, though we have dropped the vector nota-tion, we continue to call v the velocity rather than the speed because the sign of v indicates direction along the x axis. Motion at constant speed can also take place along a curved path and then obeys similar mathematical equations ($v = \Delta s/\Delta t$ and

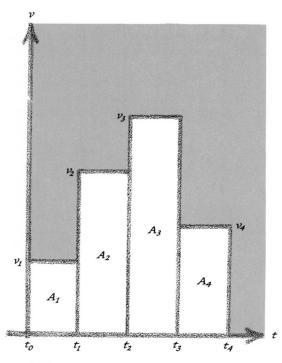

FIG. 8.21

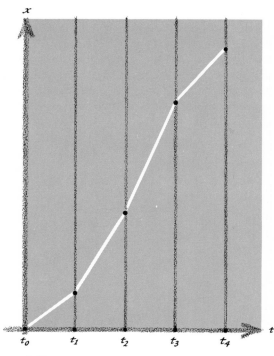

FIG. 8.22

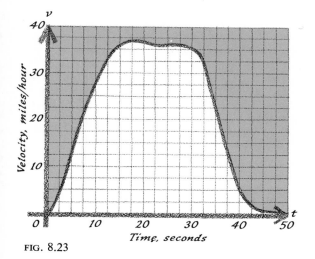

FIG. 8.23

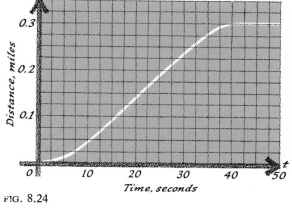

FIG. 8.24

$s = s_0 + vt$), but obviously it is not uniform motion in the strict sense, for the velocity vector changes direction.

For motion with continuous change in speed we define the instantaneous velocity as

$$v = \lim_{\Delta t \to 0} \frac{\Delta s}{\Delta t}$$

We can avoid the computation of such limits in some cases by using the fact that, when s is plotted against t in rectangular coordinates, the slope of the curve at a point is the velocity at that point.

Uniformly accelerated motion takes place when the acceleration is constant. All the formulas for this kind of motion can be developed from two simple equations,

$$\Delta x = \bar{v}(\Delta t)$$
$$\bar{v} = (v_1 + v_2)/2$$

Whether the acceleration is constant or not, when velocity is plotted against time in rectangular coordinates, the area under the curve is proportional to the distance covered in the given interval of time.

Problems

8.1. Let the distance covered during the first second by a body falling from rest be called 1 unit. During the second second (that is, between $t = 1$ sec and $t = 2$ sec) it will fall 3 units; during the third second it will fall 5 units; and so on. This is what Galileo meant in the quotation at the beginning of this chapter. Hence the total distance traveled in n seconds is $1 + 3 + 5 \ldots + (2n - 1)$ units.

1. Prove that the sum of the first n odd number is n^2. In other words, prove that

$$1 + 3 + 5 + \ldots (2n - 1) = n^2$$

(See any college algebra under mathematical induc-

tion.) If you can't prove it, convince yourself that this formula is right from $n = 1$ up to $n = 5$. (For example, for $n = 3$, $1 + 3 + 5 = 3^2$.)

2. For a uniformly accelerated body (not necessarily falling) starting from rest, $x = at^2/2$. Suppose (for convenience) that $a/2 = 1$ m/sec². By substitution find the distance traveled at the end of 1, 2, 3, 4, 5 sec. (Note that for a falling body $a/2 \cong 4.9$ m/sec². At the ends of successive seconds the total distances traveled are $4.9(1)^2$, $4.9(2)^2$, $4.9(3)^2$, $4.9(4)^2 \ldots$ m. These numbers are proportional to 1, 4, 9, 16, . . .)

3. How far (in meters) does a body released from rest fall *during* the 7th second?

8.2. A marble rolls with a uniform speed of 1 m/sec. Following Zeno, consider that it covers first 1/2 m, then 1/4 m, then 1/8 m, and so on.

1. How long, in seconds, does it take to cover these intervals? (Answer: 1/2 sec, 1/4 sec, 1/8 sec, . . .)

2. Consider the sequence of numbers s_n such that

$$s_1 = \frac{1}{2}$$

$$s_2 = \frac{1}{2} + \frac{1}{4}$$

$$s_3 = \frac{1}{2} + \frac{1}{4} + \frac{1}{8}$$

etc.

Express s_1, s_2, s_3, etc. as decimal fractions. Prove or argue plausibly that the limit of this sequence is 1. (Formal proofs are given in algebra texts under *series*.)

3. What is the sum of the time intervals given in part 1?

4. Now read Zeno's paradox again, and comment or criticize.

8.3. Consider the equation $s = s_0 + vt$ graphically. Let s_0 equal 5 m and v equal 2 m/sec. Except for units the equation becomes $s = 5 + 2t$.

1. Plot a graph of this equation by first making a table of values of s vs t (for $t = 0, 1, 2, 3, 4, 5$ sec).

2. From the graph find what distance was covered from $t = 4$ to $t = 5$ sec.

3. Plot v vs t. Note that $v = 2$ m/sec at all values of t.

4. Using $\Delta v/\Delta t$, find the acceleration involved in this motion.

8.4. Consider the example of Fig. 8.11. Choose physical units and scales along the s and t axes so that the velocities represented are within reason for ordinary automobiles.

8.5. The car in Fig. 8.12 that travels at a constant rate throughout the trip goes for four hours at 40 mph. The other car goes for three hours at 20 mph. How fast must the second car go in the next hour to catch up with the first at the end of the fourth hour?

8.6. In Fig. 8.15, find by graphical approximation the point on the curve where the instantaneous velocity is the same as the average velocity between points A and B. What is the time coordinate of this point? (You must plot the curve to get the answer. Use the data of Prob. 8.7.)

8.7. Find the instantaneous velocity at point A (Fig. 8.15) by finding the slope of the tangent line (limit

of the slope of the secant lines as Δs and Δt approach zero). To get greater precision than is possible on the graph, use the following t and s coordinates, on which the figure was based: (2.00, 3.00), (2.20, 3.22), (2.60, 3.63), (3.00, 4.00), (3.60, 4.50), (5.00, 5.50), (7.00, 6.50), (11.00, 7.60). Compute and tabulate to three significant figures the slopes of three secant lines such as AB, AB', and AB''. Does the ratio $\Delta s/\Delta t$ approach a value other than zero? What, then, is the velocity at point A?

8.8. Using equations 8.11 and 8.15, prove equation 8.16. (Hint: There are several ways of doing this, but one of the easiest is to square equation 8.11 and, working backward, manipulate equation 8.15 to get the answer.)

8.9. This problem refers to Figs. 8.23 and 8.24, the velocity-vs-time and distance-vs-time plots of an actual experiment with an automobile. By estimating the area under the velocity curve, determine the distance traveled after the first 20 seconds. Compare this with the corresponding value on the distance curve. In estimating the area, develop some systematic way of counting the squares without spending too much time. Here is one way: (a) count squares and parts of squares under the velocity curve of Fig. 8.23; (b) evaluate one square—for example,

$$2.5 \text{ mi/h} \times 2.5 \text{ sec} = 2.5 \text{ mi/h} \times 2.5/3{,}600 \text{ h}$$
$$= 0.00174 \text{ mi}$$

(c) multiply these two numbers, getting distance in miles; (d) compare with the corresponding distance value in Fig. 8.24.

The following problems are primarily for drill in the use of the formulas of this chapter.

8.10. As you are driving along at 65 mph, your glance leaves the road for 1 sec. How many feet do you travel in that time?

8.11. A snail crawls at a rate of 11 ft/day. If he decides to decrease his speed to 6 ft/day and takes 6 min to do it, what is the magnitude of his (negative) acceleration in ft/sec²?

8.12. A ball is thrown vertically into the air. It is caught on the ground 1 sec later. How high did the ball go? What was its initial velocity?

8.13. On the surface of Mars, the acceleration due to gravity is 3.92 m/sec². If a piece of rock is thrown vertically upward with a speed of 15 m/sec, what is its downward speed when it comes back to the surface?

8.14. In 1954 Don Perry climbed vertically up a rope 20 ft long in 2.8 sec. What was his average velocity?

If he let go of the rope when he reached the top, how long did it take him to reach the ground?

8.15. A man starts at point P and runs at a constant speed of 7 m/sec along a railroad track. At the instant he starts a loaded freight train leaves point P and moves in the same direction with a constant acceleration of 0.5 m/sec². How far will the runner have gone when the train reaches him?

8.16. An anti-aircraft gun developed in the Second World War could fire a projectile 11 mi straight up. Compute its muzzle velocity.

8.17. If the acceleration due to gravity on the moon is 1/6 of that on the earth, show that a man can jump 6 times as high on the moon (if he is capable of achieving the same initial velocity) as he can on the earth.

8.18. A man stands on a building of height h. He throws a ball straight up with speed u and one straight down with speed u. Compare the speeds of the two balls when they hit the ground.

8.19. Some dragsters can achieve an acceleration of 1.2 g in a quarter-mile race. If you started from rest, how long would it take to cover the quarter mile at this constant acceleration? Compute, in miles per hour, the final and average speeds.

8.20. A rock is thrown vertically downward from the top of a tall cliff with an initial velocity of 20 m/sec. What is the distance covered during the first 2.5 sec?

8.21. A hunter fires horizontally at a target 200 m away. If the muzzle velocity of the bullet is 300 m/sec, by how much will the hunter miss his mark because of the effect of gravity on the bullet?

Kinematics with Vectors

"It has been observed that missiles and projectiles describe a curved path of some sort; however no one has pointed out the fact that this path is a parabola. But this and other facts, not few in number or less worth knowing, I have succeeded in proving; and what I consider more important, there have been opened up to this vast and most excellent science, of which my work is merely the beginning, ways and means by which other minds more acute than mine will explore its remote corners."

GALILEO GALILEI, "Mathematics of Motion," in James R. Newman, *The World of Mathematics* (Simon & Schuster, New York, 1956), vol. 2, p. 734.

EVERYONE has seen the graceful curve that is followed by a stone after it leaves the hand of the thrower. The stone begins to fall, in a sense, the very instant it leaves the hand. This statement may sound strange, for we can see the stone go up before it begins to come down. We naturally think, at first, that it doesn't begin to fall until, having reached its highest point, it starts on its downward path. But let us imagine what would happen to the stone thrown upward and outward if the pull of gravity did not act. It would travel in a straight line in its original direction. In reality it departs continuously from this straight line. In this sense, it begins to fall immediately after it leaves the hand.

9.1. The Parabolic Arc

Galileo was the first to prove that, if the resistance of air and the variation in the acceleration due to gravity in the stone's path are both assumed to be zero, the path is a parabola. I shall take advantage of your knowledge of algebra to prove this, not only because the parabola is an impor-

tant curve, but in order to illustrate a modern mathematical approach to a simple problem in motion.

Suppose that a blackboard eraser is propelled along a horizontal table Fig. (9.1). It has horizontal velocity v_0 at O just as it leaves the table. We see it land at point S. We want to discuss its motion mathematically. One way to do that is to set up a system of rectangular coordinates, x and y, with the x axis horizontal and the y axis vertical (Fig. 9.2). (We have made y downward for convenience.)

Experiment and logic confirm the idea that the eraser's x component of motion progresses as if the acceleration of gravity did not exist; in other words, the motion in the x direction obeys the equation

$$x = v_0 t \qquad [9.1$$

This is the equation of uniform motion in the x direction (see equation 8.7). The moving object covers equal distances in equal times. If gravity did not act, we should find the eraser at points A, B, C, D, . . . along the horizontal x axis, on which $AB = BC = CD = v_0(\Delta t)$—$\Delta t$ being the constant time interval chosen. Starting from rest, the distances OA, OB, OC and OD are $v_0(\Delta t)$, $2v_0(\Delta t)$, $3v_0(\Delta t)$, and $4v_0(\Delta t)$, respectively, in obedience to equation 9.1.

In free fall, the eraser's downward motion would obey the equation

$$y = \tfrac{1}{2}gt^2 \qquad [9.2$$

(See equations 8.18.) Dropped from rest, it would be found at points A', B', C', and D' at the ends of the equal time intervals, Δt. The distances OA', OB', OC', and OD' are $g(\Delta t)^2/2$, $g[2(\Delta t)]^2/2$, $g[3(\Delta t)]^2/2$, and $g[4(\Delta t)]^2/2$, respectively, in accordance with equation 9.2. These distances are proportional to the numbers 1, 4, 9, and 16. In

actuality the eraser is found at points P, Q, R, and S at the ends of the successive intervals of time, Δt. The rectangular coordinates (x and y) of these points satisfy both these equations simultaneously:

$$\left.\begin{array}{c} x = v_0 t \\ y = \tfrac{1}{2}gt^2 \end{array}\right\} \qquad [9.3$$

Equations 9.3 define the motion.

If the value of t obtained from the first equation is substituted into the second equation, the result is $y = gx^2/2v_0^2$. In textbooks on analytic geometry an equation of this type is shown to be that of a parabola (Probs. 9.1 and 9.2). If you have never studied the parabola, you need not be dismayed. Just consider this imagined mechanical experiment as your introduction to the parabola. You may form any number of graceful parabolic curves with no mathematical exertion at all. Simply throw stones into the air at different speeds and at different angles. The downward part of the path in each case will bear some resemblance to Figure 9.2.

The most important point to observe in that figure is that the eraser begins to fall as soon as it leaves the table, even though it has a horizontal velocity. This behavior, as we shall see presently, is characteristic, quite generally, of all projected bodies, even when the initial direction is not horizontal. In the meantime let us consider another way of writing the results of this discussion.

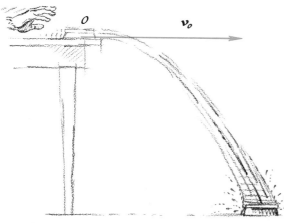

FIG. 9.1

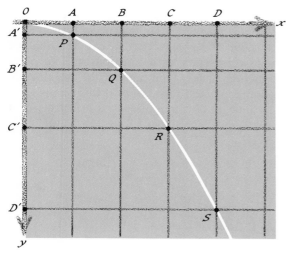

FIG. 9.2

9.2. Vectors and Motion

The displacement of the eraser in Figure 9.2 can be considered the vector sum of two displacements, one in the x direction and the other in the y direction. In Figure 9.3 the displacement **r** of point P on the eraser's path is the sum of the two vectors **x** and **y**. We therefore write the equation

$$\mathbf{r} = \mathbf{x} + \mathbf{y} \qquad [9.4]$$

in which

$$\mathbf{x} = \mathbf{v}_0 t \quad \text{and} \quad \mathbf{y} = \tfrac{1}{2}\mathbf{g}t^2$$

(Notice that we write $\mathbf{v}_0$ and $\mathbf{g}$ as vectors.) Therefore

$$\mathbf{r} = \mathbf{v}_0 t + \tfrac{1}{2}\mathbf{g}t^2 \qquad [9.5$$

is the single vector equation that defines the motion. Observe that it expresses the vector **r** as a function of t.

Paraphrasing the definition of a function given in § 1.5, we say: If the two variables **r** and t are so related that, when one value of t is chosen within its range, one value of **r** can be determined, then **r** is a function of t. This statement presumes that operations performed on t on the right-hand side of the equation have been defined. They have been: the multiplication of a vector by a scalar has already been defined. The vector $\mathbf{v}_0 t$, for example, has the direction of $\mathbf{v}_0$, the magnitude $v_0 t$, and the physical dimension L. Similarly, the vector $\mathbf{g} t^2/2$ has the direction of **g**, the magnitude $g t^2/2$, and the physical dimension L.

Some economy of thought is gained by the vectorial conception of motion. Notice that specific reference to the x and y axes has vanished from equation 9.5. The equation $\mathbf{r} = \mathbf{f}(t)$ implies that **r** is known at every instant of time. Only when numerical calculations are involved must the frame of reference be specified.

Equation 9.5 may be talked out as follows: "If **g** were zero but $\mathbf{v}_0$ were not zero, **r** would equal $\mathbf{v}_0 t$; the eraser would move only in the direction of $\mathbf{v}_0$, in uniform motion. If $\mathbf{v}_0$ were zero but **g** were not zero, **r** would equal $\mathbf{g} t^2/2$; the eraser would fall freely in the direction of **g**. If neither $\mathbf{v}_0$ nor **g** were zero, the eraser would experience the total displacement **r**, which is simply the vector sum of those two displacements."

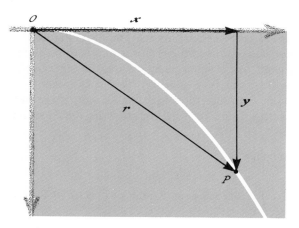

FIG. 9.3

Experiments with acceleration other than **g** confirm the general idea that the total displacement of a body can be considered as the vector sum of the several simultaneous displacements to which it is subjected. This leads us to a more general expression for the average velocity of a body.

9.3. The Average Velocity as a Vector

Let us imagine a set of operations that will give us the direction and magnitude of the displacement vector of an airplane moving in a curved path overhead. A telescope is mounted with freedom to point in any direction (Fig. 9.4). A trained observer keeps the image of the airplane always on the intersection of the cross-hairs of the telescope sight. The direction of the telescope axis is the direction of the displacement vector $\mathbf{r}_1$. (If we needed numbers to specify this direction, we could resort to the angles of altitude and azimuth as defined in any textbook on astronomy, or we could measure the angles between $\mathbf{r}_1$ and a set of rectangular axes. For the time being we can proceed without being specific about these details.) An optical rangefinder can measure the distance from O to the point, P, where the airplane is at a certain instant. This gives the magnitude of the vector $\mathbf{r}_1$. We have, therefore, given operational instructions for defining both the direction and the magnitude of the vector $\mathbf{r}_1$.

Since we can get direction and magnitude in this way at many different instants of time, we can have a set of discrete data that can be smoothed out to represent **r** as a function of t. In other words, we have a solution to the problem of motion. I proceed to show what this means.

At time Δt after reaching P, the airplane is at

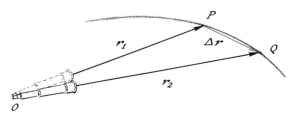

FIG. 9.4

Q, whose displacement vector is r_2. We draw the vector PQ and label it Δr. This is an appropriate label for the following reason.

Notice that the rule for adding vectors yields the equation

$$r_1 + \Delta r = r_2 \qquad [9.6$$

Therefore

$$\Delta r = r_2 - r_1 \qquad [9.7$$

We now define the average velocity in this interval as

$$\bar{v} = \frac{\Delta r}{\Delta t} = \frac{r_2 - r_1}{\Delta t} \qquad [9.8$$

This equation, in form, is identical with those used earlier for one-dimensional motion (equations 8.5 and 8.6), but now, as a vector equation, it carries very general information on direction as well as magnitude.†

Observations such as those that gave us r_1 and r_2 can now be made by radar. (The directional properties of the antenna give the direction, and the time required to bounce a radar signal from point O to the object and back gives the magnitude of r.) Though the smallest Δt separating two observations can be very small because electronic techniques are used for tracking and computing, the data are always discontinuous. In the theory of motion, however, we assume that they are continuous, and we apply the concept of limit to them as follows:

Imagine that, leaving P fixed, we could let Δt approach zero through an infinite sequence of values. This would lead to a sequence of ratios:

$$\frac{\Delta r_1}{\Delta t_1}, \frac{\Delta r_2}{\Delta t_2}, \frac{\Delta r_3}{\Delta t_3}, \dots \qquad [9.9$$

This is actually a sequence of vectors:

$$\bar{v}_1, \bar{v}_2, \bar{v}_3, \dots \qquad [9.10$$

† When we were considering motion along the x axis, we observed that a positive Δx means that $x_2 - x_1 > 0$, which implies motion in the positive direction of the x axis. A negative Δx means that $x_2 - x_1 < 0$, which implies motion in a direction opposite to that of growth on the x axis. To this extent even $v = \Delta x/\Delta t$ has a directional property. So does $v = \Delta s/\Delta t$ if s is measured in a specified direction along an arc. We did not use the vector notation in these cases because the plus or minus sign gave us all the knowledge of direction that was necessary. The motion we are now considering is not necessarily limited to a straight line or to a prescribed curve like that of a railroad track or of a wire.

The limit of this sequence (if it exists) is a vector, v, that *defines* the *instantaneous* velocity at P. The magnitude of v is the instantaneous speed. The direction of v is along the tangent at P.

All this (and more!) is implied when we write the equation†

$$v = \lim_{\Delta t \to 0} \frac{\Delta r}{\Delta t} \qquad [9.11$$

9.4. Projectile Motion Treated Vectorially

To test our understanding of these concepts, let us interpret the motion defined by equation 9.5—

$$r = v_0 t + \tfrac{1}{2} g t^2$$

—when the initial velocity vector, v_0, is inclined at an angle, θ, to the horizontal (Fig. 9.5). Let us talk out the implications of that equation: If g were zero, the displacement r would be simply $v_0 t$. This is the vector v_0 multiplied by the scalar t. At the end of 1 sec the body would be at A; at the end of 2 sec it would be at B; at the end of 3 sec it would be at C; and so on.

$$OA = AB = BC = v_0 \,\text{m/sec} \times 1 \,\text{sec}$$

But equation 9.5 says that r is the vector sum of

† This has led us to the brink of the differential calculus of vectors. We cannot and need not pursue this more deeply in this book.

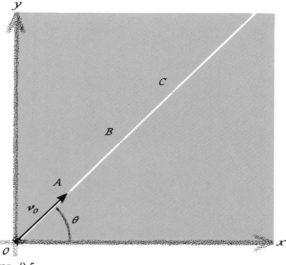

FIG. 9.5

two vectors, one in the $\mathbf{v}_0$ direction, of magnitude v_0t, and the other in the $\mathbf{y}$ direction, of magnitude $gt^2/2$. Figure 9.6 shows how the vector $\mathbf{g}t^2/2$ has been added (vectorially) to the vector $\mathbf{v}_0t$ at a general instant, t. Point P is a typical point on the body's path. Its displacement is $\mathbf{r} = \mathbf{v}_0t + \mathbf{g}t^2/2$. Also shown are points A', B', and C', obtained from the equation with t equal to 1, 2, and 3 seconds, respectively.

Now what, exactly, have we done? We have taken a vector equation (9.5) and, as an exercise, explored its graphical meaning. We see that it yields a symmetrical curve (which happens also to be a parabola), but what does this exercise have to do with physics? Do real bodies behave in this way when projected at an angle to the horizontal? The answer is "yes." Experiments confirm that to a high degree of approximation this is the way bodies behave. We say, therefore, that equation 9.5 is the general equation of a projectile. It holds even when the angle (θ) is negative—that is, when the gun (if the body is projected from a gun) is pointed below the horizontal. With vectorial language we have been able to state a very general proposition in one equation, without specific reference to x and y axes. If we want to compute numerical results, we can state

this result in terms of x and y components; and, if x is horizontal and y is vertical, we can get directly from Figure 9.6 and equation 9.5, for which we have found a very general interpretation, the x and y components of $\mathbf{r}$. They are

$$x = v_0t \cos \theta \qquad [9.12$$
$$y = v_0t \sin \theta - \tfrac{1}{2}gt^2 \dagger \qquad [9.13$$

9.5. Acceleration with Constant Speed

When a body moves at a constant speed, its acceleration is zero if it is moving in a straight line, not zero if it is moving in a curve, for now its velocity, being a vector, is no longer a constant, but is changing direction.

The average acceleration is defined, vectorially, as

$$\bar{\mathbf{a}} = \frac{\mathbf{v} - \mathbf{v}_0}{\Delta t} = \frac{\Delta \mathbf{v}}{\Delta t} \qquad [9.14$$

The instantaneous acceleration is defined, by analogy with instantaneous velocity, as

$$\mathbf{a} = \lim_{\Delta t \to 0} \frac{\Delta \mathbf{v}}{\Delta t} \qquad [9.15$$

Let us examine first the implications of equation 9.14. Consider a body moving in a curved path (Fig. 9.7.A). (The path need not be in a plane for the following argument, although in our figure we represent a plane curve.) At P the velocity is $\mathbf{v}_0$; at Q it is $\mathbf{v}$. What is the meaning of the expression $\mathbf{v} - \mathbf{v}_0$, which is needed in equation 9.14? To answer this question, redraw vectors $\mathbf{v}$ and $\mathbf{v}_0$ from a common point (Fig. 9.7.B). [Remember that two vectors parallel to each other and equal in magnitude are said to be equal vectors. Hence moving $\mathbf{v}$ to a new starting point (P) does not change it provided it retains its original direction.]

It is apparent in the figure that

$$\mathbf{v}_0 + \text{vector } \mathbf{AB} = \mathbf{v}$$

Hence

$$\text{vector } \mathbf{AB} = \mathbf{v} - \mathbf{v}_0$$

† In triangle OQD, $\sin \theta = DQ/v_0t$; therefore $DQ = v_0t \sin \theta$; and, since $QP = gt^2/2$, equation 9.13 follows. Similarly, $\cos \theta = OD/v_0t$; therefore $OD = v_0t \cos \theta$, which is equivalent to equation 9.12. The sine and cosine functions are defined in § 14.3; further information on them appears in Appendix E.

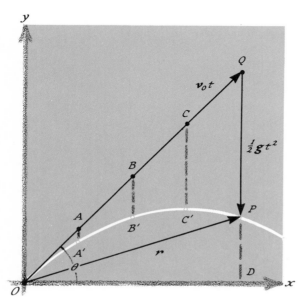

FIG. 9.6

In other words, the vector **AB** is the vector Δ**v** since it is the vector that must be added to **v₀** to produce **v**. It is obviously not zero. Hence the average acceleration defined by **ā** = Δ**v**/Δt is not zero. We have drawn the vectors **v₀** and **v** almost equal in magnitude. It is apparent that, even if **v₀** and **v** were equal in magnitude, Δ**v** would not be zero. The direction of Δ**v** is almost perpendicular to that of **v**. If Δt were permitted to approach zero and if the *speed* did not change, the direction of Δ**v** would approach that of a perpendicular to both **v** and **v₀**.

A special case of this kind occurs when a body moves in a circle (of radius r) at a constant speed (v). If we grant the logic of the preceding arguments, we can reason as follows (Fig. 9.8). The *instantaneous* velocity vector, **v**, at P points along

the tangent to the circle (part A). The *instantaneous* acceleration vector has to be perpendicular to **v**; so it must point along −**r**. (Imagine the limiting direction of Δ**v**, in Fig. 9.7.B, when the magnitude of **v** is a constant and Δt approaches 0. Observe, for example, that Δ**v** is approximately perpendicular to both **v₀** and **v** and that its direction can be reconciled with the last statement about −**r**.) Since vectors can be moved parallel to themselves, we redraw part A of the figure in parts B and C. Notice (B) that **r** and **v** and (C) that **v** and **a** have the orientations they had in part A. Now suppose (B) that it takes time T for **r** to go through one complete revolution. The distance covered by P would be 2πr; hence, using the formula v = distance/time, we get the equation

$$v = \frac{2\pi r}{T} \qquad [9.16$$

But, while **r** is going through 360°, **v** also is going through 360°. You can see this by imagining the vector **r** going through 360° in part B but even more clearly by considering what happens to the **v** drawn in part C. That **v** covers 360° in exactly the same time (T) as **r**. Now remember that **v** is the instantaneous rate of change of **r**,

$$\lim_{\Delta t \to 0} \frac{\Delta \mathbf{r}}{\Delta t}$$

and that **a** is the instantaneous rate of change of **v**,

$$\lim_{\Delta t \to 0} \frac{\Delta \mathbf{v}}{\Delta t}$$

In part C, **v** and **a** play roles analogous to those of **r** and **v**, respectively, in part B. Hence, corre-

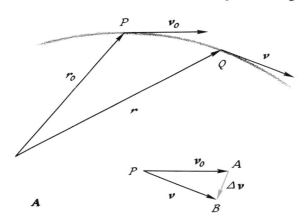

FIG. 9.7

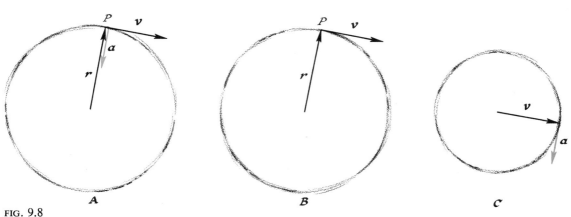

FIG. 9.8

sponding to equation 9.16 for Figure 9.8.B, we have the equation

$$a = \frac{2\pi v}{T} \qquad [9.17$$

for Figure 9.8.C.

If we divide the terms of equation 9.16 by the corresponding terms of equation 9.17, we get the equation

$$\frac{v}{a} = \frac{2\pi r/T}{2\pi v/T}$$

Therefore $v/a = r/v$, or

$$a = \frac{v^2}{r} \qquad [9.18$$

This is the magnitude of the centripetal (center-seeking, from *peto*, to seek) acceleration; its direction is perpendicular to the direction of motion. It deflects that motion but does not change its speed.

The vectorial notation applied to velocity and acceleration has enabled us to consider quantitatively two important kinds of motion: (1) the motion of a projectile near the surface of the earth; (2) circular motion at constant speed, with its attendant centripetal acceleration. One of the important ideas gleaned from the latter is that an acceleration whose direction is perpendicular to the velocity vector does not speed up or slow down the moving body; it simply deflects it. Without going into numerical details we can now begin to understand the speeding up and slowing down of a missile or an earth satellite.

9.6. Missiles and Satellites Are Falling Bodies

Figure 9.9 represents the parabolic path of a projectile. At point A in the first half of the path we have drawn the acceleration, **g**, that acts on it. The vectors $\mathbf{a}_T$ and $\mathbf{a}_N$ are the tangential and normal (perpendicular) components of **g**, respectively; that is, $\mathbf{g} = \mathbf{a}_T + \mathbf{a}_N$. Hence we can study the effects of **g** by considering the separate effects of $\mathbf{a}_T$ and $\mathbf{a}_N$ as vectors. The instantaneous velocity vector, **v**, has been drawn along the tangent.

Since $\mathbf{a}_T$ points opposite to **v**, it will slow down the projectile; $\mathbf{a}_N$, being perpendicular to **v**, represents the centripetal acceleration at that instant and is responsible for the deflection (change of direction of **v**) of the projectile but not for its speeding up or slowing down. If you make a similar analysis at B (top of the curve) and at C, you will see that the *speed* decreases up to B and increases thereafter.

A similar argument applies to Figure 9.10. The earth is at E; an earth satellite is at S. The instantaneous acceleration, **a**, points from S to E (in the same direction as the gravitational pull). The tangential component, $\mathbf{a}_T$ of **a** points opposite to **v** and slows the satellite down. The normal component, $\mathbf{a}_N$, has no effect on the speed but does deflect the motion. (The larger $\mathbf{a}_N$, the greater the deflection.) You will find it instructive to draw a similar diagram at point P. The path of a satellite is an ellipse with the earth at one focus. It is instructive also to consider the satellite motion at

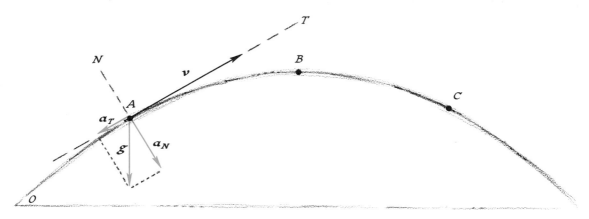

FIG. 9.9

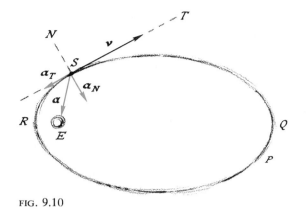

FIG. 9.10

the very special points R and Q, which are on the line joining the foci of the ellipse on which the satellite travels.

The planets move in elliptical paths with the sun at one focus. They too are falling bodies. Their acceleration vector always points from the planet to the sun.

9.7. Summary

A body moving freely under the influence of the earth's gravitational field follows an elliptic path with the earth at one focus. For a projectile moving near the earth, the path is approximately a parabola. You can prove this by analyzing the vertical and horizontal components of the motion independently and combining the results.

Another, equivalent way is to treat the displacement of the projectile as a vector, $\mathbf{r}$. From it you can get the average velocity, $\bar{\mathbf{v}} = \Delta \mathbf{r}/\Delta t$.

The limit of this as Δt approaches 0 is the instantaneous velocity, $\mathbf{v}$. The average acceleration is $\bar{\mathbf{a}} = \Delta \mathbf{v}/\Delta t$, and the limit of this as Δt approaches 0 is the instantaneous acceleration, $\mathbf{a}$. The vector equation for parabolic projectile motion is $\mathbf{r} = \mathbf{v}_0 t + \mathbf{g}t^2/2$.

Since velocity is a vector, it can change in direction or magnitude or in both. Even if the magnitude (speed) does not change, there is an acceleration if the direction changes. A body moving in a circle of radius r at constant speed v experiences a centripetal acceleration of magnitude v^2/r. Since

$$\mathbf{a} = \lim_{\Delta t \to 0} \frac{\Delta \mathbf{v}}{\Delta t}$$

is a vector equation, it is immediately apparent that the *change* in velocity, $\Delta \mathbf{v}$, has approximately the same direction as the instantaneous acceleration, $\mathbf{a}$. If $\mathbf{a}$ is decomposed into two components, $\mathbf{a}_T$ and $\mathbf{a}_N$ ($\mathbf{a}_T$ being along the tangent to the curve and $\mathbf{a}_N$ along the normal), and if $\mathbf{a}_T + \mathbf{a}_N = \mathbf{a}$, we find that $\mathbf{a}_N$ is responsible for the deflection, but does not produce instantaneous speeding up or slowing down. In the equation $a_N = v^2/R$, v is the instantaneous speed and R is the radius of the circle that best fits the curve at the point. The speeding up (or slowing down) is due to $\mathbf{a}_T$, which acts either with or against $\mathbf{v}$.

These vectorial concepts can be applied to the motion of planets, earth satellites, baseballs, and even simple pendulums. We obtain a qualitative understanding of the speeding up and slowing down of a satellite by treating velocity as a vector. The quantitative aspects also follow, but I shall not discuss them in this book.

Problems

The parabola plays an important role in the motion of projectiles. The first two problems are designed to acquaint you with some of its properties.

9.1. One definition of a parabola is: the locus of a point that moves so that it is always equidistant from both a fixed point and a fixed line. Confirm

experimentally that $y^2 = 4ax$ is the equation of a parabola as follows:

1. Draw the curve for $a = 1$ by plotting points on rectangular-coordinate graph paper and passing a smooth curve through them. (Use the same unit of distance on both axes.)

2. Measure the distance between a point on the curve and the point (1,0).

3. Measure the distance from the same point to the line $x = -1$ along a perpendicular to the line.

4. Compare the distances obtained in parts 2 and 3.

5. Repeat for several other points on the curve.

9.2. Perform the following analysis on the parabola defined by the equation $y = gx^2/2v_0^2$. Rewrite this equation so that all the constants are lumped together and appear within parentheses. Now, taking v_0 to be 7 m/sec and g to be 9.8 m/sec^2, calculate y for six values of x between 0 and 5 m. Plot these points on rectangular-coordinate graph paper to an appropriate scale. Plot also some points corresponding to negative values of x. Describe how changes in g and v_0 alter the shape of the parabola. What is the slope of the parabola at $x = 0$?

9.3. We know that the eraser (Fig. 9.1) that was pushed off the table followed the path of a parabola. Show that, if the eraser were given an instantaneous additional push in the horizontal direction the moment it left the table, its new path would also be a parabola.

9.4. 1. Use Fig. 9.6 to convince yourself by rough measurements that the distances the body falls in successive seconds are in the ratios of 1, 3, 5, 7, etc.

2. Using this fact, redraw Fig. 9.6 on a larger scale as follows: Locate points A, B, C, D, etc. where the body would have been at the end of successive seconds without gravity. Locate points A', B', C', D', etc. by drawing downward displacements in accordance with part 1.

3. Redraw Fig. 9.6 once more on the assumption that the new gravitational acceleration has half of its former value.

9.5. The problem of the hunter and the monkey is a classic, so I give it here even though I don't believe in shooting monkeys: A monkey is hanging from a limb. The hunter aims his rifle at him and fires, but the monkey lets go of the limb when he hears the shot, thereby starting to drop at practically the same instant that the bullet leaves the rifle. Using particle kinematics, you are to prove that the bullet will hit him regardless of its speed or the inclination of the rifle provided the rifle is aimed directly at the monkey. The following special case (for which Fig. 9.6 may be used as a guide) was designed to help you in your solution and to give you some practice in thinking vectorially. (The bullet speed is unrealistically slow.) The monkey is initially at Q. The bullet leaves the rifle at O with the speed $v_0 = 200$ ft/sec, inclined so that the upward component is 120 ft/sec and the horizontal component is 160 ft/sec. The displacement $\mathbf{d} = OQ$ is exactly

800 ft in magnitude. If gravity acts on neither the bullet nor the monkey, the bullet will travel in the straight line OQ and reach the monkey in 4 sec.

1. Without gravity the bullet will pass points O, A, B, C, and Q on the line OQ at 0, 1, 2, 3, and 4 sec, respectively. If you take gravity into consideration, where will the bullet and the monkey be at these instants?

2. Draw a diagram similar to Fig. 9.6, with the constants of this problem, and consider the solution

$$\mathbf{v}_0 t + \tfrac{1}{2}\mathbf{g}t^2$$

At $t = 1$ sec, $\mathbf{v}_0 t$ is AB and $(1/2)gt^2$ is 16 ft long, pointing vertically down. Put a point at the tip of the arrow representing

$$\mathbf{v}_0(1) + \tfrac{1}{2}\mathbf{g}(1)^2$$

3. Similarly, locate the tip of the arrow of

$$\mathbf{v}_0 t + (1/2)\mathbf{g}t^2$$

for $t = 2$, 3, and 4 sec.

4. Now, with gravity acting, locate the monkey at the instants 0, 1, 2, 3, 4 sec by drawing an asterisk at each of these points.

5. In general, if you use $\mathbf{d}$ to represent the fixed vector, OQ, the equation of motion for the monkey is

$$\mathbf{r}_m = \mathbf{d} + \tfrac{1}{2}\mathbf{g}t^2$$

and that for the bullet is

$$\mathbf{r}_b = \mathbf{v}_0 t + \tfrac{1}{2}\mathbf{g}t^2$$

At intersection time, t^*, $\mathbf{v}_0 t^* = \mathbf{d}$, and $\mathbf{r}_m$ and $\mathbf{r}_b$ are identical. Draw both $\mathbf{r}_m$ and $\mathbf{r}_b$ at $t = 1, 2, 3, 4$ sec.

9.6. In Fig. 9.7 let 1 cm represent a speed of 35 m/sec. Taking the time interval between $\mathbf{r}$ and $\mathbf{r}_0$ as 5.0 sec, compute the magnitude of the average acceleration. (Use equation 9.14.)

9.7. Work out this further proof of equation 9.18, using Fig. 9.11. In part A point P moves with constant speed v in a circle of radius r. At one instant the velocity is $\mathbf{v}_1$ and Δt later it is $\mathbf{v}_2$, but the magnitude is always the constant v. In part B the increment in velocity, $\Delta\mathbf{v}$, is shown. For very small Δt the arc Δs is almost straight. From similar triangles prove that $\Delta v/v \cong \Delta s/r$. Show that v is approximately $\Delta s/\Delta t$. Prove that $\Delta v/\Delta t \cong v^2/r$. Finally prove that the direction of $\Delta\mathbf{v}$ for small Δt is approximately perpendicular to $\mathbf{v}_1$.

9.8. Since the earth is rotating, everything on it must experience a centripetal acceleration (except at the poles). The radius of the earth is 6.38×10^6 m, and the speed of a point on the equator is 465

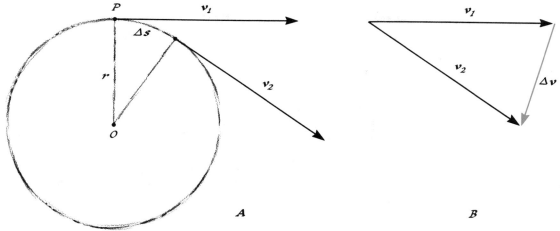

FIG. 9.11

m/sec. What is the acceleration of a man standing at the equator? What percentage of the acceleration due to gravity is this?

9.9. A sports car is capable of a maximum linear acceleration of 5 m/sec². It is on a circular track with a radius of 200 m and starts from rest, moving in this circle at maximum linear (tangential) acceleration. After how many seconds will its centripetal acceleration be numerically equal to its tangential acceleration?

9.10. The second hand on a watch is 2 cm long from the pivot to the moving tip. Think of it as a rotating vector, **r**. The motion of a point at its tip can be described by this vector. Consider an interval beginning at zero and ending at 15 sec. Use a figure and

equation 9.8 to compute the magnitude of the average velocity of this point in this interval. What is the direction of the average velocity vector in relation to the initial direction of **r**?

9.11. A string 1 m long with a nut tied to one end is twirled so that the nut travels in a circle parallel to the ground. What is the speed of the nut when the string makes a constant angle of 45° with the horizontal?

9.12. Analyze the motion of the satellite of Fig. 9.10 by considering the effect of the tangential acceleration vector in speeding up and slowing down the satellite. Find points where there is neither speeding up nor slowing down. Discuss the relative magnitudes of tangential and normal acceleration vectors at several different points, including P and Q.

10

The Evidence for Atoms and Molecules

THE STUDY of the atom plays such an important unifying role in modern physics that we shall devote the last two parts of this book to it. The main object of this chapter is to show some experimental evidence for atoms and molecules. We shall stress first some obvious properties of matter that seem to cry out for an atomic explanation. We shall not go back to Democritus and review the subject historically; we shall not even have time to praise Dalton and the early atomists adequately for their pioneering work. We shall emphasize, instead, some demonstrations and operational procedures that give circumstantial evidence of atoms and molecules. We are simply opening up a vast subject and raising many questions. The answers to some of these must wait until we have learned much more about dynamics, waves, electricity, and light.

First, what simple characteristics of matter seem to *demand* an atomic explanation?

10.1. Circumstantial Evidence

No one doubts the existence of the sun. "Seeing is believing." We see it. It is real. This is the kind of evidence we should like to have for atoms, but unfortunately we don't. What we have is circumstantial evidence; we think about that, mull it over, and conclude that atoms *must* exist.

There are many things that we believe simply

because we have been told, since our early childhood, that they are so. Most of us believe that the sun is 93 million miles away, but how many of us have taken the trouble to make the measurements that would justify this conclusion? The truth is that we have looked out of the corner of our eye (perhaps while basking in the warm rays of the sun at a beach) and have seen the cosmos go about its orderly business, but we have not observed carefully or measured.

If the sun *is* 93 million miles away, and if light travels at the rate of 3×10^8 m/sec, it must take 8.33 minutes for the sun's light to reach us. The sun we see is the sun that existed 8.33 minutes ago. If we look into the night sky with a powerful telescope, we can record on a photographic film galaxies that we cannot see with our eyes alone. Are they as real as the sun? Calculations indicate that it takes the light from some of them a million years to reach us. We see those galaxies as they were a million years ago! Is it not somehow possible to see them as they are now? When evidence comes to us by way of light, we usually give it great weight; but maybe the galaxy no longer exists! When you see something, does that prove it exists?

The bits of simple evidence of atoms, when isolated, are not convincing; when assembled from different quarters, they make a very strong case. How do we prove that atoms exist?

Let's begin with an unpretentious example that shows how we make such decisions in daily life.

"A new tenant is told by his neighbor that the garbage collector comes every Thursday, early in the morning. Later, in answer to a question from his wife about the same matter, the tenant says, 'I have been told there is a garbage collector and that he comes early Thursday morning. We shall see if this is true.' The tenant, a scientist, accepts the statement of the neighbor (who has had opportunity to make observations on the subject). However, he accepts it *tentatively* until he himself knows the evidence for the conclusion.

"After a few weeks, the new tenant has made a number of observations consistent with the existence of a Thursday garbage collector. Most important, the garbage does disappear every Thursday morning. Second, he receives a bill from the city once a month for municipal services. And there are several supplementary observations that are consistent—often he is awakened at 5:00 A.M. on Thursdays by a loud banging and sounds of a truck. Occasionally the banging is accompanied by gay whistling, sometimes by a dog's bark.

"The tenant now has many reasons to believe in the existence of the garbage collector. Yet he has never seen him. Being a curious man and a scientist, he sets his alarm clock one Wednesday night to ring at 5:00 A.M. Looking out the window Thursday morning, his first observation is that it is surprisingly dark out and things are difficult to see. Nevertheless, he discerns a shadowy form pass by, a form that looks like a man carrying a large object.

"Seeing is believing! But which of these pieces of evidence really constitutes 'seeing' the garbage collector? Which piece of evidence is the basis for 'believing' there is a garbage collector? The answer is, *all* of the evidence taken together, constitutes 'seeing.' And *all* of the evidence taken together, furnishes the basis for accepting the 'garbage collector theory of garbage disappearance.' The direct vision of a shadowy form at 5:00 A.M. would not constitute 'seeing a garbage collector' if the garbage didn't disappear at that time. (The form might have been the paper boy or the milkman.) Neither would the garbage disappearance alone consist of 'seeing' the garbage collector. (Perhaps a dog comes by every Thursday and eats the garbage. Remember, a dog's bark was heard!) No, the tenant is convinced there is a garbage collector because the assumption is consistent with so many observations, and it is inconsistent with none. Other possible explanations fit the observations too, but not as well (the

tenant has never heard a dog whistle gaily). The garbage collector theory passes the test of a good theory— it is useful in explaining a large number of experimental observations. This was true even before the tenant set eyes on the shadowy form at 5:00 A.M.

"Yet we must agree, there are advantages to the 'direct vision' type of experiment. Often more detailed information can be obtained this way. Is the garbage collector tall? Does he have a mustache? Could the garbage collector be a woman? This type of information is less easily obtained from other methods of observation. It is worthwhile setting the alarm clock, even after we have become convinced there is a garbage collector." †

I shall present the circumstantial evidence of atoms first and then move on to the demonstrations that come closest to seeing atoms.

10.2. The Simple Evidence from Solids, Liquids, and Gases

You are aware that water may be a solid, a liquid, or a vapor, for you have known it to change from one form to another and back. You have also seen solid carbon dioxide (Dry Ice) disappear without leaving a liquid trace. Perhaps you have even formed solid carbon dioxide by allowing the gas to expand rapidly out of a fire extinguisher into a woolen sock. And, if you have mixed solid carbon dioxide and alcohol, you have produced a temperature so low that it can freeze mercury hard enough to be used as a hammer. Many substances can exist in all three states of matter: as solids, liquids, and gases (Fig. 10.1). (There is a technical distinction between "vapor" and "gas," which we need not consider until later.) This fact alone demands an explanation. We explain it by the hypothesis that matter is made up of tiny building blocks called molecules. For the time being we are not concerned with the distinction between a molecule and an atom; we are simply asking: "Is matter continuously divisible, or do we reach an ultimate unit?" We seek evidence of the units that we are loosely calling molecules.

† Reproduced from *CHEMISTRY, An Experimental Science* with permission from the CHEM Study but not necessarily with its endorsement of the contextual use.

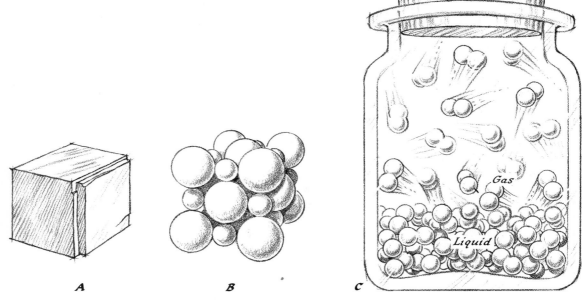

FIG. 10.1. *Solid, liquid, and gas: (A) In a solid (shown as a crystal) the molecules are rigidly and closely packed; they do not need a container; they can vibrate about fixed positions. (B) A molecular model accounts for the cubical shape of the crystal. (C) As a liquid (molecules in lower part) the molecules are spaced slightly farther apart and can move more readily; they assume the shape of their container, and a molecule could, conceivably, move from one part of the container to another. As a gas (molecules in upper part) the molecules are much farther apart, on the average, and are capable of moving about almost independently; they completely fill a closed container in the sense that they move readily throughout all parts of it. At high temperatures the amount of molecular agitation increases in all three states.*

A **solid** has a definite size and shape. Except for a free surface, a **liquid** assumes the shape of its container. A **gas** fills completely any closed volume, whatever its shape. No single molecule, obviously, has any of these characteristics; only aggregates containing a large number of molecules can have the characteristics of a solid, a liquid, or a gas. I am going to describe three experiments, one for each state of matter, as circumstantial evidence that molecules exist.

1. *Brownian Motion*

If the air in a small chamber, *C* (Fig. 10.2), is illuminated by a strong beam of light, *B*, and viewed under a microscope that has been focused on a plane slightly higher than the bottom of the chamber, we see nothing but the out-of-focus image of the chamber. If smoke is now admitted into it, we see the smoke particles moving ceaselessly in random, chaotic motion (Fig. 10.3). All the particles move, and not in any discernible current, not in any common direction, but completely at random, each particle for itself. This is a simple experiment to set up, and it is eminently worth while, for nothing else conveys so forcefully the feeling that the smoke particles are being bombarded on all sides by many smaller and hence invisible particles—the molecules of air in the chamber. Here is a bit of evidence that is hard to explain in any other way. You could, of course, invent a theory to explain just this one experiment (you could, for example, attribute the motion to life, as was once done), but it would be difficult to invent a theory that would

FIG. 10.2. *The Brownian motion of smoke particles can be seen with a low-powered microscope. Smoke from a match is illuminated with the aid of a simple magnifier set up to form a real image of a lamp filament directly beneath the microscope's objective.*

also explain all the other things that the molecular hypothesis explains.

Since the smallest particle that can be seen under a microscope cannot be much smaller than the wavelength of light, about 5×10^{-5} cm, we deduce that molecules of air must be smaller than 5×10^{-5} cm.

Brownian motion is not restricted to gases. Robert Brown himself, the botanist after whom the phenomenon is named, while looking through a microscope in 1827, observed that tiny particles from the pollen grains of flowers moved about chaotically in the water in which they were immersed. He thought at first that the motion was due to something alive but later suggested that it was due to the impacts of invisible molecules. A modern version of Brown's experiment can be done very simply with lead carbonate particles

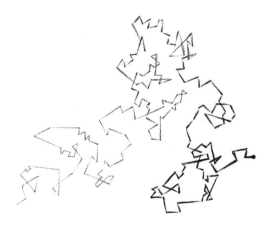

FIG. 10.3. *The vertices represent instantaneous photographs of a particle taken after equal time intervals. Between exposures the particle may have traced a path as erratic as the total one shown.*

suspended in water.† This shows that the random motion of molecules is not restricted to gases; the "dance of the molecules" goes on in liquids too. This motion helps to explain why the water left in an uncovered glass disappears in time. We theorize as follows: the fast-moving molecules escape from the liquid and begin a more independent existence as a gas.

2. Experiments with Monomolecular Layers of Liquids

Another elegant bit of evidence from liquids permits us to estimate the size of a molecule. A single drop of oil, dropped on a clean surface of water, spreads quickly into a flat layer (Fig. 10.4)

† Add about 1 cm³ of a 1% potassium carbonate solution (1 gm of potassium carbonate dissolved in 100 cm³ of water) to 250 cm³ of water in a large beaker. Then dilute 1/2 cm³ of a 1% lead acetate solution in 100 cm³ of water. Mix the two dilute solutions together in a 500-cm³ beaker, and stir. The ratio of lead to potassium compounds may vary from 1:2 to 1:4 and still give good results. The mixed solution may be diluted indefinitely once the reaction has taken place. If a cloudy or milky suspension results, the solutions used were too concentrated, and the preparation should be repeated with each solution diluted further.

whose diameter depends on the volume of the drop. This layer always assumes an approximately circular shape. Oil drops of the same size consistently spread into flat layers of the same diameter. Whether the layer is a single molecule thick we cannot say, but the reproducibility of the experiment and the fact that attempts to stretch the surface break it lend plausibility to the idea that it is a monomolecular layer.† Quantitative data can be obtained from this experiment. By measuring the total volume of 100 drops of oil, all formed by the same dropper, we can estimate the volume of one drop. The radius of the disk into which this volume spreads (Fig. 10.5) can be easily measured with a meter stick. The volume of such a disk is simply the area of the base times the altitude; that is, $V = \pi r^2 h$. Solving for h, we get

$$h = \frac{V}{\pi r^2} \qquad [10.1]$$

The quantities on the right are measurable: V is the volume of oil in a single drop, and r is the radius of the disk into which it spreads. We can therefore calculate h. This sets an upper limit to the size of a molecule: though we don't *know* that the disk is a *monomolecular* layer, we can safely say that a monomolecular layer would not be thicker than this h. Experiments with stearic

† Detailed instructions for the performance of similar experiments with oleic acid and stearic acid are given in Physical Science Study Committee, *Laboratory Guide for Physics* (D. C. Heath & Co., Boston, 1960), p. 13, and in R. M. Sutton, *Demonstration Experiments in Physics* (New York, McGraw-Hill Book Co., 1938), p. 465.

FIG. 10.4. *Monomolecular layer: One drop of a solution of 0.1 cm³ of stearic acid in a liter of benzene, when dropped on water, forms an approximately circular layer with a diameter of about 8 cm. The benzene evaporates, leaving the layer composed of stearic acid.*

FIG. 10.5. *Thickness of a monomolecular layer: The liquid in the dropper of Fig. 10.4 contains 10^{-4} part of stearic acid to one part of liquid. There is, therefore, about 10^{-5} cm³ of stearic acid in a drop. This is the volume of the cylinder shown here schematically with radius r and height h.*

acid have consistently given values of about 2×10^{-7} cm for h; oleic acid films are a little thinner.

The experiment is simple, and the result is spectacular. It gives us an order of magnitude for the height of a molecule. This figure ($\sim 10^{-7}$ cm) gives us a better estimate than the rough guess we made after looking at the Brownian motion of smoke particles (less than 5×10^{-5} cm).

The fact that a monomolecular layer resists being torn apart shows that the molecules of a liquid attract one another. A needle can float on still water as if the surface were a membrane. This and many beautiful experiments with soap films† support the idea that there is a strong mutual attraction between the molecules of a liquid.

3. *The Evidence from Crystals*

Many solid substances form themselves into crystals. Diamond is one example, but a commoner one is table salt, or sodium chloride. A

† C. V. Boys, *Soap Bubbles and the Forces which Mould Them* (Doubleday Anchor Books, Garden City, N.Y., 1959).

look at some table salt under tenfold magnification might surprise you. The great regularity of the shape of the crystals—they are all rectangular parallelepipeds—strongly suggests uniform building blocks. Even the large crystals of salt sometimes found in mines have the same shape. Other solid substances also, by the regular geometrical relations of their crystals, by their constant angles and symmetries, support the idea that they are made up of fundamental building blocks.

The next evidence of building blocks comes from cleavage. Mica has the extraordinary property of cleaving rather easily. You can take a razor blade and slice a large sheet of mica in two (Fig. 10.6). The blade simply helps you get started; after that, all you need to do is to pull the two layers apart by hand. You can take each of the new layers and split it the same way, and you can repeat the process many times. The layers finally get so thin that it is difficult to start the cleavage with the razor blade, but you get the feeling that there are always more layers and that they will always peel off with this same display of regularity. This effect, which is due to the extremely small size of the molecules, seems to support the concept of continuous divisibility, but the fact that the mica peels off in parallel planes supports the idea that the ultimate building blocks are neatly and systematically stacked in layers forming plane sheets.

Many other crystals also cleave. Nickel sulphate hexahydrate, for example, cleaves in a family of planes, as shown in Figure 10.7. The planes of cleavage are perpendicular to a certain direction in the crystal. You can cleave it along any plane that is perpendicular to that direction. Sodium nitrate will cleave if you place a single-edged razor blade along a cleavage plane and tap it lightly with the handle of a screwdriver.

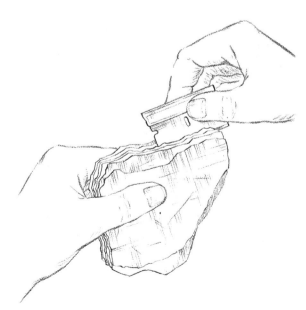

FIG. 10.6. *Cleaving a sheet of mica.*

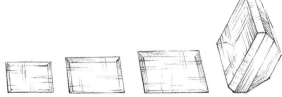

FIG. 10.7. *Cleavage of nickel sulphate hexahydrate.*

Not all crystals cleave, but those that do give us an impressive proof of the orderliness of their make-up. A model that shows what we think is happening at the atomic level is illustrated in Figure 10.8. Some of the little spheres that represent atoms lie in planes. Crystals that cleave are able to separate easily along one of these planes. The order exhibited by crystals is evidence of order at the atomic level.

The way in which crystals grow gives us more evidence. A crystal of alum, for example, can be grown in any household jar (Fig. 10.9). If the solution in the jar has the proper concentration of alum, the crystal will grow on a tiny alum crystal tied to the string and used as a seed, by the accretion of atomic layers of alum. The rate at which molecules attach themselves is tremendous; but, since they are very small, a fair-sized crystal may take weeks to grow. The molecules that make up the crystal are taken from the solution, the concentration of which diminishes as the crystal grows.†

I have chosen to cite certain properties of crystals as the main evidence from solids, but many other properties of solids can be explained atomistically. Melting, for example, we see as the change from a state in which the atoms are bound together so tightly that they cannot move around in relation to one another, and hence form a solid body, to a state in which the bonds are weak enough to allow the atoms to move around, to flow, and hence to form a liquid body. We

† Alan Holden, *Crystals* (Doubleday Anchor Books, Garden City, N.Y., 1959).

explain the expansion of a heated iron rod by imagining the atoms in the iron to be attached to one another by the forces of attraction represented in Figure 10.10 by springs (which are, of course, imaginary). The atoms can vibrate somewhat about their equilibrium positions. (Only with great

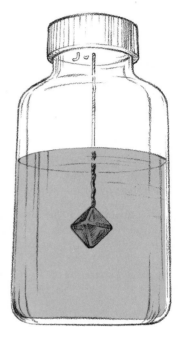

FIG. 10.9. *A crystal of alum can be grown in an ordinary household jar if the concentration and the temperature are properly chosen. The regularity of the crystal faces suggests that they grow by the addition of atomic layers.*

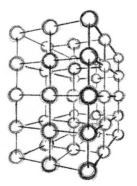 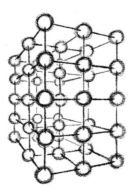

FIG. 10.8. *Cleavage model.*

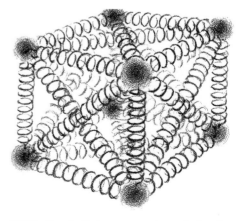

FIG. 10.10. *Symbolic representation of the forces of attraction between the atoms of a solid.*

difficulty can one atom migrate from one corner of a cube to the corner diagonally opposite. The effect is called diffusion.) Heating the rod agitates all the atoms: the average distance between two adjacent atoms increases, and hence the length of the rod increases. This increase is readily measurable, and it, along with a knowledge of the energy needed to produce the change, gives valuable numerical information about the strength of the forces that hold the atoms together in a solid. (It is only through hindsight that we know that in this case the building blocks are atoms of iron. We have used both terms, "molecule" and "atom," to mean fundamental building block. The fact that molecules are made up of atoms is not important at this stage.)

The evidence from solids, liquids, and gases all points in the same direction: matter seems to be made up of tiny things that we have been calling atoms and molecules. It tells us nothing, however, about what an atom or a molecule looks like, and we have had to use little balls to represent them in our figures. It also has not stressed the fact that there must be atoms of different kinds—atoms of iron and copper, of mercury and carbon and helium, for example. We turn now to the kind of evidence that supplies this information. It comes from chemistry.

10.3. The Evidence from Chemistry

The early history of chemistry is replete with the names of distinguished investigators. We shall consider here only two: John Dalton and Amedeo Avogadro—Dalton (1766–1844) because he was the pioneer of the modern concept of the atom, Avogadro (1776–1856) because he made an inspired guess without which the young science could never have moved forward.

It was the chemists that first gave operational meaning to the concept of atoms. They made the first measurements that supported the atomic theory. Their most powerful tool in this work was the analytical balance. It was by weighing samples before and after chemical reactions that Dalton was able to get numerical facts to support his atomic hypothesis.

In Chapter 5 we concentrated our attention on the *similarities* exhibited by all kinds of matter. We pointed out that matter of any kind has inertia and attracts other matter gravitationally. Now we start looking for *differences* between one kind of matter and another. This is what the early chemists did, and they discovered in nature not only different substances, but different kinds of substance. (A **substance** is a specific form of matter that is homogeneous and has a fixed chemical composition.) Some substances—copper, iron, mercury, and oxygen, for example—could not be decomposed (not, at least, with the means available to Dalton and his followers) and were therefore called **elements**. Other substances— water and salt, for example—could be decomposed into the elements; since they were composed, or *compounded*, of the elements, they were called **compounds**.

The earliest principle discovered in modern chemistry was that each chemical compound has a fixed and definite elemental composition. Whenever water is decomposed into its elements, eight grams of oxygen are formed for every gram of hydrogen. Attempts to synthesize water with different ratios of oxygen and hydrogen fail. However and wherever water is synthesized, its composition is always the same. Similar remarks can be made about all compounds.

The atomic theory explains this by saying that any sample of a compound is made up of molecules, that all these molecules are alike in containing the same number of atoms of each of its elements. The atoms of any one element all have the same characteristic weight† (except for isotopic differences treated in § 45.2), and the composition by weight of any compound is therefore always the same.

A simple analogy with nuts and bolts may help. You have a bunch of bolts, all alike; they weigh 1,600 grams. You have a bunch of nuts, all alike;

† The **atomic weight** of an element is obtained from its relative mass on a scale in which the mass of carbon is exactly 12 (more accurately, in which the mass of $_6C^{12}$—see § 45.2 and § 47.2—is taken as 12). The atomic weights are tabulated in Appendix F. The **molecular weight** of a compound is obtained from its relative mass on the atomic-weight scale. The molecular weight of water, for example, can be found if we know that its formula is H_2O; it is $2(1.00797) + 15.9994 = 18.01534$.

they weigh 240 grams. Now you screw two nuts on each bolt. You find that you have some nuts left over. You weigh them; they weigh 40 grams. You conclude that the weight ratio of bolts to nuts is 1,600/200 = 8/1. In this case you could see that you screwed two nuts on one bolt; so you concluded that the ratio of the weight of one bolt to that of one nut is 16/1. Observe that by weighing alone, *without knowing the total number* of bolts involved, you were able to make this deduction.

The work of the early chemists was somewhat like this. They discovered that, when oxygen and hydrogen combine to make water, the ratio of the weight of oxygen to that of hydrogen is always 8/1. But they could not see what was going on. They could not see atoms; they could only surmise that they existed. And it is no wonder, then, that they first guessed that an atom of oxygen is eight times heavier than an atom of hydrogen. They could not see that each molecule of water contained two atoms of hydrogen. They had to wait for other kinds of evidence before this was clear. Nevertheless, the first simple deduction from all these weighing experiments is what we now call the **law of definite proportions**: *Different samples of a compound contain the same elements in the same proportions.* From the fact that the ratios of the weights of the combining elements are constant we deduce that the number of atoms of one element is to the number of those of another element as the ratio of small whole numbers. Knowing that the combining ratio of the weight of oxygen to that of hydrogen is 8/1 does not determine the number of atoms of hydrogen and oxygen in one molecule of water. A clue came from experiments in which it was discovered, also by weighing, that 16 grams of oxygen combine with 1 gram of hydrogen to make, not water, but hydrogen peroxide; and 16/8 is exactly 2, a small whole number. Similar experiments with other compounds led to the **law of multiple proportions**: *When two elements combine to form more than one compound, the weights of one element that combine with the same weight of the other are in the ratios of small whole numbers.* (For example, the oxides of nitrogen, N_2O, NO, N_2O_3, N_2O_4, and N_2O_5, each with 14.008 gm of

nitrogen, have 8, 16, 24, 32, and 40 gm of oxygen, respectively. These numbers are in the ratios 1:2:3:4:5.)

Many similar experiments, decomposing compounds into their elements and synthesizing compounds out of elements, slowly enabled chemists to put the different atoms into a table in the order of their relative atomic weights (Appendix F).

The atomic theory thrust itself upon Dalton as the only explanation of all the facts that had been accumulating. We owe to him the basic idea that a sample of any compound is made up of molecules, and that the molecules of each compound are formed only by a unique combination of certain atoms. In the light of this idea, many facts of chemistry suddenly became understandable. The theory has survived because it still succeeds in correlating a multitude of new observations. Although we have, today, many new kinds of evidence of atoms, the laws of chemical composition provide the solid foundation on which our belief in the atomic structure of matter rests.

Ratios of small whole numbers appear not only in the weights of combining elements but also in the volumes of gases entering into chemical combinations. The volume of hydrogen resulting from the electrolysis† of water is always twice the volume of oxygen (see Fig. 10.13). This and many other experiments with gases seemed extremely puzzling until Avogadro made what I have called his "inspired guess"—now called **Avogadro's law**: *Equal numbers of molecules are contained in equal volumes of all gases at the same pressure and temperature.* It is now known that when the pressure is one normal atmosphere (1.013×10^5 nt/m²) and the temperature is zero on the Celsius scale, the number of molecules in 22.4 liters of any gas is 6.02252×10^{23}. This number is known as the **Avogadro constant**, N_A. (Avogadro did not know the constant; he knew only that equal volumes of all gases contain the same number of molecules.) An alternative way of defining the constant is to say that it is the number of molecules in a mole of an element or a compound. **A mole** is that quantity of an element or a compound whose mass in grams is numerically

† **Electrolysis** is the decomposition of a compound by electrical means.

equal to its molecular weight. For example, 32 grams of oxygen is a mole of oxygen, and 2 grams of hydrogen is a mole of hydrogen. Each contains 6.02252×10^{23} molecules.

It is known that Dalton considered and rejected Avogadro's hypothesis. The idea that elements might occur as polyatomic molecules (H_2 and O_2) did not occur to him. Between 1811 and 1858 chemists refused to accept the hypothesis, apparently because they felt that molecules were too theoretical. Once the hypothesis was accepted as law, however, the uncertainty about the atomic weights of the elements and about the correct formulas of compounds vanished. To be clearly understood, this point must be illustrated by many examples. This is usually done in chemistry courses. We do not have time to do it here.

It is enough to say that, with the help of Avogadro's law, chemists after 1858 wrote the formula of water as H_2O instead of HO. We can at least understand how Avogadro's law makes this plausible. In the electrolysis of water, as we have seen, two volumes of hydrogen are produced for each volume of oxygen. If we assume that a molecule of hydrogen and a molecule of oxygen each contain two atoms, we can illustrate the result of the electrolysis with Figure 10.11. At the left we show two molecules of water. In the center we show two volumes of hydrogen; at the right, one volume of oxygen. Each volume has the same number of molecules in it. (Only one molecule is shown in each volume, but 2 grams of hydrogen or 32 grams of oxygen would each

have about 6.023×10^{23} molecules in it.) By assuming the formula H_2O for water and the validity of Avogadro's law we have reached an explanation of the experimental facts. (See Prob. 10.10.)

Let us see if 6.023×10^{23} is a plausible estimate of the number of molecules in a mole. Consider a water molecule (H_2O). Its molecular weight is $2 \times 1.00797 + 15.9994 = 18.01534$. One mole (also called a **gram-molecular weight**) of water is 18.01534 grams of water. This much water contains 6.023×10^{23} molecules. Since water's density is very close to 1.00 gm/cm³, 18.01534 cm³ of water contains 6.023×10^{23} molecules. The number of molecules per cubic centimeter, if we round off to three significant figures, is

$$6.023 \times 10^{23} \text{ molecules} \div 18.01534 \text{ cm}^3$$
$$= 0.0334 \times 10^{24} \text{ molecules/cm}^3$$

If we imagine these as little cubes equally spaced in a cube one centimeter long, and if we let x^3 equal 0.0334×10^{24}, we can count x molecules along one edge. This means that $x = 0.322 \times 10^8$ molecules/cm. The inverse of this ($1/x$) is 0.311×10^7 cm/molecule. This, the average distance between water molecules, gives us a rough estimate of the size of such a molecule. Using the Avogadro constant, we have estimated the size of a water molecule, and our estimate is not out of line with what we learned of molecular sizes from our experiments with monomolecular layers of oil.

The Avogadro constant, approximately 6.023×10^{23}, is one of the few numbers that deserve to be memorized. From it we can deduce much in-

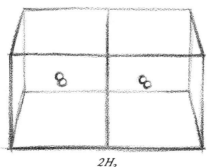
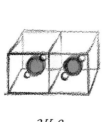

2H₂O   2H₂   O₂

FIG. 10.11. *The decomposition of water depicted schematically. Equal volumes of all gases contain the same number of molecules at the same temperature and pressure. Only one molecule is shown in each cube, but each mole of gas would occupy 22.4 liters at standard pressure and temperature.*

teresting and useful information. We shall strengthen our faith in its validity as we progress in this course. It is a good estimate of the number of molecules in a mole of any substance.

10.4. Atoms and Electricity

Our account of why we believe in atoms will not be complete unless we devote at least a few words to the atomicity of electric charge and to the intimate connection between the atom and the electron. The electron is the basic unit of electricity. I could write a separate chapter on why we believe in electrons, showing all the circumstantial evidence of these invisible but influential entities, but I shall offer only the evidence from electron beams and electrolysis.

This is not the way I should have started this discussion twenty-five years ago. Television, however, has brought into most American homes, and into many others, an instrument in which electron beams not only are taken for granted but are made to form pictures by landing precisely on the fluorescent screen of the TV tube. Let us see how. In Figure 10.12, F, a tungsten filament, is fixed in one end of a glass tube, which is evacuated by a vacuum pump and sealed. A battery (or an equivalent source of electric power), B, causes F to get hot, glow, and emit electrons; without oxygen F doesn't burn. The other end of the tube, the screen, S, is coated with a fluorescent material similar to that used in fluorescent electric-light

bulbs. The plate, A, which has a hole in it, is called an *anode*. It is connected to the positive side of another battery or an equivalent electronic device, which puts a large positive charge on it. This causes a spot to appear on the screen at P_1. We attribute this to the impact of electrons (small particles with mass and negative charges), which, having boiled off the filament, are pulled and hence accelerated by the electric field between A and F. (G is another aperture with a control function that we ignore in this elementary explanation.) The electrons have *inertial mass*, which keeps them going from A to P_1 at a constant speed in a straight line—unless, of course, an external force acts on them. Such a force can be supplied by an electric field between the deflection plates, D_1 and D_2. (This kind of deflection is used oftener in the cathode-ray tubes of oscilloscopes and radar than in television tubes, which use magnetic deflection instead.) The proof that electrons are *negative* charges is that, if D_2 is positive and D_1 negative, the electrons are attracted upward. This is shown by a deflection of the visible light spot on S from P_1 to P_2. The result is that we see something by means of this tube, but no one would claim that we see electrons. What we see is simply the effect of the impact of the electrons on the fluorescent screen.

All of this happens every day in millions of television tubes, which are designed and built on the following assumptions: (1) atoms are made up, at least in part, of electrons; (2) electrons are negatively charged particles; (3) electrons have inertial mass. Our belief in electrons, however, like our belief in atoms, is based not on any single demonstration but on an accumulation of information from widely diverse experiments, all of which find a consistent explanation in the assumption that electrons exist and that they have both inertial mass and electric charge.

The ratio of the charge to the mass of the electron was first measured with an apparatus that has some of the features of the tube shown in Figure 10.12. Still earlier in the history of electrons, before they became the tools of physicists, chemists were already aware of the existence of electric charges in atoms and were, indeed, using electric currents in chemical experiments.

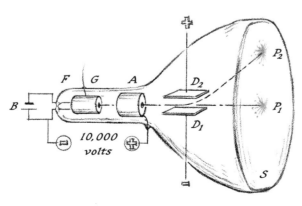

FIG. 10.12. *Cathode-ray tube.*

One such experiment is the electrolysis of water, which can be effected with an apparatus like that shown in Figure 10.13. Very pure distilled water in the W-shaped tube does not seem to be affected by the application of an electric potential to the platinum electrodes at A and B, but the slightest addition of an acid to the water starts a decomposition in which hydrogen (H_2) is collected above one electrode and oxygen (O_2) above the other. The usual chemical tests easily confirm that the gases formed are hydrogen and oxygen. If the electric current flowing into the system, as measured by the meter, is constant, the volume of gas in either column is proportional to the *time* during which the current flows. If electric current, I, is a measure of the quantity of electric charge, q, that flows in time t (that is, if $I = q/t$), then $q = It$, and the experiment indicates that dou-

bling the time doubles the total electric charge carried into the system. If we now assume that electric charge comes in little bundles called electrons, the total charge, q, is ne if n is the total number of electrons and e is the electric charge on one electron.

My choice of words has been unfortunate. If the electron is the basic unit of electric charge, we should say that e is one basic unit of electricity. Historically, however, the unit called the coulomb came first, and the number of coulombs equivalent to one electronic charge had to be measured by experiment. We know now that $e = 1.602 \times 10^{-19}$ coulomb, and I propose to show one way of arriving at this number. (For a more direct method of measuring e see § 45.3.)

We have been considering the electrons that we imagine flowing in the wires of the apparatus

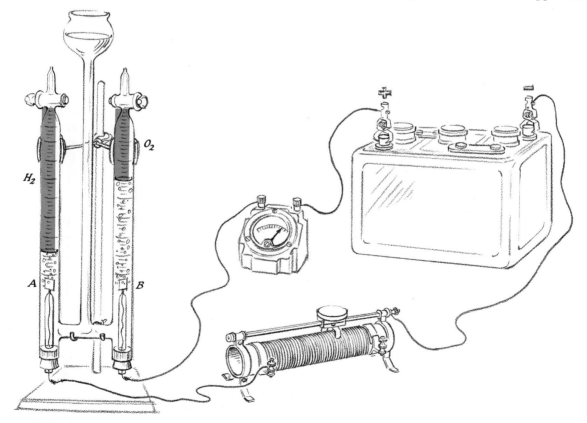

FIG. 10.13. *A typical arrangement of apparatus for the electrolysis of water. The apparatus is connected in series with a meter, a battery, and a rheostat (a variable resistor used for adjusting the current). Opening the stopcocks will release the H_2 and O_2 gases formed.*

of Figure 10.13. Now we must account for the effects in the water. To do this, we imagine that atoms are normally neutral. In Figure 10.14 two neutral atoms (A) are shown. They have electrons in them, but there are also enough positive charges (protons) in them to make the net effect neutral. If an electron could be taken from the left-hand atom (B), that atom, being left with an excess of positive charge, would now be a positively charged atom (positive **ion**). If the electron attached itself to the right-hand atom, that atom (C) would now be a negatively charged atom (negative ion). We believe that some of the hydrogen in water consists of positive hydrogen ions. The electrons coming in from the wire at A (Fig. 10.13) supply the charges needed to convert the hydrogen ions into hydrogen atoms, which pair off to form the molecules liberated in the left tube. Because of their low density these molecules rise in the tube and displace the water. To provide continuity of flow, electrons must leave the liquid at B. They come, we believe, from

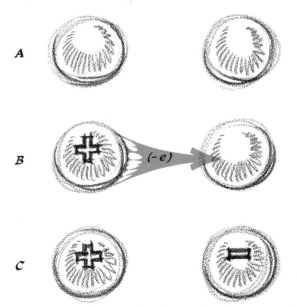

A

B   (−e)

C

FIG. 10.14. *Ionization: (A) Two neutral atoms each have equal amounts of positive and negative charge. (B) An electron removed from one atom leaves it positively charged. (C) If the electron attaches itself to the second atom, the atom becomes negatively charged. The charged atoms are called ions. The transfer of one electron from one atom to the other has ionized both.*

negatively charged oxygen ions in the right tube. This is an oversimplified version of what really happens, but it is nevertheless true that the rate at which electrons are taken up by the hydrogen at A must equal the rate at which they are given off by the oxygen at B.

These ideas apply not only to water but to many solutions. In Figure 10.15, for example, two electrolytic cells are connected in series with a battery and a meter. *Electrons flow into both cells at the same rate.* In one we see lead being deposited in the form of a spectacular tree of lead crystals. In the other we see copper being deposited on one of the electrodes.

Let M be the total mass of the atoms liberated at one electrode. Obviously $M = nm$ if n is the total number of atoms liberated and m is the mass of one such atom. Multiplying and dividing the right-hand side by ze, we get

$$M = \frac{nmze}{ze} \qquad [10.2$$

Now let's see why we write equation 10.2 as we do.

Let e be the charge of one electron. Let z stand for the number of electrons that need to be added to or removed from the ion to neutralize it; it is the **valence**, and ze is the magnitude of the net charge carried by the ion. Hence nze is the total net charge, q, carried by n ions. We therefore rewrite equation 10.2 as

$$M = \frac{mq}{ze} \qquad [10.3$$

The quanity q is measurable. The definition of current ($I = q/t$) suggests how to measure it. Write $q = It$, and substitute into equation 10.3:

$$M = \frac{Itm}{ze} \qquad [10.4$$

This may be solved for e:

$$e = \frac{Itm}{zM} \qquad [10.5$$

I is the current in amperes (coul/sec), measured with the meter; t is the time in seconds; m is the mass per atom. This is where the Avogadro constant comes to our aid. We know that there are 6.023×10^{23} molecules in one mole. From this we can compute the number of atoms per gram and hence the number of grams per atom; the valence,

z, comes from chemistry; we measure M by weighing with an analytical balance. Thus all the quantities on the right-hand side of equation 10.5 are known or measurable, and we can compute e. It comes out as 1.602×10^{-19} coulomb. This is a basic and universal constant of nature.

We have come a long way in endowing atoms with operationally measurable characteristics. Of great importance to the chemist are the relative atomic weights (Appendix F). Even more important, perhaps, to the physicist is the total number of electrons (Z) carried by each neutral atom—the **atomic number.** The atomic numbers of all the atoms are tabulated in Appendix F.

10.5. Seeing Atoms

You may remember that in the anecdote of § 10.1 the tenant actually got to see a shadowy form that could have been the garbage-collector.

But seeing that and only that would not have been convincing proof of his existence. It was the totality of evidence that convinced the tenant: the disappearance of the garbage, the monthly bills, the bark of the dog, etc. We are now in a similar position with regard to atoms.

We have two very powerful microscopes by which we can take pictures of things smaller than any optical microscope can photograph. One is the electron microscope. The picture shown in Figure 10.16 was taken with an electron microscope at a magnification of 10,400 times. Because of much circumstantial evidence we believe that each of the little spheres in the figure is a giant molecule containing about 10^9 atoms. (The diameter of one of the molecules can be estimated by comparison with the scale; $1 \mu = 10^{-6}$ m.) We can photograph giant molecules, but not individual atoms, with the electron microscope.

The photograph shown in Figure 10.17 was

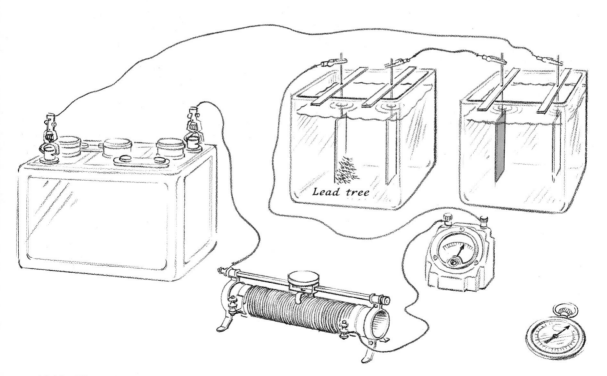

Lead tree

FIG. 10.15. *Electrodeposition: When two electrolytic cells are connected in series, as shown, the same current flows through both. You can confirm the laws of electrolysis by measuring the current with an ammeter and the time with a stopwatch and by weighing with a sensitive analytical balance, before and after the flow of charges, the electrodes on which the deposition takes place.*

made with a still more powerful device called an ion microscope. It can resolve detail much smaller than that resolved by the best electron microscope. We believe that each little dot in the picture represents a single atom. The device works somewhat like a shadow microscope.

This is the nearest thing to a picture of an atom that we have today. Does *it* convince you that atoms exist? If it were the only evidence you had, your answer would probably be "No!"

10.6. Summary

Atoms and molecules cannot be seen, but there is a great deal of circumstantial evidence of their existence. The most obvious behavior of solids, liquids, and gases—the way crystals form and cleave; the way liquid drops spread out into thin layers on other liquids; the chaotic behavior of smoke particles in air, known as the Brownian motion—all can be easily explained on the assumption that matter is made up of tiny, invisible building blocks held together by forces that become weaker as matter passes from solid through liquid to gas.

The modern concept of atoms and molecules received its strongest support, however, from the work of the early chemists who discovered that substances behave as if there were different kinds of atoms that combine to form molecules according to definite rules—one such rule being the law of definite proportions, which states that different samples of a compound contain the same elements in the same proportions.

One of the most important laws of chemistry, for physicists, bears the name of Avogadro. It says that equal numbers of molecules are contained in equal volumes of all gases at the same tempera-

FIG. 10.16. *Crystals of necrosis-virus protein. (Photograph from Dr. R. Wyckoff.)*

ture and pressure. When the pressure is one normal atmosphere and the temperature is zero on the Celsius scale, the number of molecules in 22.4 liters of any gas is $N_A = 6.023 \times 10^{23}$. This number is known as the Avogadro constant. A mole of any substance in any state contains N_A molecules.

Further evidence of the atomicity of both matter and electricity comes from experiments in electrolysis. These confirm the existence of a basic unit of electricity, called the electron, whose charge is 1.602×10^{-19} coulomb.

Problems

10.1. State carefully the circumstantial evidence that you could use to convince someone that the mail is distributed by an organized postal system.

10.2. The atomic weights of carbon (C), hydrogen (H), and oxygen (O), to three significant figures, are, respectively, 12.0, 1.01 and 16.0. Find the

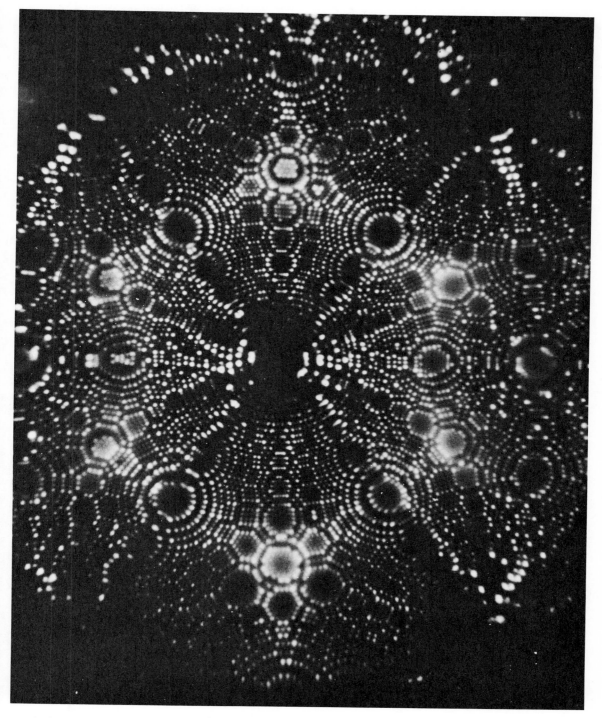

FIG. 10.17. *Field-ion microscope's image of a tungsten-crystal hemisphere with a radius of 500 A. (Photograph from Prof. E. W. Mueller of Pennsylvania State University.)*

molecular weight of aspirin ($CH_3COOC_6H_4COOH$) to three significant figures.

10.3. Molecules are made up of elements X and Y. Given the molecular weights of the following imaginary compounds, use the law of multiple proportions to find the molecular weight of X_3Y_7 and the number of grams of Y that must combine with X to form one gram of X_3Y_7: X_3Y_1, 90; X_3Y_2, 120; X_1Y_1, 50; X_3Y_4, 180; X_1Y_2, 80.

10.4. Both hydrogen (H) and nitrogen (N) form diatomic molecules (H_2 and N_2) in the gaseous state. If one liter of H_2 is combined with the proper amount of N_2, the result is pure ammonia (NH_3). How many liters of N_2 is the proper amount—the amount that will leave no excess H_2 or N_2? How many liters of NH_3 are produced? How many moles of NH_3 are produced? (Assume a standard atmospheric pressure and a temperature of zero Celsius.)

10.5. This problem requires calculations that will make vivid the great number of atoms in a mole. Consider a mole of lead (atomic weight 207.2). What is its mass in grams? What is the volume of a mole of lead of density 11.35 gm/cm^3? How long is an edge of a cube of lead containing one mole? Knowing the number of atoms in a mole, find the volume of one atom on the assumption that the atom is cubical. Find the length of one side of such a cubical atom. Imagine all the atoms in a mole placed side by side on a line segment. Find the length of this segment in centimeters. What is the length in miles? (One mile is 160,900 cm.) The answer is equivalent to about 244,000 round trips to the moon. The distance from the earth to the moon is 239,000 miles.

10.6. Using approximations of the same type as those used in Prob. 10.5, find the area in acres of a film of water one molecule thick whose volume is one gallon. (One gallon = 3,785 cm^3; 1 gm of water has a volume of about 1 cm^3; 1 acre = 4.05×10^7 cm^2.

10.7. Electric current is a flow of electrons. A kilowatt-hour (kWh) is the energy carried by 8.33 amperes for an hour across a potential difference of 120 volts. How many coulombs does this represent? How many electrons? At $0.02 per kWh what is the price in dollars of one electron obtained in this way? (You actually have to give the electron or an equivalent electron back; so the price you pay is more like a rental fee; you pay not for electrons but for the energy they give up in your appliances.)

10.8. This problem should give you an idea of the tremendous forces involved in electric interactions. Take a mole of water (18 grams, or about 1/2 ounce), and remove, to the other side of the earth, one electron from each molecule. (The diameter of the earth is 1.27×10^7 m.) Using equation 3.17 with K equal to 9×10^9 nt-m^2/$coul^2$, compute the electric force between the electrons and the remaining positive ions. (To get a feeling for the magnitude, put the answer in tons; 1 ton is 8.9×10^3 nt.)

10.9. The purpose of this problem is to test your understanding of equation 10.4 and of the consequence of having the same current flowing in the two cells of Fig. 10.15. Remember that lead is deposited in the cell on the left and copper in the cell on the right. (This happens when the circuit is closed if the proper electrolytes are used.) The ammeter reads 5.00 amp for a total of 200 sec. How many grams of copper are deposited? (The valence of copper is 2, and its atomic weight is 63.5.) What mass of lead is deposited by electrolysis in the other cell during the same interval of time? (The valence of lead is 2, and its atomic weight is 207.2.)

10.10. 1. Assuming that the formula for water is HO and that Avogadro's law is valid, try to account for the fact that in the electrolysis of water we get two volumes of hydrogen for each volume of oxygen.

2. Assuming that the formula for water is H_2O and that Avogadro's law is invalid, try to account for the experimental facts of the electrolysis of water.

3. Would it be possible to count the number of molecules in a container of gas?

The Conservation of Energy

THE IDEA that energy can neither be created nor be destroyed but can simply pass from one form to another is one of the basic concepts of physics and perhaps of all science. Known as the **principle of the conservation of energy,** it first found application in the solution of mechanical problems; then, as the meaning of "energy" was extended, the scope of the principle also expanded, and it has become one of the most solidly entrenched ideas in physics. It is now so firmly rooted that abandoning it would require a complete revolution in our thinking. When apparent contradictions of the principle have arisen, it has been found convenient to extend the meaning of "energy" in order to salvage the principle. In this chapter we shall show how heat has been accepted as a form of energy and how matter has been accepted as having potential energy. In the chapter on energy I proposed a simple test: if something can put objects into motion, it has energy. By that criterion, heat is rightly called energy, and matter has a store of potential energy.

11.1. The Sum of Potential and Kinetic Energy

Consider a man-made earth satellite moving in an elliptic path with the earth at one focus (Fig. 11.1). It has kinetic energy ($mv^2/2$) and potential energy at every point of its orbit. Since work has to be done against the gravitational forces of attraction between earth and satellite to move the satellite away from the earth, the system consisting of earth and satellite has more potential energy at B, where the satellite is far from the earth, than at A, where it is closer. The principle of the conservation of energy can be simply illustrated here by the statement that the sum of potential and kinetic energies is constant:

$$PE + KE = \text{a constant} \qquad [11.1$$

Since the kinetic energy equals $mv^2/2$, the velocity must be smallest at C, where the satellite is farthest from the earth, for the potential energy is greatest there.

This simple illustration demonstrates the great power of the principle of the conservation of energy. It enables us to make rather general statements without going into the details of the kine-

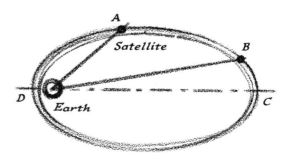

FIG. 11.1. *A system consisting of the earth and a satellite.*

matics and dynamics of the system. We don't have to analyze the forces that act on the satellite in order to say where it will be going slowest or fastest.

How long would such a system keep going? If there were no losses of energy due to friction and other causes—forever. If a system obeys equation 11.1, it is conservative. We know that the planets have been going round the sun for a very long time; they obey equation 11.1 quite well. Man-made earth satellites, we know, are not expected to keep going forever. Some, however, have already been up for several years—a more impressive result than that of any similar experiment performed in an earthbound laboratory with objects of macroscopic size. (If we go to the microscopic realm of atoms, however, we can conceive of systems that would keep going a very long time.)

In the laboratory we might set up a system (Fig. 11.2) consisting of a carbon dioxide puck moving on a horizontal glass table under the action of two springs pulling in opposite directions. The system has a natural position of equilibrium, O, where the net force exerted by the springs on the puck is equal to zero. If we displace the puck to one side and release it, the system starts to oscillate. At the ends of the swing, where the velocity goes to zero, the kinetic energy also must go to zero, and the potential energy must be a maximum. So long as there is carbon dioxide in the container, the system is nearly frictionless and continues to oscillate; but, since it is not completely friction-less, we know that equation 11.1 does not hold perfectly. Even before the carbon dioxide runs out, we begin to see that the amplitude of the oscillation is slowly diminishing, and it is not hard to realize that the oscillation, like that of a pendulum, will eventually stop at or near the equilibrium position. The equation holds well enough, however, for us to predict fairly well the system's motion during a long interval though one not nearly long enough for application to an earth satellite or planet.

There was work done against frictional forces here. Where did the energy go? Our daily experience with rubbing objects supplies the answer. Everybody knows that, when you rub your hands together, they get warm. This suggests immediately that heat is a form of energy. The accepted idea of heat is that it is the energy of random motion of the molecules (and/or atoms, ions, and electrons) in a piece of matter, but that is jumping the gun a bit. Let us go back and discuss the classical idea of heat as something that flows and show how units like the calorie (which still persists in engineering practice) first arose.

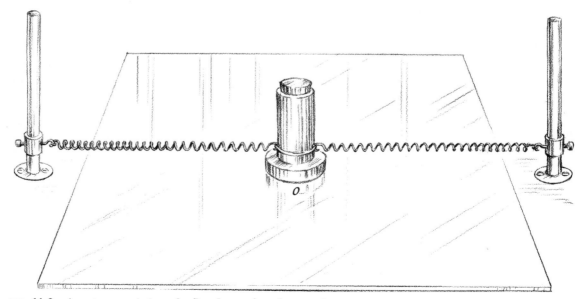

FIG. 11.2. *A system consisting of a Dry Ice puck and two springs.*

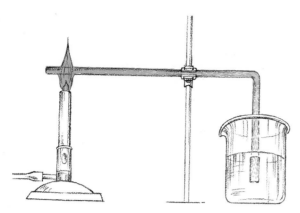

FIG. 11.3. *A molecular explanation of the flow of heat would attribute the rise in temperature to increased molecular agitation.*

11.2. The Classical Idea of Heat

We know when something is hot and when it is cold; we have in our bodies a built-in rough measure of temperature. But is temperature the same as heat?

One of the oldest ideas about heat is that it is like a fluid flowing from one place to another. Consider, as an illustration, Figure 11.3, which shows one end of a thick copper bar being heated by a Bunsen burner and the other end immersed in a beaker of water. The fact that the water is heated seems to show that heat, whatever it is, can flow along a copper rod. Many experiments confirm the idea that heat can flow from a hot body to a cold one. This is analogous to the flow of a gas from a container where it is at one pressure to a container where it is at a lower pressure. These are useful analogies, all right, but they leave unanswered the question "What *is* heat?"

Let us begin to answer that question by showing that a hot body does not necessarily contain more heat than a cold one. We shall use as our qualitative measure of heat the time during which a Bunsen burner is allowed to heat a beaker containing water. Figure 11.4 shows two beakers containing water, one (A) a small amount, the other (B) a larger amount, both at the same (room) temperature. We assume that the Bunsen burners are identical in every way and that they act for

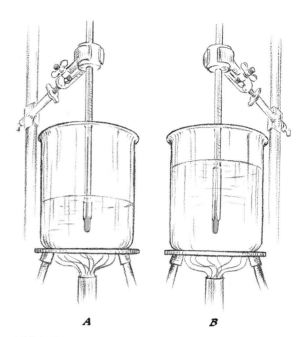

A   B

FIG. 11.4. *Identical quantities of heat fed into beakers containing different quantities of water.*

the same length of time. Heat is a form of energy, and the fire passes some of it to the water. Thermometers tell us that heat flows into the water, and the conditions of the experiment suggest that approximately the same quantity of heat flows into both beakers. The temperature goes up in both beakers, but the rise is much less in beaker B than in beaker A. Here we have two objects containing approximately the same amount of heat but at different temperatures. Even if we did not know what heat is, we should have here an operational way of measuring it. Using water as a standard, we can tentatively and approximately define the unit of heat called the calorie in the following way. A **calorie** is approximately the quantity of heat that will impart to one gram of water a rise in temperature of one degree Celsius.†

When a quantity of heat is fed into a body, there will often be a temperature rise, ΔT, which is directly proportional to the input heat, ΔQ, and inversely proportional to the mass, m, of the body being heated:

$$\Delta T = \Delta Q/ms$$

† The calorie is defined as 4.1840 joules.

Solving for s, we get

$$s = \frac{\Delta Q}{m(\Delta T)} \qquad [11.2$$

This s is a constant of proportionality called the **specific heat** of the material of which the body is composed (see Table 11.1). One consistent set of units comprises calories for ΔQ, grams for m, degrees Celsius for ΔT, and, hence, calories per gram per degree Celsius for s. If the substance is water and its mass is one gram, then, since s equals one calorie per gram per degree Celsius for water, ΔQ will come out as one calorie when ΔT equals one degree Celsius. This equation, when applied to mixtures of liquids and solids at different temperatures, leads to a consistent engineering practice, and the idea that heat is a fluid that can pass from one body to another serves well enough for certain operations in engineering. Some problems on the use of the equation are given at the end of the chapter.

Here we are more concerned with heat at the atomic level. If heat is a form of energy, how does it look from the atomic point of view? An answer to this question that is consistent with what we have said about temperature is this: whereas the temperature of a body is a measure of the *average* translational kinetic energy of the random motion of its molecules, its heat is a measure of the *total*

energy of the random motion, translational and rotational, of all its molecules. The fundamental nature of heat was first clarified, from the atomic point of view, when Count Rumford (1753–1814) observed that in the boring of cannon he could generate any amount of heat by doing more and more mechanical work. It was he who suggested that there is an equivalence between mechanical work and heat, but it was J. P. Joule (1818–1889) who first did an experiment to measure this equivalence.

11.3. The Calorie and the Joule

The foot and the meter both measure length, and there is a simple numerical relation between them: 1 foot equals 0.3048 meter. Similarly, the calorie and the joule both measure energy, and there is a simple numerical relation between them: 4.184 joules equal 1 calorie. But this relation is not quite so obvious. The operational steps we take in measuring a length in feet consist in laying off a standard foot along the length of the object we want to measure and counting. The operational steps are identical when we measure with a meter stick, but the counting gives us a different answer. The operational steps we take in measuring heat and mechanical energy, on the other hand, may be quite different from each other.

So far, we have been dealing primarily with mechanical energy. When this was kinetic energy, measurements of mass and velocity were involved; when it was potential energy, measurements of force and distance were involved. In the measurement of heat, however, measurements of mass and thermometer readings are usually involved. The classical notion that heat was a fluid did not easily suggest the relation between calories and joules.

One of the important differences is that, when we are dealing with mechanical energy, we are often concerned with the directed motion of one or more objects, but that, when we are dealing with heat, we are concerned with the random motion of the molecules that make up the objects. It is easy to go from the directed kind of motion to the random kind, as the following experiment proves. In Figure 11.5 a cardboard tube about a

TABLE 11.1

Specific Heats (calories per gram per degree Celsius)

Aluminum	at	−240°C	0.0092
		0°	0.2096
		600°	0.282
Copper		−250°	0.0035
		0°	0.091
		100°	0.095
Iron		0°	0.105
Lead		0°	0.030
		300°	0.034
Brass		0°	0.09
Glass		0°	0.16
Ice		0°	0.50
Alcohol		0°	0.55
Mercury		0°	0.0335

meter long is shown with a cork stopper in each end. Inside (A), on the lower cork, are some lead shot, and the upper cork has a hole into which a thermometer has been inserted. If the tube is suddenly inverted, the shot find themselves at the top, ready to fall (B). When the shot have fallen partway down the tube (C), they have picked up a certain speed, v_1, and hence have kinetic energy $mv_1^2/2$. Just before they reach the lower cork, they have picked up speed v and hence have kinetic energy $mv^2/2$. Very shortly thereafter they have all been brought to rest. Their average speed is now zero, and so their kinetic energy is zero. A total energy equal to $mv^2/2$ has apparently vanished. What happened to it? It is logical to think that a good part of the energy of directed motion that the shot had before impact has somehow or other been transmitted to the molecules of lead, thereby increasing the average kinetic energy of their random motion. This suggests that we look for a rise in temperature. If we push the thermometer through the cork (D) so that its bulb is surrounded by the shot, we shall probably discover that whatever rise there may have been is practically imperceptible. It will not remain imperceptible,

however, if the operation is repeated enough times. Experiment shows that even as few as fifty inversions of the tube will raise the temperature noticeably.

Let's compute the ratio of the mechanical work done in lifting the shot against the earth's gravitational field to the heat energy evolved (neglecting the heat that went into the cork, the cardboard, and the thermometer). In equation

$$W = nmgh \qquad [11.3$$

m is the mass of the lead shot, g is the acceleration due to gravity, and h is the height, measured from the lead's center of gravity after it fell to its center of gravity before it fell. The product mgh is the potential energy of the shot in position B. The letter n stands for the total number of inversions. With m in kilograms, g in meters per second per second, and h in meters, W comes out in joules. We use the formula for potential energy as a measure of the work rather than that for kinetic energy ($mv^2/2$) because it is easy to measure m and h but difficult to measure v, and we thereby assume that the total kinetic energy just before impact is equal to the potential energy at the top.

To measure the increase in heat, ΔQ, we need to know the rise in temperature, ΔT. That increase is given by the equation

$$\Delta Q = ms(\Delta T) \qquad [11.4$$

To keep the measure of ΔQ consistent in the two equations, we put m in kilograms, s in calories per kilogram per degrees Celsius, and ΔT, of course, in degrees Celsius. This yields ΔQ in calories.

The ratio W/Q is given the symbol J. The quantity J has been measured in many different ways and is certainly not limited to the value obtained in heating up lead shot. A value of J obtained from an experiment like the one described will probably differ considerably from the accepted value (4.184 J/cal) unless many precautions are taken to avoid losses of heat. The value of our demonstration lies primarily in its simplicity and in the way we almost see the transformation of the directed motion of macroscopic objects into the random motion of invisible molecules.

In the experiment just described heat was evolved from mechanical energy. It is not quite so easy to make the conversion take place in the opposite

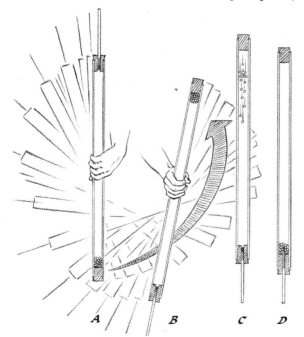

FIG. 11.5. *Conversion of potential energy into kinetic energy and of kinetic energy into heat.*

direction—that is, from heat to mechanical energy; but it is now believed that, whenever this conversion does take place, the rate of exchange remains the same: you always get 4.184 joules for every calorie. This permits us to extend the idea of the conservation of energy, not only in a qualitative but in a strictly quantitative way, to heat as a form of energy.

Today, electrical means of producing energy make it possible to measure heat in joules with great accuracy. The experimental difficulties encountered in measuring heat in calories, however, make calorimetric experiments among the least satisfactory to students. It is difficult to take all the heat losses into account. Consistent results have been achieved only by very painstaking work with the refined type of apparatus used in standards laboratories. In other words, it is now simpler to measure heat quantities directly in joules, but from sentimental or other irrational motives we often measure them in the unit 4.184 joules, a unit called the calorie. If we define the calorie thus, in terms of the joule, and if we do careful experiments, heating water electrically in a well-insulated calorimeter, we find that the specific heat of water is not precisely 1 throughout the range 0–100°C. Careful determinations of this kind yield the data presented graphically in Figure 11.6. We observe that the specific heat of water varies with the temperature—that 1 cal will raise the temperature of 1 gm of water by 1°C only in the vicinity of 20°C or 60°C. For calorimetric experiments in the elementary laboratory the value 1 for the specific heat of water is obviously good enough.

Any variation of this sort, subtle though it may

be, raises interesting questions. Why does the specific heat of water vary with temperature? If adding one calorie of heat to a substance does not always produce the same rise in temperature in that substance, why doesn't it? In more advanced texts answers to these questions are found at the atomic level.

11.4. The First Law of Thermodynamics

Problems related to the conversion of energy from heat into other forms or back again into heat belong to the branch of physics called **thermodynamics,** in which we discuss transformations of energy without going into detail about what is happening at the atomic level. The techniques of thermodynamics are very powerful and very general, but we shall not consider them here. Instead, as we strive for an understanding of what is commonly called the first law of thermodynamics, we shall continue to stress the atomic picture.

When heat is added to a mixture of ice and water and this is properly stirred, the temperature of the mixture does not rise until all the ice has melted. Why not? Rudolf Clausius (1822–1888), one of the founders of thermodynamics, assumed that there were no intermolecular forces. There are such forces, however, and it must take work to separate two molecules; this work has to come from whatever energy is fed into the system. If some of the energy goes into separating the molecules, into increasing the average distance between them, that much less is left to appear as kinetic energy of translation—that is, as a rise in temperature.

There are other forms of kinetic energy besides that due to the translation of the center of mass of a moving body. Consider a large grindstone that has been set into circular motion by a motor. When the power is turned off, the stone continues turning: it has kinetic energy even though its center of mass is at rest. Even with the power turned off, it has enough energy to make sparks fly off the edge of an axe or a knife brought to it for sharpening. It has kinetic energy of rotation.

In contrast with it, a ball moving forward at speed v has kinetic energy $mv^2/2$. This is due to

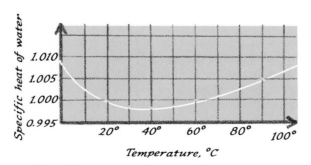

FIG. 11.6. *Variation in the specific heat of water as a function of temperature.*

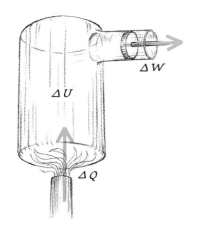

FIG. 11.7. *Schematic diagram illustrating the symbols used in the first law of thermodynamics.*

the motion of its center of mass. But it is possible for a ball to be spinning at the same time that it is moving forward. Its energy of spin is kinetic energy of rotation.

It is the ball's kinetic energy of translation that is responsible for the hardness of the ball's impact against a wall. It is the kinetic energy of translation, therefore, that is associated with the concept of temperature in Clausius' picture of molecular motion.

Real molecules, it happens, can have both translational and rotational kinetic energy. If some of the energy that is fed into a sample of gas goes into producing rotational kinetic energy, there will be that much less left to produce translational kinetic energy and therefore less energy that shows up in the form of a rise in temperature. In short, not all of the energy that is added to a gas will necessarily produce a rise in temperature.

I shall use the term "heat increment" to mean the *total* energy of random motion that is added to a collection of molecules. Some of it may go into producing rotation of the molecules; some of it may go into changing the average separation between the molecules; and some of it may go into increasing the kinetic energy of translation of the centers of mass of the molecules, and only this portion of the energy shows up as a rise in temperature. The relations among (1) the energy of random motion of molecules, (2) the energy of directed motion of a macroscopic body, and (3) heat energy

can be expressed symbolically with the help of Figure 11.7. This represents, in schematic form, a device by which heat energy can be fed into a system that can move a piston and thus do work. The substance within the container is called the "working substance." I do not specify what it is. You may think of it as a gas if that will help you visualize what may happen, but the argument is not restricted to gases.

If heat energy, ΔQ, is transmitted into the system in the direction shown, it is conceivable that a directed motion of the piston results in a quantity of work, ΔW. The agent that pushes the piston may have kinetic energy of random motion, some of which is imparted to the piston. And more than likely some of ΔQ goes into increasing the internal energy, U, of the working substance by the amount ΔU. The equation

$$\Delta Q = \Delta U + \Delta W \qquad [11.5$$

expresses the law of the conservation of energy for the system. We definitely have heat energy ΔQ and mechanical energy ΔW. We also have the quantity ΔU, which we label neither mechanical energy nor heat energy; we simply say that it is the internal energy of the working substance.

Consider mechanical energy at the atomic level. When it is in such a form that the translational kinetic energy of molecules can put pressure on a piston, then, obviously, temperature is involved, for temperature is a measure of the average translational kinetic energy of the random motion of molecules. On the other hand, ΔU may be partly in the form of rotational kinetic energy and partly in the form of the potential energy of separation between molecules that is due to attractive forces between them. In any case, all three terms of equation 11.5 can be measured in the same units, joules or calories.

It is fruitful to examine the consequences of special cases of equation 11.5 by imagining what happens in Figure 11.7 if the working substance is an ordinary gas like air. If the piston, for example, is locked so that it can't move, $\Delta W = 0$, and equation 11.5 states that $\Delta Q = \Delta U$. This means that all the heat entering the system is used to increase the internal energy of the working substance. As we have seen, this does not necessarily mean that the temperature goes up; but, if the temperature does go up, the pressure that the gas exerts on the piston certainly goes up also.

If the piston is allowed to move, part of ΔQ is used to produce ΔW; hence there must be less energy left for ΔU, and the energy available for a rise in temperature is less than in the previous case. The heat required to raise the temperature of the working substance by 1°C is greater than it was when the piston was locked; in other words, the specific heat of that substance is now greater.

Finally, if $\Delta Q = 0$ and the whole system is well insulated thermally,

$$0 = \Delta U + \Delta W$$

and therefore

$$\Delta U = -\Delta W$$

A negative ΔW means that work is done *on* the substance instead of *by* it. The signs in equation 11.5 were chosen so that a positive ΔQ means heat flowing into the system, a positive ΔU means an increase in the internal energy of the substance, and a positive ΔW means work done by the system on the piston. Any change of sign implies a reversal in direction for ΔQ, ΔU, or ΔW. If ΔW is a positive quantity, work is done by the working substance. If ΔW is a negative quantity, ΔU is positive; that is, the internal energy of the working substance increases, as we should expect of a compression.

You are urged to imagine other experiments suggested by Figure 11.7 and equation 11.5.

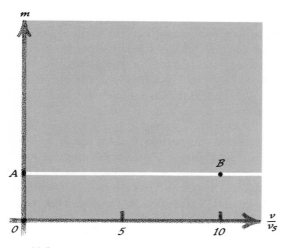

FIG. 11.8

It is apparent, according to the definition given at the beginning of this section, that we have been dealing with some basic principles of thermodynamics. I shall not pursue this subject any further except by asserting that the principle of the conservation of energy applies to heat energy as well as the other kinds of energy. This assertion, called the **first law of thermodynamics,** is summarized mathematically in equation 11.5. It is based upon a tremendous amount of accumulated evidence. The numerical relations involved have already been stated: 1 calorie of heat is produced whenever 4.184 joules of energy in any other form are completely converted into heat. When we convert heat into mechanical energy, it is difficult to convert it all; but, for the part that *is* converted, the same numerical factor holds: one calorie for every 4.184 joules.

11.5. The Kilogram and the Joule

Now that I have demonstrated in what sense the joule and the calorie measure the same thing, energy, I propose to show that, from the point of view of the modern physicist, matter has energy.

In classical physics the mass of a body was considered a constant that did not depend on velocity. But at high velocities mass does seem to depend on velocity. What is a high velocity? Sound travels in air at about 300 m/sec. High-speed bombing planes can travel at several times the speed of sound. Even at such speeds, the mass of a moving body would not show any appreciable change. Although no bombing plane has flown at ten times the speed of sound, we have reason to believe that a plot of mass against v/v_s (v is the speed of a moving object, and v_s is the speed of sound) would look like Figure 11.8; the mass would remain constant.

If we take the speed of light, c, as our standard, another situation prevails. The speed of light, 3×10^8 m/sec, is about a million times greater than the speed of sound. The range of speeds from 0 to $v/v_s = 10$ in Figure 11.8 is only $1/10^5$ times that from 0 to $v/c = 1.0$ in Figure 11.9. In other words, the whole range, AB, of Figure 11.8 would fit within the dot at m_0 in Figure 11.9. In this region the plot of m against v/c is almost level, but experiment and theory agree that, at speeds approaching that of light ($v/c \longrightarrow 1$), the mass would increase as shown in Figure 11.9. The equation that governs this variation is

$$m = \frac{m_0}{\sqrt{1 - v^2/c^2}} \qquad [11.6$$

in which m_0 is the mass of the body at rest. It comes from Einstein's special theory of relativity (§ 46.3), by which it can be shown that

mass of body in motion = mass at rest

$$+ \frac{\text{kinetic energy of body}}{(\text{speed of light})^2} \qquad [11.7$$

The implication of the second term on the right seems to be that kinetic energy has mass. The equation

$$E = mc^2 \qquad [11.8$$

which applies not only to kinetic energy but to all kinds of energy, comes from an elaboration of the theory that produced equation 11.7. (See Chap. 46.) In the short span of fifty years a wealth of experimental results has confirmed the validity of equation 11.8. It has been confirmed primarily in nuclear reactions but is believed to hold without exceptions. It can be seen at once that its terms are dimensionally correct. Both sides have ML^2T^{-2} as dimensions. Both represent energy. The factor for conversion from kilograms to joules is $c^2 = 9 \times 10^{16}$ m²/sec². This is a huge figure. It implies that one kilogram of matter has 9×10^{16} joules of energy. (The amount of electrical energy used by the City of New York in one month is about 10^{16} joules.)

Obviously a fascinating story remains to be told about how such huge quantities of energy can be obtained from matter. That forms the subject of Part VI of this book. For the present I simply wanted to introduce one more form of energy that has to be considered if a complete tally is to be kept when we tabulate heat, mechanical energy, and other energies.

11.6. Conversions of Energy

We began our consideration of energy in Chapter 6 with a simple criterion: if a body has energy, it can make something move. There are many ways to show that heat can produce motion. One of the simplest is shown in Figure 11.10. Heat makes the water inside the metal container boil. The vapor, issuing from jets J_1 and J_2, imparts a

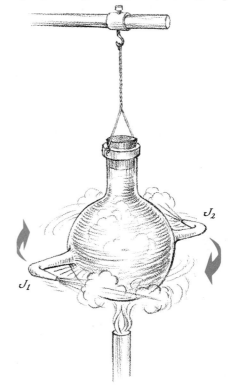

FIG. 11.10. *A simple engine for converting heat energy into mechanical energy.*

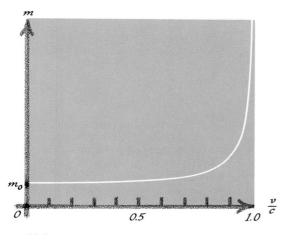

FIG. 11.9

rotary motion to the whole. This device is a simple engine. Our whole civilization leans heavily on more sophisticated heat engines that work with coal, gasoline, and diesel oil as fuels. In all of them mechanical energy is obtained from heat.

The branches of classical physics are called mechanics, heat, sound, light, and electricity. Notice that each is related to a form of energy. The basic nature of energy begins to become clear. A study of the instruments by which energy is converted from one form into another would be fascinating in itself. An electric light bulb, for example, converts electricity into heat and light, and a photoelectric cell converts light into electricity. Can you name the instrument by which heat is converted *directly* into electricity? How many other links connecting forms of energy can you name?

That energy is essential to life is apparent. A study of the supplies of energy that will be available in the future is obviously important to the human race. We cannot begin that study better than by considering the broad implications of the idea that energy can be neither created nor destroyed, but simply changed from one form to another.

11.7. Summary

The principle of the conservation of energy asserts that energy can neither be created nor be destroyed but can pass from one form to another.

The total amount of energy in an isolated system is a constant.

The equation

$$\Delta Q = \Delta U + \Delta W$$

says that in an isolated system an increment in heat energy appears as the sum of increments in internal energy, ΔU, and work, ΔW, done by the system. It is a mathematical statement of the first law of thermodynamics, which implies that the principle of the conservation of energy applies to heat as well as to mechanical energy.

The calorie, which is approximately the heat required to raise the temperature of a gram of water by 1°C, is equal to 4.184 joules.

In heat exchanges in which the dissipation of heat is minimized, the heat lost by the hot bodies is equal to the heat gained by the cold ones. The heat ΔQ is computed from the equation

$$\Delta Q = sm(\Delta T)$$

in which s is the specific heat, m is the mass, and ΔT is the temperature change.

Mass itself has energy according to the relation

$$E = mc^2$$

in which E is energy, m is mass, and c is the speed of light. This very general result of the theory of relativity implies, as a special case, that the mass of a moving body depends upon its speed. That mass is equal to the body's mass at rest plus its kinetic energy divided by the speed of light squared.

Problems

11.1. Problems in calorimetry often involve the simple idea that the heat lost by the hot bodies is equal to the heat gained by the cold bodies, always in accord with equation 11.4. An interesting deduction from this is that the final temperature of a mixture of two liquids is the weighted average of their original temperatures, with mass times specific heat as the weighting factor. You can test your understanding of these ideas by proving this as follows: You are given mass m_1 of a liquid with specific heat s_1 at temperature T_1. It is mixed with mass m_2 of another liquid, whose specific heat is s_2 and temperature is T_2. Assume that the final temperature is T and that $T_1 > T > T_2$. The heat lost involves $T_1 - T$, and the heat gained involves $T - T_2$. Equate the heat lost to that gained, and solve for T. The result should be

$$T = \frac{m_1 s_1 T_1 + m_2 s_2 T_2}{m_1 s_1 + m_2 s_2}$$

A very special case is the mixture of equal quantities of the same liquid. The final temperature comes out as the arithmetic mean of the two initial temperatures. Prove this for yourself.

11.2. The density of iron is 7.9 gm/cm³. The mass of a block of iron with a volume of 1,000 cm³ is, therefore, much greater than the mass of the same volume of water. Find the ratio of the heat required for raising the temperature of the iron by 10°C to that required for raising the temperature of the water by the same amount.

11.3. 1. Heat energy enters the water, in Fig. 11.3, at the rate of 500 W. Calculate how long it would take to heat 450 gm of water from 20°C to 80°C.

2. Repeat the calculation for an equal volume of glycerine. Its density is 1.26 gm/cm³, and its specific heat is 0.540 cal/(gm × °C).

11.4. The lead shot in Fig. 11.5 weigh 95 gm. They are allowed to drop 100 times. What is the greatest possible rise in the temperature of the shot?

2. Repeat the calculation for a mass of 190 gm.

3. If you solve the problem with symbols rather than with numbers, you should be able to prove that the rise in temperature is independent of the mass. Do you believe this—when, for example, the mass is 200 kg?

11.5. The energy of a waterfall eventually turns into heat. If the fall is high, most of this goes into evaporating the water into the air. Suppose, however, that all the energy of the Angel Falls of Venezuela were converted into a rise in the temperature of the water. Compute that rise. (This is the highest waterfall in the world—1,010 m.)

11.6. 1. Where, in Fig. 11.1, does the satellite attain its greatest speed? Explain.

2. After a very long time, the system shown in the figure loses energy. Would you expect its orbit to shrink or enlarge? Explain.

11.7. A roller coaster has practically zero speed at the top of its highest hill. Without power from the outside can it reach the top of another hill of the same height? Explain. Discuss its variations in speed in terms of energy as it moves from start to finish.

11.8. Assume that the puck of Fig. 11.2 is displaced along the common central axis of both springs and then released. Discuss its variations in speed in

terms of equation 11.1. Because of friction it gradually loses energy and does not really obey the equation precisely. In the light of this statement, what should be its ultimate speed?

11.9. We can learn from Fig. 11.6 that heat energy supplied to water at 90°C will produce a smaller increase in temperature than a similar amount of energy fed into the same system at 20°C. If the energy doesn't increase the average kinetic energy of translation of the molecules, what else might it do?

11.10. 1. If the piston of Fig. 11.7 is kept locked and the gas flame is turned off, heat leaks out of the system; that is, ΔQ is negative. What happens to the internal energy of the system? Does this necessarily mean that the temperature of the system falls?

2. Use the first law of thermodynamics to determine whether the internal energy of a certain amount of gas increases or decreases and by how much if 15 J of work is done on the gas and 3 cal of heat is allowed to flow from it.

3. Paint, insecticides, and shaving cream are now packed in pressurized cans. When they are shaken, a noticeable drop in temperature often takes place. Invent an explanation suggested by the definition of temperature as the average kinetic energy of translation of the molecules. Can molecules have other kinds of energy?

11.11. Mechanical energy, chemical energy, heat, sound, light, and electricity are forms of energy encountered in our daily living. Make a chart with those words on it. Join each word to every other with two lines, one for the device that transforms energy of type A into type B and one for the device that transforms energy of type B back into type A. Name the devices that are used for these transformations. An electric motor, for example, transforms electrical energy into mechanical energy. A generator transforms mechanical energy into electrical energy. Your ability to answer this question depends, to a great extent, on your interest in physical things. If you have difficulty, consult someone to whom this seems like a trivial question.

11.12. The mass of an electron at rest is 9.11×10^{-31} kg. The speed of the electron is increased in an accelerating machine until its kinetic energy is 8.2×10^{-14} J. What is the mass of the electron in motion? (See equation 11.7.)

12

What is Physics?

"To be surprised, to wonder, is to begin to understand. This is the sport, the luxury, special to the intellectual man. The gesture characteristic of his tribe consists in looking at the world with eyes wide open in wonder."

JOSÉ ORTEGA Y GASSET, *The Revolt of the Masses*

"A man to whom the feeling of mystery is not familiar, who has lost the ability to marvel, to be overwhelmed by awe, is like a dead man."

ALBERT EINSTEIN, as quoted in the French magazine *L'Express*

WE HAVE gone once round the spiral and have touched on space, time, matter, and motion. Kinematics, the study of motion, gave us our first glimpse of the power of mathematics in physics. The kinematics of a single particle, for example, showed us how a mathematical formulation enables us to predict the answer to a problem.

But we barely touched on the greatest triumph of classical mechanics, Newton's laws of motion (Chap. 3), which describe how forces affect the motions of bodies. We have been laying the foundation for a detailed study of this subject, called dynamics. It forms the substance of Part III.

Although our treatment of forces was mostly qualitative, we were able to introduce the concept of energy. In some ways energy is the most obvious physical reality: we feel the warm rays of the sun; we observe the growth of plant and animal life, made possible by energy from the sun; and the daily cycle of our bodies' functions transforms the chemical energy in the food we eat into energy for our countless activities. Yet in other ways energy is the most abstract concept we have dealt with, and it is probably the most far-reaching

concept in physics. Physics has been defined, indeed, as the study of energy and its transformations The time-honored subdivisions of the subject—mechanics, heat, sound, light, and electricity—all exemplify energy in its different forms.

Energy is one of the great unifying concepts of physics. Let us now review how it and the other new concepts we have learned so far have taken on meaning, and let us find out what we must do to penetrate the subject of physics to greater depth.

12.1. How the Concepts of Physics Take On Meaning

It is possible to study certain branches of physics without doing experiments. A subject called rational mechanics, for example, is sometimes taught in the mathematics departments of some British universities. The fact that it is taught as mathematics, not as physics, indicates that it is being considered abstractly and theoretically: one lays down certain postulates (such as $f = ma$) and some definitions such as

$$a = \lim_{\Delta t \to 0} \Delta v / \Delta t$$

and

$$v = \lim_{\Delta t \to 0} \Delta x / \Delta t$$

and builds on them a logical structure called mechanics.

We have been approaching the subject in a more qualitative way. I have taken such words as "length," "mass," "time," and "force" from our everyday vocabulary and have tried to sharpen their meaning in an operational way; that is, I have tried to specify, with details of the procedures to be followed, how length, mass, time, and force can be measured. We measure a length by counting the number of times a standard rod fits into it; we measure time by starting and stopping a stopwatch in coincidence with two events, and we read off a number; we calculate an average velocity by forming the ratio $\Delta x / \Delta t$; and so on. In this way I have tried to clothe the skeleton of abstract concepts with the flesh and blood that only experiments can produce.

The power of physics stems, in part, from the simple and straightforward way in which the *operation* that is performed can be communicated to other investigators so that they can repeat it and verify its results. Mathematical formulation is essential; so far I have kept mathematics to a minimum, but it should be apparent that our grasp of the subject increases not only with the number of experiments but also with our discoveries in mathematical language.

The concept of temperature (to be discussed in detail in § 29.6) illustrates nicely how we start with a certain set of operations and end with a mathematical expression that makes the concept general and useful. We begin with a bodily sense of heat and cold. (We often begin with the human body and its senses. The color of light and the pitch of sound are other physical effects that are detectable by the human body.) Next we seek a more dependable instrument for measuring the effects of temperature quantitatively. We devise the mercury thermometer and calibrate its scale against the melting and boiling points of water. With its help we investigate the properties of gases

by means of the measurable quantities pressure (P) and volume (V). This leads to a mathematical formulation, $PV = NkT$ (in which N is the number of particles, T is the temperature, and k is a constant), that predicts the behavior of gases over a wide range of temperature but begins to fail as the temperature falls below that range and fails completely when the gas turns into a liquid. Why? At this point we need a theory to describe the behavior of gases on a finer scale. The elementary kinetic theory of gases (Chap. 29) grows out of this need, and we get a microscopic interpretation of temperature—

$$T \propto \tfrac{1}{2}\overline{mv^2}$$

—the average kinetic energy of translation of the molecules. This immediately suggests new experiments and new theoretical concepts.

A concept of physics takes on meaning, we see, only if we can specify an operation or a series of operations associated with it.

As another illustration consider the centripetal force that acts on a rubber stopper, of mass m, tied to a string and twirled in a circle of radius R at speed v (Fig. 12.1). Although the precise definition of force is yet to come (in Part III), we have already used operational ways of measuring forces—for example, by comparing with one another the pulls that the earth exerts on objects like the weight, W, in the figure. A purely kinematical discussion leads to the central acceleration v^2/R, and the qualitative dynamical introduction I have given yields a formula for the force, F_c, that keeps the stopper moving in a circle. It is

$$F_c = \frac{mv^2}{R} \qquad [12.1$$

Since the quantities on the right, a mass, a velocity, and a length, have all been given operational meaning, the equation could give an operational meaning to F_c. In practice, forces are defined more simply by the linear accelerations they produce, but here we have seen how the combination of ordinary algebra and operationally defined quantities like length and velocity could yield a mathematical expression of great generality. The most general expressions of this type are called **laws.** The equation $PV = NkT$, for example, is called the general gas law.

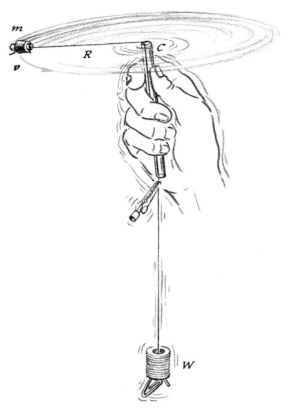

FIG. 12.1. *Simple apparatus for testing the formula for centripetal force.*

We assert, then, that the words we use in physics (velocity, acceleration, mass, time, etc.) have operational meaning. But what is *physical* meaning? What is physical truth? What is physical reality? These questions are hard to answer because it is hard to understand what they mean. Many scientists believe today that science can move forward without defining "truth" or "reality." Instead, operational meanings are given to physical concepts. The following statement of the operational philosophy is quite appropriate to our discussion:

"In nuclear physics, as in all branches of science, a unified point of view seems necessary. One that finds general but not universal acceptance among scientists today is the *operational philosophy* whose founding father was the Austrian physicist Ernst Mach (1838–1916). This philosophy was developed in its modern form largely by the members of the so-called Vienna circle (the physicist P. Frank, the mathematician

H. Hahn, and the economist O. Neurath, among others).[1]

"It is no coincidence that this development took place during the same period that saw the rise of relativity and the quantum. In our own country important contributions have been made by P. W. Bridgman, of Harvard University.[2]

"The operational philosophy is known formally as *logical positivism*. These are its main features:

"1. Quantities such as the charge, temperature, mass, and length of a body are not thought of as things 'whose nature is intuitively understood'; they are *defined* as the objective results of certain carefully prescribed operations that can, at least in principle, be carried out in the laboratory.

"2. These operational definitions, as well as all other laboratory manipulations or experiments, give rise to sets of 'pointer readings' of one sort or another. They may be actual scale readings, the numerical results of calculations, cloud-chamber photographs, oscilloscope traces, graphs, etc. Such pointer readings, taken in bulk, are the 'irrefutable facts of Nature.' Quantities for which operational definitions cannot be given, i.e., quantities that are not reducible to sets of pointer readings, are called 'unobservable'; they do not belong to the field of science.

"3. Physical laws are relationships between operationally defined physical quantities that always seem to occur when certain experiments are performed.

"4. It is the role of theory to give, on the basis of a few hypotheses, a simple unified description of as many experiments (pointer-reading sets) as possible. The question of the *ultimate truth* of either hypothesis or theory simply does not arise.

"5. Theories and hypotheses may be replaced at any time by more useful ones, i.e., by ones that describe more experiments or that describe the same experiments in a simpler way. The hypothesis of a continuous fluid of negative electricity, for example, was replaced by that of the spherical electron. This was replaced by the point electron, which, in turn, was modified by quantum mechanics with its notion of wave functions. Current troubles in quantum electrodynamics may call for other changes of the hypothesis that we now call 'the electron.' Atoms, nuclei, and 'fundamental particles' in general are hypotheses of greater or lesser usefulness.

"It is commonly held by other philosophies that the

"1. P. Frank, *Modern Science and Its Philosophy*, Cambridge, Harvard University Press, 1949.
"2. P. W. Bridgman, *The Logic of Modern Physics*, New York, The Macmillan Co., 1927.

universe is a vast reservoir of truths and that it is the function of the scientist to uncover these truths. A logical positivist, however, sees no operational way to decide whether a given theory or hypothesis represents 'absolute truth' or not. As a result he discards all concepts like 'truth' or 'reality' in his thinking. His goal is to give as economical a description as possible of the sense perceptions that come (or that can be made to come) within his experience. We marvel at the economy that is possible; many scientists identify 'reality' with this economy.

"At one time practically every physicist believed that Newton's laws of motion represented absolute truth in the field of mechanics. We now know that these laws do not hold for bodies whose speeds are appreciable compared with the speed of light. Here we must use the special theory of relativity, which arises logically when we try to give operational definitions to word groups like 'the length of a body' and 'the time difference between two events.' The point of view of the operational philosophy is not that Newton's laws are 'untrue' and the special theory 'true' but rather that the special theory, which includes Newtonian mechanics as a special case for slow speeds, represents a forward step because it correlates a great many more sense perceptions. The special theory of relativity is vastly useful in nuclear physics." †

12.2. Which is the Basic Concept of Physics?

It is too early to decide, on the basis of what has been covered so far in this book, which laws of physics stand the best chance of surviving without modification. We have not yet studied Newton's great generalizations in mechanics, which summarize, in two equations, much of what is known of classical mechanics. Nor have we studied Maxwell's mathematical treatment of electricity, which summarizes, in four equations, nearly all that is known of electromagnetic fields. (They are partial differential equations, a branch of mathematics we shall never reach in this course, but we shall study special cases of them in less general form.) I assert, nevertheless, that of all the principles known in physics the one that is least likely to be replaced is the principle of the conservation of energy.

† Reprinted with permission from David Halliday, *Introductory Nuclear Physics* (John Wiley & Sons, New York, 1950), pp. 1–5.

The idea that energy is neither created nor destroyed but simply passes without loss from one form to another received its earliest confirmation in the transformation of mechanical energy from potential energy into kinetic energy and back. Later, when theory and experiment confirmed that heat is a form of energy, the principle of the conservation of energy could be written as the equation

heat energy + mechanical energy = a constant   [12.2

You may think at first that all we are doing is making up a new form of energy and putting it into equation 12.2 in order to keep the principle of the conservation of mechanical energy from failing. You may at first think the same when I propose a new form of energy, which we shall call electromagnetic energy. Since heat energy and mechanical energy do not account for all the energy transformations involved in electrical experiments, the extension of the equation for the conservation of energy to read

heat energy + mechanical energy
     + electromagnetic energy = a constant   [12.3

seems natural; but it is an artificial trick if electromagnetic energy has no operational definition except equation 12.3. It isn't fair to say, "See, equation 12.3 is now satisfied," if we simply invent electromagnetic energy in order that the equation may be satisfied. But if we have other operational means (besides equation 12.3) of identifying electromagnetic energy, and if we then discover that putting it into that equation satisfies it, we can claim a legitimate extension of the principle of the conservation of energy. This is exactly what happened. The energy carried by radio waves, for example, is of the electromagnetic kind and, like any other kind of energy, is measurable in joules. It can be transformed into heat and into mechanical energy.

Finally, as we have already seen, mass has energy, and vice versa. Einstein proved, as he put it, that "the mass of a body is a measure of its energy content." The expression $E = mc^2$ expresses the relation between mass and energy. If a body liberates energy E, its mass decreases by the amount E/c^2. But the energy will pass to another system, whose mass will be increased by the same amount. The total mass of all the bodies concerned will remain unchanged. Since there is no net loss of mass, there is, according to the equation $E = mc^2$, no net loss of energy.

12.3. The Relation of Physics to Other Sciences

What we now call science had its first dramatic successes in the work of Galileo and Newton. Their observations, experiments, and theories eventually became the branch of science called mechanics. Physics, by way of mechanics, pointed the way for the general evolution of science. It was a model to be emulated for the scope of its generalizations and the power of its mathematical tools. No wonder, then, that physics has been called the pioneer science. Lloyd William Taylor, under the topic "Physics as the Key to All the Sciences," writes:

"Every science shares, each in its characteristic degree, the heritage called 'the scientific method.' By no means, however, is every science equally qualified to stand as an example of this heritage. There is, in fact, a wide range of gradations in the extent to which the various sciences have participated in the formation of the world view which lies at the foundation of the scientific era. Other things being equal, there is every reason for choosing the science which has been the most prominent in this respect, and which today is influencing such thought most profoundly, namely, physics.

"Physics is, by common consent, the fundamental science. This is not merely because it fell to the lot of physics, in company with astronomy, to carve the place for science out of the highly resistant intellectual world of the sixteenth to the nineteenth centuries, but more particularly because the younger sciences, without exception, consider themselves scientific to just the extent that their concepts are logically reducible to those of physics. In addition, the basic technique of laboratory observation and measurement used by all the other scientists consists primarily of adaptations of the methods of physics. Consider, for example, the astronomical telescope, the chemical balance, the biological and the petrographic microscopes, the geological seismograph, the medical electrocardiograph and X-ray, and almost the entire equipment of the engineer. The basic instruments from which these were

devised were born in the physics laboratory, and most of them, except for minor adaptations, were perfected there." [†]

At this point I should try to define "science" and describe the scientific method, showing how observation, measurement, and experiment lead to hypothesis and theory; how theory suggests new experiments, the results of which demand modification of the theory; how a generalization that is sufficiently wide in its application and that has withstood the tests of much experimental confirmation and of internal consistency is called a law. This is an interesting and important topic, but I do not have time to develop it adequately here. I shall, instead, refer you to a book that has developed this topic well,[‡] and we shall content ourselves here with analyzing some of the criticisms of certain definitions of science.

It has been said that science is organized common sense. Whoever said this was no doubt trying to emphasize the fact that the procedures followed in science are but sophisticated extrapolations of the steps taken by rational men when confronted by any dilemma. But if by "common sense" we mean the accumulated knowledge of the race that guides our thinking even at the subconscious level, we can argue that no progress in science could have been made by those who believed in the common-sense view. Common sense tells us that matter is solid and impenetrable; common sense tells us that the sun revolves round the earth; common sense tells us that heavy bodies fall faster than light ones; and so on. We could argue that progress has been made, not by organizing common sense, but by departing from it. Nonconformists have often been useful as the pioneers of new ideas that departed from the accepted common-sense view. Copernicus argued that the motion of the other planets could be more readily explained if they were thought to revolve round the sun instead of round the earth, and the earth too, he maintained, revolved round the sun. But

[†] From Lloyd W. Taylor, *Physics, the Pioneer Science* (Dover Publications, Inc., New York, N.Y.).

[‡] Gerald Holton, *Introduction to Concepts and Theories in Physical Science* (Addison-Wesley Publishing Co., Cambridge, 1952), "The Nature of Scientific Theory" and parts of Chaps. 9, 10, 12, 13, and 14.

the established metaphysical (meaning here philosophical and theological) concepts contradicted, by what was called pure reason or by some other non-empirical argument, Copernicus's view.

What happens, apparently, is that a causal explanation that is adequate for its day receives a metaphysical sanction that makes its explanation seem like common sense. When a scientific theory has met with particular success (for example, Newton's laws of motion), there is a tendency to establish it as the only legitimate basis of explanation, and this makes it difficult, even for scientists, to explore new theories (such as that of Einstein).

Philipp Frank says: "All attempts at such a justification have been based upon metaphysics. They have had their roots in the belief that the validity of some equation (e.g., Newton's equation) can be established 'philosophically' or 'epistemologically' without reference to the observable facts which have to be derived. . . . Even a slight glance at the history of scientific thought shows us that the content of yesterday's metaphysics is today's common sense and tomorrow's nonsense."† And elsewhere Frank says: "Obsolete philosophical views in physics are mostly physical theories in a state of petrifaction."

This is strong and colorful language; and, though we are not yet sufficiently well versed in science or the history of science to defend or refute Frank, we should take his words seriously. He is, in effect, arguing for the *operational* point of view: we must base our knowledge on what is observable, and our theories must be verifiable by investigation.

It may be true that physics has progressed to the extent to which it has used the tools of mathematics, but it is also true that mathematics has profited greatly from its contact with physics. The problems of physics have served as the incentive for whole branches of mathematics. The differential calculus was invented by Newton to cope with the problems of motion and other problems involving rates; the integral calculus

was invented by him when he faced the difficult problem of adding all the tiny contributions of the gravitational attraction between bodies. He made the bold guess that a body as large as the earth, in its attraction for other, even nearby, bodies, acts as if its mass were concentrated at its center. He waited twenty years before publishing his theory, but during this time he invented the integral calculus to deal with the problem of adding the quantitative effects of an infinite number of small masses. Vector analysis arose as a tool in mechanics. Mathematics, while "queen and maidservant of the sciences," profited much by her association with them, particularly physics.

Though logic plays an important part in physics, not only in the symbolic forms, such as algebra, but in the verbal forms associated with syllogistic reasoning, the logical foundation on which scientific inquiry rests is not always thought through very carefully. The book *Science is a Sacred Cow*† cites, as illustration, a man who does experiments to find the cause of drunkenness. In one case he observes that his subject, after drinking gin and soda, gets drunk. In a second case the same subject, after drinking whiskey and soda, gets drunk. In a third case the same subject, after drinking vodka and soda, gets drunk. The common ingredient in all three drinks is soda, and so, it seems obvious to the experimenter, the cause of the drunkenness in all three cases must be the soda. This example shows that a common ingredient is not necessarily the only common ingredient or the one responsible for the common outcome of the experiments.

At another level of sophistication, we have the argument that a theory is true if deductions from it have been confirmed. Einstein's special theory of relativity, for example, is based on the assumption that the speed of light is the same for two observers moving at a constant velocity in relation to each other. One deduction from this theory—that the inertial mass of a body increases as its speed increases—has been confirmed with high-speed electrons. The experiment is thought to give support to the theory. But consider Bertrand Russell's example of simple logic: Assume

---

† Philipp Frank, *Foundations of Physics*, Vol. 1, Part 2, in International Encyclopedia of Unified Science, edited by Otto Neurath, Rudolph Carnap, and Charles Morris (University of Chicago Press, 1955).

† Anthony Standen (E. P. Dutton & Co., New York, 1958).

that bread is made of stone and that stone is nourishing. The conclusion is that bread is nourishing. Now we confirm experimentally that bread *is* nourishing. Does that lend weight to our assumptions?

Does this example mean that experiments that support Newton's laws of motion do not validate those laws? Not necessarily, but it points to the need of other criteria. One such criterion arises if we can specify what kind of experimental results would *invalidate* the law. If, for example, we state the law of terrestrial gravitation as "Every unsupported body will move toward the center of the earth," we see that the law would be proved false if even *one* case contradicted it. In a true science it is always possible to specify just what would invalidate a law. No astrologer has been at a loss, when called upon, to specify the things that would, when they happened, reflect credit on his theories or predictions; but no astrologer has ever been able to say, concerning one of his predictions, precisely what would show that his theory was completely false.† For this and other reasons we call astrology a pseudo science.

I said earlier that the other sciences have looked to physics as a model. Today some of the most promising fields of research lie on the borders between physics and other sciences—biophysics and biochemistry. The contacts that physics has with biology and chemistry are most important at the molecular and atomic levels. Life as we know it on this planet seems to depend on the generation of certain types of molecules. It is conceivable that the study of a living organism, which is very complex, will require the invention of new approaches, and that these may also be of help to physics. At the molecular level it must be difficult indeed to know whether we are in physics, chemistry, or biology.‡

Finally, let us take note of one distinction be-

† I have leaned heavily here on Norwood Russell Hanson, "The Importance of Saying What is False," *The Nation* (June 27, 1959, p. 578), in which he reviews *The Logic of Scientific Discovery* by Karl P. Poppe (Basic Books, New York, 1959).

‡ At the macroscopic level a distinction between physics, chemistry, and biology, obviously invented by a physicist who has had difficulty in making demonstrations work, runs like this: If it stinks or pops, it's chemistry; if it doesn't work, it's physics; if it bites, it's biology.

tween science and technology. Technology yields inventions like the lens or the magnetic compass or the automobile. These may be of tremendous utility and importance, but discoveries of this sort, in the past, have led to no general law. Taylor puts it this way:

"The compass and the lens were inventions rather than steps in scientific progress. They were not associated in the least with the development of the idea which is fundamental to science, confidence that the world is knowable. That idea was born in the minds of the Ionian Greeks about the sixth century B.C., and after being all but lost during the Middle Ages, came to its first full fruit in the sixteenth century, through the beginnings of what is now called physics." †

12.4. The Liberating Effect of Science

Besides producing the great labor-saving and other technological devices that have been its fruits in engineering, science has had a salutary effect on the spirit of man. Science has been a liberating force. It has helped to dispel superstition and to substitute rationality. Where fear and darkness born of ignorance prevailed, science has brought light and freedom.

Rudaux and Vaucouleurs say of astronomy, which we can equate to early physics:

"Astronomy, which is without doubt the oldest of the sciences, has contributed more effectively than any other to the development of human thought. Although born of everyday needs (the calendar, the time, navigation) and the fears of primitive man in the face of the terrifying phenomena of Nature—for which reason it has remained closely associated with the superstitions of the astrologers in the minds of the uneducated, even, alas, to the present day—astronomy was nevertheless the first science to form the concept of natural physical law, which was demanded by the regularity of heavenly phenomena. . . . At a much later date, it was the Copernican revolution in astronomy that liberated men's minds from baseless superstition, and gave birth to the authentic scientific attitude and the rational outlook of the present day." ‡

† L. W. Taylor, *op. cit.*, p. 6.
‡ Lucien Rudaux and G. de Vaucouleurs, *Larousse Encyclopedia of Astronomy* (Prometheus Press, New York, 1959), p. 499.

Neither the spiritual benefits nor the material benefits of science, unfortunately, have reached enough people on the earth.

Because of the great physical power available to scientists today, they have a tremendous responsibility. They have the duty to explain the methods and limitations of science to the non-scientist. And it is clear that the non-scientist has the duty to learn something of the discipline of science. Communication between the scientist and the layman has broken down; there is a gap between them, and this can perhaps be closed more readily by the scientist than by the non-scientist.

"Closing the gap between our cultures [scientific and non-scientific] is a necessity in the most abstract intellectual sense as well as in the most practical. When these two senses have grown apart, then no society is going to be able to think with wisdom . . . for the sake of the western society living precariously rich among the poor, for the sake of the poor who needn't be poor if there is intelligence in the world, it is obligatory for us . . . to look with fresh eyes." †

I can only suggest here that there are interrelations between science and politics, science and morality, science and humanity, science and art, science and technical assistance to underdeveloped

† C. P. Snow, *The Two Cultures and the Scientific Revolution* (Cambridge University Press, New York, 1959), p. 53.

countries. They should be in the back of our minds as we pursue the study of physics, the pioneer science.

12.5. Where Do We Go from Here?

In Part I of this book we have moved rapidly and superficially over many of the concepts of physics. Our purpose has been to get our feet wet before we take a header. Or, to use a different metaphor, we have climbed a high mountain and taken a broad look at our field. We have observed the interesting pathways and the winding rivers. It is now time to descend into the valley and walk along the road. It may seem dusty, and the going may seem rough; but those who have gone before us beckon, assuring us that the journey is worth making. Whether you plan to enter a field like medicine, which demands some knowledge of physics, or simply wish a deeper understanding by which to bridge the gap between scientist and non-scientist, may you find the journey challenging and rewarding!

We shall study, in greater detail, waves, dynamics, electricity, and the electromagnetic character of light, with special emphasis on the basic principles that will enable us to understand the most elementary theories of the atom and its central constituent, the nucleus.

II

VIBRATIONS AND WAVES

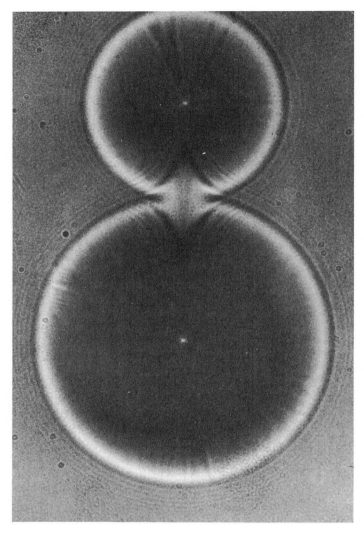

Poisson's Bright Spot   *(See § 23.5.)*
(Photograph from Clifford Miles.)

A. J. Fresnel, in 1818, submitted, to the Prize Essay Committee of the French Academy of Sciences, an essay on the theory of diffraction. One member of the committee, S. D. Poisson, who supported the corpuscular theory of light and opposed the wave theory, deduced from Fresnel's theory that a spot of light should appear at the center of the shadow of a circular object; and, not knowing that such a spot had been discovered and announced by G. F. Maraldi nearly a century earlier, he offered this deduction as evidence that Fresnel's theory was absurd. When Poisson communicated his deduction to François Arago, the latter, promptly putting the question to the test of experiment, rediscovered Maraldi's spot. It is known today as Poisson's bright spot. If two ball-bearing balls are used as shadow-casting objects, as in the illustration, other effects of diffraction are observable near their point of contact.

13

Introduction to Vibrations and Waves

THIS chapter begins Part II of our book, devoted to vibrations and waves. As physics has progressed, it has uncovered more and more phenomena whose explanation demands a knowledge of vibrations and waves. The revolution of the planets, for example, is periodic and has some of the characteristics of vibrations. Many structures that are commonly considered rigid, such as bridges and skyscrapers, actually vibrate, and great calamity has resulted when the possibility of vibration has not been taken into account by the designing engineers. The study of sound demands a knowledge of the vibrations and waves that travel through gases, liquids, and solids. The great strides in communication that we have made by means of radio, television, and radar depend upon the electromagnetic waves produced by vibrating electrons inside wires and other devices. Even more important, perhaps, are the electromagnetic waves

associated with light, visible and invisible, with x-rays, and with the radiation called gamma (γ) rays, which is emitted by atomic nuclei. In our time the best reason for studying vibrations and waves is, perhaps, that they occur in atoms and that without some knowledge of them no understanding of even the simplest atomic theories is possible.

13.1. Another Kind of Motion

If you line up some dominoes so that they stand vertically like so many soldiers on parade, with the distance between them less than the height of each of them, you can, by pushing over the domino at one end, start a disturbance that travels along the line, knocking each domino down in turn, until it reaches the other end (Fig. 13.1). If

FIG. 13.1. *Propagation of a pulse.*

the total distance along their path from the first domino to the last is Δx, and if Δt is the time it takes to bring them all down, from the first to the last, the average velocity is $\Delta x/\Delta t$. But the average velocity of what? What actually moves? Certainly the first domino did not travel the distance Δx.

We could say that the disturbance moved along; and, if we had clocked it at different positions, we should have discovered that its motion was uniform. Now, as we found earlier (§ 5.2), a moving body acted upon by no external force continues in uniform motion, but here we are obviously dealing with something else. This is certainly not the motion of a single body or particle. The motion of the dominoes is a very special example of a **pulse,** which, in turn, is related to wave motion.

Consider an example. At one end of a long corridor is an open window with a curtain over it (Fig. 13.2). At the other end is a door. What happens when someone opens the door (A)? A

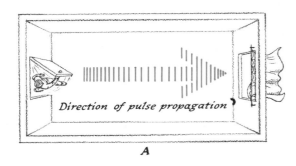

Direction of pulse propagation

A

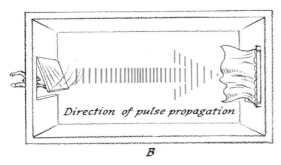

Direction of pulse propagation

B

FIG. 13.2. *Propagation of two kinds of pulse: (A) When the door is opened, a pulse of condensation travels from left to right and pushes the curtain to the right. (B) When the door is closed, a pulse of rarefaction travels from left to right and pulls the curtain to the left.*

few seconds later the curtain flaps to the right, out the window. We say that a pulse of air pressure travels from the door to the curtain. You may imagine the door pushing the air molecules near it as the cause of a pulse carried by the air, but how do you explain the fact that, if the door is now closed (B), the curtain flaps to the left a few seconds later? More detailed experiments would prove that the velocity $\Delta x/\Delta t$ (which is to the right in both parts of the figure) is a constant in this case also. This much a single body with zero force on it and a pulse seem to have in common: both travel at a constant speed.

This will serve as our introduction to waves, for a wave is something like a series of pulses traveling at a constant speed. Uniform motion seems to be natural both for a single body like a particle and for a wave, but wave motion is more complicated in its details. What precisely is a wave? Let us consider one more illustration before we give a formal definition.

Our earliest memories of waves are probably of water waves. When a pebble is dropped into a still pond, the circular ripples that move away from the spot are two-dimensional waves. (Although the water rises and falls, thus moving slightly in the third dimension, the energy carried by the ripples flows out radially in two dimensions.) The motion of a crest, measured along a radial line, obeys the formula for uniform motion, $x = v_0 t$, but a small twig floating on the surface bobs up and down as the crest passes under it. The twig does not travel along with the crest. In the study of wave motion we are concerned both with the motion of the twig and with the velocity of the crest.

Our purpose in this chapter is to get a qualitative (non-mathematical) introduction to wave motion. You want to learn the terminology, and some of the basic characteristics, of vibrations and waves. You want to learn also why waves and vibrations are important in physics.

13.2. Why We Study Vibrations and Waves

The connection between vibrations and waves has not been made clear so far. The examples given above have illustrated single pulses (the dominoes and the curtain) and a series of pulses, or train of waves (the pebble dropped into water). Suppose, however, that a wooden box is floating on a still pond and that a hand pushes it down periodically so that its vertical motion goes through regular repetitive cycles. The circular ripples that move away from their center continue to do so as long as the box continues to be pushed down and let up. A train of waves is being generated. Another box, floating on the pond, bobs up and down as the waves pass by. It is apparent that some of the kinetic energy at the source has been transferred to the other box. This example illustrates two facts: (1) the generation and continued maintenance of an unvarying train of waves requires a vibrating source; (2) energy can be transported by waves. The second fact is probably the most important reason for studying waves.

The sun, for example, although it is 93 million miles from us and is radiating energy in all directions, still delivers about one horsepower (746 watts) to each square meter of the earth's surface, thus making plant and animal life on the earth possible. But energy need not be delivered in such huge quantities to be useful. In much smaller quantities energy carried by waves is important in bringing us information rapidly across great distances. Practically all that we know about the regions of extragalactic space has been deduced from such waves, some of which have traveled billions of light-years. At the other extreme, much of what we know about the atom also comes from information carried by waves.

There is a vast difference between the power needed for heat and that needed for the communication of intelligence. The tremendous delivery of joules from the sun to the earth may be needed to promote plant and animal life, but light signals from distant stars need only extremely low power to be useful. In toasting one slice of bread, an electric toaster uses 1,000 watts of electric power for a minute. Compare that with the 50 watts of radio power used by the space probe Pioneer V, communication with which took place in 1960 at a distance of 22.5 million miles.

We have extremely sensitive detectors of waves in the ear and the eye. The ear can detect pressure waves where the power is only about 10^{-16} W/cm². The best human eyes have a sensitivity of about the same order of magnitude to waves of green light.

Since one of the purposes of this book is to present the basic concepts of atomic physics, and since light waves emanate from vibrations set up within the atom, one of our strongest reasons for stressing vibrations and waves is that without an understanding of them we shall be unable to handle even the most elementary theory of atomic structure. And now, to understand waves, we must first understand vibrations.

13.3. The Terminology and Kinematics of Vibrations

Many of the words we use in describing waves are the same as those we use in describing vibrations. The reason is simple: vibrations can set up waves. A wave is something that happens to a lot of particles along a whole line—for example, on a rope or on a spring—or to all the particles on a two-dimensional manifold of points, such as the surface of a lake. But a vibration is something that occurs to one body or one particle moving about a central point.

As a representative of all vibrations we consider the motion of a body suspended on a spring (Fig. 13.3). We are going to treat the body as if it were a particle; you may, if you like, consider just one point in it—for example, its center of mass. At first we find the body in equilibrium. Let the center of mass, when the body is resting, be the origin of our x axis. Now suppose that you stretch the spring by pulling the body down through distance A. When you release it, it oscillates up and down in a straight line in a vibratory motion. This is called **simple harmonic motion.**

There are some observations we can make immediately. If the distance from the equilibrium position to any other position of the body during the motion is called its displacement, x, we observe that the displacement is changing continuously with time. Sometimes it is positive and sometimes it is negative, and at other times it is zero. If you determined the time needed for one cycle by measuring the total time for 50 cycles and dividing by 50, and if you repeated this experiment many times, you would discover that the time for one oscillation, called the **period,** T, is quite constant. There are, then, some quantities that vary

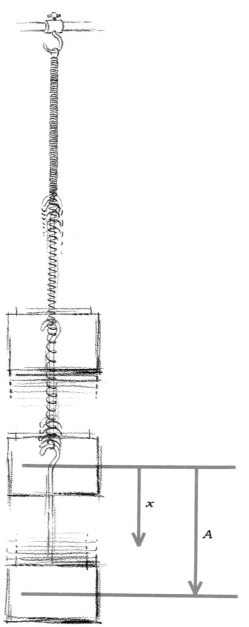

FIG. 13.3. *A vibrating body on a spring executes simple harmonic motion.*

and others that remain constant during this vibration.

It is important to understand clearly which quantities are variables and which are constants. Without the damping effect of friction we should find that the **amplitude,** A, which is the maximum displacement, is a constant. The period, T, is also a constant. Since the **displacement,** x, is a function of time, t, both x and t are variables. We tabulate for convenience the symbols we shall use:

x The displacement: the distance from the equilibrium position to any position of the particle in simple harmonic motion.
t The time.
A The amplitude: the magnitude of the largest displacement; a constant.
T The period: the time required for one complete cycle, or round trip; a constant.

We have seen before that a complete description of the motion of a moving body requires that the displacement be given as a function of time. This is a mathematical problem. We shall eventually be able to express $x = \mathrm{f}(t)$; that is, we shall be able to state the explicit mathematical formula that gives x as a function of time. But we can get a qualitative feeling for this function without putting down any equations at all.

Simply observe that x increases with time up to a certain point; then it decreases to zero; then, turning negative, it reaches a maximum negative value; then it starts coming back. But, if we look more carefully, or if we look at a body that is executing simple harmonic motion much more slowly, we shall observe that the body is moving fastest as it passes the origin and slowest at the ends of the oscillation. It makes this transition gradually, and so it should not come as a surprise that the graph of x against t looks like Figure 13.4.A.

If that figure describes accurately the behavior of a vibrating body on a spring, we should, with our knowledge that the slope of a displacement curve is numerically equal at each point to the velocity, be able to deduce from it the velocity curve. At the instant of time marked b, the slope is zero. Therefore the corresponding velocity should be zero at that point, and it is so indicated at point b' in part B of the figure. At d the slope is again zero; so the velocity curve must go through zero at that point (*d'*). The slope is positive from *a* to *b* and negative from *b* to *c*; therefore the velocity must be positive from *a'* to *b'* and negative from *b'* to *c'*; and so on. Study the relation between the velocity curve (B) and the displacement curve (A). We are using only the fact that the slope of a displacement curve at a point gives the value of the velocity at that point.

Now let us examine the physical implications of the velocity curve (B) to see if they check with our qualitative observations. It says that the velocity must have its highest positive value as the body goes through the origin in one direction and its highest negative value as the body goes through the origin in the opposite direction. In other words, the speed must be greatest at the origin. This seems reasonable enough. Curve B also says that the velocity is zero at *b'* and *d'*, which correspond to the points where the displacement is greatest, and thus that the speed is zero at the ends of the oscillation. This seems reasonable if we consider that the velocity is positive as the end is being approached and negative immediately thereafter, suggesting that it must have gone through zero somewhere in between. We can safely say of curve B that it does not contradict any qualitative observations we make of a vibrating body on a spring.

If we repeat the argument (that is, if we use the fact that the slope of the velocity curve at a point is the acceleration at that point), we can draw curve C, on which an ordinate represents the slope of the velocity curve at that instant of time. Since the slope of curve B is negative as we go from *a'* to *b'*, the values of the ordinates from *a''* to *b''* are all negative, but increasing in magnitude. The slope of curve B is zero at times *a'* and *c'* and *e'*; the acceleration curve must therefore go through zero at the corresponding instants of time, *a''*, *c''*, and *e''*.

Curve C tells us that the acceleration has its maximum values at the ends of the oscillation and zero value at the origin. At first glance, this may not seem reasonable. How can the motion have its greatest acceleration at the ends of the swing, where the velocity is zero? If we had

asked, "Where do we observe the greatest *change* in velocity?" it might seem clearer why the acceleration is greatest at the ends.

Still another feature of curve C is that it looks very similar to curve A except for a change in sign. Wherever *x* is positive, *a* is negative.

Not all oscillations in one dimension would have graphs like those of Figure 13.4. Assume that two boys playing catch throw the ball back and forth in a straight line. The ball oscillates, all right; and we can certainly see that the oscillation has a displacement, a period, and an amplitude; but, when we consider that the velocity between the two boys is almost a constant, it is apparent that the velocity curve could not look like Figure 13.4.B. (It is left for you, in Prob. 13.7, to analyze this motion qualitatively.)

The particular vibration we have been studying happens to be the simplest of a very general type.

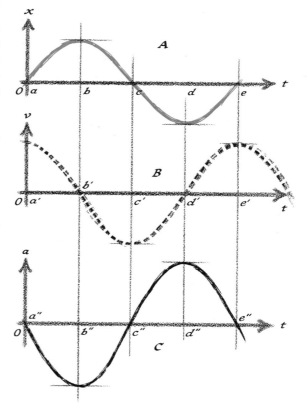

FIG. 13.4. *Displacement, velocity, and acceleration in simple harmonic motion.*

The complex vibrations that produce musical sounds can be shown to be combinations of vibrations like those of Figure 13.4, to which, for this reason, the term "simple harmonic motion" is applied. So far we have studied the kinematics of simple harmonic motion. We may now consider the dynamics of this kind of motion in a qualitative way.

13.4. Dynamics of Vibrations (Qualitative)

Vibrations can be set up in many ways other than with an object on a spring. If you hold a kitchen knife blade against the edge of a table so that the handle sticks out over the edge, and pluck the handle, it will make the knife vibrate. If you pluck a string of a guitar, it will vibrate. If you disturb the equilibrium of a chandelier, it will vibrate. If you push a child on a swing and thus displace him from his equilibrium position, he will swing back and forth when you release him; in other words, he too will vibrate.

The swing is a good illustration because most of us have had some experience with it; so we shall imagine an experiment. A small child sits in a swing. (The weight of the child is supported by the vertical component of the tension in the rope. When you push him horizontally, you push against the horizontal component of the tension.) It does not take a great force to push him horizontally and hold him in his new position. But it takes more force to push him two feet in a horizontal direction than to push him one foot from the origin in the same direction. The very fact that you push the child away from the origin indicates that a *restoring force* is acting on him. This is the first characteristic of simple harmonic vibrations. They require a force that points toward the origin of the oscillation. If you pulled the child instead of pushing him, you would again realize that it takes a greater force to pull him two feet from the origin than to pull him one foot from it. Again the restoring force points toward the origin. This, then, is the first requirement for a vibration: a restoring force.

Now suppose that you hold the child away from the origin and then release him. When you

do, the oscillation begins, and the swing begins to pick up speed. As it approaches the bottom of its path, its speed approaches a maximum. But since the horizontal force is least near the origin, the continued motion of the swing depends upon inertia. A body in motion, if not interfered with, continues its state of motion; so the swing, moving along almost horizontally near the bottom of its path, overshoots the origin. The inertia of the child and the swing keeps them going forward; but, as they pass the origin, the restoring force begins to slow them down and continues to do so until they reach the other end of the path, and then the restoring force speeds them up so that once again the speed is high as they pass the origin in the opposite direction. They overshoot and go back to where they started from, and now the cycle is ready to repeat itself. The second requirement, then, is *inertia;* the body must have inertial mass. (Inertia does not enter into the kinematical description of the motion of the shadow of a vibrating tree limb, and it is a hindrance to the motion of a piston, but it plays an important role in a large class of dynamically sustained vibrations.)

Finally, we have all observed that a swing put into motion eventually comes to rest of its own accord. We attribute this to the retarding effect of friction between the swing and the air and at various points of the swing. It is true that, if you reduce friction, a vibration does not die out so readily. If the friction is too great, the vibration cannot take place; that is, your system will not complete even one cycle. As an illustration, consider what would happen to a pendulum hanging in a very thick oil. If you displaced the bob and then released it, it would move toward the equilibrium position; but, if the oil were thick enough, it would not arrive with enough velocity to overshoot. The third requirement for vibration, then, is that the *retarding force* be small.

Simple harmonic motion requires that the restoring force be *directly proportional* to the displacement in magnitude but opposite in sense. A spring obeys this requirement quite accurately within certain limits; in other words, the graph of the restoring force (which is equal in magnitude to the force required to stretch the spring), when

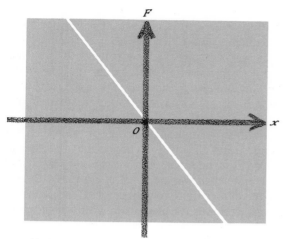

FIG. 13.5. *Plot of force against displacement in simple harmonic motion.*

plotted against the displacement, is a straight line going through the origin (Fig. 13.5). (The slope is negative because the force is negative when x is positive and positive when x is negative.) This linear relation between force and displacement is required for the kind of vibration called simple harmonic motion. (Not all vibrations require this kind of force-distance relation.)

We are now ready to add one more item of plausibility to Figure 13.4, in which, as we observed, a is proportional to $-x$. But, according to Newton's second law ($f = ma$), the magnitude of a is simply proportional to the magnitude of f. So we can say that a comparison of curves A and C of Figure 13.4 lends weight to the idea that, in simple harmonic motion, f is proportional to $-x$; that is, that the magnitude of the restoring force is proportional to the displacement, which is exactly what Figure 13.5 demands. The negative sign indicates that the force vector has a sense opposite to that of the displacement vector. (A mathematical discussion of simple harmonic motion appears in § 14.5.)

Many simple experiments can be performed with linked rubber bands instead of springs. It is easy to convince yourself experimentally that rubber bands, for sizable displacements, do not follow the curve of Figure 13.5 accurately, but for very small displacements they follow the curve in the vicinity of the origin. We can therefore use rubber bands instead of springs if we use only small displacements in our vibrations.

If you hang an iron washer from a rubber-band chain, the vertical vibration has a definite period. If you hang two washers from the chain, you will observe that the period definitely increases. We say, qualitatively, that doubling the number of washers has doubled the mass and hence the inertia, or the sluggishness, of the system. We therefore expect the round trip, or the complete cycle, to take longer, and it does. If you then take a piece of unstretchable string, hang a washer from it, and make it oscillate as a pendulum, you find that it has a definite, measurable period; but now, if you keep the length of the string the same and use two washers instead of one, you observe that the period hardly changes at all. You have increased the inertia of the system. Why doesn't it take longer to complete one cycle? (The complete answer to this is left for you to work out in Prob. 13.6.)

The motion of the pendulum bob and that of a body suspended from a spring will be used over and over again as examples of simple harmonic motion. It is true that the pendulum bob moves in a circular arc and not in a straight line; but, if the total swing of the pendulum is kept small, the path of the bob approximates a straight line. For small amplitudes, the restoring force that acts on the pendulum bob may be shown to obey a relation like that of Figure 13.5. (Even if it has the three requirements of restoring force, inertia, and low friction, a system will not vibrate of its own accord. You must put energy into it— as, for example, by stretching the spring.)

With this introduction we are ready to pass from vibrations to waves.

13.5. The Language of Waves

If a tuning fork is hit and examined under a magnifier, its prongs are seen to vibrate. They set up invisible waves that leave the region of the fork and become more nearly spherical as they move out. The waves are produced by the vibrations of the fork and can be detected by their effect on the listener's ear. Unfortunately, they are invisible; so we must seek easier examples to begin with. Another disadvantage is that they are three-dimensional; they move out in all directions. So we begin with waves that are confined to a one-dimensional path.†

A long piece of rope stretched horizontally between two posts can carry a pulse. If you strike the rope a sharp lateral blow, you produce a local distortion that travels the length of the rope rather rapidly (Fig. 13.6). (The points in the distorted region depart temporarily from their original one-dimensional positions.) The pulse is probably reflected from the farther post, returning to its starting point and then to the nearer post, where it is reflected again. The cycle continues until the energy is dissipated.

Reflection is an important property of waves, but it becomes a disturbing element in our elementary introduction. If you took one end of the rope and moved your hand in simple harmonic

† An undisturbed stretched string is a one-dimensional path; a stretched membrane—a drum-head—is a two-dimensional medium; the water in a swimming pool fills a three-dimensional region. One variable (x) suffices to locate a point on the string, two (x, y) to locate a point on the drum-head, and three (x, y, z) to locate a point in the swimming pool.

motion at right angles to the length of the rope, you would see a train of waves leaving your hand and moving along the rope, but reflected waves would probably begin interfering with the ones that you were sending out, and the pattern would become somewhat jumbled. We need to avoid the reflected wave at first if we are to find out what a wave really is.

Another very simple carrier of waves is the spiral spring that is sold under the trade name Slinky. One model of this spring can be stretched over more than thirty feet. If it is allowed to rest on the floor, friction will prevent the reflected waves from interfering much with our demonstrations. If the friction were too great, the damping effect would, of course, be too great, and the spring would not carry waves at all. We therefore require a small amount of friction.

In Figure 13.7 we are looking down on part of a Slinky that is fixed at end B. Someone moves end A by hand in approximately simple harmonic motion in a direction perpendicular to the length of the spring. If many cycles of this vibration are performed, we see a train of waves passing along the spring from A to B. These are **transverse waves**—that is, waves in which the vibrations

FIG. 13.6. *Producing a pulse in a stretched rope. You can find the speed of the pulse by dividing the distance covered by the elapsed time.*

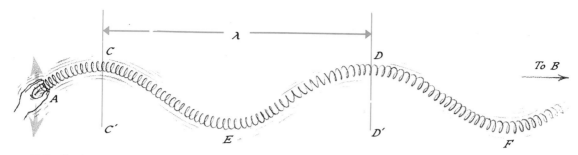

FIG. 13.7. *Studying transverse waves with a spiral spring lying on the floor. The experiment works well on a smooth floor. You can increase the speed of propagation by increasing the tension of the spring.*

take place at right angles to the direction of propagation. What we observe as we produce vibrations at A is that crests and troughs are formed in the spring (we shall call them that even though in the example everything happens on the plane of the floor, making crests and troughs interchangeable), that these travel at a uniform rate from A to B, and that there is a uniform distance between two successively formed crests (C, D) or troughs (E, F). This distance, symbolized by the Greek letter λ, is called the **wavelength.**

The **frequency** of the vibration at A is simply the number of cycles per second. We use the Greek letter ν (nu) for the frequency. Remembering that the period, T, is the time for a complete cycle (seconds per cycle), we see that the frequency is simply the inverse of the period. In symbols,

$$\nu = \frac{1}{T} \qquad [13.1$$

(The unit for T is the second; the unit for ν is therefore sec^{-1}. We say that ν is the number of cycles per second; but the number of cycles does not have the physical dimensions of mass, length, or time; hence ν has the physical dimension T^{-1}.) We speak of the frequency, not only of a vibration, but also of the wave it produces because every point on the wave vibrates with the same frequency. If you concentrate your attention on points C and D of the spring (Fig. 13.7) by tying little red ribbons to them, you observe that each vibrates at right angles to the direction of propagation. All points on the spring, in fact, execute simple harmonic motion if A executes simple harmonic motion. If A began to vibrate in some other way, C and D also, at different times, would

begin to vibrate in that way. This is one of the elementary facts about waves that you should understand right away: that, in an undamped system, whatever begins to happen at point A in the medium that carries the wave will begin to happen later at C and still later at D.

Let us assume that we are talking about an ideal situation in which there is no friction and in which the medium is infinitely long. The vibration at A is, then, identical with the vibrations at C, D, or any other point, such as E. If we take a series of snapshots, we observe that the pattern shown in Figure 13.7 moves to the right, each time, by a certain amount. Again I repeat: the particle at C does not move to the right, but the crest that we saw at C in the figure moves from C toward D. While the particle at C is executing one complete cycle of its vibration, ending it by rising to the top of a new crest, the crest that started at C is moving through the distance λ, or one wavelength. I have already defined the wavelength as the distance between two adjacent crests of a transverse wave, but this is not the only way to express the concept of wavelength. It is not, in fact, the best way, for it cannot be applied to other kinds of waves, such as the longitudinal waves that I shall soon describe.

Let us again concentrate our attention on points C and D of Figure 13.7. Forgetting the flow of the wave motion between them and looking only at these points, we observe that they move together. When C reaches the position C', its position of maximum negative displacement, we find that D has reached D', a similar position in its vibration. Two points that always have the same displacement and velocity at the same instant

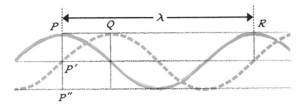

FIG. 13.8. *Wave produced by simple harmonic motion: relations among velocity, period, and wavelength.*

are, we say, **in phase** (or in the same phase). If we compare C with E, which is halfway between C and D, we observe that C and E are always moving in opposite directions. They go through their equilibrium points at the same instant, but at every other instant one is moving in a positive direction and the other is moving in a negative direction. We say that C and E are completely **out of phase.** The other points between C and D are neither completely in phase nor completely out of phase with C. Later we shall associate a number with the phase of each of these, but that is not necessary right now. Having defined "in phase" and "out of phase," we can now say that a wavelength is the shortest distance between two points on a wave that are in phase with each other.

So far we have established the following: that each particle vibrates at right angles to the direction of propagation of the wave; that two particles that are near each other reach their maximum displacements at slightly different times; that two particles that are separated by the distance λ reach their maximum displacements at the same instant; and that two particles that are separated by the distance λ/2 move so that one reaches its maximum positive displacement as the other reaches its maximum negative displacement.

We can also show that the time required for a crest to move over to the position presently occupied by the next crest is exactly equal to T, the period of vibration. While the particle at P (Fig. 13.8) is going through one complete cycle, down to P′, then to P″, and back all the way to P, the crest is moving to the right from point P to point R. When the particle at P has reached its equilibrium position, P′, the crest has moved from P to Q. All of this is happening in a continuous

way, of course. The particle at P goes to P′, to P″, and back in simple harmonic motion, and all the other particles of the wave execute their simple harmonic motions at slightly different times, but they do so in such a way that the crest travels from P to R in time T. The wave velocity, therefore, is simply the distance λ divided by the time, T, required to cover that distance. So we have a simple relation:

$$v = \frac{\lambda}{T} \qquad [13.2$$

Or, using equation 13.1, we may write this as

$$v = \nu\lambda \qquad [13.3$$

This very simple relation applies to many different kinds of waves: to waves on the surface of water, to sound waves in air, to sound waves in a solid or a liquid, to radio waves, light rays, and x-rays. We have used a simple transverse wave in a spiral spring to illustrate the terminology of wave motion, but we can apply these remarks to other wave-carrying media, even if the waves are invisible, if the terms "wave velocity," "period," "frequency," and "phase" still have meanings similar to those we have considered.

13.6. Kinds of Waves

There are different ways of classifying waves. The very fact that we can have waves on a rope or on a Slinky or on the surface of the water indicates that one way to distinguish waves would be to consider the medium in which they are propagated. We have waves propagated by solids, liquids, and gases and can distinguish them accordingly. Another way to distinguish waves is to consider the fact that we have eyes and ears—detectors that are sensitive, respectively, to the two kinds of waves that we call light and sound. It would be difficult to classify light waves by our first method, for they can be propagated even in a vacuum: light waves do not require a medium with material particles executing simple harmonic motions.

We already know that we can have electric and magnetic fields in an evacuated space. If an electric field can be caused to reach positive and

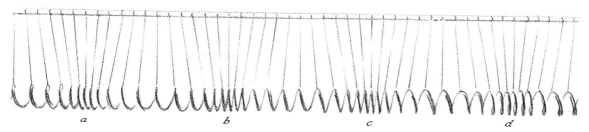

FIG. 13.9. *Longitudinal wave in a suspended spiral spring.*

negative values at a point, and if all the points in a region can be caused to simulate the electrical vibrations with due regard to phase, perhaps the concept of a wave consisting of electric fields can be understood. At any rate, we believe today that light and x-rays and radio waves and many similar waves are actually electromagnetic waves that do not require a material medium for their propagation. The purpose of our discussion so far has been to introduce the terminology of simple vibrations and waves so that we may employ it in our treatment of light and other waves of the electromagnetic spectrum.

There is still another way in which we may classify waves. They can be transverse or longitudinal or a mixture of the two. If we hang a Slinky from a horizontal rod by many thin verti-

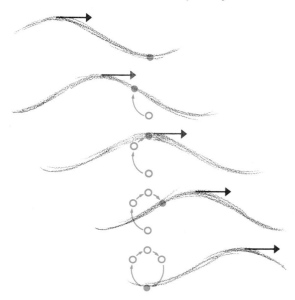

FIG. 13.10. *Wave that has both longitudinal and transverse characteristics.*

cal strings (Fig. 13.9), and if we put the end near *a* into simple harmonic motion in the direction of the spring's axis, a wave consisting of *condensations* and *rarefactions* will be propagated from left to right; that is, there will be regions where the coils are close to one another (condensations) and other regions where the coils are farther from one another (rarefactions). Two adjacent condensations, such as those centered at *a* and *b*, are separated by one wavelength; that is, the distance *ab* is the shortest distance between two points that are vibrating in phase. Once again we observe that, as the train of waves is formed, the motions of *a* are mimicked by all the points of the Slinky at successive times: *a* moves back and forth in the *x* direction, later so does *b*, and still later so do *c* and then *d*. We assume here that there is no reflected wave; strictly speaking, we demand a spring of infinite length. Each particle executes simple harmonic motion if *a* does. If *a* executes some other kind of vibration, all the other points execute that kind of vibration. If we limit ourselves to simple harmonic motions, we can continue using the terms "frequency," "period," "displacement," "amplitude," and "phase" just as we did before. A wave in which the vibrations take place along the direction of propagation, as in the example just discussed, is called a **longitudinal wave**.

Certain kinds of water waves have both longitudinal and transverse characteristics. As the wave passes by, a single molecule of water on its surface (represented by a solid green dot in Fig. 13.10) moves along an elliptic path. The positions of the dot at five successive instants show that the molecule moves both left and right and up and down; that is, it has components of motion both in the *x* directions and in the *y* directions. If, instead of

FIG. 13.11. *Profile of a wave with both transverse and longitudinal characteristics.*

concentrating on one molecule at successive instants, we focus our attention on all the molecules along a single line of the surface at the same instant, we get a snapshot of the waves' profile (Fig. 13.11). The ellipses are drawn for reference only. At a later instant the reference chords of all the ellipses will have rotated through the same angle, and the curve connecting their points will represent the new profile of the waves.

Since there are many waves whose crests and troughs are invisible to us, either because the distance between them is very short or because the vibrating particles (such as air molecules) are invisible, one of the first questions we seek to answer about a wave is whether it is transverse or longitudinal or both. Sound waves, for example, are longitudinal; this can be deduced from the kinds of stresses that gases and fluids in general can sustain or can be proved by experiment. Light waves are transverse, but the proof of this, either theoretical or experimental, requires a considerable degree of sophistication.

13.7. Properties Common to All Waves

One last set of terms must be introduced here because it applies to all kinds of waves. The terms are "reflection," "refraction," "diffraction," and "interference." I could illustrate these with sound and light and radar and other waves, but we are going to limit ourselves to one-dimensional and two-dimensional waves that can be seen with the unaided eye.

Consider **reflection.** If you mount a Slinky in the proper way to minimize friction, it is easy to show that a pulse, either transverse or longitudinal, will be reflected from the fixed end. Even a more complicated pulse, starting as two complete cycles at the free end, will travel to the fixed end and return, exhibiting two crests all the way out and all the way back.

To illustrate reflection with water waves, we resort to the ripple tank (Fig. 13.12). Figure 13.13 shows a train of parallel waves moving from left to right, hitting boundary *AB* and bouncing off in the direction *CD*. We observe that the frequency and wavelength remain the same after reflection and that only the direction has changed. The reflection of light is a very familiar occur-

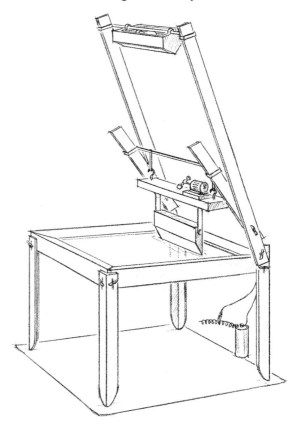

FIG. 13.12. *A ripple tank: The ripples are produced by the wooden wedge that dips into the water. The wedge is attached to a platform suspended by vertical rubber bands. When the little electric motor on the platform rotates with a weight mounted eccentrically on its shaft, it produces vibrations that are transmitted to the water. A point source of light, mounted above, casts sharp shadows of the ripples on the table below.*

rence; the reflection of other electromagnetic waves is utilized in many ways. Radar waves, for example, when reflected by objects, bring us information about those objects. Radar waves originating on the earth have been bounced off the moon and even off the sun's corona. Reflection, we see, is an important characteristic of waves.

The effect of a change of speed on the wavelength can be predicted from equation 13.3. If the frequency remains constant, a great speed implies a great wavelength. An interesting experiment is to connect two long rubber tubes of different linear densities (measured, for example, in kg/m) so that transverse waves generated in one pass into the other. In one tube (Fig. 13.14) the wavelength is λ_1; in the other it is λ_2. From the fact that the two tubes are connected, the frequency is the same in both tubes. The fact that

the wavelength has diminished in the second tube therefore indicates, according to equation 13.3, that the speed also must have diminished. Experiments show that, as waves travel from A to B and then on toward C, two things happen: the energy of the waves is partly reflected into tube AB and partly transmitted into tube BC.

All these phenomena have their counterparts in other waves. We shall see later, for example, that the speed of light diminishes as it passes from air into glass or water. A consequence of this change of speed is **refraction.** In Figure 13.15 we see parallel waves in a ripple tank passing a boundary, represented by the dashed line AB, beyond which the tank is shallower; the direction of the train has been changed, and the wavelength has become shorter. These two changes are related to each other. The fact that the wavelength has become shorter is experimental proof that the waves travel more slowly after passing the boundary. The medium on both sides of the boundary may be water, but waves travel slower in shallow water than in deeper water; there is therefore a change in speed as the waves pass from left to right across the boundary, and there is also a corresponding change in direction. Refraction, then, is the change in the direction of a wave as it passes from one medium to a medium in which the speed of propagation is different.

Figure 13.16 illustrates **diffraction.** Parallel waves, approaching from the left, pass through a small opening and beyond it spread out into approximately concentric arcs. If the opening is very small, the spreading is very noticeable. If the opening is very large (Fig. 13.17), we observe this spreading only behind the boundary; opposite the opening we see what looks like a con-

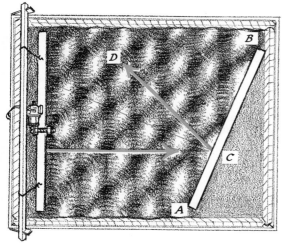

FIG. 13.13. *Reflection of wave fronts.*

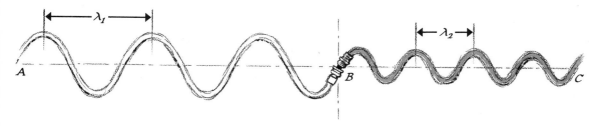

FIG. 13.14. *Change of speed as a wave passes from a lighter to a denser medium. (Filling tube BC with sand has increased its mass per unit length.)*

tinuation of the parallel waves that came from the left.

One of the early puzzles in the history of physics involved the nature of light. Because light could be reflected and refracted, it was thought that it must be a wave. But particles also can be reflected and refracted; you can bounce a ball off a wall, and you can show that, if a ball passes from a region where it moves at one speed to a region where it moves at a different speed, its path will be bent, or refracted. (An experimental way of

proving this is discussed in § 18.3.) Therefore, said the proponents of the particle theory of light, why bother with a wave theory when particles also exhibit refraction? But it was eventually shown that light can also be diffracted. Because the wavelength of light is very short (5×10^{-5} cm), the diffraction usually goes unnoticed. But the experimental evidence in favor of the wave theory of light became overwhelming in the nineteenth century.

The last of the special terms that apply to

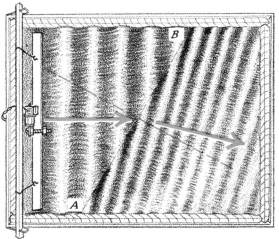

FIG. 13.15. *Refraction of waves as they pass into a medium in which they travel more slowly—shallower water in this case, the change in depth being produced by a sheet of glass laid on the bottom of the right side of the ripple tank with its edge along the line AB.*

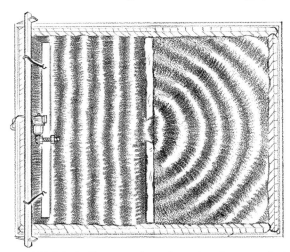

FIG. 13.16. *Diffraction through a slit that is a little longer than the wavelength.*

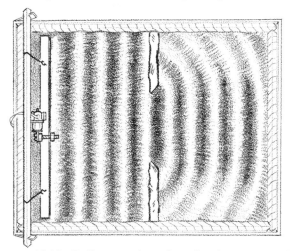

FIG. 13.17. *Diffraction through a slit that is several times longer than the wavelength.*

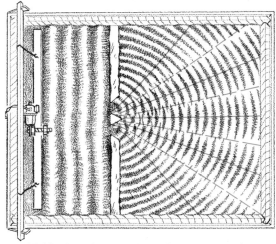

FIG. 13.18. *Interference of wavelets emerging from two slits.*

waves is **interference.** The term is somewhat misleading: in some cases illustrating it we may seem to be trying to demonstrate non-interference. If, for example, you take a long Slinky and cause identical pulses to originate at each end simultaneously, the two pulses will move toward the middle, momentarily reinforce each other there, and then go on their way as if one had no effect on the other. (A similar result can be seen with ripples on a smooth surface of water.) If the Slinky experiment is repeated so that the pulses meet out of phase with each other, their effects cancel momentarily, but after this they continue in their original directions as if they had met no opposition. This ability of waves to meet, reinforce one another if they are in phase, or cancel one another if they are out of phase, is common to all kinds of waves. It is the essence of interference.

In Figure 13.18 we see a ripple tank with waves going through two small openings. Each opening sets up its new source of wavelets on the right. We observe that there are relatively quiet regions. These are the regions in which **destructive interference** has taken place: the waves have arrived out of phase at those points and have tended to cancel one another. There are also regions in which **constructive interference** has taken place: the waves have arrived in phase and have reinforced one another. In still other regions there has been partial cancellation or partial reinforcement. The over-all result is called an **interference pattern.**

To show that something is a wave, even if we cannot readily see it with our eyes, we must show that it exhibits all four of these characteristics: reflection, refraction, diffraction, and interference.

Sound waves and light waves and x-rays and radio waves pass that test. New kinds of waves may be discovered, but one thing is certain: we shall not have proved that they are really waves until we have shown that they exhibit these characteristics.

13.8. Summary

A mechanical system having inertia, a restoring force, and low friction will vibrate if displaced from its equilibrium position and released.

The displacement, amplitude, period, frequency, and variations in velocity and acceleration characteristic of simple harmonic motion are well illustrated by a weight vibrating on a long helical spring.

In an elastic medium such as a stretched rope a vibration at one point sets up a wave. If one point vibrates in simple harmonic motion, all the other points will do approximately the same. The shortest distance between two points that have the same phase is called a wavelength. The speed of propagation, the frequency, and the wavelength obey the relation $v = \nu\lambda$, which is characteristic of all waves.

A wave is transverse if the vibration of the particles takes place at right angles to the direction of propagation and longitudinal if the vibration is parallel to the direction of propagation.

Ripples on the surface of water can be used to illustrate reflection, refraction, diffraction, and interference. These are four of the important characteristics of all waves in two- and three-dimensional media.

We study waves because of their great importance in atomic physics.

Problems

13.1. Explain why the curtain in Fig. 13.2.B moves to the left even though the pulse moves from left to right. Describe how you would measure the speed of such a pulse.

13.2. Suppose that a heavy object on the ground is tied to the rope of Fig. 13.6, about two feet from the farther post, by means of a vertical cord that is normally under tension. Describe what you should do to the rope at the near end in order to lift momentarily the weight at the other end without removing the rope from the poles. Would this be a way to prove experimentally that a wave carries energy? (It takes work to lift a heavy object.)

13.3. Which of the following cannot be illustrated by use of the Slinky as in Fig. 13.7?—displacement, amplitude, frequency, period, wavelength, reflection, refraction, diffraction, interference.

13.4. It is said that Galileo deduced some of the laws of the pendulum by observing an oscillating chandelier and timing it with his pulse. In the same spirit of inquiry make a simple pendulum by tying a small dense object like a ring to a string, and measure the *average* speed of the ring as it oscillates as follows: Use a watch or electric clock as a timer. Keeping the amplitude constant at 20 cm, use pendulum string of 20, 40, and 80 cm (or lengths proportional to these), and compute the time for one complete cycle by measuring the time for many cycles and dividing by the number of cycles. Which length gives the greatest average speed? Are there instants in each case when the speed of the ring is zero during the oscillation? If there are, where is the ring at such instants?

13.5. The body of Fig. 13.3 is pulled down, as described in the text, through distance A and is released. (Consider an upward displacement as positive.) The period is T.

1. What is the distance between the two most widely separated positions of the body?

2. What is the time required for the body to travel between those two positions?

3. What is the average speed during that interval?

4. What is the exact value of the displacement at $t = 3T$?

5. What is the exact displacement at $t = 3.5T$?

6. What is the exact displacement at $t = 3.25T$? (Assume that the body was released at $t = 0$.)

13.6. 1. Imagine two identical pendulums; both have the same length, and their bobs are alike in mass. If you release them together, they will move together thereafter. After tying the two bobs loosely together with a light thread, you could repeat the experiment, and the thread would not break. Finally, if the two bobs were bolted firmly together, they would still vibrate in unison. Pursue the imaginary experiment far enough to convince yourself that doubling the mass of a pendulum does not affect its period.

2. Now consider two identical springs suspended vertically (as in Fig. 13.3) with identical weights. Repeat the argument used in part 1 to the point where the springs are oscillating in unison with a light thread between the weights. Now criticize the following statement: The period of a system consisting of a spring and a body attached to it is independent of the mass of the body.

3. Confirm the conclusions reached in parts 1 and 2

by simple experiments using things like strings, rings, and rubber-band chains.

13.7. Two boys, A and B, are playing catch with a ball. A stands at $x = -5$ m and B at $x = 5$ m. Assume that the ball travels in a straight line at a constant speed of 10 m/sec and that it spends very little time at either end.

1. Plot what you think would be the graphs of displacement, velocity, and acceleration against time for several throws of the ball. The velocity graph is perhaps the easiest to start with. The displacement and acceleration graphs can then be drawn to correspond with it, using the principles of Chap. 8.

2. What is the period of this oscillation?

3. What is the frequency?

4. What is the amplitude?

13.8. The plot of displacement y against time for a golf ball dropped from rest and bouncing on a hard pavement is shown in Fig. 13.19. (The ball is actually moving in a vertical line, but the plot looks like the trajectory of a ball moving with a small constant speed to the right.) Using the principles of Chap. 8, make plots of velocity and acceleration against time. For convenience in interpretation they should have identical units on the time axis and be placed one above the other.

13.9. In common usage the word "wave" may refer to the breakers at the seashore, but the use of the word in physics (as regards the up-and-down motion of the water in the sea) is reserved for the kind of

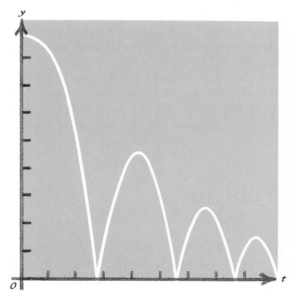

FIG. 13.19

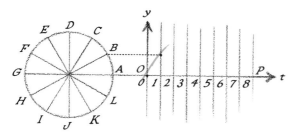

FIG. 13.20

motion possessed by points on the surface far from the region where the breakers form. At such a point a blob of liquid dye is poured onto the surface.

1. Will it travel up and down?

2. Will it arrive at the shore in a fairly short time?

3. Will it ever have an instantaneous velocity that points away from the shore?

4. Will it move in simple harmonic motion? (See Fig. 13.10 for a hint.)

13.10. 1. The lowest audible frequency for a sound wave is about 20 cycles/sec, and the highest is about 20,000 cycles/sec. The speed of sound waves in air is about 331 m/sec. What are the wavelengths of sound waves of these extreme frequencies?

2. The speed of ripples in shallow water is roughly 10 cm/sec. What frequency of vibration would produce ripples with a wavelength of 2 cm?

3. The radio broadcast band starts at 550 kilocycles per second. The speed of radio waves is 3×10^8 m/sec. What is the wavelength of such waves?

13.11. Here is a simple and instructive method for plotting simple harmonic motions.

1. Draw a circle (Fig. 13.20) of radius R. Draw radii to points on the circle, A, B, C, . . . , L, 30° apart, as shown. Extend the diameter GA to point P on the right. At point O on the line GAP erect a perpendicular. This is the axis of displacements (y). Let OP be the time (t) axis. Erect perpendiculars to OP at equal time intervals and label them 0, 1, 2, 3, etc. Associate the points A, B, C, etc. with the instants of time 0, 1, 2, etc. At $t = 0$ put the y coordinate of A (zero). On the line $t = 1$ put a point at the y coordinate of B ($R/2$); and so on. Connect all the points with a smooth curve. This is the graph of a simple harmonic motion.

2. Associate points A, B, C, etc. with $t = -1$, 0, 1, 2, etc., and draw another curve on the same set of axes.

3. Associate points A, B, C, etc. with $t = 1$, 2, 3, etc., and draw another curve. This method of drawing curves is applicable to waves as well as to vibrations.

13.12. Try to explain the following phenomena by the four basic characteristics of waves given at the end of the chapter. (An echo, for example, involves the property of reflection.)

1. Broadcast radio waves can travel several times round the earth before they are completely dissipated.

2. You can hear music from a loudspeaker even if it is in a different room.

3. If you hear a very distant explosion, you may hear a low-pitched roar rather than a sharp crack.

4. It is harder to detect the direction of the origin of a sound with one ear covered than with both uncovered.

5. If you look through a fine screen, such as a silk scarf or an umbrella, at a distant point source of light, it seems to have several side images, both up and down and to the sides.

6. Soon after you jump into a swimming pool, the entire water surface is covered with waves going in seemingly random directions.

7. A stick thrust through the surface of a calm pool appears bent.

Simple Vibrations: Mathematical Treatment

THE POWER of mathematics in physics is elegantly demonstrated in the treatment of vibrations. I shall discuss here, using elementary mathematics, the simplest of vibratory motions: simple harmonic motion. Whatever you learn here can be used later in consideration of more complex vibrations, many of which can be analyzed in terms of simple harmonic motions.

14.1. Simple Harmonic Motion

The straight-line motion that ensues when a body suspended from a spring is displaced vertically from its equilibrium position and released is, as we saw in Chapter 13, called simple harmonic motion (SHM). Since a spring produces a force, F, that depends on its stretch, x, according to the equation

$$F = -kx \qquad [14.1]$$

an equivalent definition of SHM says: **simple harmonic motion** occurs when the restoring force is proportional to the displacement. (See § 14.6 for a purely kinematic definition.)

Consider a body of mass m suspended from a spring (see Fig. 13.3). Although a gravitational force of magnitude mg is always acting on the body, the net force responsible for vibration is

$F = -kx$. (See Prob. 14.1.) The body is therefore subjected to a restoring force that is directly proportional to its displacement, and it will execute simple harmonic motion after being pulled down and released. (To avoid the complication of gravity, the SHM of a body on a frictionless horizontal surface was considered in § 11.1. For an experimental demonstration of SHM the suspended body of Fig. 13.3 is simpler and mathematically equivalent.)

The definition of simple harmonic motion given above involves its dynamics, and we wish first to consider only its kinematics. In order to delay the mathematical treatment, we resort to an experiment. In Figure 14.1, A marks the handle on a wheel that can rotate about its center, O, with constant angular velocity. Through a variable-speed drive we can adjust the frequency of rotation (in cycles per second) to match exactly the frequency of vibration of the body m, which vibrates (by definition) in SHM. We adjust the amplitude of vibration of m so that it equals exactly the radius OA. Finally we start m vibrating *in phase* with A; that is, as the shadow of A produced on a distant vertical wall by light coming from the left in a horizontal beam falls at P, we require that the shadow of m, at the same instant, also fall at P, and that the shadows of m and A move together at all times.

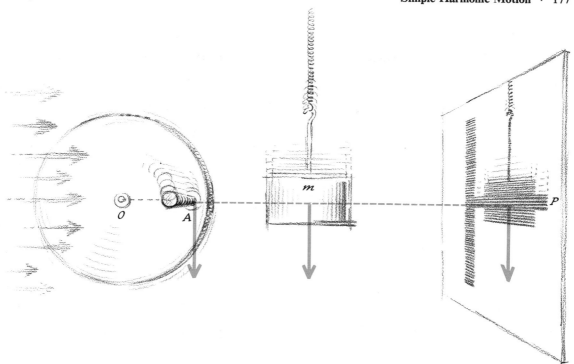

FIG. 14.1. *The shadow of the crank handle of a wheel rotating with constant angular velocity can be made to have the same instantaneous displacement, velocity, and acceleration as the shadow of a vibrating body suspended from a vertical spring.*

This requirement can be satisfied experimentally to a reasonable degree, and we proceed on the assumption that in the ideal case the coincidence of the shadows would be perfect. This means that the *vertical* motions of *A* and *m* are identical in displacement, velocity, and acceleration. We

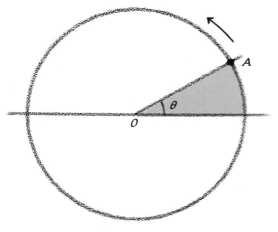

FIG. 14.2. *Illustrating the definition of constant angular velocity.*

can therefore shift the analysis from *m* to *A*. This is what I propose to do; but, in order to do so, we must learn the mathematical language of rotation.

Let us see, first, what **constant angular velocity** (a term used in the discussion of Fig. 14.1) means. Consider, in Figure 14.2, the motion of the radial spoke, *OA*. As the wheel turns in a counterclockwise direction, the spoke generates an angle, θ (theta), measured from the horizontal diameter. If the increment $\Delta\theta$ is generated in time Δt, the average angular velocity is defined as $\bar{\omega} = \Delta\theta/\Delta t$. (The expression

$$\lim_{\Delta t \to 0} \frac{\Delta\theta}{\Delta t}$$

represents the instantaneous angular velocity.) If equal increments of angle are always generated in equal times, $\Delta\theta/\Delta t$ must be constant. In this case the angular velocity, ω (omega), is simply

$$\omega = \frac{\Delta\theta}{\Delta t} \qquad [14.2$$

The unit of ω depends on the units of θ and t. A possible unit of ω is degrees per second, but, to

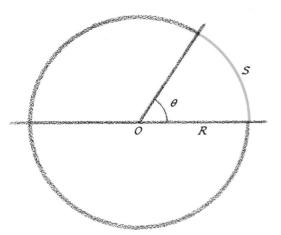

FIG. 14.3. *Illustrating the definition of radian.*

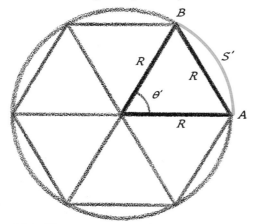

FIG. 14.4. *The construction makes it apparent that the angle θ' is 60°.*

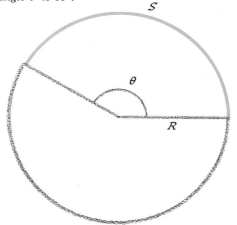

FIG. 14.5. *Illustrating the relations among arc, subtended angle, and radius.*

simplify the mathematical treatment, we shall measure ω in radians per second. Let us consider the radian as a measure of angles.

14.2. The Radian, Measure of Angles

Ever since the invention of the wheel, the translational movements of carts and carriages have been associated with the rotational motion of wheels. Every day the inhabitants of every civilized community depend upon the rotational motion of many different objects. These range all the way from the earth to the wheels that drive our automobiles. A unit of angular measure found to be very useful in all quantitative work involving rotation is the radian.

One **radian** is the angle subtended at the center of a circle by an arc equal in length to its radius. In Figure 14.3, for example, S has been drawn equal to R, and the angle θ is therefore one radian. It is obviously close to 60°, and a little thought will show that it is somewhat less. In Figure 14.4, a regular hexagon has been inscribed in a circle of radius R, and equilateral triangles have been drawn. The angle θ' is obviously 60°, but the arc S' must be greater than R, for R is the shortest distance between A and B. Therefore θ' must be a little greater than one radian. I shall now prove that one radian is 57.296°.

In Figure 14.5, θ represents any angle, not necessarily a radian. The expression

$$S = R\theta \qquad [14.3$$

is correct if θ is measured in radians. When $S = R$, equation 14.3 says that $\theta = 1$ (radian). It is obvious that the dependence of S on θ is linear (if you double θ, you expect S to be doubled); and, when θ is kept fixed, a linear dependence on R is reasonable.

If a radius turns through a complete revolution (360°), it generates the arc $S = 2\pi R$. From equation 14.3 we know that $\theta = S/R$ radians; it follows that $\theta = 2\pi R/R = 2\pi$ radians, from which we get the relation

$$360° = 2\pi \text{ radians} \qquad [14.4$$

from which we get

$$1 \text{ radian} = \frac{360°}{2\pi} = \frac{180}{\pi} \text{ degrees} \qquad [14.5$$

and, since $\pi = 3.1416$,

$$1 \text{ radian} = \frac{180°}{3.1416} = 57.296°$$

This conversion may be useful in some problems, but often the relations expressed in equation 14.5 are even more useful.

If R is constant, giving θ an increment, $\Delta\theta$, will produce an increment, ΔS, in S. Equation 14.3 therefore gives us

$$S + \Delta s = R(\theta + \Delta\theta) \qquad [14.6$$

Writing equation 14.3 beneath an expanded form of equation 14.6, we get

$$\begin{aligned} S + \Delta S &= R\theta + R\Delta\theta \\ S &= R\theta \\ \hline \Delta s &= R\Delta\theta \end{aligned}$$

Dividing both sides by Δt, we get

$$\frac{\Delta S}{\Delta t} = R\frac{\Delta\theta}{\Delta t} \qquad [14.7$$

which may be written, if ω is constant, as

$$v = R\omega \qquad [14.8$$

This equation expresses the magnitude of the tangential velocity, v, in terms of the angular velocity, ω. More generally, if ω is not constant, we obtain equation 14.8 from equation 14.7 by taking the limit as Δt approaches 0.

Starting with equation 14.8, and repeating an argument very similar to that used in arriving at equation 14.7, we get

$$\frac{\Delta v}{\Delta t} = R\frac{\Delta\omega}{\Delta t} \qquad [14.9$$

from which, by letting Δt approach 0, we get

$$a_T = R\alpha \qquad [14.10$$

Here a_T is the tangential acceleration, and α is the angular acceleration. If the angular velocity, ω, is constant, $\Delta\omega = 0$, and therefore $\alpha = 0$ and $a_T = 0$.

The tangential acceleration must not be confused with the centripetal (radial) acceleration, whose magnitude, $\omega^2 R$, we derived in the form v^2/R in Chapter 9. The centripetal acceleration, $\omega^2 R$, does not vanish when ω is constant. The tangential acceleration, a_T, depends on

$$\alpha = \lim_{\Delta t \to 0} \frac{\Delta\omega}{\Delta t}$$

and vanishes if α is zero.

EXAMPLE 14.1. We wish to find the angular velocity, in radians per second, of the minute hand of a clock. The average angular velocity is defined as $\Delta\theta/\Delta t$. When $\Delta\theta = 2\pi$ radians (once round),

$$\Delta t = 1 \text{ h} = 3{,}600 \text{ sec}$$

Therefore

$$\Delta\theta/\Delta t = \frac{2\pi \text{ rad}}{3{,}600 \text{ sec}} = 1.745 \times 10^{-3} \text{ rad/sec}$$

Note that θ, ω, and α play roles in rotation analogous to those of x, v, and a in translation. We put these and related terms in columns to exhibit the striking similarities. We assume that a in D and E, and α in D′ and E′, are constant.

x	θ	
(A) $v = \lim\limits_{\Delta t \to 0} \dfrac{\Delta x}{\Delta t}$	(A′) $\omega = \lim\limits_{\Delta t \to 0} \dfrac{\Delta\theta}{\Delta t}$	
(B) $x = \bar{v}t$	(B′) $\theta = \bar{\omega}t$	
(C) $a = \lim\limits_{\Delta t \to 0} \dfrac{\Delta v}{\Delta t}$	(C′) $\alpha = \lim\limits_{\Delta t \to 0} \dfrac{\Delta\omega}{\Delta t}$	$[14.11$
(D) $x = \frac{1}{2}at^2$	(D′) $\theta = \frac{1}{2}\alpha t^2$	
(E) $v = at$	(E′) $\omega = \alpha t$	

EXAMPLE 14.2. A grindstone wheel experiences a constant angular acceleration of 2 rad/sec². We wish to know what its angular velocity is at the end of three seconds if it starts from rest. We use equation 14.11.E′:

$$\omega = \alpha t = 2 \text{ rad/sec}^2 \times 3 \text{ sec} = 6 \text{ rad/sec}$$

14.3. The Trigonometric Functions† sin θ and cos θ if 0 ≤ θ ≤ π/2 Radians

Trigonometry, first used to solve right triangles, was later extended to the solution of all triangles. These applications are static; that is, they deal with triangles that are not changing in time. But the trigonometric functions sine and cosine, which were developed for these purposes, can serve us well in the discussion of vibrations. Let us define the sine of θ (written as sin θ) and the cosine of θ (written as cos θ) with reference to Figure 14.6. A circle of radius r is drawn with the center at O, the origin of a system of rectangular coordinates.

---

† This section and the next develop the trigonometric functions sin θ and cos θ. If you are well acquainted with them, you may go directly to § 14.5.

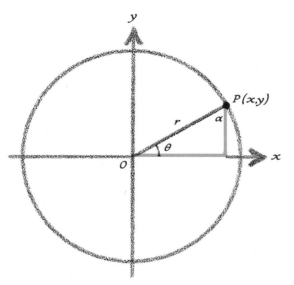

FIG. 14.6. *Illustrating the definitions of sin θ and cos θ.*

TABLE 14.1

θ	0° = 0 rad	30° = $\frac{\pi}{6}$ rad	45° = $\frac{\pi}{4}$ rad	60° = $\frac{\pi}{3}$ rad	90° = $\frac{\pi}{2}$ rad
sin θ	$\sqrt{\frac{0}{2}}$	$\sqrt{\frac{1}{2}}$	$\sqrt{\frac{2}{2}}$	$\sqrt{\frac{3}{2}}$	$\sqrt{\frac{4}{2}}$
cos θ	$\sqrt{\frac{4}{2}}$	$\sqrt{\frac{3}{2}}$	$\sqrt{\frac{2}{2}}$	$\sqrt{\frac{1}{2}}$	$\sqrt{\frac{0}{2}}$

TABLE 14.2

θ	0° = 0 rad	30° = $\frac{\pi}{6}$ rad	45° = $\frac{\pi}{4}$ rad	60° = $\frac{\pi}{3}$ rad	90° = $\frac{\pi}{2}$ rad
sin θ	0.000	0.500	0.707	0.866	1.000
cos θ	1.000	0.866	0.707	0.500	0.000

Point P on the circle has coordinates (x, y). The radius has swept out an angle, θ, measured from the positive side of the x axis. When θ is an angle in a right triangle, sin θ is defined as the ratio of the opposite side to the hypotenuse, and cos θ is defined as the ratio of the adjacent side to the hypotenuse. ("Opposite" and "adjacent" refer to θ.) That is,

$$\sin \theta = \frac{y}{r} \qquad [14.12$$

$$\cos \theta = \frac{x}{r} \qquad [14.13$$

We take r to be a constant, positive number; x and y are variables with ranges defined by the expressions

$$-r \le x \le r \qquad [14.14$$

$$-r \le y \le r \qquad [14.15$$

We can see immediately that, if $\theta = 0$, $x = r$ and $y = 0$ and that therefore sin $\theta = 0$ and cos $\theta = 1$. The values of sin θ and cos θ for certain values of θ that recur in simple problems are given in Table 14.1. They are exhibited in this form because the sequence of the numbers $\sqrt{0}$, $\sqrt{1}$, $\sqrt{2}$, $\sqrt{3}$, and $\sqrt{4}$ is easy to remember. The same data are tabulated in decimal form in Table 14.2. Values of sin θ and cos θ for other angles are given in Appendix E.

The graphs of sin θ and cos θ for values a little less than $\theta = 0$ and up to $\theta = \pi/2$ rad are shown in Figure 14.7. The θ axis is labeled in radian measure in rational fractions of π: $\pi/6$, $\pi/4$, $\pi/3$, $\pi/2$ ($\pi/2$ rad = 1.5708 rad). The ordinate (y) is drawn to the same scale (from 0.0 to 1.0) as θ, and the several functions $y = 1$, $y = \theta$, $y = \sin \theta$, and

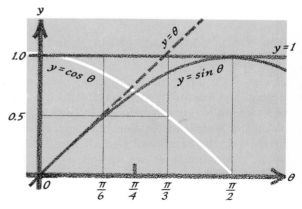

FIG. 14.7. *Plots of sin θ and cos θ in which θ has been expressed in radians. The value of θ goes up to π/2, which is approximately 1.57. The curve y = θ, which is tangent to sin θ at the origin, has a slope of 1.*

$y = \cos \theta$ are all plotted on the same set of axes. (The function $y = 1$ could have been written as $y = \theta/\theta$, showing that it is 1 for all values of θ.) Note in particular that, in the vicinity of $\theta = 0$, $y = \cos \theta$ and $y = 1$ coincide very closely, and that $y = \sin \theta$ and $y = \theta$ do also. It may be shown, by a careful consideration of the values of x and r in Figure 14.6 and equations 14.12 and 14.13, that near $\theta = 0$ the approximations

$$\sin \theta \cong \theta \qquad [14.16$$

$$\cos \theta \cong 1 - \frac{\theta^2}{2} \qquad [14.17$$

hold very well† if θ is expressed in radians. Tables 14.1 and 14.2 also show that $\sin 30° = \cos 60°$ and that $\sin 60° = \cos 30°$, and the graphs suggest, more generally, that $\sin (90° - \theta) = \cos \theta$. That this is generally true may be seen in Figure 14.6, where it is obvious that $\cos \alpha = y/r$; but $y/r = \sin \theta$; therefore $\cos \alpha = \sin \theta$. But $\alpha + \theta = 90°$; so $\alpha = 90° - \theta$. Hence $\sin (90° - \theta) = \cos \theta$ if $0 \le \theta \le 90°$. In fact, the expressions

$$\sin (90° - \theta) = \cos \theta \qquad [14.18$$

$$\cos (90° - \theta) = \sin \theta \qquad [14.19$$

are *trigonometric identities*. An **identity** is an equation that holds true for *all* values of the variable (or variables). (I shall show shortly that equations 14.18 and 14.19 hold true for *all* values of θ, even values greater than 90° and less than 0°; but first we must define $\sin \theta$ and $\cos \theta$ for such values of θ.)

The expression $x^2 + y^2 = r^2$ obviously holds true for the x, y, and r of Figure 14.6. Since $y/r = \sin \theta$ and $x/r = \cos \theta$, $y^2/r^2 + x^2/r^2 = \sin^2 \theta + \cos^2 \theta$. Hence

$$\sin^2 \theta + \cos^2 \theta = \frac{x^2 + y^2}{r^2} = \frac{r^2}{r^2} = 1$$

and we have established another useful trigonometric identity,

$$\sin^2 \theta + \cos^2 \theta = 1 \qquad [14.20$$

† It can be shown with the aid of the calculus that

$$\sin \theta = \theta - \frac{\theta^3}{3!} + \frac{\theta^5}{5!} - \frac{\theta^7}{7!} + \cdots$$

and that

$$\cos \theta = 1 - \frac{\theta^2}{2!} + \frac{\theta^4}{4!} - \frac{\theta^6}{6!} + \cdots$$

if θ is in radians. (The product of the integers from n down to 1 is written as $n!$. For example, $7! = 7 \times 6 \times 5 \times 4 \times 3 \times 2 \times 1$.)

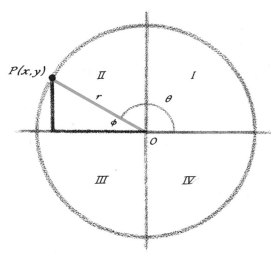

FIG. 14.8. *The sine and cosine functions are defined as y/r and x/r, respectively, regardless of the quadrant in which the terminal side lies. If "f" stands for either sine or cosine and ϕ is the acute angle between the x axis and the terminal side of θ, $f(\theta) = \pm f(\phi)$. The sign is chosen in accordance with Fig. 14.9.*

EXAMPLE 14.3. We wish to check the last identity at $\theta = \pi/6$ rad. In Table 14.1 we see that

$$\sin \frac{\pi}{6} \text{ rad} = \frac{1}{2}$$

$$\cos \frac{\pi}{6} \text{ rad} = \frac{\sqrt{3}}{2}$$

Hence

$$\sin^2 \left(\frac{\pi}{6}\right) + \cos^2 \left(\frac{\pi}{6}\right) = \frac{1}{4} + \frac{3}{4} = 1$$

14.4. The Circular Functions sin θ and cos θ for All Values of θ

We are now ready to extend the definitions of $\sin \theta$ and $\cos \theta$ to all values of θ. We can do it very simply. We merely adhere to the definitions of equations 14.12 and 14.13 no matter where the terminal side of θ lies. As an example, in which θ is about 150°, with its terminal side in the second quadrant (II), consider Figure 14.8. By definition, $\sin \theta = y/r$, and $\cos \theta = x/r$. It is obvious that y/r also equals $\sin \phi$ and that x/r equals $\cos \phi$ if ϕ is the *acute* angle between the terminal side of θ and the x axis. Since y is positive in quadrants I and II and negative in quadrants III and IV, it is apparent that the polarity† of the sine in the four quadrants is as shown in Figure 14.9.A. We obtain Figure 14.9.B for cos θ by considering that x is positive in quadrants I and IV and negative in quadrants II and III. We can summarize all these results in the single equation

$$f(\theta) = \pm f(\phi) \qquad [14.21$$

If "f" stands for the sine function, sin θ = ± sin φ if φ stands for the *acute* angle between the terminal side of θ and the x axis, the proper polarity being chosen by reference to Figure 14.9. In a similar way "f" can stand for the cosine function. All these remarks are also well summarized in the graphs of Figure 14.10.

Since φ is an angle that is equal to or less than 90°, only the sines and cosines of angles up to 90° need be tabulated, for the values of these functions for values of θ greater than 90° or less than 0° can be obtained from equation 14.21—or, what amounts to the same thing—from the information that appears graphically in Figure 14.10.

† The sign, + or −. We use the word "polarity" instead of "sign" so that "sign" will not be confused in speech with "sine."

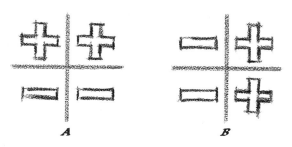

FIG. 14.9. *The polarity (sign) in the various quadrants: (A) of sin θ; (B) of cos θ.*

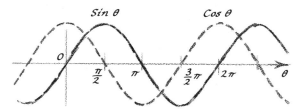

FIG. 14.10. *The polarities (signs) of sin θ and cos θ in the different quadrants can also be obtained from these graphs. Check this against Fig. 14.9.*

EXAMPLE 14.4. We want the sine of 330°.

$$\sin 330° = -\sin \phi$$
$$\phi = 360° - 330° = 30°$$

Therefore

$$\sin 330° = -\sin 30° = -0.500$$

14.5. The Equation of a Simple Harmonic Motion

At last we are in a position to discuss a simple harmonic vibration mathematically.

Using Figure 14.1, I showed that the y component of the motion of the handle of a wheel turning with constant angular velocity, ω, is a simple harmonic motion. We can think of the angle of Figure 14.11 as having been generated according to the equation

$$\theta = \omega t$$

In Figure 14.11 we have substituted ωt for θ and A (amplitude) for r, but it should be quite apparent that the y coordinate of point P is

$$y = A \sin \omega t \qquad [14.22$$

Let us consider this equation dimensionally. First observe that, since

$$[\omega t] = T^{-1}T = T^0$$

ω is a pure number. Remember that ω is measured in rad/sec; ωt, then, is measured in rad/sec × sec = rad. But a radian is dimensionless. The reason is simple. According to equation 14.3, θ = S/R. Both S and R are lengths, making θ a pure number. A quantity of which we take a sine or a cosine must be a dimensionless quantity. (Both radians and degrees are dimensionless for similar reasons.)

Next consider A. It is the amplitude of the vibration: $[A] = L$. It has the dimension of length. That is as it should be, for $[y] = L$. Of course, y is *not* a constant; it is the *dependent* variable in this function, and it varies over the range $-A \leq y \leq A$ (because $-1 \leq \sin \omega t \leq 1$).

Since one whole cycle is completed in time T, another way of writing ω is

$$\omega = \frac{2\pi}{T} \text{ rad/sec}$$

So equation 14.22 may be rewritten as

$$y = A \sin \frac{2\pi}{T} t \qquad [14.23$$

It is important to remember that the variables are y (displacement) and t (time). The constants are A (amplitude) and T (period). The period measures the number of seconds per cycle; so a related constant, the frequency, ν, meaning the number of vibrations per second, is obviously related to T:

$$\nu = \frac{1}{T} \qquad [14.24$$

This is read as "the frequency is the inverse of the period." We tabulate for convenience the relations:

$$
\begin{aligned}
&\text{(A)} \ \omega = \frac{2\pi}{T} \\
&\text{(B)} \ T = \frac{2\pi}{\omega} \\
&\text{(C)} \ \nu = \frac{\omega}{2\pi}
\end{aligned}
\qquad [14.25
$$

The plot of equation 14.22 (or of its equivalent, equation 14.23) is shown as curve I in Figure 14.12. It is to be observed from equation 14.23 that, when the variable t assumes the value 0, y must

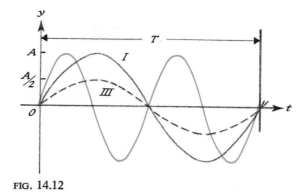

FIG. 14.12

vanish because $\sin 0 = 0$, and that, when the variable t assumes the value T, $y = A \sin (2\pi/T)T$ or $y = A \sin 2\pi = 0$, and y vanishes again because ωt has gone through a complete cycle of 2π radians (or 360°).

Curve II of Figure 14.12 completes its cycle in time $T/2$, but, since its amplitude is still A, its equation must be

$$y = A \sin \frac{T}{2} t \qquad [14.26$$

or

$$y = A \sin 2 \left(\frac{2\pi}{T} \right) t \qquad [14.27$$

which we may write, using equation 14.25 (A), as

$$y = A \sin 2\omega t \qquad [14.28$$

which is of the form

$$y = A \sin \omega' t \qquad [14.29$$

ω' being equal to 2ω.

The effect of halving the period or doubling the frequency is to crowd the graph tighter along the t axis.

EXAMPLE 14.5. What is the effect of halving A but leaving T fixed?

Suppose that $A' = A/2$. The new equation is

$$y = A' \sin \omega t$$

or

$$y = A' \sin \frac{2\pi}{T} t$$

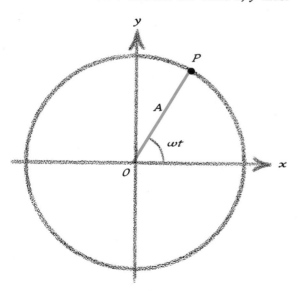

FIG. 14.11. *If an angle is generated by a radius rotating at constant angular velocity* ω, *it is equal to* ωt. *The* y *coordinate of* P *is* $y = A \sin \omega t$, *the equation of simple harmonic motion.*

Since the range of $\sin(2\pi/T)t$ is $-1 \le \sin(2\pi/T)t \le 1$, the range on y is now $-A' \le y \le A'$. Its graph is shown as curve III in Fig. 14.12.

14.6. The Period of a Simple Harmonic Motion

We now seek an expression for the period of a simple harmonic motion in terms of some of the other constants involved in that motion. We have been analyzing the motion of point M on the y axis. It moves in **simple harmonic motion** if it is the projection on a diameter of a point, P, moving in a circle with a constant angular velocity, ω.

The motion of P (Fig. 14.13) is characterized by the displacement vector $\mathbf{r}$, the velocity vector $\mathbf{v}$, and the centripetal acceleration vector $\mathbf{a}_c$. The motion of M is characterized by displacement, velocity, and acceleration vectors that are the y components of $\mathbf{r}$, $\mathbf{v}$, and $\mathbf{a}_c$. Since the y components all lie on the same line (the y axis), we shall drop the vector notation for the motion of M. The algebraic signs of the relevant quantities will indicate direction.

The motion of M is characterized by the quantities

$$y = r \sin \omega t \qquad [14.30a$$
$$v_y = v \cos \omega t \qquad [14.30b$$
$$a_y = -a_c \sin \omega t \qquad [14.30c$$

From equations 14.30a and 14.30c we get the equation

$$\frac{y}{a_y} = -\frac{r}{a_c} \qquad [14.31$$

Since a_c is the centripetal acceleration (§ 9.5), it obeys the equation

$$a_c = \omega^2 r \qquad [14.32$$

Therefore

$$\frac{y}{a_y} = -\frac{r}{\omega^2 r} \qquad [14.33$$

Since $\omega = 2\pi/T$ (equation 14.25.A), this may be written as

$$T = 2\pi\sqrt{-y/a_y} \qquad [14.34$$

The quantity inside the square-root sign is really positive since a_y is negative whenever y is positive.

The importance of equation 14.34 is this: the period of a simple harmonic motion can be deduced from it if an expression for the ratio of the displacement (y) to the acceleration (a_y) can be found.

We may go back for an example to the equation $F = -kx$, which defined simple harmonic motion dynamically. If we substitute mass times acceleration for F, we get the equation $ma = -kx$, from which we get the equation $-x/a = m/k$; that is, in this case, the ratio of displacement to acceleration (times -1) is m/k. Hence the formula for the period of an object of mass m oscillating under the action of a spring that obeys the equation $F = -kx$ is $T = 2\pi\sqrt{m/k}$.

We have cheated a bit here by using the basic equation of dynamics, $f = ma$, which we shall not study in detail until Part III; but we can excuse this digression from pure kinematics by claiming a slight acquaintance with that equation from Chapter 3. The main topic of this chapter has been kinematics—the kinematics of a *single point moving in a straight line in simple harmonic motion*. The excursions into rotational motion have simply been a means to the exposition of that topic.

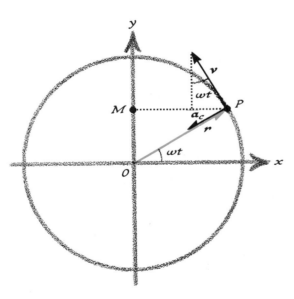

FIG. 14.13. *The displacement, velocity, and acceleration of point* M, *moving with simple harmonic motion on the diameter of a circle, can be obtained from the projection of the displacement vector, the velocity vector, and the acceleration vector of point* P, *moving with constant angular velocity on the circle.*

14.7. Summary

A body moves in simple harmonic motion if the restoring force on it is proportional to the displacement.

The projection on a diameter of a point moving in a circle with constant angular velocity moves with simple harmonic motion.

An equation for displacement y as a function of time t in simple harmonic motion with amplitude A and period T is

$$y = A \sin (2\pi t/T)$$

The period can also be expressed by the equation

$$T = 2\pi \sqrt{-y/a_y}$$

in which y is the displacement and a_y the acceleration of a point moving in simple harmonic motion.

Problems

14.1. In Fig. 13.3 let us choose down as the positive direction. The body of mass m is normally in equilibrium under the action of two forces. One is the weight, mg, and the other is the force, $-kx_0$, of the·spring on the body, x_0 being the positive elongation of the spring when the body is in equilibrium. If a further elongation, x, takes place, the total stretch is $x_0 + x$.

1. At that point, what force does the spring exert on the body?

2. At the same point, what is the force of gravity on the body?

3. What is the *net* force (the vector sum of the forces) on the body? Use the fact that $kx_0 = mg$.

4. Your result should also be valid for a position of the body above its position of equilibrium. Is it? Your answer should be reconcilable with § 14.1, paragraph 2.

14.2. The minus sign in the equation $F = -kx$ ensures that the force always points toward the equilibrium position in simple harmonic motion.

1. Consider another kind of motion, one taking place according to the equation $F = +kx$. (Assume, as before, that k is positive.) Starting at $x = 0$, for example, the body subjected to this force is first moved away from its equilibrium position by hand and then released. Describe its subsequent motion qualitatively.

2. An object attached to springs executes simple harmonic motion on a horizontal frictionless surface (Fig. 11.2). The force equation is the usual $F = -kx$. The vibrating object is made of a substance that evaporates so rapidly that it loses an appreciable fraction of its mass during one cycle.

What effect will this have on the period and amplitude of the vibration? Explain qualitatively.

3. Imagine the system of Fig. 13.3 immersed in melted butter. You start an oscillation by displacing the object from its equilibrium position and releasing it. Draw a curve of displacement against time on the assumption that the medium presents a great deal of friction.

4. Repeat part 3 on the assumption that the melted butter is so cold that it is about to solidify.

14.3. 1. Calculate the angular velocity of the earth about the sun in radians per second.

2. Use this value and the average distance between the earth and the sun (1.49×10^8 km) to find the speed of the earth as it goes round the sun.

3. Check this result: compute the speed by dividing the total distance by the total time of one revolution. (Use the fact that there are 3.156×10^7 seconds in a year.)

14.4. 1. What is the angular velocity of the earth in its daily rotation? Express the result in radians per second. The period of rotation is 8.64×10^4 sec.

2. If the diameter of the earth at the equator is 1.28×10^7 m, what is the linear speed in meters per second of a point on the equator? (You are probably better acquainted with miles per hour; note that 1 m/sec = 2.24 mi/h.)

14.5. It is common to express the angular velocity of electric motors in revolutions per minute (rpm). Calculations in dynamics, however, require the use of the radian measure for angles. An electric motor accelerates uniformly from rest to an angular velocity of 1,700 rpm in 2 sec. Calculate its angular acceleration in rad/sec².

14.6. A phonograph record is 12 in. in diameter and is designed to be played at 33.3 rpm. A certain selection lasts 19.4 min.

1. During that time a crayon mark made on the edge of the record travels how far in meters?

2. What is the centripetal acceleration of the mark, in m/sec², while the record is playing?

3. What is the tangential acceleration of the mark while the record is playing?

14.7. When a wheel rolls on the ground with a certain angular velocity, the speed of its hub is exactly what the speed of a point on its rim would have been if the hub had not moved while the wheel rotated at the same angular velocity. Use this fact to solve this problem. The radius of a bicycle wheel is 0.33 m. The bicycle accelerates uniformly from rest to a linear speed of 10 m/sec in 7 sec. What is the angular acceleration of the wheel?

14.8. This problem illustrates the similarity between a problem in linear motion and one in rotation. Solving the linear one first should help you to establish the pattern for the solution of the one in rotation.

1. A car starts from rest with uniform acceleration and covers its total distance of 90 m in 6 sec. What are the acceleration and the greatest speed reached in this interval?

2. A merry-go-round starts from rest with a constant angular acceleration. It completes 3.98 revolutions in 100 sec. What are the angular acceleration in rad/sec² and the greatest angular velocity reached in that interval? (See equations 14.11.)

14.9. A ferris wheel with a radius of 10 m starts rotating with a constant angular acceleration of 0.1 rad/sec². What will be the tangential speed of a point on the perimeter of the wheel after 5 sec?

14.10. Satellite-tracking cameras are capable of photographing a 30-caliber bullet (width of bullet is 0.30 in.) in flight at a distance of 200 mi.

1. What angle in radians is subtended at the camera by the width of the bullet?

2. What is the angular velocity of the tracking camera if it keeps the image of the bullet, moving at 300 m/sec, on the cross hairs of the tracking telescope? (This is equivalent to asking for the angular velocity of a line joining the camera and the moving bullet.)

3. A satellite 2,400 mi from the surface of the earth looks exactly like the bullet in its angular width and in its angular velocity. Assuming that it is moving in a circle with the center of the earth as its center, compute its linear speed in mi/h.

14.11. If the initial side of an angle lies on the positive x axis, in what quadrant does the terminal side lie for (1) 542°, (2) 290°, (3) 2.9 rad?

14.12. Use the identity of equation 14.20 to answer the following questions, and check your results by resorting to a table of trigonometric functions.

1. If sin θ is 0.571, what is cos θ?

2. If sin x = cos x, what is x in radians?

14.13. The sine and cosine of angles other than 30°, 45°, 60°, and 90° may be found in the table of Appendix E. With the aid of equation 14.21 and a table of values for angles up to 90° you should be able to compute the sine and cosine of any angle, no matter how large. With the aid of Tables 14.1 and 14.2 find the sine and cosine of 150°, 225°, and 300°.

14.14. Test your understanding of equations 14.16 and 14.17 by converting 5° to radians and using them to find approximate values for sin 5° and cos 5°. Check your results by looking up the values in a table.

14.15. Find the sine and the cosine of 23.5π rad.

14.16. A simple harmonic motion has an amplitude of 10 cm and a period of 2 sec. Find the maximum displacement, the maximum speed, and the maximum acceleration of a moving point.

14.17. Let A be the amplitude in centimeters and T the period in seconds. Plot simple harmonic motions with the following characteristics.

1. $A = 10$ cm, $T = 2$ sec.

2. $A = 3$ cm, $T = 2$ sec.

3. $A = 3$ cm, $T = 2/3$ sec.

14.18. One can gain some insight into the factors that affect simple harmonic motion by considering an oscillatory phenomenon in nature. The number of puncture weeds in the United States fluctuates with time. Before considering the period of that fluctuation, consider an analogous problem.

1. A body executing simple harmonic motion has a displacement of 0.05 m when its acceleration is -0.1 m/sec². What is its period? The ratio of displacement to acceleration is a constant. If we know it for one instant, we know it in general and can use it in equation 14.34. Thus

$$T = 2\pi\sqrt{-y/a_y} = 2\pi\sqrt{0.05/0.1} = 4.44 \text{ sec}$$

2. There is an insect that feeds on the puncture weed, which, in turn, depends on the insect for pollination. Insect and weed achieve an equilibrium in numbers. Occasionally a drought kills off a lot of

weeds. A lot of insects go hungry and die. This gives the plant a chance to increase in numbers. Soon there is an excess of plants and not enough insects to pollinate them; so the plants begin to diminish in number. An oscillation in numbers takes place, and we wish to calculate its period. Let us assume that the excess, over the equilibrium number, in the number of plants is proportional to the acceleration in the rate of growth of plants. Consider a hypothetical example. The equilibrium number for puncture weeds in a certain area is 10^9. For each 200 million plants below the equilibrium number the rate of growth of plants increases by 100 million plants per year *each* year. Compute the period of oscillation, assuming that it obeys the same mathematical relations as simple harmonic motion.

Mathematical Description of Waves in One Dimension

IN CHAPTER 13 I reminded you that we can generate a train of waves by pushing up and down a box that is floating on the surface of a lake. The waves thus generated travel in ever-expanding circles on the two-dimensional collection of points making up that surface. In Chapter 14 you learned an equation that describes simple harmonic motion. If the motion of the box is simple harmonic motion, that equation—

$$y = A \sin 2\pi t/T$$

—describes it.

What about the equation for the vibration of all the other particles affected by the passage of the wave? They all seem to imitate the vibration of the box, but the equation given above cannot be the exact formula for all the particles simultaneously; if it were, all the particles of the surface would go up and down together, and, of course, they do not. Somehow we must develop an expression that takes account of the fact that some vibrating particles are out of phase with one another.

15.1. One-dimensional Waves

First let us see how we shall use the word "dimensional" in this chapter. It refers to a medium that is capable of carrying a wave. A string stretched along an x axis, for example, is a one-dimensional medium. If you pluck it, the crest of a wave will travel along that axis. The wave is called one-dimensional even though the vibrations of the particles take place (in the y direction) at right angles to the direction of the wave's progress. Similar remarks apply to the two-dimensional waves that travel on the surface of water: the crests and troughs travel out on their two-dimensional medium. The condensations and rarefactions of a sound wave in air travel in a three-dimensional medium.

In order to simplify matters, we begin by considering one-dimensional rather than two- or three-dimensional waves. The waves that move along a radial line in the lake are one-dimensional, but their amplitude diminishes with increased

distance from the center, and we want to begin
with the simpler case of constant amplitude So
let us return for a moment to the vibration of a
single particle.

Suppose, for example, that you hold a piece of
chalk in your hand and move it up and down in
simple harmonic motion. (It is not easy to do this
accurately, getting the velocity and the acceleration right at every instant, but, for the sake of
argument, let us assume that you can do it.) A
trace drawn on the blackboard while the chalk is
so moving (Fig. 15.1.A) is a straight vertical line
of length $2A$ (A = amplitude). Now imagine walking at a constant speed in a horizontal direction
while you move the chalk vertically in SHM (Fig.
15.1.B). The trace is now a wavy curve that looks
like a sine curve. You get a similar result if, while
you remain standing and moving the chalk vertically in SHM, a specially prepared window
shade is unrolled along the board at a constant
speed (Fig. 15.1.C). The two curves are similar.
Let us talk about either one, but first a question:
Are these waves? The answer is "no." The chalk
vibrated in SHM. The curves we have are nothing
but graphs of the equation

$$y = A \sin 2\pi t/T$$

—that is, graphs of a simple harmonic motion.
They look wavy, and they have many of the
characteristics of a wave, as we shall see, but here
they are graphical descriptions of the vibration of
a single particle, not of a wave.

We can generate a one-dimensional wave in a
long spiral spring, such as a Slinky, or in a long
rope. If we stretch a Slinky to a length of about
thirty feet and let it rest on a smooth floor, we can
set up easily visible waves by putting one end into
SHM with an amplitude of about two feet and a
period of about one second. The shape of the

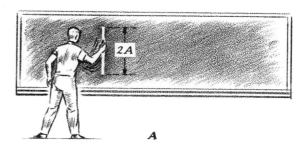

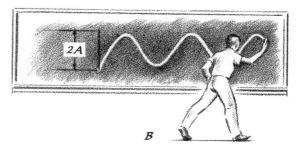

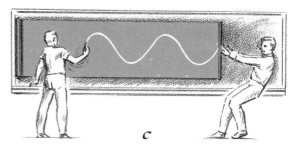

FIG. 15.1. *Simple harmonic motion and two ways of
plotting it.*

curve (Fig. 15.2) at any instant looks somewhat
like the curves of Figure 15.1; but notice an important difference. Here not only the end of the
spring, but every particle of the spring, is moving
in SHM, and not all the particles are in phase.
Particles A and C are out of phase with each other,

FIG. 15.2. *A transverse wave in a long spiral spring.*

and the phase condition changes gradually from "out" to "in" as we go from C to B. The characteristic thing about a wave is that the vibratory motion at one point is copied accurately at all other points at different times if the amplitude is constant.†

It should be apparent by now that vibrations can set up waves, but the methods of analysis that we shall develop are not limited to waves set up by vibrating bodies. With proper substitutions, they can describe electrical and pressure waves too. Electrical waves are governed by an equation

---

† A large number of people line up according to size, each with his hands on the shoulders of the person directly in front of him. If the first person moves down in a knee-bend, he pulls the person in front of him down too a little later, and in this way he begins to propagate a **pulse** (a single disturbance that travels along a medium), in the course of which each person's motion copies, a little later, that of the person just behind him. If the person who began the downward pulse now stands up, he begins an upward pulse, going in the same direction as the first, in the course of which each person stands up in turn. A continuous succession of downward and upward pulses would constitute a train of waves.

such as

$$E = E_0 \sin 2\pi t/T$$

in which E and E_0 are measured in units of electric field intensity (newtons per coulomb). The vibrations set up by a tuning fork are, in part, variations of pressure and obey an equation such as

$$p = p_0 \sin 2\pi t/T$$

in which p and p_0, for physical and dimensional consistency, are measured in the same units (for example, newtons per square meter).

To see how different vibrations might be related, consider the experiment depicted in Figure 15.3. The vibrations of the tuning fork's prong are mechanical and obey an equation such as

$$x = x_0 \sin 2\pi t/T$$

They set up a train of waves, which travels to P as well as in other directions. At P a microphone picks up the air-pressure variations—

$$p = p_0 \sin 2\pi t/T$$

—and converts them into electrical signals, ending

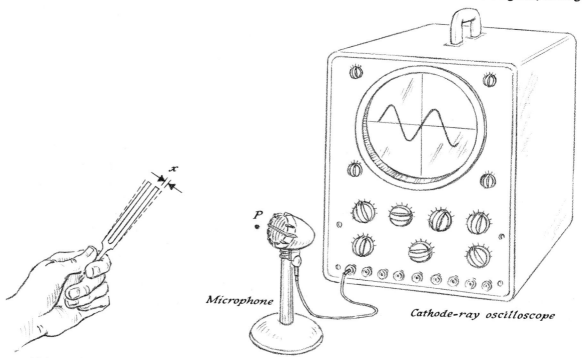

Microphone

Cathode-ray oscilloscope

FIG. 15.3. *Cathode-ray oscilloscope trace of a simple harmonic motion. What happens here is, in principle, very similar to what happened in Fig. 15.1. The curve is drawn by an electron beam instead of by a piece of chalk.*

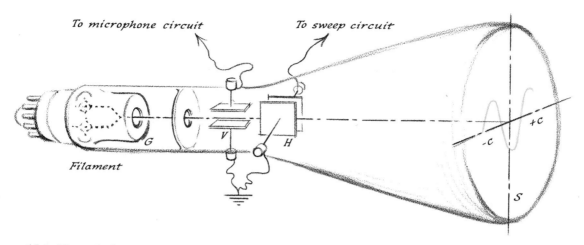

FIG. 15.4. *The cathode-ray oscilloscope: Electrons from the electron gun produce a spot of light when they land on the fluorescent screen. The oscilloscope is not limited in its use to the display of simple harmonic curves.*

as electric-field fluctuation—

$$E = E_0 \sin 2\pi t/T$$

—between the plates that control the vertical motion of the electrons inside the cathode-ray oscilloscope. These electrons trace, on the fluorescent screen of the oscilloscope, the graph of a simple harmonic motion,

$$y = A \sin 2\pi t/T$$

Since the **oscilloscope** is a very useful tool, let us pause to examine in some detail how it works (Fig. 15.4). At the left is an electron gun, G—that is, a source of electrons, which move in a stream from left to right. The electrical signal from the microphone is amplified and fed to the metal plates marked V. Between them a fluctuating electric field—for example,

$$E = E_0 \sin 2\pi t/T$$

—deflects the beam up and down, giving the final image on the fluorescent screen, S, a y component. The plates marked H are connected to another source of electric field ($E = E_0 t$), which increases with time, giving the electrons a horizontal motion at a constant velocity. When a simple harmonic vibration is picked up by the microphone, the motion of the spot on the screen is governed by the equations

$$Y = A \sin \frac{2\pi t}{T} \qquad [15.1$$

$$X = vt \qquad [15.2$$

Equation 15.1 represents the periodic motion in a vertical direction; it is like the motion of the chalk in Figure 15.1.A. Equation 15.2 is like the motion of the man in Figure 15.1.B (or of the window shade in Fig. 15.1.C) and has similar results. The main difference is that, though the man cannot suddenly move from the extreme right to the extreme left to start the trace again, the electron beam *can* suddenly jump from, say, $x = c$ to $x = -c$ (Fig. 15.4) with no loss of time; it can trace the periodic curve over and over again, doing this, if necessary, millions of times per second.

So much for vibrations and their analysis. We must now proceed to a detailed discussion of waves. Most of the waves we encounter in nature (such as water waves) and those generated by physical apparatus (for example, sound waves in air or radio waves) are actually two- or three-dimensional waves, but we can come to grips mathematically more readily with the one-dimensional waves that can be set up along strings, ropes, and springs; so we shall begin with them.

15.2. Transverse and Longitudinal Waves

We shall now consider mathematically the transverse and longitudinal waves introduced in Chapter 13.

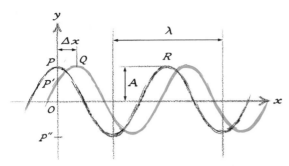

FIG. 15.5. *Two snapshots of a transverse wave.*

Consider an elastic one-dimensional medium along the x axis (Fig. 15.5). So long as no wave is traveling on it, the y coordinate of every point on it is zero; but if, at some distant point on the negative x axis, one particle is put into simple harmonic motion, it sets up a wave that travels on the x axis. If the frequency, ν, and the amplitude, A, of the particle are kept constant, we see crests and troughs, separated from one another by a constant distance, λ, move from left to right at a constant speed, v. If we take a snapshot of the wave with a camera capable of making an exposure of about 10^{-6} second (so that no blur can be seen in the picture), it will look like the black curve. The particle that was at the origin (O) before the wave came by is now at point P, with coordinates (0,A). Point R has coordinates (λ, A), and all points except those where the curve cuts the x axis have positive or negative displacement, as shown. A wave of this kind, in which the displacements occur at right angles to the direction of propagation, is, we know, called a transverse wave.

Imagine now that another snapshot is taken at time T/10 later, T being the period of the vibration. This is shown as the green curve of the figure. The top of one crest has moved from P to Q in time Δt. If the distance PQ is Δx, $\Delta x/\Delta t = v$, the speed of the wave, which is a constant.

The particle at P did not, of course, move from P to Q; it moved, instead, from P to P', then all the way down to P'', and then back to P, in simple harmonic motion, which means that it experienced the displacement, velocity, and acceleration in the y direction that are characteristic of SHM.

A given particle of the medium moves parallel to the y axis with a variable speed while the crests of the wave (and hence the wave itself) move parallel to the x axis at a constant speed, v. For the special case where $\Delta x = \lambda$, Δt is equal to one period, T; therefore $v = \Delta x/\Delta t = \lambda/T$, from which formula, since $\nu = 1/T$, we get the equation $v = \nu\lambda$ (see equation 13.3). Though what I have said of one particle of a medium (that it moves in the y direction in SHM) is true of all particles of the medium, they do not all move in unison: a crest, for example, is at P at t = 0 but does not reach Q until $t = \Delta t$.

The vibrations of the strings of musical instruments resemble those of Figure 15.5 in principle. The waves travel with such speed, however, that a wave soon bounces off each end and sets up complications (a discussion of which we must defer). The amplitude of a string's wave may be a millimeter or less, whereas that of a Slinky's wave may be a foot or more. When drawn to the proper scale, the black curve of Figure 15.5 is a graph of displacement against x at a fixed time (t = 0) for either the string or the Slinky. The green curve is a graph of displacement against x at another time ($t = \Delta t$). Each graph drawn in this way is a representation of a wave "frozen" at an instant in time (a snapshot). We observe that each looks like a sine curve, but the equation cannot be

$$y = A \sin 2\pi t/T$$

for the independent variable of each is x, not t.

As a mathematical representation of a wave, Figure 15.5 can serve even for longitudinal waves. In a longitudinal wave, you will remember, the vibratory motion is parallel to the direction of propagation. The magnitudes of the displacements are still the ordinates of the curves of Figure 15.5, but the displacement takes place to the left and to the right of the equilibrium position of the particle while y becomes negative and positive respectively.

EXAMPLE 15.1. We draw dots 1 cm apart on a line (Fig. 15.6, line x). They represent the normal positions of particles of an elastic medium. For convenience we can associate the x coordinates 0, 1, 2, 3, . . . with them. If a longitudinal simple periodic wave is passing by (line x'), the successive particles experience, respectively, displacements along the x axis proportional to 0, 0.5, 0.866, 1.0, 0.866, 0.5, 0, −0.5, −0.866, −1.0, −0.866, −0.5, 0, etc. (These values are the sines of 0°, 30°, 60°, 90°, etc.) At a later instant (line x'') the particle normally at A experiences displacement −0.5, and successive particles to the right experience, respectively, displacements 0, 0.5, 0.866, 1.0, 0.866, 0.5, 0, −0.5, −0.866, −0.5, etc. Although the new locations of the particles are shown on lines x' and x'', the displacements of all really take place on the same x axis. The use of three lines in the figure exhibits more clearly the fact that the center of condensation has shifted, in this example, from position 6 to position 7. The center of condensation is analogous to the crest of a transverse wave. If the displacements used here were applied to a y axis, a curve similar to those in Fig. 15.5 would result. You are urged to verify this. (See Prob. 15.7.)

Figure 15.7 presents drawings of a helical spring along which a longitudinal wave is passing. Notice the successive regions of condensation and rarefaction. The sequence of drawings shows how the condensations and the rarefactions move along in the same direction and at the same speed.

Figure 15.5, then, can represent mathematically either a longitudinal wave or a transverse wave. The curve looks like a transverse wave because each y displacement is drawn at right angles to the x axis, but the same set of displacements, if applied in the direction of propagation, would produce a longitudinal wave.

We are now ready to consider a mathematical expression that will give us a complete description of a one-dimensional wave.

15.3. The Mathematical Equation of a Wave

In Figure 15.1.C we saw that the graph of simple harmonic vibration, $y = A \sin 2\pi t/T$, looks very much like a wave. If x replaced t in this equation, we should, in fact, have y as a function of x, and the vibration, instead of completing a cycle in time T, would complete a cycle in distance λ. This suggests that we try the equation

$$y = A \sin \frac{2\pi x}{\lambda} \qquad [15.3$$

FIG. 15.6. *Motion of points in a longitudinal wave.*

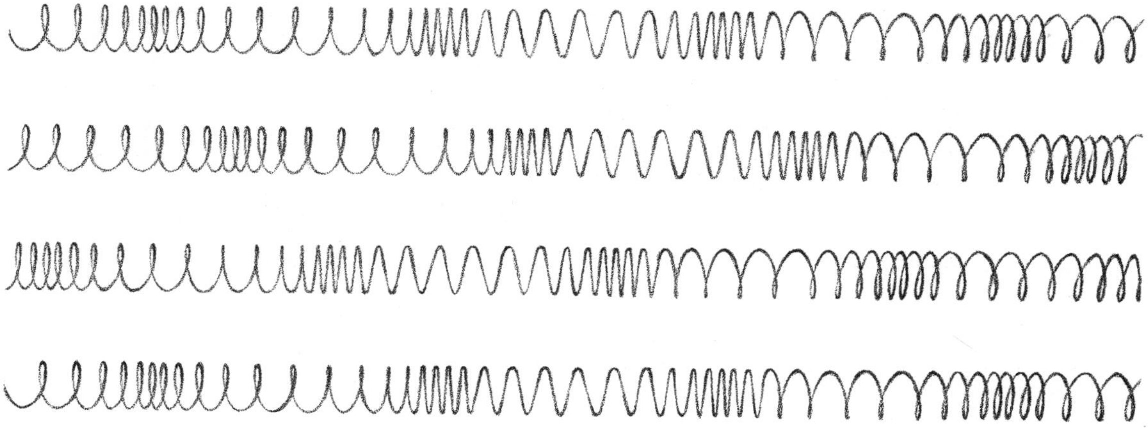

FIG. 15.7. *Longitudinal wave in a long coiled spring.*

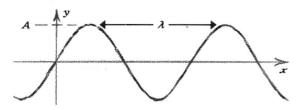

FIG. 15.8. *The graph of* y = A *sin* 2πx/λ *is identical with that of the plot of displacement against time in the simple harmonic motion of a single point, but the physical interpretation is different. The abscissa here is* x *rather than* t. *The graph shows the simultaneous displacement of many particles. It is a snapshot of a wave whose amplitude is* A *and whose wavelength is* λ.

Its graph is shown in Figure 15.8. It has the right shape and the right amplitude, and it does complete a cycle in the distance $\Delta x = \lambda$, but it does not move forward. The element of time is needed to make it do that.

Suppose (Fig. 15.9) that a boy in a stationary laboratory, L, generates a wave by vibrating one end of a very long spring in SHM. The wave moves from left to right at speed v. Let L' be a laboratory on wheels moving from left to right at the same speed. To an observer in the moving laboratory the wave going through it appears to stand still. In the primed coordinates x' and y' of L', the equation of this fixed curve is

$$y' = A \sin \frac{2\pi x'}{\lambda} \qquad [15.4$$

A point on the curve with coordinates (x',y') relative to L' would have coordinates (x,y) relative to L, for $y' = y$ and $x = x' + vt$ on the assumption that the y and y' axes coincided at $t = 0$. From the equation for x we obtain the equation

$$x' = x - vt \qquad [15.5$$

Substituting into equation 15.4, we get the equation

$$y = A \sin \frac{2\pi}{\lambda}(x - vt) \qquad [15.6$$

This is the equation of the wave as seen from L.

We can see immediately that this equation has at least some of the characteristics we expect of a wave equation. If, for example, we fix time by letting t assume a constant value, we get a snapshot of the right shape; if we let t equal 0, equation 15.6 becomes simply

$$y = A \sin \frac{2\pi x}{\lambda}$$

which is equation 15.3.

If, on the other hand, we concentrate our attention at one point in space by letting x be a constant, we get a simple harmonic motion, as we can check by letting x equal 0 in equation 15.6 This yields the equation

$$y = A \sin\left(-\frac{2\pi t}{T}\right)$$

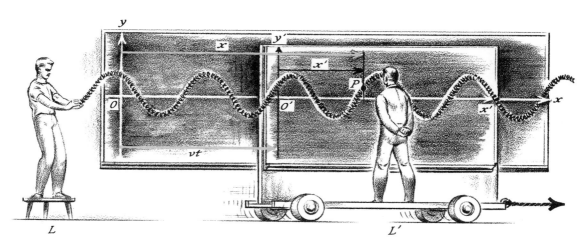

FIG. 15.9. *To the observer in the laboratory moving with the speed of the wave set up by the observer in the fixed laboratory the wave seems to be standing still.*

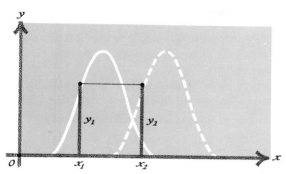

FIG. 15.10. *The expression* y = f(x − vt) *is the general equation for a wave moving in the direction of increasing* x *with speed* v.

which may be written† as

$$y = -A \sin \frac{2\pi t}{T} \qquad [15.7$$

This represents a SHM. The negative sign simply reverses the sign of the usual equation,

$$y = A \sin \frac{2\pi t}{T}$$

The way we derived equation 15.6 may make you think that *any* function of the type $y = f(x - vt)$ represents some sort of progressive wave. You are right; it does. Suppose, for example, that a pulse has the shape of the solid curve of Figure 15.10. If a point on it has coordinates (x_1, y_1) at t_1, it obeys the equation

$$y_1 = f(x_1 - vt_1) \qquad [15.8$$

Now let us consider the value of the function at x_2 at time t_2:

$$y_2 = f(x_2 - vt_2) \qquad [15.9$$

Suppose that $x_2 = x_1 + x$ and $t_2 = t_1 + t$. Then

$$y_2 = f[x_1 + \Delta x - v(t_1 + \Delta t)] \qquad [15.10$$

or

$$y_2 = f[x_1 - vt_1 + \Delta x - v(\Delta t)] \qquad [15.11$$

If Δx and Δt obey the equation $\Delta x / \Delta t = v$, we get $\Delta x = v(\Delta t)$, which, put into equation 15.11, yields

$$y_2 = f(x_1 - vt_1) = y_1 \qquad [15.12$$

† By going back to the definition $\sin \theta = y/r$ (equation 14.12), we see that y goes negative for negative values of θ, and that therefore $\sin(-\theta) = -\sin \theta$. In a similar way we can prove that $\cos(-\theta) = \cos \theta$. Any function such that $f(-\theta) = -f(\theta)$ is called an odd function; if $f(-\theta) = f(\theta)$, it is called an even function.

In other words, the point (x_1, y_1) of the curve simply moved to the right by amount $v(\Delta t)$. Since the same argument could have been applied to any point of the curve, we see that the whole configuration simply moved to the right at speed v.

We must remember that, if the displacements, y, are parallel to the direction of propagation, the pulse or the progressive wave, whichever it is (depending on the mode of excitation), is longitudinal even though it obeys precisely the same mathematical equations.

15.4. Phase

Another way of writing the equation of a wave (15.6) exhibits greater symmetry in its symbols. First let us write equation 15.6 in the form

$$y = A \sin 2\pi \left(\frac{x}{\lambda} - \frac{vt}{\lambda} \right) \qquad [15.13$$

Next, using the relation $v/\lambda = 1/T$, we substitute into equation 15.13 and obtain the equation

$$y = A \sin 2\pi \left(\frac{x}{\lambda} - \frac{t}{T} \right) \qquad [15.14$$

In this form the quantity inside the parentheses is dimensionless. To consider the *vibration* excited at point $x = x_1$, we substitute into equation 15.14 and get the equation

$$y_1 = A \sin 2\pi \left(\frac{x_1}{\lambda} - \frac{t}{T} \right) \qquad [15.15$$

Let us explore what is happening at x_2 if $x_2 = x_1 + \lambda$. Putting this into equation 15.14, we get the equation

$$y_2 = A \sin 2\pi \left(\frac{x_1 + \lambda}{\lambda} - \frac{t}{T} \right) \qquad [15.16$$

or

$$y_2 = A \sin \left[2\pi \left(\frac{x_1}{\lambda} - \frac{t}{T} \right) + 2\pi \right] \qquad [15.17$$

But we know that, in general,

$$\sin(\theta + 2\pi) = \sin \theta \qquad [15.18$$

Therefore

$$y_2 = A \sin 2\pi \left(\frac{x_1}{\lambda} - \frac{t}{T} \right) \qquad [15.19$$

The vibration at x_2 (equation 15.19) is identical with that at x_1 (equation 15.15). In other words, the vibrations are in phase with each other.

We expected this, of course, but we see that the

in-phase relation resulted from our choosing as increment $\Delta x = \lambda$, which resulted in increment 2π in the angular argument (the angle on which the sine operates) of the sine function.

If we had let Δx equal $\lambda/2$, we should have expected an out-of-phase condition. To check this, we let x_2 equal $x_1 + \lambda/2$ and put it into equation 15.15. Repeating the logic that led to equation 15.17, we now get the equation

$$y_2 = A \sin \left[2\pi \left(\frac{x_1}{\lambda} - \frac{t}{T} \right) + \pi \right] \qquad [15.20$$

But we know that

$$\sin (\theta + \pi) = -\sin \theta \qquad [15.21$$

We may check this by considering the basic definition $\sin \theta = y/r$ (equation 14.12). Therefore

$$y_2 = -A \sin 2\pi \left(\frac{x_1}{\lambda} - \frac{t}{T} \right) \qquad [15.22$$

and the vibration is, as we suspected, out of phase with that of equation 15.15.

More generally, the word "phase" can be applied to the whole or part of the angular argument of the sine function of equation 15.14. If we write that equation in the form

$$y = A \sin \left(\frac{2\pi x}{\lambda} - \frac{2\pi t}{T} \right) \qquad [15.23$$

we can, if we like, speak of $2\pi x/\lambda = \phi$ as the *phase* of the vibration and write

$$y = A \sin \left(\phi - \frac{2\pi t}{T} \right) \qquad [15.24$$

If ϕ equals 2π or any integral multiple of 2π, its effect on the vibration is the same as if it equaled 0; if ϕ does not equal 0 or an integral multiple of 2π, its effect is a lag in the vibration. If, for example, the vibration represented by the equation

$$y = A \sin (-2\pi t/T)$$

reaches its maximum displacement at time t_1, the vibration represented by the equation

$$y = A \sin (\phi - 2\pi t/T)$$

reaches its maximum displacement at time $t_1 + \phi T/2\pi$.

You need not be troubled by the concept of phase. In most of our discussions you will need to know only what "in phase" and "out of phase" mean. We can now add, however, that the phase of a simple periodic wave changes continuously

from 0 to 2π as we consider all the points from point x_1 to point $x_1 + \lambda$. The idea of phase will be most useful when we consider the *interference* of waves.

I now state—without proof here—an identity that is often useful in problems involving phase:

$$\sin (\alpha + \beta) = \sin \alpha \cos \beta + \cos \alpha \sin \beta$$

This holds true for all values of α and β. If $\alpha = 30°$ and $\beta = 60°$, for example, the right-hand side becomes

$$\sin 30° \cos 60° + \cos 30° \sin 60°$$

$$= \frac{1}{2} \cdot \frac{1}{2} + \frac{\sqrt{3}}{2} \cdot \frac{\sqrt{3}}{2} = \frac{1}{4} + \frac{3}{4} = 1$$

This checks, for $30° + 60° = 90°$, and $\sin 90° = 1$. This identity is needed in the solution of Problems 15.10 and 15.11.

15.5. Summary

The equation of a one-dimensional wave moving in the direction of increasing x may be written as

$$y = A \sin 2\pi \left(\frac{x}{\lambda} - \frac{t}{T} \right)$$

in which A is the amplitude, λ the wavelength, and T the period, all of which are constants. The variables are x, the space coordinate of points on the line on which the wave is propagated, and t, the time. This equation can represent either a longitudinal or a transverse wave. If we consider x constant, it is the equation of a simple harmonic motion. If we consider t constant, the graph of the equation represents a snapshot of the wave. If the equation is written in the form

$$y = A \sin (\phi - 2\pi t/T)$$

we can speak of ϕ as the phase of the vibration. Each constant value of x has a corresponding constant value of ϕ. The phase of the vibration changes gradually from point to point, but because of its cyclic nature there are different points with the same phase. The shortest distance between two points with the same phase is one wavelength. Another way to write this equation is

$$y = A \sin (2\pi/\lambda)(x - vt)$$

It can be shown that any equation of the type $y = f(x - vt)$ represents a one-dimensional wave moving in the direction of increasing x.

Problems

15.1. In your own words formulate as clearly as possible the distinction between a vibration and a wave.

15.2. Fig. 15.11 shows two positions of a wave moving from left to right. Write a mathematical equation that represents this wave at any time. Assume the length of the side of each square to be 1 cm and the time interval between the two positions shown to be 1 sec.

15.3. The equation of a wave, using MKS units, is

$$y = 0.2 \sin 2\pi(x/0.3 - t/0.5)$$

What is the displacement y at $x = 101$ m and $t = 45$ sec?

15.4. Write the equation of a wave moving in the direction of increasing x with the following characteristics:

(A) speed 2 m/sec, frequency 3 cycles/sec, amplitude 0.5 m

(B) speed 3 m/sec, period 0.5 sec, amplitude 0.5 m

(C) speed 300 m/sec, wavelength 0.30 m, amplitude 0.001 m

(D) frequency 1,000 cycles/sec, wavelength 3.0 m, amplitude 0.02 m

(E) wavelength 3 m, period 1.5 sec, amplitude 0.50 m

15.5. From each of the following formulas for waves determine the amplitude, frequency, period, speed, and wavelength. All quantities are in MKS units.

(A) $y = 0.15 \sin 2\pi(3x - 2t)$

(B) $y = 2.5 \sin 2(3x - 2t)$ (The omission of the π is intentional.)

(C) $y = 3.0 \sin (x - vt)$

(D) $y = 0.5 \sin (2\pi x/5 - t/6)$

(E) $y = 0.003 \sin (2\pi x - 4\pi t)$

15.6. At the point $x = 0$ a particle vibrates in accordance with the equation $y = \sin (-5\pi t)$ under the influence of a wave. The shape of the wave, on the other hand, satisfies the equation $y = \sin (7\pi x)$ when $t = 0$. Write the equation of a wave moving in the positive x direction and satisfying both of the requirements above. What are the frequency, speed, and wavelength of this wave? Assume that MKS units are used throughout.

15.7. Take the numerical values y of the displacements along the lines labeled x' and x'' in Fig. 15.6, and plot them vertically instead of horizontally against x. Compare the graphs with those of Fig. 15.5.

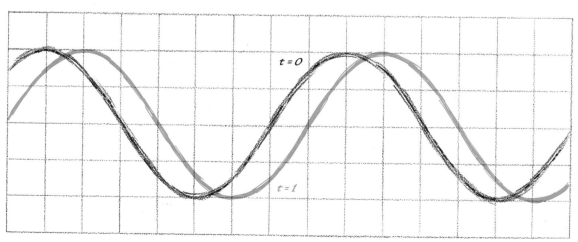

FIG. 15.11

15.8. It is important to distinguish between the speed of a wave and the speed of a particle in the wave. Consider the wave whose equation is

$$y = 0.5 \sin 2\pi(x/2 - t/3)$$

1. Find the speed of the wave by finding its wavelength, λ, and its period, T.

2. The simple harmonic motion of each point has an amplitude of 0.5 m and the same period as the wave. Find the maximum speed of the particle by considering the speed of a point on the circle of reference of radius 0.5 m, which completes 1 cycle in T sec.

15.9. All functions of the form $y = f(x - vt)$ represent waves. Study the special (and quite artificial) example $y = (x - vt)^2$ graphically as follows: The variables are x, y, and t. Let v be a constant, 1 cm/sec. Plot y against x:

(A) at $t = 0$ sec (for x between -2 and $+2$)
(B) at $t = 1$ sec (for x between -1 and $+3$)
(C) at $t = 2$ sec (for x between 0 and $+4$)

15.10. A vibration obeys the equation

$$y = \sin (2\pi t/5 + \pi)$$

Write this in expanded form by using the equation

$$\sin (\alpha + \beta) = \sin \alpha \cos \beta + \cos \alpha \sin \beta$$

and prove that it is equivalent to

$$y = -\sin (2\pi t/5)$$

What does the addition of π radians to the argument of the sine function do to its graph? Compare, for example, the graphs of

$$y = \sin (2\pi t/5 + \pi)$$

and

$$y = \sin (2\pi t/5)$$

15.11. 1. Prove that

$$\sin 2\pi \left(\frac{x + 2\lambda}{\lambda} - \frac{t}{T} \right) = \sin 2\pi \left(\frac{x}{\lambda} - \frac{t}{T} \right)$$

Hint: Use the technique employed in Prob. 15.10, letting $2\pi(x/\lambda - t/T)$ equal α.

2. Prove, similarly, that

$$\sin 2\pi \left(\frac{x}{\lambda} - \frac{t + 3T}{T} \right) = \sin 2\pi \left(\frac{x}{\lambda} - \frac{t}{T} \right)$$

15.12. 1. Prove that $y = x$ is an odd function and that $y = x^2$ is an even function.

2. Is $y = (1/x)^3$ an odd function?

16

The Superposition
of Waves

ONE OF the most remarkable properties of waves is that they can cross in the same medium without permanently damaging one another. Waves from many radio stations, for example, reach the antenna of a radio receiver simultaneously and move on very much in the same way that ripples formed by a rock dropped on a still pond pursue their own circular destiny despite the ripples formed by another rock dropped simultaneously nearby.

16.1. The Principle of Superposition

We can best learn how waves pass one another in the same medium by considering first the behavior of a single pulse as it passes through an elastic one-dimensional medium. It travels at a constant speed, preserving its shape as it goes along. In Figure 16.1 two successive positions are shown as the pulse moves from left to right. Notice that the particle at A has to move *down* to A' while the one at B has to move *up* to B' in order for the pulse to move from left to right. The pulse seems to be able to instruct a particle to move up or down as the situation requires. Actually, of course, a combination of elastic forces and the inertia of the medium are responsible for its motion. The very fact that a particle is accelerated vertically proves that a vertical force acts on it as the pulse passes.

What would happen if transverse pulses originating at opposite ends of a spring were to meet? Figure 16.2 shows the result. It can be summarized very simply. If the one pulse acting alone can produce displacement y_1 at a certain point and the other can produce displacement y_2 at the same point, the combined result is simply $y_1 + y_2$. This **principle of superposition** describes the behavior of pulses. In Figure 16.3 we see in greater detail how y_1 and y_2, added together, produce the combined displacement as the pulses approach coincidence. The dashed black curve represents the pulse causing displacement y_1, the dashed green curve represents the pulse causing displacement y_2, and the solid black curve, representing the combined pulses, results from the addition of the ordinates y_1 and y_2 at each point of the x axis.

If one pulse has positive values and the other negative values, the displacement, when they meet, is still the algebraic sum, with the results shown in Figure 16.4. In line C we see a complete instantaneous cancellation. Because one pulse is the

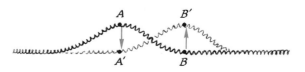

FIG. 16.1. *Behavior of particles in a one-dimensional medium as a pulse passes through it.*

mirror image of the other, their effects, at one instant of time, balance completely, and the displacement is zero, as shown by the solid line. If the pulses are alike but are not mirror images of each other (Fig. 16.5), they never cancel out completely, but there is one point (*P*) at which $y_1 + y_2 = 0$ throughout the interval of encounter.

Our illustrations have dealt only with transverse pulses, but the principle of superposition is valid for longitudinal pulses also. In these, of course, the displacements y_1 and y_2 are parallel to the direction of propagation. If a longitudinal pulse travels along the *x* axis, the displacement, y_1, of the particles is parallel to that axis. If two pulses produce $y_1 + y_2 = 0$, the instantaneous *x* displacement at that instant is zero; the particle finds itself just where it would have been if no pulses were going by.

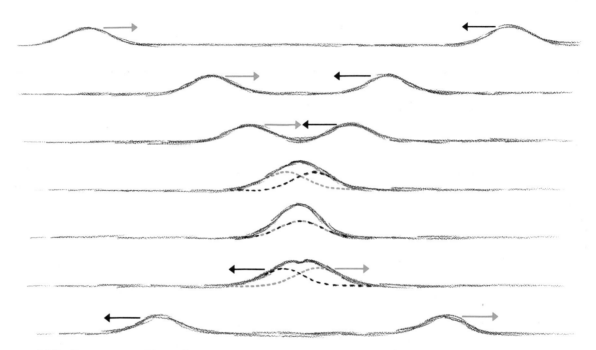

FIG. 16.2. *Superposition: Two pulses originating at opposite ends of a coiled spring move in opposite directions, cross each other, and continue after meeting. The displacement of a particle is the algebraic sum of the individual displacements produced by the two pulses.*

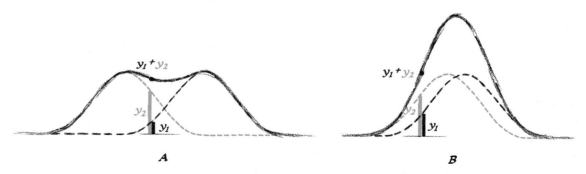

FIG. 16.3. *How superposition is effected.*

16.2. Superposition of Two Simple Harmonic Waves

1. *Mathematical Treatment*

Let us assume that the principle of superposition holds for waves as well as for pulses and consider mathematically the effect of two waves, one traveling from left to right and the other from right to left, on the same one-dimensional medium. The equations

$$y_1 = A \sin \left(\frac{2\pi x}{\lambda} - \frac{2\pi t}{T} \right) \qquad [16.1$$

$$y_2 = A \sin \left(\frac{2\pi x}{\lambda} + \frac{2\pi t}{T} \right) \qquad [16.2$$

represent waves set up by simple harmonic motions, of amplitude A, period T, and wavelength

λ, traveling in opposite directions along the x axis. The resultant displacement, y, is given by the principle of superposition:

$$y = y_1 + y_2 \qquad [16.3$$

$$y = A \sin \left(\frac{2\pi x}{\lambda} - \frac{2\pi t}{T} \right) + A \sin \left(\frac{2\pi x}{\lambda} + \frac{2\pi t}{T} \right) \qquad [16.4$$

At this point we need the following trigonometric identity (see Prob. 16.11):

$$\sin \alpha + \sin \beta = 2 \sin \left(\frac{\alpha + \beta}{2} \right) \cos \left(\frac{\alpha - \beta}{2} \right) \qquad [16.5$$

It holds for all values of α and β. Notice that on the right-hand side the argument of the sine is half of the sum of the two angles and the argument of the cosine is half of the difference of the two angles. This makes the application of equation 16.5 to equation 16.4 particularly simple, for the sum of the two angles in question here is $4\pi x/\lambda$ and the difference is $-4\pi t/T$. Hence equation 16.4

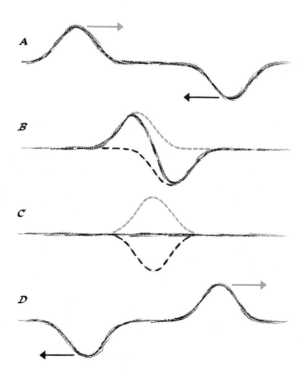

FIG. 16.4. *Superposition of pulses producing zero displacement (C).*

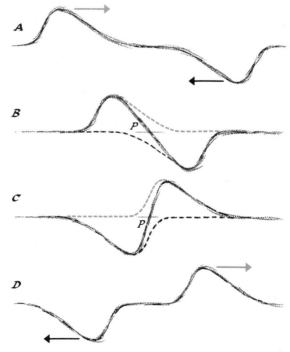

FIG. 16.5. *Superposition of two pulses that are alike but not symmetrical about the line of propagation. There is one point (P) at which $y_1 + y_2 = 0$ during the encounter.*

FIG. 16.6. *Snapshot of a standing wave produced by waves moving in opposite directions.*

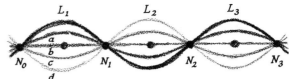

FIG. 16.7. *Graphs of a standing wave.*

becomes

$$y = 2A \sin \frac{2\pi x}{\lambda} \cos \frac{2\pi t}{T} \qquad [16.6$$

(Since $\cos -\theta = \cos \theta$, we drop the negative sign before $2\pi t/T$.)

Does this equation represent a wave? It no longer has the characteristic form involving $(x - vt)$ or $(2\pi x/\lambda - 2\pi t/T)$ in the argument. What happens, for example, at some arbitrary point, x_1? We get the equation

$$y = \left(2A \sin \frac{2\pi x_1}{\lambda} \right) \cos \frac{2\pi t}{T}$$

and, since all the quantities inside the parentheses are constant, we could write it as

$$y = A' \cos \frac{2\pi t}{T} \qquad [16.7$$

This is the equation of a simple harmonic motion, but the amplitude, A', depends on the value chosen for x_1. If, for example, $x_1 = n\lambda$ and n is an integer,

$$A' = 2A \sin \frac{2\pi n\lambda}{\lambda} = 0$$

At this particular value of x the amplitude is always zero, but at the point $x_1 = \lambda/4$

$$A' = 2A \sin \frac{\pi}{2} = 2A$$

Here the amplitude is twice the amplitude of either wave alone.

Equation 16.6 can be plotted against x if t is considered constant. At $t = 0$, for example, $\cos 2\pi t/T = 1$, and the graph is like that shown in Figure 16.6. At the subsequent times $t = T/8$, $t = T/4$, $t = 3T/8$, and $t = T/2$, the graphs are like those shown as curves a, b, c, and d, respectively, of Figure 16.7. Points like N_0, N_1, N_2, and N_3, where the amplitude of the vibration is always zero, are called **nodes**. Points like L_1, L_2, and L_3,

where the amplitude is greatest ($2A$), are called **antinodes**. The configuration is now called a **standing wave**. It does not have crests that travel at a constant speed along the x axis. In a progressive wave, you will remember, the displacement, velocity, and acceleration at any point are just like those at any other point except in phase, which varies gradually from one point to the next. In a standing wave, on the other hand, all the points from N_0 to N_1 have the same phase, which is opposite to that of all the points from N_1 to N_2; and (possibly most interesting of all) there are instants when all points have, simultaneously, a zero displacement (curve b)—something that never happens in a single progressive wave.

2. Experimental Results

So far our discussion has been purely theoretical. How well do experiments confirm our conclusions? Figure 16.8 shows drawings made from photographs of standing waves produced in a coiled spring. Instead of having two vibrating sources, one at each end, the spring was tied down firmly at one end. This fixed end produced reflected waves, which, moving in the direction opposite to that of the incoming waves, produced standing waves by superposition.

To understand how a reflected wave is set up, consider the behavior of the single pulse traveling from left to right in Figure 16.9. The spring is tied at the right end. The successive drawings show how the pulse is reflected. In the sixth line we see a situation reminiscent of Figure 16.4.C, where for a moment the superposition of two pulses moving in opposite directions produced a zero displacement for all particles. The explanation of the reversal in reflection in this: The end point is held fixed. Therefore, to balance the upward force that the incoming pulse exerts on that point, *the support has to supply an equal downward force.* This downward force, acting on the spring, sets up the pulse going in the return direction. If we have a train of waves coming from the left, it generates a train of reflected waves going to the left, and the superposition of the two trains produces the standing waves of Figure 16.8. A node is produced at the fixed end because the reflected wave changes phase.

Transverse waves are easier to visualize than longitudinal waves and are therefore chosen to illustrate graphically the concept of superposition, but bear in mind that longitudinal waves, such as sound waves, also exhibit the effects of superposition. We shall soon consider some examples under the topics *resonance* and *beats*.

We have seen the important role that the reflected wave plays in the production of standing waves. It is instructive to consider experimentally what happens when a pulse traveling in a light spring meets a heavy spring and when it meets a light thread.

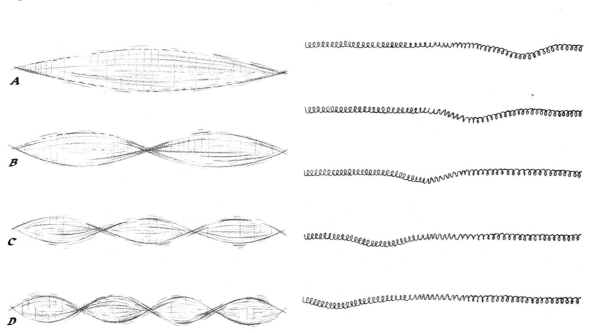

FIG. 16.8. *Standing waves in a coiled spring. The frequencies of patterns A, B, C, and D are in the ratios 1:2:3:4.*

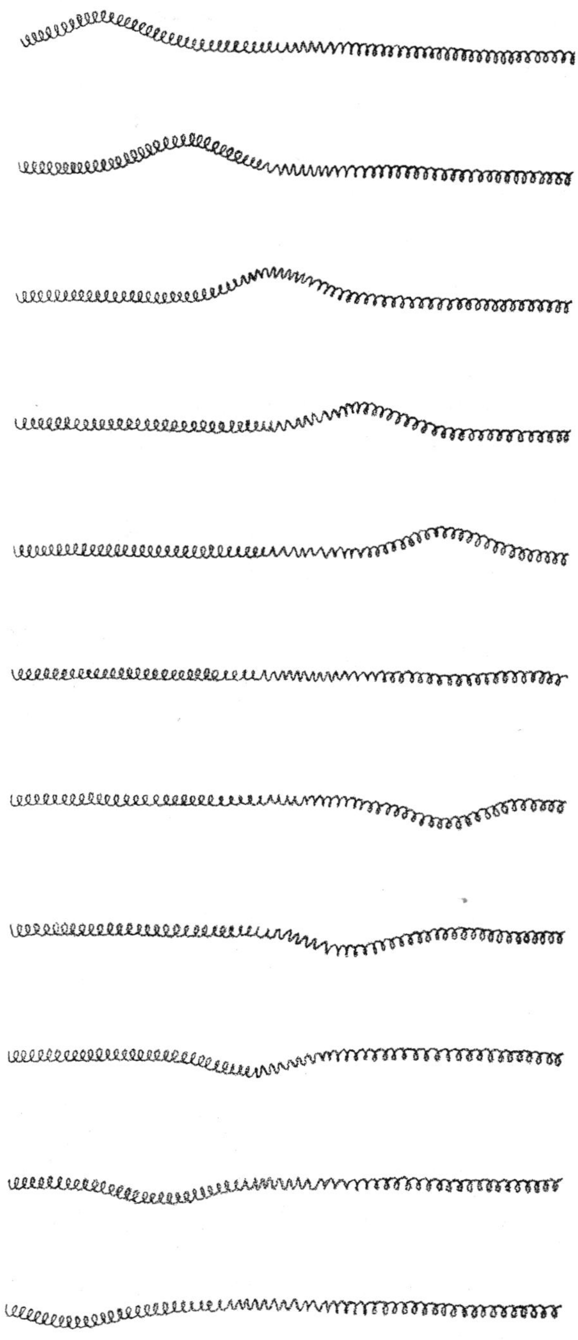

A

B

C

D

FIG. 16.9. *Reflection of a pulse in a coiled spring.*

In Figure 16.10 a pulse moving in a light spring (left) meets a heavy spring. The sequence of drawings shows that the pulse is transmitted in part, that it is reflected in part, and that the reflected pulse is upside down. In Figure 16.11 a pulse moving in a heavy spring (left) meets a light spring. ("Heavy" and "light" refer here to relative linear densities.) This sequence shows that the pulse is transmitted in part, that it is reflected in part, and that the reflected pulse is right side up. Both figures reveal still another significant fact. The pulse travels faster in the light spring than in the heavy one. Figure 16.12 shows what happens when a pulse moving in a spring meets

a very light thread. Here we see only a reflected wave, which is right side up.

It can be shown experimentally that similar phenomena take place with waves in two-dimensional and three-dimensional media. (When I speak of the latter as light or dense, I refer to the relative densities.)

I generalize these results without proof as follows: in the passage from a lighter to a denser medium, reflection, transmission, and change of phase take place, and the amplitude of the reflected pulse approaches that of the incoming pulse if the ratio of densities is considerably different from unity. When the two media have

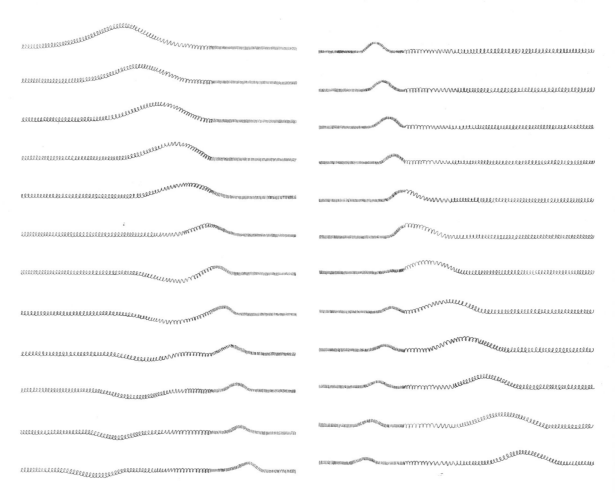

FIG. 16.10. *Pulse moving from a light spring (left) into a heavy one.*

FIG. 16.11. *Pulse moving from a heavy spring (left) into a light one.*

similar densities, no reflection takes place (only transmission). In the passage from a denser to a lighter medium, reflection without change of phase occurs.

16.3. Resonance

We can now take up the phenomenon of **resonance**. Here is a simple example of it: Anyone who has pushed a child in a swing knows that he can increase the amplitude of the swing by pushing in phase with the frequency of vibration of the swing. Another example is offered by sympathetic tuning forks—that is, forks with identical frequencies (Fig. 16.13). When one of a pair is struck (A), the sound waves from it set the other vibrating if the two are very closely matched in frequency. If the fork that was struck is silenced by hand (B), a persisting tone can be traced to the

other, resonating fork, for, when it is touched (C), the tone ceases.

Resonance occurs when a body is fed energy that is in tune with its own frequency; it occurs even in atomic vibrations. We can gain some insight into its nature by considering one further example. The column of air in a tube with one end closed (Fig. 16.14) resonates with a vibrating tuning fork that is held at its open end if the tube's length, L, has a certain relation to the fork's frequency. Suppose that, while one prong of the fork is undergoing its maximum excursion, from E to F (we neglect the effect of the other prong in order to simplify our discussion), the sound pulse in air travels from C to D and back to C. It is now ready to reinforce the motion of the prong at F; that is, the condition for resonance exists. If the period of the tuning fork is T, half of the length of the sound wave in air must be $2L$ (that is, $CD + DC$) since it takes time $T/2$ for the prong to go from E to F.

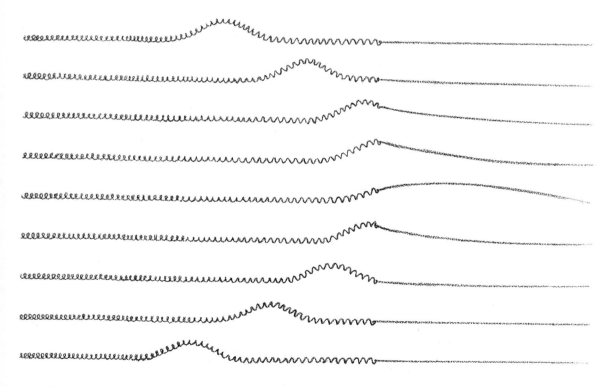

FIG. 16.12. *Pulse moving in a spring tied to a very light thread.*

Hence the full length of the sound wave is 4L. Using either of the equations $v = \nu\lambda$ and $v = \lambda/T$, we get the equation

$$v = \frac{4L}{T} \qquad [16.8$$

This equation is only approximately true because the maximum disturbance is not exactly at C, but it is interesting for two reasons: (1) it enables us, with the tuning fork acting as a kind of clock for short time intervals, to measure the speed of sound waves in air (about 330 m/sec) in a very small space; (2) the production of resonance in this way proves that the principle of superposition is valid for longitudinal waves (such as those of sound).

How superposition takes place in the tube can be depicted diagrammatically. (The dashed curve of Fig. 16.14 looks like part of a standing trans-verse wave, but it is not. It is supposed to show that the amplitude of the standing longitudinal wave in the tube is greatest at C and zero at D, with a gradual transition from one to the other.) As the sound waves traveling down the tube meet a denser medium, the reflected wave changes phase, and a node is formed at D by superposition. As the sound waves moving up the tube meet a slightly less dense medium (the open air), reflection takes place without change of phase, and an antinode is therefore formed at C. A comparison of Figures 16.6 and 16.7 shows that the distance between two successive nodes is half of a wavelength. The distance between a node and the nearest antinode is therefore a quarter of a wavelength. Hence $4L = \lambda$, which is the value we used to get equation 16.8.

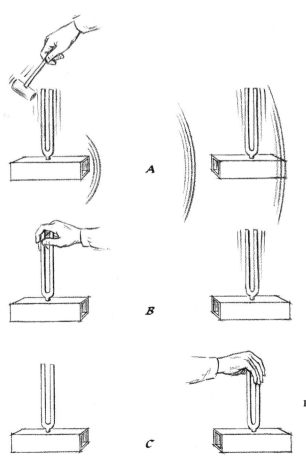

FIG. 16.13. *Resonant tuning forks.*

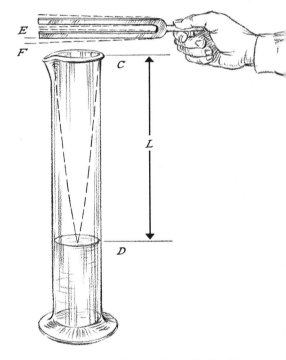

FIG. 16.14. *A resonant column of air: If the distance CD is a quarter of a wavelength of the wave produced in air by the tuning fork, the condition for resonance prevails. Resonance occurs for other lengths of air column. The criterion is that the reflected wave in air be in phase, at C, with the vibration of the tuning fork.*

16.4. Beats and Other Effects of Combining Simple Harmonic Motions

Something interesting happens when two simple harmonic motions have almost identical frequencies. Two springs, for example, may seem identical, and we may attach two bodies of apparently equal mass to them (Fig. 16.15); yet, if we pull the bodies downward by the same distance and release them simultaneously, the slightest difference in their periods will show up in time. They start off apparently in phase (A); but, if we wait long enough (Δt), we may see them moving with opposite phases (B). If we wait another interval Δt, we see them again in phase (C). The smaller the difference in their periods, the longer will be the time ($2\Delta t$) they take to come back into phase. It is apparent at once that, if we were to add the displacements of these vibrations algebraically, the resultant of the combination would go to zero after interval Δt and come back to a maximum after another interval Δt.

We can again demonstrate experimentally that the principle of superposition holds for sound waves, which are longitudinal, by setting up two wave trains from two tuning forks of periods T_1 and T_2. Considering only the variation of the waves in time, we have the equations

$$y_1 = A \sin \frac{2\pi t}{T_1} \qquad [16.9$$

$$y_2 = A \sin \frac{2\pi t}{T_2} \qquad [16.10$$

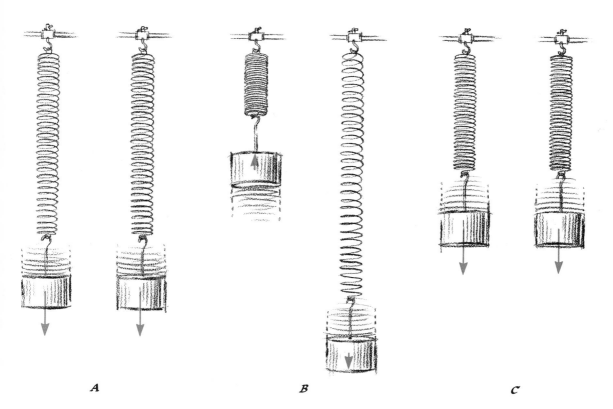

A   B   C

FIG. 16.15. *A sensitive way to detect the difference in frequency between two vibrations with almost equal frequencies: (A) The vibrations, initially in phase, remain approximately so for several cycles. (B) After time Δt they are completely out of phase. (C) By time $2(\Delta t)$ they are in phase again. The difference between the two frequencies is $\frac{1}{2}(\Delta t)$.*

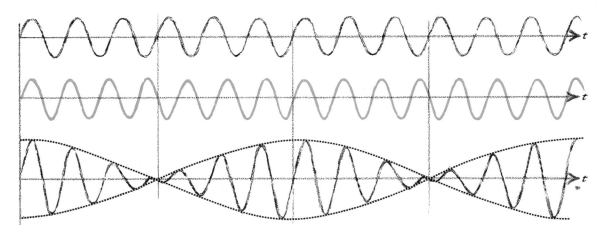

FIG. 16.16. *Graphical analysis of the superposition of two vibrations with almost equal frequencies. The curve at the top shows a simple harmonic vibration with a frequency of 6 cycles/sec. The green curve shows one with 7 cycles/sec. The curve at the bottom, obtained by algebraic addition of the ordinates of the two others, has an amplitude variation whose frequency is 1 cycle/sec.*

By the principle of superposition and equation 16.6 we get the equation

$$y = y_1 + y_2$$
$$= 2A \sin \pi t \left(\frac{1}{T_1} + \frac{1}{T_2}\right) \cos \pi t \left(\frac{1}{T_1} - \frac{1}{T_2}\right) \quad [16.11$$

or, since $\nu = 1/T$, we may write this as

$$y = 2A \sin 2\pi t \left(\frac{\nu_1 + \nu_2}{2}\right) \cos 2\pi t \left(\frac{\nu_1 - \nu_2}{2}\right) \quad [16.12$$

Now, if ν_1 and ν_2 are very similar, $\bar{\nu} = (\nu_1 + \nu_2)/2$, being the average frequency, is very close to ν_1 or ν_2. Letting $\nu_1 - \nu_2$ equal $\Delta\nu$, we get the equation

$$y = 2A \sin 2\pi\bar{\nu}t \cos 2\pi \frac{\Delta\nu}{2} t \quad [16.13$$

or

$$y = \left(2A \cos 2\pi \frac{\Delta\nu}{2} t\right) \sin 2\pi\bar{\nu}t \quad [16.14$$

The quantity inside the parentheses is not a constant; it varies slowly if $\Delta\nu$ is very small. We may write the equation

$$y = A' \sin 2\pi\bar{\nu}t \quad [16.15$$

in which

$$A' = 2A \cos 2\pi (\Delta\nu/2)t$$

may be considered the slowly varying amplitude of the vibration whose frequency is $\bar{\nu}$. The amplitude A' itself has the frequency $\Delta\nu/2$, but it reaches maxima of absolute value (regardless of sign) with the frequency $\Delta\nu = \nu_1 - \nu_2$. This is the so-called **beat frequency**. It can be heard when tuning forks

or stringed instruments or any other sources of sound waves vibrating simultaneously differ very slightly in frequency. Graphs of signals picked up by a microphone from two beating tuning forks might look like the upper two curves of Figure 16.16; a graph of the combination of the two waves, according to the principle of superposition, would then look like the lowest curve.

With the cathode-ray oscilloscope we can compare two simple harmonic motions. If we impress a signal that produces the vertical deflection

$$y = A \sin 2\pi\nu t$$

and simultaneously impress a signal that drives the spot on the screen according to the equation

$$x = A \cos 2\pi\nu t$$

the spot will trace out the circle $x^2 + y^2 = A^2$. This is most readily appreciated intuitively if you consider the projections on the y and x axes of a point on a circle moving with angular velocity $\omega = 2\pi\nu$ (Fig. 16.17). The two equations

$$y = A \sin 2\pi\nu t$$
$$x = A \cos 2\pi\nu t$$

taken together, obviously give to the point $P(x,y)$ a circular motion. The requirement is that ν be the same for both SHMs. If the two amplitudes are not exactly alike, the curve will be an ellipse; if the frequencies differ, the spot will not return to its starting point at the end of one cycle.

If you have the equations

$$y = A \sin 2\pi\nu_1 t$$
$$x = B \cos 2\pi\nu_2 t$$

you may be able to convince yourself (see Prob. 16.10) that the result (Fig. 16.18) is a plot somewhat like A if $\nu_1 = 2\nu_2$ and like B if $\nu_1 = 3\nu_3$. In other words, if ν_1 is an integral multiple of ν_2, the pattern, called a Lissajous figure (after the French physicist Jules-Antoine Lissajous, 1822–1880), closes on itself, and the number of loops (two in A, three in B) gives the value of the integer in question. In this way a standard frequency can serve as a basis for calibrating higher frequencies.

16.5. Vibrations, Waves, and Sound

I have occasionally used sound to illustrate the properties of waves and vibrations, but I shall not be able to treat the topic of sound with the thoroughness it used to receive in elementary texts. The topic is not lacking in interest or practical importance, however; a whole journal of the American Institute of Physics (*The Journal of the Acoustical Society of America*) is devoted to sound and related topics, and there are many engineering journals devoted to the science of sound recording and reproduction. Interest in high-fidelity sound recording and reproduction has never been higher.

Today, however, vibrations and waves, in the study of physics, are more important in relation to electricity, light, and atomic physics than in relation to sound alone, and we therefore leave the study of sound—reluctantly—to more specialized books.

Observe, however, how the wave nature of sound can be graphically portrayed (Fig. 16.19).

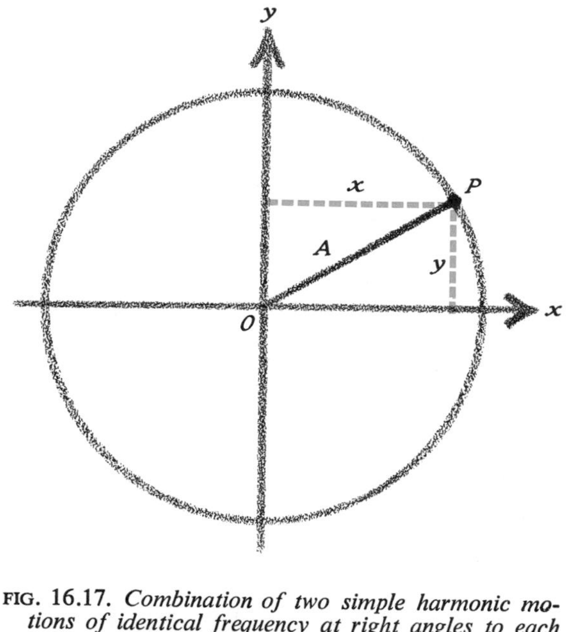

FIG. 16.18. *Lissajous figures.*

FIG. 16.17. *Combination of two simple harmonic motions of identical frequency at right angles to each other, producing circular motion. Working backward, we see that a point moving in a circle of radius A with constant angular velocity* $\omega = 2\pi\nu$ *obviously has the displacement components*
$$x = A \cos 2\pi\nu t \quad and \quad y = A \sin 2\pi\nu t$$

FIG. 16.19. *The pattern of sound waves produced by a scanning technique. A tiny microphone and a 110-V neon lamp scan the sound-wave field while the camera is set for a time exposure. (Photograph from Bell Telephone Laboratories.)*

Sound waves in air are invisible, but a lamp whose brilliance varies with the instantaneous amplitude of the sound vibration produces this photograph (ten-minute exposure) when it is moved through the sound field. (The waves look like standing waves but are not. The superposition of waves produces the maxima and minima, seen here as light and dark regions.)

16.6. Summary

Several waves can travel over the same medium simultaneously without destroying one another.

The principle of superposition states that the displacement produced by several waves at a point is the algebraic sum of their individual displacements.

When two waves of the same frequency move in opposite directions in the same medium, the result is a standing wave.

Beats occur when two waves of almost identical frequencies move in the same medium; the beat frequency is the difference between the two frequencies.

Resonance occurs when a body is fed energy that is in tune with its own frequency.

Problems

16.1. Outdoors, on a very still day, an electronic device for generating sound waves of controllable frequency (called an audio-frequency oscillator—AFO) sets up a wave with a frequency of 1,000 vibrations per second. The sound is reflected from a single vertical wall. The incident and reflected waves combine according to the principle of superposition, and the maxima and minima can be located with the aid of a microphone. Describe the probable location of intensity maxima and minima on a line through the source and perpendicular to the wall. What is the distance between successive maxima if the speed of sound waves is 330 m/sec?

16.2. A wave travels from left to right at a speed of 2 m/sec along a coiled spring. It has an amplitude of 50 cm and a frequency of 5 cycles/sec. Write its equation. Write the equation of a wave going in the opposite direction with the same speed, amplitude, and frequency. Write the equation of the standing wave set up as a result of superposition. Make a sketch of the standing wave pattern. What is the distance between successive maxima of amplitude? What is the speed of propagation of the standing wave?

16.3. In Fig. 16.15 the two systems have periods of 2.00 and 2.01 seconds. If they are started together, as in part A, how long will it be before they are out of phase, as in part B?

16.4. A tuning fork with a frequency of 500 vibrations/sec can vibrate with an amplitude of 0.2 cm at point P in space. Another tuning fork, vibrating

separately, can produce the same amplitude at P with a frequency of 502 vibrations/sec.

1. Describe what happens in time to the magnitude of the maximum displacements at P when both tuning forks vibrate.

2. How many times per second does the maximum of greatest magnitude occur at P when both tuning forks vibrate simultaneously?

16.5. An AFO (see Prob. 16.1) produces an audible vibration simultaneously with a tuning fork whose frequency is 500 vibrations/sec. Describe what will be heard as the AFO frequency varies continuously from 450 to 550 vibrations/sec while the tuning fork frequency remains constant.

16.6. Beats are often used in the tuning of musical instruments. A tuning fork is sounded, and the instrument's frequency is varied until the beat frequency goes to zero.

1. If a tuning fork vibrates at 440 vibrations/sec and a violin string vibrates at 444 vibrations/sec, what will be the length of time between successive maxima in amplitude?

2. A tuning fork with a frequency of 440 vibrations/sec produces 5 beats/sec when sounded together with a violin string. What is the frequency of the string if the slightest increase in its frequency produces fewer beats per second than before?

16.7. A tuning fork produces resonance in the air column above the water (Fig. 16.14) when the distance between the free surface of the water and the open end of the tube is 45 cm. If resonance does not occur for any shorter distance, what is the approximate frequency of the tuning fork if the speed of sound waves in air is 344 m/sec? If the container were very much taller, at what subsequent depths would resonance occur?

16.8. Draw two curves representing the displacements due to two separate sine waves traveling in the same direction and out of phase with each other by $\pi/2$ radians. Construct graphically the wave that is the resultant according to the principle of superposition.

16.9. Two plots of displacement against time are shown in Fig. 16.16. Assume that the total time interval is 1 sec. In the top curve, for example, there are 12 complete vibrations. Count the number of vibrations in the second curve. Estimate the average number of amplitude maxima per second from the third curve. Is the third curve drawn accurately according to the principle of superposition? If not, be specific about departures from this principle. What is the beat frequency?

16.10. To account for the shape of Fig. 16.18.A, combine two simple harmonic motions at right angles to each other graphically as follows. (Use the technique of Fig. 13.20, Prob. 13.11.) On a set of rectangular (x,y) coordinates draw a circle with a radius of two units and with its center at $(0,5)$;

draw another circle with a radius of one unit and with its center at $(4,0)$. Locate points $15°$ apart on the large circle, starting at $(2,5)$, labeled 0, and going round counterclockwise, numbering the successive points 1, 2, 3, . . . 24, the 24th point coinciding with 0. Similarly, locate points $30°$ apart on the smaller circle. Starting at $(5,0)$, labeled 0, go round counterclockwise, labeling subsequent points 1, 2, 3, . . . 12, the 12th point coinciding with 0. Go round once more, labeling the same points 13, 14, . . . 24. Now take the x coordinate from a point on the large circle and the y coordinate from the correspondingly labeled point on the small circle, and locate 24 points such as $(2,0)$, $(2 \cos 15°, 0.5)$, etc. Join all these points with a smooth curve. It should resemble Fig. 16.18.A.

16.11. In Chap. 15 it is stated without proof that

$$\sin (\alpha + \beta) = \sin \alpha \cos \beta + \cos \alpha \sin \beta$$

From this find the value of $\sin (\alpha - \beta)$, and show, by adding this to the first expression, that

$$\sin (\alpha + \beta) + \sin (\alpha - \beta) = 2 \sin \alpha \cos \beta$$

and, equivalently, that

$$\sin A + \sin B = 2 \sin \left(\frac{A+B}{2}\right) \cos \left(\frac{A-B}{2}\right)$$

Standing Waves and Natural Modes of Vibration

THERE are many examples of bodies with cyclic motions, and in general those with long periods are either large or massive or both. The earth takes 365 days to complete its cycle round the sun; the moon takes only 28 days to pass round the earth. A swing about 4 meters long has a period of 4 seconds, but a simple pendulum 1 meter long has a period of about 2 seconds. It is not difficult to find a spring on which a body with a mass of 1 kilogram has a period of 1 second, but a body with a mass of 10 grams has a period of 1/10 second on the same spring.

The formula for the period of a planet is $T = 2\pi\sqrt{R^3/MG}$ (R is the radius of the orbit, M the mass of the sun, and G the universal gravitational constant). For a pendulum $T = 2\pi\sqrt{l/g}$ (l is the length, g the acceleration due to gravity). In both of these motions the period gets longer as a length increases.

Even as we approach the atomic realm, it remains true that, as things get smaller, their periods of vibration get shorter. A whole tuning fork, for example, considered as a vibrating unit, can easily have a frequency of 1,000 cycles/sec, but the atoms of a quartz crystal (in a crystal-controlled radio transmitter, for example) can have a frequency of 10^6 cycles/sec. The nitrogen atom in an ammonia molecule has a frequency of 24×10^9 cycles/sec. The electromagnetic waves of the green light produced by electrically excited mercury vapor have a frequency of 5.5×10^{15} cycles/sec. If we go to even smaller things than the atom and even larger things than the solar system, we still find that, the larger a system is, the longer is its period of oscillation.

The formulas given above indicate that a system with a given set of constants has a certain frequency of its own. We shall call this a **natural frequency,** They also imply that we can change a period continuously by changing a mass or a length continuously. Since we know that continuity is only a convenient macroscopic illusion (§ 10.2), however, we may suspect that in atomic systems it is not possible to vary the period continuously—that only certain frequencies are permitted.

This suspicion turns out to be well founded. The fact that only certain frequencies produce orderly **modes** (patterns) **of oscillation** (and, for reasons to be made clear later, are called permitted, or natural, frequencies) is first encountered, however, in the macroscopic realm, in the phenomenon of standing waves; and we shall now study these waves for the insight they can give us into the deeper problems of atomic oscillations.

17.1. One-dimensional Standing Waves

For an illustration of standing waves we return to the transverse waves that can be set up in a rope. A rope (Fig. 17.1) is passed over a pulley (A) and tied to an object (B) that is capable of vibrating vertically. A weight (W) hung from one end of the rope supplies the tension. A variable-speed motor (M) is connected to a mechanism that gives B a vertical simple harmonic motion. As we speed up the motor and thus increase the driving frequency, we suddenly reach a critical frequency that sets up a natural mode of oscillation in the rope. This oscillation is actually a standing wave produced by the superposition of two progressive waves going in opposite directions. Observe that a standing wave is, in a sense, more like a complex pattern or mode of vibration than like a wave, for it does not travel. Particular modes of vibration are associated with certain frequencies, which we shall call natural or **permitted frequencies.**

Since we have nodes at A and B and an antinode in the middle, the distance, L, from A to B is half of a wavelength. Hence in the equation $v = \nu\lambda$ we can put 2L for λ, obtaining $v = 2\nu L$.

The speed of propagation of a wave along such a rope obeys the equation

$$v = \sqrt{\frac{\text{tension}}{\text{linear density}}} \qquad [17.1$$

We may write tension as f (force), measurable in newtons. The linear density of the rope, symbolized by ρ (rho), is measurable in kilograms per meter.

The units of $\sqrt{f/\rho}$ are

$$\sqrt{\frac{\text{newtons}}{\text{kg/m}}} = \sqrt{\frac{\text{kg-m/sec}^2}{\text{kg/m}}} = \sqrt{\frac{\text{m}^2}{\text{sec}^2}} = \frac{\text{m}}{\text{sec}} \qquad [17.2$$

We have thus proved that equation 17.1 is correct in its units. We shall accept it for the present without further proof. (It can be proved on dynamical principles; see Chap. 25.) Let us now put the expression $v = \sqrt{f/\rho}$ into the equation $v = \nu 2L$ and solve for ν. We get

$$\nu_1 = \frac{\sqrt{f/\rho}}{2L} \qquad [17.3$$

This is the equation of the **fundamental mode** of oscillation of the rope (the mode with the lowest

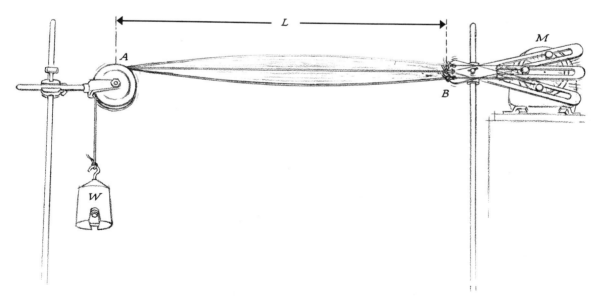

FIG. 17.1. *Apparatus for setting up standing wave patterns in a stretched rope.*

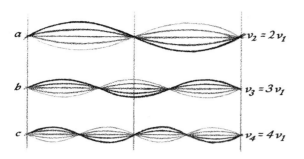

$v_2 = 2v_1$

$v_3 = 3v_1$

$v_4 = 4v_1$

FIG. 17.2. *The standing waves (in a rope) corresponding to integral multiples of the fundamental frequency illustrated in Fig. 17.1.*

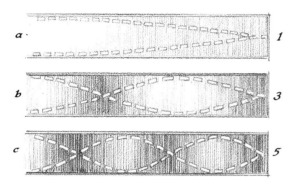

FIG. 17.3. *Natural modes of vibration of air in a pipe closed at one end. The curves suggest greatest amplitude (antinodes) where they are farthest apart and zero amplitude (nodes) where they meet. The longitudinal nature of the vibration is suggested by the shading, which gets darker in the regions of smaller amplitude.*

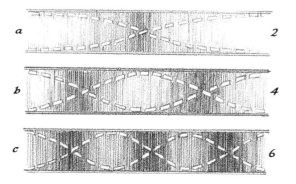

FIG. 17.4. *Natural modes of vibration of air in a pipe open at both ends. The darkest regions are nodes, and the lightest regions are antinodes. The amplitude of the vibration is also suggested by the separation between the two curves in each pipe.*

frequency), and for this reason the subscript 1 is used.

If the driving frequency is now increased gradually, no orderly pattern is produced until the frequency $v_2 = 2v_1$ is reached. Since the standing wave is produced by superposition, and since our method of support demands a node at each end, the simplest pattern after the fundamental one must be that of Figure 17.2.a, where the wavelength is half of what it was before. This requires twice the frequency. Figures 17.2.b and 17.2.c show the next permitted standing-wave patterns, those with frequencies $v_3 = 3v_1$ and $v_4 = 4v_1$. The important thing to observe is that only certain definite frequencies are permitted.

The strings of musical instruments obey the same conditions as the rope, but the amplitudes are often so small that the oscillations cannot be seen. We can analyze the frequencies, however, by picking up the sound energy with a microphone, amplifying the signal, and displaying it on a cathode-ray oscilloscope in the manner discussed in § 15.1. We discover that a string may vibrate with several of the permitted frequencies simultaneously. (One way to visualize this result is to impress the signal from the microphone on the y axis and a variable frequency from a variable-frequency oscillator on the x axis. When the latter reaches $v = v_2$, a pattern like that of Figure 16.18.A appears; when it reaches $v = v_3$, a pattern like that of Figure 16.18.B appears; and so on.)

The analysis of musical sounds has been greatly simplified by the cathode-ray oscilloscope. Using it, we find that one of the things that distinguish musical instruments from one another is that, even when two instruments are playing the same note (with the same fundamental frequency), the relative amplitudes at which the other permitted frequencies (called overtones, in music) appear vary greatly from the one to the other. The overtones are, in large part, responsible for the quality of the musical tone. Middle C on a piano sounds different from middle C on a trumpet, for example, mainly because the two instruments produce the overtones of that tone with different relative amplitudes.

Another illustration of standing waves in one dimension is afforded by the longitudinal vibration of air in long pipes (Figs. 17.3 and 17.4). As in Figure 16.14, the dashed lines look like transverse wave patterns, but they simply serve to give an idea of the varying amplitude of the standing waves—longitudinal in this case—within the pipe. Where they cross, the amplitude is zero and there is a node. Where they are farthest apart, there is an antinode. For reasons outlined in § 16.3, the fundamental mode of a pipe closed at one end contains one quarter wavelength. The principle of superposition demands a node at the closed end and an antinode at the open end. Hence the first three permitted patterns of such a pipe are those shown schematically in Figure 17.3, in which the numbers 1, 3, and 5 indicate the number of quarter wavelengths that fit in the pipe under these conditions. Hence the frequencies are in the ratios $1:3:5$. Figure 17.4 represents the first three permitted longitudinal standing waves of a pipe open at both ends. Since the pipe contains 2, 4, and 6 quarter wavelengths, the first three frequencies are in the ratios $1:2:3$. A pipe open at both ends has, we see, a fundamental frequency twice as great as that of a similar pipe closed at one end. The closed pipe selects frequencies in the ratios $1:3:5:7$ etc., whereas the open pipe selects those in the ratios $1:2:3:4:5$ etc. The open pipe has all the overtones that the closed one has—and more.

The vibrations of long thin rods also present some interesting features. One of the most interesting is the establishment of a longitudinal standing wave with the antinode-node-antinode pattern of Figure 17.4.a. If an aluminum rod about a meter long is held by hand at its center and struck longitudinally with a hammer (Fig. 17.5), the vibration set up persists, and is even audible in a large auditorium, for a long time. There are regions in the room where, by the principle of superposition, the sound waves from the two ends of the rod arrive out of phase and produce a less intense sound. We can find these regions by covering one ear and moving the head to and fro to explore the intensity of the sound field. We can prove that the vibrations at the ends run parallel to the rod by bringing one end to touch a table-tennis ball suspended by a long thin string. The ball is visibly deflected by the longitudinal impacts of the rod. Usually transverse vibrations are also set up simultaneously, but we can dampen them by running the fingers of one hand over one end,

as shown in Figure 17.6. This does not stop the longitudinal vibrations, which audibly persist.

The xylophone is evidence that we can also produce musical tones by striking rods transversely.

17.2. Two-dimensional Standing Waves

One of the simplest and most beautiful demonstrations of standing waves in two dimensions is afforded by **Chladni plates.**† These thin plates, made of glass or of some metal like brass and supported firmly in the center, are excited by being stroked on the edge with a violin bow. Sand or salt sprinkled on the surface will show up the standing wave pattern. Nodes—in fact, whole nodal lines—will be formed where fingers touch the edge of a plate while it is being stroked elsewhere, and the sand particles will accumulate on the nodal lines. Chladni patterns on plates in the

† Named after E. F. F. Chladni (1756–1824), a German physicist.

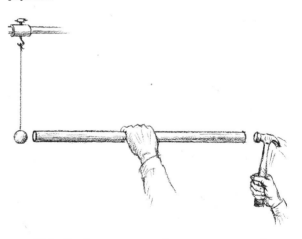

FIG. 17.5. *Setting up a standing wave pattern (corresponding to Fig. 17.4.a) in an aluminum bar.*

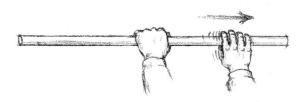

FIG. 17.6. *Stopping the transverse vibrations of a bar.*

shape of a violin are shown in Figure 17.7. If a plate is made of glass, a strong light under it will project its patterns as shadows of the sand on the ceiling (Fig. 17.8).

Standing waves can often be seen on the surface of puddles of water that form on a vibrating platform—in the sink of the washroom in an airplane, for instance, where the vibration of the engines produces standing waves on the water surface. A simple demonstration can be made in the classroom with a glass dish containing water and placed on a projector with a horizontal stand (Fig. 17.9). An electric drill connected to a variable autotransformer and with an eccentric piece of metal on its shaft can produce vibrations of different frequencies. At certain frequencies standing waves are produced on the surface of the water. The variable refraction of the nodes and antinodes makes their projection visible on the screen.

The magnitudes of the permitted frequencies are called, in advanced works, the **eigenvalues.** What these demonstrations show is that eigenvalues exist in many different kinds of vibrating systems. The systems have a natural ability to vibrate at these frequencies and at no others. The standing-wave patterns that are set up at these

frequencies are called the **natural modes of vibration.**

It is more difficult to demonstrate these phenomena in three dimensions, but three-dimensional bodies do have natural modes of vibration. The earth, for example, considered as an elastic solid, can be made to vibrate by a severe explosion on its surface. The modes of vibration are harder to

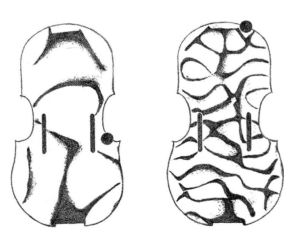

FIG. 17.7. *Chladni plates: Patterns produced on a violin-shaped brass plate covered with sand. Bowing the plate at different points, indicated by the dark round dots, produces different frequencies of vibration and different patterns. Low frequencies produce a pattern of a few large areas, high frequencies a pattern of many small areas.*

FIG. 17.8. *Projection of Chladni plate patterns: A large shadow of the pattern on a glass plate, produced by a point source below it, can be cast on the ceiling of the classroom. Students can observe how the plate is stroked and how nodal lines can be forced by a finger pressed on a point on the edge of the plate.*

detect than those in one- or two-dimensional systems, but they are used all the time in modern seismography. The standing waves of sound that can occur in a room could be made visible by the procedure described in § 16.5.

17.3. The Significance of Standing Waves to Modern Physics

The relevance of standing waves to modern physics appears at different levels. First, because light and radio waves are members of a very extensive family of radiations called electromagnetic waves, any insights we can gain into the behavior of waves will be useful to us in the electromagnetic realm. Standing waves of electromagnetic energy,

in a very small container, have been used to measure the speed of propagation of electromagnetic waves.

You will recall that the speed of sound in air could be measured in a small space by means of resonance (Fig. 16.14). Waves of audible sound are about 2 feet or so long; with a resonance column only one-fourth as long as the wavelength, we could find the speed of sound by using the equation $v = \nu\lambda$.

Sound waves, it is true, are not electromagnetic. Nevertheless, the same technique can be applied to electromagnetic waves (and any other kind of waves). What we need is a way of measuring the frequency directly (as we did with the tuning fork) and of measuring the wavelength in terms of some related measurable length of apparatus. If, for

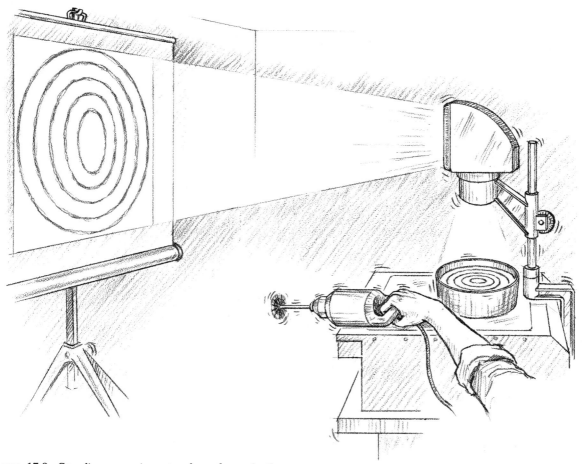

FIG. 17.9. *Standing waves in water shown by projection.*

TABLE 17.1
Electromagnetic Waves

Frequency (cycles/sec)	Designation or Use	Wavelength (meters)	
10^{23}			
	Cosmic-ray photons,	10^{-14}	
10^{22}	gamma rays		
		10^{-13}	
10^{21}			
	-------------------------------	10^{-12}	
10^{20}	-------------------------------		
		10^{-11}	
10^{19}			
	X-rays	10^{-10}	(1 angstrom)
10^{18}			
		10^{-9}	
10^{17}			
	-------------------------------	10^{-8}	
10^{16}	Ultraviolet radiation		
		10^{-7}	
10^{15}			
	Visible light		
	-------------------------------	10^{-6}	
10^{14}		10^{-5}	
	Infrared radiation,		
10^{13}	useful for heating	10^{-4}	
10^{12}			
		10^{-3}	(1 millimeter)
10^{11}			
	-------------------------------	10^{-2}	(1 centimeter)
10^{10}			
	Radar, microwave	10^{-1}	
10^{9}	communication		
	-------------------------------	1	(1 meter)
10^{8}	Television, FM radio		
		10^{1}	
10^{7}	Police, fire-department, and		
	experimental radio	10^{2}	
(1 megacycle/sec) 10^{6}	AM radio		
	-------------------------------	10^{3}	(1 kilometer)
10^{5}	Federal Government radio		
		10^{4}	
10^{4}	-------------------------------		
		10^{5}	
(1 kilocycle/sec) 10^{3}	Long radio waves of little		
		10^{6}	
10^{2}	present use; hard to		
		10^{7}	
10	produce		

example, we know the frequency of a radio wave very accurately, and if we know with equal accuracy the geometrical dimensions of a metallic container within which standing waves can be set up and detected, we can compute the speed of the wave from the equation $v = \nu\lambda$. By such a technique the speed of electromagnetic waves (and hence of light, as we shall see) has been measured as 2.997925×10^8 m/sec.

Because of their importance, the different kinds of electromagnetic waves, and the frequencies associated with them, are tabulated here (Table 17.1).

It is interesting to compare the wavelengths and frequencies of sound with those of light. Sound waves are pressure waves, carried usually by the air but also by solids and liquids. Since the average ear can detect only frequencies between about 20 and 20,000 cycles per second, a range of about ten octaves (ν_2 and ν_1 cover one octave if $\nu_2/\nu_1 = 2$), the associated wavelengths, computed from the equation $v = \nu\lambda$ with v as 334 m/sec, range from 16.7 m to 1.67 cm. The eye is sensitive only to wavelengths between about 4×10^{-7} m and 7×10^{-7} m, its frequency range thus being less than one octave. The spread of frequencies in the electromagnetic spectrum is so great that octaves are less suited to them than powers of ten. Between cosmic rays and long radio waves the ratio of frequencies is 10^{20}.

Another reason for studying waves in our approach to the study of atoms is that light waves emanate from atoms and that something akin to standing waves exists within the atoms. The first successful mathematical model of the simplest atom, that of hydrogen, was invented by Niels Bohr (1885–1962), who used a mixture of classical concepts and some of the new ideas about the wave nature of particles and the particle nature of waves. Bohr's model has been dropped because the new quantum-mechanical ideas have produced better mathematical models, but his vivid picture —with electrons whirling in circular orbits—still serves a pedagogical purpose. Bohr was led to make an assumption that is equivalent to saying that standing waves can take place even in a circular path.

To visualize such an occurrence, you may take a circular bandsaw blade and support its top by hand (Fig. 17.10). If you move your hand up and

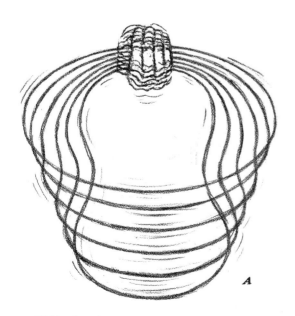 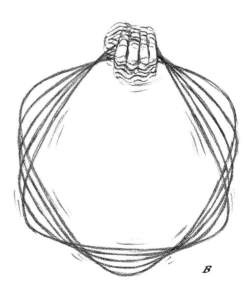

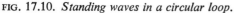

FIG. 17.10. *Standing waves in a circular loop.*

down slightly (A) at the proper frequency, a vibration, whose maximum amplitude is opposite your hand, will be set up. We can think of the top as a node and the bottom as an antinode. If you move your hand up and down faster (B), the blade will vibrate in a new mode at a certain higher frequency and with a new set of nodes and antinodes. This is only suggestive of the possibility of nodes and antinodes in a wave associated with a particle moving in a circle.

One must be careful about macroscopic models that purport to describe how atoms really work. It must be granted, however, that eigenvalues, permitted modes of vibration, and standing waves have all played a very important role in the development of the modern theory of the atom—of an atom in which waves exist.

17.4. Summary

Certain standing-wave patterns, or modes of vibration, produced in macroscopic objects in obedience to the principle of superposition, are physically permitted and are called natural modes of vibration. Their associated frequencies are called natural frequencies. The simplest examples are the permitted modes and frequencies of vibration of stretched strings, but two-dimensional patterns exist (on a stretched drum head, for example) and three-dimensional as well. Natural modes of vibration are important in acoustics and in other branches of engineering, but they are most important in our study of physics, for the discrete energy levels of atoms are related to the standing waves that exist in the atoms.

Problems

17.1. 1. As a problem in mathematics it is easy to calculate the length of a simple pendulum that would have a period of 5,080 sec (approximately the time it takes an earth satellite to orbit closely once round the earth). Do so.

2. As a problem in physics, however, it may not be very meaningful. Discuss some of the physical difficulties to be expected in the construction of such a pendulum. Compare its computed length with the earth's radius.

17.2. 1. Would it be possible to construct a simple pendulum with a period of 1 millisecond? Explain your answer.

2. It is possible, in a special centrifuge, to produce an acceleration as high as 500,000 times the acceleration of gravity on the surface of the earth. If a simple pendulum were set up to vibrate with a period of 10^{-3} sec in an artificial gravitational field of magnitude 100,000 g, what would be its length?

17.3. A piece of steel piano wire is 0.005 cm² in cross-sectional area. It will support, at most, a pull of 1.35×10^3 nt (about 300 lb). Steel has a density of 7.9 gm/cm³. What would be the fundamental frequency of a 10-cm length of the wire subjected to its maximum tension? (Hint: Convert all quantities to MKS units and check the units of the expression

before substituting numbers. Linear density, for example, should be in kg/m.)

17.4. If you have alternating current in your home, you can adapt the apparatus of Fig. 17.1 to measure the frequency of that current (this is not uniform throughout the world). Instead of a motor, an electromagnet, driven at the house-current frequency, imparts a vibration to a light string, at the other end of which weights are attached until it is vibrating in the mode of Fig. 17.2.c, with four loops. Here are typical data: total mass of string between the pulleys, 4.89×10^{-4} kg; length of the string, 1.60 m; tension produced in the string by weights, 0.490 nt. Calculate the frequency of vibration, which is the same as that of the electric current. (This is a variation of an experiment devised by F. Melde in 1859.)

17.5. The E string of a violin has a mass of 0.125 gm and a length of 33 cm. What force does it exert on the violin when it is tuned to 640 vibrations/sec? (This may give you a rough idea of the tremendous forces exerted on the piano, which has more than 100 strings.)

17.6. 1. Three of the different frequencies at which the air in an open organ pipe can vibrate are 400,

6 00, and 1,000 cycles/sec. If the speed of sound in air is 340 m/sec, what is the length of the pipe?

2. If the same pipe were closed at one end, what would be the three lowest frequencies at which the air in it could vibrate?

17.7. The velocity of sound in a gas is given by the formula $v = \sqrt{\gamma P/\rho}$, in which γ is a pure number (the ratio of the two specific heats of the gas), P is the pressure, and ρ is the density of the gas.

1. Check this equation for dimensional consistency.

2. What MKS units would you use for P and for ρ?

3. Describe what happens to the fundamental frequency of a whistle if it is blown with hydrogen instead of air. The density of air is about 18.7 times that of hydrogen. Compute the ratio of frequencies for hydrogen and air. (Hint: Assume that all factors except density are constant. Square both sides of the equation. Write it twice, once for air and once for hydrogen. Take the ratio of these two expressions.)

17.8. A new type of pile-driver, called a "sonic hammer," utilizes sound waves instead of a pounding steam hammer to drive piles. The fundamental longitudinal vibrational mode, excited in the pile shaft itself, achieves maximum amplitude at the ends. The shaft is solid steel and 9.15 m long (30 ft). The speed of sound in steel is 5,000 m/sec. Assume that the pile vibrates (like an open organ pipe) with antinodes at both ends.

1. Find the frequency of vibration.

2. If the amplitude of the motion of the bottom part of the shaft is 1 cm, use the frequency to find the maximum instantaneous speed of that part. (Hint: Remember that simple harmonic motion is the projection on a straight line of simple rotary motion. This should enable you to relate frequency, amplitude, and maximum speed without resort to special formulas.)

17.9. An aluminum rod 1 m long is held lightly in the center. It is struck longitudinally on the end so that a vibration is set up.

1. Describe where the node(s) and antinode(s) will be found for the fundamental frequency.

2. It is found that the rod vibrates at a fundamental frequency of 2,550 cycles/sec. What is the speed of sound in aluminum?

3. What is the wavelength of the sound wave set up in the air at this frequency if its speed is 334 m/sec?

4. Do the two ends of the rod vibrate longitudinally in phase with each other; that is, do they move in the same direction at the same instant?

17.10. It is mentioned in the text that the human ear can detect frequencies in a range of about ten octaves. (A tone is one octave above another if its frequency is twice that of the other.) What is the frequency of a tone ten octaves above 25 vibrations/sec?

Another Look at Waves in Two Dimensions

SO FAR we have given most of our attention to one-dimensional waves. The most important waves in physics, however, are probably the three-dimensional waves associated with atoms and the electromagnetic waves. (Light waves and radio waves are examples of these. Sources of light or of radio waves can send out waves in all directions. Sound waves, which are not electromagnetic, are also three-dimensional.) Before considering waves in three dimensions, however, we must return to two dimensions for a more detailed look at the general behavior of waves. Before we can prove, for example, that light is a wave, we must know how to recognize a wave when we meet one. What are the general characteristics of all waves? What criteria can we use to tell that we are dealing with a wave? If we can give general answers to these questions and illustrate them with two-dimensional waves, we shall have criteria to apply to the three-dimensional waves of light.

We have already encountered some of a wave's characteristics in considering one-dimensional waves. We observed, for example, that a wave may be partly transmitted and partly reflected when it comes to a different medium, that a reflected wave may change phase, that the principle of superposition holds, and that a wave may speed up or slow down as it enters a new medium. All these phenomena are also exhibited by two-dimensional waves. In addition to them we find, in two-dimensional waves, some interesting new characteristics that had no counterpart in one dimension.

18.1. How Waves Go Round Obstacles and Through Openings

We can study the new characteristics with surface water waves in a ripple tank. (The speed of such waves in shallow water, about 20 cm/sec, varies somewhat with the depth of the water. If the depth is constant, the speed is constant.) Let us consider first the effect of frequency on the waves. A straight vibrating stick sets up waves whose crests run along parallel and equally spaced lines. At a particular instant the waves might appear as in Figure 18.1. If the stick vibrates faster, the wavelength, in conformity with the equation $v = \nu\lambda$, becomes shorter, as in Figure 18.2. (The straight lines represent **wave fronts.** The vibrations at each point of a wave front all have the same phase.) The most interesting of the new characteristics, probably, is the behavior of waves at obstacles and openings.

The behavior at obstacles varies with the wavelength. Figures 18.3 and 18.4 show the behavior of waves meeting a circular obstacle. The behavior at obstacles of other shapes does not differ appreciably from this. If the wavelength is some-

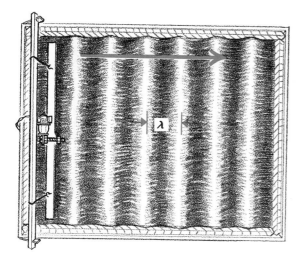

FIG. 18.1. *Straight waves produced in a ripple tank.*

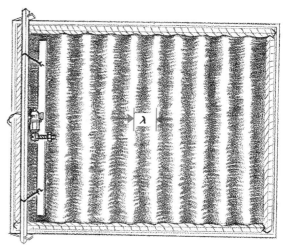

FIG. 18.2. *The frequency of the vibrating stick of Fig. 18.1 has been increased, and the distance between crests (the wavelength) is therefore decreased.*

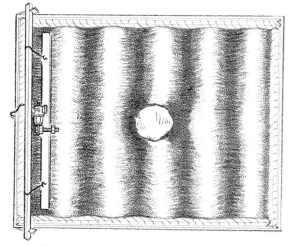

FIG. 18.3. *Waves in a ripple tank passing an obstacle whose diameter is shorter than the wavelength. The wave fronts are only slightly affected by their encounter with the obstacle.*

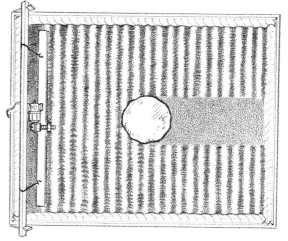

FIG. 18.4. *Waves in a ripple tank passing an obstacle whose diameter is considerably longer than the wavelength. The wave fronts are noticeably altered by their encounter with the obstacle. An absence of wavelets (a shadow) is found to the right of the obstacle.*

what longer than the diameter of the obstacle, the waves bend round the obstacle, merging again as they pass it (Fig. 18.3). If the wavelength is considerably shorter than the diameter of the obstacle, a waveless region—we might call it a shadow—is evident (Fig. 18.4). As the wavelength gets shorter and shorter, the edges of the shadow become sharper and sharper.

If parallel wave fronts meet an obstacle with an opening that is much wider than the wavelength (Fig. 18.5), the waves go through the opening with little bending at the edges, and there is a sharp contrast between the great amplitude opposite the opening and the slight amplitude in the shadow region. As the opening is narrowed and its width approaches one wavelength, the wave front fans out after passage through it (Fig. 18.6). This behavior of waves at obstacles and openings is called **diffraction.** It is the size of the obstacle or the opening, in relation to the wavelength, that governs diffraction effects.

The direction of propagation of waves is represented by lines, called **rays,** that are perpendicular to the wave fronts. If an opening is much wider than the wavelength (Fig. 18.5), the direction is, of course, not appreciably changed as the waves go through; if it is much narrower (Fig. 18.6), there is, because of diffraction, a drastic change in direction. If the behavior resembles that shown in Figure 18.5, we say that the waves go

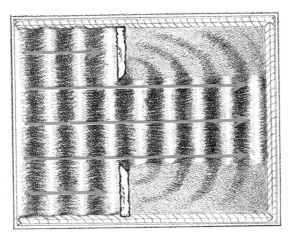

FIG. 18.5. *Waves whose direction is not altered by diffraction.*

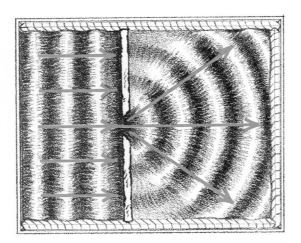

FIG. 18.6. *Waves whose direction is altered by diffraction.*

through the opening like a **beam,** which can be thought of as a bundle of rays. In other words, it seems that we can handle certain wave phenomena with the language of rays traveling in a straight line if the effects of diffraction are negligible; and, in general, diffraction becomes less and less noticeable as the wavelength gets shorter and shorter. Diffraction is, however, a property of all two- and three-dimensional waves, and its occurrence indicates that the phenomena under observation have the nature of waves.

18.2. Huygens's Principle

To explain diffraction and many other wave phenomena, Christian Huygens (1629–1695) suggested a new principle: that each point of a wave front is the source of new wavelets and that the new wave front is the envelope of all of these wavelets.† In Figure 18.7, for example, a curved wave front, *AB*, exists at some instant. A short time later each point of the wave front has generated circular wavelets. The curve *A'B'*, which is tangent to all these wavelets, is the new wave front. Since the waves do not go backward, the envelope drawn to the receding part of the wavelets is not physically meaningful. (For an example

† The envelope of a set of curves is a curve that is tangent to each curve of the set.

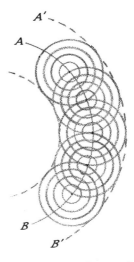

FIG. 18.7. *Huygens's principle illustrated.*

starting with a straight wave front see Prob. 18.3.) The application of this idea to the waves going through a very small opening (Fig. 18.6) makes plausible the curved nature of the wave front that emerges.

Another characteristic of waves is that they can be reflected at a smooth surface. If a ray incident on a plane surface makes angle i with the normal to the surface, and the reflected ray makes angle r with the normal, experiment shows that $i = r$. The statement that the incident ray, the normal to the surface, and the reflected ray all lie in a plane and that $i = r$ is called the **law of reflection.** Huygens's idea that the wave front is a tangent to the family of wavelets enters into the explanation of the law of reflection as follows (Fig. 18.8): PA and QB are the extreme rays of a beam. AB is a wave front moving toward the reflecting surface MM'. The point A is about to become the center of reflected Huygens wavelets. While the other end of the wave front travels from B to C, the radius (AE) of the wavelet originating at A must increase to a length equal to BC. Say this takes time Δt. In time $\Delta t/2$, B travels to C', and the wave front now touches the reflecting surface at D. During the next interval of $\Delta t/2$, C' travels to C, and the radius of the reflected wavelet originating at D increases to a length equal to $C'C$ or $BC/2$. The wavelet whose center is at A and the one whose center is at D

have a common tangent in the line EFC. Actually, every point from A to C has become the center of a wavelet, the largest wavelet originating at A and the smallest (of zero radius) at C. The line EFC, which is tangent to all these wavelets, represents the new, reflected wave front, whose direction is given by the rays AP' and CQ'. It is not difficult to prove that triangles ABC and AEC are congruent. From this it follows that $\angle BCA = \angle EAC$; that is, the rays QC and AP' (and hence CQ') make equal angles with MM'. Usually the angles of the incident (QC) and reflected (CQ') rays are measured from a normal (CN). It follows that the angle of incidence, i, between the incident ray and the normal is equal to the angle of reflection, r, between the normal and the reflected ray. Huygens's principle holds for the reflected wave front EC and all subsequent wave fronts in the reflected beam. We see, then, that the law of reflection is a natural consequence of the way waves are propagated. The law is not peculiar to waves, however; a ball making a perfectly elastic collision with a frictionless surface also bounces in accordance with this law of reflection (Fig. 18.9).

Another application of these ideas is in **refraction,** the change that takes place in the direction of a wave front as it passes a boundary between two media in which the wave travels at different speeds. Let MM' (Fig. 18.10) be such a boundary.

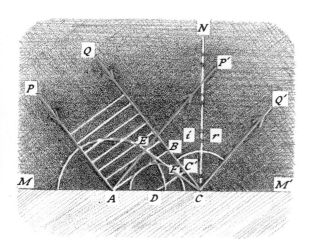

FIG. 18.8. *Huygens's principle applied to reflection of waves at a straight boundary.*

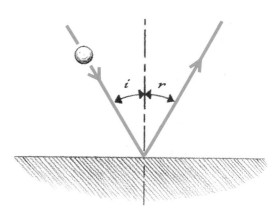

FIG. 18.9. *A perfectly elastic particle encountering a frictionless wall.*

Above it, the speed of the wave is v_1; below it, it is v_2. Let us assume that $v_1 > v_2$. The explanation of refraction runs like this: We have an incoming wave front, AB, just as we did in Figure 18.8. While the front moves from B to C in time Δt at speed v_1, the front at A has been generating a wavelet of radius $AE = v_2\Delta t$ in the second medium. All points between A and B become the centers of wavelets in the new medium, which, by the end of time Δt, all have the common tangent EC. This is the new wave front to which Huygens's principle applies. As time progresses, it moves in the direction AP' (which is parallel to CQ' and perpendicular to EC.)

Notice that the beam is bent *toward the normal when it enters a medium in which the wave travels more slowly*. (It would bend away from the normal if it entered a medium in which the wave traveled more rapidly.) This is a characteristic of all waves.

Consider the incoming ray PA, making angle θ_1 with the normal to the surface, and the *refracted* ray AP', making angle θ_2 with the normal. We seek a relation between θ_1, θ_2, v_1, and v_2. We observe that in the right triangle ABC the angle BAC is equal to θ_1 (because its sides are perpendicular to PA and NA). Similarly, angle $ACE = \theta_2$. Using historical hindsight, we examine the ratio v_1/v_2 for a clue:

$$\frac{v_1}{v_2} = \frac{v_1\Delta t}{v_2\Delta t} = \frac{BC}{AE} = \frac{BC/AC}{AE/AC} = \frac{\sin\theta_1}{\sin\theta_2} \quad [18.1$$

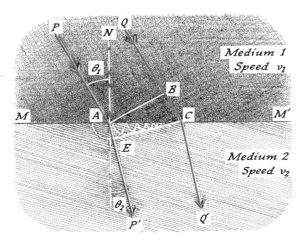

FIG. 18.10. *Huygens's principle applied to refraction at a straight boundary.*

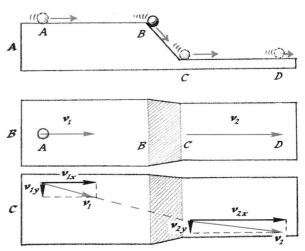

FIG. 18.11. *Refraction of particles illustrated by a rolling ball.*

Here is a simple and symmetrical relation between the sines of the angles of incidence (θ_1) and refraction (θ_2) and the speeds (v_1 and v_2) in the different media. It says clearly that, if $v_2 = v_1$, $\theta_2 = \theta_1$; that is, there is no refraction if the speed is the same in the two media.

The waves we have just considered, like the waves on a string meeting a different medium, can be both reflected by and transmitted into the second medium. Only the transmitted wave front is shown in Figure 18.10, but some of the incoming energy is reflected exactly as in Figure 18.8. Again like the waves on a string, these waves change phase on reflection and undergo superposition. The new thing in Figure 18.10, possible in two dimensions but not in one, is the change in the direction of the wave.

18.3. Refraction of Particles

Particles, as well as waves, experience refraction if their speed is changed as they pass from one region to another. One way to increase their speed is to let them move down an incline, as in Figure 18.11. In part A of the figure a small ball (an imperfect but practical illustration of a particle) rolling on a horizontal plane, AB, moves at a constant velocity, $\mathbf{v}_1$. From B to C it increases its velocity by $\Delta \mathbf{v}$, and its velocity on the new horizontal plane, CD, is $\mathbf{v}_2 = \mathbf{v}_1 + \Delta \mathbf{v}$. What we should see from above is depicted in parts B and C of the figure. The ball has velocity $\mathbf{v}_1$ at B and $\mathbf{v}_2$ at C. If it approaches the boundary along a normal (part B), its path is not bent as it passes the boundary. If it approaches the boundary obliquely (part C), the velocity $\mathbf{v}_1$ has, as shown, components $\mathbf{v}_{1x}$ and $\mathbf{v}_{1y}$, of which $\mathbf{v}_{1x}$ increases under the action of the force of gravity as the ball crosses the boundary and loses potential energy, but $\mathbf{v}_{1y}$ is not affected, for there is no change of potential energy due to the motion in the y direction (remember that we are looking down from above). The resultant vector, $\mathbf{v}_2$, leans toward the normal to the boundary. In this kind of refraction the path is bent toward the normal as the particle enters a region of higher velocity. This is just the opposite of what happens with waves.

18.4. Superposition in Two Dimensions

In a ripple tank (Fig. 18.12) we have a generator, AB, sending parallel wave fronts, such as CD, to the right. At O and O' are openings in a barrier. To the right of the barrier we have the wave fronts originating at those openings. At point P, on the perpendicular bisector of OO', the two waves always arrive in phase because

they started in phase at O and O' (all the points on an incident wave front, such as EF, have the same phase) and because the distance OP equals the distance $O'P$. By the principle of superposition, the two waves reinforce each other there and, indeed, at all points on the perpendicular bisector. At some point not on that bisector, such as P', it may happen that $OP' - O'P' = \lambda/2$, in which case the two waves arriving at P' have opposite phases and cancel each other. There are many points for which $OP' - O'P' = \lambda/2$, and these lie on the **nodal lines,** along which vibration is at a minimum. The pattern produced by the principle of superposition over the whole two-dimensional region is, we know, called an interference pattern; this one, in particular, is called the **double-slit interference pattern.** Interference is called **constructive** if the vibrations are in phase and **destructive** if the vibrations are out of phase. Interference is simply the result of superposition. In this particular illustration, since diffraction was responsible for the production of the two wave patterns, both interference and diffraction are illustrated.

A similar (though invisible) pattern can be set up in the air by two loudspeakers set in vibration by **audio-frequency oscillators** (AFO). (An **AFO** is an electronic device that can produce electrical vibrations of predetermined audio frequency. An audio frequency is one that lies between 20 and 20,000 cycles per second.) In Figure 18.13, AFO_1

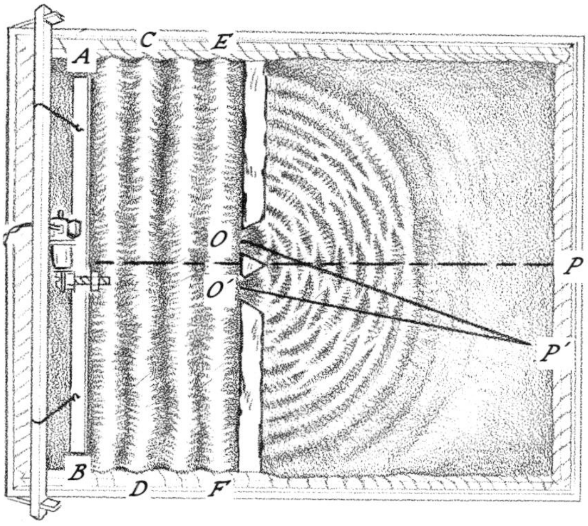

FIG. 18.12. *Interference of ripples from two sources.*

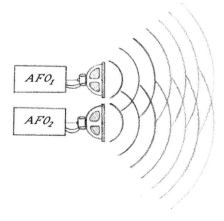

FIG. 18.13. *Interference of sound waves from two loud-speakers.*

sets one loudspeaker vibrating with frequency ν_1; AFO$_2$ sets another loudspeaker vibrating with frequency ν_2. We let ν_2 equal ν_1. If the loudspeakers are vibrating with the same phase, the waves coming from them interfere with each other, for the principle of superposition holds, and regions of high and low amplitude are produced. The waves are longitudinal rather than transverse: they are pressure variations in the air (detectable with a microphone), not altitude variations (as on the water surface of the ripple tank), and they are three-dimensional, although a two-dimensional region can be studied in which the pattern of interference resembles that of Figure 18.12. The nodal lines, though invisible, are detectable with a microphone, an amplifier, and some display device such as a meter or a cathode-ray oscillograph. They could also be rendered visible by a technique similar to that used to produce Figure 16.19.

We can deduce mathematically the direction in which a maximum or minimum of intensity will be found in the two-dimensional case. (It can be shown that the intensity is proportional to the square of the amplitude.) In Figure 18.14, $ABCD$ is a barrier with slits (perpendicular to the plane of the paper) at B and C. At a distant point, P, we find that $PB - PC = \lambda/2$; in other words, the waves reaching P from B and C, being out of phase with each other, interfere destructively, and the amplitude at P is therefore zero (or very small),

as indicated by a minimum on the curve FGH, which is simply a plot of amplitude against location on the y axis. At point E the waves, being in phase, interfere constructively and produce the maximum amplitude (and hence intensity). If the separation, d, between slits is very small and the distance L is very great, $\angle\theta = \angle POE \cong \angle BCM$. Therefore $\sin\theta = \lambda/2d$. This value of θ corresponds to the first minimum in the curve FGH on either side of the central point, E, on the y axis. (The approximations made here in setting $\angle POE$ equal to $\angle BCM$ are very good if d/L is much less than 1.) If the two interfering waves are not in phase at C and B, the whole nodal pattern will shift.

We can now summarize by observing that, though we have chosen illustrations using only water waves in a ripple tank and sound waves in air, reflection, refraction, diffraction, and interference are properties of *all* waves in two and three dimensions. We shall test new phenomena for their wave-like character by looking for these properties.

18.5. The Doppler Effect

Another phenomenon peculiar to waves originates in moving sources or moving receivers or in both. Called the **Doppler effect,** it is most commonly observed in sound (but its real importance lies in its production by light waves).

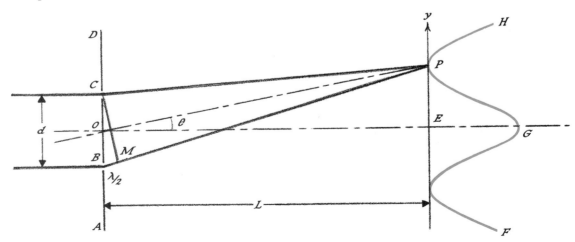

FIG. 18.14. *Mathematical analysis of the interference pattern of Figs. 18.12 and 18.13.*

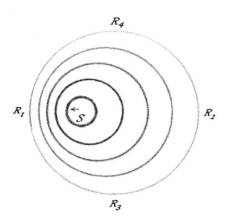

FIG. 18.15. *The Doppler effect: the pattern of waves produced by a source vibrating with constant frequency and moving with constant speed toward the left. To test your understanding of this diagram, try Prob. 18.11.*

Imagine a locomotive with a horn emitting a tone whose frequency is ν. As it approaches a stationary listener, the frequency actually heard is $\nu + (\Delta\nu)_1$; as it recedes, the frequency heard is $\nu - (\Delta\nu)_2$. For moderate speeds of travel, $\Delta\nu_1$ and $\Delta\nu_2$ are close but not precisely equal. The stationary listener hears a pitch higher than the fundamental pitch as the train approaches and a pitch lower than the fundamental pitch as the train recedes. (We are not considering loudness here; I am simply saying that the tone heard by the listener would not be in tune with the same horn if it were stationary.)

The pattern produced in a ripple tank by a moving source of waves (Fig. 18.15) illustrates what actually happens. The source, S, is moving to the left. Stationary receiver R_1 receives more crests per second than if S were not moving. Stationary receiver R_2 receives fewer crests per second than if S were not moving. Stationary receivers R_3 and R_4 receive approximately the normal number of crests per second—that is, the number they would receive if S were stationary.

The conveyor belt offers a useful analogy from which the right mathematical relation follows. Suppose that a conveyor belt (Fig. 18.16) can carry parts from a sender, S, to a receiver, R, at a constant speed, u. If S puts parts on the belt at the rate of ν per second, the time interval between them, T, is $1/\nu$, and the distance between them, λ, is uT, from which it follows that $u = \nu\lambda$. If there is no relative motion between S and R, the latter picks up ν parts per second; that is, the frequency at R is the same as that at S. We have used the symbols ν and λ because the parts play the role of crests of waves moving at speed u.

If S now approaches R at speed v, the distance between parts on the conveyor belt is less than before. Since the speed of S *in relation to the conveyor belt* is $u - v$, the new separation between parts, λ', is

$$\lambda' = (u - v)T = \frac{(u - v)}{\nu} \qquad [18.2$$

At the receiving end, parts are coming in at speed u, but, since their separation is λ', their frequency, ν_R, obeys the equation

$$u = \nu_R\lambda' \qquad [18.3$$

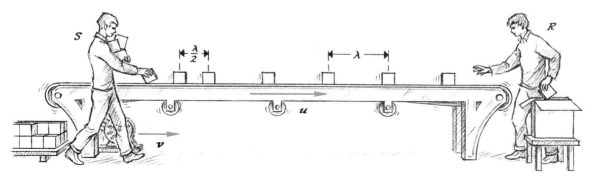

FIG. 18.16. *A model for the Doppler effect.*

Using in this equation the λ' of equation 18.2, we get

$$u = \nu_R \frac{(u - v)}{\nu} \qquad [18.4$$

or

$$\nu_R = \nu \frac{u}{u - v} \qquad [18.5$$

If the sender recedes instead of approaching, the formula is

$$\nu_R = \nu \left(\frac{u}{u + v}\right)$$

If the sender is stationary and the receiver approaches him at speed w, the separation between parts, λ, does not change. It is still u/ν, but, since the speed of the receiver in relation to the conveyor belt is $u + w$, the time between pick-ups, T', is $\lambda/(u + w)$. The frequency at the receiving end is the inverse of this, or

$$\nu_R = \frac{u + w}{\lambda} \qquad [18.6$$

Using the value $\lambda = u/\nu$, we get

$$\nu_R = \nu \left(\frac{u + w}{u}\right) \qquad [18.7$$

If the receiver recedes from a stationary sender, the formula is

$$\nu_R = \nu \left(\frac{u - w}{u}\right)$$

You are urged to convince yourself that the formula

$$\nu_R = \nu \frac{(u \pm w)}{(u \mp v)} \qquad [18.8$$

will take care of both a moving receiver and a moving sender. The upper signs in both numerator and denominator are used when sender and receiver approach each other, the lower signs when they recede from each other.

EXAMPLE 18.1. An airplane carrying a siren whose frequency, ν, is 1,000 cycles/sec approaches a stationary listener on a landing field at a speed of 176 ft/sec. We wish to know the frequency, ν_R, heard by the listener.

The speed of sound in air is 1,100 ft/sec. Since a moving source is approaching a stationary receiver, we use equation 18.5:

$$\nu_R = \nu \frac{u}{u - v} = 1,000 \text{ cycles/sec} \times \frac{1,100}{1,100 - 176}$$
$$= 1,000 \times 1.19 \text{ cycles/sec}$$
$$= 1,190 \text{ cycles/sec}$$

If the same siren were on the field and the listener were in an airplane coming in at the same speed, the frequency heard would not be 1,190 cycles/sec. (See Prob. 18.13.)

It is obvious from the way we deduced these formulas, using simple Galilean relativity, that they are not applicable to speeds that approach the speed of light; and even the speed of sound sets an interesting limitation on the use, for example, of equation 18.5. If the speed (v) of the sender approaches the speed (u) of the wave, $u - v$ approaches zero. What does that imply about the frequency ν_R? What does it mean physically? What happens when v exceeds u (as is possible with modern aircraft)? These interesting questions are left for you to explore in the problems.

18.6. Summary

Waves in two and three dimensions are characterized by reflection, refraction, diffraction, and interference. The ripples on the surface of water can be used to illustrate all of these characteristics in two dimensions. The explanation of them is greatly aided by Huygens's principle, which states that every point of an advancing wave front is a center of disturbance from which emanate independent wavelets whose envelope constitutes a new wave front at each successive stage of the advance.

The explanation of interference depends upon the principle of superposition: the resultant amplitude at a point where several waves are crossing is simply the algebraic sum of the amplitudes of the individual waves.

Another wave effect—the Doppler effect—accounts for the change in frequency at the receiver when there is relative motion between the sender of a train of waves and the receiver. With sound waves it is observed as a change in pitch.

Problems

18.1. In Fig. 18.1 the frequency of the waves is governed by the number of revolutions per second of the motor attached to the stick that generates them. If the wavelength is 12 cm and the frequency is 2 vibrations/sec, what is the speed of the ripples on the surface of the water? The ripples are in constant motion; how, then, would you measure the wavelength? Describe also an operational procedure that might be used to measure the frequency.

18.2. If a match is dropped onto a large flat field of dry grass on a calm day, the fire will spread in all directions in a manner reminiscent of the ripples that spread out on a still pond from a point where a stone has been dropped. Describe some aspects of fire propagation that seem closely related to Huygens's principle and others that do not. If the edge of a grass fire is a straight line, it spreads in a direction perpendicular to the line. Consider the possibility of reflection, refraction, and diffraction of the fire, comparing its behavior with that of ripples on the surface of water. Does the concept of wavelength enter into a discussion of the propagation of the fire?

18.3. 1. If the wave front *AB* of Fig. 18.7 were a straight line (as it would be if the source were very distant), what would be the shape of the envelope (*A′B′*) of the wavelets that originated at different points of *AB*?

2. Draw a set of successive wave fronts on the assumption that the speed of the wavelets increases gradually for successive positions of *AB*.

18.4. There is an interesting and surprisingly accurate way of estimating the speed of a rapidly moving airplane that is within audible range. Using both ears, the average person can, under favorable conditions, estimate the angle between the direction of the source of sound and the line of sight of the airplane within 5°. Such an airplane is always seen in a position far in front of the point at which the sound originated. Assuming that light travels with infinite speed when compared with the speed of sound (the ratio of the speeds is about $10^6 : 1$), devise a method of measuring (by eye) the angle, θ, between the line of sight to the airplane and the line along which the sound has come. From a knowledge of the speed, c, of sound in air (about 700 mi/h)

derive the formula $\sin \theta = v/c$ for the speed, v, of an airplane in the simple case in which the line of sight is perpendicular to the path of the airplane. What is the speed of the airplane if θ is 30°?

18.5. Study Fig. 18.9, in which the angle of incidence equals the angle of reflection. Draw a picture of incident and reflected directions, taking into consideration the frictional force that the surface exerts on the ball. Consider, for example, the effect of the frictional force on the velocity components parallel to and perpendicular to the surface.

18.6. Consider a purely hypothetical situation to test your comprehension of the factors that entered into the construction of Fig. 18.8. Make a drawing to determine what direction the reflected ray would take if the speed of propagation of the reflected wave were greater than that of the incident wave. (Although this problem may seem artificial, it may aid you to understand how Huygens's principle is used in Fig. 18.10.)

18.7. A car traveling rapidly along a road runs off onto the shoulder, which happens to be made of soft sand. The right front tire is the first to hit the sand and is slowed down before the left front tire touches the sand at all. In which direction will the car tend to turn? Draw a diagram to illustrate your answer. Does the car's behavior resemble the refraction of a wave (Fig. 18.10) or the refraction of the particle discussed in connection with Fig. 18.11? Does the concept of wavelength enter the discussion of the car?

18.8. The particle model of Fig. 18.11 gives results that are opposite to those observed with light. Does this mean that light cannot consist of particles? Discuss.

18.9. A beam of light passing from air into water bends as indicated in Fig. 18.10. This is one of the indications that light has wave-like characteristics. On the assumption that equation 18.1 is applicable to light, calculate the angle θ_2 for the following values of θ_1: 0°, 30°, 45°, 60°, and a value very close to 90°. It is known, from other experiments, that $v_1/v_2 = 1.33$ when the media are air and water, respectively.

18.10. Light, sound, and ripples on water normally travel in straight lines, but their direction of travel can be changed by reflection (as in Figs. 18.8 and 19.9), by refraction (as in Fig. 18.10), and by diffraction (as in Fig. 18.6). Which of the three phenomena is the most convincing proof of the wave nature of light? Describe in words what you think would happen to the ripples of Fig. 18.5 if the wavelength were kept constant and the width of the opening were gradually diminished. Would you expect a similar effect to take place with light?

18.11. With a pair of compasses reconstruct Fig. 18.15. Starting with the center of the largest circle, mark the centers of the successive circles with dots numbered 5, 4, 3, 2, 1, and 0. Now try to state the meaning of the figure in words—for example: "The largest circle represents the pulse that started five seconds ago at the point marked 5. The next largest circle represents . . ." and so on, down to the point labeled 0. In which direction are the waves traveling with the greatest speed?

18.12. 1. What would happen physically if the sender of Fig. 18.16 ran along with the conveyor belt at exactly the same speed as the belt?

2. What does equation 18.8 predict algebraically about the sound frequency at the receiving end when the sender moves toward a fixed receiver at a speed that approaches the speed of sound?

3. How is part 2 related to part 1?

4. An airplane "breaks the sound barrier" when its speed exceeds that of sound in its ambient atmosphere. Describe, utilizing the ideas of this problem, what you think happens.

18.13. When there is relative motion between the sender and the receiver, one may analyze the behavior of sound by using the conveyor-belt analogy (Fig. 18.16). Use it to justify the following statements:

1. When the sender moves toward a fixed receiver, the wavelength is decreased; hence the frequency at the receiver is increased.

2. When the receiver moves toward a fixed sender, the frequency at the receiver increases but the wavelength is unaltered.

3. The increase in frequency for a given relative speed is more pronounced in case 1 than in case 2.

18.14. A speed boat travels through shallow water at constant speed v and sets up a bow wave that moves at the lower but constant speed c. Prove that the angle ϕ between the line along which the boat travels and the front of the bow wave obeys the relation $\sin \phi = c/v$. (Hint: While the circular wave produced by the bow travels distance ct, the boat travels distance vt. Study the case in which $v < c$, discussed in Prob. 18.12 and illustrated in Fig. 18.15.)

18.15. The sound of a horn on a moving automobile is recorded on a stationary tape recorder both as the automobile approaches and as it recedes. By comparing the pitch of the two tones with those of a piano, we calculate the apparent frequencies, from which we derive the speed of the automobile.

1. Derive a formula for the speed of the automobile in terms of the two apparent frequencies and the speed of sound in air. (Hint: Write down the relevant cases of equation 18.8, and take their ratio.)

2. Calculate the speed of the automobile for the case where the ratio of frequencies is 1.15 and the speed of sound in air is 1,100 ft/sec.

18.16. 1. Two loudspeakers vibrating in phase with each other are separated by a distance equal to three times the wavelength of the sound waves they are producing in air. Use graphical methods to find the regions in a horizontal plane where the vibrations interfere constructively with one another. Use enough points to get a general idea of what the pattern will look like, and sketch in the rest. What would you expect to hear at such points?

2. Check your results by performing the following experiment: Fill a sink with water. Hold two fingers of one hand so that the tips are just touching the surface of the water and are about three inches apart. Now try to achieve a steady up-and-down vibratory motion of the fingers. It may help to brace your palm against the edge of the sink. Look for a pattern similar to the one you constructed graphically.

18.17. In an experiment with light having geometrical features like those of Fig. 18.14 it is found that, when $d = 0.05$ cm and $L = 87$ cm, the distance EP, from the central bright spot at E to the dark spot at P, is 0.0435 cm. Using the fact that $\sin \theta$, for a small θ, is approximately equal to EP/L, find the wavelength of the light.

The Nature of Light

THE DICTIONARY says about light: "that which makes it possible to see." As an operational definition of light this leaves something to be desired; but the emphasis on seeing is justified, for, if we did not have eyes, we should not even know that there is such a thing as light. Because we do have eyes, and because there is light, we can enjoy seeing the rainbow, the sunset, the flowers, the moon, the stars—and sometimes one another. Light has made knowledge of the whole universe possible. Almost all we know about the distant galaxies and the innermost structure of atoms has been learned through light (and the other electromagnetic radiations). In our daily lives we gain most of our information through light from the television screen, the movie screen, and the printed page. No wonder the word "light" has also come to mean knowledge, enlightenment, and inspiration.

19.1. Light: a Wave or a Particle?

But what is the physical nature of light? What are the measurable properties of it that do not depend on the human eye? The fact that light comes along with heat from the sun suggests that it may be energy. But energy, as we have seen, can be transported by both waves and particles. Is light a train of waves? Or is it a stream of particles? What produces colors? Is the speed of light finite? Can light travel in a vacuum? These and many other questions have led thinking men to speculate about the nature of light for many centuries.

I shall begin by stating the commonly accepted facts and theories about light and shall then show how the evidence for the present view of light accumulated. In other words, I shall not uncover the clues, one by one, and then put all the pieces together, as if we didn't know the answer. We do know the answer. I shall give the answer first in order to show why it took so long to uncover some of the clues.

There is much evidence to support the theory that light is an electromagnetic wave. Like any other wave, it obeys the equation $c = \nu\lambda$, and its speed, which is given the special symbol c, is about 3×10^8 m/sec in a vacuum. The wavelengths, λ, visible to the eye run from about 4×10^{-7} m to about 7×10^{-7} m. The corresponding frequencies, ν, therefore run from about 4.3×10^{14} cycles/sec to about 7.5×10^{14} cycles/sec. The equation of the electric field associated with a light wave traveling along the x axis can be written as

$$E = E_0 \sin 2\pi \left(\frac{x}{\lambda} - \frac{t}{T} \right) \qquad [19.1$$

Here E_0 and E measure electric field intensity (in newtons/coulomb: E_0 is a constant, E a variable). We have already seen that the order of magnitude is 10^{-7} m for λ and 10^{-14} sec for T. Using the equations $c = \nu\lambda$ and $\nu = 1/T$, we may write equation 19.1 as

$$E = E_0 \sin \frac{2\pi}{\lambda} (x - ct) \qquad [19.2$$

A similar equation describes the magnetic field associated with the wave, but I shall defer consideration of it until Part IV.

There is also evidence that light has a particle-like nature; in many experiments it behaves like a stream of particles. If the frequency associated with the light as a wave is ν, the energy, W, of each particle, or **photon,** of the light obeys the equation $W = h\nu$, in which h is a universal constant of nature (the **Planck constant:** 6.6256×10^{-34} J-sec). In a sense, then, light is both a wave and a particle. We do not resolve the dilemma by saying that it must be either one or the other, for it behaves in some experiments like one and in other experiments like the other.

Visible light exhibits differences in brightness and in color. These subjective characteristics are related, respectively, to the power (watts) of the source and the wavelength of the light. The shortest visible wavelengths look violet or bluish, and the longest ones look red; but in most physical problems the wavelength, not the appearance, is the important characteristic.

Having said so much, I have summarized a lot of what is known about the basic nature of light, but this can become operationally meaningful to us only if we go back and discuss or perform some of the basic experiments that culminated in this view. It would not be wise to do this in historical order, for the search led into many blind alleys. We must, nevertheless, present some of the arguments in favor of each of the two theories of light.

How shall we go about proving that light is a wave? For a clue, let us first consider the experiments by which we prove that sound and radio waves are waves.

Sound waves are invisible, but their wave nature is suggested by the vibration of sources of sound. The mechanical vibration of a tuning fork or a stringed instrument is detectable by touch and is often easily visible. This vibration immediately suggests waves. A microphone can pick up the pressure variations due to sound waves in air and convert them into electrical impulses that can be displayed on a cathode-ray oscilloscope; even the frequency of the sound can be measured directly with a calibrated oscilloscope. Radio waves also are invisible, but their electric fields can be picked up by an antenna, amplified, and displayed on a cathode-ray oscilloscope; and their frequency,

although much higher than that of sound waves, can readily be measured with a calibrated oscilloscope. The wavelength of both sound waves and radio waves can be measured by means of the standing waves produced by superposition. Since some sound waves are about 30 cm long and the radio waves used in television and FM radio are about a meter long, the wave nature of sound waves and radio waves can be demonstrated directly by simple laboratory experiments.

Can we do similar experiments with light? Can we, for example, by some means or other, detect electrical vibrations in a source of light? At present we have no direct way of measuring frequencies of the order of 10^{14} cycles/sec. How about standing waves? These and other effects of superposition have been demonstrated experimentally, and now we know why the task was so difficult: the wavelengths involved, about 5×10^{-7} m, are shorter than the smallest objects that can be seen by the best light microscopes.

We have considered the terms ν and λ in the equation $c = \nu\lambda$ and have found no direct way to measure them for light. How about c, the speed of propagation? Attempts to measure the speed of light began with Galileo, who used lanterns on two hills. A man on one hill was instructed to uncover his lantern as soon as he saw the operator on the other hill uncover his. If light were slow, the operator would have noticed an interval between the time when he first exposed his lantern and the time when he saw the light from the other lantern. With our present knowledge of the speed of light (about 186,000 mi/sec) we can see why this experiment was bound to fail. Nevertheless, of the three quantities c, ν, and λ, it was c that was first measured with some accuracy. (By 1676 Olaus Roemer had used astronomical methods to obtain approximately 2.6×10^8 m/sec as a value for the speed of light.) Measuring the speed of light did not prove that light is a wave, but it did supply our first numerical quantity for the equation $c = \nu\lambda$.

Since direct proof of the nature of light seems difficult, we turn to indirect evidence. Of all the properties of waves (reflection, refraction, diffraction, and interference), diffraction should give us the first convincing proof of the wave nature of light. Can we show that light spreads out when we let it pass through a tiny opening?

19.2. Diffraction: Support for the Wave Theory of Light

Consider (Fig. 19.1) a light-tight box with a hole, *H*, of variable size in the center of one wall. Over a large opening in the opposite wall we put a flat piece of ground glass, *GG'*. Suppose now that a Christmas tree with little colored light bulbs at *R* (for red) and *B* (for blue) stands in front of our **pinhole camera**. If an observer, *O*, throws a dark, opaque cloth over both his head and the back of the camera (as the early photographers had to do) in order to exclude unwanted light, and if he waits long enough for his eyes to become dark-adapted, what will he see on the ground glass if the hole is about 2 mm in diameter? He will

probably first notice a red blur at *R'* and a blue one at *B'*. If the hole is made smaller, he will see the blurs transformed into recognizable images of the two light bulbs. If a photographic film is inserted in place of the ground glass, exposed sufficiently, and developed, not only the two bulbs but also a great amount of detail on the tree and in the nearby scene will be clearly seen. Careful measurements of the image on the film will show that the light from the tree had traveled in straight lines such as *BHB'* and *RHR'*. The similarity of triangles *BHR* and *B'HR'* reveals the relation between the size of the object, *BR*, and the size of the image, *R'B'*:

$$\frac{\text{object size}}{\text{image size}} = \frac{BR}{R'B'} = \frac{p}{q} = \frac{\text{object distance}}{\text{image distance}} \quad [19.3$$

All the facts we have considered so far fit the idea that light travels along straight lines and does *not* bend—is not diffracted—in going through a hole. If light *is* a wave, it must have an extremely short wavelength. (We saw in § 18.1 that, the

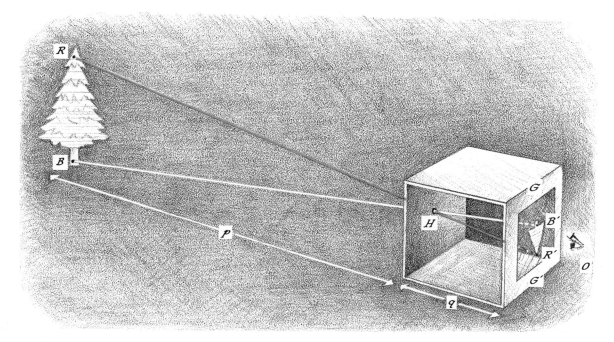

FIG. 19.1. *Pinhole camera: The totality of rays coming from different points on the tree produces an image of the tree on the ground glass.*

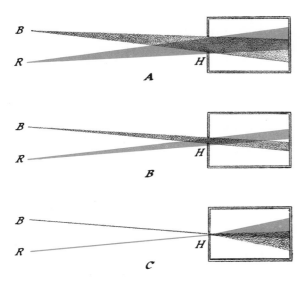

FIG. 19.2. *Pinhole camera: effect of reducing the diameter of the pinhole.*

shorter the wavelength, the less noticeable is diffraction.) Let us examine more closely the behavior of our pinhole camera (Fig. 19.2). The concept of rays leads us to believe that our pictures should get sharper as we diminish the hole. Light from two distant small sources, *B* and *R*, passing through a large hole, *H*, produces two overlapping blurs on our film (A). Diminishing the hole diminishes the blurs, thus separating the images of *B* and *R* (B). But since, as we saw in § 18.1, diffraction of a wave increases as the hole becomes smaller in relation to the wavelength, we suspect that, if light really is a wave, further diminishing of the hole may result in *diffraction and spreading* (C), which would destroy the resolving power of the pinhole. This is exactly what happens, as illustrated by Figure 19.3, which shows six photographs of a set of words printed in type of several sizes.† When the pinhole's diameter was reduced below a certain length, diffraction caused blurring instead of the greater sharpness that would have been expected if light did not have wave-like characteristics. Although

† From the Unesco Pilot Project "The Physics of Light." The "pinholes" were really transparent circular areas in an otherwise opaque, fine-grained photographic film. They were produced photographically.

the hole had to be made so small that the light was too dim for the effect of diffraction to be seen by the eye on a ground glass, a long exposure on a photographic film recorded the effect.

19.3. Inverse-square Law of Illumination: Support for Both the Wave Theory and the Particle Theory

Our eyes tell us, in a qualitative way, that the illumination produced by a source of light diminishes with distance. In a cave, with only a single candle lit, you can't read a book unless you bring the candle near the book.

Although, if we depend on our eyes, we are fairly good at judging relative degrees of illumination, we are very poor at judging absolute degrees. A photoelectric exposure meter, on the other hand, by converting incident light energy into electric energy, enables us to read degrees of illumination on its face. Readings taken with this, instrument at distances of one, two, and three meters from a very small electric light bulb (Fig. 19.4) are found to be proportional to 1, 1/4, and 1/9; that is, an inverse-square law prevails.

This fact is established without an exposure meter as follows: Two identical small sources (tungsten-filament bulbs or even candles), *A* and *B*, illuminate a white board (Fig. 19.5). A rod casts shadows on this board. The region *A'* is illuminated only by *A*, for the rod blocks the light from *B*. The region *B'* is illuminated only by *B*. This may be easier to see in the schematic drawing of Figure 19.6. If *A'* and *B'* look similar, *A* and *B* must be equally bright. By this means we find four lamps that are identical in luminous intensity. We then find experimentally that the illumination by the cluster of four identical lamps (in a vertical line), *C*, is the same at *C'* as the illumination by *A* at *A'* if $AA'/CC' = 1/2$.

By experiments of this sort we can convince ourselves that the inverse-square law of illumination *does* hold. Does this result support the wave theory or the particle theory? It supports both and is therefore not a conclusive proof of either, as we shall see.

The particle theory seems to provide the simpler

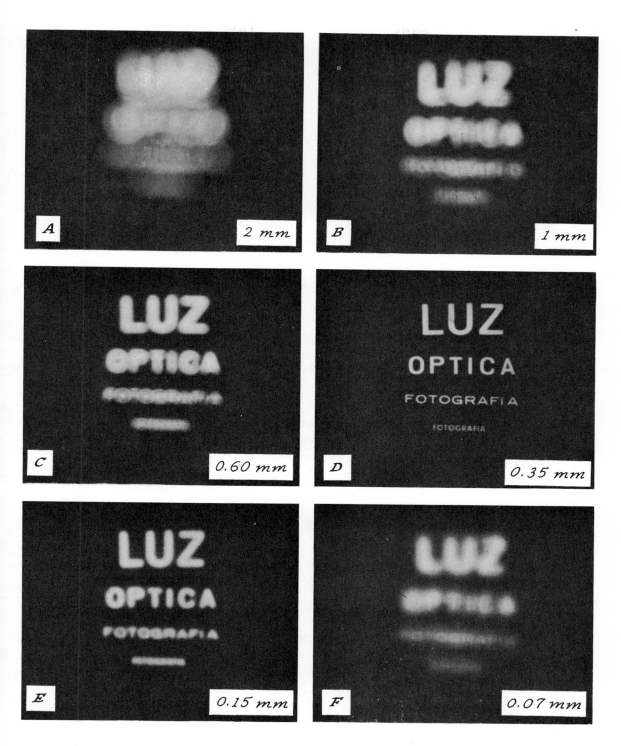

FIG. 19.3. *Pinhole-camera photographs taken with pinholes of different diameters. (Photographs from UNESCO, Paris.)*

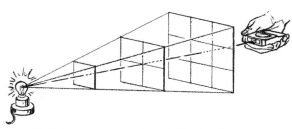

FIG. 19.4. *Inverse-square law of illumination.*

FIG. 19.5. *The eye is capable of detecting very slight differences of illumination in this way.*

explanation. If we assume (Fig. 19.7) that a point source, S, throws out n particles (photons) per second in all directions, the total number intercepted per second by an imaginary sphere of radius R_1 is the same as the total number intercepted later by a concentric imaginary sphere of radius R_2. The number of photons per unit area is $n/4\pi R_1^2$ and $n/4\pi R_2^2$ respectively. If we take this number as a measure of illumination, I, we see that

$$\frac{I_1}{I_2} = \frac{n/4\pi R_1^2}{n/4\pi R_2^2} = \frac{R_2^2}{R_1^2} \qquad [19.4$$

An inverse-square law of illumination is very plausible for particles.

The application of the law to waves is simplified by the concept of *energy carried by a wave*. The total amount of energy passing through the first sphere in unit time must equal the total amount of energy passing through the second sphere in unit time. If we now associate energy *per unit area* per unit time with illumination, an inverse-square law again follows.

The fact that the inverse-square law of illumination holds does not, we see, confirm exclusively

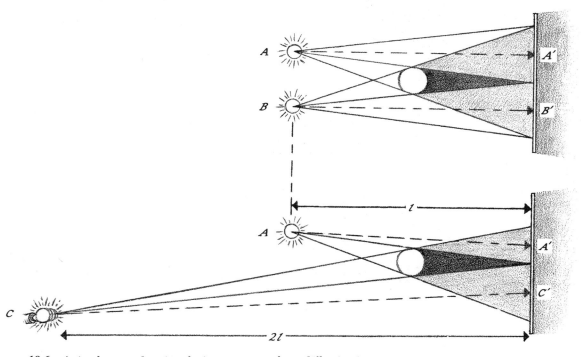

FIG. 19.6. *A simple way of testing the inverse-square law of illumination.*

either the wave theory or the particle theory. I introduced it at this time as a prelude to an experiment that does make one theory more plausible than the other.

19.4. The Photoelectric Effect: Support for the Particle Theory of Light

The photoelectric exposure meter works by the simple ejection of electrons from matter by light. We can demonstrate this ejection, called the **photoelectric effect,** in a direct way. We put (Fig. 19.8) a piece of recently sandpapered zinc (galvanized iron will do), Zn, on an electroscope,† E; and charge it negatively. When we turn on a germicidal lamp (a source of near ultraviolet light),‡ nearby, the electroscope is discharged. The explanation is that light from the lamp liberates electrons from the zinc, which, having already

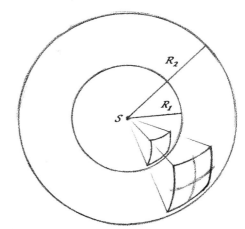

FIG. 19.7. *Light as particles and the inverse-square law of illumination.*

an overabundance of electrons, repels those so liberated, thus losing its negative charge. If the electroscope started with a positive charge, the liberated electrons would be attracted back to the zinc and hence would not be permanently lost, and the electroscope would remain charged.

We can check the inverse-square law roughly

---

† The electroscope is described in detail in Chap. 36.
‡ A crude carbon arc consisting of two hand-held carbon rods in series with a lamp bank also works. Tape the rods to protect yourself from shock.

FIG. 19.8. *Demonstration that some of the ultraviolet light produced by a mercury source is stopped by ordinary window glass.*

with this apparatus: we find that the time required for the electroscope to discharge increases as the lamp is placed farther and farther away.

Let us now try an interesting variation. If we hold a piece of ordinary window glass, *G*, between the lamp and the negatively charged electroscope, the electroscope is *not* discharged when the light is turned on. Only after the glass is removed, letting the light shine directly on the zinc, is the electroscope discharged. Even if the lamp is very close to the electroscope, the discharge does not take place if the glass is put between the lamp and the zinc.

The modern explanation of this effect is as follows: The light source (mercury vapor at low pressure, electrically excited) puts out radiation of discrete frequencies, ν_1, ν_2, ν_3, ν_4, etc. Some of these correspond to radiation in the visible part of the spectrum, but one to a strong invisible radiation (with a wavelength of 2,537 A, in the ultraviolet), and this is primarily responsible for the ejection of the electrons from the zinc. The glass passes visible light but not this strong invisible radiation.

According to the photon hypothesis, the amount of energy carried by each photon is $h\nu$ (*h* being the Planck constant and ν the frequency). Hence photons with a large ν (high frequency, low wavelength) are more energetic than photons with a small ν. Since photons in the ultraviolet part of the spectrum are more energetic than the visible-light photons, they can eject electrons that are bound to the zinc in such a way that it takes a certain minimum energy per photon to dislodge them. No matter how near you place the lamp to the zinc, the glass, if it is interposed, lets through only the less energetic photons, no one of which is energetic enough to dislodge an electron. You can allow billions of visible-light photons to strike the zinc for a long time, and their effects will not be cumulative; that is, you can not pile up enough energy from weak photons to dislodge even one electron.

An analogy may help. You may have seen at county fairs or in an amusement park a device that is designed to test your strength (Fig. 19.9). A weight sliding on a vertical wire can be pushed up by a lever, which is moved by the impact of a

FIG. 19.9. *An analogy for the photoelectric effect.*

large hammer. If you hit the lever hard enough, the weight on the wire climbs all the way to the top and rings a bell. (The vibration of the wire introduces a complication that we shall disregard here.) If a small boy hits the lever, he can not hit it hard enough to ring the bell, no matter how many times he tries. It takes a minimum amount of energy to ring the bell, and no single blow of his has that much energy. He can hit the lever over and over again, and expend a lot of energy, but the bell will never ring.

The photoelectric effect is somewhat like this. If the energy of an incoming photon is sufficiently high, it can knock out an electron; if the energy of each of a number of photons is below a certain level, no single one of them can eject an electron, no matter how many of them hit the zinc, and there is no way in which the energy from a number of weak photons can accumulate, act on one electron, and eject it.

This experiment seems to demand a particle model for light. For the time being let us simply admit that light has a dual nature. There will be times when we invoke the wave picture to help us, and there will be other times when we lean heavily on the particle picture. Light seems to be complex enough to demand both.

But now we must get better acquainted with the way light behaves in many different kinds of experiments. Then, after we have studied electricity and atomic physics, we can return to basic questions about the nature of light.

19.5. Summary

Diffraction and other effects confirm that light has wave-like characteristics. These effects eluded early observers because the wavelength of light is very short (about 5×10^{-7} m). Other properties of light, such as the inverse-square law of illumination, can be explained by either a wave or a particle hypothesis; but we can explain the photoelectric effect only by considering light as a stream of particles. Light is complex enough to behave like a wave or like a particle according to the means of observation we use.

Problems

19.1. With the help of a friend and two lanterns, you plan to repeat Galileo's experiment on the speed of light. You are sure that it will work if the distance between observers is great enough. Let us suppose that your reactions are very fast—that you can have your lamp uncovered 0.2 sec after you see your friend uncover his.

1. How far apart would you have to be in order that the total time elapsed between the instant he uncovers his lamp and the instant he sees your lamp be twice your reaction time? (This would set a limit to the ability to detect the finite velocity of light.)

2. Could this experiment be done with two observers on earth? Describe how.

19.2. A device using a laser (a new source of light in which many atoms, vibrating in the same phase, produce a powerful but extremely short burst of light) can be used to measure the distance to an object by measuring the time it takes for the light to travel to the object and back. The timing device (which might be a cathode-ray oscilloscope) can measure an interval of time as short as 15 nanoseconds (a nanosecond is 10^{-9} sec). What is the shortest distance measurable with this device?

19.3. The maximum electric field intensity produced at a point by a certain light is 1 nt/coul.

1. What is the maximum force (in newtons) felt by an electron in such a field? The electron charge is 1.6×10^{-19} coul.

2. Using a non-relativistic approximation, find the upper limit of the acceleration experienced by an electron in such a field.

19.4. In the text, light waves are described in terms of variations in an electric field. Sound waves are variations in what kind of field quantity? Is this quantity a vector or a scalar? (See § 4.2 and § 4.3.)

19.5. If the speed of light is 3.00×10^8 m/sec, what is the frequency of the light from the germicidal lamp, described in § 19.4, whose wavelength is 2,537 A? What is the wavelength of an FM radio signal of 98.6 megacycles/sec?

19.6. At what frequency would a source of sound have to vibrate in air in order to produce a wavelength of 5,000 A? Take the speed of sound in air as 330 m/sec. (Electromagnetic radiation with a wavelength of 5,000 A is a greenish-yellow light.)

19.7. The trace produced on a cathode-ray oscilloscope by a simple harmonic oscillation is a sine curve regardless of its origin. (The 60 cycles/sec of the electric voltage from a wall outlet, the 1,000 cycles/sec originating in a tuning fork driven at constant amplitude, and the 550 kilocycles/sec of the carrier frequency of a broadcasting station can all be made to look alike on the oscilloscope by adjustment of its sweep frequency.) Assume that as oscilloscope (of the future) can be made to operate at 10^{15} cycles/sec, the frequency associated with a monochromatic light. Considering that light originates in many different atoms, all producing the same frequency, would you expect the oscilloscope pattern produced by a monochromatic light to resemble (a) that produced by many identical tuning forks all started simultaneously or (b) that produced by the same tuning forks started at random but continuing to vibrate with fixed frequency and phase thereafter or (c) that produced by the same forks started, and allowed to stop, at random?

19.8. To illustrate the short wavelength of visible light, consider the problem of setting up standing waves of light, of wavelength 5,000 A, in a way analogous to the way standing waves were produced on a rope (§ 17.1)—that is, by letting the reflected wave from a mirror interfere with the incident wave of the same frequency and amplitude. How many nodes would there be between a source and a mirror 1 cm away? (Otto Wiener, in 1890, successfully recorded on photographic film the nodes and antinodes of standing waves of light.)

19.9. An observer, using his ear as a detector, observes a rise in pitch when the frequency of a sound source goes up and an increase in loudness when the amplitude increases. Describe the analogous subjective effects that an observer experiences when his eye, used as a detector, is subjected to the electromagnetic wave (equation 19.1) produced by a light source (a) as the frequency is increased and (b) as the amplitude is increased.

19.10. A pinhole camera (Fig. 19.1) can be made with any light-tight box—for example, a shoe box that has been well taped to exclude extraneous light. (The image $B'R'$ is formed on a photographic film placed inside the box instead of on the ground glass, GG', shown in the figure.) The hole, H, may be pierced with a needle in a piece of thin aluminum foil and taped over a larger hole.

1. If the separation between the lights R and B is 2 m, at what distance (p) should the tree be placed to produce an image height ($B'R'$) of 1.5 cm? The length (q) of the box is 30 cm.

2. Under these circumstances, what is the greatest pinhole diameter permitted if the images of two tiny lamps, one placed 10 cm above the other on the tree, are to appear as two non-overlapping images on the film?

19.11. The solar constant is the amount of energy from the sun impinging normally (perpendicularly) on a unit area per second. At the surface of the earth, if we ignore atmospheric absorption, the solar constant is 0.033 cal/cm²/sec. The earth is 93×10^6 miles from the sun, and the planet Pluto is 3.7×10^9 miles from the sun. What is the approximate value of the solar constant on Pluto?

19.12. If the exposure meter of Fig. 19.4 reads 1.00 unit at a distance of 1.00 m from a point source of light and 0.25 unit at a distance of 2.00 m, what will it read at a distance of 2.37 m? Give the answer to three significant figures.

19.13. The argument related to Fig. 19.6 runs like this: If one lamp at A produces illumination of 1 unit at A', the same lamp at twice the distance will produce an illumination of 1/4 unit. It takes four identical lamps at C, therefore, to produce illumination of 1 unit at C'. Suppose that one of the four lamps at C burns out. At what distance from the screen will the bank of three lamps produce illumination of 1 unit at C'? (Assume that l is 1 m.)

19.14. Here is a simple illustration of the conservation of energy. A tiny 1-W (one-watt) bulb is placed at the center of a cubical box.

1. How many joules of energy impinge on one side of the cube if its edge is 1.50 m long?

2. How many joules impinge on one side of the cube if its edge is 2.75 m long?

19.15. 1. What is the energy in joules of individual photons associated with monochromatic light of wavelength 5,000 A?

2. How many such photons does a monochromatic 1-W lamp put out in one second (assuming 100% efficiency in that wavelength)?

3. How many photons per second hit an area of 1 m² at a distance of 1 km from the light? (Assume a spherical surface, and remember that the area of a sphere is $4\pi r^2$).

19.16. Assume that photons, when they enter the eye at the rate of 1,000/sec, are just barely visible. Using the data of Prob. 19.15 and assuming no loss by absorption, say how far away a monochromatic 100-W source of 5,000-A light could be seen if the aperture of the eye had an area of 0.50 cm².

19.17. Suppose that it takes 50 J of work to ring the bell of Fig. 19.9. A boy can produce only 10 J of work every time he hits the lever. He does this twenty times in succession.

1. What is the total work done?

2. How many times does he ring the bell?

Reflection and Refraction of Light at a Smooth Interface

A PRIMITIVE fisherman who harpooned a fish by throwing a spear at it obliquely into the water knew from experience that he had to aim low in order to hit it. The reason is that, since light bends away from the perpendicular to the water surface as it passes from water to air, the apparent position of the fish is higher than its real position.

This bending, or refraction, of light was one of the earliest scientific phenomena subjected to measurement and analysis. Ptolemy's observations on refraction (125–151 A.D.) are thought to be the oldest collection of experimental measurements outside astronomy. Alhazen (965?–1039) devised an apparatus for studying refraction. The precise law of refraction, though stated by Willebrord Snell as late as 1621, antedated Newton's work in mechanics by about sixty years. Optics, or the study of light, has always been an important and stimulating part of physics. Recently a focused beam of radiation has been sent from the earth to a small area of the moon. This suggests that physicists are still as interested in optical problems today as they have been in the past.

20.1. Reflection and Refraction at a Plane Surface

When a beam of light hits a surface of water obliquely, some of it is reflected, and some of it is refracted as it enters the water.† This behavior is characteristic of light meeting a smooth transparent interface. In Figure 20.1 the behavior is summarized diagrammatically. Single rays indicate the directions of the incident, reflected, and refracted beams. The angle of incidence, θ_1, is the angle between the incident ray and the normal to the surface; the angle of reflection, θ_1', and the angle of refraction, θ_2, are similarly defined. Since we are dealing with a plane wave, successive crests of a train of waves are drawn one wavelength apart, but these, of course, cannot be seen. We can deal with reflection and refraction by using rays, without recourse to waves.

† The relations between intensity of the beam and angle of incidence are discussed in more advanced books.

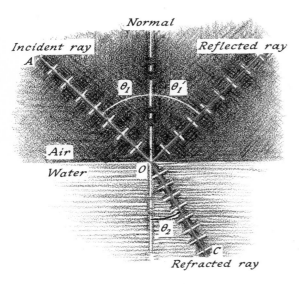

FIG. 20.1. *Diagrammatic representation, using rays, of reflection and refraction at an air-water interface.*

1. *Snell's Law*

The experimental facts can be simply summarized: (1) The reflected and refracted rays lie in the plane determined by the incident ray and the normal to the surface. (2) The angle of incidence equals the angle of reflection:

$$\theta_1 = \theta_1' \qquad [20.1$$

(3) In refraction,

$$\frac{\sin \theta_1}{\sin \theta_2} = n \qquad [20.2$$

Here n is a constant, called the **index of refraction** of the medium that the light enters in relation to the medium that it leaves. The index of refraction of water in relation to air, for yellow light, is 1.33. (In relation to a vacuum it is slightly different but is still 1.33 to three significant figures.)

Equation 20.2 is known as **Snell's law.** We have already seen (equation 18.1) that a wave front obeys the relation

$$\frac{\sin \theta_1}{\sin \theta_2} = \frac{v_1}{v_2}$$

if v_1 and v_2 are the speeds of the wave in the two media. The refraction of Figure 20.1 indicates that light, if it is a wave, must travel more slowly in water than in air. (See § 18.3.) Experiments

confirm that light *does* travel more slowly in water than in air. (That is why, in the figure, the distance between crests was drawn shorter in the water than in the air.) Equation 20.2, we see, implies the *rectilinear propagation of light;* for, if the medium is homogeneous, a light ray will not be bent by refraction.

We are dealing here with **geometrical optics,** the branch of optics that treats the propagation of light waves in terms of rays, or lines perpendicular to wave fronts. In this treatment the ray properties of light predominate over the wave properties, not because light is not a wave, but because its wavelength is very short. Observe that we demand a *smooth* interface. The measure of smoothness is related to the wavelength of the light being used. It is easy to judge smoothness qualitatively, for a surface produces **specular** (mirror-like) **reflections** of the kind illustrated in Figure 20.1 only if its irregularities, measured as heights from a perfectly smooth base, are shorter than the wavelength being used. At grazing incidence, however, many surfaces produce specular reflections even though they would not do so at normal or nearly normal incidence; with a piece of slate or ground glass held close to the eyes you can get good specular reflections formed by rays at grazing incidence.

We can, it is clear, properly speak of rays of light; but whether a surface will behave like a smooth mirror and reflect rays specularly depends upon the wavelength of the radiation that strikes it. A choppy sea behaves like a mirror to radio waves several meters long, but not to light.

2. *Behavior of a Ray Entering a Region of Greater Speed*

A ray traveling along the path *AOC* in Figure 20.1 can be sent back along the same path; starting at *C* and passing through *O*, it follows the path *OA*. In other words, it bends *away* from the normal as it passes from one medium into another in which it travels more rapidly.

A simple way to let a ray pass out of water into air, permitting us to study the behavior of the emergent beam, is to allow a beam to enter the water normally, as shown in Figure 20.2. *S* is a source of light; F is a filter that lets violet light through. Since the beam enters the water normally, no refraction occurs at this passage. The beam, being reflected from an adjustable mirror, M, proceeds from M to O, where both reflection (toward B) and refraction (toward A) take place. By changing the tilt of M and thereby changing the angle θ_2, we can bring the angle θ_1 close to 90°; for, as θ_2 is increased, θ_1 increases. A white screen placed to catch the ray OA shows a violet spot where it hits.

3. Color and Wavelength

If we now remove the violet filter so that a beam of white light enters the water, the white screen reveals a whole spectrum of colors above A. All the colors of the rainbow are seen, from red, the highest one, at A', down through orange, yellow, green, blue, and violet.

This experiment demonstrates not only that the emergent beams are bent away from the normal but that the different colors have different indices of refraction—or, more precisely, that the index of refraction is a function of wavelength. Color is subjective; it is a sensation; and it is not yet completely understood. Though it is true that light of all wavelengths from 7,000 A to 4,000 A, if the wavelengths are separated as in this experiment,

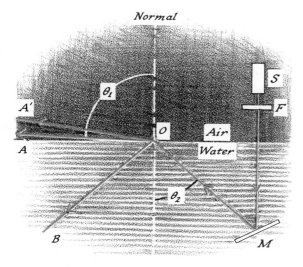

FIG. 20.2. *Demonstration of reflection and refraction at a water-air interface.*

looks to most people like a spectrum beginning with red and ending with violet, and though this fact makes it plausible that light of wavelength 5,461 A looks green to most people,† the sensation of green (or of any other color) can, in fact, be created by many different combinations of many different wavelengths. I shall therefore specify wavelength as the physically measurable characteristic of color and shall leave the difficult but interesting subject of color perception to other books.

4. The Critical Angle

Again we have had to digress from our consideration of geometrical optics in order to consider a characteristic of light—color—that is related to its wave-like properties. Light of a single wavelength is difficult to produce experimentally, but this will not prevent us from using the convenient fiction of a **monochromatic beam** of light. With a filter, as we know, it is possible to narrow the range of wavelengths. The ideal result of this process is the monochromatic beam. For such a beam, at each wavelength, there is (Fig. 20.2) a special value of θ_2 for which θ_1 is 90°. This value of θ_2 is called the **critical angle**, c. If θ_2 is greater than c, all the energy goes into the reflected beam, and **total internal reflection** occurs. From the way in which c was defined it is apparent that

$$\frac{\sin 90°}{\sin c} = n \qquad [20.3$$

EXAMPLE 20.1. We wish to find the critical angle for yellow light of wavelength 5,890 A, for which water has an index of refraction of 1.33.

Using equation 20.3, we get

$$\sin c = \frac{\sin 90°}{n} = \frac{1}{1.33} = 0.752$$

A table of sines reveals that $c = 48°45'$.

5. The Prism and Dispersion

We can analyze the behavior of light passing through a glass prism by considering the refrac-

† Sensations are difficult to compare. We all agree to call the color of the sky blue, but I have no way of knowing if your sensation of blue is the same as mine.

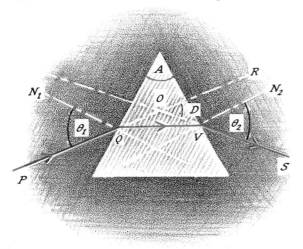

FIG. 20.3. *Deviation of light by a prism: minimum deviation.*

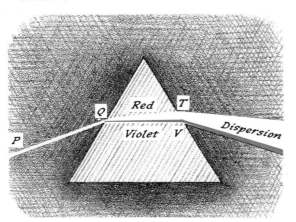

FIG. 20.4. *White light entering the prism at* Q *spreads out into a spectrum. The violet rays emerge at* V *and the red rays at* T.

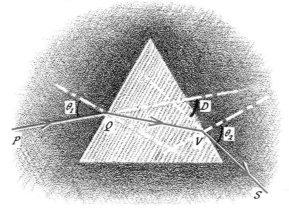

FIG. 20.5. *Deviation of light by a prism: deviation greater than the minimum.*

tions that occur at the interfaces (Fig. 20.3). First consider the monochromatic violet ray *PQ*. It bends toward normal N_1, follows path QV through the prism, and then, bending away from normal N_2, leaves the prism along path *VS*. The angle, *D*, between the incoming and outgoing rays is called the **deviation**. If the incoming monochromatic ray had been red, it would have bent less than the violet at each interface, with the result that its total deviation would have been less (Fig. 20.4). The angle between two outgoing rays of different wavelengths is a measure of their **dispersion**.

If the incoming beam is white, all its component wavelengths are dispersed, and a whole spectrum of colors emerges from the prism. To each wavelength between those of the red and the violet rays there corresponds a unique deviation. The deviation of a ray of a particular wavelength passing through a prism of a particular vertex angle *A* (Fig. 20.3) and made of a particular material depends upon the angle of incidence, θ_1. Figure 20.3 was drawn for the case of **minimum deviation** of a violet ray. Figure 20.5 shows what happens to this ray when the prism is rotated so that angle θ_1 is changed. The ray QV no longer makes equal angles with the faces, and the deviation is greater than it was in Figure 20.3. (If the prism is set for the minimum deviation of a ray of wavelength λ_1, it is not set for the minimum deviation of a ray of a different wavelength, λ_2.) For a ray of a particular color, as we let θ_1 range through all possible values—by rotation of the prism, for example—we can find the position for which the emerging ray has the minimum deviation. (It can be shown both experimentally and by use of the calculus that this occurs when $\theta_1 = \theta_2$, as in Fig. 20.3.)

By applying Snell's law at each interface we can prove† that

$$n = \frac{\sin \frac{1}{2}(A + D_{\min})}{\sin \frac{1}{2}A} \qquad [20.4$$

If we examine the right side of this equation, we see that we need to measure two angles, *A* and

† From Fig. 20.3 it may be shown that the angle of incidence, θ_1, is equal to $(D_{\min} + A)/2$ and that the angle of refraction is $A/2$. Application of Snell's law yields equation 20.4.

D_{min}, in order to calculate the index of refraction of the glass for light of a specific wavelength. The wavelength of light cannot be measured with a prism; but, once the wavelengths of a certain source of light have been measured in some other way and tabulated, we can get the index of refraction of the glass for the different wavelengths by using the prism and equation 20.4.

The graph of the variation of the index of refraction with wavelength is called the **dispersion curve** of the refracting material (usually in relation to air or to a vacuum). The dispersion curve of crown glass is shown in Figure 20.6. The index of refraction of this and many other refracting materials is greatest at the violet end (short wavelength) of the spectrum and least at the red end (long wavelength). The curve indicates that the trend of the dispersion in the visible range holds also for waves shorter than the shortest visible waves (4,000 A) and longer than the longest visible waves (7,000 A), and thus implies that we have means of detecting the invisible rays called ultraviolet (<4,000 A) and infrared (>7,000 A). We shall see later that these rays are playing a more and more important role in physics.

20.2. Reflection and Refraction at Smooth Curved Surfaces

The laws of reflection and refraction were stated in terms of the angles between incident, reflected, and refracted rays and the normal to a plane surface. How shall we apply these laws to curved surfaces? We need to know first what is meant by "normal" to such a surface. Imagine a plane tangent to a curved surface at a given point. A line perpendicular to the tangent plane at the point of tangency is, by definition, the normal to the curved surface at that point. With "normal" thus defined, the laws of reflection and refraction, as stated for a plane surface, hold without modification for a smooth curved surface. At a curved interface of air and glass (the material most commonly used for lenses) both reflected and refracted rays are found to lie in the plane determined by the incident ray and the normal.

Since straight lines, surfaces, tangents, and normals are involved, it should not be surprising that

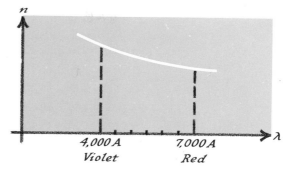

FIG. 20.6. *Dispersion curve of crown glass.*

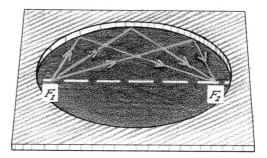

FIG. 20.7. *Focal property of elliptic reflector.*

these considerations belong to geometrical optics. Some geometrical shapes, especially all the conic sections (parabola, ellipse, hyperbola, and degenerate forms such as the circle and the straight line), so called because they may result from the intersection of a plane and a circular cone (see Fig. 34.8), and also the surfaces obtained from those sections by revolution, have interesting optical properties. We shall briefly consider elliptical and spherical surfaces.

1. Reflection

The ellipse has the interesting property of concentrating light from one of its foci on the other. Imagine that the elliptical reflector of Figure 20.7 is two-dimensional, with a point source of light at focus F_1. All the rays that reach the reflector from the source are reflected so that they converge at the other focus, F_2.† Rays starting from any

† In three dimensions the almost egg-shaped surface formed by rotation of the ellipse round the line joining its two foci can reflect *all* the radiant energy from a point source at one focus and concentrate it precisely at the other focus.

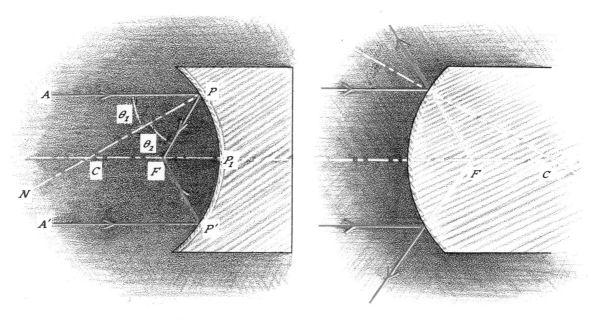

FIG. 20.8. *Concave spherical reflector (diagramed in one plane).*

FIG. 20.9. *Convex spherical reflector (diagramed in one plane).*

point except a focus will not converge precisely at any other point even if the reflector is a perfect ellipse. In practice, moreover, the reflector is never perfect, and therefore not all the rays from a source at one focus converge precisely at the other focus. It is impossible to make a mathematically perfect surface: the reflector always has small bumps—deviations from the ideal surface.

The curved surfaces most commonly used in optical work are spherical. The practical reason for this is simple: the sphere is the only surface that we can generate by rubbing together, with a motion whose directions are random, two hard surfaces, such as glass, with an abrasive between them. By using finer and finer abrasives we can generate spherical surfaces capable of producing specular reflection and refraction. A spherical reflecting surface may be concave or convex.

A *concave* spherical surface reflects parallel rays as shown in Figure 20.8. At each point of the surface (at P, for example) angle θ_1 (between the incident ray, AP, and the normal, NP) is equal to angle θ_2 (between the normal and the reflected ray, PF), and all three—incident ray, normal, and reflected ray—lie in the same plane. In principle

this is the only rule that we need in order to predict the behavior of all the reflected rays. In practice the application of the rule may lead to complicated and lengthy computations. We shall avoid these by considering the problem graphically and only in a single plane. We consider, therefore, a circular reflector.

Only two parallel rays, AP and $A'P'$, are shown. If they are equidistant from the center, C, of the circular reflector, the reflected rays meet at a point lying on that diameter of the circle which is parallel to the incident rays. The circle has the mathematical property that all other rays parallel to AP and $A'P'$ and lying between them will meet at points such as F, each of which is approximately halfway between the circle and its center. They miss going exactly through the halfway point not because of imperfections in the reflector—we have assumed that our circle is a slice of a perfect sphere—but as a consequence of its being circular. If the limiting rays AP and $A'P'$ are sufficiently close to each other, the reflected rays will be as close as we please to the halfway point. If the limitation of the incoming beam has been effected by an aperture, and if the size of the aperture is

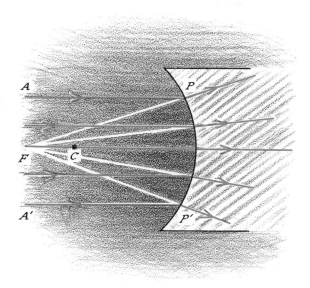

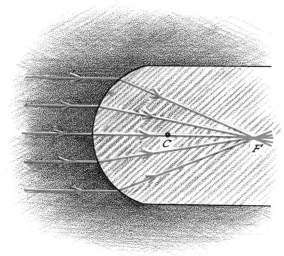

FIG. 20.10. *Refraction of parallel rays at a single concave interface.*

FIG. 20.11. *Refraction of parallel rays at a single convex interface.*

reduced below a certain limit, diffraction, which cannot be accounted for by geometrical optics, begins to predominate, and the predictions of ray optics cease to be correct. We shall defer consideration of these effects and continue to assume here that the principles of geometrical optics hold. On that assumption, if the reflector were parabolic instead of circular, and if all the incident rays were parallel to the axis of the parabola, all the reflected rays would meet precisely at one point, called the focus of the parabola.

A *convex* spherical surface, treated here in one plane, as a circle, reflects parallel rays as shown in Figure 20.9. The reflected rays, extended backward, converge at point F, which is approximately halfway between the circle and its center, C; in other words, the reflected rays seem to diverge from this point.

2. Refraction

The behavior of light as it is refracted at spherical surfaces is of particular interest because many camera lenses and eyeglasses have spherical or nearly spherical surfaces. Thin spherical lenses

will be treated in § 21.5. Light is refracted twice by them, once on the way in and again on the way out. For the present let us consider graphically the behavior of parallel light rays passing a single spherical air-glass interface.

A *concave*, transparent glass surface refracts parallel rays as shown in Figure 20.10. The refracted rays obey Snell's law at each point and diverge as if they originated approximately at point F. As in the case of reflection from a spherical mirror, the more the separation of the limiting parallel rays AP and $A'P'$ is reduced, the more accurately do the refracted rays (extended backward) converge at F.

A *convex*, transparent glass surface refracts parallel rays as shown in Figure 20.11. The refracted rays, each bending toward its normal, converge approximately at point F.

Since the precise determination of the behavior of a large set of rays involves a lengthy computation with many steps and many opportunities for error, electronic computers are now commonly used in the design of optical apparatus that depends upon the reflection or refraction of light at smooth interfaces.

20.3. Summary

When a ray of light meets the boundary between two media in which light travels at different speeds, some of the light may be reflected, and some of it may enter the second medium and be refracted in accordance with Snell's law, which says that the sine of the angle of incidence divided by the sine of the angle of refraction is a constant —the ratio of the speeds of light in the two media.

A ray of light can be bent as it enters a prism and as it leaves it. The angle between the incoming and outgoing rays is called the deviation. Because deviation varies with wavelength, refraction by a prism is accompanied by dispersion, the separation of the wavelengths composing a beam of light.

The laws of reflection and refraction that apply to light striking a plane surface also apply to light striking a curved surface, and it is possible, in principle, to account for the convergent and divergent effects of curved mirrors and refracting surfaces with these two laws alone.

Problems

20.1. Two plane mirrors are placed at right angles to each other. Prove that a ray that is incident on one mirror in a plane perpendicular to both mirrors and is reflected by both mirrors in succession emerges parallel to the incident ray. Draw several cases to convince yourself of the generality of the statement, and then devise a geometrical proof. (A device consisting of three mutually perpendicular plane mirrors is called a corner reflector. It can be proved that any ray entering a corner reflector emerges parallel to the incident ray.)

20.2. An archer fish, by ejecting a powerful stream of water into the air above the medium in which it swims, may knock down an insect.

1. If such a fish sees an insect when looking up through the water at an angle of 15° with the normal, what angular correction must it make when it shoots in order to hit the insect?

2. Draw a diagram to explain your reasoning.

20.3. In a special case of Fig. 20.1 the refracted ray and the reflected ray are perpendicular to each other. Compute the angle of incidence, θ_1, for this case, letting n equal 1.33. If you use the identity $\sin \theta_2 = \cos \theta_1$, which is valid when $\theta_1 + \theta_2 = 90°$, and remember that $(\sin \theta)/(\cos \theta) = \tan \theta$ (§ 14.3 and Appendix E), you can find the solution mathematically. Otherwise, make a drawing that looks plausible, and measure θ_1. Using this value of θ_1 in Snell's law, compute the angle between reflected and refracted rays. If it is too large or too small, start again with a better estimate of θ_1, and repeat the foregoing procedure.

20.4. Diamond, one of the most highly refractive materials known, has an index of refraction of 2.42. What is the smallest angle that a ray of light inside a diamond can make with the surface and still pass from the interior into the air?

20.5. A flat, unpolished piece of aluminum behaves like a smooth mirror for electromagnetic waves of frequency 3,000 megacycles/sec. Explain why. (See § 20.1.1.)

20.6. In prism binoculars light enters a 45°-45°-90° glass prism normal to the hypotenuse.

1. Trace the path of a ray into and out of such a prism by drawing a diagram.

2. Give a numerical argument to show why, if the index of refraction of the glass is 1.50, no silvering is needed at the other surfaces to achieve 100% reflection.

20.7. 1. Prove mathematically that by looking into a glass cube of index 1.52 you can never see out through a side adjacent to the one through which you are looking in.

2. Calculate the highest index of refraction that would permit you to see out of the adjacent side of a glass cube.

20.8. In Fig. 20.2 start with M horizontal, using white light (filter F removed). Describe the changes in color of the reflected ray B when the mirror is rotated counter-clockwise, from the moment total reflection begins until the last visible refracted ray (A') sinks down to grazing emergence. (To answer this you must consider the spread of colors in the refracted part of the beam as grazing emergence is approached.)

20.9. Water is lighter than carbon disulphide and can rest on top of it. The index of refraction of carbon disulphide is 1.63, and that of water is 1.33.

1. What is the ratio of the speed of light in carbon disulphide to that in water? (Hint: Let the speed in air be v_1, that in carbon disulphide v_2, and that in water v_3. We know, by the definition of index of refraction, that $v_1/v_2 = 1.63$ and that $v_1/v_3 = 1.33$.)

2. A ray of light in the carbon disulphide makes an angle of 15° with the normal to the carbon disulphide–water interface. What angle with the normal will the ray make in the water?

20.10. A beam of light enters one face of a prism (index 1.53) at an angle of 30° to the normal. The angle between the normals to the two faces of the prism at which refraction takes place is also 30°. What angle will the emergent beam make with the normal to the second face? (Hint: Draw a sketch to rule out the solution that involves total internal reflection at the second face.)

20.11. Prove that equation 20.4 is valid, assuming that the angle of minimum deviation occurs when $\theta_1 = \theta_2$ in Fig. 20.3. (You need to remember that the angle between the normals to two lines is either the same as the angle between the lines or equal to its supplement.)

20.12. How would you measure the angles of a prism to ±2°? to ±0.1°? (Hint: Use rays reflected from the surface of the prism when it is put on a spectrometer.)

20.13. Reconstruct Figs. 20.8–20.11 with ruler and compass. Use the law of reflection (for the mirrors) and the law of refraction (for the rays penetrating the spherical glass surface). The objective is to confirm, geometrically, the facts mentioned in the text concerning the relative positions of points F and C.

20.14. Everyone knows that both glass and water are transparent. Fill a drinking glass with water and put it on a white piece of paper. Let the glass intercept the light from an electric light bulb or a candle. Observe that the glass of water casts a shadow. Why does it? Can you explain the variations of intensity that you see within the shadow?

Image-formation

THE ULTIMATE receiver of optical images is usually the retina of the eye. We can form images by artificial lenses and display them on movie or television screens, but we do so only in order to form corresponding images on the human retina. Since most of our information reaches us through that wonderful instrument the eye, it is important to understand how the eye works, but this is impossible unless we first understand how mirrors and lenses form images.

21.1. The Human Eye—a First Look

The human eye is not a pinhole camera, but treating it as such gives a rough first picture that we can refine later (§ 22.1). Let us think (Fig. 21.1) of the pupil, P, as a very small aperture. Light from two luminous objects at A_1 and B_1—such as small electric light bulbs hung on a Christmas tree—lands on the retina, that from A_1 at A_1', that from B_1 at B_1'. This information is somehow transmitted to the brain, and the person sees the bulbs at A_1 and B_1.

If we hang a decorative ball (not a lamp) on the tree at C, we can see it too, for it reflects the light from the two bulbs. We can even see the green needles of the tree, for they reflect some light diffusely (not specularly). Most objects, in fact, reflect light diffusely, and this reflection makes them visible.

An object may look large to us simply because its image fills a large part of the retina, but our impression of its size is influenced by our knowledge, or our estimate, of its distance. If we move the tree (Fig. 21.1) closer to the eye, with bulbs at A_2 and B_2, the angle they subtend at the pupil is larger, and the image, extending from A_2' to B_2', is also larger; but we are able to perceive that the tree is of the same size as before. We can estimate an object's distance partly because we have two eyes, which see slightly different images; but psychological and other factors assist us, especially one-eyed people, in judging distance.

We can also judge direction. Experience has taught us to interpret a ray striking a low place on the retina, such as A_2', as coming from above and a ray striking a high place, such as B_2', as coming from below. Similar remarks can be made about left and right. The image on the retina is inverted, but experience has taught us to interpret the image and perceive the direction of objects. (Experimenters wearing special glasses that invert the image on the retina have adjusted themselves to this inversion and have pointed accurately to an object even while wearing the glasses.)

With this highly simplified description of the eye in mind, we proceed to discuss the formation of images by mirrors and lenses. After that we shall come back to the eye and discuss it in a more sophisticated way (§ 22.1).

21.2. The Plane Mirror

Consider a smooth plane of glass coated with silver or aluminum on its front face, AB (Fig. 21.2). (Most mirrors have the metallic coat on the back; the glass protects the coat, but reflection from the front glass surface can be disturbing in critical experiments.) Light from point O sends out spherical waves, which have a common center at O. Huygens's principle, applied to the wave fronts reaching AB, yields a set of spherical waves that have a common center at I, a point behind the mirror.

We don't need waves, however, to locate I; we can use rays instead. Of all the rays leaving O, in Figure 21.3, we choose two: OC, which is normal to the mirror, is reflected on itself; OP, which makes angle θ_1 with the normal to the mirror at P, is reflected, according to the law of reflection

($\theta_1 = \theta_1'$), as ray PQ. Extending the lines QP and OC backward till they intersect, we can see that the reflected rays, PQ and CO, behave as if they originated at the intersection, I. Since triangles OPC and PCI are congruent (angle, side, angle), the object distance, OC, equals the image distance, CI. The point I is called the **image** because, although the reflected rays do not really come from I, an observer interprets them (in accordance with what we found about the ability of the eye to judge direction) as coming from I. It is called a **virtual image** because no light rays pass through

FIG. 21.1. *The human eye treated as a pinhole camera.*

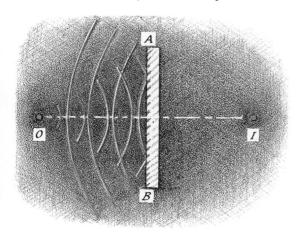

FIG. 21.2. *The plane mirror: reflection of spherical waves of light from a point source.*

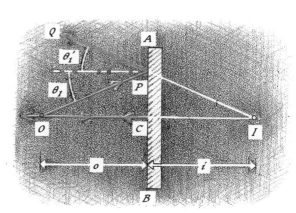

FIG. 21.3. *The plane mirror: location of the image of a point source.*

point *I*. An image at a point is said to be a **real image** if light rays actually cross at the point.

Since *P* represents any point other than *C*, the argument is general, and we conclude from it that *all* rays emanating from *O* and hitting the mirror are seen precisely as if they came from *I*. This generality is essential to image-formation, for the eye always catches a *bundle* of rays. Figure 21.4 shows such a bundle emanating from *O* and reaching the eye after reflection. (Wave fronts also are drawn, although it is apparent that rays suffice to locate point *I*.)

Most sources of light, however, are not point sources. Even the tiniest filament in a lamp is extended and can be conceived as an aggregate of many point sources. All the visible objects of the macroscopic world are, in fact, extended objects. To consider the formation of an image of such objects, whether they are luminous or not, we must imagine them as manifolds containing many point sources. In Figure 21.5 the light from two points, O_1 and O_2, of an extended object (in this case a match) is analyzed as it is reflected by a mirror so that, apparently having originated at I_1 and I_2, it reaches an eye at *E*. Only two rays are drawn from O_2 and followed all the way to the eye. Actually many rays leaves O_2 and are reflected as if they came from I_2. Ideally, for every ray leaving O_2 and hitting the mirror, there is a reflected ray apparently emanating from I_2. This

one-to-one correspondence between rays from O_2 and rays apparently from I_2 suggests that the concept of function could yield a mathematical treatment of image-formation. In principle this is true, but we shall not pursue it further. The plane mirror, moreover, is the only image-forming device for which it is *mathematically* true, in a rigorous sense, that all rays emanating from an object point produce a point image.

Two obvious properties of the image formed by a plane mirror can be summarized as follows: (1) the image of a point object lies on the perpendicular drawn from that object to the plane of the mirror; (2) the image distance, *i* (Fig. 21.3), is equal to the object distance, *o*. These statements, which apply, point by point, to all the points of an extended object, show us why the image of a left hand held before a plane mirror looks like a right hand that is as far behind the mirror as the left hand is in front of the mirror. If a partially reflecting mirror is used, one that behaves like a window as well as like a mirror, an observer can put his right hand behind the mirror so that it coincides (approximately) with the image of his left hand.

A humorous demonstration based on the fact that even an unsilvered pane of glass is both a window and a reflecting mirror is illustrated in Figure 21.6. Two identical light sockets and bulbs are located symmetrically, as shown, one in front of the glass and one behind it. The rear socket

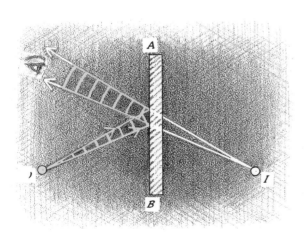

FIG. 21.4. *The plane mirror: reflection of a bundle of rays from a point source.*

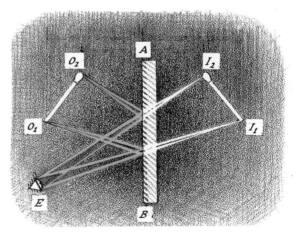

FIG. 21.5. *The plane mirror: the image of an extended object.*

sits exactly where the mirror image of the front socket would be. When we turn on the front bulb, its image appears bright, making it look as if the rear bulb were turned on. Next, after turning off the front bulb and putting a cloth over the rear bulb, we smash the rear bulb with a hammer. When the cloth is removed, there is, of course, no bulb in the rear socket; but, as soon as we light the front bulb again, its image reappears over the rear socket, making it seem that a new bulb has appeared there by magic.

Any serious photographer who has tried to take a picture of an image in a plane mirror knows that he has to focus his camera on a distance equal to the sum of the distance from camera lens to mirror and the distance from mirror to object.

One method of locating images depends on our ability to tell when one object lies closer than another. To demonstrate how this works, place a finger of your right hand so that it is completely hidden by the corresponding finger of the left hand when you close your left eye and look with only your right eye; now, when you close your right eye and open your left eye, the rear finger is no longer completely hidden behind the front finger. The front finger seems to have moved to the right; or, what amounts to the same thing, the rear finger seems to have moved to the left. Only if the fingers had been coincident would there have been no apparent displacement between them as we changed from one eye to the other.

Instead of changing from one eye to the other, you can keep one eye open and move from one side to the other. A distant object will seem to move in the direction in which you are moving. As you look—even with both eyes open—through the window of a train moving west, for example, the nearby telephone poles seem to move east, but the distant hills seem to move west along with the train. As two objects get closer to each other, their apparent relative motion diminishes; if they become coincident, they seem to move together. (This method of determining the coincidence of two objects or of an object and an image—virtual or real—is called the **method of parallax**.)

In Figure 21.7 the lower half of the image of candle A can be seen (A') in an opaque mirror. Candle B is placed by trial and error so that it

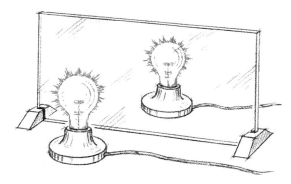

FIG. 21.6. *Using a sheet of glass as both a window and a mirror.*

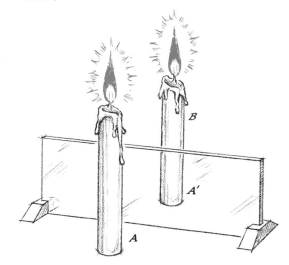

FIG. 21.7. *The method of parallax.*

coincides with the image of A. It looks this way from all directions, for, if there is no relative motion between the image and candle B, they are coincident. The method of parallax is especially useful in locating the virtual images produced by mirrors and lenses.

21.3. Spherical Mirrors

You can get a general idea of what curved mirrors do by looking at a polished spoon. If you look into the concave side, holding it very near your eye, you see an enlarged, erect (right-side-up) image of the eye. Holding the spoon farther away, you see a reduced inverted image. When you look

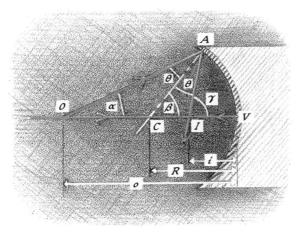

FIG. 21.8. *The concave spherical mirror: location of the image point by graphical analysis.*

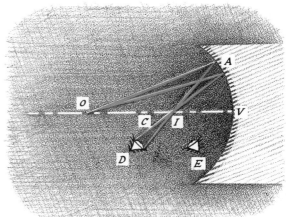

FIG. 21.9. *The concave spherical mirror: reflection of a bundle of rays from a point source.*

at the convex side, the image is always erect and reduced. Though a spoon is only approximately spherical, these are general characteristics of spherical curved mirrors. Let us see why.

In Figure 21.8, light from a point source at O strikes a concave spherical mirror of radius R whose center is at C. A line through O and C serves as a reference axis. The ray OC travels along the axis to point V (called the **vertex**) on the mirror and is reflected on itself, since OCV is normal to the mirror. (Every radius of a circle is normal to the circle.) Another ray, OA, making angle α with the axis, intersects the axis at I after reflection. For these two rays at least, I is the image of O. It is a real image, for light energy actually travels through I.

Since an exterior angle of a triangle is equal to the sum of the two opposite interior angles,

$$\gamma = \alpha + 2\theta$$
$$\beta = \alpha + \theta$$

Solving the second equation for θ and substituting in the first, we get

$$\alpha + \gamma = 2\beta \qquad [21.1$$

In radians, an angle is equal to the arc it subtends divided by the radius of the arc. For small values of α,

$$\alpha = AV/o \qquad \beta = AV/R \qquad \gamma = AV/i$$

The first and third of these expressions are not precisely true, for o and i are not radii of arc AV.

Putting these values into equation 21.1 and dividing through by AV, we get

$$\frac{1}{o} + \frac{1}{i} = \frac{2}{R} \qquad [21.2$$

Here o is the object distance and i the image distance, both measured from V. Observe that, as R approaches ∞, the mirror surface approaches a plane, and the $2/R$ of equation 21.2 approaches 0; so $o = -i$. The negative sign before i is our first introduction to a sign convention (discussed below) that holds for mirrors. If object and image are on the same side of the mirror, as in Figure 21.8, both o and i are positive. If o and i have opposite signs, object and image lie on opposite sides of the mirror.

To see the image, the eye must receive a bundle of rays. In Figure 21.9 a bundle of rays leaving O is reflected from A through I to the eye at D. Since the rays are reversible, a ray from D to I would go back to O. If the eye is placed at E, it will not see the image, for no bundle of rays from O can reach that position. You may confirm this by observing that a line from E through I would not touch the mirror.

Equation 21.2 holds equally well for convex mirrors, as you may prove by applying the preceding analysis to Figure 21.10.

In using equation 21.2, we must take care to give the quantities o, i, and R their proper signs according to the following conventions: (1) the

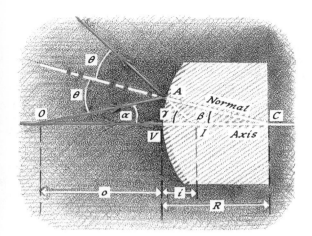

FIG. 21.10. *The convex spherical mirror: location of the image point by graphical analysis.*

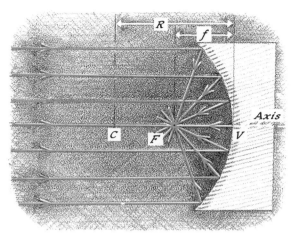

FIG. 21.11. *The concave spherical mirror: the focal point.*

object distance, o, is positive for light diverging from real objects or from images formed by other mirrors or lenses; (2) the image distance, i, is positive if the image, I, lies on the same side of the mirror as the object, O; (3) the radius of curvature, R, is positive for mirrors that are concave toward the object (Fig. 21.8), negative for those that are convex (Fig. 21.10). It helps to remember one standard case: in Figure 21.8, for example, the quantities o, i, and R are positive.

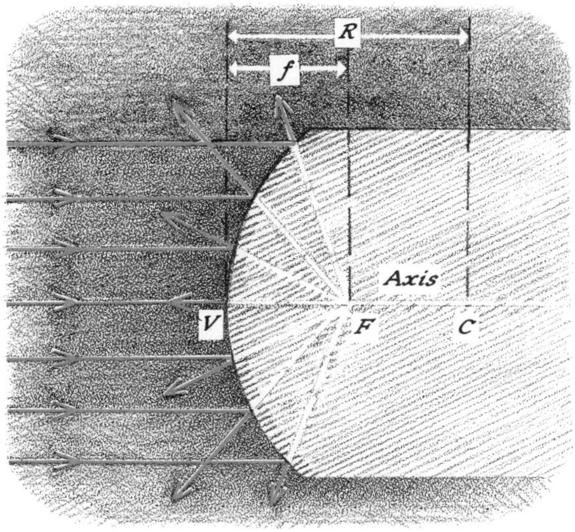

From this one could infer that i and R are negative in Figure 21.10.

The **focal point** of a spherical mirror is the image point (real or virtual) produced by parallel rays of light hitting the mirror. Figure 21.11 shows the focal point, F, of a concave mirror, and Figure 21.12 shows the focal point, F, of a convex mirror. The **focal length**, f, is the distance between the vertex, V, and F; in other words, it is the value of i when $o \longrightarrow \infty$. Equation 21.2, in such a case, yields

$$\frac{1}{f} = \frac{2}{R}$$

We may therefore rewrite equation 21.2 as

$$\frac{1}{o} + \frac{1}{i} = \frac{1}{f} \qquad [21.3$$

This is an equation relating three variables: o, i, and f.

We solve equation 21.3 graphically by drawing three lines making an angle of 60° with one another, as shown in Figure 21.13. We consider these the $o, f,$ and i axes, whose values increase in the direction of the arrows from their common origin at O. A straight line such as L meets the three axes at points whose coordinates, $o_1, f_1,$ and i_1, are solutions of equation 21.3. The accuracy of the solution is limited only by the accuracy with which the angles and lengths are constructed. The main value of this graph, perhaps, is that it enables us to sense quickly the qualitative variation

FIG. 21.12. *The convex spherical mirror: the focal point.*

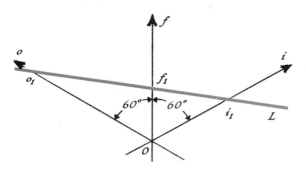

FIG. 21.13. *Graphical construction for solution of the equation* $1/o + 1/i = 1/f$.

of o and i when f remains fixed: we can see, just by considering the intersections of a line of variable inclination going through a fixed point on the f axis, that, as $o \longrightarrow \infty$, $i \longrightarrow f$; that, when $o = 2f$, $i = 2f$; and that, as $o \longrightarrow f$, $i \longrightarrow \infty$.

The method of **ray-tracing** is helpful in locating the image of an extended object such as a small electric light bulb on a tree. The behavior of three of the many rays that leave point O on the bulb (Fig. 21.14) is easily predicted. Ray a, traveling parallel to the axis, is reflected through F; ray b, passing through F, is reflected parallel to the axis; ray c, passing through C, comes back on itself after reflection. The three reflected rays all go through I, the image of the point O. Any two of the rays suffice to locate I, and the third can serve

as a check. All the rays that leave O and hit the mirror are reflected through I (approximately). Figure 21.15 presents a similar ray diagram for a convex mirror. We must modify our description of the rays' behavior to take into account the fact that, since C and F are on the opposite side of the mirror from O, real rays from O never reach C or F.

21.4. Images Formed by Refraction

As we saw in the introduction to Chapter 20, fishermen who hunt by spearing know that they must aim low in order to hit the fish. The reason is apparent if we consider Figure 21.16. The fish's eye, labeled O, is illuminated by the sunlight that penetrates the water. A bundle of rays from O, obeying the law of refraction, reaches the fisherman's eye at E. He sees the fish on the extension of line EP. If he throws the spear in that direction, he misses the fish. The fish sees the top of the man's eye on the extension of line OP.

21.5. Thin Spherical Lenses

Figure 21.17 shows a glass lens of thickness d ground so that its faces are spheres with centers at C and C' and with radii R and R'. The line

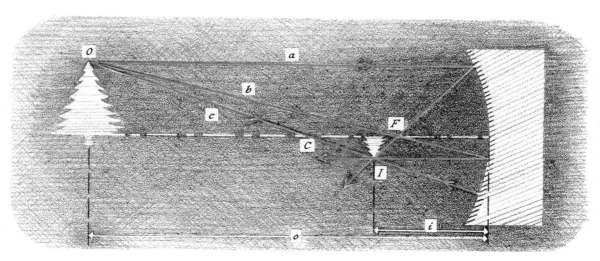

FIG. 21.14. *The concave spherical mirror: the image of an extended object.*

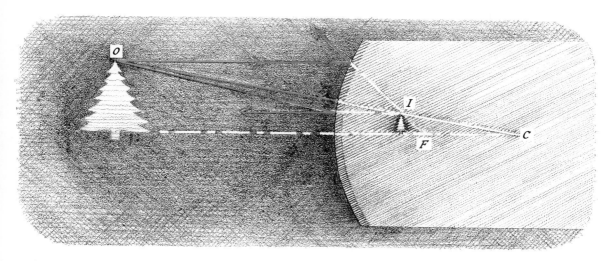

FIG. 21.15. *The convex spherical mirror: the image of an extended object.*

joining C and C' is the axis. A ray leaving point O on the axis at angle α is bent toward the normal at A, is bent away from the normal at B, and hits the axis at I. Ray OC, along the axis, goes through unbent (since it enters and emerges normally); so I, at least for rays OC and OA, represents the image of O. We let n stand for the index of refraction of the glass, relative to air. We see intuitively that the image distance, $i = V'I$, is related to the object distance, $o = OV$, to the index of refraction, n, and to the radii, R and R'. It also depends on d; but, since we are considering thin lenses,

whose d is very small compared with o and i, the relation between o and i does not involve d and can be expressed by the equation

$$\frac{1}{o} + \frac{1}{i} = (n-1)\left(\frac{1}{R} + \frac{1}{R'}\right) \qquad [21.4$$

This equation holds only for rays that are very close to the axis. I shall not prove it here, but we shall test its plausibility.

We observe that, since n is dimensionless, both sides of the equation have the dimension L^{-1}. The following conventions are observed: (1) the

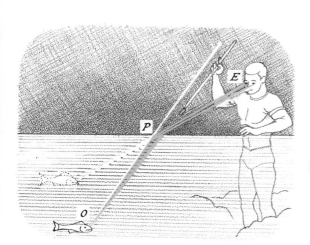

FIG. 21.16. *The image of a fish as seen by an observer above the water.*

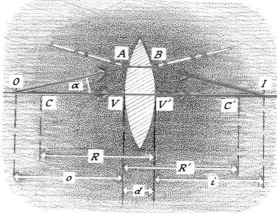

FIG. 21.17. *Graphical representation of distances and points related to image-formation by a double convex lens.*

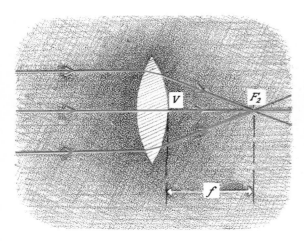

FIG. 21.18. *Behavior of rays parallel to the axis of a double convex lens.*

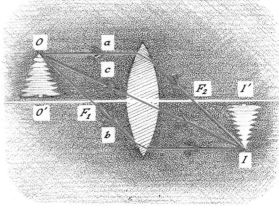

FIG. 21.19. *Image-formation by ray-tracing through a converging lens.*

object distance, o, is positive for light diverging from real objects or from images formed by lenses or mirrors; (2) the image distance, i, is positive if I lies on the opposite side of the lens from O; (3) the radii, R and R', are both positive if both surfaces of the lens are convex. It will help us to remember that o, i, R, and R', in Figure 21.17, are all positive.

If $(1/R + 1/R')$ is not zero, the right-hand side of the equation vanishes if $n = 1$. In this case $o = -i$. The interpretation of this equality is that the image is exactly where the object is; in other words, the lens has no effect—a result that is to be expected when we consider that the expression $n = 1$ implies no refraction at all. Even when $n \neq 1$, $o = -i$ whenever $(1/R + 1/R')$ vanishes, as it does when $R \longrightarrow \infty$ and $R' \longrightarrow \infty$. The physical meaning of this is that the surfaces of the lens are virtually parallel planes, which do not focus rays. Finally, the lens has no effect, even when $n \neq 1$, if $(1/R + 1/R')$ vanishes because $R = -R'$, implying that one surface is convex and the other concave.

The behavior of light rays parallel to the axis is shown in Figure 21.18. The rays converge to point F_2 on the axis and diverge thereafter. This point is called the **second focal point** of the lens. The **first focal point** is a point on the axis on the other side of the lens. A point source of light placed there would cause rays parallel to the axis to

emerge from the lens on the right side. The distance from point V on the lens to point F_2 is the **focal length,** f, of the lens; it is the value of i that we obtain by letting o approach ∞. (For a thin lens the distance from the first focal point to the nearest point on the lens is also f.) Substituting this in equation 21.4, we get the lens-maker's equation,

$$\frac{1}{f} = (n - 1)\left(\frac{1}{R} + \frac{1}{R'}\right) \qquad [21.5]$$

so called because it enables us to compute the focal length of a thin lens in terms of the radii of curvature and the index of refraction of the material. Combining equations 21.4 and 21.5 permits us to write the thin-lens equation as

$$\frac{1}{o} + \frac{1}{i} = \frac{1}{f} \qquad [21.6]$$

Since this is identical with equation 21.3, the graphical solution of Figure 21.13 is applicable to thin lenses as well as to mirrors. A positive focal length implies that the lens will cause parallel rays to converge; a negative focal length implies that the lens will cause parallel rays to diverge.

We can locate images by tracing rays (Fig. 21.19): (1) a ray, a, parallel to the axis passes through the second focal point, F_2; (2) a ray, b, through the first focal point, F_1, emerges parallel to the axis; (3) a ray, c, through the center of the lens goes through undeflected. Any two of these

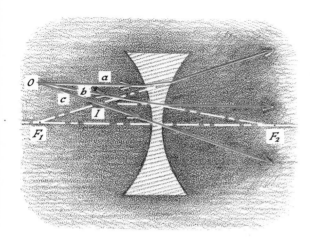

FIG. 21.20. *Image-formation by ray-tracing through a diverging lens.*

rays suffice to locate the image point, *I*. The third serves as a check. Any other ray that leaves *O* and gets through the lens passes through *I*. Any ray that leaves any other point of the line object *OO'* and gets through the lens passes through a point of the extended image *II'*.

A ray diagram for a diverging lens is shown in Figure 21.20. Follow rays *a*, *b*, and *c* to determine that they emerge from the lens as if they originated at *I*.

The formation of images by mirrors and lenses has made possible the microscope, the telescope, the camera, and a host of other devices that are in daily use. The main value of such devices to science is that they have enabled us to see objects that are invisible to the unaided eye and have extended our knowledge of the physical world inward toward the atom and outward toward stellar space. Because of the great utility of these instruments as aids to human vision, I shall discuss a few of them in the next chapter.

21.6. Summary

The eye sees an object when light originating from it or reflected by its enters the eye and forms an image on the retina. The object's size and direction are judged by the size and orientation of the retinal image.

To understand how the eye works, you must first understand how mirrors and lenses produce real and virtual images by bending the light from an object. Simple and useful approximate formulas, which we derive by applying the laws of reflection and refraction to rays, summarize the image-forming properties of mirrors and lenses, whose surfaces are usually either plane or spherical.

Problems

Additional drill in the use of the lens and mirror formulas is offered by the problems of Chap. 22.

21.1. Suppose that the distance between your eyes is 6.0 cm and that you look through a window pane at a meter stick that is 5 m from you. The stick is perpendicular to your line of sight and is oriented with the zero end to the left. The pane is parallel to the stick. Your right eye alone sees a fly on the pane directly in line with the 47-cm mark on the stick, and your left eye alone sees the fly at the same instant in line with the 51-cm mark. How far away from you is the fly? (Hint: Draw a figure.)

21.2. Fig. 21.21 shows a simplified optical range-finder. The eye sees the distant object, *O*, through a half-silvered mirror, *M*. (In practice, an ordinary mirror can be used, but then it is necessary to look over it to see the object directly.) It also sees an image of the distant object produced by reflections in the rotatable mirror, *M'*, and in the fixed mirror, *M*. By adjusting screw *S*, one can make the direct and reflected images of the object coincide. The distance *MO* is *D*, that between *M* and *M'* is *s*, and the length of the lever that rotates *M'* is *l*. When *M'* is set for an object at infinity, let the displacement of the free end be $x = 0$. In general, x/l is approximately the angle in radians through which *M'* has to be rotated from the position for which $x = 0$ if you are to see the image of *O* along the line *MO*. Prove that x/l is approximately equal to $\theta/2$ if θ is

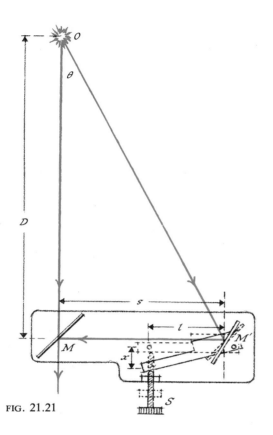

FIG. 21.21

the angle MOM'. Using the fact that for small angles expressed in radians $\tan \alpha \cong \alpha$, prove that the expression $D \cong sl/2x$ holds for values of D much larger than s.

21.3. When you look at yourself in the mirror, where does your image seem to be? We have used logic to prove that it appears to be just as far behind the mirror as you are in front of it, but some untrained observers insist that they see it at the surface of the mirror, as if it were a picture in a frame. Here is a test for such unbelievers. Hold a piece of clear glass (an ordinary microscope slide will do) vertically in your hands between your face and a wall on which a dot has been penciled at the height of your nose. Have a helper measure the distance between your nose and the wall. Using the glass as both a window and a mirror (it both transmits and reflects light), move it toward the wall until the dot on the wall seems to be exactly at the tip of the image of your nose, as judged by stereoscopic vision (with both eyes open). Have your helper measure the distance between the glass and the tip of your nose. Repeat this several times for different distances between you and the wall. What do you conclude?

21.4. "A mirror interchanges left and right but not up and down." To support this misleading statement, the fact that the image of a left hand held in front of a mirror looks like a right hand (§ 21.2), but still looks right side up, is often cited. As further "proof," hold a magazine or a book toward a mirror. Observe that the print is reversed—runs from right to left—in the image but is still right side up. A dilemma arises when you ask how a plane surface like a mirror distinguishes left and right from up and down. (It doesn't. What seems like the logical way to turn a book toward a mirror is to spin it round a vertical axis. If you spin it round a horizontal axis, however, its image is upside down.) There is, however, an important reversal. Suppose that a vertical mirror stands in an east-west plane. (Draw a picture.) You stand in front (south) of it facing the reflecting side of the mirror. Take a step to the west. Which way did the image step? Take a step to the east. Which way did the image step? Take a step to the north. Which way did the image step? Take a step to the south. Which way did the image step? Summarize your conclusions about image-reversal.

21.5. Two plane mirrors intersect at right angles. They stand vertically—one on the positive x axis (east-west), the other on the positive y axis (north-south). Draw a sketch. At the point $x = 3$ m, $y = 2$ m put a shoe on the floor. From heel to toe it points south.

1. A camera at $x = 2$ m, $y = 3$ m can see images of the shoe in three different places. Sketch them. One of these images is formed by rays that bounce off both mirrors. To photograph that one sharply, a photographer must focus his camera on what distance?

2. A person looking at himself in such a combination of mirrors "sees himself as others see him" (not as he sees himself in a single ordinary mirror). Comment on this statement. Better still, try the experiment, or analyze it graphically.

21.6. A low-power microscope is focused on a coin inside an empty water glass. The glass is then filled with water to a depth, d, of 5 cm. We can now find the image of the coin by raising the microscope through distance x. Calculate x. (By drawing, from a point on the coin, rays that diverge as they leave the water, try first to prove that the apparent depth, a, is related to the real depth, d, according to the equation $d/a = n$, in which n is the index of refraction of water. For a small angle θ, $\sin \theta \cong \tan \theta$.)

21.7. Imagine a device that can send a pulse of light to an object, receive the light reflected from the object, and measure with extreme accuracy the time it takes for the light to make the round trip. Such a device could then be used to measure the distance to any visible object.

1. This device is pointed down at the coin lying at the bottom of the glass of Prob. 21.6. If it is 5 cm away from the coin, and if there is no water in the glass, how long will it take the light pulse to make the round trip?

2. If the glass is filled to a depth of 5 cm with water, how long will the round trip take?

3. What would be the calculated distance to the coin for the latter case if the device were set for judging distances in air?

4. Compare this result with that of the previous problem.

21.8. A lighted small electric light bulb sits at the bottom of a clear lake. Draw a number of representative rays originating at the bulb and penetrating the surface into the air. For each of several bundles of rays determine from a sketch just where the bulb will appear to be when viewed from outside the lake. Convince yourself by logic or experiment, or by both, that the bulb, when viewed from the edge of a distant shore, will appear to be just under the surface of the water. (In other words, prove that the apparent depth approaches zero for rays at grazing emergence.)

21.9. A small electric light bulb is suspended at height h above the surface of a lake. Prove the following: When the bulb is viewed along a normal to the surface from a point within the water, the ratio, h'/h, of the apparent height to the real height is equal to n, the index of refraction of the water. (See Prob. 21.6.) When the bulb is viewed along any other direction, the apparent height is even greater than it is along the normal.

21.10. From equation 21.3 (which applies both to mirrors and to lenses) plot i roughly as a function of o in rectangular coordinates as follows: Choose values of o equal to $4f$, $3f$, and $2f$, and find, quickly, by measurement on a diagram such as Fig. 21.13, the corresponding values of i. Note, for example, that, as o approaches f, i becomes infinite. It is important to understand the physical meaning of points on the resulting graph. Express in words the significance of points corresponding to values of o between zero and f, first for a mirror and then for a lens. Points for which o is negative also have a physical significance, but we shall defer their interpretation until later.

21.11. 1. An object stands on the axis of a concave spherical mirror at a distance of 15 cm. The radius of curvature of the mirror is 10 cm. Compute the image distance algebraically. Check your results graphically by tracing rays (Fig. 21.14) and also using Fig. 21.13.

2. Solve the same problem for a convex spherical mirror whose radius is 10 cm.

21.12. 1. An object stands on the axis of a convergent lens of focal length 10 cm at a distance of 30 cm. Compute the image distance algebraically. Check your results graphically by tracing rays (Fig. 21.19) and also by using Fig. 21.13.

2. Solve the same problem for a divergent lens of focal length -10 cm.

21.13. A simple double convex lens is held so that an object 10 cm above the lens is focused on a screen held 15 cm below the lens. The index of refraction of the glass is 1.5.

1. If the curvature is the same on both sides of the lens, what is the radius of curvature of either side?

2. How far from the lens should a light source be placed in order that a set of parallel rays emerge from the other side of the lens?

Optical Instruments

"There are reasons to think that the vertebrate eye . . . originated on the surface of the body, and that it was the most potent single factor in the rise and further evolution of the vertebrate phylum."

Encyclopaedia Britannica, 1960 edition, Vol. 9

THE HUMAN eye is, without doubt, the most important optical instrument. Almost all man-made optical instruments serve to produce images or signals that will eventually reach the human retina. And it is through the eye that we have picked up the information that has led to our present knowledge of how the eye itself operates.

I shall not attempt to do justice to the subject.† The following is merely the barest outline of how the eye works. Although the eye is a physiological organ, we shall consider primarily its physical properties as they are manifested in image-formation.

22.1. The Human Eye—a Second Look

The eye (Fig. 22.1) is more than just a pinhole camera. The *pupil, P,* is an aperture whose diameter is varied by the movements of the diaphragm called the *iris, I,* the colored part of the eye. The iris's response to light is automatic: reflex actions cause it to contract and diminish the pupil when the intensity of light is high, and vice versa. The eye's focusing is due to refraction. We can think of the eye as having a single lens, but refraction

† The *Encyclopaedia Britannica*, quoted above, has a good article on the eye.

actually takes place not only at the *lens, L,* but also at the *cornea, C,* and to some extent at the boundary of the transparent *vitreous humor, H,* which fills the body of the eye. When the muscles, *M* and *M'*, affecting the lens are relaxed, parallel rays of light are focused at a point on the *retina, R.* (For simplicity's sake we draw the ray that passes through the center of the lens as if it were not refracted.) Here a complex physiochemical process generates signals that eventually reach the brain by way of impulses in the system of nerves,

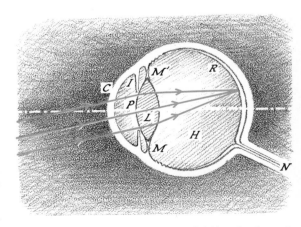

FIG. 22.1. *The human eye—a simplified and schematic representation.*

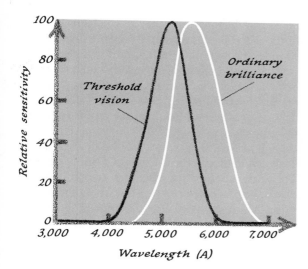

FIG. 22.2. *Relative sensitivity of the eye to different wavelengths. Wavelengths below 4,000 A and above 7,000 A produce the sensation of black. The wavelengths in between produce the sensation of colors in the order found in the rainbow.*

N. The retina is somewhat like a photographic film with renewable emulsion: the cells affected by light are damaged but are ready to work again after a short rest.

The normal eye can detect differences in intensity and in color. In Figures 22.2 and 22.3 we may compare the color sensitivity of the eye with that of three different types of photographic film. Notice especially that the sensitivity of films does not go to zero at about 4,000 A, as the sensitivity of the eye does. Electromagnetic waves with lengths from about 4,000 A to about 7,000 A can be detected by the average eye. With light of ordinary brilliance the peak sensitivity occurs at about 5,500 A, but in weak light it is closer to 5,000 A. Some eyes are slightly sensitive to the near ultraviolet, but for most people the wavelengths below 4,000 A and above 7,000 A fail to register. The visible spectrum begins out of black and ends in black. The colors in between range from violet at the short-wave end to red at the long-wave end.

The eye's lens has a variable focal length. The muscles at *M* and *M′* (Fig. 22.1), acting on instructions from the brain, can change the radii of curvature of the lens and hence the focal length.

[According to the lens-maker's equation (21.5), the effect of increasing the radii *R* and *R′* (Fig. 21.17) is to increase the focal length.] An eye set to see objects at infinity would produce an unsharp image of a nearby object [as *o* decreases, *i* increases (equation 21.6)]. If the focal length of the lens is decreased, its converging power increases. This almost automatic change of focal length enables the viewer to shift his attention fairly rapidly from distant to nearby objects.

The average eye can not comfortably adjust itself to seeing sharply objects much closer than 25 cm (about 10 inches); if an object, *O*, is brought much closer than that to the eye (Fig. 22.4), the rays converge toward a point, *Q*, that lies beyond the retina and therefore produce a blur on the retina. What is needed, obviously, is an increase in the converging power of the eye. A converging lens, placed in front of the eye, produces the required total convergence and brings the rays to a sharp focus on the retina.

A crude but effective model of the eye can be made (Fig. 22.5) out of a spherical flask, filled with water to which a little fluorescein has been added,

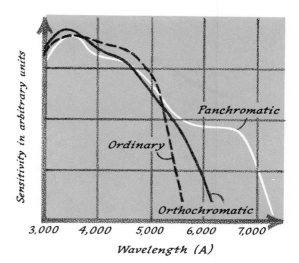

FIG. 22.3. *Sensitivity of three photographic films as a function of wavelength. Notice that ordinary film is insensitive to the wavelengths above about 5,500 A, whereas orthochromatic film is sensitive to about 6,200 A and panchromatic film has some sensitivity to wavelengths beyond 7,000 A. All three films can detect ultraviolet light of wavelength less than 4,000 A, which is invisible to the eye.*

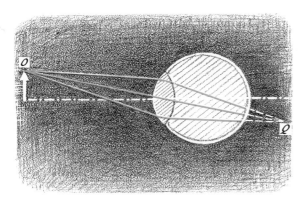

FIG. 22.4. *Effect of bringing the object too close to the eye.*

FIG. 22.5. *Spherical-flask model of the eye.*

FIG. 22.6. *A converging lens added to the model of the eye.*

and a variable-aperture stop, *S*, which fills the role of the iris. The fluorescein makes the light beams passing through the flask clearly visible. Light from a small automobile headlight bulb, *O*, produces a beam that converges, as a result of the refractions encountered, at a point, *I*, outside the flask. A converging lens, *L*, of the proper strength, placed before *S* (Fig. 22.6), converges the rays enough before they enter the flask so that the flask can converge them to point *I* on its surface. This illustrates how eyeglasses can correct vision—that is, help to produce sharp images on the retina. With the model of Figures 22.5 and 22.6 we can demonstrate not only the converging and diverging effects of different real eyeglasses but also the effect of diminishing the aperture in *S*, which is to sharpen fine details such as the images of the coils of wire in the filament of the bulb. (The explanation of this sharpening is discussed in § 22.5.)

The eye loses its sensitivity to color below a certain intensity. The dark-adapted eye seems capable of responding to flashes of light of wavelength 5,070 A that deliver as few as 100 photons to the cornea. Ten or fewer of these photons may actually be absorbed by the sensitive receptors of the retina.[†] One such photon carries 3.92×10^{-19} joule.

The eye's **persistence of vision,** which enables it to hold an image for about 1/16 second, makes the illusion of continuity in modern motion pictures (24 frames per second) almost perfect.

The preceding array of facts forms only an outline of what is known about the human eye. What is still not known will no doubt fill future volumes. The eye is "fearfully and wonderfully made," and it offers enough problems to keep many investigators busy for a long time. Now, with this brief introduction, we must proceed to consider some of the instruments that man has designed to aid the eye.

22.2. The Camera and the Projector

The photographic camera is like the eye in many ways. It is essentially a light-tight box (Fig. 22.7) with a lens at one end and a photographic film

† M. H. Pirenne, "Light Quanta and Vision," *Endeavour,* Vol. XX.

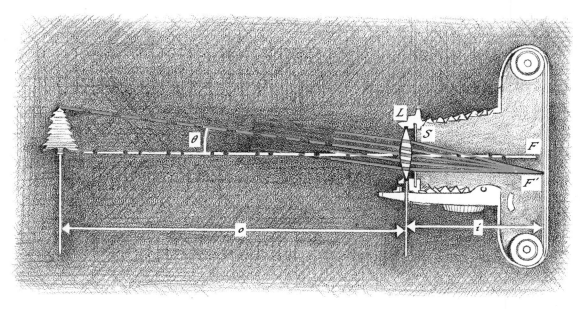

FIG. 22.7. *A very simple photographic camera: The image distance,* i, *may be adjusted in accordance with the object distance,* o.

in the **focal plane,** which is perpendicular to the axis and contains the second principal focus, F. A bundle of rays entering the lens parallel to its axis is focused at F. Some other set of parallel rays, making angle θ with the axis, is focused at some other point, F', on the focal plane. (This last statement is only approximately true, but the approximation is adequate for most applications of photography.) In practice the object is often placed at a distance that is much greater than the focal length of the lens, the result of this being that the image distance is very nearly equal to the focal length. The image distance, i, obeys the lens equation

$$\frac{1}{f} = \frac{1}{o} + \frac{1}{i}$$

EXAMPLE 22.1. We wish to take an extreme close-up with a camera of focal length f so that the image size is the same as the object size. What should be the value of i in terms of f?

Putting $o = i$ in the lens equation, we get

$$\frac{1}{f} = \frac{1}{i} + \frac{1}{i}$$

Therefore

$$\frac{1}{f} = \frac{2}{i}$$

and

$$i = 2f$$

The total distance between object and film plane in this case is $4f$.

The camera represented in Figure 22.7 is very simple, without mechanical or optical refinements. It has a single, thin, converging lens, L, behind which is a shutter stop, S, with an aperture of variable diameter. Today, however, all but the cheapest cameras have **compound lenses**—that is, lenses composed of many (in some cases as many as twelve) different lens elements, which serve to correct the different kinds of aberration (see § 22.5). The shutter is sometimes placed between two elements or two groups of the elements of the lens.

The image of an extended object consists of light and dark areas in the focal plane, corresponding to the light and dark areas of the object. Light hitting the emulsion of the photographic film induces an invisible chemical change, which, when the film is developed and fixed in a series of chemical baths, becomes visible: the areas hit by light are darkened. This process results in a **negative,** in which white objects appear black, and black objects appear as transparent areas of the film. The darkening effect of the light at a point on the focal plane depends on the film's sensitivity to light of the given color (see Fig. 22.3), on the light's intensity, on the length of time during which the light strikes the film, and on the area of the aperture through which the light passes. If the aperture is very small, it is apparent, from the properties of similar triangles, that a little square of area $\Delta x \times \Delta x$ in the object plane will look like a little square of area $(\Delta x)^2(i/o)^2$ in the image plane. (This is true even if the aperture is large, but we shall simplify the analysis by considering, for the moment, only the rays going through a tiny aperture.)

The blackening effect at a point on the film is proportional to the density (in J/cm², for example) of the energy hitting it. The total energy originating in a little square source of area $\Delta x \times \Delta x$ and passing through a lens aperture of diameter d at distance o is proportional to $\pi d^2/4 \times (\Delta x)^2/o^2$. If all of this is focused on a square of area $\Delta y \times \Delta y$, the energy density at the film is proportional to $d^2(\Delta x)^2/o^2(\Delta y)^2$. But this is equivalent to d^2/i^2 since $\Delta x/\Delta y = o/i$. As a camera is generally used, i is very close to the focal length, f, of the lens. We conclude that the blackening effect is proportional to $(d/f)^2$. What is called the **speed of a lens** is usually expressed as d/f.†

It is impossible to list here, in any useful form, all the characteristics of the great variety of photographic emulsions now commercially available, but color sensitivity, speed, and resolving power demand a brief description. Most of the film used today in ordinary snapshot work is **panchromatic**—that is, is sensitive to all the colors to which the eye is sensitive, though not to the

† The *f*-stop of a lens is a number whose reciprocal is d/f. The *f*-stop $f/11$ (read as "*f* eleven"), for example, means that the ratio of aperture to focal length is $1/11$. Since $d/f = 1/11$, $d = f/11$. Given the focal length, we simply divide it by 11 to get the aperture; but the figure that determines the light flux on the film is d/f. All lenses rated at $f/11$, regardless of focal length, produce similar blackening of the same film from the same exposure, for they all have the same value of d/f—namely, $1/11$.

same degree (see Fig. 22.3). The sensitivity of photographic emulsions can be extended, in the infrared, to about 10,000 A. Films sensitive to ultraviolet rays and x-rays are common. An exceptionally fast film, not long ago, had a speed index (ASA) of 100; films of that speed are available today wherever film is sold, even in drugstores, and one film now has a speed index of 3,000. Ordinary emulsions can resolve—that is, produce a distinct image of—about 500 equally spaced lines per centimeter, but the emulsion of the plates used in spectroscopy can resolve 10,000 lines per centimeter. Even the development of special films into natural-color transparencies (film slides) is now a routine process. The most spectacular novelties, however, are the Polaroid film that can deliver a paper positive ten seconds after it is exposed and another than can produce a color picture in one minute.

Figure 22.8 shows how a projector for transparencies works. (The basic idea applies equally well to movie projectors and to still projectors for films and plates of all sizes.) A transparency is placed in the object plane, OO'. Light from an incandescent filament, F (some of it reflected by the mirror, M), passes through a condensing lens system, L_1, which is placed in such a way that any point such as A in the object plane is illuminated by light from different parts of the filament. (The rays from the filament to point A are omitted because they would make the figure unduly complicated.) For our purpose it is sufficient to consider point A as the origin of a bundle of light rays to be focused on the screen by the projection lens, L_2 (shown as a single lens but in practice often a compound lens). The ratio, m (for magnification), of image size to object size is equal to the ratio of image distance to object distance; that is, $m = i/o$. From the equation

$$\frac{1}{f} = \frac{1}{o} + \frac{1}{i}$$

we get

$$\frac{i}{f} = \frac{i}{o} + 1$$

or

$$\frac{i}{f} = m + 1 \qquad [22.1$$

This is a useful formula.

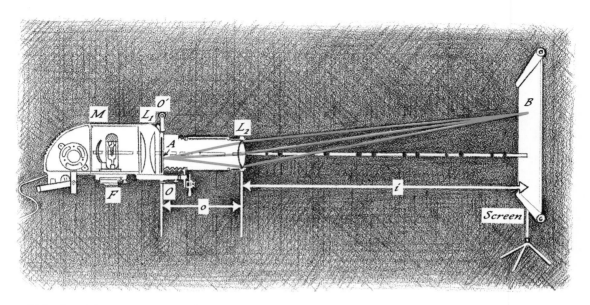

FIG. 22.8. *Simplified diagram of a projector for transparencies.*

EXAMPLE 22.2. We wish to fill a screen 2 m square from a transparency 5 cm square with a projector lens having a focal length of 5 in. How far from the lens should the screen be placed?

Solving equation 22.1 for i, we get $i = f(m + 1)$. Since $m = 40$ and $f = 12.7$ cm, we get

$$i = 0.127 \times 41 \text{ m} = 5.2 \text{ m}$$

22.3. The Simple Magnifier

A simple experiment helps you to understand what a converging lens actually does and demonstrates its value as a simple magnifier. Face a distant wall on which there is some fixed object, such as a light-switch plate. Hold a pencil at arm's length, and focus your attention on its tip. As you bring the pencil closer and closer to your eye, its image on the retina gets larger, and the pencil therefore looks bigger and bigger. Bring it so close to one eye that even with considerable strain you can not see it clearly. Now, relaxing the eye muscles, look at the switch plate with both eyes. The eye strain is gone, and the pencil is now hopelessly out of focus, but the blurred image is big.

We should like, while retaining the advantages of relaxed viewing and bigness, to sharpen the image. We can do this if we put a converging lens between the pencil and the eye (Fig. 22.9.A). By adjusting the distance between the lens and the eye while keeping the pencil fixed and the eye as relaxed as it was when looking at the switch plate, we can get a large, sharp image of the pencil. The converging lens, called a **simple magnifier** when used in this way, has apparently thrown the image of the pencil out to the plane of the wall. With a little practice, keeping both eyes open, you can see at the same time, with one eye, the distant switch plate and, with the other eye, an enlarged image of the pencil *that seems to be in the plane of the wall* (Fig. 22.9.B). You can check the italicized clause by moving your head slightly to the left or right: if conditions are right, there will be no parallax between the switch plate and the image of the pencil; that is, the images of the pencil and the switch plate will not move in relation to each other.

It is important to understand the experiment you have just performed, for the microscope, the telescope, and the spectroscope, to be described shortly, all contain a magnifier. It is not always a simple magnifier, but it performs the function just described for the simple magnifier.

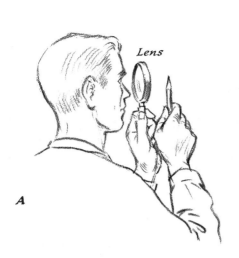

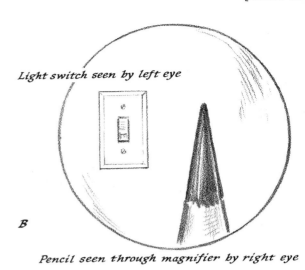

Light switch seen by left eye

A

B

Pencil seen through magnifier by right eye

FIG. 22.9. *Experiment with a simple magnifier.*

Let us look at a ray diagram (Fig. 22.10) to see just what the lens does. The pencil stands between the converging lens, C, and its first principal focus, F_1. Two rays are drawn from the pencil's tip, P, one through the center of the lens and the other parallel to the axis. The emerging rays appear to come from point Q, which is the image of P. A point at the intersection of pencil and axis, such as P', has an image point, Q', also on the axis. An object of size PP' would have an image of size QQ'. Notice that the similar triangles QCQ' and PCP' yield the useful relation

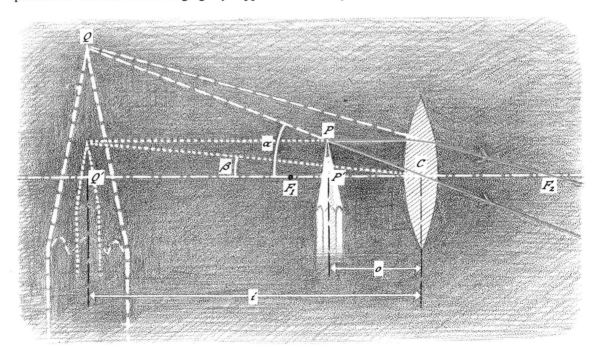

FIG. 22.10. *Ray diagram for a simple magnifier.*

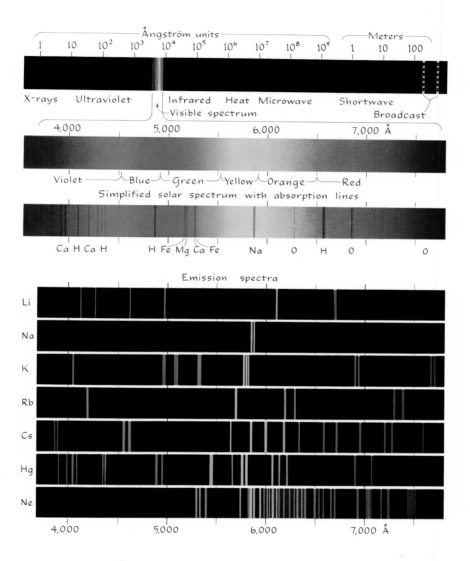

Spectra produced by different sources of light.

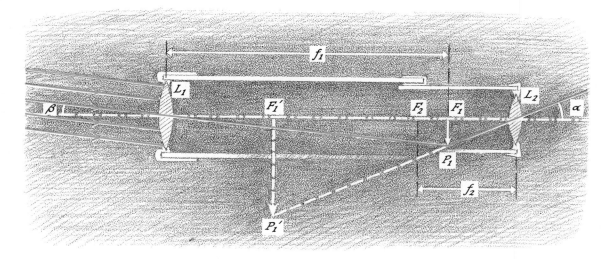

FIG. 22.11. *Schematic diagram of an astronomical telescope.*

$$\frac{\text{size of image}}{\text{size of object}} = \frac{\text{distance from lens to image}}{\text{distance from lens to object}}$$

As the distance, CP', from lens to object approaches the focal length, f, of the lens, the distance, CQ', from lens to image becomes infinite, and so does the size of the image. That would seem to make the magnification infinite. But the angle, α, subtended by the image does not, if the eye is kept close to the lens, change appreciably as we move P' closer to F_1.

The important thing about a virtual image is not how large it is but how large it seems to be, and this is determined by the angle it subtends at the lens. This does not vary appreciably. Hence a definition of magnification (Fig. 22.10) is the ratio of angle α, subtended by the image, to angle β, subtended by the object when it is placed at a distance of 25 cm from the unaided eye. (The choice of 25 cm depends on the fact that an object usually produces a blurred image on the retina if brought closer than 25 cm to the unaided eye.) What a magnifier does, then, is to permit us to bring an object close to the eye, thereby subtending a large angle and making the image seem big, and at the same time to throw the image far enough away to be focused sharply on the retina.

With a lens of focal length 2.5 cm (approximately 1 in.) we can bring an object close to 2.5 cm from the eye. Without a lens the object would have to be placed at a distance of 25 cm. The angle

subtended by the image, therefore, when the lens is used, is 10 times as great as that subtended by the object without the lens. The magnification of the lens is 10. More generally, the magnification of a lens of focal length f is $25/f$ if f is expressed in centimeters.

If the image (Fig. 22.10) is 25 cm away instead of at infinity, the magnification is

$$m = \frac{\alpha}{\beta} \cong \frac{\tan \alpha}{\tan \beta} = \frac{PP'/P'C}{PP'/Q'C} = \frac{Q'C}{P'C} = \frac{25}{o}$$

(The tangent function is defined in Appendix E.) Multiplying both sides of equation 21.6 by 25 cm, we see that $25/o = 1 + 25/f$ since $i = -25$ cm. Summarizing, if the image is at infinity, the magnification is $25/f$; if the image is 25 cm away, the magnification is $25/f + 1$, which is only a little larger than $25/f$ when f is much shorter than 25 cm.

22.4. The Telescope and the Microscope

A simple telescope can be made with two converging lenses, one of long and the other of short focal length. In Figure 22.11 parallel rays coming from a star are focused by lens L_1, of focal length f_1, at point P_1. (Only the central ray, for simplicity's sake, is shown going through the lens, but all rays entering parallel to it are focused at P_1.) Rays from another star, entering parallel to the axis, are focused at F_1, the second principal focus

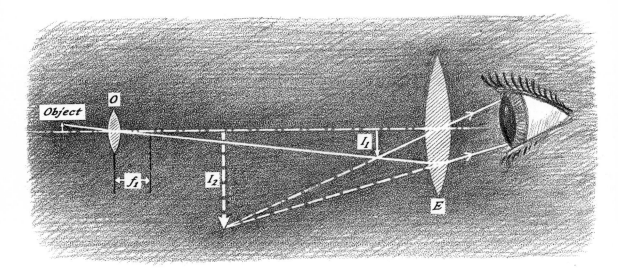

FIG. 22.12. *Schematic diagram of a compound microscope.*

of L_1. The angle subtended at L_1 by the rays from the two stars—that is, the angular separation between the stars—is β. The images at F_1 and P_1 are real and can be viewed through a simple magnifier (or a converging combination of lenses). If the distance from F_1 to that magnifier—the *eyepiece*, L_2, of focal length f_2—is a little less than f_2, the virtual image formed by L_2—the image, P_1', of P_1—is far enough away to be viewed comfortably. The angular separation between the virtual images of F_1 and P_1 is α. The magnification of the telescope is the ratio of angle α to angle β.

Using the approximation $\tan x \cong x$, we get the expression

$$m = \frac{\alpha}{\beta} \cong \frac{\tan \alpha}{\tan \beta} \cong \frac{P_1 F_1/f_2}{P_1 F_1/f_1} = \frac{f_1}{f_2} \qquad [22.2$$

We can increase the magnification either by increasing f_1 or by decreasing f_2, or by both means. This combination of lenses is called an **astronomical telescope**. The final image is inverted, but this is of no consequence in astronomical work.

The optical components of a **compound microscope** (Fig. 22.12) are usually an *objective*, O, a lens of short focal length, f_1, and an *eyepiece*, E, which is used as a simple magnifier. The ray diagram gives enough details to show you that I_1 is the real image formed by O and that I_2 is the virtual image, formed by E, of I_1. The eye sees I_2 at a comfortable distance.

22.5. Aberrations of Lenses

Deviations of sets of rays from their intended point focus are called **aberrations**. We shall consider only two kinds.

Chromatic aberration, as the name suggests, is due to the fact that light rays of different colors are dispersed—that is, are differently refracted. Because the refractive index of glass and other materials is a function of wavelength (Fig. 20.6), blue light bends more than red (Fig. 22.13) and focuses (B) closer to the lens than red (R). To demonstrate this effect, catch the image of a small, distant, white source on a white screen at B. The image will have a red outline. If you move the screen to R, the image will have a bluish outline.

An **achromatic pair of lenses** (which are often in contact with each other) is one that minimizes dispersion. A lens of ordinary crown glass, for example, can be combined with a flint-glass lens of the proper shape so that a blue ray and a coincident red ray experience identical total deviations. The deviations of all the other colors will be approximately the same. A white object will therefore produce a white image—a result that is particularly important in color photography.

Spherical aberration is due to the fact that even monochromatic light, entering in a parallel beam along the axis, is not precisely focused to a single point by a lens with spherical surfaces (Fig. 22.14). The rays (R, R') that are close to the axis are focused at one point, B, but the rays (P, P') that are far from the axis are focused at another point, A, which is nearer the lens. The aberration is measured as the distance AB, which is proportional to d^2/f if d is the diameter of the circular aperture admitting light to the lens and f is the focal length. It also depends on the shape of the lens and its orientation to the incoming rays. A plano-convex lens, for example, has, under certain circumstances, a smaller aberration when the plane side faces the image than when it faces the object.

The simplest way to reduce spherical aberration is to stop down the lens—that is, to stop all rays except a small bundle near the axis; but this reduces the total amount of light passing through the lens. The most effective way is to grind non-spherical surfaces. This method requires refined optical techniques, but it is being used more and more for instruments, such as telescopes and microscopes, that require both large aperture and sharp images.

Interest in optics has increased because new telescopes, to be placed in orbiting satellites, have recently been developed. These instruments are expected to pick up such radiations as ultraviolet rays and x-rays in the region of the spectrum that does not get through the earth's atmosphere. A half century ago interest in telescopes was nearly limited to the worldwide fraternity of astronomers. Today articles on new kinds of telescopes may be found not only in the *Journal of the Optical Society of America*, and in its counterparts published in other countries, but in journals devoted to astronomy, geophysics, and space research.

Optics is a specialized branch of physics, and optical engineering is an applied branch of optics. Designers of lenses and mirrors now use the most modern computing techniques to minimize all the aberrations besides the spherical and the chromatic and to maximize speed. Since it is impossible to correct all aberrations at the same time in one system, mathematical optimization, according to the limitations under which the system will be used, is desirable.

22.6. Television

The motion-picture camera and projector use standard optical parts—light sources, films, mirrors, and lenses—to produce images on a screen. The basic ideas were known a hundred years ago. Television utilizes some techniques of image-formation that are barely more than twenty-five years old. The link between movies and television is electronics. Since there are more than 100 million television sets in the world, the new techniques have obviously proved their worth as a means of conveying visual information (some of it of doubtful value). Let us look very briefly into this marriage of optics and electronics.

In the television studio is a camera (Fig. 22.15). It has an ordinary optical lens, but the image is formed on a special tube (known by the trade names Orthicon and Vidicon in the United States), which converts the light landing on it into a series

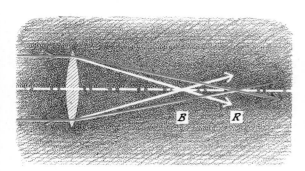

FIG. 22.13. *Chromatic aberration.*

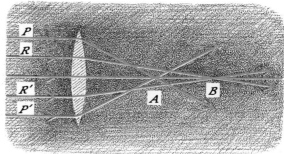

FIG. 22.14. *Spherical aberration.*

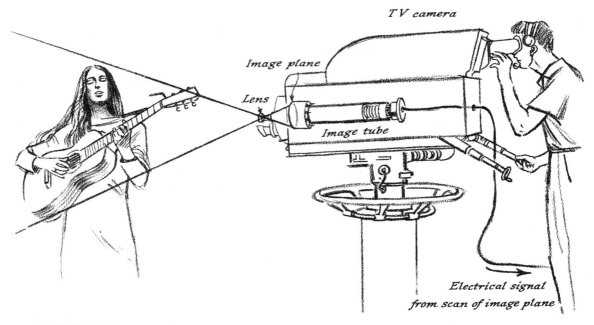

FIG. 22.15. *Television camera in use.*

of electrical impulses by means of the photoelectric effect (§ 19.4).

Essential to the technique is the process of **scanning.** Imagine (Fig. 22.16) an electron beam, represented by the spot S, moving across the first line, from A to B, and sampling the image plane of the image tube for light intensity. Whenever the spot is in a light region, it sends a strong electrical signal; whenever it is in a darker region, it sends

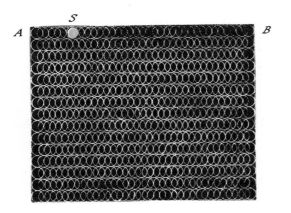

FIG. 22.16. *Scanning of the television camera's image plane.*

a weaker signal. Having scanned from A to B, it immediately sweeps across the second line, then across the third line, and so on. In an ordinary television image there are 500 lines like AB (this number could, in principle, be increased considerably), and the complete scan of one image takes only 1/30 second; that is, thirty complete scans are made each second.

A highly schematic diagram (Fig. 22.17) shows the electrical links between studio and receiver. The fluctuating signals from the TV camera are amplified and broadcast as signals that modify the electromagnetic waves transmitted by the antenna. At the receiving end these signals, after being again amplified, are fed to the horizontal plate in a cathode-ray picture tube (Fig. 22.18). These plates control the vertical motion of the electron beam and thus of the scanning spot. The horizontal location of the spot is determined by a sweep circuit acting through the vertical plates. (Magnetic deflection is generally used in commercial television receivers, but the scanning principle is the same.) The brightness of the spot depends on the changing intensity of the electron beam. Mathematically, we want the intensity and location of the beam hitting the tube's screen to be a function

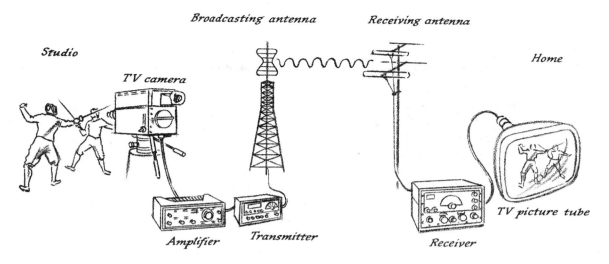

FIG. 22.17. *The varying electrical impulses created in the TV camera are broadcast by a radio transmitter, picked up by a receiver, and converted into a visible picture on the TV picture tube.*

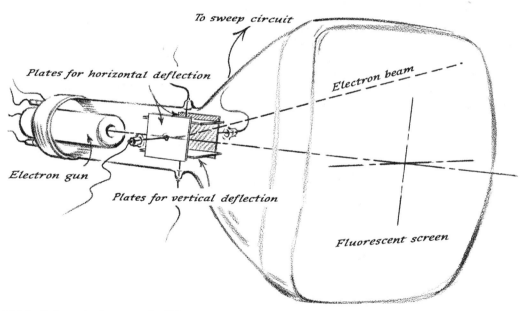

FIG. 22.18. *Schematic diagram of a TV picture tube: An electron beam originating in the electron gun is deflected horizontally and vertically by electric fields. A spot of light appears wherever electrons hit the screen. The picture is built up of light and dark spots as the beam scans the screen in obedience to the original scanning—that of the image plane of the TV camera, as in Fig. 22.16.*

of time and proportional to the similar function at the image plane of the camera.

If you could take extremely fast motion pictures of the images on a television receiver screen and slow them to a normal projection speed, you would see nothing but a flying spot of light that was sometimes brighter and sometimes darker. The spot would start (Fig. 22.19) at the upper left-hand corner, *A*, and move slowly toward *B*, then start at *A′* and move toward *B′*,

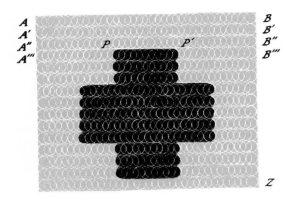

FIG. 22.19. *Building up a picture on the screen of a TV picture tube.*

and so on. It would be bright until it reached P (line $A'''B'''$); there it would go dark, and it would remain dark until P', lighting up thereafter. In such a way the picture of a simple black cross on a light background could be built up. All the scans from A to Z really took only 1/30 second; but it was a single moving dot, lighting up and going out, that produced the final picture. No matter how complicated the object, the image on the screen is built up in this piecemeal way. The

eye's persistence of vision alone enables us to integrate the pieces into the illusion of a picture.

Television, in brief, has replaced film by an electronic device, the image tube, that produces a time-dependent sequence of electrical impulses, and these impulses transmit information normally carried by a photograph. The advantages of this system of forming and displaying images may be summarized as follows: (1) The TV camera can be put into dangerous and otherwise inaccessible places (deep in a shaft, in an orbiting satellite, in a room full of dangerous radioactivity). (2) The resolving power of the system can equal that of photographic film. (3) The display is instantaneous and is simultaneous at any number of receivers. (4) The sensitivity of the image tube to color can be extended far into the infrared and ultraviolet and x-ray regions; display in natural color is possible for the visible wavelengths. (5) Since it is possible to record a time sequence of electrical signals on a magnetic tape, it is possible to store a whole program of entertainment, or of scientific information picked up by TV cameras on orbiting satellites, until it is needed (see Fig. 1.1, taken by the weather satellite TIROS V).

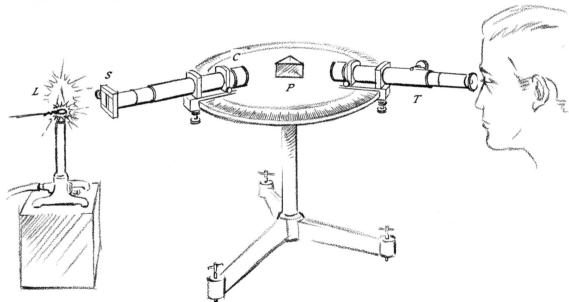

FIG. 22.20. *A simple spectroscope: The collimator, C, passes a beam of parallel rays aimed at the prism, P. The prism bends the light to new directions, keeping a beam of parallel rays for each wavelength. The telescope, T, forms an image of the slit, S, for each of the wavelengths produced by the source of light, L.*

22.7. The Spectroscope

Thus far I have described instruments whose main function is to produce optical images of extended objects. There is another class of instruments, however—those designed to *disperse* light, to spread it out into its component colors. (This, as we saw in § 22.5, is the phenomenon that produces chromatic aberration.) The simple **spectroscope** (Fig. 22.20)—an instrument for the production and examination of spectra—is such an instrument. We shall emphasize here the role played by its different lenses: the **collimating lens**, C, produces a beam of parallel rays; the eyepiece, used as a simple magnifier, and the objective act together as a telescope, T.

We adjust the telescope first (Fig. 22.21) by moving the eyepiece, E, in relation to the objective, O, so that we can clearly see the image of a very distant object. The telescope, thus set, is said to be focused at infinity. The **collimator** (Figs. 22.20 and 22.22) consists of a tube with a slit, S, at one end and a converging lens, C, at the other end. The slit is illuminated by a lamp, L. We adjust the distance between C and S to equal the focal length, f, of C and thereby cause the light from S to emerge from C as a beam of parallel rays; in other words, light passing through C seems to come from a slit at infinity. We can set the distance SC at f by placing the telescope on the same axis and looking through it (Fig. 22.22). Since the telescope was previously focused at in-

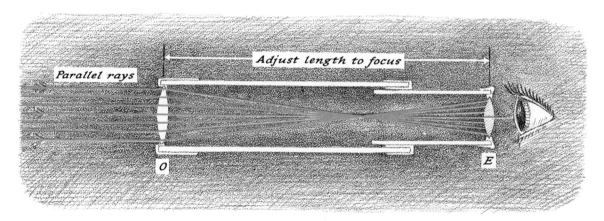

FIG. 22.21. *The telescope of a spectroscope.*

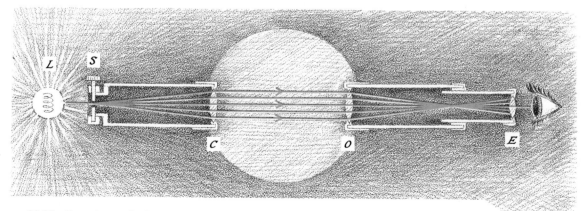

FIG. 22.22. *Experimental adjustment of the collimator of a spectroscope.*

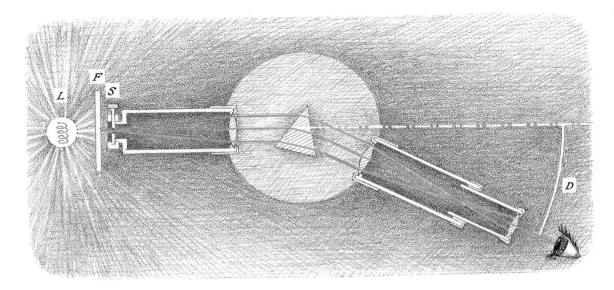

FIG. 22.23. *The simple spectroscope in use.*

finity, the image of the slit will be seen in focus when $SC = f$.

All we have so far is a telescope receiving an image from a collimator. But now, if we put a prism between the telescope and the collimator, we have a spectroscope. Light from the collimator is deviated by an amount that depends on the index of refraction of that prism for the wavelength of that light. If (Fig. 22.23) a filter, F, permits only perfectly monochromatic light of a certain wavelength to enter the slit, and if the prism is turned so that the beam emerges with the minimum deviation, an image in that wavelength can be seen after the telescope is rotated through the proper angle of deviation, D. If the filter is green, for example, a green image of the slit will be seen at the angle shown. Since, as we know, a prism has a different index of refraction for each wavelength, different wavelengths require different values of D. If white light without a filter is used, overlapping images of the slit, giving the impression of a continuous spectrum, will be seen.

If the source of light is a neon glow lamp such as those used for signs. the spectrum consists of many images of the slit, each of a different wavelength (see the color plate facing p. 270). The discovery that each chemical element produces a unique set of such images, or **spectral lines**, gave

birth to chemical analysis by spectroscopy, which has already been extended (with suitable modifications of equipment) into the ultraviolet and x-ray regions and into the far infrared. Since much of what we know about atoms comes from spectroscopy, the atomic explanation of spectra is one of the goals of this book.

22.8. Summary

The human eye is an image-forming mechanism of great sensitivity and adaptability. In some respects it is like a camera that can take color pictures. It has a lens system and a retina whose function is like that of the color film in a camera. A complete understanding of its functioning would involve chemistry and biology as well as physics.

Many optical aids to vision have been devised. They include the simple magnifier, the compound microscope, and the telescope.

The photographic camera and projector have made it possible to store and retrieve visual information in a simple way. A knowledge of how images are formed by lenses is essential to the understanding of these instruments.

Recently electronics has been utilized, in television, to produce images in a new way.

With the combined help of cameras, television, and orbiting satellites it is possible to see an event occurring almost anywhere on the earth with practically no loss of time.

The dispersion produced by a prism has made possible the spectroscope, by means of which the chemical components of substances can be identified.

Problems

22.1. A government health agency, in order to prevent damage to eyes, recommended the following adaptation of an old and well-known device to observations of a recent solar eclipse: A box one m long, without a cover, is pierced on one side with a small hole one mm in diameter, and this is pointed at the sun; the image of the sun on the inside of the box on the face opposite the hole can then be observed safely and easily. It is known that the sun subtends an angle of 0.5° at the earth and delivers about 495 W/m² to the earth's surface.

1. Calculate the diameter of the image of the sun on the wall of the box. It may help to use the approximation $\sin \alpha \cong \tan \alpha \cong \alpha$ for angle α expressed in radians.

2. If all the energy that enters the hole is evenly distributed over the whole image, what is the power density at the image in W/cm²?

22.2. The word DANGER is painted in red on a black background. Describe how this would look in a black-and-white photograph made (1) with panchromatic film, (2) with orthochromatic film. (See Fig. 22.3.)

22.3. The greatest distance a certain nearsighted man can see sharply without glasses is 0.4 meter. Should he get glasses with converging or with diverging lenses, and what should be their focal length if he is to be able to focus sharply on very distant objects? (Hint: It is possible to solve this problem mathematically by using the lens equation, but you can solve it much more simply by calculating the focal length of the eyeglass lens that will make an object at infinity look as if it were 0.4 meter away.)

22.4. A camera having a lens with a focal length of 7.5 cm is pointed perpendicularly at the side of a building 1 km away. The width of the building is 70 m, and the height is 100 m. What is the area in mm² of the image of the building on the film?

22.5. Suppose you want to take a picture of a bush 1.00 m high at a distance of 10.0 m and you want the image on the film to be 1.00 cm high. What should be the focal length of the lens (to three sig-

nificant figures)? (To any amateur photographer it is obvious that the answer must be very close to 10 cm. One way to get the precise answer is to start with equation 21.6 and multiply both sides by o.)

22.6. The lens of a camera can usually be moved in and out a little so that it will focus on objects at different distances. The focal length of a certain camera is 5.00 cm. How much movement of the lens must be provided if it is to focus from 1.00 m to infinity? Express the result to three significant figures.

22.7. The opacity of a processed photographic film depends (within certain limits) on the product of the area of the aperture and the exposure time. A picture taken at $f/16$ with an exposure of 0.1 sec produces an adequately exposed negative. What exposure time would produce the same opacity on the same type of film at $f/4$? at $f/32$?

22.8. One way to get a larger image from a projector on a screen is to move the two farther apart. (This can, at times, be very inconvenient; see part 2, below.) Another way is to use a special lens of variable focal length (the so-called "zoom" lens). A typical home projector for 35-mm transparencies has a focal length of 12.7 cm. In Example 22.2 we saw that such a lens produced a magnification of 40 at a distance of 5.2 m. (The 35-mm dimension of a slide, for example, appears as the length 35 mm $\times$ 40 = 1.40 m on the screen.)

1. Compute the new focal length (to three significant figures) that is needed to double the image dimensions on the screen if the lens-to-screen distance remains fixed at 5.2 m.

2. If the focal length had remained fixed at 12.7 cm, what should the lens-to-screen distance be (to three significant figures) to double the image dimensions?

22.9. 1. What is the magnification of a simple magnifier with a focal length of 3 cm?

2. What would be the magnification of the same lens if it were used by a horse that could focus sharply no closer than 65 cm?

22.10. 1. If you put a light source at the first focal point (see § 21.5) of a thin converging lens of focal length f and then put an identical lens just beyond the first one, what will be the separation of the source from its image?

2. What is the effective focal length of the system?

3. If, instead of a second lens, a plane mirror is placed beyond the first lens and perpendicular to its axis, where will the image be formed?

4. What is the focal length of the new system?

5. Now consider the problem of observing the iris of your eye. Suppose that you place a mirror 5 cm away from your eye and a thin lens in front of and up against the mirror. What focal length of lens will make your iris appear at infinity?

22.11. Show that the focal length, f, of a system of two thin lenses placed right next to each other obeys the equation

$$1/f = 1/f_1 + 1/f_2$$

if f_1 and f_2 are the focal lengths of the individual lenses. (Hint: You may check the validity of the result immediately by considering a point object at the focal point of the first lens. Draw a diagram. The general analytical proof requires using the lens formula twice. The negative of the first image distance becomes the object distance for the second lens.)

22.12. A certain optical instrument can make an object 1 cm long appear to be 40 cm long at a distance of 10 m. Another instrument makes the same object appear to be 20 cm long at a distance of 4 m.

1. Which instrument produces the image that subtends the larger angle on the retina?

2. Could you obtain an even larger sharp image on the retina, without the use of these instruments, simply by bringing the object closer to the eye? Discuss.

22.13. 1. The magnification of a compound microscope (Fig 22.12) is $(i/o) \times 25/f_2$. The first factor is produced by the objective lens, and the second is simply the magnification of the eyepiece treated as a simple magnifier. In a crude microscope the focal length (f_1) of the objective is 3 cm, and that (f_2) of the eyepiece is 5 cm. The distance between them is 25 cm. What is the magnification of the microscope?

2. The same lenses may be used for a telescope. This time let the lens of focal length 5 cm be the objective and the other be the eyepiece (Fig. 22.11). A distant tree subtends an angle of 1° when viewed with the naked eye. How large an angle will the image of the tree subtend as seen through this telescope?

3. If the tree is 1 km away, how far away will it seem as seen through the telescope?

22.14. 1. If a complete TV picture of 500 lines is scanned in 1/30 sec, and if the lines happen to be alternately light and dark, what is the frequency of the electric signal generating this particular picture?

2. Within a single horizontal scan the beam goes alternately light and dark for equal intervals 500 times. The final picture looks like a checkerboard with 250×250 dark squares. What frequency has the electric signal in this case?

3. A high-fidelity phonograph record can store electric signals with a frequency no higher than 15,000 cycles/sec. Could the information being carried by the electric waves between the transmitter and the receiver of part 2 be stored on such a record? Explain.

22.15. Assume that the prism of Fig. 22.23 is equilateral, is made of fused quartz, and has been set for minimum deviation (see § 20.1.5) for one of the yellow lines (5,893 A) of sodium, for which the index of refraction of the prism is 1.45848. Calculate the angle of minimum deviation to the nearest second of arc.

23

Physical Optics

OUR consideration of reflection and refraction, as manifested in optical instruments, has used geometrical optics almost exclusively; that is, we have treated light as rays. In this chapter we shall consider, in some detail, experiments that show that light travels in waves; we shall use **physical optics**, which stresses the wave aspects of light. The treatment will not specify what kind of wave is under consideration, for we are not yet ready to discuss the electromagnetic theory of light (Part IV); but the experiments described will demonstrate that light, whatever kind of wave is involved, obeys, for example, the principle of superposition.

Before considering an experiment on interference with light, let us seek some clues in a similar experiment with other waves. In § 18.4 we saw that sound waves from two loudspeakers fed by audio-frequency oscillators can set up an interference pattern (see Fig. 18.13). We need only two sources of the same frequency. Exploration of such a field proves that there are maxima and minima of intensity in accordance with the principle of superposition.

23.1. Two Independent Light Sources Produce No Fixed Interference Pattern

The experiment with two loudspeakers suggests that we try two small electric light bulbs as sources (Fig. 23.1). We make the light nearly monochromatic by using filters, F. We find, however, that the photographic film, AB, does not record the expected pattern of interference maxima

and minima; and we can think of many reasons why such an experiment may fail.

The wavelength, for example, may be so short that, with the given spatial relations of lights and film, the pattern is too fine to be recorded on film of even the greatest resolving power. Let us see whether the experiments *ought* to work if the wavelength is 5,000 A (5×10^{-5} cm). The argument of § 18.4 shows that the maxima on a screen, AB, that is at distance L from the sources emitting light of wavelength λ should be separated by distance $x = L\lambda/d$. Let us prove this by referring to Figure 23.2, in which $x/L = \tan \theta$, $\lambda/d = \sin \theta$, and d is the separation between the two point sources. Using the fact that $\sin \theta \cong \tan \theta$ for a small θ, we get the equation

$$\frac{\lambda}{d} = \frac{x}{L} \qquad [23.1$$

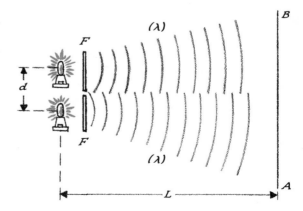

FIG. 23.1. *Two independent light sources produce no fixed interference pattern.*

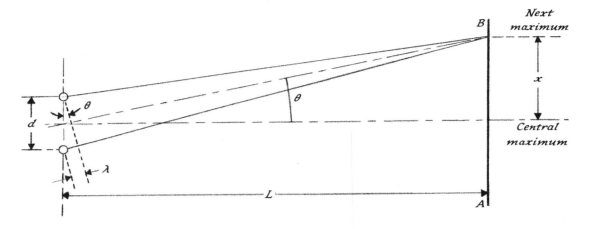

FIG. 23.2. *Schematic diagram for analysis of interference.*

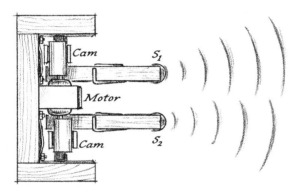

FIG. 23.3. *Device for producing mechanical vibrations with the same frequency and a range of different phase relations.*

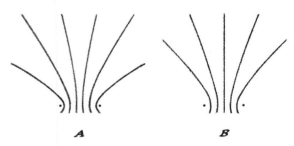

FIG. 23.4. *Interference patterns produced by two sources in phase (A) and out of phase (B).*

FIG. 23.5. *The lengths of the paths PS_1 and PS_2, as well as the phases of S_1 and S_2, determine whether constructive or destructive interference (or something in between) occurs at P.*

Hence

$$x = \frac{L\lambda}{d} \qquad [23.2$$

Let us, for the constants, choose values that could be easily realized experimentally: let $L = 100$ cm, $d = 1$ cm, and $\lambda = 5 \times 10^{-5}$ cm. Putting these values into equation 23.2, we get the result

$$x = \frac{100 \times 5 \times 10^{-5}}{1} \text{ cm}$$

$$= 5 \times 10^{-3} \text{ cm}$$

This is not too small a distance for a fine-grained film. The film at AB is explored by eye with a $10\times$ magnifier, and the interference maxima and minima, if there were any, would be visible. But none can be seen. We must seek the cause of failure elsewhere.

Let us explore an interference pattern made with a ripple tank. Figure 23.3 illustrates how the relative phases of the two sources, S_1 and S_2, can be changed. Figure 23.4 shows the curves along which maximum destructive interference takes place (the **nodal lines**) when the two sources are in phase (A) and the corresponding pattern formed when they are out of phase by 90° (B). The reason for the change is this (Fig. 23.5): if the vibrations from S_1 and S_2 arrive at point P in

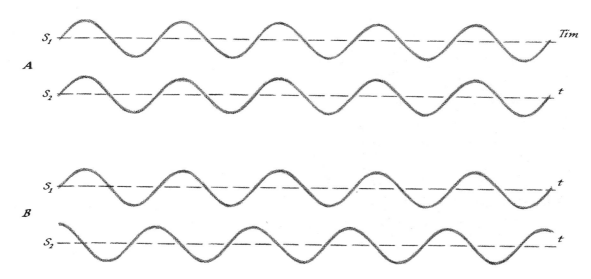

FIG. 23.6. *Graphs of two vibrations with no difference in phase (A) and with a constant difference in phase (B).*

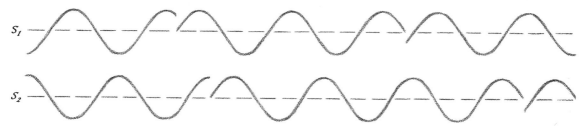

FIG. 23.7. *Sudden and random changes of phase and duration.*

phase, there will be a maximum amplitude at that point. If the phase of one source changes in relation to that of the other, the waves may arrive at P completely out of phase, producing there a minimum amplitude. The curve containing the points of maximum amplitude will shift to a new location. As long as the difference in phase between S_1 and S_2 remains constant, the interference pattern will remain fixed in space. If the variation in time of the displacement of sources S_1 and S_2 has graphs like those of Figure 23.6.A (always in phase), a fixed interference pattern in space is possible. If Figure 23.6.B depicts the displacement of sources S_1 and S_2 (with a constant phase difference of $\pi/2$), a different but still fixed interference pattern in space is possible. But, if each source changes its phase suddenly and at random, as depicted in Figure 23.7, the interference pattern in space does not remain fixed for any perceptible

length of time. We have reason to believe that two light bulbs, as sources, behave somewhat like the sources of Figure 23.7.

23.2. Young's Double-pinhole Experiment

Thomas Young (1773–1829) was the first to perform an experiment that avoided the chaotic condition suggested by Figure 23.7. Light (Fig. 23.8) from a single source, S, after passing through a monochromatizing filter, F, and a pinhole, P, illuminated two other pinholes, which became new sources, S_1 and S_2. (Compare § 18.4.) An interference pattern was observed around point O. Because of the common origin, at P, the graphs of the vibrations coming out of S_1 and S_2 might have looked like those of Figure 23.9. During the interval AB the sources were in phase and pro-

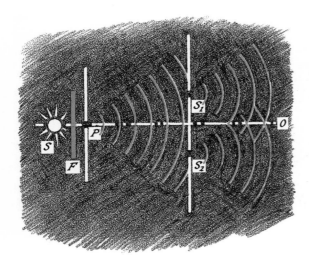

FIG. 23.8. *Young's double-pinhole experiment. The interference pattern can be observed directly through a magnifier at O or can be recorded photographically.*

duced a fixed pattern in space. During interval *BC* they were still in phase even though both had changed phase abruptly at *B*. *The interference pattern in space remained fixed*—then and during each subsequent time interval. Young deserves special credit for this experiment because he did it at a time when Newton's weighty opinion favored a special form of the particle theory of light rather than a wave theory.

A modern version of Young's experiment (Fig. 23.10) uses slits instead of pinholes to permit the passage of more light. A lamp with a single straight filament, used as a line source, obviates the need for the first pinhole. The light leaving slits S_1 and S_2 at angle θ from the axis can be focused on a film or a screen at distance f by a converging lens, C, of focal length f. The expression $x/f = \lambda/d$ holds quite accurately for a small θ. Figure 23.11 is a photograph of an interference

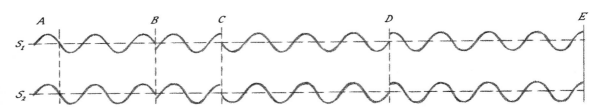

FIG. 23.9. *Vibrations due to the sources* S_1 *and* S_2 *of Fig. 23.8.*

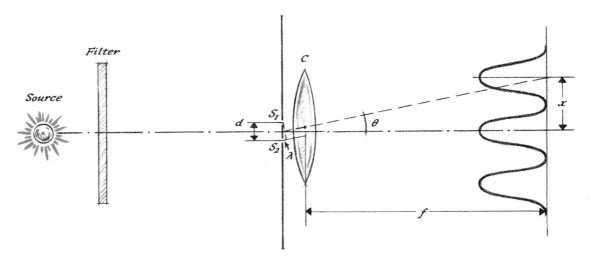

FIG. 23.10. *A modern version of Young's experiment.*

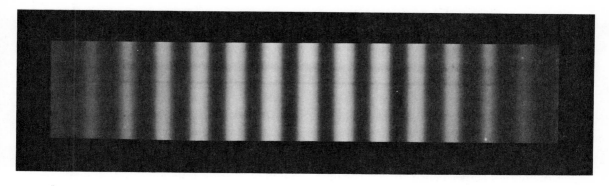

FIG. 23.11. *Photograph of double-slit interference pattern. [From Michel Cagnet, Maurice Françon, and Jean Claude Thrierr, Atlas of Optical Phenomena (Springer-Verlag, Berlin-Göttingen-Heidelberg, 1962), through the courtesy of Prof. Françon.]*

pattern taken with an apparatus like that described in Figure 23.10. But lens C is not really needed; the lens of the eye can be used instead, and the retina then serves as the screen.

Many variations of this experiment have been performed with waves of different lengths. A very striking classroom demonstration, made with radio waves ($\lambda \cong 10$ cm), is diagrammed in Figure 23.12. A large, flat sheet of aluminum, A, serves as a reflector. The source, S_1, has a virtual image at S_2. The receiver, R, picks up radiation coming apparently from S_2 and coming directly from S_1 (path length S_1R). As the receiver is moved vertically, the maxima and minima of amplitude that it picks up are displayed by an output meter, M. The interference pattern can be reconciled with the thinking that led to equation 23.2.

23.3. The Diffraction Grating

A diffraction grating consists, in principle, of many equally spaced parallel slits in the same plane. An actual grating consists of fine parallel grooves ruled by a diamond point on a smooth, hard surface.† Plastic casts of this surface have equally spaced grooves. These replicas—as the casts are called—serve as inexpensive diffraction gratings.

In Figure 23.13 a plane, monochromatic wave

† Why grooves on a transparent surface produce the same diffraction effects as slits in an opaque surface is explained, by Babinet's principle, in texts on physical optics. See, for example, R. W. Wood, *Physical Optics*, 3rd edition (Macmillan, New York, 1934).

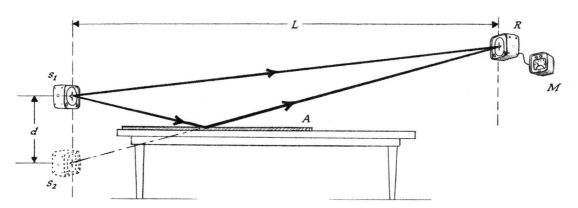

FIG. 23.12. *Apparatus for experiment on interference of microwaves.*

front, W_1, of wavelength λ, is approaching diffraction grating G, in which the adjacent slits, A, C, E, and H, are separated by distance d. Huygens wavelets originating at the slits produce a wave front (not shown) parallel to the incoming wave front and moving in the direction of the axis—a line perpendicular to both the grating and the lens and going through the center of the lens. Let us, however, consider the wave front W_2, which goes off at angle θ. The lines CB, ED, and HF, extended, are rays perpendicular to W_2. The lines AB, CD, and EF are at right angles to these rays. Since the triangles of which they are parts are congruent, the distances CB, ED, and HF are equal. The angle CAB and both the corresponding angles (ECD and HEF) are equal to θ. Suppose that CB is one wavelength, λ. The points B, J, and K, which are the intersections of the line AB, extended, with the rays, are at distances equal to λ, 2λ, and 3λ, respectively, from slits C, E, and H. The line AB, extended, is tangent to circles of radii λ, 2λ, and 3λ, with centers at C, E, and H, respectively. $ABJK$ is a new wave front, which will move later to position W_2. A convergent lens, L, can focus the rays of this front to point P. All the rays entering the lens have the same inclination, θ, from the axis. From triangle ABC we see that

$$\sin \theta = \frac{\lambda}{d} \qquad [23.3$$

Since a certain value of θ corresponds to each value of λ, a grating, like a glass prism, disperses light; it is apparent, however, that it bends the long waves more than the short ones (a large θ corresponds to a large λ)—just the opposite of what a glass prism does.

There is another important difference between the grating and the prism. The deviations produced by a prism yield a measure of variations in the index of refraction but not a measure of the wavelengths. With a grating-and-lens system, however, we can measure θ and get from it, by means of equation 23.3, the corresponding wavelength. At last we have a simple device by means of which we can measure wavelengths of the order of 5×10^{-5} cm. Before taking up the instrument designed for that purpose, let us consider how a diffraction grating can be used without a lens.

If an illuminated slit or a lamp with a single straight filament is viewed through a grating held close to the eye with its grooves parallel to the line source (Fig. 23.14), the lens of the eye will produce images of the source that correspond to the image at P in Figure 23.13. Since each image is a line if the source is a line, a series of lines will

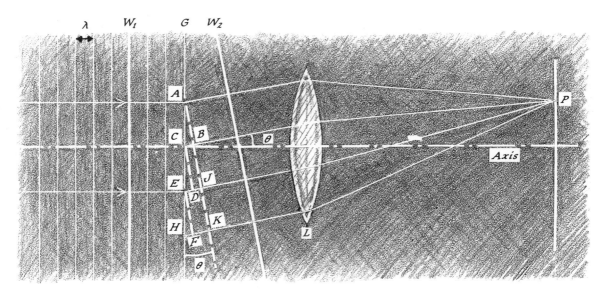

FIG. 23.13. *The diffraction grating used with a lens.*

FIG. 23.14. *Viewing a single-filament lamp through a diffraction grating held close to the eye.*

be seen, all parallel to one another and to the source, and separated by a distance that depends on the wavelengths of light emitted by the source. A tungsten filament produces a continuous spectrum in which all wavelengths within a certain range are present. The corresponding lines blend into a continuous array with no breaks. The complete visible spectrum (from red to violet) will be seen not only at I but also at I'. Every line of a certain color at angle θ on the left will be duplicated, symmetrically, by a similar line at angle θ' on the right. These spectra (I and I') are called the first-order spectra. There may be second- and higher-order spectra as well. The second-order spectra appear at the value of θ for which the distance corresponding to the CB, ED, and HF of Figure 23.13 is 2λ instead of λ. Generally, a line in the nth-order spectrum occurs at the value of θ that satisfies the equation

$$\sin \theta = \frac{n\lambda}{d} \qquad [23.4$$

It is possible for the red end of the first-order spectrum to overlap the blue end of the second-order spectrum.

The spectroscope discussed in § 22.7 can be adapted for use with a diffraction grating instead of a prism. Figure 23.15 shows how the parallel rays of monochromatic light coming out of the collimator are deviated by the grating through angle θ and emerge from the grating as parallel rays, which, entering the telescope, form a virtual image of the slit in the color associated with the wavelength. A spectroscope adapted for measuring the wavelengths of light is called a **spectrometer.** A spectroscope adapted for photographing

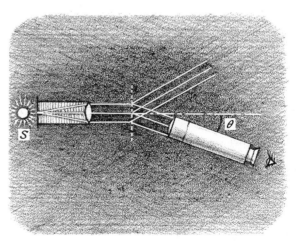

FIG. 23.15. *A diffraction grating replacing the prism of a spectroscope.*

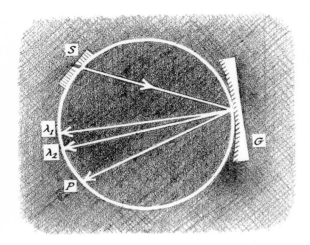

FIG. 23.16. *By ruling a grating on a concave spherical mirror we get both dispersion and a focused real image of the slit.*

spectra is called a **spectrograph.** The best of such instruments use gratings rather than prisms.

By ruling a grating on a concave spherical mirror we can get both dispersion and a focused *real* image of the slit (Fig. 23.16). The concave grating mirror, G, whose radius of curvature is $2r$, is tangent to a circle whose radius is r. Light passing through a slit, S, anywhere on the circle obeys the ordinary law of reflection at the grating and produces a focused real image of the slit (its zeroth-order spectrum) at point P on the same circle. The lines of the first-order spectrum are also displayed at different places on the same circle. Since not only visible rays but also those of the infrared and ultraviolet regions are reflected, the spectra of those regions can be explored with such a curved grating. Modifications of the same technique have been used with x-rays of wavelength of about 1 A.

The spectrometer is one of the important tools of modern physics because changes in the energy levels within atoms show up as differences in wavelength in the spectrum. By observing a spectrum we can tell not only what kind of atom produced it but also what energy states the atom was in. The spectroscope and the spectrograph are powerful tools in astrophysics: with their aid the chemical constitution and temperature of stars have been studied, and much has been learned

even about stars so distant that it takes many years for their light to reach us.

Of great current interest is the possibility of picking up the extremely short ultraviolet rays and x-rays from space. Before the advent of orbiting satellites and high-altitude rockets, this possibility was not seriously considered, for most of the x-rays and ultraviolet radiation that bombard the earth from outer space are absorbed by the earth's atmosphere, which blocks practically all radiation of wavelengths between 3,000 A and about 1 A. Grating spectrographs carried by rockets have given us evidence that the sun emits x-rays and that atoms in certain regions of space emit ultraviolet radiation. It is hoped that spectral analysis of this radiation will yield new information concerning the temperature, the constitution, and the origin of the stars.

23.4. The Single Slit

Thus far—since interference implies superposition and hence at least two different sources—we have considered the interference produced by two or more slits. Starting with the two-slit experiment and going on to the diffraction grating, which is a multiple slit, we have explained the maxima and minima of intensity as the result of superposition. Now let us see what happens when we look through a single slit at a monochromatic line source.

A good single slit of variable width can be produced with the jaws of a vernier caliper (Fig. 23.17). Almost as good is a slit made of tongue-depressors mounted as shown in Figure 23.18;

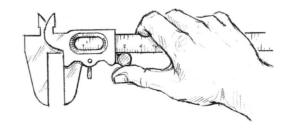

FIG. 23.17. *A vernier caliper used as a single slit of variable width.*

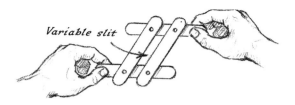

FIG. 23.18. *A variable slit made with tongue-depressors.*

painting the sticks a flat black helps to avoid unwanted scattering and reflection. The spreading of the central beam that we expect because of diffraction is readily observed, and a row of alternating light and dark bands, which represent the maxima and minima of light intensity, can also be seen. A photograph of a monochromatic line source taken with a slit in front of the camera lens is shown in Figure 23.19. This is the type of pattern you will see even when you look through the slit between two fingers; you can vary the width of this crude slit by pressing with the fingers of the other hand, as shown in Figure 23.20. You will see that, as the slit between the fingers gets narrower, the central bright band broadens out. (The interference associated with the two-slit experiment occurs even inside this central region.) The dark bands suggest destructive interference.

Since we are using only one slit, we have to ask, "Where are the multiple sources usually needed for interference?" The answer suggested by A. J. Fresnel (1788–1827) is that even the region within one slit can be thought of as made up of many adjacent sources. He refined the idea to the point

where he could even make a mathematical analysis of the intensity pattern so produced. For us it will suffice to show why maxima and minima should be observed at all.

The argument runs somewhat as follows (Fig. 23.21). A plane wave approaches from the left along the axis, which is perpendicular to the plane of the slit *AB*. Every point from *A* to *B* becomes the source of Huygens wavelets. Consider the

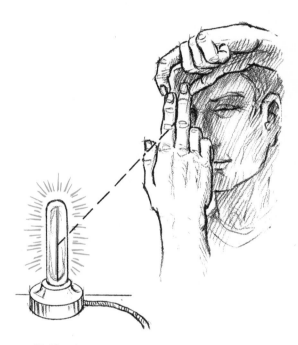

FIG. 23.20. *A crude single slit made by the chinks between fingers.*

FIG. 23.19. *Photograph of a diffraction pattern formed by a single slit in front of the camera lens. (From Cagnet, Françon, and Thrierr, op. cit., through the courtesy of Prof. Françon.)*

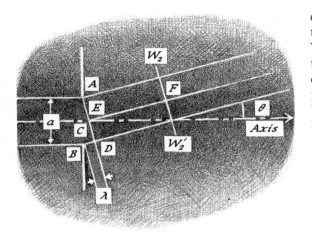

FIG. 23.21 *Elementary analysis of single-slit interference: If* BD = λ, CE = λ/2; *hence* E *and* D *are out of phase and can interfere destructively. Taken in suitably chosen pairs, all points of* AED *interfere destructively.*

possible wave front AED moving at angle θ to the axis. It is perpendicular to the rays that define the diffracted beam. Let us assume that $BD = \lambda$, the wavelength of the incoming monochromatic wave. Let the line W_2W_2' be perpendicular to the rays and hence be a possible future position of the wave front AED. The distance BW_2' is one wavelength longer than AW_2; so we expect these two extreme rays to interfere constructively if focused by a lens. This might lead us to think that all the rays perpendicular to AD would interfere constructively, but they do not; on the contrary, they interfere destructively, and an accurate math-

ematical analysis confirms this. We must be content here with the following simplified analysis: The distance CF is just half a wavelength longer than AW_2; so rays CF and AW_2 will interfere destructively if focused. Many similar pairs of points can be found; a point a small distance below A and another point the same distance below C, for example, are such a pair, and there are infinitely many other such pairs. Two by two, their effects cancel out, through destructive interference, in the direction θ.

Focused by the lens of the eye on the retina or by any other converging lens on a screen, the totality of these pairs of rays produces a minimum of intensity. This appears as one of the dark bands bordering the central bright area. At a value of θ for which $BD = 3\lambda/2$, on the other hand, we expect some but not complete cancellation and hence a moderate intensity. This is borne out by experiment. Measurements made on Figure 23.19 confirm the fact that for values of θ that obey the equation

$$\sin \theta = \frac{n\lambda}{a} \qquad [23.5$$

in which a is the width of the slit, we have minima of intensity when $n = 1, 2, 3, \ldots$ and maxima when $n = 1/2, 3/2, 5/2, \ldots$ There are intermediate values of intensity for other than half-integral values of n. The graph of the intensity displayed on a screen illuminated by a single slit is shown in Figure 23.22. According to equation 23.5, the first minimum, when $n = 1$, occurs approximately at $\theta = \lambda/a$ (if we use the approximation $\sin \theta \cong \theta$).

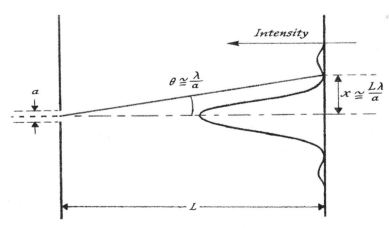

FIG. 23.22. *The graph of intensity produced by diffraction through a single slit.*

A diffraction grating, we know, can be conceived as a collection of evenly spaced single slits. If the slit width, a, is very small, the angular spread, θ, due to single-slit diffraction will be large. The maxima and minima of the multiple-slit interference pattern are governed, however, by equation 23.4, which looks very similar to equation 23.5 but has a d instead of an a. Since the single-slit aperture, a, is usually considerably smaller than the separation, d, between adjacent slits, the maxima and minima due to interference will be closer to one another than those of the single-slit diffraction pattern. The intensity curve for a double slit at which $d/a = 3$ is shown in Figure 23.23. In general, the ratio d/a determines the relative location of interference minima within the diffraction envelope. If d/a is constant, the addition of more slits increases the sharpness of the pattern.

23.5. Other Diffraction Phenomena

We saw in an earlier chapter that, when we let a wave pass through a very small opening, it spreads out as it goes through, or is *diffracted*. Now we have seen that, when a wave of light passes through a single slit, there are maxima and minima of intensity within the spread-out beam, and we attributed these to the *interference* of wavelets having their individual sources on different parts of the wave front coming through the slit. In other words, diffraction and interference are often seen together. The interference stresses

the role played by the superposition of waves.

Knowing that these effects are subtle because the wavelength of light is very short, we can look for them in places where ordinary geometrical optics would not predict them. A simple illustration is the fine detail along the edge of the shadow of an object with a well-defined edge, such as a razor blade. Geometrical optics would predict darkness in the shadow, light in the direct beam, and a clean break between light and shadow. But physical optics suggests that the light should be diffracted round the edge and fall a little into the geometrical shadow area, and the concept of interference suggests that within this diffracted beam there may be maxima and minima of intensity due to the superposition of waves from adjacent areas of the wave front near the edge of the obstacle. Figure 23.24 is a schematic representation of a simple experiment in which an opaque straight edge, A, illuminated by a very small monochromatic source, S, casts a shadow on a screen, CD. A straight line drawn from S to A and extended to meet the screen at B would mark the limiting ray in a description of the experiment according to geometrical optics. The shadow ought to begin at B. Actually, because of diffraction, some light reaches points below B; and, because of the superposition of waves that originate in the wave front at points a little above A, interference maxima and minima may be observed in the area above B. A photograph of the effects is shown in Figure 23.25.

These effects are blurred out, of course, if the

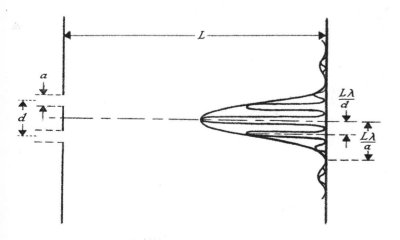

FIG. 23.23. *The double-slit interference pattern with maxima and minima close to one another has the single-slit diffraction pattern as an envelope.*

source is not small (different parts of it then contribute their maxima at different places in the shadow) or is not monochromatic (different wavelengths then produce their in-phase interference effects at different places). A zirconium arc lamp that produces a spot smaller than 0.1 mm in diameter is commercially available. Available interference filters let through a frequency band only 50 A wide. With this combination, diffraction effects such as those shown in Figure 23.25 can

be photographed or can be viewed by the eye if, taking the place of the camera, you look from B toward A (Fig. 23.24) through a $5\times$ magnifier. All shadow effects described below can be produced in the same way. The shadows produced by a screw are shown in Figure 23.26.

When the wave theory of light was new, its proponents were often ridiculed. To show how absurd the wave theory was, S. D. Poisson (1781–1840) pointed out that, if it were true, the shadow

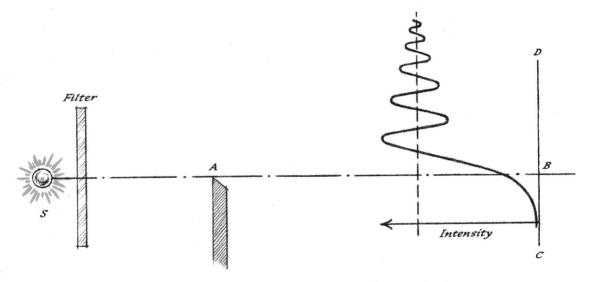

FIG. 23.24. *Diffraction of a plane wave at an opaque plane boundary with a straight edge.*

FIG. 23.25. *Photograph produced by the experiment depicted in Fig. 23.24. (From Cagnet, Françon, and Thrierr,* op. cit., *through the courtesy of Prof. Françon.)*

of a circular object would have a bright spot in the center because all the diffracted waves would arrive there in phase. François Arago (1786–1853) accepted the challenge and did the experiment. He found that the shadow of a circular obstruction did indeed have a bright spot in the center, and he brought a photograph of it to prove his point at the next meeting of the French Academy of Sciences. An interesting variation of that experiment is illustrated in the photograph on page 158, which shows the shadow of two bearing balls, one resting on top of the other. We see not only the bright spot at the center of each circle but also an interesting and highly symmetrical pattern in the region around the contact of the balls.

Another interesting set of shadows is to be ob-

served if we send light through a circular opening. Figure 23.27 shows the complicated diffraction pattern produced in this way. The fact that all the circles are concentric leads us to the idea that the space inside a circular hole can be regarded as a set of concentric bands, each of which can produce the same phase at a given point on the axis. In Figure 23.28, for example, a band of radius r and width Δx within the circular opening AB has points equidistant from point P on the axis. Hence the contributions received at P from the elementary wavelets originating on this band will all be in phase. Since the contributions from an adjacent band of slightly different radius would each produce a constant but different phase at point P, Fresnel thought of closing a series of circular bands

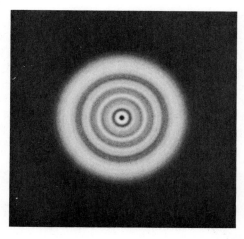

FIG. 23.27. *Photograph of diffraction effects produced by a circular opening. (From Cagnet, Françon, and Thrierr, op. cit., through the courtesy of Prof. Françon.)*

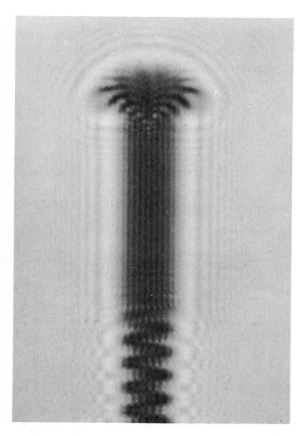

FIG. 23.26. *Photograph of diffraction shadow cast by a screw. (From Cagnet, Françon, and Thrierr, op. cit., through the courtesy of Prof. Françon.)*

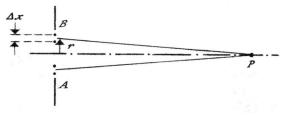

FIG. 23.28. *A circular opening considered as a set of concentric bands each of which contributes wavelets with a fixed phase at P. The total intensity at P depends on the proper composition of phases due to the separate bands.*

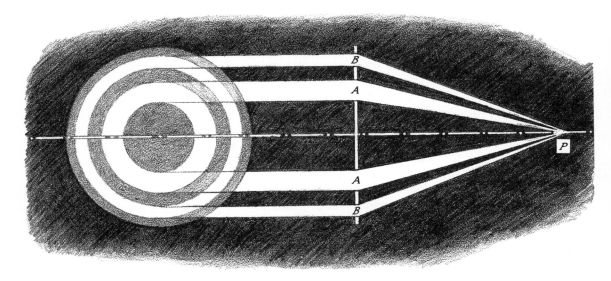

FIG. 23.29. *Fresnel zone plate with alternating opaque and transparent zones.*

within AB and leaving open only those whose contributions would all arrive in the same phase at P. Figure 23.29 shows a set of circular bands drawn according to Fresnel's scheme and a schematic representation of wave contributions arriving in phase at P. Figure 23.30 shows a photograph of a zone plate made of gold. Since the radial struts make it self-supporting, there is no need for glass or plastic as a support, and the open regions are therefore transparent to many different kinds of radiation. In Figure 23.29, all points on the circle AA are at the same distance from P. All points on the circle BB are one wavelength farther from P than the points of A. The contributions from circle AA and circle BB are therefore in phase at P, and light collects there as if focused by a lens. The Fresnel zone plate has, we see, lens-like properties. Figure 23.31 shows, for comparison, a photograph of a screen made with a simple lens and one of the

FIG. 23.30. *Photograph of a Fresnel zone plate made of gold. The clear regions are completely devoid of matter and will therefore let through some radiations that would not pass through a lens.*

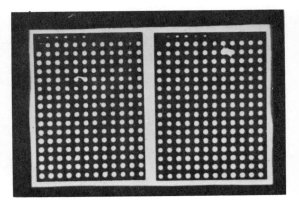

FIG. 23.31. *Photographs of a screen made with a lens (left) and with a Fresnel zone plate (right).*

FIG. 23.32. *A wire loop designed to pick up a soap film from the soap solution below.*

same screen made with a zone plate of the same aperture and focal length.

The advantage of the zone plate with open zones is conspicuous in certain regions of the ultraviolet, where ordinary glass is opaque and hence cannot serve as a lens.

23.6. Other Interference Phenomena

There are other interference phenomena that deserve mention because they produce beautiful colors and because they show how the wavelength of light can be used to measure very short distances with great precision.

Consider, as a first example, the ordinary soap bubble, which consists of a thin film of soapy water. The varied colors seen on the bubble are due to interference. We can control the soap film better by forming it on a metal ring, as shown in Figure 23.32. If we form it inside a closed box

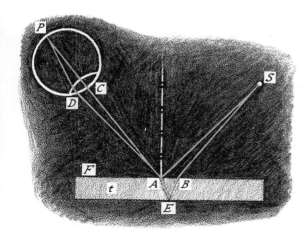

FIG. 23.33. *Analysis of interference in a thin film.*

(with a glass window for observation), it will not evaporate readily and will last much longer than in the open air.†

Let us now consider an elementary explanation of these phenomena (Fig. 23.33). A thin film, F, of thickness t receives light from a point source, S. Consider the ray SA. It is reflected as AC, enters the eye, and strikes P on the retina. The point P is also the image formed by all the rays that leave the point A. Now consider the ray SB, which is bent as it enters the film, is reflected at E, and emerges at A as the ray AD. Since P is the image of A, this ray proceeds from D to P. Now consider the lengths SA and $SBEA$. It is obvious that $SBEA$ is longer than SA. The phase at A due to $SBEA$ could therefore be different from the phase at A due to SA. The difference in length is $SBEA - SA$. The difference in phase depends on the index of refraction of the film and also on changes in phase that may take place on reflection at A (where the boundary is air-water in the case of a soap film) and at E (where the boundary is water-air). Taking all these factors into account, we see that, if the difference in phase is 2π (as it would be if the difference in length were the equivalent of precisely one wavelength in air), the contributions arrive at P in phase and hence interfere constructively to produce a maximum of intensity there. If we repeated the argument for a different point S and a different point A, the difference in phase might be exactly π; this would mean destructive interference at a different point P and a minimum of intensity there. Thus, if we have a monochromatic *extended* source (we need more than one point S), we shall see a pattern of light and dark bands.

Now consider the meaning of the dark bands we obtain when we use monochromatic light. What does the darkness mean? It means—if our monochromatic light is, let us say, red—that the effects of red light cancel out by destructive interference and produce an intensity minimum. Red light has, in a sense, been removed there. If the red source is now replaced by a white one, the

† See Physical Science Study Committee, *Physics* (D. C. Heath & Co., Boston, 1960), Figs. 19-19 and 19-20, for good color photographs of such a film, taken in white and in red light.

red part of the spectrum will be missing wherever the dark bands had appeared before. But now the bands are not dark; they are filled by a blend (effected subjectively) of all the other colors of the visible spectrum. This blend is said to be the complement of red.

The **complement** of any other color is defined in a similar way; it is the sensation produced subjectively by the mixture of all the colors of the visible spectrum except the one (or the totality of those) in question, which is (are) missing. We produce the colors in a soap film by removing, through destructive interference, different colors from white light. The result is a set of colors, complementary to those removed. The colors in a soap film cannot be found in the rainbow or in the spectrum of white light formed by a prism. If green light, for example, is subtracted from white light by the destructive interference produced by a soap film, you are left with a mixture of red from one end of the spectrum and violet from the other (along with the continuous array of other colors). Where the green should have been you will see a purple, which is the subjective blend of all the colors except the green. Since a vertical soap film tends to get thicker at the bottom than at the top, it is actually a thin wedge. The variation in thickness adds one more variable to complicate the colors of the bands.

A thin wedge of air can have a similar effect. If two microscope slides (Fig. 23.34) are held together by a rubber band at one end and separated by a paper spacer of thickness s at the other end, the air space between them is a wedge. Monochromatic light coming in from the right (D) is reflected down by a glass plate, E, enters the region bounded by the slides, and produces interference. Thus the light reflected upward to the lens of a microscope experiences interference, constructive or destructive, according to the width of the air space through which it has traveled, and produces a row of alternate light and dark bands.† If the separation between two dark bands is Δx, the slope of the upper slide must be $(\lambda/2)/\Delta x$, for an increase of $\lambda/2$ in the width of the wedge produces an increase of λ (which is required for a repetition

of a given phase condition) in the length of the path. Since the slope is also s/L, we can compute the thickness of the paper by equating these slopes and solving for s. In practice, of course, we get better accuracy by counting the number of bands of the same kind between two distant points on the glass and measuring the separation between the first and the last. Knowing that each new dark (light) band means an increment of $\lambda/2$ in the thickness of the wedge, we can evaluate λ very precisely.

The bands called Newton's rings can be seen when a convex lens resting on a flat glass surface is viewed by monochromatic light. Since the curves of constant phase are now circles, we see circular interference bands.

The following demonstration can be seen by many people at one time. Two thick, flat plates, one on top of the other, are illuminated from above by an extended monochromatic source. (A large piece of ground glass illuminated by a sodium arc works well.) Slight differences in the separation of the plates show up as interference bands, which are usually broad and somewhat diffuse. Using an elegant research technique, one can increase the reflectivity of the two glass surfaces that bound the air space. By this means one can increase the sharpness of the bands to the

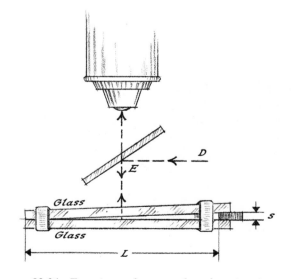

FIG. 23.34. *Experimental set-up for observing interference bands produced in a thin wedge of air.*

† For a photograph of such bands see Physical Science Study Committee, *op. cit.*, Fig. 19-21.

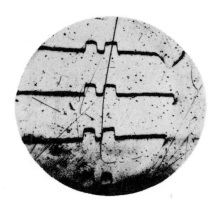

FIG. 23.35. *Interference bands produced by multiple reflections of monochromatic light between two glass plates whose reflectivity has been increased by thin metallic coats.*

responsible for spectral lines. These and many other things must wait until we have studied electricity, for it turns out that the atom is, to a great extent, an electrical entity. So we are not through with light. We shall return to it when we can treat it as an electromagnetic wave.

The study of light has attracted some of the best minds in science. I cannot leave the subject without mentioning three modern physicists—James Clerk Maxwell, Albert Einstein, and Max Planck—who made great contributions to it. Those contributions, to be presented in Chapters 43 and 49, would have been impossible without the earlier work of the investigators mentioned in this chapter, who first put the concepts of physical optics on a firm basis.

point where even a slight increase in height can be made to show up as a conspicuous discontinuity. Figure 23.35 was made with this technique. The double discontinuity in each band indicates a double ridge whose height was about 800 A. The method can be used to detect variations as slight as 50 A on the surface of polished glass.

23.7. Concluding Remarks About Light

In this chapter I have stressed experiments that tend to show that light is a wave. I have not proved that the wave is electromagnetic, that it is transverse, or that changes of energy in an atom are

23.8. Summary

The wave theory of light had its first major breakthrough in Young's interference experiment. Since then a great many experiments have confirmed the fact that light bends round obstacles and that light waves, obeying the principle of superposition, give rise to constructive and destructive interference.

A simple wave theory accounts for such diverse effects as the colors in a soap bubble and the action of the diffraction gratings by means of which the wavelengths of spectral lines have been calculated with great accuracy. These measurements were the basis upon which a theory of atomic structure was later built.

Problems

23.1. In § 23.1 we saw that two ordinary electric light bulbs cannot produce an interference pattern as two loudspeakers do. In a new source of light called the laser a great many atoms emit their light in phase with one another. With two of these lasers an effect of interference has been observed. In order to photograph such an effect, is it necessary that both lasers have the same phase, or is it sufficient that their phases, though different, remain constant long enough to expose the photographic film? Explain in terms of diagrams such as Figs. 23.6, 23.7, and 23.9.

23.2. A long aluminum rod can be set into vibration (Fig. 17.5) so that the ends vibrate longitudinally. Under these circumstances there would be, at some point on the line AB of Fig. 23.2, a central maximum. Find the distance, x, to the next maximum if the length of the rod is 0.896 m, the frequency is 958 cycles/sec, and the distance, L, is 7.52 m. (Use 340 m/sec as the speed of sound in air, and calculate results to three significant figures.)

23.3. The electric current (i) picked up by a microphone from a single tuning fork varies with time (t) according to the equation

$$i = A_1 \sin 2\pi(\nu t + \phi_1)$$

The variables are i and t; the other quantities, including the frequency (ν), the amplitude (A_1), and the phase (ϕ_1), are constant. (In practice, if a tuning fork is electrically driven, it has a constant amplitude; otherwise its amplitude diminishes with time, and the tone dies out.) It is a fact that many identical tuning forks, all acting together, produce the current

$$i = A \sin 2\pi(\nu t + \phi)$$

In other words, a lot of identical tuning forks together produce at a point a tone identical with that of a single tuning fork (except for loudness and phase—hence A and ϕ). Suppose, in Fig. 23.8, that the light source, S, is replaced by a group of 100 identical, electrically driven tuning forks (since all have the same frequency, no filter is required) and that the slit systems are scaled up in size to correspond with the wavelength of sound.

1. Would you expect a microphone to detect interference beyond S_1 and S_2 if each tuning fork kept a constant phase? Explain.

2. If the tuning forks were suddenly stopped and then started one by one at random times, would you expect the same interference as in part 1 beyond S_1 and S_2? Explain in terms of Figs. 23.6, 23.7, 23.9.

23.4. Young's experiment (Fig. 23.10) may be repeated with parallel razor-blade cuts in the emulsion of an exposed photographic plate as slits 0.15 mm wide. Let the separation between slits S_1 and S_2 be 1.0 mm, the distance between the filament source and the double slit be about 0.5 m, and the focal length, f, of the lens be 2.00 m. You may observe the interference pattern directly by viewing the light from the double slit through a magnifier, or you may photograph it by putting a photographic film at distance f from the lens. What is the wavelength of the light if the dark (or light) bands are found to be 1.3 mm apart?

23.5. 1. Find two values of angle θ (Fig. 23.13) at which a diffraction grating with 5,900 parallel rulings per cm will produce maxima of the green line of mercury whose wavelength is 5.461×10^{-7} m.

2. What is the greatest number of orders (§ 23.3) of this radiation that can be produced by this grating?

23.6. With a single microwave source and a flat sheet of metal as a mirror (Fig. 23.12) the equivalent of Young's experiment can be done with microwaves of wavelength about 10 cm. When the separation, d, between S_1 and its image, S_2, is 30 cm, what will be the vertical distance between successive maxima of intensity at the detector, R, if the distance, L, between the plane of the sources and the parallel plane in which the detector moves is 3 m? (The source and its image are equivalent to the two sources of Fig. 23.2.)

23.7. 1. An ordinary LP phonograph record behaves like a diffraction grating. You can confirm this experimentally by looking at a single-filament light source (or even the flame of a candle) reflected at grazing incidence. An LP record ($33\frac{1}{3}$ rev/min) that plays 26 min and 18 sec has grooves covering 8.52 cm. If a beam of white light (produced by an ordinary 35-mm projector with an opaque piece of cardboard with a slit in it in the slide carriage) hits the face of the record almost normally, and if equation 23.4 applies, what is the angle (θ) between the white reflected ray and the first-order beam with wavelength 5,500 A?

2. By tilting the record and showing that this angle can be increased, confirm experimentally the fact that the effective distance between grooves is decreased by reflection at grazing incidence.

23.8. 1. Look for the diffraction effect produced by a distant light bulb as seen through a metal window screen (or a curtain, a handkerchief, or a silk umbrella acting as a fine-mesh screen). The effect is enhanced if you look through a low-powered telescope or a pair of binoculars.

2. Calculate the angle between the undiffracted and the first-order image of a light bulb 1 km away as seen through a metal screen with 20 wires to the inch. Assume that the average wavelength of light is 5,000 A. (You will need to accept without proof that the diffraction pattern of Fig. 23.23 is unaltered if the transparent and opaque regions of the screen are interchanged.)

3. (Optional—slightly difficult.) The intensity pattern you will see through the screen is explainable in terms of Fig. 23.23. A very definite dark band, especially noticeable if the light source is monochromatic, occurs where one of the orders is missing. (In Fig. 23.23, for example, the third order is missing. We find, therefore, that λ/a divided by λ/d is, in this case, equal to 3.) Suppose that the sixth order is missing when you view the light through the screen of part 2. What is the diameter of the wire used in the screen? (Observe that with only a ruler and a telescope you are able to measure a length that would normally require a microscope.)

23.9. Describe in words what happens to the single-slit diffraction pattern when the width of the slit approaches the wavelength of the light being diffracted.

23.10. Suppose, in Fig. 23.33, that S is a monochromatic red source and that F is a thin film of water (as in a soap bubble). The changes of phase due to reflection, the index of refraction, and the thickness of film are such that rays AC and AD produce completely destructive interference at P. Now imagine that a white source replaces the red one at S. The sensation of what color will be produced at point P on the retina? (If you do not know the answer, think what color or colors are missing from the totality of colors needed to produce white.) Is this color one of the colors of the rainbow? Describe the change in color expected at P if the film gets very slightly thinner.

23.11. The number of dark interference bands per centimeter produced in an air wedge such as that of Fig. 23.34 is 28. Distance L is 9.85 cm. What is the thickness (s) of the paper sheet separating the glass slides at one side? Monochromatic light of wavelength 5,890 A is used. Express the result to a number of significant figures that is consistent with the data given.

III
FORCE AND MOTION

Airplanes in Almost Vertical Upward Flight
near Mount Kilimanjaro
(British official photograph [Air Ministry]; Crown Copyright reserved.)

Unlike the hovering of the imaginary rock of Magritte's painting (Part I), the motion of airplanes can be accounted for by the precise laws relating force and motion—the laws of dynamics, which apply to all bodies. Our study of them begins with a simplification—the dynamics of a particle.

The Dynamics
of a Particle

THE STUDY of motion apart from the forces involved is, as we saw in Chapter 8, called kinematics. The formulas $s = \frac{1}{2}at^2$ and $v^2 = 2as$, which apply to uniformly accelerated motion, are kinematic formulas; they involve displacement, velocity, acceleration, and time, but not force and mass. We observe, however, that real moving objects have mass and that forces can affect their motion. The study of the relation between force and mass in an accelerated body is, we know, called dynamics.

The science of dynamics, as developed by Newton, has been held up as the crowning glory of man's intellectual achievement. We must try to understand at least why it deserves this high praise.

We shall begin our study of dynamics by considering the simplest case, one force acting on one body, and we assume the body to be a particle. Mathematically speaking, a **particle** has no extension; in dynamics it is a mere point endowed with the characteristics of mass. The concept "particle" is a useful fiction. All real objects, including atomic particles, have extension, but even large objects, such as a ball or a rocket or a moon, can be treated as particles if we deal only with their translational motion. The complications introduced by rotation will be dealt with later.

Everything that moves does so in obedience to the formula

$$F = \lim_{\Delta t \to 0} \frac{\Delta \mathbf{p}}{\Delta t}$$

in which $\mathbf{p} = m\mathbf{v}$. This is the basic equation of dynamics and was first stated by Newton. To understand its importance, we must notice very briefly the ideas about force and motion developed by Galileo (1564–1642). (A rapid review of Chap. 3, where the concept of force was first introduced, should provide a good foundation for the next section.)

24.1. Motion Without Force

The common but mistaken idea that it always takes a force to keep something moving seems to be supported by our daily observations. You have to push the pedals of a bicycle to keep it rolling (unless you are coasting); you have to row a boat to keep it gliding (unless a current carries it along); and a rocket has to burn fuel and eject gases in order to keep going. Galileo, however, through a combination of real and imagined experiments, came to the conclusion that bodies will keep moving without being pushed if friction does not interfere. He reasoned along these lines (Fig. 24.1): If you allow a ball to roll down one slope of a curve (A), it picks up speed until it gets to the bottom and then loses speed as it climbs the opposite slope. Frictional losses of energy keep it

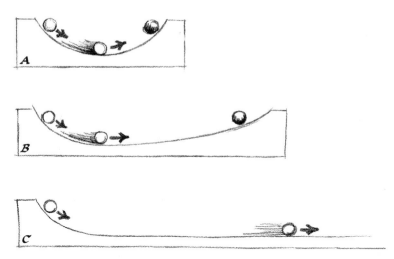

FIG. 24.1. *Imaginary experiment showing why a moving body with no net force acting on it should keep moving in a straight line at a constant speed.*

from reaching the height from which it started, but it does reach a point that is almost as high. If the experiment is repeated on a curve of a different shape (B), the ball rolls farther before it reaches its highest point, which is again a little below the starting point. What would happen if, instead of the second slope, we had a horizontal platform (C) extending without end beyond the bottom of the first slope? The conclusion reached by Galileo was that, if there were no friction, the ball would roll on forever without loss of speed. (A block sliding on a frictionless surface without rolling would be conceptually a better experiment, but less simple to do.) This conclusion is the basis of the concept of inertia: a body in motion, as we saw in § 5.2, does not need the application of a force to continue in motion. This statement is an idealization; it is approximated better and better as friction is diminished. It also expresses one of the most revolutionary ideas in the history of thought.

Galileo was a pioneer in the science of mechanics. He insisted upon doing experiments and upon reasoning from their results about the fundamental laws of nature. He was a strong exponent of ideas he arrived at in this way whether or not they conformed to the accepted theories handed down by the ancients. He was also a master at expounding his ideas in an interesting

manner for non-scientists† and so would have delighted the modern novelist C. P. Snow. He is rightly called the father of experimental science, and the dramatic life of this fiery and outspoken pioneer (he was forced by the Inquisition to recant his belief in Copernicus's views on the solar system) is still an inspiration to scientists. We shall now see how Newton incorporated Galileo's ideas into his broader formulation of the laws of mechanics.

24.2. Newton's Laws of Motion

The person who has had the profoundest effect upon the development of physical science is Sir Isaac Newton (1642–1727). He invented the differential and integral calculus, discovered the

† See, for example, Galileo's "Discourse and Demonstrations Concerning Two New Sciences," which presents conversations between the fictional characters Salviati, Sagredo, and Simplicio. Salviati speaks for Galileo; Sagredo, who usually supports Galileo, for the man of general education and good will; Simplicio for the Aristotelian philosophers, who disdain experiment and oppose Galileo. Parts of the discourse are incorporated, along with a great deal of other interesting material, in a pocket book of the Physical Science Study Committee: I. Bernard Cohen, *The Birth of a New Physics* (Anchor Books, Doubleday & Co., Garden City, N.Y., 1960). *The World of Physics*, edited by Arthur Beiser, contains a chapter entitled "Falling Bodies from Galileo's Two New Sciences" (McGraw-Hill Book Co., New York, 1960).

universal law of gravitation, laid down the basic laws of mechanics, and made contributions to optics. For any one of these achievements his name would have been engraved on the honor roll of history. Yet he was also a theologian who hoped that he would be remembered for his theological treatises. Very few people read Newton's theology today; but, if the barriers between the scientific and literary worlds—the "two cultures" that C. P. Snow speaks of—are demolished, every schoolboy in the world will be at least exposed to Newton's three laws of motion. Here they are, adapted to modern usage and stated in a way that permits easy transition to Einstein's modern formulation.

Newton's first law: *A body remains in its state of rest or of motion with constant velocity if it is acted upon by no net external force.* Mathematically, this means that $\mathbf{a} = \mathbf{0}$ when $\mathbf{F} = \mathbf{0}$.

Newton's second law: *The net force on a body is equal to the instantaneous rate of change of momentum.*† Mathematically, this means that

$$\mathbf{F} = \lim_{\Delta t \to 0} \frac{\Delta \mathbf{p}}{\Delta t} = \lim_{\Delta t \to 0} \frac{\Delta(m\mathbf{v})}{\Delta t}$$

If the mass is constant, we may write

$$\mathbf{F} = m \lim_{\Delta t \to 0} \frac{\Delta \mathbf{v}}{\Delta t} \quad \text{or} \quad \mathbf{F} = m\mathbf{a}$$

Newton's third law: *Whenever two bodies interact, the force exerted by the first body on the second is equal and opposite to the force exerted by the second body on the first.*

Consider the first law. Mathematically, it seems to be just a corollary of the formula $\mathbf{F} = m\mathbf{a}$: when the force is zero, the acceleration must be zero since the mass cannot vanish. A book lying on a table, for example, is at rest. The force of gravity is acting on it, but there is also an upward push, due to the table. (If there were no upward

† In § 3.3 I called $m\mathbf{v}$ momentum and $\Delta(m\mathbf{v})/\Delta t$ the rate of change of momentum. Strictly speaking, the latter is the *average* rate of change of momentum, and

$$\lim_{\Delta t \to 0} \frac{\Delta(m\mathbf{v})}{\Delta t}$$

is the *instantaneous* rate of change of momentum. This may be written as

$$\lim_{\Delta t \to 0} \frac{\Delta \mathbf{p}}{\Delta t}$$

force, the book would fall.) This reminds us that forces are vector quantities. The vector sum of the weight of the body and the force of reaction of the table is zero. There being no *net* force, the book remains at rest until it is moved by some unbalanced external force. As another illustration, consider an object suspended from a spring (Fig. 24.2). If it has reached equilibrium, it is at rest. Once again there are two forces acting on the object: its weight (the pull of the earth on it, $\mathbf{w} = m\mathbf{g}$) and the tension, $\mathbf{T}$, of the spring. The net effect of these two forces is zero. The object will remain at rest until it is moved by an unbalanced force.

The tendency of a body to stay put can be illustrated in several rather dramatic ways. The classic way is to pull the tablecloth from under a glass of wine without spilling any wine. A difficult but probably less messy variation on this can be performed with a wooden slide rule. Lay a sheet of writing paper on a smooth horizontal table, and stand the slide rule carefully on end on the paper

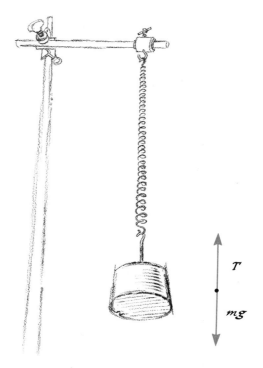

FIG. 24.2. *An object in equilibrium under the action of two equal and opposite forces.*

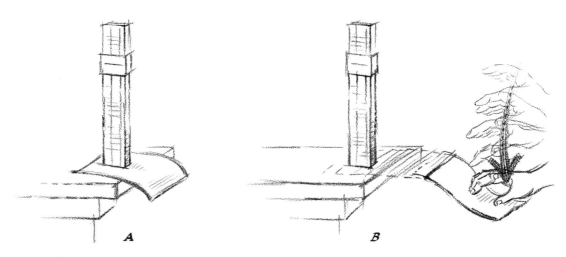

FIG. 24.3. *Illustration of inertia.*

(Fig. 24.3). Attempts to pull the paper out from under the slide rule without upsetting it usually fail. You may succeed after a little practice, however, if you let part of the paper extend over the edge of the table (A), then wet your hand and bring it down sharply on the paper (B). You thereby exert a force on the paper very rapidly.

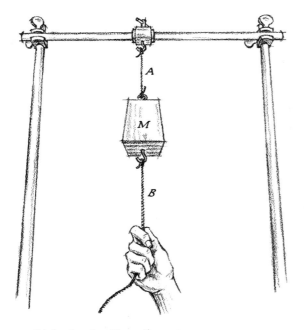

FIG. 24.4. *Another illustration of inertia.*

You can make the product $F(\Delta t)$ small by making Δt small. We shall see later the role played in mechanics by $F(\Delta t)$.

Another demonstration is illustrated in Figure 24.4. A body of large mass, M, is suspended as shown. If string B is pulled down with gradually increasing force, string A will break. If the force exerted on B is sudden, string B may break, and not A. (See Prob. 24.7.)

All these demonstrations illustrate matter's inertia, its reluctance to change its state of rest or motion. This reluctance is measured, as we saw in Chapter 5, by matter's inertial mass—which is not the same as its weight. It takes a strong push to move a loaded boat away from a pier even though the boat's weight is supported by the water and friction is slight. In a qualitative sense we can see what we mean when we say that a loaded boat has more inertia than an empty one. We should say, more precisely, that the inertial mass of the loaded boat is greater than that of the unloaded boat.

Figure 24.5 shows a Dry Ice puck resting on a rotating platform with a smooth glass top. The friction between the platform and the puck is very slight, and the other forces on the puck—its weight and the upward reaction of the carbon dioxide—are balanced. There is practically no net external force on the puck; so it remains at rest even though the platform is racing by beneath it. If the puck were moving in relation to the platform, it would continue to do so at a constant velocity.

A classroom demonstration of inertia can be performed with a long plank resting on rollers of the kind found at the delivery exits of some big food markets. A boy running along the floor suddenly steps on the plank (Fig. 24.6). Because this arrangement gives him a platform with relatively small mass and very little friction, he continues moving at almost the same speed without further effort.

It takes work to lift a rocket to a point far from the earth (Fig. 24.7); but, once out there, the rocket may experience only a slight net force (due to the gravitational pulls from the earth and other heavenly bodies) and almost no friction. Under these circumstances it moves approximately in a straight line at a constant velocity.

This last illustration brings up an important question: "a constant velocity relative to what?" The frame of reference must be specified. If we take the so-called fixed stars as a frame of reference, motions relative to this frame obey Newton's laws of motion. Any frame in which Newton's laws hold is called an **inertial frame.** We shall see that the earth (on which Newton's laws were discovered) is, strictly speaking, not an inertial frame, but it is so close to being one that only very refined experiments can detect departures from Newton's laws on it.

Later we shall devote a whole chapter to examples of the operation of the second law. Here let us consider the operational meaning of three of its terms: force, mass, acceleration. Of the three, acceleration is the easiest to measure, at least in principle. In kinematics we learned that a record of distance and time contains all the information we need in order to compute velocities and hence accelerations. In other words, if we have adequate instruments for measuring distance and time, we can calculate accelerations.

We can do a simple laboratory experiment (Fig. 24.8) by tying long rubber bands to a little cart or a Dry Ice puck to which ticker tape has been attached. The tape runs through a simple timer made from an old-fashioned doorbell. By counting

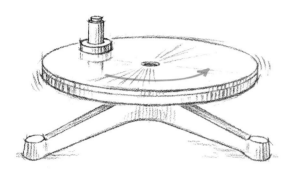

FIG. 24.5. *An example of Newton's first law: a Dry Ice puck remains almost at rest while the glass platform beneath it is rotated. Can you determine how it will actually move because the frictional force is not really zero?*

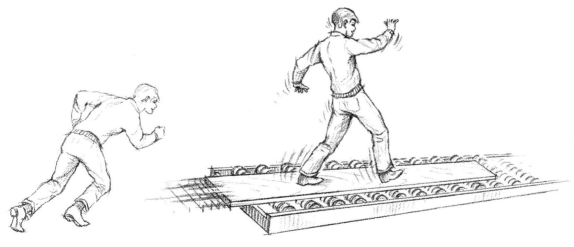

FIG. 24.6. *A laboratory demonstration of inertia.*

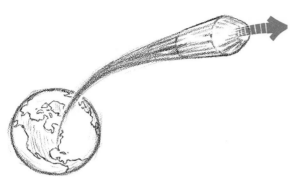

FIG. 24.7. *Another illustration of inertia: a rocket's motion.*

the dots on a tape that has been run through the timer for a known interval of time, the frequency of the timer can be measured. When the cart is released, it moves under the influence of the forces and accelerates. Since we have a trace consisting of spots made on the tape at equal time intervals, we can obtain the average speed within any interval from the equation $v_1 = \Delta x/\Delta t$. We measure the quantities on the right-hand side with a meter

stick and by counting the number of time intervals indicated by the dots. Repeating this procedure somewhere else on the tape, we get another value, v_2, for the speed. Now we can find the average acceleration within the interval between the two regions of the tape. We can refine this experiment as much as we please—within the limitations set by the apparatus and by our ingenuity. We have an experimental means of measuring acceleration.

How about mass? How do we measure *inertial* mass? Let us try to answer this question by seeing how masses can be compared. Briefly, the logic is somewhat like this: Suppose that two bodies of masses m_1 and m_2 interact (they may collide, for example). During the interaction m_1 experiences a force, F_1, and hence an acceleration, a_1, such that $F_1 = m_1 a_1$. Simultaneously, m_2 experiences an acceleration, a_2, under the influence of a force, F_2, such that $F_2 = m_2 a_2$. Now the third law comes to our rescue. It says that $F_1 = -F_2$. Therefore $m_1 a_1 = -m_2 a_2$. We now have a relation from which the explicit mention of the force has dropped out. We can therefore compare masses *dynamically* simply by observing the accelerations

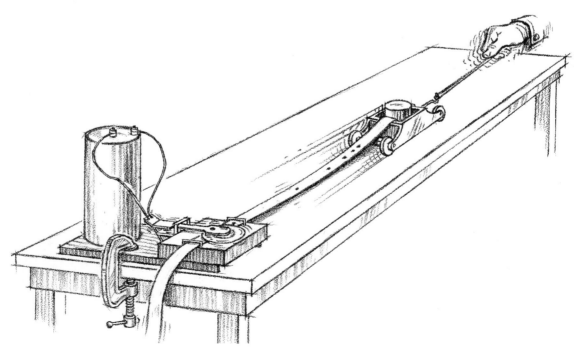

FIG. 24.8. *Measuring the accelerating effect of a constant force on a body.*

produced during an interaction in which the two forces are numerically alike. We don't need to know the values of the forces; it is enough to know that they are equal and opposite. Let us, for example, assume that m_1 is the prototype standard kilogram. That makes m_1 equal to 1 kg. Let us solve the last equation for m_2:

$$m_2 = -\frac{m_1 a_1}{a_2}$$

If the ratio a_1/a_2 comes out as -2, for example, the inertial mass m_2 is exactly 2 kg. We can, in principle, compare any mass with our standard mass in this way and thus obtain a list of the masses of different objects. By this procedure we define mass operationally.

It is easy, in practice, to compare masses by means of a platform balance. Because inertial mass is proportional to gravitational mass, we can compare the masses of objects, as we saw in Chapter 5, by weighing the objects at the same place on the earth. If the first object weighs three times as much as the second object, the first has an inertial mass that is three times as great as that of the second. Comparison of two masses by weighing at the North Pole would yield the same ratio as a comparison of the same two masses by weighing at the Equator, for two objects with the same gravitational mass experience the same gravitational pull at any one place on the earth's surface. If two objects weigh the same at the Pole, they weigh the same at the Equator. By weighing, therefore, we should arrive at the correct conclusion: they have the same inertial mass. In a similar way, if one object weighs twice as much as another at one place, it will weigh twice as much as the other everywhere.

And now, force. Since we know how to measure acceleration, the equation $F = ma$ can be used to define force in terms of mass or mass in terms of force, but it cannot do both. We have chosen to define mass by choosing an arbitrary standard, the kilogram, and giving operational instructions for comparing other masses with it. The second law, then, permits us to define the **newton** as the unbalanced force that will impart to an object with a mass of 1 kg an acceleration of 1 m/sec/sec. The operational way to measure a force is to measure the acceleration it produces on an object of known mass. I am saying that the formula $F = ma$ is essentially a definition of force.

The procedure we usually follow in confirming Newton's laws in the laboratory runs somewhat like this: First, we observe that two bodies identical in volume and made of the same homogeneous material stretch a spring twice as much as one alone: the stretch of a spring varies linearly with force (of gravity in this case). Even if the spring's stretch does not vary linearly, we know, if it is reproducible, that a certain stretch means a certain constant force; we don't have to know, numerically, what the force is. If we pull an object by a spring attached to it, and keep the stretch constant throughout the pull, we can, as we saw earlier (Fig. 3.10), measure the acceleration. Experiments of this sort confirm the idea that a constant force produces a constant acceleration on the same object. Next, attaching two similar springs side by side or otherwise doubling the force, we repeat the experiment with the same object. (We don't yet need to know its mass.) We discover that doubling the force does indeed double the acceleration. Finally, keeping the force constant, we double the mass, choosing an object whose gravitational mass (determined on a platform balance) is twice that of the first object. We discover that the acceleration is halved when we double the mass. In this way we begin to build up confidence in the formula $F = ma$. In the long run we rely on the fact that many experiments of this kind all indicate that the formula is correct—not, indeed, by perfect direct confirmation but because none of the results, analyzed to minimize the effect of friction and other forces, has ever contradicted it for speeds much lower than that of light (and no contradictions to the formula

$$\mathbf{F} = \lim_{\Delta t \to 0} \frac{\Delta(m\mathbf{v})}{\Delta t}$$

have been found even for speeds close to that of light).

It is beyond the scope of this book to go into a rigorous critique of Newton's laws. We should have to go deeply into some matters that I have treated superficially, such as the importance of the frame of reference in which experiments are performed. There are also other difficulties, which I am glossing over in this elementary treatment.

Is the relation $F = ma$ a discoverable law of nature? In the introductory discussion of Chapter 3, I treated it as such; but, in doing so, I had to give a rather intuitive account of how masses are compared. Now, as we try to put that relation on a firmer basis, we find that we need the third law to describe operationally how masses are compared, and the second law emerges as a definition of force. (Some writers feel that Newton's third law is the most interesting and important of the three.)

Despite the difficulties we have left unresolved, we can assert that Newton's laws constitute the first important generalization in physics. They have served as the base from which departures have been made for more accurate descriptions of the laws of mechanics (such as Einstein's formulation). Newton's laws are valid and precise enough to be used in a wide range of scientific experiments, and they give us a firm grasp on many problems involving space, time, matter, and motion.

24.3. Units of Force

The formula $F = ma$ indicates immediately that a unit of force will produce a unit of acceleration on a unit of mass; that is, when $m = 1$ and $a = 1$, $F = 1$. In the MKS system a newton, we have seen, is the force that, if unbalanced, imparts to a mass of one kilogram an acceleration of one meter per second per second. This is the system that we shall use most of the time.

In atomic physics the CGS system is often used. Its unit of force is the dyne. A **dyne** is the force that, if unbalanced, imparts to a mass of one gram an acceleration of one centimeter per second per second; briefly, it is a gram-centimeter per second per second. The dyne is a very small unit of force. An ordinary postage stamp weighs about 50 dynes.

We shall use the CGS system occasionally. Its units are related by simple decimal factors to those of the MKS system. Since there are 1,000 grams in a kilogram and 100 centimeters in a meter, one newton is 100,000 gram-centimeters per second per second, or 100,000 dynes.

In the British engineering system the **pound** is the force that gives to the unit of mass called the **slug** an acceleration of one foot per second per second.

A table of conversion factors appears on the front flyleaf, and a fool-proof method of converting from one system to another is given in Appendix B. When a force is given in pounds, for example, it may be converted to newtons by reference to this table.

24.4. Introductory Examples in Dynamics

Even the simplest illustration of how Newton's second law should be used requires that we understand how to isolate a body whose motion we wish to analyze. Suppose that a smooth wooden block with a mass of 7 kg is going to be pulled by a horizontal force of 8 nt. We have a spring balance calibrated in newtons. It is convenient, when we use the second law, to draw a **free-body diagram**—that is, a diagram in which we isolate the body, perhaps by drawing a dashed curve round it (our artist has laid a patch of color over it)—and draw vectors representing all the external forces acting on it. In Figure 24.9 the block is drawn with three vectors on it: **W**, the weight, which is the gravitational pull of the earth on the block; **R**, the force of reaction of the table on the block; **F**, the pull exerted by the cord connecting the block and the spring balance. We assume that **R** exactly balances **W**, for, if it didn't, there would be a vertical acceleration, and there is none. That leaves only **F** as the unbalanced force, which is, then, the **F** that is used in the second law. On the assumption that there is no friction (which may not be a good assumption in some cases) we can predict what the acceleration will be. From the second law, $\mathbf{a} = \mathbf{F}/m$, we get

$$a = \frac{8 \text{ nt}}{7 \text{ kg}}$$

$$= \frac{8}{7} \frac{\text{m}}{\text{sec}^2}$$

$$= 1.14 \frac{\text{m}}{\text{sec}^2}$$

Suppose that the same block is pulled by a force, F, of 8 nt at an angle, θ, of 30° above the hori-

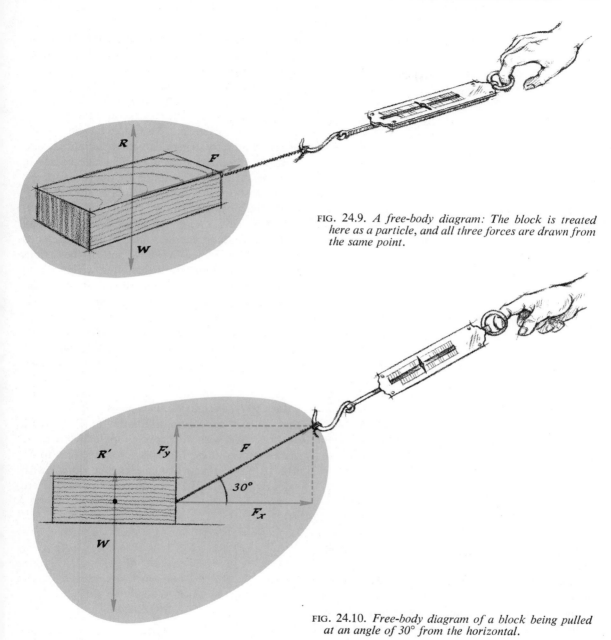

FIG. 24.9. *A free-body diagram: The block is treated here as a particle, and all three forces are drawn from the same point.*

FIG. 24.10. *Free-body diagram of a block being pulled at an angle of 30° from the horizontal.*

zontal. In the free-body diagram (Fig. 24.10) F has been replaced by its horizontal and vertical components, F_x and F_y, respectively. The other forces are R' and W, but this R' does not equal the R of Figure 24.9. Newton's second law can be applied to the resultant of the forces in the x direction and separately to the resultant of the forces in the y direction. Treating R', W, and F_y as magnitudes only, we see that $R' + F_y - W = 0$, for there is no vertical acceleration; that is, the vector sum of the vertical forces is zero. That leaves F_x (if we assume that there is no friction) as the only unbalanced force. Therefore

$$a = \frac{F_x}{m}$$

$$= \frac{F \cos \theta}{m}$$

$$= \frac{8 \text{ nt} \times 0.866}{7 \text{ kg}}$$

$$= 0.99 \frac{\text{m}}{\text{sec}^2}$$

At this point we can consider a simple question in kinematics. If the block starts from rest and the acceleration remains constant, how far will the block move in 12 sec? The formula $s = \frac{1}{2}at^2$ for constant acceleration applies here:

$$s = \frac{1}{2} at^2$$

$$= \frac{1}{2} \left(0.99 \frac{\text{m}}{\text{sec}^2} \times 12^2 \text{ sec}^2 \right)$$

$$= 72 \text{ m}$$

We have now seen (1) how the basic dynamic formula, $F = ma$, is used to evaluate a and (2) how this value of a is substituted into the kinematic formulas that govern motion under constant acceleration. This "divide and conquer" method will be useful very often in more difficult problems.

24.5. Forces in Equilibrium

The motion of an arrow as it leaves the bow demonstrates qualitatively that the force propelling it is a vector quantity, for it moves in the direction of the resultant of the two vectors whose directions are those of the string under tension. It would be difficult to confirm the vector addition of the forces in this example because, as the arrow picks up speed, it is acted upon by forces that vary in time. But consider the instant just before the arrow is released (Fig. 24.11). Treating the arrow as if it were a particle, we can conceive of two forces, $\mathbf{F}_1$ and $\mathbf{F}_2$, due to the cord and one force, $\mathbf{F}_3$, exerted by the hand that draws the cord. We find it reasonable that $\mathbf{F}_1 + \mathbf{F}_2 + \mathbf{F}_3 = \mathbf{0}$ since $\mathbf{a} = \mathbf{0}$. This idea suggests that we can test the vector nature of forces in *static* situations quite

readily. We can make the test with very simple equipment and with fair accuracy as follows (Fig. 24.12):

We make chains by looping rubber-bands together. We tie the chains to a small ring, R, with strings. (The smaller the ring the more nearly does it resemble a particle.) We fasten the other ends of the chains to strings, which we thumbtack to a board at T_1 and T_2 and T_3. The ring comes to equilibrium under the action of the three forces. We now slip a sheet of paper under the ring and mark the positions of the chains by lines coincident with RT_1, RT_2, and RT_3. On these lines we mark the lengths, L_1, L_2, and L_3, of the stretched rubber-band chains. We now detach the strings from the board and, by suspending weights from the first chain, measure and record the force, F_1 (in grams, for example; the units are not important here), that stretches that chain to length L_1. We find F_2 and F_3 from L_2 and L_3 in the same way.

We now have the direction and the magnitude of the forces acting on the ring, and we can draw them to scale simply by marking off, on these lines, lengths proportional to the experimental values of F_1, F_2, and F_3. This gives a diagram like that of the three forces originating at C in Figure 24.13.A. We wish to prove graphically that the vector sum of these forces is zero. One way to do it is to prove that a triangle can be drawn with sides that are parallel to $\mathbf{F}_1$, $\mathbf{F}_2$, and $\mathbf{F}_3$ and that are

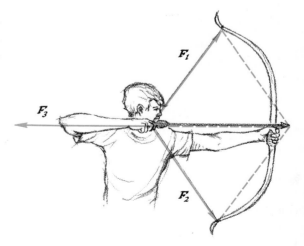

FIG. 24.11. *Forces acting on an arrow.*

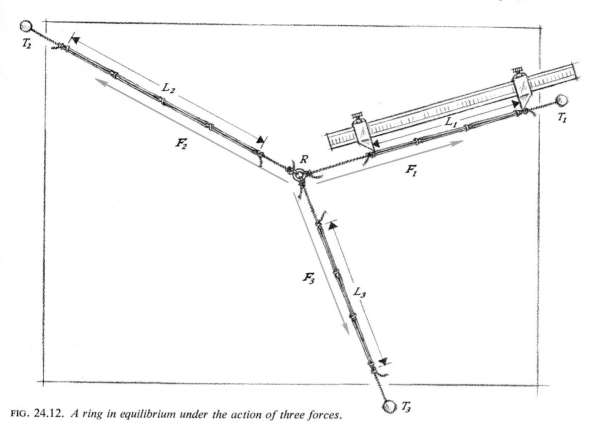

FIG. 24.12. *A ring in equilibrium under the action of three forces.*

proportional in length to their magnitudes. We shall try to do it by moving vector $\mathbf{F}_2$ so that its initial point coincides with the terminal point (arrowhead) of $\mathbf{F}_1$ and then moving $\mathbf{F}_3$ so that its initial point coincides with the terminal point of $\mathbf{F}_2$. We want to see if this set of connected line segments is a triangle; that is, we want to see if the terminal point of $\mathbf{F}_3$ falls exactly on the initial point of $\mathbf{F}_1$.

With a ruler and a celluloid triangle we can, leaving $\mathbf{F}_1$ fixed, move $\mathbf{F}_2$ parallel to itself so that its initial point coincides with the terminal point of $\mathbf{F}_1$ (Fig. 24.13.A). We extend the line of $\mathbf{F}_2$ and place side CD of the celluloid triangle against it. Resting the ruler against side DE of the triangle and holding it firmly against the paper, we slide the triangle along the ruler to a new position ($C'D'E'$, for example). Since line $C'D'$ is parallel to CD, we can now draw the directed line segment $D'B$ as equal to $\mathbf{F}_2$. (It is much easier to do this than to describe it.) In a similar way (Fig. 24.13.B)

we can move $\mathbf{F}_3$ parallel to itself and attach it to $\mathbf{F}_2$. If the terminal point, S, of $\mathbf{F}_3$ fell exactly at the initial point, O, of $\mathbf{F}_1$, it would confirm the fact that the forces involved obey the law of combination of displacements (§ 3.4) and hence are indeed vectors. It is more likely that S will miss O by a small distance, labeled e in the figure (for error of closure). It should be possible to obtain experimentally a value of e that is about a tenth of the smallest of the three magnitudes F_1, F_2, and F_3. In this way the vector nature of three or more forces acting at a point can be confirmed experimentally quite readily.

We have evolved, we see, the condition for the **equilibrium of a particle.** It can be stated symbolically:

$$\sum_{i=1}^{n} \mathbf{F}_i = \mathbf{F}_1 + \mathbf{F}_2 + \dots \mathbf{F}_n = \mathbf{0} \qquad [24.1$$

The notation means simply that the vector sum of n forces ($\mathbf{F}_1$, $\mathbf{F}_2$, . . . , $\mathbf{F}_n$) acting on a mass particle

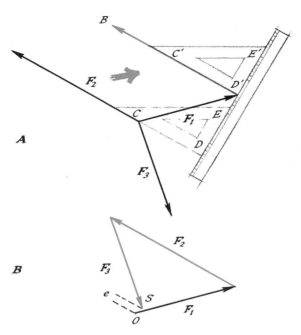

FIG. 24.13. (*A*) *Moving a vector parallel to itself.* (*B*) *Applying the polygon rule for vector addition.*

must be zero to produce equilibrium. The expression

$$\sum_{i=1}^{n} \mathbf{F}_i$$

(the Greek letter Σ, sigma, here means sum) is another way of indicating the net force on the body.

Experiments of the type described are instructive because they furnish practice in dealing with vectors quantitatively. Since we are more interested in dynamics than in statics, the main virtue of such an experiment is that it confirms, in a special case, the fact that forces are vector quantities and hence that the net unbalanced force mentioned in the second law is the vector sum of all the forces acting on the body.

24.6. Action Equals Reaction

I am going to devote a whole chapter to Newton's third law, but I want to point out here some interesting features of it. As I stated it, two objects

are involved: object A acts on object B with force $\mathbf{F}_1$, and B simultaneously acts on A with force $\mathbf{F}_2$ such that $\mathbf{F}_1 = -\mathbf{F}_2$. An apple, for example, falls to the earth because it feels a pull, and, simultaneously, the earth feels an equal but opposite pull. *The earth falls toward the apple!* Since the accelerations of apple and earth (relative to a frame of reference connected to the fixed stars) are inversely proportional to their masses, only the acceleration of the apple is of appreciable magnitude. This illustrates the fact that there are interactions without springs or strings, and, in each of these, every force exerted by body A on body B is accompanied simultaneously by an equal but opposite force exerted by B on A. (See Prob. 24.15.)

We shall see later that the meaning of "simultaneous" is not as obvious as we may think. When two billiard balls collide, the fact that opposite forces act simultaneously seems obvious, but we can cite interactions in which it becomes more difficult to test Newton's third law. Consider a hypothetical example. Suppose that by some miracle an object with a gravitational mass a million times greater than that of the sun is created instantaneously at a point in space forty light-years away. Since the object has gravitational mass, it must pull on the earth, but does the earth feel the effect instantaneously, and does the hypothetical object *simultaneously* feel the gravitational pull exerted by the earth? If the new celestial body is born with a flash of light, we shall not see this flash on earth for forty years. Does the gravitational signal travel faster? Is it really instantaneous? I shall not answer this question, I have asked it merely to show that we may encounter difficulties in applying Newton's laws to some cases. In all the experiments dealing with mechanical forces that you will encounter in ordinary laboratory work, however, forces will occur in equal and opposite pairs.

In conclusion, consider what is possibly the simplest (although not a trivial) example of pairs of equal and opposite forces. We observe that two spring scales (Fig. 24.14) read alike when a weight, A, is suspended from the string. If the weight is changed, both scales give new readings, but the two readings are still alike. The pull exerted by

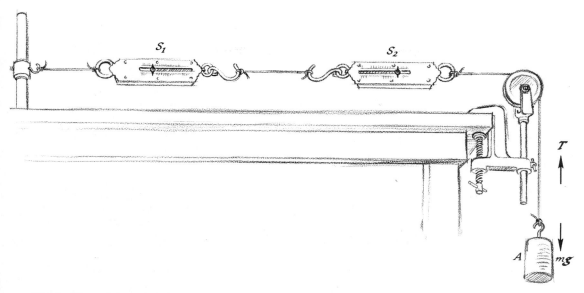

FIG. 24.14. *Forces in equal and opposite pairs.*

scale S_1 on scale S_2 is equal to the pull exerted by S_2 on S_1, but oppositely directed. It is instructive to isolate the parts of the system and label the forces exerted on them. Suppose that A has mass m. It feels not only a downward pull, $m\mathbf{g}$, but also an upward pull, $\mathbf{T}$, which is due to the tension in the string. It is true that, vectorially, $\mathbf{T} = -m\mathbf{g}$, but this pair ($\mathbf{T}$ and $m\mathbf{g}$) is not a valid illustration of the force pairs of the third law, for both $\mathbf{T}$ and $m\mathbf{g}$ act on the same body. There are many third-law force pairs in Figure 24.14, however, and you are urged to find some and discuss them. The test is simple: one force must be the force exerted by body A on body B, and the other must be the force simultaneously exerted by body B on body A. Two forces and two bodies are always involved in Newton's third law.

24.7. Summary

Casual observations seem to indicate that it takes a force to make something move, but a detailed analysis suggests that in the absence of friction and other retarding forces a moving body will continue to move at a constant velocity without the application of a force.

More generally, if the vector sum of all the forces acting on a body is zero, the body is in equilibrium. This means that, if at rest, it will remain at rest, and that, if in motion, it will continue to move in a straight line at a constant speed. This summarizes the inertial property of matter, first described by Galileo and later expressed in Newton's first law. The branch of mechanics called *statics* deals with bodies at rest or moving with constant velocity in relation to an inertial frame of reference.

Bodies in motion obey the basic equation of *dynamics*, known as Newton's second law: $\mathbf{F} = m\mathbf{a}$. In the MKS system the force is measured in newtons, the mass in kilograms, and the acceleration in meters per second per second. An unbalanced force of 1 nt produces an acceleration of 1 m/sec² on an object whose mass is 1 kg.

Of even greater interest, perhaps, is Newton's third law, which says that, when body A acts on body B with force $\mathbf{F}$, body B acts simultaneously on body A with force $-\mathbf{F}$. Newton's second and third laws will be discussed in detail in subsequent chapters.

Problems

24.1. A body sliding from left to right on a flat, frictionless board speeds up when the slope of the board is negative and slows down when the slope is positive. What should be expected on a long stretch where the slope is zero? Is this in accord with Newton's first law? Draw a diagram, and explain.

24.2. Suppose a huge vehicle could be built to ride on a cushion of air the way a frictionless puck rides on carbon dioxide. According to Newton's first law, no fuel would be needed to keep it moving at a constant speed. Would energy be needed to speed it up? to slow it down? to keep it floating on air at rest in one spot? Explain.

24.3. Imagine a simple pendulum consisting of a heavy lead ball attached to a thin steel wire about 1,000 m long. The ball, when oscillating, moves approximately in a straight line at a constant speed. What does this imply about the sum of all the forces acting on the ball? Draw a diagram showing each of those forces. Do they ever really add up vectorially to zero?

24.4. In Fig. 24.3 a piece of paper is jerked out from under a slide rule. What would happen if the paper were moved very, very slowly? What would happen if the paper were pulled out rapidly, as suggested in the text, but were about 3 ft long instead of about 1 ft long? Try to become clear in your own mind on what, exactly, allows the rule to remain standing in some cases and not in others. If there are apparent contradictions of Newton's laws, describe and explain them.

24.5. Prove algebraically that Newton's first law is merely a special case of the second law. Prove algebraically that, if there is no net force on a body, its velocity is constant. Begin by writing the algebraic definitions of average acceleration and velocity.

24.6. Draw a diagram of a taut string that is horizontal and at rest. Imagine it to have negligible weight and to be made up of three consecutive parts labeled A, B, and C.

1. Consider the forces exerted by A on B, by B on A, by B on C, and by C on B.

2. Invoke the second law to show that the net force on B is zero. Use this and the third law to prove that the force exerted by B on A is equal and opposite to the force exerted by B on C.

24.7. Consider a horizontal modification of the experiment shown in Fig. 24.4. Instead of strings imagine two identical light bands of rubber, A and B (Fig. 24.15), each of which will break when the tension reaches exactly the value F_b. They are tied to a heavy block of lead, which rests on a slab of solid carbon dioxide so that friction with the horizontal table is reduced to a negligible quantity.

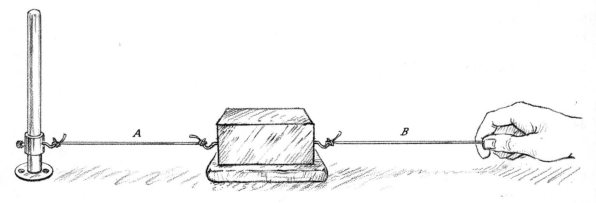

FIG. 24.15. *Illustrating Prob. 24.7.*

1. What will happen if B is suddenly jerked to the right so that the tension in it exceeds F_b?

2. Suppose that B is pulled rapidly to the right without having the tension in it quite reach F_b and is held extended. Will A break?

3. Suppose that B is pulled very slowly and continuously to the right. Will A break before B?

4. If strings replaced the rubber bands, would the results be the same?

5. Can you now devise a way to pull so that both strings of Fig. 24.4 break at the same time?

24.8. A huge block of Dry Ice rests in the middle of the smooth floor of a special railroad car that is at rest and empty. Assume that there is almost no friction between the block and the floor.

1. The car starts to move slowly to the right. Describe the behavior of the block as seen by an observer in the car and as seen by another on the ground.

2. After a while the train comes suddenly to rest. Assuming that the block is not against a wall, describe its behavior as seen by the same two observers.

24.9. Consider an experiment like the one illustrated in Fig. 24.8. (The following numerical values are hypothetical and were chosen only to illustrate the procedure.) The mass of the little cart is 3 kg, and the timer makes a mark every 1.0 sec. The cart is standing still initially. The timer is started as soon as the constant force is applied. Marks are found at the following distances from the initial point: 0.0 cm, 1.0 cm, 4.0 cm, 9.0 cm, 16 cm, 25 cm, 36 cm, 49 cm, . . . What is the acceleration of the cart in cm/sec² and the applied force in nt?

24.10. This problem, requiring only simple substitutions, is mathematically trivial, but it illustrates the fact that Newton's laws hold, within certain limits, even for the constituents of the atom.

1. An electron has a mass of 9.1×10^{-31} kg. In an electric field whose strength is 1 nt/coul it experiences a force of 1.6×10^{-19} nt. What acceleration will it experience?

2. Using the formula $v^2 = 2ax$ (equation 8.18), compute what the electron's speed will be after it has traveled 0.1 m.

3. Using the formula $v = at$, compute what the electron's speed will be after it has traveled 1 sec. Compare this with the speed of light. Does the comparison suggest an erroneous assumption? If so, what is it?

24.11. With a scale that does not register more than 5 nt you cannot weigh an object whose mass is about 2 kg. So you pull the object with a force of 4.36 nt (as measured with the scale) in a straight line along a frictionless horizontal table, and you find its acceleration to be 2.15 m/sec². How much does the object weigh? (Assume that an object whose mass is 1.00 kg weighs exactly 9.80 nt.)

24.12. If the arrow of Fig. 24.11 is pulled back until the upper and lower parts of the cord make 45° angles with the arrow and the tension in the cord is 100 nt, what force must the hand apply to hold the arrow? What would be the instantaneous acceleration of the arrow upon being released if it had a mass of 0.15 kg?

24.13. As a laboratory exercise you should perform the statics experiment with three rubber-band chains, described in § 24.5. In preparation for this and to offer you some practice in the adding of vectors, data on magnitudes and directions of forces are given below. Add these graphically as carefully as possible. Do not worry if there is an error of closure; the data are not perfect (any more than your experimental data would be).

Magnitude:	Direction:
13 nt	northwest
20 nt	30° east of north
27 nt	due south

Add these vectors by drawing the vector triangle in the order given; then add them in a different order, starting with a different vector. Draw in the error-of-closure vectors. Would you expect these to be the same regardless of the order of adding the vectors?

24.14. The branch of mechanics dealing with particles and rigid bodies in equilibrium is called statics. Its applications are very important, and considerable space used to be devoted to it in physics textbooks. Here is a typical problem in statics: A boy is hanging by his hands from a rope whose ends are tied at the same height to two trees. One end of the rope makes an angle of 60° with the horizontal, and the other makes an angle of 30° with the horizontal. If the boy weighs 900 nt, what is the tension in each end of the rope? Draw a diagram. Isolate the forces affecting the boy. Use the fact that the vector polygon must close or the fact that the sum of both the vertical and the horizontal components of the forces must be zero.

24.15. Determine the distance the earth falls from rest toward a 70-kg man if he falls 1 m toward the earth. (Hint: First prove that the initial instantaneous accelerations of earth and man are inversely proportional to their masses. Then prove that the initial distances are approximately proportional to the accelerations. The mass of the earth is 6.0×10^{24} kg.) Compare the earth's displacement with the approximate diameter (10^{-10} m) of an atom.

25

More About
Newton's Second Law

IT IS one thing to translate words from one language to another but another to transform these words into meaningful concepts. We can accomplish the latter for the laws of motion only by doing experiments and solving problems that give meaning to the words. Newton published his laws in a work entitled *De Motu Corporum*. One of the translations of his second law from the Latin reads: *The alteration of motion is ever proportional to the motive force impressed and is made in a direction of the right line in which the force is impressed.* Even in this day of automatic translation by high-speed electronic computers it is difficult to conceive that the same set of words now appears in books as: *The acceleration produced by an unbalanced force on a body is proportional to the magnitude of the net force, in the same direction as the force, and inversely proportional to the mass of the body.* The important thing to do, obviously, is not to memorize either definition but to grasp the meaning of the formula $\mathbf{F} = m\mathbf{a}$, which summarizes both of them accurately. I shall indicate how you can do this by performing experiments and solving problems.

25.1. Friction

Let us pull a block of wood with a chain of rubber bands as shown in Figure 25.1. By tying enough bands end to end, we can diminish the stiffness of the combination to the point where great elongations produce only small forces. (We can produce greater forces by attaching one or more chains alongside the first one.) We observe that we can stretch the rubber-band chain without moving the block. Only as we stretch the chain farther and farther does the block suddenly begin to move.

Let us isolate the block and consider all the forces acting on it. Its weight, $m\mathbf{g}$, acts downward. The normal reaction, $\mathbf{N}$, of the table is upward. The vertical forces must be numerically equal ($\mathbf{N} = -m\mathbf{g}$), for otherwise we should have a vertical acceleration. The force, $\mathbf{F}$, exerted by the chain must be balanced by an equal and opposite force $\mathbf{f} = -\mathbf{F}$, which is due to friction, if the block is to remain stationary. We see at once that the magnitude of the force of friction depends on the magnitude of the pull exerted by the chain. If $\mathbf{F}$ goes to zero, the force of friction will be zero; a block resting on a perfectly horizontal table ex-

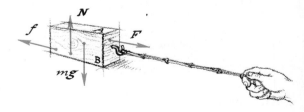

FIG. 25.1. *The forces acting on a block.*

periences no frictional force at all. Remember this when we consider a formula for the maximum friction; that formula will give erroneous results unless you remember that the real force of friction is equal to *or less than* the maximum force of friction.

To find the maximum force of friction, we stretch the chain more and more, as shown by the vectors (**F**) of parts A–C of Figure 25.2: the vector sum of the pulling force, **F**, and frictional force **f**, is zero; the *net unbalanced force* is zero, and the block remains at rest. In C, however, we reach a point where the block is almost ready to move. In D we do reach that point. There **F** is larger than **f** in absolute value; the net unbalanced force, still written vectorially as **F + f**, is greater than zero, and the block suddenly accelerates to the right. The largest value of the frictional force was the value of **f** in C, and it remains almost the same in D. (Actually it is a little smaller.) The maximum

value is proportional to **N** and is independent of the area of contact between the table and the block.

To prove the last statement, we need only turn the block so that the face opposite B, rather than that opposite A (see Fig. 25.1), is in contact with the table. This changes the area of contact but not force **N**. If we now repeat the experiment of Figure 25.2, we find that the rubber-band chain has to be stretched approximately the same amount as before to start the block moving (Fig. 25.3). The maximum frictional force is, we see, approximately independent of the apparent area of contact between surfaces. (Some of the laws of friction are just rough approximations, and precise experimental confirmation is not possible. Friction is always present, however, and we are attempting here to consider it in a quantitative way.)

If we now put a second block, identical with the first, on top of the first, we have to stretch the

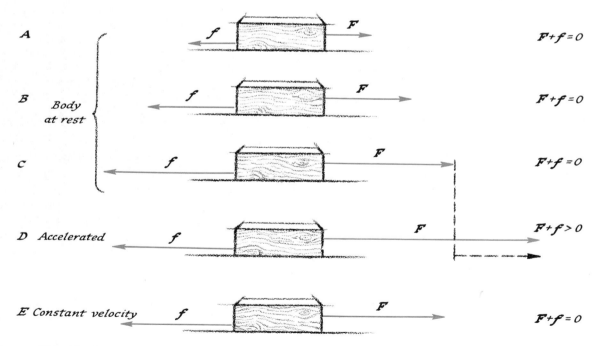

FIG. 25.2. *The force of friction,* **f***, arises in opposition to the applied force,* **F***. In A, B, and C,* **f** *is numerically equal to* **F***. Hence* **F + f = 0***. In D the magnitude of* **F** *exceeds that of* **f***, which has reached its maximum value; so the net force,* **F + f***, produces an acceleration. In E the block is kept moving at constant speed by a new value of* **F***, which is smaller than that of C.*

FIG. 25.3. *Showing that the force of friction for a given normal force does not depend upon the apparent area of contact of the surfaces.*

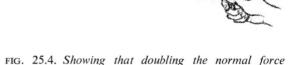

FIG. 25.4. *Showing that doubling the normal force doubles the friction.*

rubber-band chain more than before to make the blocks move. If we then attach, beside the rubber-band chain, a second chain identical with the first (Fig. 25.4), we have to stretch the pair just as much, to make the two blocks move, as we had to stretch one chain to make one block move. This proves that doubling the normal force, **N**, doubles the *maximum* frictional force, f_s.

In the following equation we drop the vector notation and consider only magnitudes because f_s is perpendicular to **N**. Many experiments of the same kind have confirmed the following as an experimental law:

$$f_s = \mu_s N \qquad [25.1$$

Again I must stress the approximate nature of the laws of friction. This equation represents only an approximation to the truth. The constant of proportionality, μ_s, is called the **coefficient of static friction.** (The symbol μ is the Greek letter mu, and the subscript s stands for "static"; read μ_s as "mu sub s.") The value of the coefficient depends on the materials of which the block and the table are made and on their degree of roughness. The coefficients of static friction listed in tables usually range, for unlubricated surfaces, from about 0.2 to 1.0. One can reduce the coefficient to about 0.1 by oiling the surfaces. Once motion has started, the coefficient changes to a lower value, μ_k, called the **coefficient of kinetic friction.** That is why, in part E of Figure 25.2, we can maintain constant velocity with a force smaller than that of part C. We are all familiar with the fact that it does not take as much force to keep something going as to get it started.

Since friction wastes energy, the reduction of friction is a serious and important branch of engineering. Yet, if there were no friction, walking,

for example, would be impossible: it is the frictional force exerted by the ground on our feet that propels us. We shall not study friction much further, but we must consider it whenever we pass from ideal, hypothetically frictionless experiments to those involving the real world, in which friction is always present. Let us consider how to solve a simple problem involving friction.

EXAMPLE 25.1. A block of wood (Fig. 25.1) is pulled along a horizontal table by a constant horizontal force of 2.0 nt (as we ascertain by stretching the rubber-band chain vertically and hanging weights on it until the stretch is the same as it was during the pulling experiment). The mass of the block is 0.5 kg. The coefficient of kinetic friction between the block and the table is 0.3. We wish to know the increase in velocity experienced by the block in 3 sec.

Since the table is horizontal,

$$N = mg = 0.5 \text{ kg} \times 9.8 \text{ m/sec}^2 = 4.9 \text{ nt}$$

Therefore

$$f_k = \mu_k N = 0.3 \times 4.9 \text{ nt} = 1.47 \text{ nt}$$

The magnitude of the net unbalanced force, $f_k + \mathbf{F}$, is $2.0 - 1.47 = 0.53$ nt. The acceleration is

$$a = \frac{f}{m} = \frac{0.53 \text{ nt}}{0.5 \text{ kg}} = 1.06 \frac{\text{m}}{\text{sec}^2}$$

Using the formula $\Delta v = a(\Delta t)$, we obtain

$$\Delta v = 1.06 \frac{\text{m}}{\text{sec}^2} \times 3 \text{ sec}$$

$$= 3.18 \frac{\text{m}}{\text{sec}}$$

It is usually better to solve such a problem with symbols before substituting numerical values. One reason for this is that a check by dimensional analysis is then possible at each step. Another is that some quantities cancel out algebraically, thereby proving that the answer is independent of those quantities. Following this method and considering first the last thing we want (Δv), we write

$$\Delta v = a(\Delta t)$$

But, since $a = f/m$ (f is the unbalanced force),

$$\Delta v = \frac{f}{m}\Delta t$$

Now

$$f = F - f_k = F - \mu_k N = F - \mu_k mg$$

Therefore

$$\Delta v = \frac{(F - \mu_k mg)}{m}\Delta t$$

We can make the dimensional check by inspection. Since mg is a force and μ_k is a dimensionless constant, the whole quantity within the parentheses is a force. This, divided by a mass, is an acceleration, which, multiplied by time, has the dimensions of velocity.

Now, putting in numbers, we get

$$\Delta v = \frac{(2.0 - 0.3 \times 0.5 \times 9.8)\,\text{nt}}{0.50\,\text{kg}} \times 3\,\text{sec}$$

$$= \frac{0.53 \times 3.0}{0.50}\,\frac{\text{m}}{\text{sec}}$$

$$= 3.18\,\frac{\text{m}}{\text{sec}}$$

A problem worked out in this fashion exhibits the logic and the units more clearly than one done numerically throughout.

25.2. The Inclined Plane

Consider first the ideal case of a block of mass m sliding down a frictionless inclined plane (Fig. 25.5). The height of the block is initially h and finally zero. The plane's inclination is θ; its length is l.

A question in kinematics might be: How long will it take the block, starting from rest, to traverse the distance l? If the acceleration, a, is a constant (as we shall prove it to be), the block should move according to equation 8.18: $l = at^2/2$. From this we obtain the equation

$$t = \sqrt{\frac{2l}{a}} \qquad [25.2$$

The dynamical part of the problem consists in finding an expression for a.

Let us first isolate the block (Fig. 25.6). There are two forces acting on it: the earth pulls it down vertically with force mg; the plane exerts on it only the normal force **N**. (Remember that even frictionless surfaces can exert normal forces; a hockey puck is pushed upward by the ice on which it rests or moves.) We could find the resultant of these two forces by the parallelogram rule if we knew the magnitude of **N**; it would point downward along the plane as shown by the green vector, **f**. We can proceed more readily if we resort to rectangular components. Since we know from experiment that the block moves along the plane, we choose an x axis along the plane and a y axis normal to it (Fig. 25.7) and thereby replace mg by its x and y components. The magnitude of the x component, OC, is $mg \sin \theta$, and that of the y component, OA, is $mg \cos \theta$ (equations 6.13 and 6.14). First we prove that angle AOB is equal to θ.

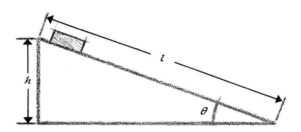

FIG. 25.5. *A block of mass* m *about to slide down a frictionless inclined plane.*

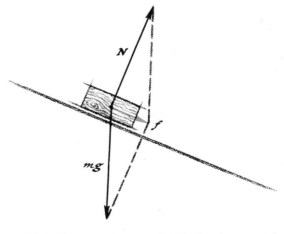

FIG. 25.6. *Forces acting on the block of Fig. 25.5.*

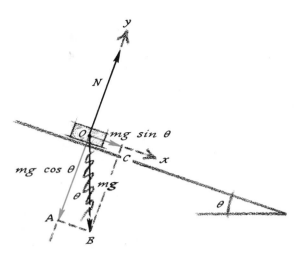

FIG. 25.7. *Rectangular axes set up for the block of Figs. 25.5 and 25.6. The wiggly line through the vector* **mg** *indicates that it has been replaced, conceptually, by its* x *and* y *components.*

Next, in the right triangle OAB, we see that

$$\cos \theta = \frac{\text{adjacent side}}{\text{hypotenuse}}$$

$$= \frac{OA}{OB}$$

Therefore

$$OA = OB \cos \theta$$
$$= mg \cos \theta$$

In a similar way

$$OC = mg \sin \theta$$

The problem of Figure 25.6, with forces mg and N, has now been replaced by an equivalent problem (Fig. 25.7), with forces along the y axis of magnitude N and $mg \cos \theta$. Since there is no acceleration in either y direction, these forces must be equal in magnitude and opposite in direction. They cancel each other. They contribute nothing to the net unbalanced force, which is now seen to be simply $mg \sin \theta$ along the x axis. Using Newton's second law, we find that the acceleration is

$$a = \frac{mg \sin \theta}{m} \qquad [25.3$$

This equation illustrates the advantage of handling the problem symbolically first: we see that the mass cancels out. The physical meaning of this is

that the acceleration of the block is independent of the mass. Blocks of different masses all reach the bottom in the same time if there is no friction.

Substituting into equation 25.2, we obtain the equation

$$t = \sqrt{\frac{2l}{g \sin \theta}} \qquad [25.4$$

Let us check this dimensionally: since $\sin \theta$ is a dimensionless constant, our dimensions inside the square-root sign are

$$\frac{L}{LT^{-2}} = T^2$$

and both sides of the equation therefore have the physical dimension of time. As a proof by *reductio ad extremum* consider what happens when we give θ the values 0° and 90°. At 90°, $\sin \theta = 1$, and, therefore,

$$t = \sqrt{\frac{2l}{g}}$$

Solved for l, this equation becomes

$$l = \tfrac{1}{2}gt^2$$

which we recognize as describing the motion of a body falling freely (equation 8.18). As θ approaches zero, $\sin \theta$ approaches zero and t approaches infinity. This also makes sense.

To find the acceleration when friction is present, let us assume that the block is given a little tap to start its movement; we can then use μ_k instead of μ_s. The maximum force of friction is the product of the normal force between block and plane and the coefficient of kinetic friction. The net unbalanced force, in the presence of friction, is

$$mg \sin \theta - \mu_k N = mg \sin \theta - \mu_k mg \cos \theta$$

Hence the acceleration is

$$a = \frac{mg(\sin \theta - \mu_k \cos \theta)}{m} \qquad [25.5$$

Once again the mass cancels out.

The expression in the parenthesis may be zero; for example, if θ_1 is the special value of θ for which the expression vanishes,

$$\sin \theta_1 - \mu_k \cos \theta_1 = 0$$

This leads to an interesting result,

$$\sin \theta_1 = \mu_k \cos \theta_1$$

or

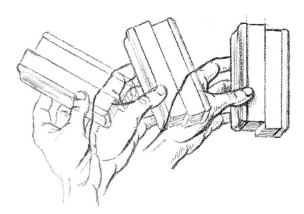

FIG. 25.8. *Demonstrating, with two blackboard erasers, that the limiting angle of repose may approach 90°. This implies that the coefficient of static friction approaches infinity.*

$$\frac{\sin \theta_1}{\cos \theta_1} = \mu_k$$

which is equivalent† to

$$\tan \theta = \mu_k \qquad [25.6$$

Notice that, when $\sin \theta - \mu_k \cos \theta$ vanishes, the acceleration equals zero (equation 25.5). This implies that the block moves *down* the incline at a *constant velocity*.

This result gives us another way of determining μ_k. We simply increase angle θ until the block slides down (after being prompted by a slight tap) at a constant velocity. We thus determine θ_1 experimentally. The tangent of this angle (sometimes called the limiting angle of repose) is the coefficient of kinetic friction.

Many combinations of substances have a coefficient of static friction that is close to 1. This implies a limiting angle of repose close to 45°, since tan 45° = 1. (See Appendix E.) But, if two blackboard erasers are used, one as the inclined plane and the other as the block (Fig. 25.8), they can be tilted slowly until the angle of inclination approaches 90°. This implies (equation 25.6) that μ_s approaches infinity. Occasionally, in fact, one can increase θ all the way to 90°. The objects of this demonstration are to show that coefficients of static friction considerably greater than 1 are pos-

† In Appendix E, I show that $(\sin x)/(\cos x) = \tan x$.

sible and to make you ponder a little on the ultimate causes of the forces (whether they are friction or not) that permit θ to approach 90° in the case of the erasers.

25.3. The Elevator

An elevator of mass m_1 contains a passenger of mass m_2 (Fig. 25.9). What must be the magnitude, T, of the tension in the cable if the elevator experiences upward acceleration a_1?

First we isolate the elevator with the man in it and consider the forces acting on it. Since both the man and the elevator experience the same acceleration, we may consider a downward force (due to gravity), equal to $(m_1 + m_2)g$. The tension, T, is an upward force. Let us consider the upward vertical direction positive; we can then drop the vector notation by considering the downward direction of g negative. If g is a positive number, the acceleration of gravity must by symbolized as $-g$. Since the net unbalanced force is

$$T - (m_1 + m_2)g$$

the upward acceleration is

$$a_1 = \frac{T - (m_1 + m_2)g}{m_1 + m_2} \qquad [25.7$$

Solving the equation for T, we get

$$\begin{aligned} T &= a_1(m_1 + m_2) + g(m_1 + m_2) \\ &= (m_1 + m_2)(a_1 + g) \qquad [25.8 \end{aligned}$$

Now let us imagine the passenger, still inside the elevator, standing on a bathroom scale of negligible mass (Fig. 25.10). Let us isolate him. There are two forces acting on him. One is the pull of gravity, m_2g. The other is the upward push, F_1, of the bathroom scale. Let us assume that the magnitude of his upward acceleration is again a_1. The net unbalanced force on him is $F_1 + m_2g$. Resorting to algebraic symbols with proper signs, we may write this as $F_1 - m_2g$. Applying Newton's second law to the man alone, we may express his acceleration as

$$a_1 = \frac{F_1 - m_2g}{m_2}$$

Solving for F_1, we get

$$\begin{aligned} F_1 &= m_2a_1 + m_2g \\ &= m_2(a_1 + g) \qquad [25.9 \end{aligned}$$

FIG. 25.9. *The forces acting on a rising elevator containing a passenger.*

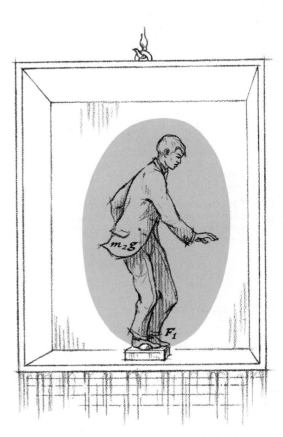

FIG. 25.10. *The forces acting on a man standing on a bathroom scale in a rising elevator.*

Now we are ready to consider the reading on the bathroom scale. By Newton's third law, the push exerted by the scale on the man is the same in magnitude as the push exerted by the man on the scale; that is, the numerical value of the reading on the scale must be $m_2(a_1 + g)$. But normally (when the reading is taken on an unaccelerated platform) the reading on the scale is simply m_2g. The passenger's weight has apparently increased by m_2a_1. To the passenger himself it seems that an additional force, m_2a_1, is acting *downward* on him; an observer in a fixed frame of reference outside the elevator would say that a net force of m_2a_1 is acting *upward* on the passenger. Who is right?

To minimize confusion, we can limit ourselves to a simple question that we can answer operationally. What is the reading on the bathroom scale when the elevator experiences the upward acceleration a_1? The answer is $m_2(a_1 + g)$. We can call this the apparent weight if we like, but the simple fact remains that the reading on the scale is $m_2(a_1 + g)$.

You are urged to repeat the analysis for a case where the acceleration (a_2) is downward.

25.4. Atwood's Machine

Another classical and very instructive problem involves a machine invented to illustrate such problems by George Atwood (1746–1807). A pulley on a string supports two bodies of masses m_1 and m_2 as shown in Figure 25.11. We want to express the linear acceleration, a, of one of the bodies in terms of the acceleration due to gravity and the masses and to find an expression for the tension, T, of the string. First let us state our simplifying assumptions. We assume that the pulley is massless and frictionless. We assume that the string is massless and inextensible; the latter property ensures that displacement Δy_1 of m_1 will be matched by displacement Δy_2 of m_2 so that $\Delta y_1 = -\Delta y_2$. (If both y_1 and y_2 are considered positive when measured upward, one displacement will be positive and the other negative.) Our assumption also implies that $v_1 = -v_2$ and that $a_1 = -a_2$ if v and a are velocity and acceleration respectively. We dispense with vector notation by symbolizing the acceleration due to gravity as $-g$.

We now isolate the body of mass m_1. Since the net unbalanced force on it is $T_1 - m_1g$,

$$a_1 = \frac{T_1 - m_1g}{m_1} \qquad [25.10$$

Similarly, isolating the body of mass m_2, we get the equation

$$a_2 = \frac{m_2g - T_2}{m_2} \qquad [25.11$$

Rewriting these equations, and using the equation $a_2 = -a_1$, we get the pair of equations

$$\left.\begin{array}{l} T_1 = m_1a_1 + m_1g \\ T_2 = m_2a_1 + m_2g \end{array}\right\} \qquad [25.12$$

There still seem to be three unknowns, T_1, T_2, and a_1, and only two equations, but we can see as follows that $T_1 = T_2$. If the pulley had mass, T_1 would have to be different from T_2 to account for its angular acceleration, but a massless pulley does not require such a difference. Therefore $T_1 = T_2$. We can therefore rewrite equations 25.12 as

$$\left.\begin{array}{l} T_1 = m_1a_1 + m_1g \\ T_1 = -m_2a_1 + m_2g \end{array}\right\} \qquad [25.13$$

Changing all the signs in the lower equation and adding it to the first, we obtain

$$0 = m_1a_1 + m_2a_1 + m_1g - m_2g$$

or

$$a_1(m_1 + m_2) = g(m_2 - m_1)$$

Solving this for a_1, we obtain

$$a_1 = \frac{g(m_2 - m_1)}{m_1 + m_2} \qquad [25.14$$

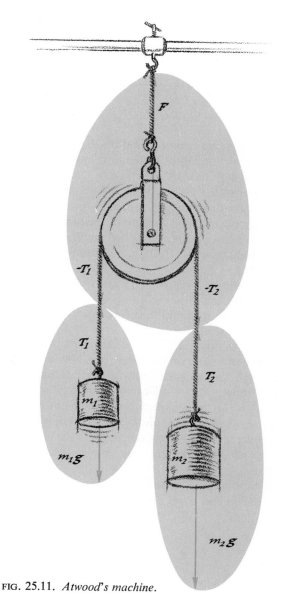

FIG. 25.11. Atwood's machine.

Now the *last* thing in the world you should do is to memorize this formula. That is the least important point of this discussion. The important thing to learn is the proper *approach* to a dynamical problem. A QAD† approach might, of course, yield the right answer. What is the net unbalanced force? After inspection of the system we say that it is $m_2g - m_1g$. What is the total mass of the

† We shall let QAD stand for "quick and dirty."

moving system? Answer: $m_1 + m_2$. Therefore the acceleration ought to be the net unbalanced force divided by the total mass:

$$a = \frac{m_2 g - m_1 g}{m_1 + m_2}$$

$$= \frac{g(m_2 - m_1)}{m_1 + m_2}$$

This is the same answer (equation 25.14), obtained in one blow instead of by detailed analysis. What is wrong with the QAD method?

One answer is: There is nothing wrong with it if you have done enough problems to realize why it comes out all right in spite of the fact that you had *two* masses being accelerated in *different* directions (which was certainly not implied by the formula $\mathbf{f} = m\mathbf{a}$).

The other answer is: You are trying to learn basic approaches that will be applicable to many problems. You should therefore learn to analyze, step by step, *all* the details of even such a simple problem as this, learning especially how to isolate the different parts of the system and how to apply Newton's law independently to each of them. If there happen to be relations (such as $a_1 = -a_2$ and $T_1 = T_2$), you can then use them instead of ignoring them. In the solution of this problem, for example, the QAD method disregards the tensions of the string, which may be important in some cases.

If we divide the first of equations 25.13 by m_1 and the second by m_2, we get

$$\left.\begin{array}{r} \dfrac{T_1}{m_1} = a_1 + g \\[2mm] \dfrac{T_1}{m_2} = -a_1 + g \end{array}\right\} \qquad [25.15$$

Adding, we get

$$\frac{T_1}{m_1} + \frac{T_1}{m_2} = 2g$$

Taking out the common factor T_1, we get

$$T_1 \left(\frac{1}{m_1} + \frac{1}{m_2} \right) = 2g$$

or

$$T_1 \left(\frac{m_2 + m_1}{m_1 m_2} \right) = 2g$$

which yields

$$T_1 = 2g \frac{m_1 m_2}{m_1 + m_2} \qquad [25.16$$

It is instructive to check this in some simple cases. If, for example, $m_1 = m_2$, the numerator of the fraction is m_1^2, the denominator is $2m_1$, and we get $T_1 = m_1 g$, which checks with common sense, since there would be no acceleration in this case. And, if $m_1 = 0$, then $T_1 = 0$. This means that, if we cut m_1 from the system, m_2 would fall freely with no tension in the string.

25.5. One More Example

Having thoroughly analyzed the example of Atwood's machine, let us reverse the procedure and discuss, by the QAD method first, another classical example: a block of mass m_1 accelerated by a weight of mass m_2, the two connected by a string passing over a frictionless and massless pulley, as shown in Figure 6.5. (The initial position of the block was, of course, farther to the left.)

The problem is very simple. The net unbalanced force is $m_2 g$. The total moving mass is $m_1 + m_2$. We therefore expect the acceleration to be

$$a = \frac{m_2 g}{m_1 + m_2} \qquad [25.17$$

Let us test this equation dimensionally. On the right-hand side we have

$$\frac{MLT^{-2}}{M} = LT^{-2}$$

which we recognize as the dimensions of an acceleration. Next we try the *reductio ad absurdum* (or *reductio ad extremum*).

What happens, according to the equation, if $m_2 = 0$? Answer: $a = 0$. This agrees with our intuition.

What happens if $m_1 \longrightarrow 0$? Answer: $a \longrightarrow g$. This too seems reasonable; m_2 falls freely.

What happens if $m_1 \longrightarrow \infty$? Answer: $a \longrightarrow 0$. This also seems reasonable.

Equation 25.16 has stood some pretty severe tests. If we now ask, "What is the tension in the string?," we are forced to isolate one mass or both masses. If we isolate m_1 (we must draw vectors for *all* the forces acting on it), we find that the net force on it is T. The acceleration in the horizontal, or x, direction is, therefore,

$$a_x = \frac{T}{m_1}$$

If we use $m_2 g/(m_1 + m_2)$ for a_x, we get

$$T = \frac{m_1 m_2 g}{m_1 + m_2} \qquad [25.18$$

As a check we may isolate m_2. The net force on it is $mg - T$. Its acceleration (in the vertical, or y, direction) is therefore

$$a_y = \frac{m_2 g - \dfrac{m_1 m_2 g}{m_1 + m_2}}{m_2}$$

$$= g - \frac{m_1 g}{m_1 + m_2}$$

$$= \frac{g(m_1 + m_2 - m_1)}{m_1 + m_2}$$

$$= \frac{m_2 g}{m_1 + m_2} \qquad [25.19$$

Equation 25.19 is identical with equation 25.17. Everything seems to be in order.

25.6. Forces in Simple Harmonic Motion

In all the examples cited so far the acceleration has been constant. But the formula $\mathbf{f} = m\mathbf{a}$ holds instantaneously for variable accelerations as well. Earlier we considered a special case of variable acceleration in simple harmonic motion—that of the simple pendulum. We are now ready to con-sider the motion of a simple pendulum dynami-cally.

Figure 25.12.A isolates a pendulum bob of mass m at an instant when its angular displacement is θ; it is acted upon by its weight, mg, and by the tension, τ, of the string. Fig. 25.12.B replaces vector mg by two components: one, $mg \sin \theta$, along the tangent to the circle of radius l (the length of the pendulum); the other, $mg \cos \theta$, along the string. Since there is no acceleration along the string, τ and $mg \cos \theta$ balance each other (we drop the vector notation). The net unbalanced force is $mg \sin \theta$, which is directed along the tangent to the circle. For small values of θ this force is almost parallel to the horizontal x direc-tion. The horizontal component of acceleration is, therefore, very nearly

$$a_x = -\frac{mg \sin \theta}{m}$$

(When θ is positive, the acceleration is negative.) Figure 25.12.C shows that the x displacement of the bob obeys the equation

$$\frac{x}{l} = \sin \theta$$

Therefore

$$a_x = -g \frac{x}{l} \qquad [25.20$$

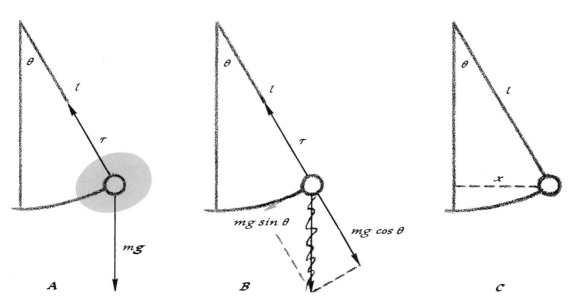

FIG. 25.12. *The forces acting on a simple pendulum.*

We learned earlier (equation 14.34) that the period of a simple periodic motion is

$$T = 2\pi \sqrt{-x/a_x} \qquad [25.21$$

Using equation 25.20, we obtain the formula

$$T = 2\pi \sqrt{l/g}$$

We have used this before (§ 7.5) but have not derived it precisely until now, for Newton's second law was required in the proof.

The period of vibration of a body of mass m suspended on a spring of stiffness constant k may be obtained in a similar way. The force acting on the body is $F = -kx$. (The constant of proportionality, k, is called the stiffness constant of the spring.) Using the second law, we get the formula $ma = -kx$, and therefore $-x/a = m/k$. Using equation 25.21, we get the formula $T = 2\pi \sqrt{m/k}$. (See § 7.5.)

You will find that your understanding of Newton's second law improves (up to a point) with the number of problems you solve. A representative sample of problems is given below, but, since the law applies to every body that is accelerated, you should try to invent problems of your own in order to get a firm grasp of this very important relation.

25.7. Summary

The best summary of this chapter is simply the formula $F = ma$. It describes the acceleration of a particle acting under the influence of forces whose vector sum is F. If we make certain simplifications (which will be spelled out in detail later), it applies also to rigid bodies. In this chapter we have simply treated rigid bodies as if they were particles. It is sometimes thought that the formula applies only in the absence of friction. This is not so. Friction is one of the forces that must be taken into account when we calculate F. Of all the simplifications made concerning friction between bodies that can slide on one another, perhaps the most useful is that the maximum force of friction is proportional to the total normal force.

Problems

25.1. The idea that the frictional force between the table and the block (Figs. 25.1 and 25.3) is independent of the apparent area of contact may be intuitively difficult to understand. Consider, however, what happens to the pressure of the block on the table as you change from a small apparent area of contact (Fig. 25.1) to a larger apparent area of contact by putting the side opposite B in contact with the table (Fig. 25.3). Is it true that, when the pressure is greater, the apparent area of contact is smaller? Does this suggest that the real area of contact is different from the apparent area? Explain.

25.2. Think through this experiment to test your understanding of the physical implications of Fig. 25.2: The rubber-band chain of Fig. 25.1 is stretched to the right by the right hand until the largest value of the static frictional force is reached. The block is then tapped slightly with the left hand to prompt it to move. If the rubber bands are so weak that only a sizable stretch will produce the desired force,

and if, once they are stretched, the right hand remains fixed, describe the motion of the block as a function of position.

25.3. We are told that the coefficient of kinetic friction is less than that of static friction. Suppose the opposite were true. Describe under what conditions you could induce the block of Fig. 25.1 to accelerate rapidly just by tapping it if the rubber bands pulling it had originally been stretched just barely enough to produce the maximum static frictional force? In a real situation will a car have more traction on the road when it is skidding as a result of braking than when it is rolling without skidding?

25.4. A car moving in a straight line reaches a long stretch of road that is covered with ice. The driver slams his brake pedal down to the floor, and the car skids for 200 meters before coming to rest. If the coefficient of friction between the locked wheels and the ice was 0.10, how fast was he going (in meters per second) before he reached the ice? Using the fact that 60 mph is almost 30 m/sec, do you consider your numerical result reasonable?

25.5. What is the maximum vertical acceleration that can be imparted to an object whose mass is 2 kg if it is pulled upward by a string that will break when the tension in it reaches 65 nt?

25.6. A jet plane with a mass of 985 kg has a landing speed of 125 m/sec relative to the deck of an aircraft carrier. It is brought to rest in a distance of 148 m by a force applied to a hook on the plane by cables connected to a hydraulic braking device on the carrier. What is the average value of the force?

25.7. Book learning has been decried in science because it has sometimes been used in place of experiment. Here is a simple experiment that can be performed with books. Use a large book as a platform, and tilt it until another book, resting flat on it, starts to slide down. Use other books to prop up the platform at the minimum angle at which sliding takes place. Now increase the weight on the sliding book by locking another book on top of it by interleaving their covers. Does the minimum angle change appreciably? What is the coefficient of friction of the two rubbing surfaces as measured by the ratio of the rise to the run of the platform? (This ratio is the tangent of the angle of inclination.)

25.8. A car is rolling down an incline of 30°. The driver puts on the brakes, and the tires skid. The car neither speeds up nor slows down under these circumstances. What is the coefficient of kinetic friction?

25.9. When a block rests on a horizontal board, the frictional force on the block is zero. It also approaches zero as the board is tilted as close as we please to 90°. Having been given data for these two points, sketch a plot of frictional force against angle of inclination θ for values of θ from 0° to 90°. (This problem is not easy, but it does not require great mathematical skill. It requires a comprehension of the physical factors that entered into the proof of equation 25.5.)

25.10. What is the steepest angle of inclination possible for a conveyor belt if the coefficient of friction between it and the objects to be carried on it is 0.900?

25.11. A man is standing on a bathroom scale in an elevator. His mass is 82 kg, and that of the scale is 2 kg. The elevator is accelerating upward at the

rate of 3 m/sec². Isolate the scale, and find the magnitude of all the forces on it. Remember: the man pushes down, the elevator pushes up, and gravity pulls down on the scale.

25.12. 1. Analyze Prob. 25.11 when the elevator's acceleration is downward. Deduce algebraic expressions and numerical values for the forces felt (a) by the man, (b) by the bathroom scale, and (c) by the elevator (assuming that its mass is 500 kg).

2. Which of these forces can be measured directly with the bathroom scale?

3. Review your analysis when the acceleration is downward and equal to g.

25.13. In a modification of the experiment shown in Fig. 6.5, a block of mass m_1 is pulled not only to the right by the weight of an object of mass m_2 but also to the left by the weight of an object of mass m_3, connected to the block by a string over a separate pulley.

1. First consider an easy problem that can be solved by the QAD method: derive a formula for the acceleration of the block.

2. Now consider a slightly more difficult question, which cannot be answered by the use of the QAD method alone: what is the tension in the string connecting the block and the object of mass m_2? (Assume that $m_2 > m_3$.)

25.14. A long, straight trough has a semicircular cross-section of radius R. When the trough is horizontal, a small ball (such as a marble), released near one edge of its concave surface, will move in a curve of radius R, in a vertical plane, with an almost repetitive motion and a fairly constant period. Except for the fact that it rolls, the ball's motion is very similar to that of the bob of a simple pendulum (Fig. 25.12) of length R.

1. Review the similarities and differences between the forces acting on such a ball of mass m and those acting on the pendulum bob.

2. If there were no friction between ball and trough, the ball would slide without rolling. Derive a formula for the ball's period of oscillation in this ideal case.

3. If the trough were inclined and its concave surface had been painted black, a tennis ball dipped in chalk dust and released near one edge of the concave surface, at the higher end of the trough, would leave an oscillatory trace as it rolled down the trough. Sketch a curve that might be traced by such a ball, and explain how this experiment might give you data with which to measure linear acceleration.

Newton's Third Law

A TRADITIONAL way of stating Newton's third law is: *To every action there is an equal and opposite reaction.* A more modern version reads: *Whenever two bodies interact, the force exerted by the first body on the second is equal and opposite to the force exerted by the second body on the first.*

The law implies, for example, that, when a horse pulls on a cart and accelerates it, the cart pulls back on the horse with an equal force. How can the cart accelerate under these circumstances? I shall try to answer this and other questions related to this important and apparently paradoxical law.

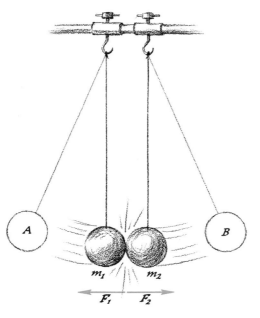

FIG. 26.1. *Illustrating the conservation of linear momentum.*

26.1. The Third Law and the Conservation of Linear Momentum

Consider an elastic collision between two steel balls suspended so that the line joining their centers is horizontal (Fig. 26.1). While one ball, B, of mass m_2, remains at rest, we displace the other ball, A, of mass m_1, to the left and then release it. When the balls meet, force $\mathbf{F}_1$ acts on A for time Δt, and, during the same interval, force $\mathbf{F}_2$ acts on B. The second law ($\mathbf{f} = m\mathbf{a}$) requires that

$$\mathbf{F}_1(\Delta t) = m_1(\Delta \mathbf{v}_1) \qquad [26.1$$
$$\mathbf{F}_2(\Delta t) = m_2(\Delta \mathbf{v}_2) \qquad [26.2$$

It is easy to prove experimentally (especially if $m_1 = m_2$ but also quite generally) that linear momentum is conserved in such a collision: it follows that

$$m_1(\Delta \mathbf{v}_1) = -m_2(\Delta \mathbf{v}_2) \qquad [26.3$$

From this equation we deduce that $\mathbf{F}_1 = -\mathbf{F}_2$ —in other words, that the force exerted by m_1 on m_2 is equal and opposite to that exerted by m_2 on m_1. This amounts to saying that Newton's third law can be deduced from the conservation of linear momentum (a generalization of this idea will be stated more precisely in Chap. 30). If, on the other hand, we assume Newton's third law, conservation of linear momentum follows from equations 26.1 and 26.2 without further experiments.

Which is the correct procedure? The answer depends on experimental evidence. Some exceptions to Newton's third law have been observed.

FIG. 26.2. *Forces come in equal and opposite pairs.*

Other possible exceptions have been thought of: instantaneous transmission of gravitational pulls, for example, would require transmission of signals with a speed greater than that of light, and this, in modern physics, is believed to be impossible. No exceptions to the conservation of linear momentum have been found. The modern view is, then, that we can treat Newton's third law as a corollary of a broader principle called the conservation of linear momentum (Chap. 30).

In the rest of this chapter we shall consider examples in which Newton's third law does hold. We dismiss for the time being further speculative questions like "which came first, the chicken or

the egg?" and get on with the more mundane business of learning how to fry the egg rather than wondering how it got here.

26.2. The Third Law Applied to Problems in Statics

When you hold a heavy suitcase, it seems to be pulling down your hand. It is! And your hand is pulling the suitcase up. This pair of forces acting on different objects illustrates what happens in all examples of the operation of Newton's third law. The wall pulls the hook, in Figure 26.2, and the hook pulls the wall; the rope pulls the hook, and the hook pulls the rope; the hand pulls the rope, and the rope pulls the hand. The forces occur in equal and opposite pairs. Try to find, in your daily living, such pairs of forces. This should not be difficult; the simple acts of cracking a nut and stepping on the brake of a car illustrate pairs of forces each acting on different objects. It is these that Newton's third law deals with.

EXAMPLE 26.1. A block with mass, m, of 2 kg resting on a horizontal table is being pulled by a horizontal rope (Fig. 26.3.A) with a force of 5 nt.

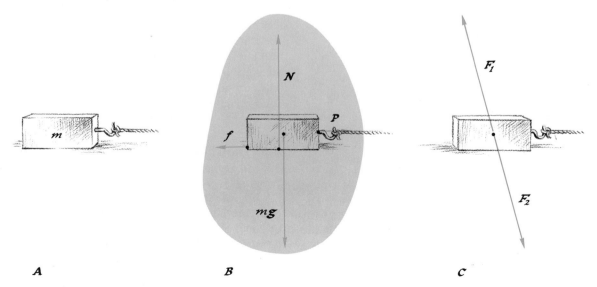

A   *B*   *C*

FIG. 26.3. *The forces acting on a block pulled by a rope.*

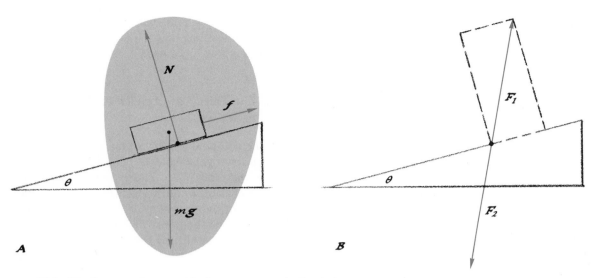

FIG. 26.4. *The forces acting on a block at rest on an inclined plane.*

The coefficient of static friction between the block and the table is 0.3. We observe that the maximum frictional force between block and table is

$$f = \mu_s N = 0.3 \times 2 \text{ kg} \times 9.8 \text{ m/sec}^2 = 5.88 \text{ nt}$$

Therefore, when the rope pulls with a force, **P**, of only 5.0 nt, the opposing frictional force is only 5.0 nt. A free-body diagram (Fig. 26.3.B) shows all the forces acting on the block. Notice that all these forces are acting on one body only: the block. Vectorially, they add up to zero. The forces that the table exerts on the block are **N** and **f**. Hence the total force exerted on the block by the table is $\mathbf{F}_1$, the vector sum of **N** and **f**, and the total force exerted on the table by the block is $\mathbf{F}_2 = -\mathbf{F}_1$ (Fig. 26.3.C).

EXAMPLE 26.2. The same block rests on a board inclined at an angle, θ, of 15° to the horizontal. We assume that $\mu_s = 0.3$. The free-body diagram is shown in Fig. 26.4.A. The forces acting on the block are its weight, mg, and the reaction of the board, which has as components the normal reaction of the board, **N**, and the force of friction, **f**. The weight can be replaced by components (not shown): $mg \cos \theta$ in the normal direction and $mg \sin \theta$ in the direction along the board. Notice that the maximum frictional force is

$$f = \mu_s N = \mu_s \, mg \cos \theta$$
$$= 0.3 \times 2 \text{ kg} \times 9.8 \text{ m/sec}^2 \times \cos 15° = 5.65 \text{ nt}$$

Since the component of mg pointing down along the board is

$$mg \sin \theta = 2 \text{ kg} \times 9.8 \text{ m/sec}^2 \times \sin 15° = 5.40 \text{ nt}$$

the actual frictional force is only 5.40 nt. The two forces exerted on the block by the board are therefore **f** and **N**. Their resultant, $\mathbf{F}_1$, is shown in Fig. 26.4.B. The force exerted on the board by the block is, as shown, $\mathbf{F}_2 = -\mathbf{F}_1$.

So far I have shown how to apply Newton's third law to objects at rest. Now we must consider the forces acting on objects that are being accelerated. Physicists maintain that Newton's third law holds even for such objects—that is, that forces occur in equal and opposite pairs even when they act on accelerated bodies; but this bears closer scrutiny.

26.3. The Third Law Applied to Problems in Dynamics

A boy, *A*, sits on a cart (Fig. 26.5) and holds a rope; another boy, *B*, pulls on the other end of the rope, producing on *A* force **P**, which gives to the cart an acceleration, **a**. Let us isolate the cart with the boy sitting on it. Force mg, which is the weight of cart and boy, acts downward. The normal reaction, **N**, of the floor acts upward. The force **P** acts to the right. The force of friction, **f**, acts to the left. Since the effects of **N** and $m\mathbf{g}$ cancel each other, the net unbalanced force on the boy and the cart is the *vector sum* **P** + **f**. The acceleration of the cart is $\mathbf{a} = (\mathbf{P} + \mathbf{f})/m$. Dropping the vector notation, $a = (P - f)/m$.

All of this seems quite straightforward. The only novelty is that we assume that Newton's third law applies (**P** acts on boy A, $-\mathbf{P}$ on the rope) *while the body is being accelerated*. There is no difficulty in accepting the fact that the boy and the rope exert pulls in opposite directions, but the equality of the magnitudes of these pulls, though important, is not obvious.

There is another way—without recourse to boy B—in which we can accelerate boy A and his cart (Fig. 26.6). We can tie one end of the rope to a hook on a wall. Now, if boy A pulls the rope toward himself with force $-\mathbf{P}$ (taking up the slack and this time doing the work), he is accelerated toward the wall. While the boy pulls on the rope, *the rope also pulls on the boy* with force **P**. Let us isolate the boy and the cart: **N** balances $m\mathbf{g}$; if the frictional force is **f**, the acceleration is, once more,

$$\mathbf{a} = \frac{\mathbf{P} + \mathbf{f}}{m}$$

or, if we drop vector notation,

$$a = \frac{P - f}{m}$$

Experimental evaluation of **a** would confirm the value of **P** given by this equation as numerically equal to the tension in the rope.

Still another way for the boy to accelerate the cart is to push against the wall (Fig. 26.7). The corresponding push *of the wall on the boy* accelerates him and the cart.

Perhaps the oldest example used to illustrate Newton's third law in dynamics is the problem of the wagon and the horse, sometimes posed as a dilemma. The horse is pulling the wagon with force $\mathbf{F}_1$ and accelerating it. But the wagon is pulling the horse back with force $\mathbf{F}_2 = -\mathbf{F}_1$. How can the wagon accelerate under the action of two equal and opposite forces?

The answer is simple if we take the trouble to isolate the wagon (Fig. 26.8) and take *all* the forces acting on it into account. The vertical force is $\mathbf{N}_1 = -m_1\mathbf{g}$. The net horizontal pull is $\mathbf{F}_1 + \mathbf{f}_1$

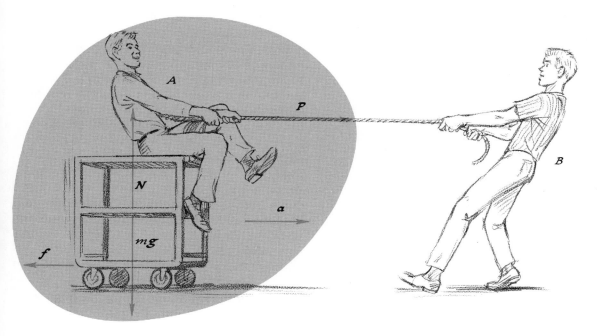

FIG. 26.5. *One way to accelerate a boy and a cart.*

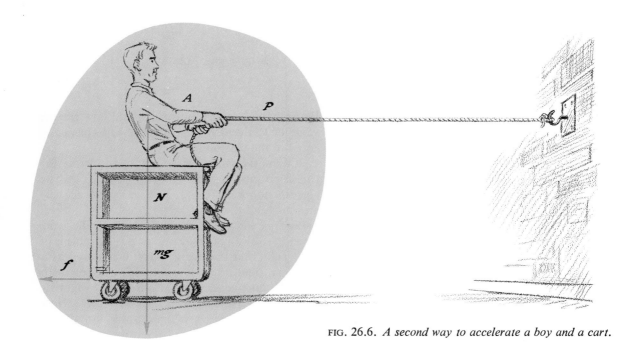

FIG. 26.6. *A second way to accelerate a boy and a cart.*

($\mathbf{f}_1$, the sum of all the frictional forces opposing the motion, points to the left). The wagon will accelerate if the vector sum $\mathbf{F}_1 + \mathbf{f}_1$ is greater than zero: $\mathbf{a}_1 = (\mathbf{F}_1 + \mathbf{f}_1)/m_1$. *There is no need to consider* $\mathbf{F}_2$, *the force exerted by the wagon on the*

FIG. 26.7. *A third way to accelerate a boy and a cart.*

horse; only the forces exerted on the wagon play a role in accelerating the wagon.

How about the horse? It experiences a force, $\mathbf{F}_2$, to the left. How can it accelerate to the right? Let's isolate it. Its weight, $m_2\mathbf{g}$, points down. The normal reaction of the ground is $\mathbf{N}_2 = -m_2\mathbf{g}$. The harness that transmits the pull of the wagon to the horse exerts force $\mathbf{F}_2 = -\mathbf{F}_1$ to the left. The fact that the horse accelerates to the right shows that we have neglected some horizontal force. That is the force of traction, $\mathbf{f}_2$, exerted by the ground on the horse's hoofs. This points to the right. Analyzing it in more detail, we see that the horse's hoofs push back on the ground and that the ground therefore pushes the horse forward with a frictional force, $\mathbf{f}_2$. If there were no friction between the horse's hoofs and the ground (or, as we usually say, if the horse had no traction), the horse could not propel itself at all. The net unbalanced force on the horse is $\mathbf{f}_2 + \mathbf{F}_2$. The acceleration of the horse is $\mathbf{a}_2 = (\mathbf{f}_2 + \mathbf{F}_2)/m_2$.

Let us write the two equations in the following way:

$$m_2\mathbf{a}_2 = \mathbf{f}_2 + \mathbf{F}_2 \qquad [26.4$$
$$m_1\mathbf{a}_1 = \mathbf{f}_1 + \mathbf{F}_1 \qquad [26.5$$

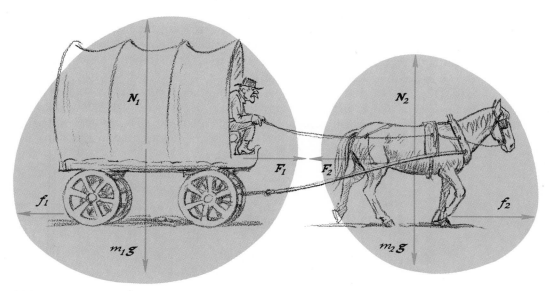

FIG. 26.8. *The horse pulls the wagon with force* $\mathbf{F}_1$. *The wagon pulls back on the horse with force* $\mathbf{F}_2$, *and* $\mathbf{F}_2 = -\mathbf{F}_1$. *These, however, are forces acting on different bodies. Analysis of the forces on the horse alone shows that traction,* $\mathbf{f}_2$, *on the horse exceeds* $\mathbf{F}_2$; *so forward acceleration takes place. A similar analysis can be made for the wagon:* $\mathbf{F}_1$ *exceeds the retarding frictional force,* $\mathbf{f}_1$. *If the combination of wagon and horse is taken as a system, internal forces* $\mathbf{F}_1$ *and* $\mathbf{F}_2$ *cancel out; acceleration is due to the excess of forward traction,* $\mathbf{f}_2$, *over retarding friction,* $\mathbf{f}_1$.

Now, remembering that $\mathbf{a}_1 = \mathbf{a}_2$ (call each one $\mathbf{a}$) and that $\mathbf{F}_1 = -\mathbf{F}_2$, let us add the corresponding sides of the two equations:

$$(m_1 + m_2)\mathbf{a} = \mathbf{f}_1 + \mathbf{f}_2 \qquad [26.6$$

This says that the whole system, consisting of wagon and horse, accelerates in accordance with the second law. The net unbalanced *external* force acting on that system is, as we might have suspected, the vector sum of $\mathbf{f}_1$ and $\mathbf{f}_2$.

Now let us consider an example (Fig. 26.9.A) in which the frictional force between two bodies that slip over each other plays an important role. As a railroad flatcar moves with velocity $\mathbf{v}$, a boy drops gently down on it, and his feet slip over its floor. Let us isolate the boy while he slips (Fig. 26.9.B). The two vertical forces on him ($\mathbf{N}$ and $m\mathbf{g}$) balance each other. The force of friction, $\mathbf{f}$, on the boy points to the right. This causes him to accelerate to the right. When his velocity reaches $\mathbf{v}$, there is no further frictional force. He continues to share the velocity of the car. The vector sum, $\mathbf{N} + \mathbf{f} = \mathbf{F}_1$, of the forces exerted on the boy by

the car is drawn in Figure 26.10. The force exerted on the car by the boy is $\mathbf{F}_2 = -\mathbf{F}_1$.

We have assumed that the velocity of the car is not affected by the experiment. This is approximately true if the mass of the car is much greater than that of the boy. Actually a force, $-\mathbf{f}$, acts on the car while $\mathbf{f}$ acts on the boy. If the car is moving by its own momentum, the effect of force $-\mathbf{f}$ is to reduce the car's speed. All of this makes good sense. The boy picks up speed, and the car loses speed. The forces on the two were the same in magnitude but opposite in direction.

26.4. The Third Law Applied to Gravitational, Electrical, and Magnetic Forces

In Chapter 3, I said that there are three basic types of forces: gravitational, electrical, and nuclear. I also said that bodies can exert forces of these kinds on one another without touching. I did not then ask whether such forces occur in equal and opposite pairs, but there is evidence to support the claim that they do. When body A acts on body B with force $\mathbf{F}$, body B acts on A with force $-\mathbf{F}$ even when they do not touch.

One example of this is that a celestial body and its satellite can revolve in circles about their common center of mass (Fig. 26.11). The body, of mass m_1, feels a force, $\mathbf{F}_1$, whose direction is toward the satellite, of mass m_2, which feels a

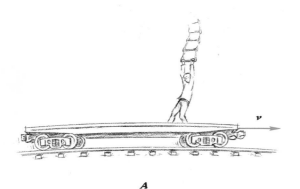

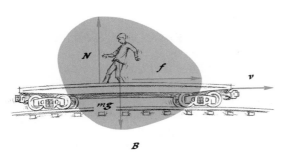

FIG. 26.9. *Some forces involved as a boy drops onto a moving flatcar.*

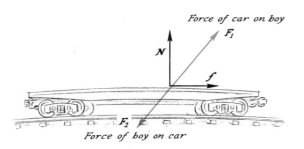

Force of car on boy

F_1

N

f

F_2

Force of boy on car

FIG. 26.10. *Another illustration (from Fig. 26.9) of equal and opposite forces.*

force, $\mathbf{F}_2$, toward m_1. If the distance, L, between them remains fixed, the magnitudes of $\mathbf{F}_1$ and $\mathbf{F}_2$ remain equal and constant. Both $\mathbf{F}_1$ and $\mathbf{F}_2$ are directed to a common point, C. Hence m_1 moves in a circle of radius r_1 with angular velocity ω and acceleration $\omega^2 r_1$ while m_2 moves in a circle of radius r_2 at the same angular velocity, ω—that is, with acceleration $\omega^2 r_2$. Therefore $F_1 = m_1\omega^2 r_1$ and $F_2 = m_2\omega^2 r_2$. Equating the magnitudes of the forces, we get

$$m_1\omega^2 r_1 = m_2\omega^2 r_2$$
$$m_1 r_1 = m_2 r_2$$

In § 30.4 I shall prove that the point for which this relation is true is the center of mass. The main conclusion, however, is that the force felt by m_1 is identical in magnitude to that felt by m_2. The gravitational force F_1 is

$$\frac{m_1 m_2 G}{(r_1 + r_2)^2}$$

It is also possible to have elliptical orbits about a common center of mass, but their analysis is more complicated.

If an electrically charged body, A, exerts a force on another electrically charged body, B, it is found that B, according to Newton's third law, exerts a

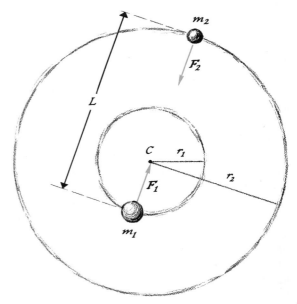

FIG. 26.11. *Two bodies, attracted to each other by the force of gravity, circling about a common point.*

force on A. Now, however, instead of considering forces due to static electric charges or to currents in wires, let us consider a simple experiment that can be done with magnets. [You will learn later (§ 39.3) that magnetic forces actually result from electric currents within the atoms of the magnet, but for the time being we are concerned primarily with the gross behavior of magnets.]

A certain toy consists of a set of circular magnets whose north and south poles are on the flat circular faces (Fig. 26.12). If a pencil, passed through the holes of several magnets that are oriented to repel one another, is held vertical (A), the magnets reach the equilibrium positions shown. If (B) magnet A is pushed down by hand, it exerts on B a force that pushes B downward; but simultaneously A feels an upward force due to B (and, to a lesser extent, due to D). The existence of this upward force on A can be readily demonstrated (C): if A is released, it jumps up, proving that an upward force existed.

Both gravitational and magnetic effects are acting simultaneously on any magnet of this toy. Magnet B, for example, experiences a downward force due to its weight (the gravitational attraction of the earth), the magnetic pull of D, and the downward push of A; it also feels an upward force due to C. (There are also much weaker gravitational forces between the magnets. The magnets have gravitational mass, of course, but the effect of this is very much weaker than the magnetic interactions mentioned.) As soon as A is pushed down, B momentarily feels an increase in downward force. When B gets displaced downward, the upward force of repulsion due to C increases, and B finds a new equilibrium position. Many pairs of forces to illustrate Newton's third law may be found here.

Suppose, however, that two huge magnets were very far apart—even light-years apart. If one of them suddenly approached the other, would it *immediately* feel an increased repulsive force? The question hinges, in part, on the word "immediately." In Chapter 43 we shall see that certain electromagnetic effects are propagated with speed $c = 3 \times 10^8$ m/sec. One type of difficulty encountered with Newton's third law arises from the consideration that the force exerted by body A on body B may not produce *simultaneously* an equal and opposite force on A. The speed of propagation of effects enters into the picture, and, in the case of gravitational forces, this speed is not yet known.

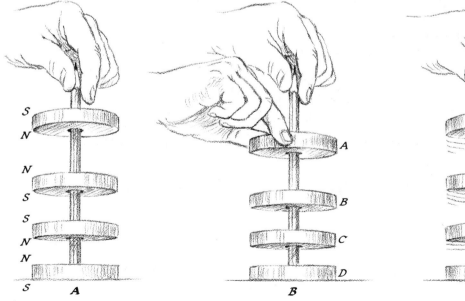
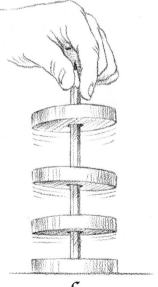

FIG. 26.12. *Circular magnets arranged to illustrate pairs of forces.*

Another type of difficulty occurs in the mathematical treatment of the force between a moving charge within a wire and free electrons outside it. The theory assumes forces of equal magnitude but not always in exactly opposite directions. It seems, then, that Newton's third law has exceptions, but for the ordinary forces of pushing and pulling between macroscopic objects not too far apart it works very well indeed.

26.5. The Concept of Inertial Reaction

I have pointed out that it does not require a force to keep a body moving with constant velocity. If a carbon dioxide puck of mass m is moving with velocity $\mathbf{v}$, no tension is needed in the string (Fig. 26.13) to keep it moving with that velocity; to accelerate the puck, however, we must apply to it a force, $\mathbf{F}$, equal to $m\mathbf{a}$. This force is supplied by tension in the string. But, while the string pulls on the puck with force $\mathbf{F}$, *the puck pulls back on the string* with force $-\mathbf{F}$. This is called the **inertial reaction.** We can now look upon the inertial mass of a body in a slightly different light. An inert mass actively resists a force applied to it, and it resists with a force that is equal in magnitude to the applied force. Whether you pull a body by a string, as in Figure 26.13, or push it by means of a compression spring, as in Figure 26.14, a body of mass m that is being accelerated

exerts a reactionary force of magnitude ma on whatever agent is pushing or pulling it.

For this reason it is not necessary to have a wall to push against, as in Figure 26.7, in order to feel

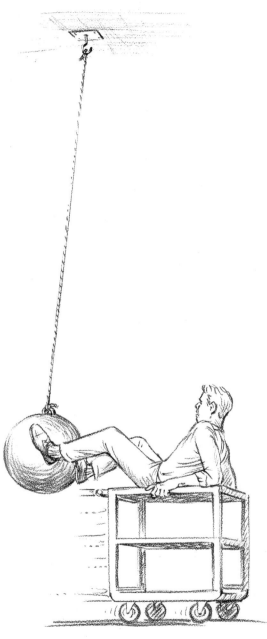

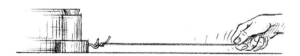

FIG. 26.13. *Inertial reaction illustrated by a frictionless puck.*

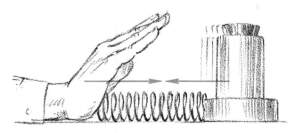

FIG. 26.14. *Inertial reaction illustrated by another frictionless puck.*

FIG. 26.15. *Inertial reaction: When the ball is accelerated to the left by a push, its inertial reaction pushes the boy to the right.*

the reaction force. You could push against any large mass resting on a frictionless surface and feel that force. Or, sitting on the cart, you could push with your feet (Fig. 26.15) against a 100-pound ball suspended by a long cable from a beam in the ceiling. The equal but opposite push felt by you would send the cart rolling to the right.

FIG. 26.16. *Inertial reaction: Since the force acting on the boy is equal and opposite to that acting on the man, their accelerations are inversely proportional to their masses.*

A similar experiment can be done by people on roller-skates. If a very light boy, of mass m_1, pushes a very heavy man, of mass m_2 (Fig. 26.16), they both feel a force of the same magnitude, F; but the acceleration of the boy is F/m_1, and the acceleration of the man is F/m_2, in magnitude.

If two sleds rest on almost frictionless ice and a boy sitting on one sled pulls a rope tied to a heavy body (for example, an automobile) on the other sled (Fig. 26.17), the sleds move in opposite directions. The boy feels the inertial reaction of the automobile whenever he pulls. If the masses are m_1 and m_2 and the corresponding accelerations are $\mathbf{a}_1$ and $\mathbf{a}_2$, the third law demands that $m_1\mathbf{a}_1 = -m_2\mathbf{a}_2$.

The reaction force that the earth exerts on buildings is probably the most important use of static reaction forces, but in the realm of dynamics the most important use of reaction forces is probably in the jet engines used to propel aircraft and missiles. I shall discuss these in detail in § 31.6. Their qualitative aspects can easily be understood in terms of Newton's third law.

A rocket expels products of combustion by pushing on them with force $\mathbf{F}_1$. By Newton's third law, they, in turn, push on the rocket (Fig. 26.18) with force $\mathbf{F}_2 = -\mathbf{F}_1$. The acceleration of the rocket is in the direction of $\mathbf{F}_2$. We need not consider $\mathbf{F}_1$, for it acts, not on the rocket, but on a different object—in this case, the combustion products. (If we call $\mathbf{F}_1$ the action, $\mathbf{F}_2$ is the reac-

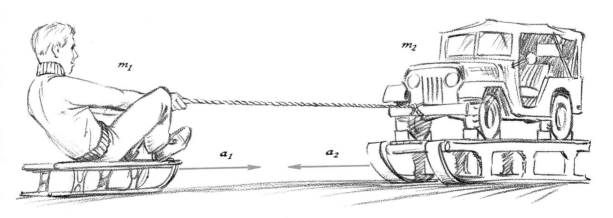

FIG. 26.17. *Inertial reaction: The accelerations of the boy-and-sled and the jeep-and-sled obey the formula* $m_1\mathbf{a}_1 = -m_2\mathbf{a}_2$.

tion, and vice-versa.) Hence a rocket does not need the earth's atmosphere to push against. It pushes against matter that it has carried with it. (See also Fig. 31.9.)

As a final example, consider a carbon dioxide puck moving in a circle under the action of the

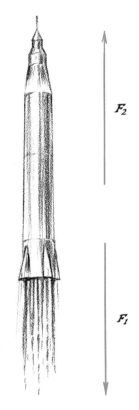

FIG. 26.18. *Inertial reaction: a reaction engine.*

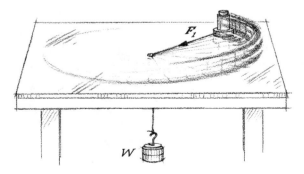

FIG. 26.19. *Inertial reaction: a carbon dioxide puck moving in a circle under the action of the tension in a string. The force exerted by the puck on the string is called the centrifugal reaction.*

tension in a string (Fig. 26.19). The string exerts a centripetal force, F_1, on the puck. (Its magnitude is equal to ma if m is the mass of the puck and a is its centripetal acceleration, defined in § 9.5.) By Newton's third law, the puck exerts a force, $F_2 = -F_1$, on the string. This is sometimes called the **centrifugal reaction**. It is the other half of a third-law pair, *but it does not act on the puck*. Strictly speaking, it is wrong to say, in an inertial frame of reference, that the puck is acted upon by both a centripetal and a centrifugal force. If it were, the vector sum of the forces acting on it would be zero, and it could move only in a straight line at constant speed.

The centrifugal reaction is, however, a real force. It creates, in the string, the tension that holds up the weight, W; but it does not act on the puck.

You may have wondered why we spend so much time on Newton's third law. The reason is that the solution to many physical problems would be impossible without it. Yet it seems to have escaped all men before Newton. If others were aware of it, they did not consider it important enough to use as one of the cornerstones of the science of mechanics. One can criticize the first law (the law of inertia) by saying that it is simply a corollary of the second law (corresponding to $f = 0$, from which it follows that $a = 0$ or v is a constant). One can criticize the second law by saying that it is just a definition, either of force in terms of mass and acceleration or of mass in terms of force and acceleration. Anyone who studies the great range of applicability of the third law, however, must pause to honor the genius of Newton.

26.6. Summary

Newton's third law says that, whenever one body exerts a force upon a second body, the second exerts an equal and opposite force upon the first. The two bodies might be the sun and the earth, or a tennis ball and a racket, or a rocket and the gas it expels. The term "body" applies equally well to atomic particles and to aggregates of these in any of the three states of matter. Interactions at levels all the way from the atomic to the astronomical require an understanding of this fundamental law.

Problems

26.1. Assume, in Fig. 26.1, that m_1 is 1.4 kg and m_2 is 2.5 kg. At a certain instant during the collision, ball A feels a force, due to impact with B, of 85 nt to the left. At that instant what is the acceleration of ball B? What is the direction of this acceleration?

26.2. Ten men are trying to break a rope by pulling on it. At first two teams of five men each take the ends of the rope and pull against each other; then one end of the rope is fastened to a brick wall, and all ten men pull on the other end. In which case will they be able to exert the greater force? Explain in terms of Newton's third law.

26.3. Assume, in Fig. 26.3, that the maximum frictional force is 5.25 nt and that the pull of the rope is 7.63 nt.

1. If the weight of the block is 8.04 nt, what is the magnitude of the resultant force exerted by the block on the table? Using the value $g = 9.80$ m/sec², express your result to three significant figures.

2. Repeat the problem for the case where all other factors remain the same but the pull of the rope is 8.37 nt.

26.4. A conveyor belt is moving a block of wood up an inclined plane at a constant speed without slipping. The belt exerts two forces on the block. One is the normal reaction, and the other is friction. Draw a diagram. The block weighs 9.56 nt, the coefficient of static friction is 0.57, and the angle of inclination is 10°. Find the magnitude of the resultant force exerted by the block on the belt. (Fig. 26.4 may be used for reference although it does not show a conveyor belt.)

26.5. In Fig. 26.7 the force exerted by the boy on the wall is 125 nt. The combined mass of the cart and boy is 132 kg. The total retarding force on the cart is 27 nt.

1. Calculate the acceleration of the cart.

2. If this acceleration can be kept constant while the cart travels a distance of 0.63 m, what speed will the cart pick up?

26.6. While being accelerated to the right the wagon (Fig. 26.8) pulls back on the horse with a force of 1,750 nt. The acceleration of the wagon is 1.86 m/sec². The mass of the wagon is 525 kg. What is the magnitude of the retarding force on the wagon alone?

26.7. A large prism of wood whose cross-section is a right triangle sits on a horizontal table so that the hypotenuse is an inclined plane on which a rectangular block can slide. (The arrangement resembles that of Fig. 26.4.A, but remember that both prism and block are free to move.) Assume that all surfaces are frictionless.

1. Describe the motion of the prism when the block is placed on it and released.

2. What is the direction of the vector sum of all the forces acting on the prism? (Hint: Isolate the block, and analyze the forces acting on it; then isolate the prism, and consider all the forces acting on it.)

3. If the prism were very much lighter than the block, what would be the result?

26.8. In Fig. 26.9 the frictional force acting on the boy is 250 nt. The mass of the boy is 56 kg. The mass of the car is 10^4 kg, and it was moving at a speed of 2.5 m/sec before the boy landed. What will be the change in the car's speed if the frictional force acts for four seconds? Try to solve the problem without recourse to the formulas of § 26.3. Begin, for example, with the fact that $\Delta v = a(\Delta t)$.

26.9. Two boys are tossing a heavy ball to each other as they stand near opposite ends of a stationary flatcar similar to that of Fig. 26.9 but very much lighter than a real flatcar. Assume that there is good traction between their soles and the flatcar. Describe the forces acting on the boys and the resulting changes of motion of the flatcar, as the ball is caught and thrown, if the possible motion of flatcar is not retarded by friction.

26.10. Let the mass of the ball in Fig. 26.15 be 100 kg. The combined mass of cart and boy is 86 kg. The boy exerts an average force of 175 nt on the ball for 2 sec. If the cart starts from rest, what will be its maximum speed?

26.11. 1. What would be the radius of the circle traversed by the center of mass of the sun if it had only the planet earth pulling on it? The mass of the sun is 390,000 times that of the earth.

2. If the earth made one revolution every 365 days and moved in a circle of radius 93 million miles, how long would it take the sun to complete its circular journey?

26.12. In Fig. 26.19 the inertial reaction of the Dry Ice puck on the string supports the weight of the object hanging from the string beneath the table. The mass of the puck is 1.5 kg. It moves in a circle of radius 45 cm, making one revolution every 2.2 sec. What is the mass of the hanging object if it is in equilibrium under these circumstances?

Potential and Kinetic Energy

WE ARE now ready to return to the ideas of potential and kinetic energy, first introduced in Chapter 6. During this second turn round the learning spiral we shall put these concepts on a more solid mathematical basis. This does not necessarily mean that we shall get deeply involved in mathematical manipulations. Wherever possible, on the contrary, and with a minimum of formal mathematics, we shall use graphical interpretations to help us grasp, conceptually, the essence of the matter.

27.1. Work and Power

The formal definition of work has been stated mathematically (§ 6.3) as follows: $W = \mathbf{F} \cdot \mathbf{d}$. The work done by force $\mathbf{F}$ acting through displacement $\mathbf{d}$ is the scalar product of the vectors $\mathbf{F}$ and $\mathbf{d}$. We recall that this may also be written as

$$W = \mathbf{F} \cdot \mathbf{d} = Fd \cos \theta \qquad [27.1$$

The angle θ is the angle between the directions of the two vectors. The product $Fd \cos \theta$ has two physical interpretations: one arises from considering it as $(F \cos \theta)d$, the other from considering it as $(d \cos \theta)F$.

Let us interpret $(F \cos \theta)d$ first. Figure 27.1.A represents a ship as moving northward through displacement $\mathbf{d}$ while under the force of a wind, $\mathbf{F}$, blowing toward the northwest. $F \cos \theta$ is simply the northward component of $\mathbf{F}$; for, if we ask,

"What part of $\mathbf{F}$ is effective in the $\mathbf{d}$ direction?" the answer is "$F \cos \theta$." If we multiply the effective part of $\mathbf{F}$ by the displacement, we get $(F \cos \theta)d$, which is the work done by $\mathbf{F}$.

In Figure 27.1.B the ship moves northeast through displacement $\mathbf{d}$. The force, $\mathbf{F}$, of the wind is due north. If we ask, "What is the effective part of $\mathbf{d}$ in the $\mathbf{F}$ direction?" the answer is $d \cos \theta$. If we multiply the effective part of $\mathbf{d}$ by $\mathbf{F}$, we get $(d \cos \theta)F$, which is, again, the work done.

It is instructive to consider under what circumstances no work is done. The product $Fd \cos \theta$ vanishes if one or more of the terms F, d, and $\cos \theta$ vanish; that is, $W = 0$ if at least one of the following is zero: F, d, $\cos \theta$. In Figure 25.1, for example, a block resting on a table is fastened to a chain of rubber bands. When the chain is slack, it exerts no force on the block. In that case, since $\mathbf{F} = \mathbf{0}$, $W = 0$. When the rubber-band chain is first stretched, it does exert a force on the block, but, because of friction, there is no displacement; since $\mathbf{d} = \mathbf{0}$, it remains true that $W = 0$. In Figure 26.19 a carbon dioxide puck, pulled by the tension, $\mathbf{F}_1$, of the string, moves in a circle. If it moves with a constant angular velocity, the magnitude of $\mathbf{F}_1$ is constant; but, since the infinitesimal displacements are always at right angles to $\mathbf{F}$, angle $\theta = 90°$ and $\cos \theta = 0$. The force does no work because it is perpendicular to the displacement.

In the MKS system the basic unit of work is the **joule** (J), which is the same as the newton-meter.

The physical dimensions of work are ML^2T^{-2}. **Power** is the rate at which work is done. If work ΔW is done in time Δt, the average power, P, is $\Delta W/\Delta t$. One **watt** (W) is one joule per second.

EXAMPLE 27.1. A force of 5 nt inclined at an angle of 30° to the horizontal (Fig. 24.10) pulls on a block that rests on a horizontal table. We wish to know what is the average power expended if a horizontal displacement of 2 m takes place in 0.5 sec.

$$P = \frac{\Delta W}{\Delta t} = \frac{(F\cos\theta)d}{\Delta t} = \frac{5\text{ nt} \times \cos 30° \times 2\text{ m}}{0.5\text{ sec}}$$

$$= \frac{5 \times 0.866 \times 2}{0.5}\frac{\text{J}}{\text{sec}}$$

$$= 17.32\text{ W}$$

We may also write

$$P = \frac{\Delta W}{\Delta t} = \frac{\mathbf{F}\cdot\Delta\mathbf{d}}{\Delta t} = \mathbf{F}\cdot\frac{\Delta\mathbf{d}}{\Delta t} = \mathbf{F}\cdot\bar{\mathbf{v}}$$

It can be shown that, if we use the instantaneous power,

$$\lim_{\Delta t\to 0}\frac{\Delta W}{\Delta t}$$

instead of the average power, $\Delta W/\Delta t$, and if $\mathbf{v}$ represents the instantaneous velocity, the formula $\mathbf{F}\cdot\mathbf{v}$ is exact. If $\mathbf{F}$ and $\mathbf{v}$ are in the same direction, we may, of course, dispense with the vector notation and write simply $P = Fv$.

27.2. Work Done by a Force in an Unaccelerated System

Suppose that a block is being pulled along at *constant velocity* on a horizontal table (as in Fig. 25.1). Isolating the block, we see that four forces are acting on it: $m\mathbf{g}$, $\mathbf{N}$, $\mathbf{F}$ (the tension of the rubber-band chain), and $\mathbf{f}$ (the force of friction). The vector sum is zero. The work done by any one of these forces during displacement $\mathbf{d}$ along the table can be calculated from equation 27.1.

Because $\mathbf{F}\cdot\mathbf{d}$ is positive ($\theta = 0°$, $\cos\theta = 1$), we say that $\mathbf{F}$ does positive work on the block. Similarly, because $\mathbf{f}\cdot\mathbf{d}$ is negative ($\theta = 180°$, $\cos\theta = -1$), we say that $\mathbf{f}$ does negative work on the block. Notice that, because the forces $\mathbf{N}$ and $m\mathbf{g}$ are perpendicular to the displacement, each does no work on the block. The procedure is straightforward: to find how much work a force, $\mathbf{F}$, does in displacement $\mathbf{d}$, we simply form the scalar product, $\mathbf{F}\cdot\mathbf{d}$, of the two vectors.

What about the work done by the reaction force mentioned in Newton's third law? The block pulls on the rubber-band chain with force $\mathbf{F}' = -\mathbf{F}$. The work done *by the block on the chain* is therefore $\mathbf{F}'\cdot\mathbf{d}$, which comes out, of course, as the negative of the work done by the chain on the block.

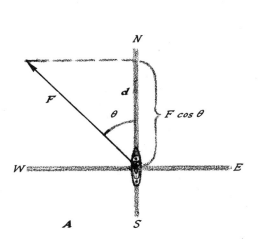

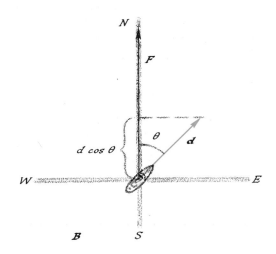

FIG. 27.1. *The movements of a ship as illustrations of the definition of work.*

We have been considering a force exerted by means of a physical object (the rubber-band chain). There are forces, such as gravity, that act without chains to pull or rods to push. Let us calculate the work done by gravity in a simple example.

A block is being moved upward at a *constant velocity* along an inclined plane (Fig. 27.2.A) by force F_1, which is parallel to the plane; F_2 is the frictional force. What work is done by gravity, mg, during upward displacement **d** along the plane? The answer is mg·**d**. Now, if the angle of inclination of the plane is 30°, the angle between the vectors mg and **d** is 120°. (It may be easier to see, instead, that the angle between F_2 and mg is 60°; compare an appropriate pair of similar triangles.) Therefore

$$m\mathbf{g}\cdot\mathbf{d} = mgd \cos 120° = -\tfrac{1}{2}mgd$$

The work done on the block by gravity is negative. By similar reasoning, the work done on the block by gravity as the block moves downward along the plane at a constant velocity (Fig. 27.2.B) is positive, for the angle between mg and the displacement, **d**′ (pointing down the plane), is 60°, and the cosine of 60° is positive.

If the block is moved first from A to B and then back from B to A, the total work done on the block by gravity will be zero, for the negative work done on the block by gravity on the way up is numerically equal to the positive work done on the block by gravity on the way down. Forces that behave in this way—so that the total work done by them during a round trip is zero—are called

conservative forces. A system in which only conservative forces act is called a **conservative system.**

Let us now consider the work done by friction. On the block's way up, friction, F_2, points down the plane. The work done by friction is therefore

$$\mathbf{F_2}\cdot\mathbf{d} = F_2 d \cos 180° = -F_2 d$$

On the block's way down, friction, F_2', points up the plane, and the displacement, **d**′, points down the plane. The work done by friction is

$$\mathbf{F_2}'\cdot\mathbf{d}' = F_2' d' \cos 180° = -F_2' d'$$

The total work done by friction during a round trip is not zero: friction is not a conservative force. The total work done by friction is always negative.

So far we have dealt with forces that remain constant throughout the motion. Consider now the work required to move a bead along a stiff wire, OB, of variable slope, as in Figure 27.3, at a constant speed. Suppose that **F** is a force along the tangent to the curve.† As motion along the very small arc Δs takes place along the curve, the work done by force **F** is $F\Delta s$. Since the force and the displacement are in the same direction, we have dropped the vector notation. This is an approximation that gets better as Δs gets smaller and approaches a rectilinear displacement in the direction of **F**. A plot of F against s is shown in Figure 27.4. We find the total work done by F in moving the bead from A to B (Fig. 27.3) by considering

† You will see, if you are careful, that, as the block moves along arc AB, even at constant speed, there must be a centripetal component of force. This acts along the same line as **N**.

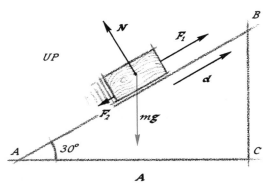

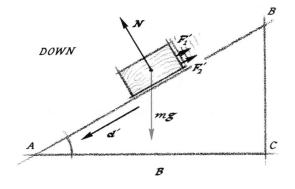

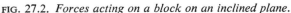

FIG. 27.2. *Forces acting on a block on an inclined plane.*

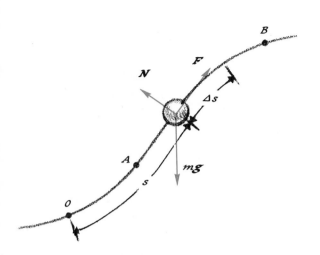

FIG. 27.3. *It takes a force,* **F**, *of variable magnitude and direction to move a bead up along an incline (a stiff wire,* **OB**) *of variable slope at constant speed. The work done in an infinitesimal displacement,* Δs, *is* F(Δs). *The total work done in moving a finite distance is simply the sum of the infinitesimal increments of work.*

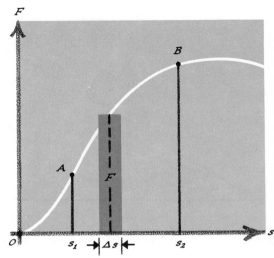

FIG. 27.4. *The exact value of the work done by the variable force* F *between* s_1 *and* s_2 *is equal to the area bounded by the curve of* F *against* s, *the* s *axis, and the lines at* A *and* B. *An infinitesimal increment in work is depicted by the area of the rectangle with base* Δs *and altitude* F.

the sum (indicated by the symbol Σ) of all the small increments of work done:

$$W = \Sigma F \Delta s = F_1(\Delta s)_1 + F_2(\Delta s)_2 + F_3(\Delta s)_3 + \ldots$$

The exact value of the total work done by F is equal to the area (Fig. 27.4) bounded by the curve of F against s, the s axis, and the lines at A and B (provided we use the proper units for F and s).

I shall not take the trouble to evaluate the work done in this case. I simply wanted to show how work is computed when the force is variable. We compute the area under the curve of F against s.

27.3. Work Done by the Resultant Force in an Accelerated System

Suppose that the vector sum of the forces we are considering is not zero. In Figure 25.1, for example, suppose that **F** is numerically greater than **f**. There is a net unbalanced force, and the block accelerates to the right. The net unbalanced force is

$$\mathbf{F'} = \mathbf{N} + m\mathbf{g} + \mathbf{F} + \mathbf{f}$$

The acceleration is

$$\mathbf{a} = \frac{\mathbf{F'}}{m} \qquad [27.2$$

Since $\mathbf{N} + m\mathbf{g} = 0$, we may write this as

$$\mathbf{a} = \frac{\mathbf{F} + \mathbf{f}}{m} \qquad [27.3$$

Now consider the work done by **F'** in a positive displacement, **x**, starting from rest. Since $\theta = 0°$,

$$W = \mathbf{F'} \cdot \mathbf{x} = F'x = (ma)x \qquad [27.4$$

If the final velocity is v, we know that $v^2 = 2ax$ (§ 8.4); therefore $ax = v^2/2$. Putting this into equation 27.4, we get

$$W = \frac{mv^2}{2} \qquad [27.5$$

We have derived the formula for kinetic energy by considering the work done by the resultant of all the forces acting on a body. This formula was given without proof in § 6.7. The important difference, here, is that we have not asked what work was done by **F** (or **f** or **N** or $m\mathbf{g}$); we have asked what work was done by the *net unbalanced force* acting on the object.

We can arrive at a more general result as follows. Let the work done by a force, **F**, moving a body through any small displacement, Δ**d**, be ΔW:

$$\Delta W = \mathbf{F} \cdot \Delta \mathbf{d} \qquad [27.6$$

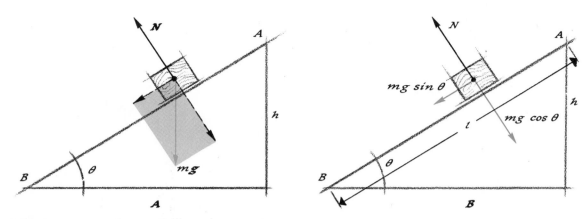

FIG. 27.5. (A) A block sliding down a frictionless plane is acted upon by two forces: its weight, mg, and the reaction of the plane, N. (B) To simplify the analysis, we replace mg by its components: along the plane, mg sin θ; perpendicular to it, mg cos θ. The effects of N and mg cos θ cancel out. The work done is simply (mg sin θ)l.

Using the equation $\mathbf{F} = m(\Delta\mathbf{v}/\Delta t)$, we get

$$\Delta W = m\frac{\Delta\mathbf{v}}{\Delta t} \cdot \Delta\mathbf{d} \qquad [27.7$$

or

$$\Delta W = m(\Delta\mathbf{v}) \cdot \frac{\Delta\mathbf{d}}{\Delta t} \qquad [27.8$$

We recognize $\Delta\mathbf{d}/\Delta t$ as the average velocity and $\Delta\mathbf{v}$ as the increment in velocity. Therefore, if $\mathbf{v}_1$ stands for initial velocity and $\mathbf{v}_2$ for final velocity,

$$\Delta W = m(\mathbf{v}_2 - \mathbf{v}_1) \cdot \frac{\mathbf{v}_2 + \mathbf{v}_1}{2} \qquad [27.9$$

We know that $(\mathbf{v}_1 + \mathbf{v}_2)/2$ is precisely the average velocity only when the acceleration is constant; but, even when the acceleration is not constant, that expression is an approximation that gets better as Δt approaches 0. We can therefore write, quite generally,

$$\Delta W = \frac{m}{2}\left(v_2{}^2 - \mathbf{v}_1 \cdot \mathbf{v}_2 + \mathbf{v}_1 \cdot \mathbf{v}_2 - v_1{}^2\right)$$

or

$$\Delta W = \frac{mv_2{}^2}{2} - \frac{mv_1{}^2}{2} \qquad [27.10$$

We recognize the right-hand side as the increment in the kinetic energy of the body. *The total work done by the net unbalanced force on a body is equal to the increment in the body's kinetic energy:*

$$\Delta W = \Delta K \qquad [27.11$$

This equation has important implications. We saw earlier that the work done by gravity on a block starting at A, going to B, and coming back to A is zero because the negative work done by gravity on the way up is exactly balanced by the positive work done by gravity on the way down. In the complete round trip, therefore, the total work done by gravity is zero. In symbols, $\Delta W = 0$; and therefore, if there is no friction, so that gravity is the only force doing work, ΔK is also zero; that is, the kinetic energy is the same at the end of the round trip as at the beginning if no force other than gravity acts. We have here another criterion for conservative force: *if a body moves under the action of a conservative force, its kinetic energy is the same at the end of a round trip as at the beginning.*

Here is an example in which gravity is the only force that does work on a body: A block slides down a frictionless inclined plane (Fig. 27.5.A). At A its speed, pointing down the plane, is v_1. What is its speed, v_2, at B? The net unbalanced force is $mg \sin\theta$ (Fig. 27.5.B). The work done by it is $(mg \sin\theta)l$ if l is the length of the incline. Therefore $\Delta K = \Delta W = (mg \sin\theta)l$.

$$\tfrac{1}{2}mv_2{}^2 - \tfrac{1}{2}mv_1{}^2 = (mg \sin\theta)l \qquad [27.12$$

You may have noticed that

$$\sin\theta = \frac{h}{l} \qquad [27.13$$

Therefore

$$\tfrac{1}{2}mv_2{}^2 - \tfrac{1}{2}mv_1{}^2 = mgh \qquad [27.14$$

The final speed, v_2, can be computed from equation 27.14. Note that the physical dimensions of mgh are ML^2T^{-2}, as we should expect from an examination of the left-hand side. We recognize mgh as the gravitational potential energy of the body at the top of the incline. Since the gravitational potential energy at the bottom is zero, mgh can be thought of as the amount of potential energy lost by the body in going from A to B. In this example, clearly, the gain in kinetic energy is equal to the loss in potential energy. I shall have more to say about this shortly.

27.4. Potential Energy

Consider a system consisting of two bodies. If the relative positions of the bodies are changed, we say that the configuration has changed. Similar remarks apply to a system consisting of many bodies. The energy that such a system has because of its configuration is called the potential energy of the system (see § 6.8). Even a single body, such as a lump of clay, may be considered a system made up of many smaller parts. A change in the shape of the lump of clay would be a change in the configuration of the system. The energy that such a body has because of its shape is potential energy (see § 6.8).

It is sometimes easy to see that the potential energy of a system is increased. The system shown in Figure 27.6, for example, consisting of the earth (with its center at O) and a rocket, has greater potential energy when the rocket is at B than when it is at A. (We assume that O, A, and B are all on a straight line.) The *applied force* that moved the rocket from A to B did positive work. At B the rocket feels the force of gravity pulling it toward A. A body tends to move to a position of lower potential energy.

The system shown in Figure 27.7, consisting of a spring, has greater potential energy in case B than in case A. The force applied to the spring by the hands does positive work in stretching it. Since the system shown in B, if released, would begin to return to the state shown in A, it must have had a greater potential energy than that of A.

In both figures the force involved is variable. In Figure 27.6 it decreases with distance; in Figure 27.7 it increases with distance. Let us see how to calculate the work done when the force is variable.

We consider the spring first. (In the following, vector notation will not be used, for force and displacement are in the same or in opposite directions.) We know (§ 25.6) that the force, F, exerted *by the spring* obeys the equation $F = -kx$ if x is the elongation. The applied force that stretches the spring in opposition to F is $F_a = -F$. The work done in stretching the spring by the small positive increment Δx is therefore $F_a(\Delta x)$. Since $F_a = -F = kx$, the graph of F_a against x is a straight line (Fig. 27.8). The total work done in stretching the spring from O to x_1 is proportional to the total area between O and $x_1 A$ and below the line representing the equation $F_a = kx$, for, as we

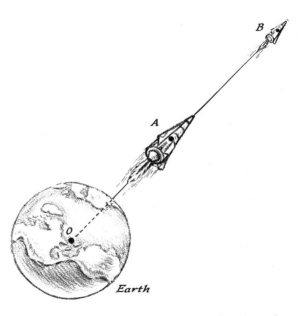

FIG. 27.6. *A system consisting of the earth and a rocket.*

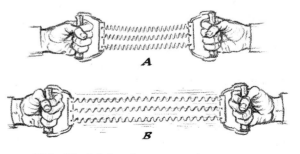

FIG. 27.7. *Work being done on a spring.*

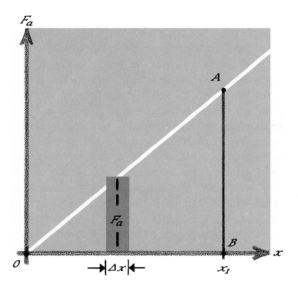

FIG. 27.8. *Graphical illustration of the work done on the spring of Fig. 27.7.*

saw in § 27.2, it must be the limit of the sum of all the quantities like $F_a(\Delta x)$. In symbols we write

$$W \cong (F_a)_1(\Delta x)_1 + (F_a)_2(\Delta x)_2 \\ + (F_a)_3(\Delta x)_3 + \ldots \quad [27.15$$

The approximation becomes exact if we pass to the limit, which is simply the area of the triangle OAB. The base of this triangle is $OB = x_1$, and the altitude is BA (the value of F_a at x_1) $= kx_1$. The area of the triangle is therefore

$$\tfrac{1}{2}(x_1)(kx_1) = \tfrac{1}{2}kx_1{}^2$$

This is the amount by which the potential energy of the spring has increased as the spring stretched from O to x_1.

A variable force is also involved in moving a body from A to B in the earth's gravitational field (Fig. 27.6), and in Chapter 34 we shall accurately calculate the work done; for the moment let us consider lifting a body only a short distance above the surface of the earth. Notice (Fig. 27.9) that, when a body of mass m is raised from A to B, the work done *by gravity* is $m\mathbf{g} \cdot \mathbf{h} = -mgh$. The work done *against gravity*—that is, the work done by the *applied force* (without acceleration)—is therefore $(-m\mathbf{g}) \cdot \mathbf{h} = mgh$. The potential energy of the body has been increased by the amount mgh.

Now suppose that the body is released from position B. It falls toward A and gains kinetic energy. Its final velocity just before hitting the

ground obeys the equation $v^2 = 2gh$; its kinetic energy then is therefore

$$\tfrac{1}{2}mv^2 = \tfrac{1}{2}m(2gh) = mgh$$

In falling from B to A the body gets back as kinetic energy the exact equal of the potential energy it gained in rising from A to B. Its energy at B was, literally, potential—that is, was available.

A conservative force (such as gravity or the force exerted by a stretched or compressed spring) is, we see, one that behaves in such a way that the potential energy, U, of the system in which the force acts is related to the kinetic energy, K, of that system† by the equation

$$\Delta U = -(\Delta K) \quad [27.16$$

The gain in potential energy is always equal to the loss in kinetic energy. This is true only for conservative forces. If the initial potential energy is U_0 and the final potential energy is U, equation 27.16 becomes

$$U - U_0 = -(\tfrac{1}{2}mv^2 - \tfrac{1}{2}mv_0{}^2) \quad [27.17$$

This may be written as

$$U + \tfrac{1}{2}mv^2 = U_0 + \tfrac{1}{2}mv_0{}^2 \quad [27.18$$

This says that *the sum of potential and kinetic energies at one point in a conservative system is equal to the sum of potential and kinetic energies at any other point in that system.* Since this sum is a constant, we may symbolize it by E. The equation

$$U + K = E \quad [27.19$$

is an expression of the law of the conservation of mechanical energy.

The formula for kinetic energy, $\tfrac{1}{2}mv^2$, holds in all cases where v is much less than the speed of light, but no single formula for potential energy holds in all cases. If, for example, we set the zero of gravitational potential energy at the surface of the earth (as, for practical reasons, we usually do), the expression mgh expresses the potential energy of a body of mass m lifted to height h above the ground provided h is much shorter than the earth's radius. The potential energy of a spring, however, is $\tfrac{1}{2}kx^2$. The formula for potential energy depends, obviously, upon the nature of the conservative force we are dealing with. Usually we are con-

† From now on let us use the generally accepted symbols U and K instead of the abbreviations (PE and KE) used earlier.

cerned with *differences* in potential energy, and the addition of an arbitrary constant to the potential-energy function does not affect its usefulness. If, for example, we write $U_0 + c$ and $U + c$ instead of U_0 and U, respectively, the difference $(U_0 + c) - (U + c)$ is simply $U_0 - U$; the constant drops out in subtraction.

We must remember that only for conservative forces do we have a potential-energy function.

From equation 27.16, since $\Delta K = \Delta W$, we obtain, for the one-dimensional case, the equation

$$\Delta U = -(\Delta W) = -F_c(\Delta x)$$

which says that, if a conservative force, F_c, is the only force that acts, the work, ΔW, that it does in the one-dimensional displacement Δx is $F_c(\Delta x)$. This equation may be rewritten as

$$F_c = -\frac{\Delta U}{\Delta x} \qquad [27.20$$

an expression that has a useful interpretation. (Equation 27.20 leads to a statement found in more advanced texts: a conservative force is derivable from a potential function.)

Consider, for example, the potential energy of a spring, of force constant k (see § 3.2), that is stretched through distance x. The formula is $U = \frac{1}{2}kx^2$. The plot of U against x is shown in Figure 27.10. The geometrical interpretation of $\Delta U/\Delta x$ is the *slope of a secant line to the curve.* (Strictly speaking, we should take

$$\lim_{\Delta x \to 0} \frac{\Delta U}{\Delta x}$$

which is the slope of a tangent line.) At a point like A, to the right of the U axis, this slope positive. Therefore F_c is negative when x is positive. At a point like B, to the left of the U axis where x is negative, $\Delta U/\Delta x$ is negative, and F_c therefore positive. The force always points to the position of equilibrium.

Because the system is conservative,

$$U + K = E$$

Since the ordinate of Figure 27.10 is U (see point B), the distance from a point on the curve up to the line $U = E$ must be K, for $U + K = E$ everywhere. At point C, we notice, $K = 0$. This implies that $\frac{1}{2}mv^2 = 0$, or that the speed is zero. At the same time we notice that for points on the curve corresponding to values of x between $-x_1$ and x_1

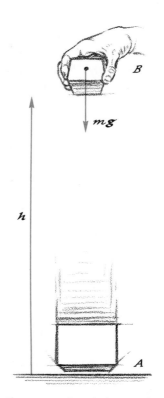

FIG. 27.9. *Illustration of work done against gravity and by gravity.*

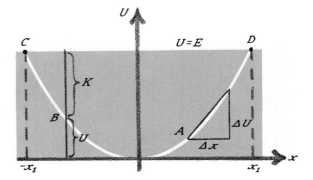

FIG. 27.10. *The potential energy, U, of a spring is a function of elongation,* x. *At a typical point such as* B *the length of the segment from* B *to the line* CD *represents the kinetic energy,* K, *since* U + K = E. *The ratio* ΔU/Δx *represents the slope of a secant line at* A. *The limit of this is the slope of the tangent line at* A. *The sign of the force* F_c *is opposite to that of* ΔU/Δx.

the slope, $\Delta U/\Delta x$, is largest (in absolute value) at C (also at D). The interpretation is that, as a body moving under the influence of the conservative force in question comes to rest ($v = 0$) at $-x_1$, it experiences a great positive force there. Hence it is accelerated to the right, losing potential energy and gaining kinetic energy. At $x = 0$ we find that $U = 0$ and therefore that $K = E$, its maximum value. With the high positive value of v the body has there, it moves to the right, but now the force is negative ($F_c = -(\Delta U)/\Delta x$) and slows the body down. At D, we see, $K = 0$, and $U = E$, and the force, which has reached its greatest negative value, starts moving the body to the left, to repeat the cycle. The potential-energy curve of Figure 27.10 is characteristic of simple harmonic motion.

We can learn a great deal by studying the shape of a potential-energy graph. See, for example, the curve of Figure 27.11, which represents a potential-energy function. Consider point B. The ordinate AB is U; the length BC therefore represents K (since $U + K = E$). This implies that the body under consideration is in motion, for $\frac{1}{2}mv^2$ is not zero. It doesn't tell us the direction of v, for v^2 is positive, and v could therefore be either positive or negative. Let us assume that v is positive. This means that the body is moving to the right, but the force, since it is negative ($F_c = -(\Delta U)/\Delta x$, the

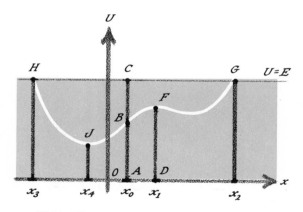

FIG. 27.11. *The potential energy,* U, *of a hypothetical system plotted against the displacement,* x. *It is possible to analyze the motion by an examination of this curve. Wherever the slope is zero, for example, as at* J *and* F, *the force, and hence the acceleration, is zero. At the typical point* B, *AB represents the potential energy, and BC represents the kinetic energy. The kinetic energy is zero at* H *and* G. *The velocity must be zero at these points.*

slope being positive near B), is slowing the body down. At x_1 the slope is instantaneously zero, and therefore F_c is momentarily zero, but the velocity is still positive.

You should pursue the analysis carefully to x_2, all the way back to x_3, and back again to x_0. The fact that the curve meets the line $U = E$ at H and G implies that a cyclic motion takes place between x_3 and x_2; but it is definitely not a simple harmonic motion, for the velocity has a relative maximum at x_1 and a relative minimum at x_4.

We shall run into potential-energy curves in many applications, from the gravitational field of the sun to the field that surrounds an atomic nucleus. We shall find that, if $\Delta U/\Delta x$ is positive when x is positive, F_c is an attractive force, but that, if $\Delta U/\Delta x$ is negative when x is positive, F_c is a repulsive force.

27.5. Summary

There is a single formula for the kinetic energy of a body moving with speed v. It is $\frac{1}{2}mv^2$ (if v is much less than the speed of light). There is, on the other hand, no single formula for the potential energy of a system, which depends on the nature of the force involved in the change of shape or configuration of the system. Gravitational potential energy, for example (for a body near the surface of the earth), can be expressed as mgh; the potential energy of a stretched spring is $\frac{1}{2}kx^2$. Other formulas hold for other types of force.

A simple relation that permits the solution of many problems of motion holds for a conservative system: the sum of the potential and kinetic energies at any point is equal to the sum of the potential and kinetic energies at any other point. A conservative system is one in which only conservative forces act. One criterion for a conservative force is this: the total work done by the force during a round trip must be zero. Another criterion is this: if a body moves under the action of a conservative force, its kinetic energy must be the same at the end of the round trip as at the start. In a conservative system the gain in potential energy is equal to the loss in kinetic energy. Real systems can be only approximately conservative, for they involve friction.

Problems

27.1. A grocer stacks six identical boxes one on top of another. Each has a mass of 10 kg and a thickness of 0.4 m.

1. Calculate, in joules, how much work he does in stacking them by adding the work done to lift the second box on top of the first, the third on top of the second, and so on.

2. Calculate the potential energy of the stack, using the formula mgh, in which m is the total mass and h is the height of the center of mass above the ground.

3. Why don't you get the same result from the two calculations?

27.2. A locomotive was about to push a flatcar. A giant intervened and put his back against the locomotive and his feet against the flatcar. In this way the locomotive succeeded in pushing the car a kilometer or so down the track. The giant was exerting a force of several thousand newtons all the time. The giant actually pushed the flatcar with great force over a long distance. The question is this: did he actually do work? (If the giant had not intervened, the locomotive would have had no difficulty in pushing the flatcar.)

27.3. When ships go through the Panama Canal, they are usually pulled through the locks by specially made locomotives that run on each side of the locks. Suppose that a small ship is being pulled by two of these locomotives, one on each side of the lock. Cables run from each locomotive to the bow of the ship, making angles of 45° with the walls of the lock (and the direction of movement of the ship). The tension in each of the two cables is 10,000 nt, and the forward velocity of the ship is 1 m/sec.

1. Analyze one of the cables, and calculate the power it delivers.

2. Calculate both the resultant force due to the two cables and the total power delivered to the ship.

3. Is the power calculated in part 1 half of the power calculated in part 2? Explain.

27.4. A sled is moved horizontally for a distance of 3 m by a force of 125 nt in a rope inclined at an angle of 30° to the horizontal.

1. What is the horizontal component of the force?

2. What is the work done by the horizontal component?

3. What is the vertical component of the force?

4. What is the work done by the vertical component?

5. Compute directly the work done, using the formula

$$W = \mathbf{F} \cdot \mathbf{d} = Fd \cos \theta$$

27.5. A boy pulls on a rope in a game of tug-of-war with a force of 250 nt. The teams are so well matched that, for a whole minute, the boy does not move. Compute the work done by the boy during that minute, using the formula

$$W = \mathbf{F} \cdot \mathbf{d} = Fd \cos \theta$$

27.6. A Dry Ice puck weighing 5 nt moves along a horizontal surface at a constant speed of 13 cm/sec for a distance of 3.5 m. How much work was done on the puck by the force of gravity?

27.7. A bale of hay weighing 495 nt is being lifted vertically at a speed of 0.65 m/sec by a rope going over a pulley and attached to a horse.

1. What power in watts is being expended?

2. Express this in horsepower (746 W = 1 hp).

3. Do you think a man could deliver more than 1 hp? Explain.

27.8. A 30-lb chimpanzee can climb to the top of a 150-ft tree in 20 sec. Find the average power output in horsepower (1 hp = 550 ft-lb/sec).

27.9. Let the inclination of the board in Fig. 27.2.A be 36° and the weight of the block be 12 nt. The block is pulled through a distance of 1.8 m by a force, F_1, of 9.87 nt at a constant speed against the force of friction.

1. What is the coefficient of kinetic friction in this case?

2. What is the work done by the force of friction?

27.10. In a situation similar to that of Fig. 27.2.B (with F_1' equal to **0**), consider the angle of inclination to be 25°. The block slides freely down the incline of length 0.85 m at a constant speed. It has a mass of 575 gm.

1. How much work is done on the block by gravity?

2. How much work is done on the block by the normal reaction, **N**, during the same time?

3. If the block is pulled up along the inclined plane at a constant speed and later permitted to slide down the plane at constant speed, what is the total work done by friction during the round trip?

27.11. A wire is bent into the shape of curve *HJBFG* of Fig. 27.11. A bead of mass 20 gm is permitted to slide without friction along this wire.

1. The bead is started at position *G* and released from rest. It passes the point *B* at a certain speed. On the return trip from *H* toward *G*, will its speed at *B* be the same as it was when it was going to the left?

2. In practice, with friction present, the speed at *B* as the bead moves to the left is 0.35 m/sec. On the return trip its speed at *B* is 0.31 m/sec. If the distance along the wire from *B* to the highest point reached near *H* is 0.67 m, what, in newtons, is the average force of friction acting on the bead?

27.12. A spring has a stiffness constant of 50 nt/m.
1. Determine graphically the amount of work required to stretch it from a position 0.90 m from equilibrium to a position 1.7 m from equilibrium. Do this by plotting the force against distance and determining the area under the curve.

2. Now recalculate the work by finding the difference in potential energy, and show that the answer is the same.

27.13. The first U.S. orbiting solar-observatory satellite had a mass of 208 kg and an orbital radius of 6,940 km. It made a complete orbit every 96 min. Calculate its kinetic energy.

27.14. A ball of mass 0.25 kg is thrown straight up with a speed of 3.7 m/sec.

1. Using the concepts behind equation 27.19, discuss how high the ball will go (assuming no friction).

2. Calculate its speed at a point halfway up.

27.15. In which regions of the curve *HJBFG* (Fig. 27.11) is $\Delta U/\Delta x$ negative? What does this indicate about the direction of the force in these regions? At what points on the curve is the force zero? At what point on the curve does the force have its greatest negative value?

27.16. The purpose of this problem is to test your understanding of the relations, discussed in this chapter, among motion, force, potential energy, and kinetic energy.

1. On a sheet of graph paper, sketch the potential-energy curve of Fig. 27.11. Leave enough room above and below it so that several graphs can be made with the same *x* coordinate but displaced vertically.

2. Make a plot of the force acting on a particle whose energy is described by the potential-energy curve. (Use the formula $F_c = -(\Delta U)/\Delta x$.) It is important only to get the proper direction, inflection points, relative magnitudes, and general shape. Sketch in lightly with a pencil at first, and do not hestitate to make changes as you perfect the graph.

3. Since the force graph yields acceleration ($F = ma$), use it to evolve a plot of velocity. Remember that the total area swept out under an acceleration curve by a moving ordinate is proportional to velocity. Use the same care in making this plot as you used in making the first.

4. From the velocity graph make a graph of the kinetic energy of the particle.

5. Finally, since the total energy of the particle stays the same, plot the potential-energy curve. Compare this final curve with the original curve, and decide where the difference in shape came about. It would be exceptional to obtain a final graph that looked exactly like the original. The important items to note are the points of maxima and minima and the slope of various parts of the curve.

The Conservation of Energy Applied to Mechanical Problems

THE PURPOSE of this chapter is to show, by simple examples, how useful the concept of the conservation of energy can be in the solution of certain kinds of mechanical problems. When, for example, it is the final speed that is sought, we can often find it without going through a detailed analysis involving Newton's laws of motion.

28.1. The Speed of a Body Dropped from Rest

A body of mass m is dropped from height h at a place where the acceleration due to gravity is g (Fig. 28.1). The potential energy at the top (A) is mgh (§ 6.8 and § 27.4). The kinetic energy at the bottom (B), just before the body hits the floor, is $\frac{1}{2}mv^2$. Setting these equal to each other, we obtain the equation

$$\tfrac{1}{2}mv^2 = mgh \qquad [28.1$$

We see immediately that the mass drops out† and that

$$v^2 = 2gh \qquad [28.2$$

We recognize this as the formula, deduced

† Strictly speaking, $\frac{1}{2}m_iv^2 = m_ggh$. The equality of gravitational mass (m_g) and inertial mass (m_i)—see § 5.3— permits us to cancel these.

earlier under kinematics, for the speed of a freely falling body. Here we obtained it by using principles of energy in a simple two-line derivation. What we have done, essentially, is to assume the law of the conservation of mechanical energy:

$$\Delta K + \Delta U = 0 \qquad [28.3$$

This is equivalent to

$$(K - K_0) + (U - U_0) = 0 \qquad [28.4$$

or

$$K + U = K_0 + U_0 \qquad [28.5$$

Here K is the final kinetic energy, $\frac{1}{2}mv^2$, and U is the final potential energy. The initial kinetic energy, K_0, is zero, and the initial potential energy, U_0, is mgh. Substituting into equation 28.5, we get

$$\tfrac{1}{2}mv^2 + 0 = 0 + mgh$$

which is the same as equation 28.1.

Now it is found by observation (Fig. 28.1) that a loosely crumpled piece of paper does not fall as fast as a a smaller and denser body, such as a marble. Because we also know from experiment that they fall at the same rate in a vacuum, we attribute the difference to the retarding force produced by the air during descent. It is clear that equation 28.3 is not valid in this case, for it would lead to the formula $v^2 = 2gh$ regardless of size,

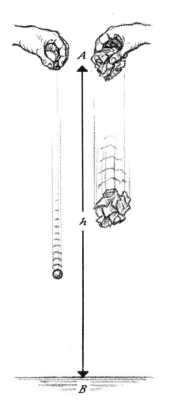

FIG. 28.1. *For a dense spherical object dropped from rest the kinetic energy at the bottom is very close to the potential energy at the top because air friction is negligible. A loosely crumpled piece of paper, on the other hand, is slowed down noticeably by air friction.*

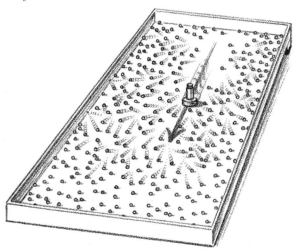

FIG. 28.2. *Model for the conversion of kinetic energy into heat energy.*

shape, or mass of the body. I shall show presently that the equation

$$\Delta K + \Delta U + \Delta Q = 0$$

is valid if ΔQ stands for the energy dissipated in the form of heat during the descent. We write

$$(K - K_0) + (U - U_0) + \Delta Q = 0 \qquad [28.6$$

$$\tfrac{1}{2}mv^2 - 0 + 0 - mgh + \Delta Q = 0 \qquad [28.7$$

$$\tfrac{1}{2}mv^2 = mgh - \Delta Q \qquad [28.8$$

or

$$v^2 = 2gh - 2\frac{\Delta Q}{m} \qquad [28.9$$

The final speed is now, as we should expect, smaller than that predicted by equation 28.2. We cannot get the correct value for v, obviously, without knowing the heat energy lost, ΔQ.

The total energy of random motion of the molecules of air is increased by the encounter with the falling piece of paper. That energy, as we have seen, is what we mean by "heat." Let us illustrate by considering a model (Fig. 28.2). Imagine a huge billiard table with plate glass for a horizontal surface. Resting on that surface, scattered at random, are hundreds of steel balls. A massive frictionless puck, resting at one end of the table, is given an initial push. It moves through the balls, making a series of collisions, approximately at a constant speed and in a straight line because of its inertia. (Actually both the magnitude and the direction of its velocity are affected by the impacts, but the effect of any one impact may be imperceptible.) The collisions impart velocities to the balls that are hit, and they proceed to hit other balls, which, in turn, eventually bounce off the walls and continue colliding with still other balls. Because the collisions obey the laws of dynamics, the result is a kind of complex order; but, when the number of balls is very large, the motions are so complex that we may describe them as chaotic. The massive puck moves steadily along but leaves chaos in its wake. It is not, however, unaffected by these encounters: since it experiences a force every time it imparts a force to a ball, it is gradually slowed down by the impacts and eventually comes to rest. If the collisions were all perfectly elastic, they would go on forever. The kinetic energy of translation of the puck moving in a definite direction eventually becomes converted into the chaotic motion of the balls and the puck.

It is important to reflect on one aspect of this experiment: it began with order and ended in chaos. The puck initially had a definite speed and a definite direction; and the balls were initially at rest. After a while the balls were moving in what looked like random motion, and the puck was apparently at rest although actually sharing imperceptibly the chaotic motion of the balls. The energy of *ordered motion* of one heavy body was converted into the energy of *random motion* of the heavy body and the many lighter ones.

This model illustrates what we believe happens when the crumpled piece of paper falls. It hits millions of invisible air molecules and increases their energy of random motion—that is, their heat energy. This energy is lost as far as the falling body is concerned.

In this chapter I shall use the symbol ΔQ to represent the energy that is lost to the system under consideration by being dissipated in the form of heat. Though we can, in some cases, actually measure ΔQ by the rise in temperature it causes, we are not interested, at present, in measuring it. We need to be aware of its existence, however, in order to balance accounts in our experiments with energy.

28.2. The Conservation of Mechanical and Heat Energy

Let us now consider a more elaborate example. A block of mass m is to be pulled up an inclined plane (Fig. 28.3) by an external force, which we shall call, in this example, the applied force $\mathbf{F}_a$. We obtain the resultant, $\mathbf{F}$, of all the forces acting on the body by adding applied force, normal force, frictional force, and gravitational force vectorially:

$$\mathbf{F} = \mathbf{F}_a + \mathbf{N} + \mathbf{F}_f + m\mathbf{g} \qquad [28.10$$

According to the principle summarized in equation 27.11, $\Delta W = \Delta K$; that is, the total work done by the net unbalanced force on a body is equal to the increment in the body's kinetic energy. Hence the work, ΔW, done in displacement Δx is equal to the increment in kinetic energy, ΔK. Therefore

$$\Delta K = \Delta W = \mathbf{F} \cdot \Delta \mathbf{x}$$
$$= (\mathbf{F}_a + \mathbf{N} + \mathbf{F}_f + m\mathbf{g}) \cdot \Delta \mathbf{x} \qquad [28.11$$

Therefore

$$\Delta K = \mathbf{F}_a \cdot \Delta \mathbf{x} + \mathbf{N} \cdot \Delta \mathbf{x} + \mathbf{F}_f \cdot \Delta \mathbf{x} + m\mathbf{g} \cdot \Delta \mathbf{x} \qquad [28.12$$

The terms on the right stand for the following: $\mathbf{F}_a \cdot \Delta \mathbf{x}$ is the work done by the applied force, $\mathbf{N} \cdot \Delta \mathbf{x}$ is the work done by the normal reaction of the plane, $\mathbf{F}_f \cdot \Delta \mathbf{x}$ is the work done by friction, and $m\mathbf{g} \cdot \Delta \mathbf{x}$ is the work done by the force of gravity, all during the displacement $\Delta \mathbf{x}$. It is obvious that $\mathbf{N} \cdot \Delta \mathbf{x}$ is zero, for $\mathbf{N}$ and $\Delta \mathbf{x}$ are perpendicular to each other. We shall write $\mathbf{F}_f \cdot \Delta \mathbf{x}$ in the scalar form $-F_f(\Delta x)$, in which F_f is the magnitude of the frictional force $\mathbf{F}_f$, Δx is the magnitude of the displacement, and the negative sign appears because $\mathbf{F}_f$ and $\Delta \mathbf{x}$ have opposite directions:

$$\mathbf{F}_f \cdot \Delta \mathbf{x} = F_f \Delta x \cos 180° = -F_f \Delta x$$

It is left to you to prove similarly that the work done by $m\mathbf{g} \cdot \Delta \mathbf{x}$ may be written in scalar form: $-(mg \sin \theta)\Delta x$.

Making all these substitutions in equation 28.12, we get

$$\Delta K = \mathbf{F}_a \cdot \Delta \mathbf{x} + 0 - F_f(\Delta x) - (mg \sin \theta)\Delta x \qquad [28.13$$

or

$$\mathbf{F}_a \cdot \Delta \mathbf{x} = \Delta K + (mg \sin \theta)\Delta x + F_f(\Delta x) \qquad [28.14$$

Since $\Delta h/\Delta x = \sin \theta$, we may write $\Delta h = \Delta x \sin \theta$. Hence $(mg \sin \theta)\Delta x = mg(\Delta h)$, which we recognize as the increment in gravitational potential energy, ΔU. The positive number $F_f(\Delta x)$ repre-

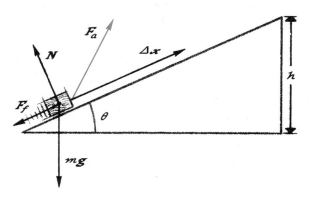

FIG. 28.3. *Illustrating how the work done by an applied force goes into increments of mechanical and heat energy.*

sents the increase, ΔQ, in the heat energy; it is due to friction. We may therefore write

$$\mathbf{F}_a \cdot \Delta \mathbf{x} = \Delta K + \Delta U + \Delta Q \qquad [28.15$$

This equation says that the work done by an external force is not lost but goes into increments of kinetic energy, potential energy, and heat energy.†

Equation 28.15 is a powerful tool for use in the solution of mechanical problems. Let us show what a time-saver it can be by using it to solve a problem of motion on an inclined plane. We can check the solution by using the formula $f = ma$.

28.3. Motion on an Inclined Plane and in a Pendulum Deduced from the Energies Involved

A block of mass m starts from rest at the top of a frictionless inclined plane (Fig. 28.4). We wish to find the speed of the block at the bottom.

Having assumed that $\mathbf{F}_a = \mathbf{0}$ and that $\mathbf{F}_f = \mathbf{0}$, we use equation 28.15 and get

$$0 = \Delta K + \Delta U + 0$$
$$= (K - K_0) + (U - U_0)$$
$$K + U = K_0 + U_0$$
$$\tfrac{1}{2}mv^2 + 0 = 0 + mgh$$
$$v^2 = 2gh$$

This interesting result is the same as that obtained (equation 28.2) for a body dropped vertically from rest. Let us compare it with the result of a solution (Fig. 28.4) using the formula $f = ma$. Since $N = -mg \cos \theta$, we need consider only $mg \sin \theta$ as the net force. Putting this in place of f in the formula $f = ma$, we get

† We can put the forces acting on a body into more general categories—for example, the external applied force, $\mathbf{F}_a$; the forces that do no work, $\mathbf{F}_n$; the conservative forces, $\mathbf{F}_c$, which, as we showed in equation 27.21, are derivable from a potential function, U, such that $-\Delta U/\Delta x = F_c$ (these can be produced by gravitational and electrical fields, for example, but also by ideal springs); and the frictional forces, $\mathbf{F}_f$. The increment, ΔK, in kinetic energy is equal to the work done by the vector sum of all these forces:

$$\Delta K = (\mathbf{F}_a + \mathbf{F}_n + \mathbf{F}_c + \mathbf{F}_f) \cdot \Delta \mathbf{x}$$
$$= \mathbf{F}_a \cdot \Delta \mathbf{x} + \mathbf{F}_n \cdot \Delta \mathbf{x} + \mathbf{F}_c \cdot \Delta \mathbf{x} + \mathbf{F}_f \cdot \Delta \mathbf{x}$$
$$= \mathbf{F}_a \cdot \Delta \mathbf{x} + 0 - \Delta U - \Delta Q$$

or

$$\mathbf{F}_a \cdot \Delta \mathbf{x} = \Delta K + \Delta U + \Delta Q$$

There are, however, other forms of energy, not included in this formula.

$$mg \sin \theta = ma \qquad [28.16$$

Since the acceleration is constant, we can use the formula from kinematics, $v^2 = 2ax$:

$$v^2 = 2gx \sin \theta \qquad [28.17$$

But, since $h/x = \sin \theta$, $h = x \sin \theta$; and therefore

$$v^2 = 2gh \qquad [28.18$$

This confirms the result predicted by the conservation of mechanical energy. Although it may not appear so in this very simple case, the solution using principles of energy is often considerably less elaborate than that obtained from dynamical and kinematical formulas.

Now consider a ball of mass m suspended as a simple pendulum (Fig. 28.5). Two forces act on it. One is the tension, τ, which is perpendicular to the direction of the motion and hence does no work. The other is the force of gravity, a conservative force. Once again, assuming that $\mathbf{F}_a = \mathbf{0}$ and that $\Delta Q = 0$, we can use equation 28.15. The analysis is identical to that of the inclined plane.

$$\Delta K + \Delta U = 0$$
$$K + U = K_0 + U_0$$
$$\tfrac{1}{2}mv^2 + 0 = 0 + mgh$$
$$v^2 = 2gh$$

The speed at the bottom of the swing is the same as that of a body falling freely through height h.

Whereas the force acting on the body was constant in the case of the inclined plane, it is variable in the case of the pendulum. If we are interested only in the final speed, that does not matter.

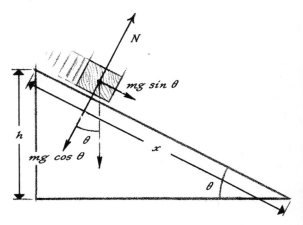

FIG. 28.4. *Finding the speed of a block sliding down a frictionless plane.*

28.4. The Roller Coaster

Although a car rolling along a roller coaster speeds up when it is rolling down and slows down when it is rolling up, we could use the principle of the conservation of energy to discuss its motion. But, in order to avoid complications such as those due to rotation of the wheels, we shall consider, instead, an almost equivalent problem, that of a bead sliding along a wire (Fig. 28.6). We assume

that a frictional force, F_f, retards the motion. The normal force, N, does no work, for it is always perpendicular to the motion. The only other force acting on the bead is conservative: the force of gravity, mg. Since there is no external applied force, $F_a = 0$. From equation 28.15 we get

$$\Delta K + \Delta U + \Delta Q = 0$$
$$(K - K_0) + (U - U_0) + \Delta Q = 0 \quad [28.19$$

We are given that the bead's initial speed is v_0 (not zero) and that its final speed is v. We are asked to find the average force of friction during the bead's motion. Let the speed be v when the height, h, is zero.

We tabulate what we know:

$$K_0 = \tfrac{1}{2}mv_0{}^2 \qquad U_0 = mgh$$
$$K = \tfrac{1}{2}mv^2 \qquad U = 0$$

Putting this into equation 28.19, we get

$$\tfrac{1}{2}mv^2 - \tfrac{1}{2}mv_0{}^2 + 0 - mgh + \Delta Q = 0 \quad [28.20$$
$$\Delta Q = mgh - (\tfrac{1}{2}mv^2 - \tfrac{1}{2}mv_0{}^2) \quad [28.21$$

If we assume that $\Delta Q = \overline{F_f}s$ (F_f being the magnitude of the average frictional force), we get

$$\overline{F_f}s = mgh - (\tfrac{1}{2}mv^2 - \tfrac{1}{2}mv_0{}^2) \quad [28.22$$
$$\overline{F_f} = \frac{mgh}{s} - \frac{(\tfrac{1}{2}mv^2 - \tfrac{1}{2}mv_0{}^2)}{s} \quad [28.23$$

We can now compute the average frictional force.

The energy method has enabled us, rather simply, to get at least partial knowledge of some of the forces involved in a problem for which the dynamical method, using the formula $f = ma$, would have been very complicated. We begin to see that the complications introduced by the shape of the path don't affect us very much when we use the energy method. We now consider another example, which, though it looks formidable, is nevertheless fairly simple by that method.

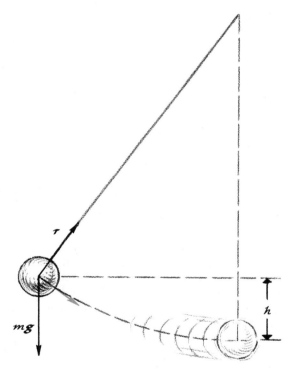

FIG. 28.5. *Finding the speed of a pendulum at the bottom of its swing.*

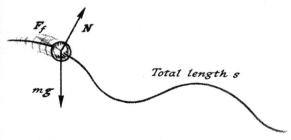

FIG. 28.6. *Finding the average force of friction during the motion of a bead sliding along a wire.*

28.5. The Loop-the-loop

A bead moves along a wire that is curved, in one part, into a loop (a spiral) that we assume to be a circle standing in a vertical plane (Fig. 28.7.A). This time let us assume that the bead slides without friction. It starts from rest at A at height h_1 above an arbitrary reference plane. Point B, at the top of the circular loop, is at height h_2. The radius

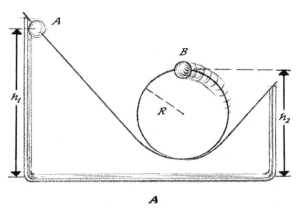

FIG. 28.7. *The loop-the-loop: If we disregard friction, the motion of a bead (or of a car) moving in such a curved path can be determined by use of the principle of the conservation of energy.*

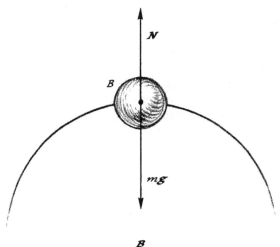

of the circle is R. We ask: What is the magnitude of the force that the wire exerts on the bead at point B?

Without the energy method this would indeed be a formidable problem. Using that method, we analyze the problem as follows: Since there is no friction, the only force the wire can exert on the bead is along a perpendicular to its path. At B the forces acting on the bead are mg, pointing down (Fig. 28.7.B), and the normal reaction, $\mathbf{N}$, which is drawn pointing up although in some cases, as we shall see, it might point down. In any case, $\mathbf{F} = \mathbf{N} + m\mathbf{g}$ must point to the center of the circle, for it takes a centripetal force to keep a body moving in a circle.

The formula for centripetal force is

$$F = m \frac{v^2}{R} \qquad [28.24$$

If we can find v^2 at B, we shall have the necessary information to put into equation 28.24. We tabulate what we know:

$$K_0 = 0 \qquad U_0 = mgh_1 \qquad \Delta Q = 0$$
$$K = \tfrac{1}{2}mv^2 \qquad U = mgh_2 \qquad F_a = 0$$

From equation 28.15 we get

$$(K - K_0) + (U - U_0) + \Delta Q = 0$$
$$\tfrac{1}{2}mv^2 - 0 + (mgh_2 - mgh_1) + 0 = 0$$
$$\tfrac{1}{2}mv^2 = mg(h_1 - h_2)$$
$$mv^2 = 2mg(h_1 - h_2) \qquad [28.25$$

Putting this value into equation 28.24, we get

$$F = \frac{mv^2}{R} = \frac{2mg}{R}(h_1 - h_2) \qquad [28.26$$

Observe that, if the difference in heights, $h_1 - h_2$, is less than $R/2$, F is less than mg; this can happen only if $\mathbf{N}$ points up, as in our example. If $h_1 - h_2 = R/2$, $F = mg$; and, since $\mathbf{F} = \mathbf{N} + m\mathbf{g}$, $\mathbf{N}$ must be zero. If $h_1 - h_2 = R$, $F = 2mg$; in this case $\mathbf{N}$ must point in the same direction as $m\mathbf{g}$ and be equal to it. Equation 28.26 holds for any case, and we can get N by considering the fact that F (the magnitude of $\mathbf{F}$) is equal to the magnitude of $(\mathbf{N} + m\mathbf{g})$, which equals

$$\frac{2mg}{R}(h_1 - h_2) \qquad [28.27$$

28.6. The Conservative Force of a Spring

So far our examples have dealt with the force of gravity as the conservative force in the system. Since the force exerted by a steel spring is approximately conservative, we can apply the energy equation to it.

An object of mass m, embedded in a block of Dry Ice, slides with negligible friction on a horizontal glass plate (Fig. 28.8). The object is at rest at O, and the spring attached to it is in equilibrium. If the object is moved through distance A, from

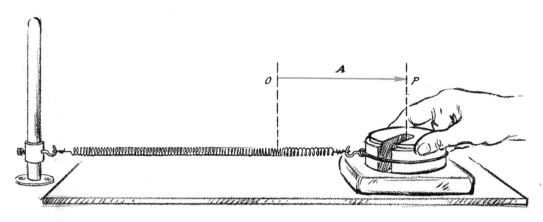

FIG. 28.8. *Studying the motion of an object moved by a force produced by a stretched spring.*

O to P, the spring thereby being stretched through the same distance, and the object is then released, how fast will it be going as its center passes O? The stiffness constant of the spring is k; that is, the force, F, that the spring exerts on the object when stretched by length x is $-kx$. (The sign is negative because the force points toward O.)

Let us consider the problem in two parts. We first apply force $\mathbf{F}_a$ to move the object from O to P. The forces acting on the object are shown in Fig. 28.9. Since we have assumed that $\Delta Q = 0$, we may write equation 28.15 as

$$\mathbf{F}_a \cdot \Delta \mathbf{x} = \Delta K + \Delta U + 0$$

The kinetic energy at the start and at the end is zero; therefore $\Delta K = 0$, and

$$\mathbf{F}_a \cdot \Delta \mathbf{x} = U - U_0 \qquad [28.28$$

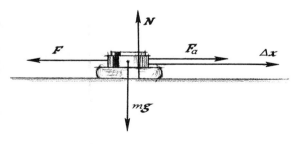

FIG. 28.9. *The forces involved in the experiment of Fig. 28.8.*

The potential energy is now due, not to gravity, but to the spring's change of shape. Assuming that $U_0 = 0$ at O, let us use the average force, $\overline{F}$, for the F_a, and the total distance, A, for the Δx, of equation 28.28:

$$\overline{F}A = U \qquad [28.29$$

Since the initial applied force is zero and the final applied force is kA, the average force, $\overline{F}$, is $kA/2$. Putting this into equation 28.29, we get

$$\frac{kA}{2} A = U \qquad [28.30$$

$$U = \frac{kA^2}{2} \qquad [28.31$$

The potential energy of the stretched spring is $kA^2/2$.

We are now ready to release the object. This time we tabulate the initial conditions at $x = A$ and the final conditions at $x = 0$.

$$K_0 = 0 \qquad U_0 = \frac{kA^2}{2} \qquad F_a = 0$$

$$K = \tfrac{1}{2}mv^2 \qquad U = 0 \qquad \Delta Q = 0$$

Substituting into equation 28.15, we get

$$K + U = K_0 + U_0$$

which yields

$$\tfrac{1}{2}mv^2 + 0 = 0 + \frac{kA^2}{2}$$

$$v^2 = \frac{kA^2}{m}$$

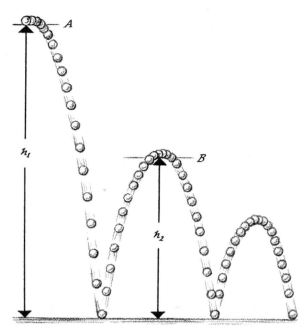

FIG. 28.10. *One way in which mechanical energy is converted into heat energy.*

$$v = A\sqrt{k/m} \qquad [28.32$$

Let's check this dimensionally:

$$[A] = L$$
$$[k] = [F/x] = MLT^{-2}/L = MT^{-2}$$

Therefore

$$[A\sqrt{k/m}] = L\sqrt{MT^{-2}/M} = LT^{-1}$$

These are the dimensions of a velocity, and the solution looks all right.

Now let's make a common-sense check. A large m means great inertia; the final velocity ought to be low, and equation 28.32 predicts this. A large k means a very stiff spring; the final velocity should be high, and equation 28.32 predicts this. Finally, a large value of A means that a lot of work was put into the system; we should expect a high final velocity, and equation 28.32 confirms this. Everything seems to be in order, and, in fact, the solution can be confirmed by the use of the formula $f = ma$. We see, therefore, that a conservative force need not be gravitational to be used in the method applying the conservation of energy.

28.7. Mechanical Energy Converted to Heat

A steel ball, of mass m, released from rest at A, at height h_1, falls and bounces back to B, at height h_2. The horizontal velocity is supposed to be negligible, but the horizontal displacements in Figure 28.10 have been exaggerated so that the different movements will be easier to see. Height h_2 may be very close to h_1, but the concepts of this chapter make it clear that it will always be less than h_1. Considering A and B as initial and final points, respectively, we tabulate:

$$K_0 = 0 \qquad\qquad U_0 = mgh_1 \qquad \Delta Q \neq 0$$
$$K = \tfrac{1}{2}mv^2 = 0 \qquad U = mgh_2 \qquad F_a = 0$$
$$\Delta K + \Delta U + \Delta Q = 0$$

(We have assumed that the horizontal velocity is negligible throughout.) In this case, $\Delta K = 0$; therefore

$$\Delta Q = -\Delta U = -(U - U_0) = -(mgh_2 - mgh_1)$$
$$= mg(h_1 - h_2)$$

Obviously, $mg(h_1 - h_2)$ is a measure of the energy converted into heat.

Suppose that the falling object is something like clay, also of mass m, which does not bounce back up at all:

$$K_0 = 0 \qquad U_0 = mgh \qquad \Delta Q \neq 0$$
$$K = 0 \qquad U = 0 \qquad F_a = 0$$
$$\Delta Q = mgh$$

In MKS units—that is, with m expressed in kilograms, g in meters per second per second, and h in meters—ΔQ comes out in joules (J). Now the temperature rise, ΔT, of a body is given by the equation

$$\Delta Q = m \cdot s \cdot \Delta T$$

If m is in kilograms, s (the specific heat) is in J/(kg × °C). [In equation 11.4 s is in cal/(gm × °C). Table 6.1 shows that 4.184 J = 1 cal.] If we assume that all of the energy converted into heat is retained by the clay, we may write

$$mgh = ms(\Delta T) \qquad [28.33$$

$$\Delta T = \frac{gh}{s} \qquad [28.34$$

This interesting result states that the rise in temperature is independent of the mass!

28.8. Relativistic Mass

So far we have used $\frac{1}{2}mv^2$ as the formula for kinetic energy. This formula was derived from the idea that the increase in kinetic energy, ΔK, is equal to the work done by the resultant of all the forces acting on a body. If we write the force as $f = ma$, the work done in a small displacement, Δx, in the direction of f is $\Delta W = f(\Delta x) = ma(\Delta x)$. We know that, when a is a constant, the correct kinematical formula for motion starting from rest is $v^2 = 2a(\Delta x)$. Hence $a(\Delta x) = v^2/2$ and $\Delta w = mv^2/2$. Hence $\Delta K = mv^2/2$. This formula is correct even when a is not a constant *if the mass of the body is constant*.

In many experiments this is practically a valid assumption, but for bodies moving with speeds close to that of light it is no longer valid. The speed of light is huge (3×10^8 m/sec), and we don't often encounter massive objects moving with anything close to that speed. Electrons, however, have a very small mass; when they are accelerated by certain electrical forces (which can be created with rather simple laboratory apparatus), it is fairly easy to give them speeds that are sizable fractions of the speed of light. In a television tube, for example, where the accelerating potential is 20,000 volts, the electrons' speed is about a fourth of the speed of light.

Experiments with electrons and other atomic particles indicate that the inertial mass of an object increases with its speed. The relation is shown graphically in Figure 28.11. The ordinate is the mass, m; it starts at value m_0 for $v = 0$. The abscissa is the speed, v, expressed in units of the speed of light, c. In other words, the ordinate represents the ratio v/c, in which $c = 3\times 10^8$ m/sec. The significance of this curve is that the mass of an object increases with its speed, approaching infinity for $v/c = 1$ (that is, for $v = c$).

Figure 28.11 is a graph of the formula

$$m = \frac{m_0}{\sqrt{1 - v^2/c^2}} \qquad [28.35$$

which comes from Einstein's theory of relativity. This may be written as

$$m = km_0 \qquad [28.36$$

in which

$$k = \frac{1}{\sqrt{1 - v^2/c^2}} \qquad [28.37$$

This is the value of k that I introduced in discussing the relativity of time in Chapter 7.

If we replace the formula $f = ma$ by the more generally correct formula†

$$f = \frac{\Delta(mv)}{\Delta t} \qquad [28.38$$

and compute the work done in displacement Δs as

† Strictly speaking, we should write

$$f = \lim_{\Delta t \to 0} \frac{\Delta(mv)}{\Delta t}$$

or, in words, "force is the instantaneous rate of change of momentum."

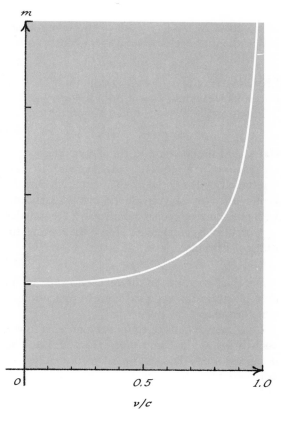

FIG. 28.11. *Plot of the mass of an object against the ratio of its speed to the speed of light.*

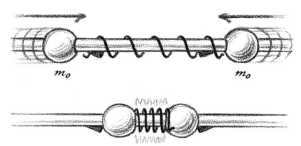

FIG. 28.12. *The result of the change depicted is to increase the potential energy, and therefore also the mass, of the system.*

$W = f \cdot \Delta s$, we can still compute the increase in kinetic energy as $\Delta K = \Delta W$, but the computation is complicated, since m cannot be considered constant but must be replaced by the expression

$$\frac{m_0}{\sqrt{1 - v^2/c^2}}$$

of equation 28.35. The result of this computation is that the increase in kinetic energy comes out as

$$\Delta K = mc^2 - m_0 c^2 \qquad [28.39$$

[For low speeds ($v/c \longrightarrow 0$) equation 28.39 reduces, as we should expect, to $\Delta K = m_0 v^2 / 2$.]

Equation 28.39, since it can be written as

$$\Delta K = (m - m_0)c^2 \qquad [28.40$$

states that the increase in the kinetic energy of a moving body is equal to its increase in mass multiplied by the speed of light squared. But that is not all. Not only is kinetic energy associated with mass, but any form of energy, E, is equivalent to a certain mass times c^2. Hence the famous formula of Einstein:

$$E = mc^2 \qquad [28.41$$

We shall perform, in thought, two experiments that illustrate the wide variety of applications of this formula.

Imagine two balls of equal mass moving toward each other at the same speed (Fig. 28.12). They compress a massless spring between them as they come to rest. A device locks the system in the compressed state. The potential energy of the system is increased by this compression. The work done in compressing the spring is U. The rest mass of each ball is m_0. The total mass of the com-

pressed system is now not just $2m_0$ but $2m_0 + U/c^2$.

This idea, fantastic as it sounds, is the basis on which we explain the energy stored in the atomic nucleus. In the illustration above it took work to compress the spring. If, instead, it had taken work to stretch it, we should have a situation vaguely resembling what happens in a nucleus. It takes work to pull the constituent parts of a nucleus apart. They therefore have more energy when they are apart. Hence they are more massive when apart. The relation between change in energy, ΔE, and change in mass, Δm, is the familiar $\Delta E = (\Delta m)c^2$.

Consider another illustration. A candle is allowed to burn inside a closed glass bell-jar. Oxygen is provided, from a small tank inside the bell-jar, so that the burning can proceed for an appreciable time. All the substances inside the jar are weighed before and after combustion. It is a basic tenet of classical chemistry that mass is conserved, and we expect the total mass of the substances inside the jar to remain unchanged. It does so to a very high degree of accuracy. But how do we reconcile that fact with the fact that radiant energy (light and heat) appeared and got out of the jar? If this radiant energy represents a loss of mass, why doesn't the loss register?

Let us make a calculation to find out why. We assume that the candle is the equivalent of a 10-watt bulb and that it burns for 10,000 seconds (not quite three hours). The energy that appears is

$$\Delta E = 10 \text{ W} \times 10^4 \text{ sec}$$

$$= 10 \frac{\text{J}}{\text{sec}} \times 10^4 \text{ sec}$$

$$= 10^5 \text{ J}$$

Using the formula $\Delta E = (\Delta m)c^2$, we get

$$\Delta m = \frac{E}{c^2}$$

$$= \frac{10^5 \text{ J}}{(3 \times 10^8)^2 \text{ m}^2/\text{sec}^2}$$

$$= \frac{10^5}{9 \times 10^{16}} \text{ kg}$$

$$\cong 10^{-12} \text{ kg}$$

$$\cong 0.000000000001 \text{ kg}$$

No balance in existence can detect such a small mass in this experiment (although there are, as we shall see, other means of detecting even smaller masses). The difficulty is in detecting such a small change of mass in a mass as great as that of a candle.

There are compelling reasons for believing, nevertheless, that gain in energy and loss of mass are here, and everywhere, related by the formula $\Delta E = (\Delta m)c^2$. Therefore, while most of our daily transactions involving energy are expressed by the equation

$$\mathbf{F}_a \cdot \Delta \mathbf{x} = \Delta U + \Delta K + \Delta Q$$

we lean heavily, in atomic physics, on the concept of energy expressed by the formula

$$\Delta E = (\Delta m)c^2$$

28.9. Summary

For a body moving under the action of conservative forces, the sum of potential and kinetic energies at a point is a constant. Hence

$$U_0 + K_0 = U + K$$

Another useful expression is

$$\mathbf{F}_a \cdot \Delta \mathbf{X} = \Delta K + \Delta U + \Delta Q$$

It says that the work done on a body by applied force $\mathbf{F}_a$ appears as an increment in its kinetic energy, ΔK; as an increment in its potential energy, ΔU (which presumes it is subject to conservative forces); and as an increment in heat, ΔQ, which, in general, represents a loss of useful energy. Many problems involving heat loss can be solved with this equation, even those in which there is no applied force ($\mathbf{F}_a = 0$). At speeds approaching that of light, the fact that the increase in the mass of a body is a function of the body's speed becomes apparent. At all speeds the increment in kinetic energy obeys the formula

$$\Delta K = (m - m_0)c^2$$

in which m is the mass of the body, m_0 is its rest mass, and c is the speed of light; but at speeds much lower than that of light the approximate formula

$$K = m_0 v^2 / 2$$

holds very well.

Problems

28.1. A large ball made of 125 gm of loosely crumpled newspaper is released from rest, in a room, at a height of 3.5 m. It lands on the floor with a speed of 8 m/sec.

1. Just before the ball hits the floor, how much heat energy in calories has been gained by the room?

2. After it hits, what is the total amount of energy, in calories, that has been converted into heat?

3. Compare this with the heat that you could obtain by burning the paper if it is capable of yielding 4,500 cal/gm.

28.2. This problem is mathematically simple but requires a clear understanding of the basic concepts. Suppose, in Fig. 28.3, that a block of mass 0.13 kg is pulled up from rest along the inclined plane for a distance of 0.76 m by a constant force, $\mathbf{F}_a$, of 12 nt that is parallel to $\Delta \mathbf{x}$. The average frictional force is 0.18 nt. The angle of inclination is 30°. What is the speed of the block at the top?

28.3. A 10-kg block, with an initial velocity of 100 m/sec, starts up a slope that makes an angle of 30° with the horizontal. The frictional force produces a drag of 60 nt.

1. What distance will the block go up along the slope before it stops?

2. After it stops (and is given a light tap to get it started), will it slide down the hill?

3. If so, how fast will it be going when it hits the bottom?

28.4. A small boy in a swing wants to go clear round over the bar supporting the swing. If the swing has ropes 3.00 m long, how fast must his father push him at the bottom in order for him to go over the top without having the ropes go slack?

28.5. A simple pendulum of length 0.75 m with a bob of mass 0.49 kg is displaced through an angle of 30° and then released from rest in a medium so viscous that the bob's speed is exactly zero when it reaches the bottom.

1. Compute the average force of friction on the pendulum.

2. In another experiment the same thing happens with a pendulum of length 0.50 m. Compute the average force of friction on the pendulum.

3. If you use symbols first and substitute numerical values only at the end, you will understand why there is a simple relation between the answers of part 1 and part 2.

28.6. An airplane with a total mass of 605 kg, traveling in horizontal flight at a speed of 150 mph, turns off its engine at an altitude of 1,000 ft and glides down in a sinuous path a mile long before it lands at a speed of 50 mph. Compute the average value of all the retarding forces acting on it during its descent. (Hint: The logic is very similar to that used in § 28.4. Since we have stressed MKS units for work and energy, it would probably be easiest to convert everything to MKS units.) Give the answer in newtons.

28.7. The car of a real loop-the-loop rolls on a track like that of Fig. 28.7.A. When the car is in position B, the passenger is upside down.

1. If R is 3 m, what is the minimum value of $h_1 - h_2$ that will keep him from exerting a pressure on his cushion when he is passing point B? Hint: Argue the solution out first by common sense: the centripetal force, mv^2/R, at B must be supplied by his weight. In a frictionless case $v^2 = 2g(h_1 - h_2)$. Substitute and solve for $(h_1 - h_2)$.

2. Reconcile your result with the treatment of § 28.5.

28.8. The purpose of this problem is to test your understanding of § 28.6.

1. Compute the speed of the block of Fig. 28.8 in a frictionless case at a point halfway between P and O if the block is released from rest at P. Given: $m = 0.1$ kg, $OP = 0.25$ m, and $k = 89$ nt/m.

2. Repeat for a case in which the coefficient of kinetic friction is a constant and is equal to 0.2.

28.9. A lump of clay of mass 1.4 kg is dropped from a height of 56 m. Assuming that, when it lands, all the kinetic energy it has just before hitting the ground goes into heating the clay, compute its rise in temperature. The specific heat of the clay is 0.15 cal/gm/°C. Be sure to adjust the units of physical quantities on both sides of the equation before you substitute numerical values and solve.

28.10. Calculate the increase in mass of a 1-kg chunk of lead as a result of the increase in potential energy produced when it is lifted vertically through a distance of 1 m.

28.11. The mean solar intensity at the surface of the earth is 495 W/m²; the mean radius of the earth is 6.37×10^6 m. The area of a sphere is $4\pi r^2$; the mass of the earth is 5.9×10^{24} kg.

1. Compute the total rate, in watts, at which the earth receives solar radiation.

2. The age of the earth is about 4.5×10^9 years. Compute the total amount of radiant energy it has received from the sun in that time.

3. Compute the mass, in kilograms, equivalent to that amount of energy.

4. What fraction of the earth's mass does the mass of part 3 represent?

28.12. Starting with equation 28.39, substitute for m the value

$$\frac{m_0}{\sqrt{1 - v^2/c^2}}$$

To compute ΔK as v/c approaches zero, it is not sufficient to substitute zero for v/c in that expression, since, as you may easily verify, it would yield zero. Instead, use the approximation

$$\frac{1}{\sqrt{1 - \epsilon}} \cong \sqrt{1 + \epsilon}$$

and then the approximation

$$\sqrt{1 + \epsilon} \cong 1 + \frac{\epsilon}{2} \quad (\text{if } \epsilon \ll 1)$$

and prove that, if $v/c \ll 1$, ΔK comes out as $m_0 v^2/2$.

An Introduction to the Kinetic Theory of Gases

IN OUR study of the motion of a single particle (Chap. 8) we were building up the idea of order and predictability in nature. By means of equation $s = gt^2/2$, for example, we were able to predict where a falling body would be at any instant of its fall. Predictability on a large macroscopic scale, on the other hand, had its first dramatic triumphs in astronomy: applying Newton's laws of motion, astronomers could foresee the motion of the planets well enough to predict events like eclipses very accurately long before they occurred.

But what happens when we look through a microscope at smoke particles in Brownian motion? The particles seem to be moving in a completely unpredictable way. The velocity of any particle changes abruptly both in direction and in magnitude many times per second. If this is happening to the smoke particles, imagine what must be happening to the much tinier molecules that are responsible for this random motion—the molecules of the gases that constitute air. How are we to predict the motion of such particles?

29.1. The Dilemma of Chaos

Our difficulty springs, in part, from the fact that we are dealing with so many particles at one time. It's a very big jump from predicting the motion of one particle to predicting the motion of 10^{23} particles. Remember that the Avogadro constant, N_A (§ 1.3), tells us that there are about 6.023×10^{23} molecules in a mole. The mole is a sample of reasonable laboratory size; but, even if we took only 0.001 mole, we should still have about 10^{20} molecules to deal with. This is a very large number. It is about a million times larger than the total number of leaves on all the trees in the world, which is about the number of all the hairs on all the heads of all the people in the world. The total human population of the world is about 3×10^9. The total number of stars in the universe from which radio telescopes might pick up signals is about 10^{20}. It has been estimated that of all the heavenly bodies in the universe capable of supporting life only about 10^8 could possibly support life as we know it on the earth. If you populated each of these 10^8 worlds with 3×10^9 people, the total number of human beings would be about 10^{17}. We must remember, then, that, when we talk about 10^{20} molecules, we are talking about a huge number.

How do we handle the behavior of such a fantastically large aggregate in any reasonable way? We have no doubt that the laws of motion hold when any two particles collide; we bog down simply because there are so many particles to consider. If, by some miracle, we tabulated the position and velocity of 10^{20} particles at a certain instant, no computing machine in the world could calculate the exact position and velocity of any one of these particles one second later. The task is just too big.

How do we handle such a situation? We can take our cue from the fact that insurance companies have survived and made money by predicting, statistically, the behavior of a large population. Using the statistical methods employed by insurance firms, we cannot predict what will happen to any individual, but we can predict with great accuracy, for example, how many people are going to die within the next year.

This suggests that we might get somewhere with molecular motion if we considered the *average* behavior of the molecules. We can sense intuitively that some molecules must be going very fast and others very slowly; that some molecules travel a great distance, others a short distance, before they collide with another molecule. This leads us to the concept of the mean speed of a molecule and the so-called **mean free path** (the average distance between collisions). There are reasons for believing that molecular speeds as low as 1 cm/sec are very improbable. There are other reasons for believing that molecular speeds approaching the speed of light are also very improbable. There must be a most probable speed, an average or mean speed of some sort. We shall see that this is of the same order of magnitude as the speed of sound waves in air (344 m/sec). By making a series of simplifying assumptions, of which the substitution of average behavior for actual behavior is the first, we can build up a theory that enables us to make predictions in spite of the chaotic nature of the motions we are considering.

29.2. Order Out of Chaos: the Assumptions of Clausius

It seems that men like to bring order out of chaos, and the kinetic theory of gases is one example. (The word "gas" came from "chaos.") The chaos is still there; the order is really in men's minds. The apparently smooth behavior of things observed on the macroscopic scale results from our inability to see things at the atomic level. We observe only the smoothed-over, average, macro-

scopic effects produced by the random motion of microscopic particles.

We can illustrate the smoothing effect of large numbers by using only hundreds, rather than millions or billions, of objects. In Figure 29.1 this is illustrated by the behavior of a light balsa-wood piston that fits fairly snugly into a plastic cylinder. Inside this cylinder are several hundred tiny steel balls. The bottom of the container is sufficiently elastic so that, when it is hit repeatedly by an eccentric on the shaft of a high-speed motor, it imparts motion to the balls, which dance about at random. They push the piston up (A) to a certain height, h, and keep it there, except for small fluctuations, as long as they are kept in random motion. The fluctuations in the position of the piston are diminished if we increase the number of steel balls and make them smaller. This suggests what we think is happening with the invisible molecules of the air.

While the motor is running, we put a small weight, w, on the piston. This forces the piston down (B) to a lesser height, h_1, and keeps it there, except for small fluctuations, as long as the motion of the balls continues. If the weight is removed while the motor is still running (C), the piston moves back to its original height, h.

If air behaves in the same way, we should be able to do a similar experiment with it. We can do it easily with a large hypodermic syringe such as those used by a veterinary doctor (Fig. 29.2). The piston of the syringe is held at height h by the molecules of the air compressed below it (A). If the air is allowed to leak out of the syringe by removal of the stopper, B, the piston gradually falls; if the stopper is kept in place, the piston stays at height h without apparent fluctuations. This supports the idea that very many tiny, invisible particles in rapid random motion are holding up the piston by continuous bombardment. If we put a weight, W, on the piston (B), it goes down to a lesser height, h_1; when we remove the weight (C), the piston rises to its original height, h. This implies that our model of Figure 29.1 may approach the truth, and it suggests the next simplifying assumption: that molecules behave like tiny, hard, elastic spheres.

The first systematic attempt to state a complete

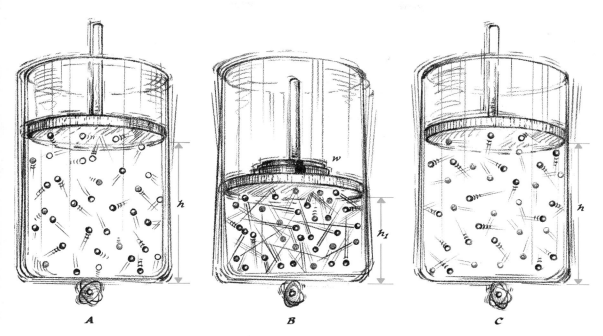

FIG. 29.1. *Model, using steel balls, for the kinetic theory of gases.*

set of simplifying assumptions that could lead to a usable kinetic theory of gases was made by Rudolf Clausius, who, beginning in 1857, worked out a theory based on the following assumptions: (1) the molecules of a monatomic† gaseous element are identical solid spheres that move in straight lines until they collide with one another or with the wall of the containing vessel; (2) the time occupied in collision is negligible, and the collision is perfectly elastic; (3) the volume of the molecules, compared with the volume of the container, is negligible; (4) there is no mutual attraction or repulsion between the molecules.‡

If you try to imagine or build a model with real balls, such as tennis balls, bouncing around inside a room, you will see that sooner or later all the balls will be lying on the floor, having fallen under the action of gravity. But molecules do not end up

on the floor of the container. Instead, they keep hitting one another and bouncing off the walls indefinitely. The real clue to the ceaseless motion of the molecules is the fact that collisions are, for all practical purposes, perfectly elastic. This implies that no kinetic energy is lost in collision. Since no energy is lost, the system must have the same total kinetic energy at the end of the experiment as at the beginning. The molecules could not wind up lying motionless on the floor of the container.

In the argument that follows we shall deal with the dynamical considerations (those involving forces) only in a qualitative way and with the kinematics of the motion only in a very special, highly simplified form.

29.3. Forces During Collisions

We attribute the pressure that a gas exerts on the walls of its container to the numerous impacts of its molecules on the walls. This implies that an elastic sphere can exert a force on a plane object

---

† A diatomic molecule behaves somewhat like a pair of spheres or a dumbbell.

‡ As we saw in Chap. 6, the ordinary behavior of gases involves molecular interactions requiring less than 1 ev per molecule, and the molecules are classed as particles without internal structure. We simply treat them as impenetrable fundamental particles.

like a wall. Let us examine this idea in a qualitative way. (A quantitative treatment appears in § 31.6.)

Before we do that, however (since we are going to treat the spheres as identical), let us consider the force that one ball can exert upon another during a collision. Suppose that two identical steel balls are hung so that their supporting strings are parallel and the balls are touching each other, as in Figure 29.3. (Steel is highly elastic, and the collision will approximate that of perfectly elastic

spheres.) If the ball at the left is moved to the left, to position A', and released, it will have a velocity pointing to the right at A; shortly thereafter it will come to rest while the second ball moves to the right with a velocity equal to that formerly possessed by the first ball. If the instantaneous direction of motion of the first ball is coincident with the line joining the two centers at impact, all its energy is transmitted to the second ball. (If the collision is a glancing one, such as you might have

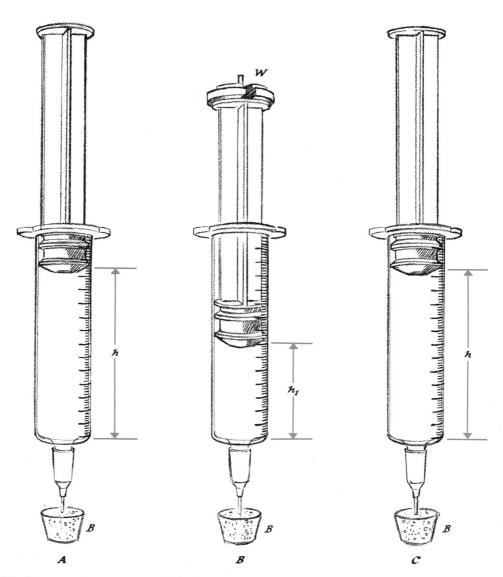

FIG. 29.2. *Demonstration, using air, of the kinetic theory of gases.*

between two billiard balls, both balls may move after impact.) We see that during the collision, if all the kinetic energy of the first ball is transferred to the other, a force pointing to the left slows the first ball down, and a force pointing to the right speeds the second ball up. In this way, one ball can exert a force upon another during the short interval in which they are in contact.

Figure 29.4 illustrates the forces that act when a ball strikes a wall. A hard steel ball is now suspended near a flat vertical wall of glass, G. This time we find that, if the ball is displaced to position A and released, it swings to the wall and bounces back toward A. The cycle may repeat itself many times, but friction eventually brings the ball to rest. Once again the ball, which is moving to the right just before it hits the wall, is slowed down; that fact indicates that a force pointing to the left acts on the ball during the first half of the collision; and the fact that the ball starts moving back toward A immediately after the collision indicates that a force pointing to the left acts on it during the second half of the collision. Throughout the whole collision it experiences a force pointing

to the left. The wall, therefore, must experience a force pointing to the right.

There are two ways in which we can increase the momentary force exerted by the ball on the wall. One way, obviously, is to lift the ball to a position higher than A, and farther from the wall, before releasing it. This would give it a greater speed on impact. In other words, we can increase the effect of the collision by increasing the speed of the ball. Another way is to increase the inertial mass of the ball. A steel ball hits harder than a table-tennis ball even if both move at the same speed. It seems reasonable, then, that the product of the mass and the velocity—in other words, the momentum, mv —plays an important role in the force that is created during collision. It is not difficult to imagine that a table-tennis ball can be bounced against a window pane but that a steel ball hitting the same pane at the same speed will shatter it. The product mv is higher for the steel ball.

No laboratory model using a steel or table-tennis ball produces sufficiently elastic collisions to permit more than fifty or so collisions before the ball comes to rest. The very fact that we hear a

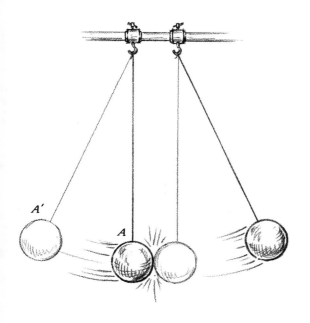

FIG. 29.3. *Elastic collision of two steel balls.*

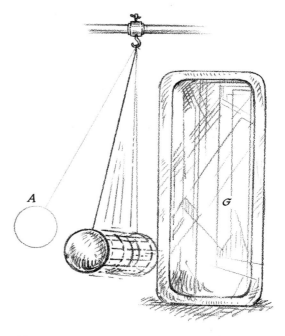

FIG. 29.4. *Elastic collision of one steel ball with a plane wall.*

click when two steel balls hit indicates that some of the collision energy goes into the energy of sound waves, which is radiated irretrievably.

Since our next step is to consider the logical consequences of the assumptions made by Clausius, it will pay you to make sure that you understand these qualitative ideas well before proceeding. We shall carry these ideas over to the motion of the molecules in a container.

29.4. The One-molecule Model of a Gas†

A fundamental rule in elementary kinetic theory seems to be that you should make as many simplifying assumptions as you can get away with because any reduction in the number of assumptions usually leads to enormous complications in the mathematical treatment. I listed, in § 29.2, four assumptions made by Clausius. If you reduce that number of assumptions to three by giving up any one of them, you will find that the mathematical treatment becomes more difficult. If, for example, you give up the fourth assumption, that there are no mutual forces of attraction or repulsion between the molecules, you will somehow or other have to deal with those forces (which do exist even though they are small). Try to think through the complications that will ensue if you do not assume, for example, that the molecules are identical spheres or that their collisions are perfectly elastic.

If it is true that increasing the number of assumptions simplifies a theory, we might even try making a few more assumptions. In the standard textbook treatment of this subject, in order to deal statistically with motions in random directions, it

† A quantitative treatment for N molecules appears in § 31.7.

is further assumed that all the molecules have the same speed, and that, if there are N molecules inside a container, $N/3$ are moving parallel to the x axis, $N/3$ are moving parallel to the y axis, and $N/3$ are moving parallel to the z axis, on the average. We are now going to assume that there is only one molecule in a cylinder, that it is moving with a constant speed, v, and that its collisions, which are with the two vertical plane walls, are perfectly elastic. We do this, not because we think there is a strong resemblance between this model and a real gas, but because we hope to learn something even from this over-simplified model.

Imagine, then, that we have a single molecule, of mass m, moving horizontally, with speed v, between two vertical walls consisting of a piston and the opposite end of its cylinder. We assume that the average force and hence the pressure exerted by the molecule on the piston (and by the piston on the molecule) is proportional to the number of impacts per second. Since speed times time equals distance, the time required to make one round trip between the two walls, separated by distance L, is $2L/v$ (Fig. 29.5.A), and the number of impacts per second is $v/2L$. If we arbitrarily call the pressure 1 in some system of units, and the volume 1, the product, PV, is 1.

We now change the volume by moving the piston to a new position, where the distance between it and the other wall is $L/2$ (Fig. 29.5.B). (We have to imagine that we can do this without touching the molecule in transit, for otherwise its speed would not remain constant.) Since the number of impacts per second on the piston is now twice what it was before, we expect the pressure to be 2, but the volume is now 1/2, and the product, PV, is therefore still 1. We repeat this process so that the distance between the piston

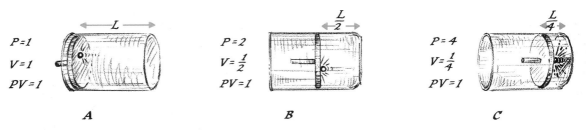

$P=1$	$P=2$	$P=4$
$V=1$	$V=\frac{1}{2}$	$V=\frac{1}{4}$
$PV=1$	$PV=1$	$PV=1$
A	**B**	**C**

FIG. 29.5. *Elastic collisions of one molecule with two opposite plane walls.*

and the other wall is $L/4$ (Fig. 29.5.C). Since the number of impacts per second has now been quadrupled, the pressure is now 4, and the volume is $1/4$, but the product, PV, is still 1.

Despite the great number of simplifying assumptions we have made, the result has physical significance. This model predicts that the product of pressure and volume will remain constant if the speed of the single molecule remains constant. You might begin consideration of a two-molecule case by imagining one molecule momentarily at rest in the middle of the cylinder while another one of the same kind, moving from right to left, is about to hit it head on. Since the collision is perfectly elastic and takes place between molecules of equal mass, all the energy of one is transferred to the other, which now moves to the left, hits the piston, bounces off it, and hits the first molecule, imparting to it all its kinetic energy. In a similar way, if you take the trouble to introduce other complications one by one, you may be able to convince yourself that the product of pressure and volume remains constant even if you have many molecules. If the molecules have the characteristics demanded by Clausius, it is not hard to convince yourself that PV is always a constant. More severe complications begin to set in when the molecules do not move parallel to the x axis, but here vector components come to our rescue. The x component of the velocity of a molecule that hits the piston will remain unchanged after impact except for a reversal of direction. The y and z components will be completely unaltered, and the speed,

$$\sqrt{v_x{}^2 + v_y{}^2 + v_z{}^2}$$

will be the same as before impact.

29.5. Experimental Test of the Gas Laws

Historically, experiments with gases came first, and theorizing came later. We have begun the other way round by formulating a very simple theory, and now we had better consider how to check it experimentally. We need to measure the pressure and the volume of a gas, and we shall use air as the gas. Figure 29.6 shows, in principle, how

we might do this. In practice one has to take into account the pressure that the sea of air in which we live exerts on everything submerged in it. But we can carry out, in thought, the experiment suggested by the figure, and we might follow this with a real laboratory experiment taking atmospheric pressure into account.

Figure 29.6.A shows a cylinder with a piston. We can calculate the volume of the air under compression simply by taking the cross-sectional area, A, of the cylinder and multiplying it by the height,

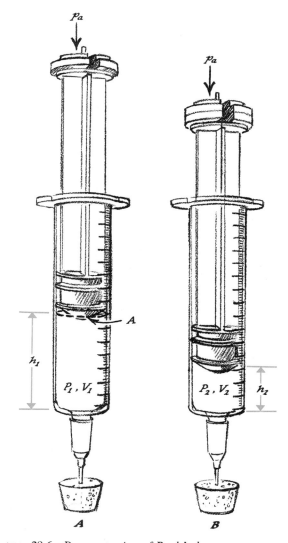

FIG. 29.6. *Demonstration of Boyle's law.*

h_1. We can obtain part of the pressure by taking the sum of the weight of the piston and any weight we have added to it and dividing by the cross-sectional area of the cylinder. To get the whole pressure, P_1, we should have to add the atmospheric pressure, p_a.

Figure 29.6.B shows what would happen to the volume if we put more weight on the piston. The new total weight, divided by the cross-sectional area, would give the new partial pressure, and the sum of this and the atmospheric pressure would be the new total pressure, P_2. Experiments of this sort, done with refined apparatus and with time for thermal equilibrium to set in before readings are taken, confirm the fact that

$$P_1V_1 = P_2V_2 = P_3V_3 = \ldots$$

That is, the product of pressure and volume actually is, experimentally, a constant. You can confirm this in the school laboratory with very simple apparatus. With the same apparatus you can also show that a slight warming of the air increases the pressure. The law that the product of pressure and volume is a constant—known as Boyle's law after Robert Boyle (1627–1691)—holds, therefore, only if the temperature is kept constant.

This confirms the predictions of our absurdly simple one-molecule model; and, since in that model we required the speed to be constant, we have demonstrated, at a very simple level, an interaction between theory and experiment. We see our first clue to the meaning of temperature. Since the theory required a constant speed and the experiment required a constant temperature, it looks as if temperature were related, somehow, to molecular speed.

Anyone who has pumped air into a tire knows that the pump gets hot. It can get appreciably warm from about twenty strokes. It is easy to show that this heat does not come primarily from friction between the piston and the cylinder: if the valve of the pump is left open, and the piston is stroked twenty times without compression, the pump does not get as warm as it did before. The heating must therefore have something to do with what the piston does to the molecules of the air when they are confined. The downward motion of the piston does, in fact, cause an increase in the average speed of the molecules. A simple illustration of this fact is represented in Figure 29.7. A table-tennis ball, suspended from the ceiling, is made to bounce between a tennis paddle, P, and a large glass brick, G. The ball is thrown against the glass brick; when it bounces, the paddle, simulating the motion of a piston, is moved toward the brick. The number of impacts per second with the paddle and the brick increases noticeably, but that alone is not proof that the average speed has increased, for a decrease in separation alone can increase the number of impacts per second. If the paddle is brought in slowly to a point near the brick, the final speed can be judged by the number of clicks heard per second; and if now, when the operation is repeated, the paddle is moved in much more rapidly to the same point, the number of clicks per second is greater, showing that moving in fast does increase the speed of the ball. It can also be shown that moving the paddle away from the brick decreases the speed of the ball. The classical example of speeding up on impact occurs in baseball. The speed of the ball before it is hit is obviously less than after it is hit—if the batter makes a good connection that will send the ball over the fence.

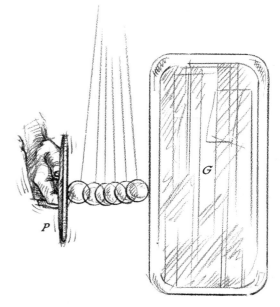

FIG. 29.7. *Analogy between the motion of a table-tennis ball and that of a gas molecule.*

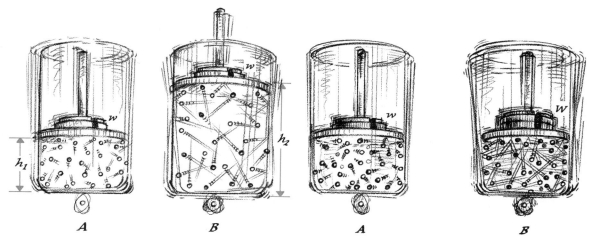

FIG. 29.8. *Model for the gas laws: increasing the average speed of the balls, at the same pressure, increases the volume.*

FIG. 29.9. *Model for the gas laws: increasing the average speed of the balls, at the same volume, increases the pressure.*

Going back to Figure 29.5, we can imagine how, even if the piston moves in at a speed considerably less than that of the molecule, it does, nevertheless, increase the molecule's speed a little every time the two collide, the result being that the molecule is going faster when the piston is halfway in than in the case (at constant speed) first illustrated by Figure 29.5.B. Another illustration of this idea can be obtained from Figure 29.8, in which the piston, with a weight, w, on it (A), is held up at height h_1 when the balls have a certain speed. If we drive the mechanism faster, thus increasing the average speed of the balls (B), the piston and the weight are lifted to a greater height, h_2. The pressure due to the piston and its weight has remained the same, but an increase in the average speed of the balls has produced an increase in volume. In the gaseous counterpart of this experiment (with molecules instead of steel balls) we can increase the volume of a gas at a constant pressure simply by raising its temperature.

We have been inadvertently led into using words like "temperature" and "heat." The word "temperature" belongs to our common vocabulary, and we know when certain things are hot or cold; but, as often happens in physics, our bodily sense is not good enough for accurate measurement—for that we need a thermometer. We know that a ther-

mometer can detect and measure changes in temperature that are either too small or too large to be sensed by our bodies. But, aside from the simple operational definition of temperature that we get from using thermometers, this chapter seems, so far, to be leading us into a direct association between the speed of molecules and this thing that we call temperature. Let us see if we can sharpen the meaning of this association.

We begin by performing, in thought, one more experiment with the apparatus of Figure 29.8. In Figure 29.9 we begin (A) with the situation as it was in Figure 29.8.A. The balls have a certain average speed and hold up a piston that supports a weight, w. If we now increase the average speed of the balls by increasing the speed of the driving mechanism, we may, instead of allowing the piston to rise to a greater height, as it did in Figure 29.8.B, put a greater weight, W, on it and thus keep it at the same height as before. In other words, we increase the pressure in order to keep the volume constant.

The experiments of Figures 29.8 and 29.9 may be summarized in the following two statements: (1) if the pressure is kept constant, the volume increases with the average speed of the balls; (2) if the volume is kept constant, the pressure increases with the average speed of the balls. Since we have already found, in our one-molecule model, a reason for believing that the product of pressure and volume remains constant when the speed of the molecule is constant, and since we have also seen, in experiments with real gases, that the product of the pressure and the volume of any sample of a gas is, as stated by Boyle's law, a constant when the temperature remains constant, we can now give "temperature" a quantitative mechanical meaning by writing

$$PV \propto NT \qquad [29.1$$

Here P stands for pressure, V for volume, N for the number of molecules in the sample, and T for temperature.† Expression 29.1 implies the existence of a constant of proportionality, which we shall call k. We may therefore rewrite the proportionality as an equation:

$$PV = kNT \qquad [29.2$$

Since this is a simple linear equation of the form $y = mx$ $[P = (kN/V)T]$, the plot of pressure against temperature, if the volume is constant, is a straight line going through the origin (Fig. 29.10). Since two points determine a line, and

† Strictly speaking, we should first prove that $P \propto N$ when T is constant. We can make this plausible by returning to the one-molecule model and imagining what happens to the pressure when we have two molecules moving at the same speed instead of one. The number of impacts per second doubles; so the pressure doubles. Next, we should have to prove that $P \propto T$ when N is fixed. Instead, since we are defining T, we are demanding that pressure be proportional to temperature. This particular temperature will be the so-called **absolute temperature**.

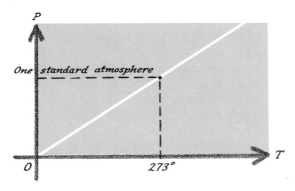

FIG. 29.10. *The plot of pressure,* P, *as a function of the absolute temperature,* T, *of a gas; it is a straight line whose slope is* kN/V.

since one point, the origin, is already determined for us, it is apparent that we can determine the constant, k, if we can make a reasonable choice for one set of P, V, N, and T. For P let us choose one standard atmosphere expressed in nt/m^2. For V we choose 22.4 liters. For the number of particles, N, we choose the Avogadro constant, $N_A = 6.02252 \times 10^{23}$. To keep the temperature constant, we decide to immerse the container of the gas in a mixture of ice and water at the temperature of melting ice.† We are at liberty to choose the numerical value of T to be associated with this; so, using foresight (to be explained in § 29.6), we choose 273.16°. Putting all these numbers into equation 29.2 and solving for k, we get $k = 1.38054 \times 10^{-23}$ J/°K. In other words, if you take a mole of a gas at standard pressure and temperature and choose 273.16 as the numerical value for T, you get $k = 1.38054 \times 10^{-23}$ J/°K. (This is called the Boltzmann constant.) For a moment in this discussion it was apparent that I was free to choose any number I pleased for the melting point of ice. Why did I choose the improbable-looking number 273.16? The explanation, which is rather involved, is presented briefly in the following section.

29.6. Temperature and Its Measurement

We've been considering temperature in a rather theoretical way. Let us back up and describe a set of operational steps that will help us to understand, first, how temperature is measured and, second, how the measurements made with practical thermometers can eventually be reconciled with the theoretical concept of temperature summarized in equation 29.2.

Everyone has seen a mercury thermometer. It is a glass capillary tube, with a bulb at one end, containing some mercury, which fills the bulb and part of the tube. If the bulb is warmed, the mer-

† Strictly speaking, we should use the temperature (273.16°K) at which ice, water, and water vapor can exist as a mixture—the so-called **triple point** of water. This is what is done in a standards laboratory. The temperature of an ice-water mixture at normal atmospheric pressure is close enough (273.15°K) to serve for our introductory discussion.

cury expands, and its expansion seems greatly magnified because the tube has a small bore: small changes in volume appear as great changes in length along the tube. Without numbers on it this instrument would be simply a *thermoscope;* it could tell us only that some objects were warmer or colder than others. But now we want to know how to calibrate an uncalibrated mercury thermometer. We need to have some standard temperatures.†

Here is a simple way to calibrate a thermometer (Fig. 29.11). First (A) we put our uncalibrated thermometer into a mixture of ice and water on a day when the atmospheric pressure is standard. After the mercury stops moving, we scratch a line on the tube at the top of the mercury and mark it 0. Next (B) we put the thermometer into a region that is full of the steam produced by water boiling at standard pressure. The new height of mercury is labeled 100. If we now divide the scale into 100 equal parts, we have a Celsius thermometer, named after Anders Celsius (1701–1744), who suggested the use of the melting and boiling of water for standard points on the thermometer. (The scale has often been called a centigrade scale because of the division into 100 equal parts.)

Having calibrated our thermometer, we can now go about exploring temperatures. If the thermometer is allowed to come to equilibrium in a room, for example, and we find that the mercury has climbed to a point that is one-quarter of the distance between 0 and 100, we label the point 25 and write the temperature as 25°C. (The C stands for Celsius. The procedure I have outlined is easy to visualize, but, as we saw earlier, the scale it produces is slightly different from the modern Celsius scale, which is based on the triple point of water.)

This is not the only way of making a thermometer. We could use, instead of the expansion of mercury, the changes in the pressure of a gas of constant volume. Figure 29.12 illustrates a device for doing this. We immerse container C, containing a gas such as hydrogen, in a mixture of ice and

† The Celsius scale is based on one fixed point, the triple point of water, not on two. The two-point method to be described yields a calibration that is distinguishable from the Celsius scale only with very refined instruments.

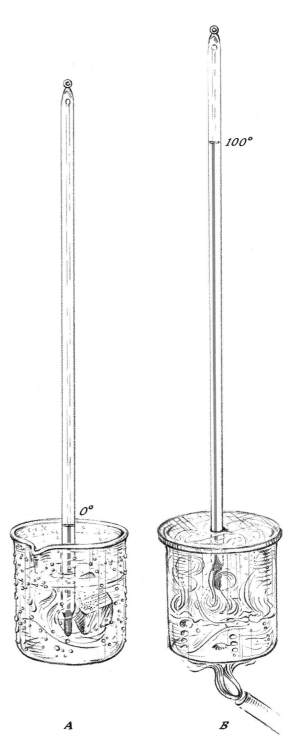

FIG. 29.11. *Calibrating a Celsius thermometer.*

water, and we find the pressure, as shown by a dial gauge, G, to be P_i. Next we immerse the container in steam and get the reading P_s (s for steam). Finally, we bring the container out—into the room, for example—and let it come to equilibrium. This time we find the pressure P. We now have three readings of pressure, P_i, P_s, and P. How do we get a temperature reading out of these? This equation tells us how to get a reading based on the Celsius scale:

$$t = \frac{P - P_i}{P_s - P_i} \times 100 \qquad [29.3$$

Instead of trying to derive this equation, I shall simply show that it is reasonable. When the variable P takes on the value P_i, for example, $t = 0$; when the variable P takes on the value P_s, $t = 100$; and this shows that we have created a Celsius thermometer, for it reads 0 when immersed in icewater and 100 when surrounded by steam at standard pressure. If we now allow this thermometer to come to equilibrium in the room in which the mercury thermometer reads 25°C, for example, what reason have we to believe that it also will read 25°C? The truth is that we don't have any

FIG. 29.12. *A constant-volume gas thermometer.*

good reason for believing so, but the experimental fact is that the two thermometers agree pretty closely.

There are other **thermometric properties**—that is, properties that vary with the temperature. The resistance of electrical conductors is one example. From such properties we could obtain numbers to substitute for the several values of P in equation 29.3. In other words, there are many ways of building a thermometer with fixed points at the freezing and boiling points of water, and fortunately there is fairly good agreement among the different kinds, at least in the range between melting ice and boiling water. The constant-volume gas thermometer has certain advantages that make it a better standard than the ordinary mercury thermometer. Nevertheless, I shall describe an experiment that can be done in the laboratory with a mercury thermometer as the temporary standard to give some idea of where the number 273 came from originally.

If, using the apparatus of Figure 29.12, we obtain different pressures, P, at different temperatures, t, the temperature being read from a mercury thermometer, we find that, when we plot pressure against temperature, as in Figure 29.13, the points lie fairly accurately on a straight line—not only the three points corresponding to melting ice, steam, and room temperature, but the points corresponding to other temperatures of the bath that surrounds container C. The amount of gas first introduced into C was arbitrary. If we now repeat the experiment with a different mass of gas, the data plotted land on a different straight line, but it is found that the two straight lines, when extended, meet at a point on the negative side of the t axis. This point is close to $-273°$ on the Celsius scale. And we get this same number (approximately) whatever the number, and whatever the kind, of molecules in container C. This suggests immediately that, if a new temperature (T) scale is chosen with its zero at the point of intersection of all these lines so that the zero of the new P axis occurs at the same point, and if the temperature variable is now called T instead of t, the equation for these lines will always be of the form

$$P = (\text{constant})T \qquad [29.4$$

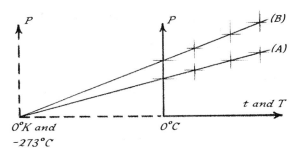

FIG. 29.13. *Experimental values of the pressure,* P, *in a gas, plotted against the Celsius temperature,* t, *on a straight line* (A) *within a certain range of values of* P. *Another set of values of* P, *obtained with a different mass of the same gas, lie on a different straight line* (B) *when plotted against* t. *Extrapolating these lines to the left, we find that they both meet the* t *axis very close to* t = −273°C.

I must emphasize here that real experiments do not give perfect agreement in the intersection of the curves for *P* against *t*. A severe extrapolation is called for, and a careful examination would reveal that the experimental points do not land perfectly on a straight line. This treatment of the subject must be considered only a rough introduction to the ideas that led eventually to the **absolute scale of temperature,** also called the **Kelvin scale** after Lord Kelvin (1824–1907), which is related to the Celsius scale according to the formula

$$T = t + 273.16 \qquad [29.5$$

We have now reconciled our experiments with the theoretical equation $PV = kNT$. Since this equation (29.2) is correct whatever gas is used, k is a universal constant. When pressure is measured in newtons per square meter and volume in cubic meters, the product PV comes out in joules. Hence the unit of k is J/°K, which is read as joules per degree Kelvin.†

29.7. Summary

An ordinary sample of a gas has so many particles in it that the only way to deal with their motion is to study their average behavior. By making several simplifying assumptions about them, Clausius evolved a model that accounts very well for many of the properties of gases. He assumed, for example, that the molecules of a gas behave like tiny elastic spheres. It is necessary, therefore, to understand the forces that arise when one elastic sphere hits another or hits the wall of a container.

By such considerations we are led in a very natural way to understand the gas laws and, in particular, why the product of pressure and volume in a gas is a constant if the temperature is constant. We are led, in fact, to the concept of absolute temperature itself. The expression $PV = kNT$, in which $k = 1.38054 \times 10^{-23}$ J/°K, representing the energy per molecule per absolute (Kelvin) degree in a gas, follows logically.

In practice the transition from t, the temperature on the Celsius scale, to T, the temperature on the Kelvin scale, is made by use of the equation $T = t + 273.16$.

† The constant k, whose value is 1.38054×10^{-23} J/°K, represents the average kinetic energy of translation per molecule per degree Kelvin if the number of molecules is large enough so that we may consider the properties of the gas to be statistically predictable and if the density of the molecules is low enough so that Clausius' assumptions hold.

Problems

This chapter is a simple and almost completely qualitative introduction to § 31.7, in which the kinetic theory of gases is developed in a more rigorous and quantitative manner. If you find these problems too simple, do not despair; the problems of Chap. 31 will be more sophisticated.

29.1. In order to hold up w in Fig. 29.1, the average force exerted by the little balls must be greater in B than in A. Considering the explanation given in the text, do you think it likely that this increased force is due to a greater average speed of the balls or only to a greater number of impacts per second on the piston?

29.2. Suppose that the transition from A to B, in Fig. 29.2, is achieved very suddenly. If the weight is left on the plunger of the syringe for a few minutes after the compression, would you expect h_1 to increase or to decrease slightly with time? Explain.

29.3. If the ball on the left of Fig. 29.3 is 1/10 as massive as the ball on the right, describe what you think will be the subsequent behavior of the balls once the former has been displaced and released. Consider especially the speeds of the balls. If both heavy and light balls are moving around inside a cylinder, which do you think will be going faster, on the average? Explain.

29.4. Two identical balls of putty collide after traveling in the same straight line in opposite directions with equal speeds. After they hit, they come to a dead stop. Compare the force that one ball exerts on the other with the force that would have been felt by the first ball if the second ball had been replaced by a smooth and solid wall. Explain your answer in terms of $\Delta(mv)/\Delta t$.

29.5. 1. Imagine, in Fig. 29.5, two balls instead of one, moving parallel to each other and at right angles to the wall and the piston. What effect does this assumption have on the argument that led to the statement that PV is a constant?

2. If the two balls were identical except that one had twice the mass of the other, what effect would this have on the argument that led to the statement that PV is a constant?

29.6. In Fig. 29.6, $P_1 = 1.5$ atm (1 atm is very close to 10^5 nt/m²), $V_1 = 8.0 \times 10^{-6}$ m³, and A is 10^{-4} m².

1. If $P_2 = 2.0$ atm, what is V_2?

2. What is the total weight, in newtons, of the piston and the object on it shown in A?

3. What is the weight, in newtons, of the extra object on the piston in B?

29.7. (This is just a straight "plug-in" type of problem, but you must use correct units to get the right answer.) A container has a volume of 2.0×10^{-3} m³. It is full of molecules of a homogeneous gas. The pressure is 0.49×10^5 nt/m² (about 1/2 atm) at a temperature of 22°C. How many molecules does it contain?

29.8. In Fig. 29.13, which graph, A or B, represents the experiment with the larger mass of gas? Explain your answer. In which case would you expect to be able to get experimental points at a lower temperature? (Remember that, as a gas gets colder, it tends to turn into a liquid.)

The Conservation
of Linear Momentum

THE CONCEPT of momentum was intro-
duced in a footnote as early as Chapter 3 and has
often recurred, for it was used in the definition
of force (§ 24.1) and in the discussion of Newton's
third law (Chap. 26), but I have waited until
now to illustrate quantitatively the meaning and
importance of the conservation of linear momentum. Wherever I use the word "momentum"
without a modifier, such as "angular," I mean
linear momentum.

30.1. Linear Momentum

If you raise a steel ball above the floor and
release it, it picks up speed as it falls. You can
increase the damage it does to the floor in two
ways. One way is to drop it from a higher position; this increases the speed with which it lands.
The other way is, while keeping the height fixed
and thereby keeping the speed at impact constant,
to increase the mass; if the ball is hollow, for
example, you can do this by adding lead shot to
its interior, or you can use a heavier ball. The
factors we are dealing with are the mass, m, and
the velocity, $\mathbf{v}$. Their product is called the **linear
momentum,** for which we use the symbol $\mathbf{p}$:

$$\mathbf{p} = m\mathbf{v}$$

Momentum is a vector. Its direction is that of
the velocity, and its magnitude is m times the
magnitude of the velocity vector.

We all have an intuitive appreciation of momentum. We don't hesitate to play table tennis
near a window, for we know from experience
that, even if the ball hits the window at high
speed, it won't break it. Because its mass is slight,
we sense intuitively that it cannot exert too great
a force on the window pane. But no one would
throw at the window, at the same speed, a steel
ball of the same size—unless he wanted to break
the window. We *know* that a greater mass gives
the ball the ability to exert a greater force.

We have already encountered a particular combination of m and v—namely, $\frac{1}{2}mv^2$ (kinetic energy), which plays an important role in mechanics.
Around it and the other forms of energy has
evolved the very useful concept of the conservation of energy. Mechanical energy, we found, is
never completely conserved, for some is always
dissipated in the form of heat. The momentum
of a set of particles, on the other hand, is always
conserved in a collision, even when the mechanical energy is not. In the principle of the conservation of linear momentum, as in that of the
conservation of energy, we have a powerful generalization that will simplify the solution of many
problems.

That the momentum of a single particle is conserved is nothing new. I have asserted all along
that a single particle moving with velocity $\mathbf{v}$ will
continue to do so unless acted upon by an ex-

ternal force. Since the velocity is constant, the momentum, $\mathbf{p} = m\mathbf{v}$, is constant. The great power of this generalization arises from the fact that it is true even when we deal with *many particles*, each moving with its own velocity. The vector sum of the individual momenta is conserved if there are no external forces. This is an experimental fact of such importance that it deserves emphasis: the bodies of a system may collide, and each may change its velocity, but the *vector sum of their momenta remains constant if no external force acts on them*. This is an illustration of the **law of the conservation of linear momentum**, which states that the linear momentum of a system is constant if the vector sum of the forces acting on it is zero.

I shall show many examples of this law in the next chapter. For the present, I wish to discuss the basic role that the product $m\mathbf{v}$, called momentum, plays in the theory of dynamics.

30.2. Force as Rate of Change of Momentum

In this Einstein and Newton agree: *force is the rate of change of momentum;* that is, if $\mathbf{p} = m\mathbf{v}$, the resultant force, $\mathbf{F}$, acting on the body obeys the equation

$$\mathbf{F} = \lim_{\Delta t = 0} \frac{\Delta \mathbf{p}}{\Delta t} \qquad [30.1$$

This expression of Newton's second law, which is the mathematically precise one, requires passing to the limit as Δt approaches zero. The ratio $\Delta \mathbf{p}/\Delta t$ alone is only an approximate value of $\mathbf{F}$; it is the value of the average force in the interval Δt. For the sake of mathematical simplicity we shall continue to use only $\Delta \mathbf{p}/\Delta t$ in this chapter. The approximate value will not invalidate the physical principles we develop, but we need to keep in mind that it is only an approximation, which becomes better as we take smaller and smaller values of Δt.

What was not, for good reasons, apparent to Newton is that the momentum of a body does not increase *linearly* with velocity. Until Einstein came along, it was believed that the graph of momentum against velocity was a straight line through the origin (Fig. 30.1, curve A). It was

believed that momentum varied directly with velocity and that you could, by the application of a force, increase the velocity of a body indefinitely. This is equivalent to saying that the m in $m\mathbf{v}$ is a constant.

But we have already seen (§ 28.8) that experiments with electrons prove that their mass increases with their speed. For this and other reasons we now think that the m in the formula $\mathbf{p} = m\mathbf{v}$ cannot be considered a constant. A constant m would imply a curve of momentum like the straight line A of Figure 30.1. Instead, experiment and Einstein's theory of relativity agree that curve B is the graph of momentum against velocity.

For values of v/c less than about 0.3 it is difficult to distinguish between the values of A and those of B. As v/c goes from 0.8 to 0.9, however, curve B predicts a substantially greater increase in momentum than curve A, and many experiments have been done to test this prediction. The relativistic expression for momentum is still $m\mathbf{v}$, but in terms of the rest mass, m_0, we should write

$$\mathbf{p} = \frac{m_0 \mathbf{v}}{\sqrt{1 - v^2/c^2}} \qquad [30.2$$

We can no longer assume that we shall always be dealing with particles that move much more

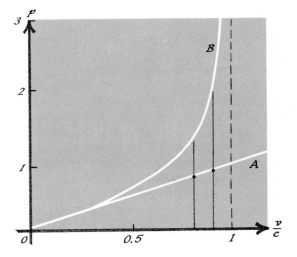

FIG. 30.1. *Two plots, the old (A) and the new (B), of momentum against velocity.*

slowly than light. Right in your living room there is probably a TV receiver in which electrons may be moving at a speed 0.3 of the speed of light or even faster.

Since the formula $\mathbf{F} = \Delta\mathbf{p}/\Delta t$ is applicable at high speeds, we can still say that, if $\mathbf{F} = 0$, $\Delta\mathbf{p} = 0$ or—what amounts to the same thing— if $\mathbf{F} = 0$, $\mathbf{p} - \mathbf{p}_0 = 0$, and therefore $\mathbf{p} = \mathbf{p}_0$. *The momentum of a particle is conserved if no unbalanced force acts on it.* If such a force does act on it, the magnitude of this force is simply $\Delta\mathbf{p}/\Delta t$.

EXAMPLE 30.1. 1. A body's initial momentum, p_0, is 2.0 kg-m/sec; its final momentum, p, is 3.0 kg-m/sec. We wish to know the average force acting on the body if the change was effected in 0.2 sec. Assume that the motion took place in a straight line.

Our given quantities are

$$p = 3.0 \text{ kg-m/sec}$$
$$p_0 = 2.0 \text{ kg-m/sec}$$
$$\Delta t = 0.2 \text{ sec}$$

Using the formula

$$\mathbf{F} = \frac{\Delta\mathbf{p}}{\Delta t} = \frac{\mathbf{p} - \mathbf{p}_0}{\Delta t}$$

and dropping the vector notation, we get

$$F = \frac{(3.0 - 2.0) \text{ kg-m/sec}}{0.2 \text{ sec}}$$

$$= \frac{1 \text{ kg-m}}{0.2 \text{ sec}^2}$$

$$= 5.0 \text{ nt}$$

We don't know whether the body was moving with a high relativistic speed, and we don't care, for the *momenta* were given, and the formula $\mathbf{F} = \Delta\mathbf{p}/\Delta t$ applies to any speed.

2. Assuming that the body's mass is 1 kg, let us find its final speed.

Using the formula

$$p = mv$$

we get

$$v = \frac{p}{m} = \frac{3.0 \text{ kg-m/sec}}{1 \text{ kg}}$$

$$= 3 \text{ m/sec}$$

Compared with the speed of light, c, this is a very small value for v. We are safely in the non-relativistic realm.

3. We now assume that the body's mass is 10^{-8} kg. (Since 10^{-8} kg $= 10^{-8} \times 10^3$ gm $= 10^{-5}$ gm $= 10 \times 10^{-6}$ gm $= 10$ micrograms, it is a small mass, but it is weighable on a sensitive modern balance.) Let us find the final speed.

Using again the formula

$$p = mv$$

we get

$$v = \frac{p}{m} = \frac{3.0 \text{ kg-m/sec}}{10^{-8} \text{ kg}}$$

$$= 3 \times 10^8 \text{ m/sec}$$

This, we know, is the speed of light, c, and hence our assumption about the body's mass cannot be true. If we mean, however, that the body's *rest mass* (m_0) is 10^{-8} kg, we can proceed as follows:

$$p = \frac{m_0 v}{\sqrt{1 - v^2/c^2}}$$

$$\frac{p}{m_0} = \frac{v}{\sqrt{1 - v^2/c^2}}$$

Earlier in this example you were told that $p/m_0 = c$. Therefore

$$c^2 = \frac{v^2}{1 - v^2/c^2}$$

$$c^2 \left(1 - \frac{v^2}{c^2}\right) = v^2$$

$$c^2 - \frac{c^2 v^2}{c^2} = v^2$$

$$c^2 = 2v^2$$

$$v = \frac{c}{\sqrt{2}}$$

$$= \frac{\sqrt{2}}{2} c = 0.707c$$

We conclude that a body whose rest mass is 10^{-8} kg can have a momentum of 3.0 kg-m/sec if it is moving with a speed about 0.7 that of light!

30.3. Momentum of Several Particles

It is an experimental fact that the vector sum of the momenta of the different particles comprising a system of particles remains unchanged if no forces external to the system act. Let us investigate some of the implications of this fact.

First let us try to illustrate what we mean by forces that are internal to a system. In Figure

30.2 the force exerted by the spring on the body of mass m_1 acts simultaneously but in the opposite direction on the body of mass m_2. Such forces are internal. The force applied to either body by a string tied to it alone would be an external force.

Imagine the system consisting of a body, having mass m_1 and moving so its momentum is $\mathbf{p}_1$, and another body, having mass m_2 and moving so its momentum is $\mathbf{p}_2$, the two bodies being connected by a spring, of negligible mass, that can exert a force on each of them. The total momentum is

$$\mathbf{p} = \mathbf{p}_1 + \mathbf{p}_2 \qquad [30.3$$

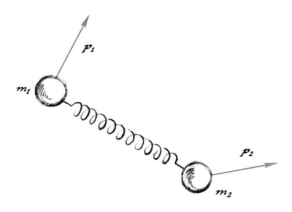

FIG. 30.2. *System consisting of two moving bodies connected by a spring of negligible mass.*

A small interval of time, Δt, later, each of these quantities has changed to new values, $\mathbf{p}'$, $\mathbf{p}_1'$, $\mathbf{p}_2'$, such that

$$\mathbf{p}' = \mathbf{p}_1' + \mathbf{p}_2' \qquad [30.4$$

Subtracting, we get

$$\mathbf{p}' - \mathbf{p} = (\mathbf{p}_1' - \mathbf{p}_1) + (\mathbf{p}_2' - \mathbf{p}_2) \qquad [30.5$$

$$\Delta\mathbf{p} = \Delta\mathbf{p}_1 + \Delta\mathbf{p}_2 \qquad [30.6$$

Dividing through by Δt, we get

$$\frac{\Delta\mathbf{p}}{\Delta t} = \frac{\Delta\mathbf{p}_1}{\Delta t} + \frac{\Delta\mathbf{p}_2}{\Delta t} \qquad [30.7$$

Using equation 30.1, we get

$$\frac{\Delta\mathbf{p}}{\Delta t} = \mathbf{F}_1 + \mathbf{F}_2 \qquad [30.8$$

The force, $\mathbf{F}_1$, acting on m_1 could have an internal component, $\mathbf{F}_{1i}$, and an external component, $\mathbf{F}_{1e}$. Similar remarks apply to $\mathbf{F}_2$. Therefore

$$\frac{\Delta\mathbf{p}}{\Delta t} = \mathbf{F}_{1i} + \mathbf{F}_{1e} + \mathbf{F}_{2i} + \mathbf{F}_{2e} \qquad [30.9$$

$$\frac{\Delta\mathbf{p}}{\Delta t} = (\mathbf{F}_{1i} + \mathbf{F}_{2i}) + (\mathbf{F}_{1e} + \mathbf{F}_{2e}) \qquad [30.10$$

Generalizing to many bodies and many forces, we get

$$\frac{\Delta\mathbf{p}}{\Delta t} = \Sigma\mathbf{F}_i + \Sigma\mathbf{F}_e \qquad [30.11$$

The experimental fact that $\Delta\mathbf{p} = 0$ when $\mathbf{F}_e = 0$ *requires* that $\Sigma\mathbf{F}_i = 0$. One way to explain this condition is to assume that the internal forces occur in equal and opposite pairs—as stated by Newton's third law.

Once again we see the intimate relation between

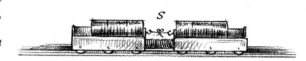

FIG. 30.3. *System illustrating Example 30.2.*

the conservation of momentum and Newton's third law. The present view is that the conservation of momentum is the basic principle, being derivable from experiment. From it we *deduce*, in certain cases, that each force has an equal and opposite counterforce. What we believe is always true is that

$$\frac{\Delta\mathbf{p}}{\Delta t} = \Sigma\mathbf{F}_e \qquad [30.12$$

That is, the vector sum of the external forces is the rate of change in the momentum of the whole system. If the vector sum of the external forces is zero, $\Delta\mathbf{p} = 0$; that is, *the total momentum of a system of particles is conserved if the vector sum of the external forces acting on the system is zero.*

EXAMPLE 30.2. A system (Fig. 30.3) consists of two carts, of masses m_1 and m_2, resting on a frictionless horizontal table, with a spring compressed between them, and held together by a string, S. We must describe the motion of the carts that occurs when the string is burned. What happens, of course, is that the carts move apart so rapidly that we shall call this an explosion.

Let the final velocity of m_1 be $\mathbf{v}_1$ and that of m_2

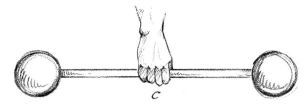

FIG. 30.4. *The center of mass,* C, *of a dumbbell is half-way between the centers of the balls. If pulled at* C, *the dumbbell can be lifted without rotation; the total weight acts as if it were concentrated there.*

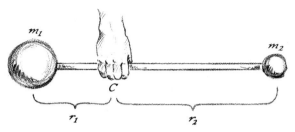

FIG. 30.5. *Lifting a dumbbell with balls of unequal masses.*

be v_2. Since there are no external forces (weight and normal reactions cancel), linear momentum is conserved: $\Delta\mathbf{p} = 0$, $\mathbf{p} - \mathbf{p}_0 = 0$, $\mathbf{p} = \mathbf{p}_0$.

The total momentum after the explosion must equal the total momentum before the explosion. Remember, momentum is a vector.

$$m_1\mathbf{v}_1 + m_2\mathbf{v}_2 = \mathbf{0} \qquad [30.13$$

$$m_1\mathbf{v}_1 = -m_2\mathbf{v}_2 \qquad [30.14$$

This says that vectors $\mathbf{v}_1$ and $\mathbf{v}_2$ have opposite directions.

Dropping the vector notation and solving for v_2, we get

$$v_2 = -\frac{m_1}{m_2}v_1 \qquad [30.15$$

If $m_1/m_2 = 10$, for example, the cart of mass m_2 will move ten times as fast as the cart of mass m_1. Notice that, though we don't have enough information to specify what v_1 is numerically (that depends on the energy stored in the spring), we can specify the ratio of the two speeds.

30.4. Center of Mass of a System of Particles

Everyone knows that a heavy dumbbell (Fig. 30.4) can be lifted by a force equal to its total weight applied at the midpoint of the rod joining

the balls. The weight of the dumbbell acts as if it were concentrated at that point.

If the balls (Fig. 30.5) have unequal masses, m_1 and m_2, an upward force equal to $(m_1 + m_2)\mathbf{g}$, applied at a point, C, located so that $m_1r_1 = m_2r_2$, can lift the whole system without rotation. This point is the **center of mass** of this system.†

A mathematical formula for the center of mass of two particles can be given in vector form. Let $\mathbf{r}_1$ be the vector that locates the particle of mass m_1; let $\mathbf{r}_2$ be the vector that locates the particle of mass m_2 (Fig. 30.6). The vector that locates the center of mass is, by definition,

$$\mathbf{r}_c = \frac{m_1\mathbf{r}_1 + m_2\mathbf{r}_2}{m_1 + m_2} \qquad [30.16$$

I shall show that this gives the right result in a few special cases.

If, for example, $m_1 = m_2$, then

$$\mathbf{r}_c = \frac{\mathbf{r}_1 + \mathbf{r}_2}{2} \qquad [30.17$$

In Figure 30.7 we see the resultant vector, $\mathbf{r}_1 + \mathbf{r}_2$. Because the diagonals of a parallelogram bisect each other, it is apparent that $(\mathbf{r}_1 + \mathbf{r}_2)/2$ is a vector whose terminal point lies halfway between m_1 and m_2, which we know intuitively to be the location of the center of mass. In other words, equation 30.16 holds in this trivial case.

Next consider (Fig. 30.8) a case in which $m_1 =$

† The **center of gravity** is the same as the center of mass if the gravitational field is constant in direction and magnitude for all particles of the system.

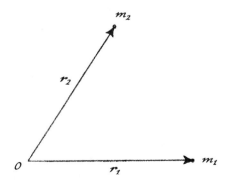

FIG. 30.6. *Locating two particles by two vectors from a common origin.*

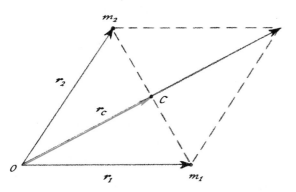

FIG. 30.7. *Locating the center of mass of the two particles of Fig. 30.6.*

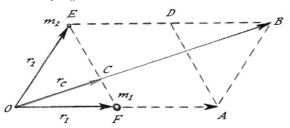

FIG. 30.8. *Locating the center of mass when the mass of one particle is twice the mass of the other.*

2 kg and $m_2 = 1$ kg. Equation 30.16 becomes

$$\mathbf{r}_c = \frac{2\mathbf{r}_1 + \mathbf{r}_2}{2 + 1} = \frac{2\mathbf{r}_1 + \mathbf{r}_2}{3}$$

Let **OA** represent $2\mathbf{r}_1$. We use the parallelogram construction: $\mathbf{OB} = 2\mathbf{r}_1 + \mathbf{r}_2$. Since $\mathbf{OF} = \mathbf{r}_1 = \mathbf{FA} = \mathbf{DB}$, we can prove that the point, C, located by $\mathbf{r}_c = \mathbf{OB}/3$ is on the line joining m_1 and m_2 and is nearer the particle with the greater mass.

Finally, let us use, as the origin of our vectors, point C, which is the center of mass of the system consisting of particles of masses m_1 and m_2 (Fig. 30.9). We locate m_1 by $\mathbf{r}_1$ and m_2 by $\mathbf{r}_2$. Since C is the center of mass, $\mathbf{r}_c = \mathbf{0}$. Equation 30.16 therefore becomes

$$m_1\mathbf{r}_1 + m_2\mathbf{r}_2 = \mathbf{0}$$
$$m_1\mathbf{r}_1 = -m_2\mathbf{r}_2$$

As far as magnitudes are concerned, this is what we learned from Figure 30.5.

There are many practical ways of finding the center of mass of solid objects. In general, if an object is homogeneous in density and has an

axis of symmetry, the center of mass is on that axis. This alone simplifies the problem in many cases. We can find the center of mass of a flat object by suspending it from a point (such as P in Fig. 30.10) on the object. The center of mass lies on the vertical line produced by a plumb bob suspended from that point. Suspending the object and the bob from two different points (P and P') yields two different lines. Since the center of mass, C, is on each of these, it must be on their intersection.

We are not, however, primarily interested in the practical problem of locating the center of mass of different objects. Let us turn to the application of equation 30.16 to the dynamical behavior of a set of particles.

30.5. Acceleration of the Center of Mass of a System of Particles

In the early part of the chapter, I stressed $\mathbf{F} = \Delta\mathbf{p}/\Delta t$ as the proper equation of motion. We now consider a non-relativistic example in which we can write, instead, with good approximation,

$$\mathbf{F} = m\frac{\Delta v}{\Delta t}$$

That is, we shall deal with mass as a constant. Our formula is, of course (in the limit as Δt approaches 0), equivalent to $\mathbf{F} = m\mathbf{a}$.

The system in Figure 30.11 consists of two particles of masses m_1 and m_2. By letting M equal $m_1 + m_2$ we write equation 30.16 in the form

$$M\mathbf{r}_c = m_1\mathbf{r}_1 + m_2\mathbf{r}_2 \qquad [30.18$$

We now let each vector take on an increment in time Δt:

$$M\Delta\mathbf{r}_c = m_1\Delta\mathbf{r}_1 + m_2\Delta\mathbf{r}_2 \qquad [30.19$$

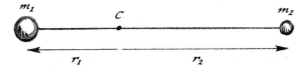

FIG. 30.9. *If we use as the origin the center of mass of two particles of masses* m_1 *and* m_2, *the magnitudes of the vectors* $\mathbf{r}_1$ *and* $\mathbf{r}_2$ *are in the ratio* m_2/m_1.

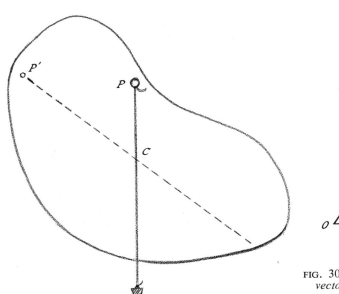

FIG. 30.10. *Finding the center of mass of a flat object.*

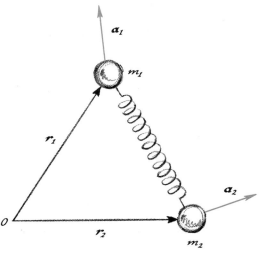

FIG. 30.11. *One particle, of mass* m_1 *and located by vector* $\mathbf{r}_1$, *has acceleration* $\mathbf{a}_1$. *Another particle, of mass* m_2 *and located by vector* $\mathbf{r}_2$, *has acceleration* $\mathbf{a}_2$. *The acceleration,* $\mathbf{a}_c$, *of the center of mass is the vector sum of the external forces divided by the sum of the masses.*

We divide by Δt:

$$M \frac{\Delta \mathbf{r}_c}{\Delta t} = m_1 \frac{\Delta \mathbf{r}_1}{\Delta t} + m_2 \frac{\Delta \mathbf{r}_2}{\Delta t} \qquad [30.20$$

or

$$M\mathbf{v}_c = m_1 \mathbf{v}_1 + m_2 \mathbf{v}_2 \qquad [30.21$$

Repeating the argument, we get

$$M \Delta \mathbf{v}_c = m_1 \Delta \mathbf{v}_1 + m_2 \Delta \mathbf{v}_2 \qquad [30.22$$

$$M \frac{\Delta \mathbf{v}_c}{\Delta t} = m_1 \frac{\Delta \mathbf{v}_1}{\Delta t} + m_2 \frac{\Delta \mathbf{v}_2}{\Delta t} \qquad [30.23$$

from which we may obtain, in the limit as Δt approaches 0,

$$M\mathbf{a}_c = m_1 \mathbf{a}_1 + m_2 \mathbf{a}_2 \qquad [30.24$$

We suppose that m_1 is acted on by $\mathbf{F}_1$, which is external, and $\mathbf{F}_{12}$, which is internal. Then

$$\mathbf{F}_1 + \mathbf{F}_{12} = m_1 \mathbf{a}_1 \qquad [30.25$$

Similarly,

$$\mathbf{F}_2 + \mathbf{F}_{21} = m_2 \mathbf{a}_2 \qquad [30.26$$

Adding, we get

$$\mathbf{F}_1 + \mathbf{F}_2 + (\mathbf{F}_{12} + \mathbf{F}_{21}) = m_1 \mathbf{a}_1 + m_2 \mathbf{a}_2 \qquad [30.27$$

Assuming that the sum of the internal forces vanishes, we get, for the sum of the external forces,

$$\Sigma \mathbf{F}_e = m_1 \mathbf{a}_1 + m_2 \mathbf{a}_2 \qquad [30.28$$

Putting this into equation 30.24, we get

$$M\mathbf{a}_c = \Sigma \mathbf{F}_e \qquad [30.29$$

$$\mathbf{a}_c = \frac{\Sigma \mathbf{F}_e}{M} \qquad [30.30$$

This expression means that *we can find the acceleration of the center of mass by taking the vector sum of all the external forces and dividing it by the total mass of the system.*

The equation (30.16) that defines the center of mass of two particles can be extended to more than two particles, and the analysis that leads to equation 30.30 can be shown to hold quite generally for many particles. The center of mass is, indeed, a unique and useful point. We can predict its behavior if we know the vector sum of the external forces, wherever they may be applied. Here are a few examples.

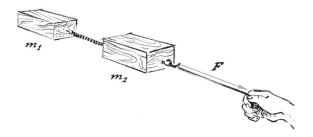

FIG. 30.12. *System illustrating Example 30.3.*

EXAMPLE 30.3. Two blocks, of masses m_1 and m_2, are connected by a massless spring (Fig. 30.12). They rest on a frictionless horizontal table. A force, **F**, pulls on m_2 to the right. We are to discuss the acceleration of the system. Putting equation 30.30 into the form that is applicable to this case, we get

$$\mathbf{a}_c = \frac{\mathbf{F}}{m_1 + m_2} \qquad [30.31$$

Let us see if we can get the same result by isolating first m_2 and then m_1 (Fig. 30.13, in which **T** is the tension in the spring). Dropping the vector notation, we have

$$m_2: \quad F - T = m_2 a_2$$
$$m_1: \quad T = m_1 a_1$$

Eventually $a_1 = a_2 = a_c$. Therefore, adding these equations, we get

$$F - T + T = (m_1 + m_2)a_c$$
$$a_c = \frac{F}{m_1 + m_2}$$

which confirms equation 30.31, which, you will note, implies that, if **F** is constant, the acceleration of the center of mass will be constant. Since the block of mass m_2 starts moving first, the center of mass will, of course, start moving at the same time, even before m_1 picks up the same speed as m_2.

EXAMPLE 30.4. Suppose now (Fig. 30.14) that, instead of pulling, we push on m_1 with force **F**. Equation 30.31 once again predicts that

$$\mathbf{a}_c = \frac{\mathbf{F}}{m_1 + m_2}$$

Dropping the vector notation, we analyze this ex-

periment (Fig. 30.15) by isolating first m_1 and then m_2:

$$m_1: \quad F - T = m_1 a_1$$
$$m_2: \quad T = m_2 a_2$$

Again T is the tension in the spring. Eventually $a_1 = a_2 = a_c$. Therefore, adding these equations, we get

$$F - T + T = (m_1 + m_2)a_c$$
$$a_c = \frac{F}{m_1 + m_2}$$

which again confirms equation 30.31. Notice that the initial behavior is different: the block of mass m_1 will start moving first. This will push the center of mass to the right immediately, but in both cases the acceleration of the center of mass of the system depends on the vector sum of the applied forces, whatever their points of application. It is quite plausible, therefore, that the behavior of the center of mass is accurately described by equation 30.30. The essential point to remember is that, regardless of the points of application of the forces that make up $\Sigma \mathbf{F}_e$, the center of mass acts as if all the mass of the system were concentrated there.

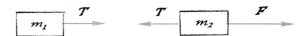

FIG. 30.13. *Analysis of the system of Fig. 30.12.*

FIG. 30.14. *System illustrating Example 30.4.*

FIG. 30.15. *Analysis of the system of Fig. 30.14.*

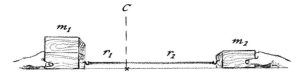

FIG. 30.16. *System illustrating Example 30.5.*

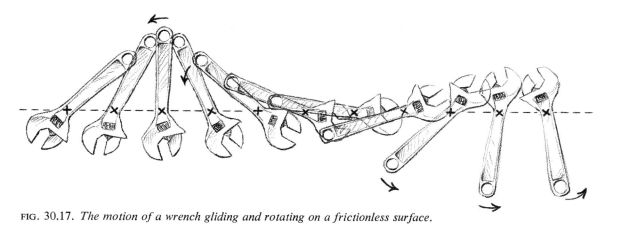

FIG. 30.17. *The motion of a wrench gliding and rotating on a frictionless surface.*

EXAMPLE 30.5. Consider the behavior of two blocks initially at rest but released simultaneously and pulled together by a rubber band, as in Fig. 30.16. Since the forces supplied by the rubber band are internal, $\Sigma \mathbf{F}_e = 0$ if there is no friction, and $\mathbf{a}_c$ should therefore be zero. We can locate C at the start by using the formula $m_1 r_1 = m_2 r_2$. According to equation 30.30, the center of mass should experience no acceleration. The blocks should therefore move so that they collide pretty close to C. Their final position should be such that C is the center of mass of the system at the end, as it was at the beginning. (If the bodies are of the same size and shape but have different masses, their proximate faces cannot meet precisely at C.)

Finally, consider the behavior of a wrench that can move without friction on a flat horizontal table. The wrench may be considered a system of particles. Suppose that it is tossed onto the table with a twisting motion. As soon as it leaves the hand, the vector sum of all the external forces on it is zero. In this case, again, $\Sigma \mathbf{F}_e = 0$. According to equation 30.30, therefore, the acceleration of the center of mass should be zero. That is, the velocity of the center of mass is constant. Figure 30.17 is a drawing made from a multiple-exposure photograph taken at equal time intervals. The center of mass is marked with a cross. Lay a ruler on the picture, and prove to yourself that the center of mass travels in a straight line. Measure the distance between successive crosses to prove that it travels at a constant speed.

It is obvious that these principles must be important in space travel, in which the condition that $\Sigma \mathbf{F}_e = 0$ is satisfied to a high degree.

Because the principle of the conservation of linear momentum plays an important role in physics, I shall devote the whole of the next chapter to a discussion of problems in which it is useful. To lay the proper groundwork for that discussion, you should work out in detail many of the problems at the end of this chapter.

30.6. Summary

Linear momentum, $\mathbf{p}$, is a vector quantity defined by the equation $\mathbf{p} = m\mathbf{v}$, and force is rate of change of momentum. In many experiments the magnitude of the momentum seems to be directly proportional to the speed of the body, but we now know that this is only an approximation—which is excellent, however, at speeds that are much lower than that of light.

The momentum of a particle is conserved if no unbalanced force acts on it. The total momentum of a system of particles is conserved if the vector sum of the external forces acting on the system is zero.

The center of mass of a system is a point that has the unique property that its acceleration is simply the vector sum of all the forces acting on the system divided by the total mass of the system. In this sense the total mass of the system behaves as if it were concentrated at its center of mass.

Problems

30.1. As an exercise in logic consider a variation of the argument presented in § 30.3. Assume, in equation 30.10, that the force exerted by m_2 on m_1 is equal and opposite to the force exerted by m_1 on m_2. (That is, assume that Newton's third law applies to these forces.) Prove that the rate of change of momentum of the system is equal to the sum of the external forces acting on it. Then *deduce* that, when the vector sum of the external forces is zero, the momentum of the system is conserved.

30.2. This problem suggests the value of high-speed particles of slight rest mass as carriers of energy in disintegration experiments. In Example 30.1 it was shown that a particle with a rest mass of 10^{-8} kg can have a momentum of 3.0 kg-m/sec if it has a speed 0.707 of that of light.

1. Calculate the kinetic energy of this particle at that speed. (See equation 28.39.)

2. Is this greater or less than the value predicted by the non-relativistic expression for kinetic energy for a particle of the same rest mass and speed?

3. Compare this with the energy of an object that has a rest mass of 1 kg and the same momentum.

30.3. The non-relativistic expression for kinetic energy may be used in this problem.

1. One object has a mass of 1 kg, and another has a mass of 2 kg. Both have a momentum of 10 kg-m/sec. Which has the greater kinetic energy?

2. If two particles have the same momentum and their masses are in the ratio a/b, what is the ratio of their kinetic energies?

3. If two particles have the same momentum and their speeds are in the ratio a/b, what is the ratio of their kinetic energies?

30.4. The momentum of a body changes from 80 kg-m/sec to 90 kg-m/sec in 0.12 sec.

1. What is the magnitude of the average force acting on the body?

2. What does this information tell about the initial speed of the body?

30.5. It is not difficult to give an electron an acceleration of a million g (9.8×10^6 m/sec²) in an electric field.

1. If the acceleration could be kept constant, calculate, using the formula $v = at$, the final speed of an electron that started from rest at the end of 1, 10, 100, and 1,000 sec.

2. If you do the calculation properly, some of your answers will be physically impossible. Explain where the error has crept in.

30.6. 1. Calculate

$$k = \frac{1}{\sqrt{1 - v^2/c^2}}$$

to three significant figures for the following values of v/c: 0.900, 0.930, 0.960, 0.990.

2. What is the relevance of these values of k to the mass of a body moving at these speeds?

30.7. Redraw, carefully, the vectors $\mathbf{r}_1$ and $\mathbf{r}_2$ of Fig. 30.8. Assume, this time, that $m_1 = 3$ kg and that $m_2 = 1$ kg, and find the center of mass graphically.

30.8. 1. Where is the center of mass of a doughnut? (If you are a mathematician and don't know what a doughnut is, substitute the word "torus.")

2. Where is the center of mass of a doughnut out of which one substantial bite has been taken?

3. Describe by what experiment or graphical construction you would find the center of mass of a teacup; of a horseshoe.

30.9. The point of this problem is to consider the concept of center of mass from a different point of view. Assume that the dumbbell of Fig. 30.5 is pivoted on a horizontal axis at the fixed point C. It is rotated clockwise from the horizontal by a very small angle (x radians).

1. Prove that the gain in potential energy of one ball is equal to the loss in potential energy of the other ball.

2. Prove that the same result holds when the dumbbell is rotated in a counterclockwise direction.

3. If a body tends to minimize its potential energy by its motion, is there any reason to believe that the dumbbell will rotate in either direction?

30.10. 1. Locate graphically the center of mass of the following system of two particles. One particle has a mass of 3 kg and is located at a point with rectangular coordinates (1,4). The other has a mass of 2 kg and is located at (3,1). (Hint: As in Fig. 30.8, use vectors with their common point at the origin.) Check your answer against the simpler method of determining center of mass suggested by Fig. 30.5.

2. Keeping the particles in the same places, move the origin of the system of coordinates to the point (1,1) of the original system. Again, find graphically the center of mass, and show that it is the same regardless of the origin.

30.11. Two identical cars are on two parallel highways. One is standing still, and the other is moving at a constant speed of 60 mph.

1. Show graphically that the center of mass of the system moves with a constant velocity.

2. What is the speed of the center of mass?

30.12. Consider an experiment with two rectangular carts like those of Fig. 30.3. They are initially at rest and have masses of 3 kg and 1 kg.

1. What is the initial momentum of the system?

2. If the speed of the lighter car is 30 cm/sec when the spring is released, where will the cars be 3 sec after the spring explodes? (Neglect friction and the mass of the spring.)

3. Locate the center of mass of the system 3 sec after the explosion.

4. What is the total momentum of the system (considered as a vector) at that instant?

30.13. Answer each of the questions, 1–4, of Prob. 30.12 with the following modification: Assume that the carts had an initial speed of 20 cm/sec before the explosion. When the spring is released, the speed of the lighter car, *relative to the center of mass of the system*, is 30 cm/sec and, relative to the laboratory, is 50 cm/sec.

30.14. A mallet whose mass is 0.5 kg is lying on a frictionless horizontal surface (Fig. 30.18) under the action of three equal forces, each of magnitude 2.5 nt, making angles of 120° with one another.

1. What is the vector sum of these forces?

2. What is the acceleration of the center of mass, C, under these circumstances?

3. If force $\mathbf{F}_3$ is suddenly removed, what will be the magnitude of the resultant force?

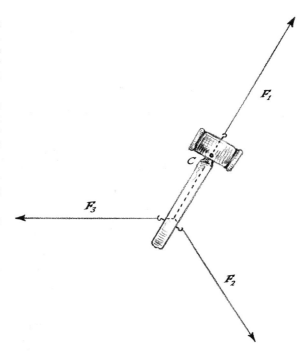

FIG. 30.18. *Illustrating Prob. 30.14.*

4. What will be the magnitude of the resultant instantaneous acceleration of C?

5. What will be the instantaneous direction of motion of C?

6. Will all the points of the body tend to move parallel to C?

7. Will they all have the same instantaneous speed?

30.15. Assume, for Fig. 30.17, that the interval between pictures is 0.1 sec and that 1 cm on the paper represents 10 cm in reality.

1. Compute the average speed of the center of mass.

2. Is it a constant?

3. What do you conclude about the vector sum of the forces acting on the wrench?

4. Compute the angular velocity (degrees/sec) of the wrench.

5. Is it a constant?

Collisions and Other Examples of the Conservation of Linear Momentum

CONSERVATION laws play an important role in physics. Among them are the laws of conservation of total energy (including rest mass), charge, angular momentum, and linear momentum. The strength of these laws lies in the fact that no experiment performed so far has violated them. We cannot, however, predict that no future experiment will ever violate them. In fact, certain other supposed conservation laws in nuclear physics (parity, antiparticle symmetry) have been found to have exceptions. Among the laws in which we have built up the greatest confidence is the law of the conservation of linear momentum, which is of particular importance because it permits the solution of certain mechanical problems that would seem formidable without it. When two steel balls collide, for example, they are in contact for a very short time, during which they exert variable forces on each other. One of the advantages of the law of the conservation of linear momentum is that it enables us to predict the effect of such forces without a detailed knowledge of how they vary during their short duration.

31.1. Impulsive Forces

Imagine a rather massive frictionless puck to which a light string is attached. If the string is suddenly jerked to the right (Fig. 31.1), it will break. Let us say that from previous static experiments we know that it takes a force of 2 newtons to break this particular kind of string. Once the string is broken, the resultant force on the puck is zero; so we expect the puck to move at a constant velocity. Can we predict how fast it will move?

It is obvious that we need to know the mass of the puck. Let's say it is 4 kilograms. A little reflection now tells us that, if the string breaks when it is under a tension of 2 newtons, the force exerted on the puck must have reached a *maximum* value of 2 newtons. But we don't know how long this variable force acted on the puck. We may surmise that the graph of force against time looks like Figure 31.2. This suggests that the average force, $\bar{F}$, might be about 1 newton. From Newton's second law we know that

FIG. 31.1. *If the string attached to a massive frictionless puck is suddenly jerked, it will break.*

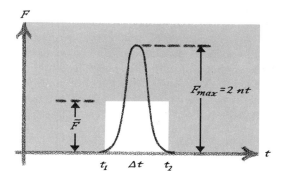

FIG. 31.2. *Possible shape of the graph of force against time for the experiment of Fig. 31.1. The area of the white rectangle is equal to the area bounded by the curve and the t axis. The altitude of this rectangle is the average force, $\overline{F}$.*

$$\overline{F} = m\frac{\Delta v}{\Delta t} \qquad [31.1$$

From this we see that

$$\overline{F}(\Delta t) = m(\Delta v) \qquad [31.2$$

and, since $\Delta v = v - v_0$, that

$$\overline{F}(\Delta t) = mv - mv_0 \qquad [31.3$$

We now list what we know:

$$m = 4 \text{ kg}$$
$$v_0 = 0$$
$$\overline{F} = \text{possibly about 1 nt}$$

We don't know Δt, and we don't know $\overline{F}$ exactly. From the suddenness of the jerk we may *guess* that Δt is about 10^{-3} sec. So we estimate, using equation 31.3:

$$1 \text{ nt} \times 10^{-3} \text{ sec} = 4 \text{ kg} \times v$$
$$v = 2.5 \times 10^{-4} \text{ m/sec}$$

Pretty slow! This is only 0.25 mm/sec.

The argument so far has shown how difficult it is to predict the effect of impulsive forces. We need an accurate knowledge of the product $\overline{F}(\Delta t)$ even if we do not know $\overline{F}$ and Δt separately.

Now let us reverse the procedure. The meas-

urement of the final speed is not difficult. A meter stick and a stopwatch are all we need. Suppose that we discover *experimentally* that $v = 3$ cm/sec. That gives us

$$m(\Delta v) = mv = 4 \text{ kg} \times 3 \times 10^{-2} \text{ m/sec}$$
$$= 0.12 \text{ kg-m/sec}$$

By equation 31.2 we see that we have found an *experimental value* (0.12 nt-sec) of $\overline{F}(\Delta t)$. This quantity is called the **impulse**. In our discussion of collisions, the impulse of a force will play a theoretical part, but in general we shall not need to know $\overline{F}$ or Δt separately. Their product (the impulse) is the essential thing, as we shall see. With a modern oscilloscope, the actual trace of a curve such as that of Figure 31.2 could be found even for time intervals of a few microseconds, but Galileo and Newton learned a lot about impulsive forces without oscilloscopes, and we propose to do the same.

If we somehow know the impulse of a force, we can use it to compute the change in momentum it produces. That is the significance of equation 31.3. If, for example, a croquet mallet exerts an impulse of 0.5 nt-sec on a frictionless puck of mass 0.2 kg (Fig. 31.3), what is the final speed of the puck?

$$\overline{F}(\Delta t) = mv - mv_0$$
$$0.5 \text{ nt-sec} = 0.2 \text{ kg} \times (v - 0)$$
$$v = 2.5 \text{ m/sec}$$

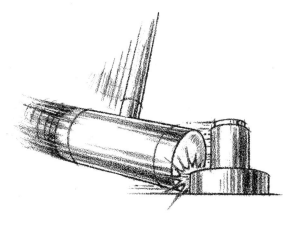

FIG. 31.3. *Croquet mallet exerting an impulse on a frictionless puck.*

FIG. 31.4. *Collision of two moving frictionless pucks.*

31.2. Collisions and Newton's Third Law

Newton's third law is particularly useful in simple collision problems. Let us consider the collision of two frictionless pucks (Fig. 31.4). We shall treat them as particles, disregarding their rotation. One puck has mass m_1 and velocity $\mathbf{u}_1$; the other has mass m_2 and velocity $\mathbf{u}_2$. For simplicity's sake we assume that they are both moving in the same direction along the same straight line on a horizontal table (A), but our treatment is more general than it appears to be. The positive direction points to the right. If the pucks collide (B), puck 1 experiences a force, $\mathbf{F}_1$, to the left, and, simultaneously, puck 2 experiences a force, $\mathbf{F}_2$, to the right. It is therefore conceivable that puck 1 slows down and puck 2 speeds up. Let their new velocities, after collision, be $\mathbf{v}_1$ and $\mathbf{v}_2$, respectively. Let us apply equation 31.2 to each puck separately:

$$\bar{\mathbf{F}}_1(\Delta t) = m_1\mathbf{v}_1 - m_1\mathbf{u}_1 \qquad [31.4$$

$$\bar{\mathbf{F}}_2(\Delta t) = m_2\mathbf{v}_2 - m_2\mathbf{u}_2 \qquad [31.5$$

According to Newton's third law, the force that puck 1 exerts on puck 2 is equal and opposite to the force that puck 2 exerts on puck 1, and, since the interval of time, Δt, during which they act is the same for both,

$$\bar{\mathbf{F}}_1(\Delta t) = -\bar{\mathbf{F}}_2(\Delta t) \qquad [31.6$$

Putting this into equations 31.4 and 31.5, we get

$$m_1\mathbf{v}_1 - m_1\mathbf{u}_1 = -(m_2\mathbf{v}_2 - m_2\mathbf{u}_2) \qquad [31.7$$

or

$$m_1\mathbf{v}_1 + m_2\mathbf{v}_2 = m_1\mathbf{u}_1 + m_2\mathbf{u}_2 \qquad [31.8$$

The total momentum after the collision is equal to the total momentum before the collision. This is nothing new to us, of course, for in Chapter 30 we saw that linear momentum is conserved whenever the vector sum of the external forces acting on a system is zero. Apparently $\mathbf{F}_1$ and $\mathbf{F}_2$ are properly considered internal forces if our system consists of the two pucks.

Equation 31.8 is, of course, only a special case of the broad principle of the conservation of linear momentum. Stated vectorially, as above, it applies to collisions in general. For motion in a straight line we can drop the vector notation and write simply

$$m_1v_1 + m_2v_2 = m_1u_1 + m_2u_2 \qquad [31.9$$

This holds for collisions of objects moving in the same straight line.

Let us see if we can use this equation in a very special case. Assuming that the two pucks have equal mass ($m_1 = m_2 = m$) and that the puck of mass m_2 is initially at rest ($u_2 = 0$), we tabulate our quantities, letting question marks stand for the unknown quantities.

$$v_1 = ? \quad m_1 = m \quad u_1 = u_1$$
$$v_2 = ? \quad m_2 = m \quad u_2 = 0$$

Using equation 31.9, we get

$$mv_1 + mv_2 = mu_1 + 0$$
$$v_1 + v_2 = u_1$$

This tells us something about the sum of the velocities after collision, but it does not tell us anything about the velocity of each puck. It seems that we must have more knowledge about the collision than what we have assumed so far. I shall return to this problem after I have discussed inelastic collisions.

31.3. Inelastic Collisions

A railroad car of mass m_1 is moving along the track with velocity $\mathbf{u}_1$. It bumps into a stationary car of mass m_2 and becomes coupled to it so that both move with the same velocity after the collision (Fig. 31.5). Can we, by using the law of the conservation of momentum, find the final velocity?

Dropping the vector notation, we are given that $u_2 = 0$ and that $v_1 = v_2 = v$. Using equation 31.9, we get

$$m_1 v + m_2 v = m_1 u_1 + 0 \qquad [31.10$$

$$(m_1 + m_2)v = m_1 u_1$$

$$v = \frac{m_1 u_1}{m_1 + m_2} \qquad [31.11$$

If $m_1 = m_2$, $v = u_1/2$, which seems plausible.

In this case we were able to deduce the final velocities because we added another restriction: that both bodies should move together after the collision. Such collisions are called **completely inelastic collisions.**

Is mechanical energy conserved in inelastic collisions? Let us compute the kinetic energy before and after impact.

Before impact

$$K_1 = \tfrac{1}{2} m_1 u_1{}^2 \qquad [31.12$$

After impact

$$K_2 = \tfrac{1}{2}(m_1 + m_2)v^2 \qquad [31.13$$

$$\frac{K_2}{K_1} = \frac{(m_1 + m_2)v^2}{m_1 u_1{}^2} \qquad [31.14$$

From equation 31.11 we get

$$\frac{v^2}{u_1{}^2} = \frac{(m_1)^2}{(m_1 + m_2)^2} \qquad [31.15$$

Putting this into equation 31.14, we get

$$\frac{K_2}{K_1} = \frac{(m_1 + m_2)}{m_1} \cdot \frac{m_1{}^2}{(m_1 + m_2)^2} \qquad [31.16$$

$$= \frac{m_1}{m_1 + m_2} \qquad [31.17$$

(As a special example: if $m_1 = m_2$, $K_2/K_1 = 1/2$.)

The total kinetic energy after impact was less than the total kinetic energy before impact. Since the collision took place on a horizontal track, no

change in potential energy has taken place. We are forced to conclude that the lost kinetic energy went into heat. (To put it another way, some of the ordered kinetic energy of the cars went into random kinetic energy of the molecules of the cars.)

31.4. The Speed of a Rifle Bullet

We can use an inelastic collision to help us deduce the speed of a rifle bullet, but let us first consider an even simpler experiment. A rifle is resting on the ground and pointing upward. A bullet of mass m has velocity v as it leaves the barrel. It rises to height h. Let K and U stand for kinetic and potential energy, respectively. From these data we calculate v:

$$\Delta K + \Delta U = 0$$
$$K + U = K_0 + U_0$$
$$0 + mgh = \tfrac{1}{2} mv^2 + 0$$
$$v^2 = 2gh$$
$$v = \sqrt{2gh} \qquad [31.18$$

This formula should look quite familiar by now.

In principle, our solution looks all right. It is a reasonable approximation to let ΔQ equal 0, for the air resistance would probably be slight. But, as a practical means of determining v, our procedure is not very good—for the simple reason that h would be very great and very difficult to measure. Consider, instead, an inelastic collision of the bullet and a block of wood of mass M (Fig. 31.6). Using the conservation of momentum, we get the equation

$$mv = (m + M)V \qquad [31.19$$

in which V is the speed of block and bullet immediately after impact. Mechanical energy is not conserved during this impact, but we may assume that it *is* conserved in the rise to height h. Therefore

$$\tfrac{1}{2}(m + M)V^2 = (m + M)gh \qquad [31.20$$

Hence

$$V = \sqrt{2gh} \qquad [31.21$$

Putting this into equation 31.19 and solving for v, we get

$$v = \frac{(m + M)}{m} \sqrt{2gh} \qquad [31.22$$

FIG. 31.5. *Collision of a moving railroad car with a stationary one.*

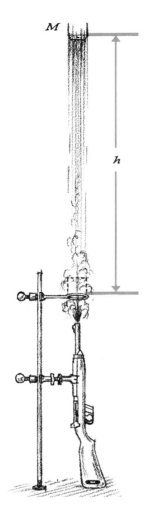

A typical set of data obtained in a laboratory is:

$$h = 3\text{ m}$$
$$m = 10\text{ gm}$$
$$M = 300\text{ gm}$$

Using equation 31.22, we get

$$v = \frac{310}{10}\sqrt{2 \times 9.8\,\frac{m}{\sec^2} \times 3\text{ m}}$$
$$= 232\text{ m/sec}$$

Putting this value of v into equation 31.18 yields

$$h = 2{,}720\text{ m}$$

It would have been difficult, indeed, to measure the maximum height of the bullet if it had not entered the wooden block.

31.5. The Reaction Engine

A boy of mass m_2 drops gently onto a railroad flatcar of mass m_1 moving with velocity $\mathbf{u}_1$ (Fig. 31.7). If we analyze the internal forces, we see that a force, $\mathbf{F}_2$, acts to the right on the boy as he slides to a halt in relation to the car while his actual velocity increases from zero to some final velocity, $\mathbf{v}$. At the same time the car experiences a force, $\mathbf{F}_1 = -\mathbf{F}_2$, to the left. This slows the car to its final velocity, $\mathbf{v}$. Dropping vector notation, we have

$$m_1u_1 = (m_1 + m_2)v \qquad [31.23$$

If m_2 is much smaller than m_1, v will be almost equal to u_1.

The car is now moving at its new speed, v, and, if friction is absent, it will continue to do so. What can the boy do, without leaving the car, to change its speed? The box resting on the car contains some lead bricks, each of mass m_3. The boy decides to throw one ahead of the car (to the right in Fig. 31.8). Since the brick experiences a force to the right, the boy and the car experience a force to the left. This slows the car down a bit. Every time the boy tosses a brick to the right, the car feels a force to the left, and this slows the car down a little more. If he could throw bricks forward often enough and fast enough, the effect on the car would eventually be noticeable. This is the principle of the **reaction engine.**

FIG. 31.6. *A practical way to determine the speed of a rifle bullet.*

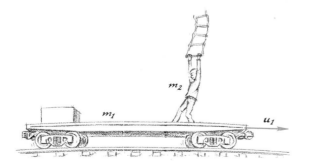

FIG. 31.7. *Dropping gently onto a moving flatcar, the boy not only acquires velocity to the right but also slows down the flatcar.*

If the boy can set up a machine gun to shoot bullets to the right (Fig. 31.9), he can generate a fairly steady push to the left on the car. Suppose that the speed of each bullet, relative to the car, is u, that the mass of each is m, and that the gun shoots n bullets per second. Since each bullet represents mu units of momentum, nmu is the rate at which the momentum carried by the bullets *increases* to the right. We know that the rate of change of momentum is a force. It can be shown that nmu (which, quite properly, has kg-m/sec² as its units) is the *average* force exerted by the bullets on the car. It is apparent that, to increase this force, we can increase any or all of the factors n, m, and u.

A rocket works by expelling gases at a high velocity. Notice that nm has kg/sec as its units. If we write nm in the form $\Delta m/\Delta t$, we see that $(\Delta m/\Delta t)u$ is a formula for the force exerted on a rocket by gases being expelled at the rate of $\Delta m/\Delta t$ kg/sec and at speed u relative to the rocket. This is called the **thrust**, T, on the rocket:

$$T = \frac{\Delta m}{\Delta t} u \qquad [31.24$$

31.6. Elastic Collisions

In some collisions so little energy is lost to heat that we may take ΔQ as equal to zero. A collision for which $\Delta Q = 0$ is called an **elastic collision**. Real collisions are only approximately elastic. Two pucks making an elastic collision conserve their total kinetic energy. We use the notation of equation 31.9:

MOMENTUM CONSERVED:

$$m_1 u_1 + m_2 u_2 = m_1 v_1 + m_2 v_2 \qquad [31.25$$

KINETIC ENERGY CONSERVED:

$$\tfrac{1}{2}m_1 u_1^2 + \tfrac{1}{2}m_2 u_2^2 = \tfrac{1}{2}m_1 v_1^2 + \tfrac{1}{2}m_2 v_2^2 \qquad [31.26$$

Consider a special case in which the second puck, of mass m_2, is initially at rest ($u_2 = 0$). Equations 31.25 and 31.26 become

$$m_1 u_1 = m_1 v_1 + m_2 v_2 \qquad [31.27$$

$$\tfrac{1}{2}m_1 u_1^2 = \tfrac{1}{2}m_1 v_1^2 + \tfrac{1}{2}m_2 v_2^2 \qquad [31.28$$

$$m_1(u_1 - v_1) = m_2 v_2 \qquad [31.29$$

$$m_1(u_1^2 - v_1^2) = m_2 v_2^2 \qquad [31.30$$

Equation 31.30 becomes

$$m_1(u_1 - v_1)(u_1 + v_1) = m_2 v_2^2 \qquad [31.31$$

Dividing equation 31.31 by equation 31.29, we get

$$u_1 + v_1 = v_2 \qquad [31.32$$

Putting this into equation 31.27, we get

$$v_1 = \frac{u_1(m_1 - m_2)}{m_1 + m_2} \qquad [31.33$$

Let us check this by considering some specific values. If $m_2 = 0$ in equation 31.33, we get $v_1 = u_1$. This makes sense; the speed of the first puck should remain unchanged. Suppose that $m_2 = m_1$ (see the end of § 31.2). Equation 31.33 predicts that v_1 will equal zero; the first puck stops dead. To conserve momentum and energy, the speed of the second puck must be $v_2 = u_1$, as confirmed by equation 31.32. Now suppose that m_2 approaches infinity. We rewrite equation 31.33 by dividing both numerator and denominator by m_2:

$$v_1 = \frac{u_1(m_1/m_2 - 1)}{m_1/m_2 + 1} \qquad [31.34$$

$$\lim_{m_2 \to \infty} v_1 = -u_1$$

The first puck bounces back with its original speed. This makes sense too. A massive wall against which a puck could bounce would react like a puck of infinite mass. The small puck would bounce back from it with a change of direction but not of speed.

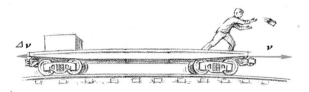

FIG. 31.8. *Illustration of the principle of the reaction engine.*

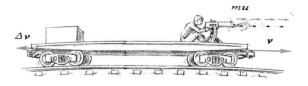

FIG. 31.9. *Another illustration of the principle of the reaction engine.*

I have discussed special cases to keep the algebra simple, but the general case of elastic collisions between pucks is implicit in equations 31.25 and 31.26. (Steel balls suspended by long strings can also be used to illustrate experimentally the properties of elastic collisions.) Now I wish to apply the concept of elastic collisions to the impacts of the invisible molecules of a gas against the wall of their container.

31.7. Kinetic Theory of Gases

In this section we extend to N molecules the treatment begun in § 29.4.

Consider the hypothetical case of a single molecule bouncing elastically between two opposite vertical walls of a box (Fig. 31.10). The momentum just before impact (A) is $\mathbf{p}_1 = m\mathbf{v}_1$. The momentum after impact (B) is $\mathbf{p}_2 = m\mathbf{v}_2$. The change in momentum, $\Delta\mathbf{p}$, is

$$\mathbf{p}_2 - \mathbf{p}_1 = m(\mathbf{v}_2 - \mathbf{v}_1)$$

Vectorially this is the same as

$$\Delta\mathbf{p} = m[\mathbf{v}_2 + (-\mathbf{v}_1)]$$

If we add $m\mathbf{v}_2$ and $m(-\mathbf{v}_1)$ graphically, we get a vector pointing to the left whose magnitude is twice that of $m\mathbf{v}_1$ (Fig. 31.11).

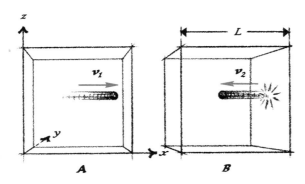

FIG. 31.10. *Analysis of the force on a single molecule bouncing between two parallel walls.*

FIG. 31.11. *The vector sum of* $m\mathbf{v}_2$ *and* $-m\mathbf{v}_1$ *is a vector pointing to the left. In the case illustrated its magnitude is* $2m\mathbf{v}_1$.

Since the speed is not changed by elastic collisions with the wall, we may write the magnitude of $\Delta\mathbf{p}$ as $2mv$. (We have dropped the subscripts from v since v_1 and v_2 are equal in magnitude.) The change in momentum per collision at one wall is therefore $2mv$. Now suppose that the molecule makes n collisions per second with that wall. The product $n2mv$ is now the *average rate of change of momentum* experienced by the molecule at one wall. Another way of writing average rate of change of momentum is $\Delta p/\Delta t$, which we recognize as the *average force* felt by the molecule. We therefore write

$$\bar{F} = n2mv \qquad [31.35$$

Let us now calculate n, the number of impacts per second at one wall. Using the formula "velocity × time = distance," we see that the number of seconds per round trip equals $2L/v$ and that the number of round trips per second is $v/2L$. Since the number of impacts per second against that wall is the same as the number of round trips per second, $n = v/2L$. Putting this into equation 31.35, we get

$$\bar{F} = \frac{v}{2L} 2mv$$

$$\bar{F} = \frac{mv^2}{L} \qquad [31.36$$

Remember what this means: $\bar{F}$ is the *average force exerted on the molecule by the wall*. (The instantaneous peaks of force would be much higher.) By Newton's third law, $\bar{F}$ is also the average force exerted on the wall by the molecule.

Now we imagine N molecules in the box bouncing around at random. Some are going fast and some slow, but there is an average v and hence an average v^2. If N is very great, one can imagine that, on the average, $N/3$ of these molecules are moving parallel with the x axis and hence colliding with the vertical wall. The average force on one wall is therefore

$$\bar{F} = \frac{N}{3} \frac{mv^2}{L} \qquad [31.37$$

If the box is a cube, the area of the wall is L^2. The average *pressure* on that wall is therefore

$$P = \frac{\bar{F}}{A} = \frac{\bar{F}}{L^2} = \frac{N}{3} \frac{mv^2}{L^3} \qquad [31.38$$

But L^3 is the volume, V, of the box. Therefore

$$P = \frac{Nmv^2}{3V} \qquad [31.39$$

Since Nm is the total mass, Nm/V is the density, ρ; so we may write

$$P = \frac{\rho v^2}{3} \qquad [31.40$$

We may also rewrite equation 31.40 as

$$PV = \frac{N}{3} mv^2 \qquad [31.41$$

Notice that we have substituted an artificial model in which $N/3$ molecules move parallel to an axis for the real situation in which all molecules move at random; on the average, however, it gives reasonable results. This purely theoretical equation may be compared with the experimental equation (29.2) that describes approximately the behavior of real gases,

$$PV = kNT \qquad [31.42$$

in which k is the universal constant 1.38054×10^{-23} J/°K. Equating the right-hand sides of equations 31.41 and 31.42, we get,

$$\frac{N}{3} mv^2 = kNT \qquad [31.43$$

or

$$T = \frac{2}{3k} \left(\frac{1}{2} mv^2 \right) \qquad [31.44$$

We can, therefore, associate the absolute temperature of a gas with the average kinetic energy of translation of the random motion of its molecules. The important point here is that two samples of different gases at the same temperature would have the same average value of $\frac{1}{2}mv^2$ for their molecules.

Consider a sample of a gas characterized by P_1, V_1, T_1, N_1 and a sample of another gas characterized by P_2, V_2, T_2, N_2. Since each obeys equation 31.42,

$$P_1V_1 = kN_1T_1 \qquad [31.45$$

$$P_2V_2 = kN_2T_2 \qquad [31.46$$

Let us take the ratio of these quantities:

$$\frac{P_1V_1}{P_2V_2} = \frac{kN_1T_1}{kN_2T_2} \qquad [31.47$$

If we now demand that the volumes be equal, the pressures be equal, and the temperatures be the same, we find that

$$N_1 = N_2 \qquad [31.48$$

This is Avogadro's hypothesis: that *equal volumes of different gases at the same pressure and temperature contain the same number of molecules.* We see how elementary kinetic theory makes Avogadro's "inspired guess" plausible.

31.8. Collisions in Nuclear Physics

We have applied the conservation of linear momentum to objects that range in size all the way from railroad cars to molecules and atoms. Notice that we used a very simple model for the molecules. We treated them like elastic spheres, and we found that by using the principle of the conservation of linear momentum we were able to evolve a theory that agrees quite well with experiment.

Is this the end? You have heard about the nucleus inside the atom. Is it possible that even a nucleus can behave like an elastic sphere in certain kinds of encounters with other nuclei? The answer is "Yes." The laws of the conservation of energy and momentum do hold at the nuclear level, and both elastic and inelastic types of collisions are encountered among nuclei.

Remember that the diameters of nuclei are about 10^4 times shorter than those of atoms, that the diameters of atoms are about 5,000 times shorter than the wavelength of light, and that the wavelength of light is about as short as the diameter of the smallest hole you could ever make in a thin aluminum foil with a very sharp needle. Nuclei are far below the range of visibility of even the most powerful electron and ion microscopes. Yet nuclear events can be made visible by the condensed-vapor trails they leave in gases (see Fig. 54.1) and by the tracks they leave in specially prepared photographic emulsions (see Fig. 1.2).

Let us see how a glancing collision between two balls can serve as a model for nuclear events (Fig. 31.12). A moving ball with momentum $m_1\mathbf{u}_1$ approaches a stationary ball of mass m_2. After

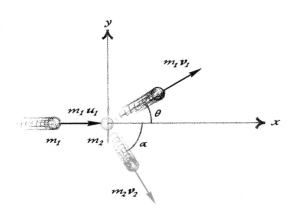

FIG. 31.12. *Glancing collision between two balls.*

encounter the respective momenta are $m_1\mathbf{v}_1$ and $m_2\mathbf{v}_2$ and are not necessarily in the same line. The conservation of momentum requires that

$$m_1\mathbf{u}_1 = m_1\mathbf{v}_1 + m_2\mathbf{v}_2 \qquad [31.49$$

Let us decompose this into two equations, one for the x components and the other for the y components of momentum:

$$m_1u_1 = m_1v_1 \cos \theta + m_2v_2 \cos \alpha \qquad [31.50$$

$$0 = m_1v_1 \sin \theta - m_2v_2 \sin \alpha \qquad [31.51$$

If the collision is elastic,

$$\tfrac{1}{2}m_1u_1{}^2 = \tfrac{1}{2}m_1v_1{}^2 + \tfrac{1}{2}m_2v_2{}^2 \qquad [31.52$$

If we can get θ and α experimentally, and if we know m_1 and m_2 from other considerations, we have three equations (31.50, 31.51, and 31.52) in the unknowns u_1, v_1, and v_2.

If some of the quantities u_1, v_1, and v_2 can be measured experimentally, we can, of course, use these equations to find relations between m_1 and m_2. We shall look into these matters more thoroughly in Part VI of this book.

31.9. Summary

The average force multiplied by the interval of time during which it acts is called the impulse of the force. The impulsive forces of short duration that act between bodies during a collision play an important theoretical role in mechanics.

The observable quantity, in practice, is often the change in momentum produced by the force, and it is then unnecessary to know just how the force varied during the collision.

One of the important generalizations of physics is that, if no external forces act on a system of colliding bodies, the total momentum before impact equals the total momentum after impact. Even in collisions in which mechanical energy is not conserved, linear momentum is conserved if no external forces act. The conservation of momentum is also useful in explaining the thrust produced by a jet engine and in determining the energy and momentum of nuclear particles.

Problems

31.1. Although we have used lower-case p for momentum and capital P for pressure, confusion might arise from the use of the same letter. Use a dimensional check to discover which of the following refer to pressure and which to momentum: (a) energy/volume, (b) watt-sec/m³, (c) cal-sec/m.

31.2. A collision between two bodies takes place in 0.01 sec. One of the bodies experiences a change in momentum of 6 kg-m/sec. What is the smallest possible value of the maximum force felt by that body?

31.3. In more advanced texts it is shown that the exact area bounded by the force curve (Fig. 31.2) and the t axis (in units of newtons × seconds, for example) is the impulse.

1. Prove that this is equivalent to $\overline{F}(\Delta t)$ if $\overline{F}$ is the average force during the interval Δt (see § 6.6).

2. From an oscilloscope trace the impulse is calculated to be 1.56×10^{-2} nt-sec. If the frictionless puck of Fig. 31.1 has a mass of 3 kg and starts from rest, what will be its final speed, as a result of this impulse?

3. What is the average force if $\Delta t = 0.0013$ sec?

31.4. A skilled carpenter hits a nail at the rate of 3 strikes/sec for 4 sec. Assume that the hammer and the nail are in contact with each other for 2×10^{-3} sec each time the hammer hits and that the force during the interaction rises linearly with time to a maximum of 3×10^4 nt and then decreases linearly to zero.

1. What is the average force exerted by the hammer on the nail? (Hint: Draw a graph of force against time. Divide the total area under the force curve by the total time.)

2. Since this is less than the weight of the carpenter, why couldn't he just lean on the nail and drive it home?

31.5. A shower emits water at the rate of 0.1 kg/sec. The mass of each droplet is 5×10^{-5} kg. The speed of the drops is 7 m/sec. Calculate the average force on the man taking the shower as follows (make the simplifying assumption that all the drops hit him and stick to him):

1. What change of momentum, in kg-m/sec, does a drop experience as it sticks to the man?

2. What, in nt-sec, is the impulse of the force exerted by the drop on the man?

3. The mass per second leaving the shower being equal to the mass per drop times the average number of drops, N, hitting the man per second, compute N and its inverse, the average number of seconds between drops.

4. Calculate the average force exerted by the drops on the man during some interval by dividing total impulse by total time.

31.6. When a ball whose mass is 0.10 kg hits a ball, initially at rest, whose mass is 0.40 kg, the former bounces to the left while the latter moves to the right. Suppose they are suspended from long strings of equal strength. When these are vertical, the balls touch, and the line joining their centers is horizontal. You pull the lighter ball to the left, keeping the string tight, until the ball is 10 cm above its lowest point. You release it. It hits the heavier ball, initially at rest, which now rises to a height of 1.2 cm.

1. Using the formula $v^2 = 2gh$, deduce the speed of the lighter ball just before impact.

2. Using the formula $v^2 = 2gh$, deduce the speed of the heavier ball just after impact.

3. Using § 31.6, deduce the speed of the heavier ball just after impact, and compare your result with that of part 2.

4. What do you conclude about the nature of the collision?

31.7. The experiment described here is a fascinating one to observe, especially after you have tried to predict the results. When two hardened steel balls (mass ratio 1/4) are suspended as in Prob. 31.6, this is what happens if, starting with the heavier one at rest, you displace and release the lighter one: After the first impact they fly apart, but $T/2$ seconds later (T is the period of either pendulum) they hit again, and this time the heavier one stops dead and only the lighter one flies back toward the position it had at the start of the experiment.

1. Treat the impacts as elastic, and explain mathematically why the heavier ball stops dead. This can get involved mathematically, but here is a simple way of looking at it: Let the original momentum of the lighter ball be m_1u_1. Let the velocities immediately after the *second* impact be v_1 and v_2. Conservation of momentum requires that

$$m_1v_1 + m_2v_2 = -m_1u_1$$

The negative sign appears because the direction of both balls was reversed when they swung back after the first impact. Conservation of energy requires that

$$m_1v_1^2 + m_2v_2^2 = m_1u_1^2$$

Prove by substitution that

$$v_1 = -u_1$$
$$v_2 = 0$$

is a solution. A mathematical search for a solution will turn up another that is physically impossible.

2. If the mass ratio is 1/3, will the heavier ball stop dead after the second impact? Explain.

3. If the mass ratio is 1/1, does the ball that was originally at rest stop dead after the second impact?

4. If the experiment starts with the mass ratio 1/4, and with the lighter ball, at rest, being hit by the heavier one, will the lighter ball stop dead after the second impact?

31.8. Two railroad cars are moving (with negligible friction) toward each other along a track. The left-hand one has a mass of 4.0×10^4 kg and a speed of 0.60 m/sec to the right. The right-hand one has a mass of 3.0×10^4 kg and a speed of 0.50 m/sec to the left. On collision, they couple.

1. What is their velocity (direction and magnitude) after the collision?

2. How much energy was turned into heat (in joules)?

3. Convert this to calories.

4. Assume that all this heat is in the couplings, which are made of iron and have each a mass of 100 kg. By how much is their temperature raised? (The specific heat of iron is 0.105 cal/gm/°C.)

31.9. A ball caught by a boy sitting at rest in a swing should make both the boy and the swing rise.

1. How fast would a ball of mass 0.2 kg have to be moving to produce a rise of 1 cm in the swing and boy (mass = 50 kg) when caught by the boy?

2. Is this a practical way of measuring the speed of a baseball?

3. If the boy were capable of catching such a fast ball, how much energy would go into heat during the encounter?

31.10. A boy whose mass is 50.2 kg is standing on a stationary sled whose mass, including that of some lead bricks, is 45.5 kg. He throws a lead brick, whose mass is 1.07 kg, horizontally to the left with a speed, *relative to the sled*, of 4.03 m/sec.

1. What is the maximum speed that the boy, the sled, and the remaining bricks can pick up in this way? (Compute your answer to three significant figures.)

2. Suppose the boy throws two bricks per second for three seconds. What is the average force he can exert on the sled and its contents?

3. Compute the final speed of the sled, which starts from rest, using the formula $\overline{F}(\Delta t) = \Delta(mv)$. The answer will be approximate because you will have to use the average mass of the sled and its contents.

31.11. An Atlas rocket has a mass of about 5.0×10^5 kg. The engine, which expels gas at a speed of 2.0×10^3 m/sec, must accelerate the rocket from rest to a speed of 100 m/sec in 1.5 sec. What is the total mass of the gas that it must expel? (Assume that the force of gravity is negligible compared with the forces of acceleration.)

31.12. The purpose of this problem is to test your understanding of the derivation of the gas laws from kinetic theory. If you have difficulty with it, study § 31.7 again. The symbols used here are those of that section. Put the following symbols on a line: $L, A, V, \overline{F}, v, m, n, P, N, \rho, T$. Directly beneath each put the new value of that variable required by the conditions of each of the problems below.

1. Assume, in the one-molecule model, that the cube of length L suddenly becomes a cube of length $2L$ without affecting v. (Under L you would put

$2L$, under A you would put $4A$, under N you would put 1, and so on.)

2. Suppose, in the many-molecule model, that L remained fixed but v changed to $v/2$.

3. Suppose, in the many-molecule model, that the mass of each molecule changed from m to $2m$ while L and v remained constant.

31.13. For hydrogen at standard temperature and pressure the density is 0.0899 kg/m³ and the pressure is 1.013×10^5 nt/m².

1. Calculate the average speed of a hydrogen molecule.

2. A little helium is liberated in the container otherwise filled with hydrogen. Helium molecules are about twice as massive as hydrogen molecules. Calculate the average speed of the helium molecules, assuming that the temperature has not changed. (Hint: Consider equation 31.44 for hydrogen and helium separately.)

31.14. One way to exert a force on a wall from a distance is to hit the wall with a succession of missiles. Suppose that we throw 10 balls per second at the wall, each with a mass of 0.40 kg and a speed of 15 m/sec. The force on the wall will, of course, be far from constant, but we can calculate the average force in the way we did for the molecules of a gas striking the walls of a container. Find the average force on the wall if we use

1. something like tennis balls (which make perfectly elastic collisions);

2. something like putty balls (which make completely inelastic collisions).

3. Since, in either case, we do the same work in throwing the balls, is this result reasonable?

31.15. Let Fig. 31.12 represent the glancing collision between two billiard balls of equal masses. We have means of measuring speed v_2 after the collision and angles θ and α. Speed v_2 is measured as 2.5 m/sec, θ is 30°, and α is 60°. What is the speed of the incoming ball? (In nuclear physics the by-products of a collision sometimes leave traces from which angles like θ and α can be determined. Instead of the speeds, the energy of the resultant particles can sometimes be measured with the proper equipment. In this way the energy and momentum of nuclear particles can be deduced.)

32

The Conservation
of Angular Momentum

WE HAVE seen how useful the principles of the conservation of energy and of linear momentum are. There is another conservation principle, and it is applicable not only to large bodies like the planets and to small bodies like the atomic constituents, but, so far as we know, to all bodies, large and small. It is called the principle of the conservation of angular momentum.

32.1. Rotational Inertia

We are all familiar with rotating objects that have angular momentum (Fig. 32.1): a phonograph turntable has it (A); so does a grindstone (B); and so does a merry-go-round (C). In its usual mode of operation a massive grindstone has more angular momentum than a turntable, and a merry-go-round has more than a grindstone. How can you tell? A simple criterion is this: *The one that is the hardest to stop has the greatest angular momentum.*† Once the power has been turned off, each of these rotating bodies tends to keep on turning, to conserve its angular momentum; and we believe that they would never slow down if no frictional or other retarding forces acted. But it is harder to stop a grindstone than

† If you are a careful reader, you will realize that this is a vague statement. To make it precise, I have to describe operationally what "hard" means. This requires the concept of torque, which I am about to define.

a turntable. We attribute this difference to the grindstone's greater angular momentum. Let's see what factors are involved.

We see at once that the grindstone is more massive than the turntable and is turning fast. That reminds us of the factors that entered into linear momentum. Linear momentum was defined as mv, the product of inertial mass and linear velocity. This suggests that angular momentum might have an inertial factor to play the role of m and a velocity factor to play the role of v; and, in fact, if I is the rotational inertia of a body and ω is its angular velocity, $I\omega$ is its **angular momentum**.

Now let us see what determines the rotational inertia of a body. Because of the comparison between the turntable and the grindstone, we suspect that the mass of a body enters into the evaluation of its rotational inertia, but that is not all; the *placement* of masses relative to the axis of rotation plays an important role. We can demonstrate this in the classroom by using a low-friction turntable with some weights on it (Fig. 32.2). We start by stacking four 2-kg weights on the axis of the turntable (A) and spinning it so that it makes one revolution per second. (We judge the speed by watching a chalk mark on the turntable and listening to a metronome ticking off seconds.) A blackboard eraser pressed gently against the side of the turntable will bring it to rest in a certain number of turns—three, for example. If

FIG. 32.1. *Objects with rotational inertia.*

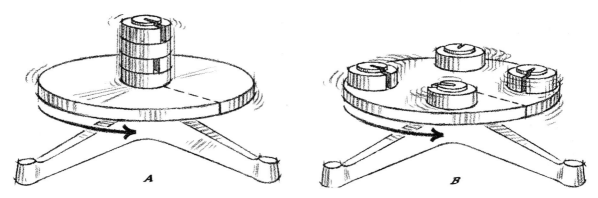

FIG. 32.2. *Demonstration that mass near the axis of rotation has less rotational inertia than the same mass farther from the axis.*

the weights are now redistributed near the edge of the turntable (B) and it is brought to the same angular velocity (one revolution per second), application of the same pressure with the eraser (as judged by the operator) will now require a longer time and a correspondingly larger number of revolutions to bring the turntable to rest. *Without changing the total mass we are able to increase the rotational inertia of the system simply by moving the weights farther away from the axis of rotation.*

The precise formula for rotational inertia must involve not only mass but distance. We shall dis-

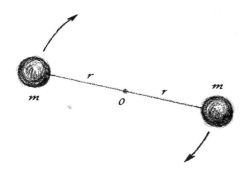

FIG. 32.3. *Illustrating the definition of rotational inertia of a particle.*

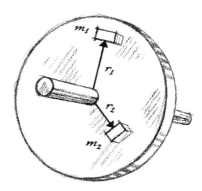

FIG. 32.4. *Illustrating the general definition of rotational inertia.*

cover the exact relation by considering next the kinetic energy of rotation of a body, and then we shall return to angular momentum.

32.2. Rotational Kinetic Energy

Consider first a pair of particles of equal mass separated (and joined) by a massless rod (Fig. 32.3). An axis of rotation at right angles to the rod is at its midpoint, O. (Imagine, in the figure, an axis perpendicular to the plane of the paper at O.) The particles move in a circle of radius r with linear speed v. The kinetic energy of each particle is $\frac{1}{2}mv^2$. If the angular velocity is ω, then $v = r\omega$ (equation 14.8). Putting this into the formula $\frac{1}{2}mv^2$, we get

rotational kinetic energy per particle
$$= \tfrac{1}{2}mr^2\omega^2 \quad [32.1$$

If we use the symbol I to represent mr^2, we can write the rotational kinetic energy of one particle as

rotational kinetic energy per particle $= \tfrac{1}{2}I\omega^2$ $\quad [32.2$

This formula is of the same *form* as $\frac{1}{2}mv^2$, with I replacing m, and ω replacing v. In rotation, we see, I does indeed play the role that m (inertial mass) does in translation. We therefore define the **rotational inertia of a particle** as $I = mr^2$. We have thus found the logical combination of mass and length that gives rotational inertia.

If a body is made up of many particles (Fig. 32.4), of mass m_i ($i = 1, 2, 3, \ldots n$), each at dis-

tance r_i ($i = 1, 2, 3, \ldots n$) from the axis, the total **rotational kinetic energy,** since all the particles have the same angular velocity, ω, is the sum of all the terms of the type $\frac{1}{2}m_ir_i^2\omega^2$. We may write it as

$$\sum_{i=1}^{n} \tfrac{1}{2}m_ir_i^2\omega^2 = \tfrac{1}{2}m_1r_1^2\omega^2 + \tfrac{1}{2}m_2r_2^2\omega^2$$
$$+ \ldots \tfrac{1}{2}m_nr_n^2\omega^2 \quad [32.3$$

Since $\frac{1}{2}\omega^2$ is a factor common to all the terms, we rewrite this as

total rotational kinetic energy $= \tfrac{1}{2}\omega^2 \sum_{i=1}^{n} m_ir_i^2$ $\quad [32.4$

This suggests that the *general* expression for **rotational inertia** is

$$I = \sum_{i=1}^{n} m_ir_i^2 \quad [32.5$$

Substituting this into equation 32.4, we get

total rotational kinetic energy $= \tfrac{1}{2}I\omega^2$ $\quad [32.6$

The calculation of the rotational inertia of a body (Fig. 32.5) amounts to an evaluation of the sum expressed in equation 32.5. It is simple if all the particles are at the same distance from the axis, as they are, for example, in a ring of radius R. The rotational inertia, according to equation 32.5, is

$$I = m_1R^2 + m_2R^2 + m_3R^2 + \ldots$$
$$= R^2(m_1 + m_2 + m_3 + \ldots) \quad [32.7$$
$$= MR^2$$

if M is the total mass. A disk (of a different substance) of the same radius and the same mass as

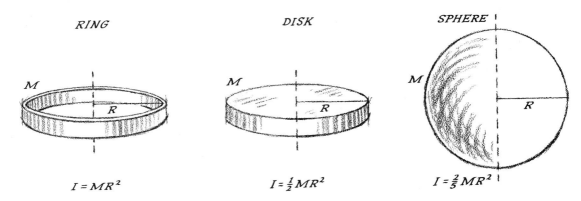

RING   DISK   SPHERE

M M M

R R R

$I = MR^2$ $I = \frac{1}{2}MR^2$ $I = \frac{2}{5}MR^2$

FIG. 32.5. *Rotational inertia about an axis of symmetry.*

the ring must have less rotational inertia than the ring for reasons that should be intuitively obvious if the physical significance of equation 32.5 is understood. Each particle of mass m contributes mr^2 to the total rotational inertia. If a particle is far from the axis of rotation (large r), its contribution is greater than if it is near, because of the multiplier r^2; in fact, since the multiplier is r^2 rather than r, its moment, or importance, increases much faster than r does. (The term **moment of inertia** is often used for what I call simply rotational inertia.) What is not intuitively obvious is that the formula for the disk comes out as $\frac{1}{2}MR^2$ and that for a solid sphere of the same mass and radius as $\frac{2}{5}MR^2$. The calculations for these and more complicated solids have to be effected by the integral calculus.

We shall not concern ourselves with formulas for the rotational inertia of bodies of any other shapes. We do need to remember that the dimensions of rotational inertia are simply those of mr^2—namely, ML^2. That knowledge and an intuitive understanding that objects whose mass is concentrated near the axis of rotation have relatively little rotational inertia is all that we require at present.

The principle of the conservation of energy provides simple solutions to certain kinds of problems involving rotation. Suppose, for example, that a disk of radius R can roll from height h without slipping down an inclined plane (Fig. 32.6). How fast will its center of mass be moving

at the bottom? There is no applied force, and we assume that, even though a frictional force is needed to keep the disk from slipping, no energy is lost to heat by the action of this frictional force; therefore $\Delta Q = 0$. Hence (equation 28.15)

$$\Delta K + \Delta U = 0$$

But the disk has kinetic energy of translation, $\frac{1}{2}mv^2$, and kinetic energy of rotation, $\frac{1}{2}I\omega^2$, at the bottom. Tabulating what we know as

$$K_0 = 0 \qquad K = \tfrac{1}{2}I\omega^2 + \tfrac{1}{2}mv^2$$
$$U_0 = mgh \qquad U = 0$$

we see that

$$mgh = \tfrac{1}{2}I\omega^2 + \tfrac{1}{2}mv^2 \qquad [32.8$$

For a disk, $I = \frac{1}{2}mR^2$, and the velocity, v, of the center of mass is related to the angular velocity by the formula $v = R\omega$. Therefore

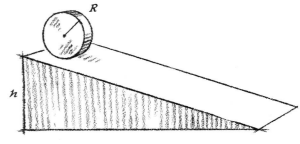

FIG. 32.6. *The speed of a disk rolling down an inclined plane can be deduced from the conservation of energy: the potential energy at the top is equal to the sum of the linear and rotational kinetic energies at the bottom.*

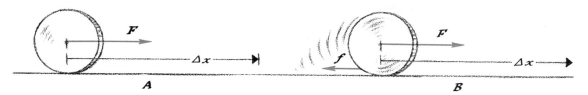

FIG. 32.7. *When force* **F** *acts over distance* Δx *on a body that slips without rotating (A), the work done,* **F**·Δ**x,** *appears as the linear kinetic energy,* $\frac{1}{2}mv^2$. *If the disk rolls without slipping (B), the work done appears as the sum of linear and rotational kinetic energies,* $\frac{1}{2}mv^2 + \frac{1}{2}I\omega^2$.

$$mgh = \tfrac{1}{2}(\tfrac{1}{2}mR^2)\omega^2 + \tfrac{1}{2}mv^2$$
$$= \tfrac{1}{4}mv^2 + \tfrac{1}{2}mv^2$$
$$= \tfrac{3}{4}mv^2$$
$$v^2 = \tfrac{4}{3}gh$$
$$v = \sqrt{(4/3)gh} \qquad\qquad [32.9$$

If the disk slips without rolling, $v = \sqrt{2gh}$ (equation 28.18). It moves slower when it rolls because part of its kinetic energy is rotational.

When an applied force, **F**, acts on a disk that is resting on a frictionless horizontal table (Fig. 32.7.A),

$$\mathbf{F}\cdot\Delta\mathbf{x} = \Delta K = \tfrac{1}{2}mv^2$$
$$v^2 = 2\frac{\mathbf{F}\cdot\Delta\mathbf{x}}{m}$$

All the work goes into translational kinetic energy. If the table is not frictionless, and if the disk rolls without slipping (Fig. 32.7.B),

TABLE 32.1

Quantities Used in the Study of Motion

Translation	Rotation
x	θ
v	ω
a	α
$s = \tfrac{1}{2}at^2$	$\theta = \tfrac{1}{2}\alpha t^2$
$v^2 = 2as$	$\omega^2 = 2\alpha\theta$
m	I
$\tfrac{1}{2}mv^2$	$\tfrac{1}{2}I\omega^2$
mv	$I\omega$
$\bar{F} = \dfrac{\Delta(mv)}{\Delta t}$	$\bar{\tau} = \dfrac{\Delta(I\omega)}{\Delta t}$

$$\mathbf{F}'\cdot\Delta\mathbf{x} = \Delta K = \tfrac{1}{2}mv^2 + \tfrac{1}{2}I\omega^2$$
$$v^2 = 2\frac{\mathbf{F}'\cdot\Delta\mathbf{x}}{m} - \frac{I}{m}\omega^2$$

Here $\mathbf{F}' = \mathbf{F} - \mathbf{f}$. The final velocity must be less than in the previous case because, first, $2\mathbf{F}'\cdot\Delta\mathbf{x}/m$ is smaller than $2\mathbf{F}\cdot\Delta\mathbf{x}/m$ and, second, the term $I\omega^2/m$ is subtracted from it. This can be reconciled with the fact that the acceleration of the center of mass is now $(\mathbf{F} - \mathbf{f})/m$, since the frictional force, $\mathbf{f}$, acts in a direction opposite to $\mathbf{F}$.

We now return to the topic of angular momentum.

32.3. Angular Momentum and Torque

Table 32.1 shows, on the left, some of the quantities we have used in the study of translational motion and, on the right, the corresponding quantities used in the study of rotational motion. Only kinematical quantities appear in the first five rows, but below that are some formulas from dynamics. I have already discussed all but the last two rows.

We have already seen that I is the rotational analogue of m, and that ω is the rotational analogue of v. This leads naturally to the formula $I\omega$ for the angular momentum of a rotating body. Experiments indicate that, as the frictional and other retarding forces acting on a rotating body approach zero, it tends to conserve its angular momentum.

In a well-known classroom demonstration of this fact a student sits on a strong turntable with good low-friction bearings (Fig. 32.8). He holds a dumbbell in each hand, arms outstretched (A), and another student starts him rotating at angular velocity ω_1. When he pulls the dumbbells in close to the axis of rotation (B), he speeds up to a new angular velocity, ω_2. If we demand that angular momentum, $I\omega$, be conserved, we require that

$$I_1\omega_1 = I_2\omega_2 \qquad [32.10$$

The explanation is now clear. By bringing the dumbbells in toward the axis, the student decreases the rotational inertia of the system (remember that $I = mr^2$ for a particle). Since I_2 is less than I_1, ω_2 must be greater than ω_1. (A numerical illustration of this is given in Prob. 32.5).

Analogies have a way of leading us on. I have likened $I\omega$ in rotation to mv in translation. We know that the rate of change of momentum, $\Delta(mv)/\Delta t$, is the force that produces a translational acceleration of a body. That raises a natural question: What is the physical significance of the rate of change of angular momentum, $\Delta(I\omega)/\Delta t$? As indicated in Table 32.1, this quantity plays a role in rotation that is analogous to that of force in translational motion. It is called torque. If it is correct to say that force causes translational acceleration, it is also correct to

say that torque causes angular acceleration. Let us give **torque** the symbol τ (the Greek letter tau) and define† it by the expression

$$\tau = \frac{\Delta(I\omega)}{\Delta t}$$

We analyze torque dimensionally. We know that

$$[I] = ML^2 \qquad [\omega] = T^{-1} \qquad [\Delta t] = T$$

Therefore

$$\left[\frac{\Delta(I\omega)}{\Delta t}\right] = \frac{ML^2 T^{-1}}{T} = ML^2 T^{-2}$$

We know that MLT^{-2} are the dimensions of a force; therefore $ML^2 T^{-2}$ has the same dimensions as the product of a force and a distance.

We saw above that torque is analogous to force, but closer examination has led us to see that it involves both force and distance and that, in fact, a product of force and distance has just the right physical dimensions to be a torque. We speak of the torque of a force, which means, loosely speaking, the turning effect of that force.

† Strictly speaking,

$$\tau = \lim_{\Delta t \to 0} \frac{\Delta(I\omega)}{\Delta t}$$

but we shall continue to use the approximate form.

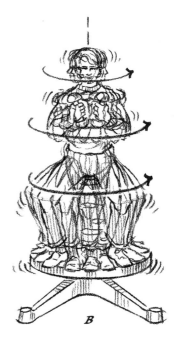

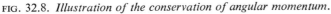

FIG. 32.8. *Illustration of the conservation of angular momentum.*

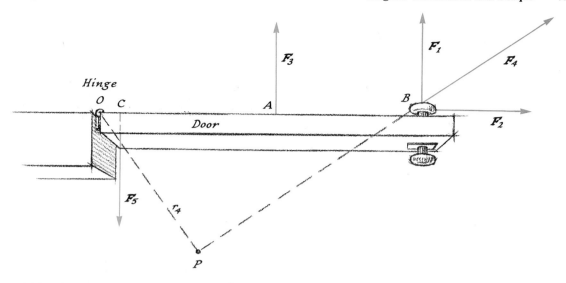

FIG. 32.9. *The turning effect of a force depends both on its magnitude and on its lever arm. The lever arm of force F_4 is illustrated. The turning effect of $\mathbf{F}_2$ is zero because its lever arm is zero.*

The torque of a force about a fixed point depends on the distance from the point to the line of action of the force. In Figure 32.9, for example, the turning effect of force F_4 about point O is measured by the product of F_4 and the perpendicular distance, OP, from the point to the line of action of the force (extended if necessary). The distance $OP = r_4$ is called the **lever arm** of force F_4. A definition of torque† that is consistent with the definition $\tau = \Delta(I\omega)/\Delta t$ is

$$\tau = \text{(lever arm)} \times \text{force}$$

This definition makes it clear that the torque produced by a force depends not only on the magnitude of the force but also on its point of application and its direction. In Figure 32.9, for example, force F_1, applied at B, is more effective in turning a door about its hinge, at O, than force F_3 of the same magnitude, applied at A, which is closer to O. Let us call torques positive if they tend to produce a counterclockwise motion about the given axis (perpendicular to the plane in which the forces act). The torques due to forces labeled in Figure 32.9 are, accordingly, as follows: F_1, great and positive; F_2, zero; F_3, small and positive; F_4, great and positive; F_5,

† Strictly speaking, torque is a vector defined as $\mathbf{r} \times \mathbf{F}$ (§ 33.2). In this chapter we deal with forces that are all in the same plane, and we treat torque as a scalar.

very small and negative. The preponderance of positive torques would produce an angular acceleration in the positive (counterclockwise) direction. The algebraic sum of the torques is

$$\Sigma\tau = (OA)F_3 + (OB)F_1 + (OP)F_4 - (OC)F_5$$

The angular acceleration, α, of this system can be computed from the equation

$$\Sigma\tau = \frac{\Delta(I\omega)}{\Delta t} = I\frac{\Delta\omega}{\Delta t} = I\alpha$$

EXAMPLE 32.1. Force F_1, of 10 nt, acts on a winding drum of radius $r_1 = 15$ cm, attached to disk D, of radius $R = 25$ cm and mass 18 kg (Fig. 32.10).

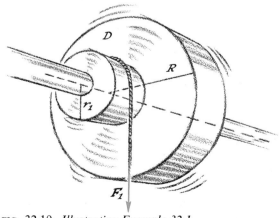

FIG. 32.10. *Illustrating Example 32.1.*

We want to find the angular acceleration of the system.

Using the formula

$$\Sigma\tau = I\alpha$$

we get

$$\alpha = \frac{\Sigma\tau}{I}$$

In this case there is only one force, F_1, producing torque:

$$\tau = r_1F_1 = 0.15 \text{ m} \times 10 \text{ nt} = 1.5 \text{ nt-m}$$

Neglecting the mass of the winding drum and using the disk formula $\frac{1}{2}MR^2$, we have

$$I = \tfrac{1}{2}MR^2 = \tfrac{1}{2} \times 18 \text{ kg} \times (0.25 \text{ m})^2$$
$$= 0.5625 \text{ kg-m}^2$$

Therefore

$$\alpha = \frac{\tau}{I} = \frac{1.5 \text{ nt-m}}{0.5625 \text{ kg-m}^2} = 2.67 \frac{\text{rad}}{\text{sec}^2}$$

Having defined torque, we can now state the **principle of the conservation of angular momentum**: *the angular momentum of a body remains constant unless acted upon by an external torque.*

I conclude this chapter with a discussion of some special cases in which the sum of the external torques is zero.

32.4. The Condition for Rotational Equilibrium

If the algebraic sum of the torques is zero, $\alpha = 0$. This is obviously a requirement for **rotational equilibrium.**

We can now summarize the requirements for equilibrium:

FOR TRANSLATIONAL EQUILIBRIUM:

$$\sum_{i=1}^{n} \mathbf{F}_i = \mathbf{0}$$

FOR ROTATIONAL EQUILIBRIUM:

$$\sum_{i=1}^{n} \tau_i = 0$$

The first guarantees that the linear velocity of the center of mass is constant. The second guarantees that the angular velocity is constant. In each case zero is a special instance of the constant.

It is possible for a body with neither external forces nor external torques acting on it to have

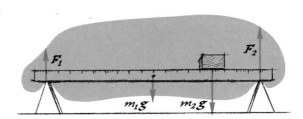

FIG. 32.11. *Illustrating Example 32.2.*

both translational and rotational motions—for example, the wrench sliding on a frictionless surface in Figure 30.17. Notice that its center of mass moves with constant linear velocity and that it rotates at constant angular velocity. It is conserving (only approximately since some retarding forces and torques act on it) both its linear momentum and its angular momentum.

32.5. Complete Equilibrium

If a body is in translational and rotational equilibrium, with no motion of either kind in the system under observation, we may say that it is in complete equilibrium. In this case the velocity of the center of mass and the angular velocity are both zero in relation to the chosen frame of reference. We shall now consider a few examples.

EXAMPLE 32.2. A meter stick rests on sharp-edged supports placed at the 5-cm and 95-cm marks (Fig. 32.11). It has a mass of 300 gm. A 500-gm object rests on it at the 75-cm mark. We want to know what forces, F_1 and F_2 (in newtons), are exerted by the supports.

The first condition of equilibrium demands, vectorially, that

$$\mathbf{F}_1 + \mathbf{F}_2 + m_1\mathbf{g} + m_2\mathbf{g} = \mathbf{0}$$

The weight, $m_1\mathbf{g}$, of the meter stick is assumed to act at the 50-cm mark. Dropping the vector notation, we have

$$F_1 + F_2 - m_1g - m_2g = 0$$
$$F_1 + F_2 = (m_1 + m_2)g$$
$$= (0.3 \text{ kg} + 0.5 \text{ kg})9.8 \text{ m/sec}^2$$
$$= 7.80 \text{ nt}$$

Now let us use the condition $\Sigma\tau = 0$. We arbitrarily calculate torques about the left support:

$$-m_1g(0.45) - m_2g(0.70) + F_2(0.90) = 0$$
$$-2.94(0.45) - 4.9(0.70) + F_2(0.90) = 0$$
$$0.90F_2 = 1.32 + 3.43$$
$$= 4.75$$
$$F_2 = 5.28 \text{ nt}$$

Since $F_1 + F_2 = 7.80$ nt,

$$F = 2.52 \text{ nt}$$

EXAMPLE 32.3. Consider a ladder (Fig. 32.12) leaning against a frictionless wall and standing on a frictionless floor. It is 20 ft long and weighs 30 lb. It makes an angle of 60° with the horizontal. A 100-lb boy is standing at the 15-ft mark on the ladder. The ladder is kept from slipping by a rope tied to the wall and to the bottom of the ladder. We want to find the tension of the rope.

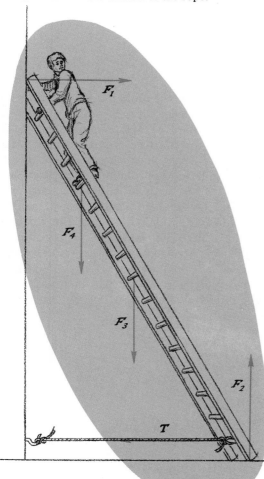

FIG. 32.12. *Illustrating Example 32.3.*

We first draw the vectors for all the forces acting on the ladder: F_1, the normal reaction of the wall; F_2, the normal reaction of the floor; F_3, the weight of the ladder; F_4, the weight of the boy; T, the tension of the rope. We require that $\Sigma F = 0$ and that $\Sigma \tau = 0$. The first equation means that

$$\mathbf{F_1 + F_2 + F_3 + F_4 + T = 0}$$

In other words, the sum of these vectors is a vector whose magnitude is zero. Such a vector has both its x component and its y component equal to zero. Now consider that the x component of a sum of vectors is equal to the sum of their x components and that the y component of a sum of vectors is equal to the sum of their y components. This leads to the conclusion that the sum of the x components of a set of forces in translational equilibrium must be zero and that a similar remark can be made about the sum of the y components. Hence, adding y components only and dropping the vector notation, we get

$$F_2 = F_3 + F_4$$

Adding x components only, we get

$$F_1 = T$$

Using our requirement that $\tau = 0$ and computing torques about the top of the ladder, we get the equation

$$F_2 r_2 = F_3 r_3 + F_4 r_4 + Tr$$

(in which we assume that the lowest rung is virtually at the floor).

$$r_2 = 20 \sin 30° = 10.00 \text{ ft}$$
$$r_3 = 10 \sin 30° = 5.00 \text{ ft}$$
$$r_4 = 5 \sin 30° = 2.5 \text{ ft}$$
$$r = 20 \cos 30° = 17.32 \text{ ft}$$
$$F_3 = 30 \text{ lb}$$
$$F_4 = 100 \text{ lb}$$
$$F_2 = F_3 + F_4 = 130 \text{ lb}$$

Substituting the numerical values, we get

$$130 \text{ lb} \times 10 \text{ ft} = 30 \text{ lb} \times 5 \text{ ft} + 100 \text{ lb}$$
$$\times 2.5 \text{ ft} + T \times 17.32 \text{ ft}$$
$$1{,}300 - 150 - 250 = 17.32 \, T$$

$$\frac{900}{17.32} = T$$

$$T = 51.9 \text{ lb}$$

EXAMPLE 32.4. We make three rubber-band chains by linking several rubber bands together for each, and we punch three holes at random in a piece of cardboard. With string we attach one rubber-band chain at each hole. We stretch the chains out in a

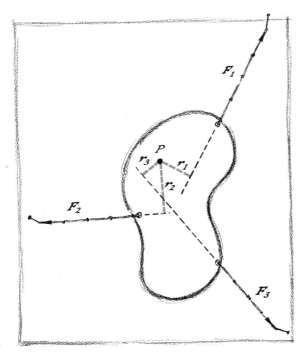

FIG. 32.13. *Illustrating Example 32.4.*

horizontal plane and loop them over nails driven into a flat piece of wood. Looking down on the configuration (Fig. 32.13), we see a body in equilibrium under the action of three forces. We measure the stretched rubber-band chains. The length of each enables us to find the magnitude of the force exerted by it, as we did for Figure 24.12. (After the demonstration is finished, we hang weights from each chain until its length is the same as it was in the demonstration.)

We trace the directions of the forces on a piece of paper slipped under the cardboard. Using this sketch, we draw a vector diagram (see Fig. 24.13) to check the fact that $\Sigma \mathbf{F} = \mathbf{0}$. On the same paper we choose an arbitrary point, P, to represent an axis of rotation. Figure 32.13 illustrates how the lever arms r_1, r_2, and r_3 can be measured from P. We can now compute

$$\Sigma \tau = F_1 r_1 + F_2 r_2 + F_3 r_3$$

being sure to give a positive sign to each counterclockwise torque and a negative sign to each clockwise torque. In this way we check both conditions of equilibrium and confirm the important fact that the point of application of the forces does not influence the vanishing of $\Sigma \mathbf{F}$.

The same procedure may be used for four or more forces. See Prob. 32.8, where it is pointed out that the problem with only three forces is a very special case.

32.6. Summary

The rotational inertia of a body is expressed by terms like mr^2. Hence its dimensions must be ML^2. It plays a role in rotation analogous to that played by mass in translation. In fact, every term used in rectilinear kinematics and dynamics has an analogous term in rotation. This preserves the form of the rectilinear equations, rotational terms replacing the analogous rectilinear terms. The formula for rotational kinetic energy, for example, is $\frac{1}{2}I\omega^2$ instead of $\frac{1}{2}mv^2$. The concept of torque, in this analogy, replaces that of force; so, in place of $F = ma$, we have $\tau = I\alpha$. When τ is zero, α must be zero, and this implies rotational equilibrium just as $a = 0$ implied translational equilibrium.

Problems

32.1. A phonograph record (45 rpm) has a mass of 37.8 gm. The radius, R, of its outer circle is 8.25 cm, and the radius, r, of its central hole is 1.92 cm. Find its rotational inertia as follows:

1. Prove that its rotational inertia is $m(R^2 + r^2)/2$. (Hint: As suggested by equation 32.5, the rotational inertia of the whole is equal to the rotational inertia of its parts, and the final formula must have the dimensions ML^2. Consider the record as a disk from which a small central disk has been removed. The mass of a disk is $\pi r^2 \rho$ if ρ is mass per unit area.)

2. Substitute numerical values into this formula.

32.2. Just as we can find the mass of an object, without weighing, by measuring its period of oscillation when it is suspended from a spring and using the formula $T = 2\pi\sqrt{m/k}$, we can find the rotational inertia of a homogeneous rod by measuring its period of angular oscillation when it is suspended at its center by a long vertical wire whose torsion supplies the restoring torque and using the analogous formula $T = 2\pi\sqrt{I/c}$. Here is an experiment that illustrates how to find the rotational inertia of the rod without knowing the torsion constant c. First the rod, of length $2r = 0.30$ m, is suspended, alone, horizontally at its midpoint. Its period of angular oscillation is 10.2 sec. When a small weight is added to each end, the period becomes 11.3 sec. Each weight has a mass, m, of 0.025 kg.

1. What increment in the rotational inertia of the system is due to the two weights?

2. Show that the periods T_1 and T_2 of the system, before and after the weights are added, are related to the corresponding rotational inertias I_1 and I_2 by the equation

$$T_1^2/T_2^2 = I_1/I_2$$

3. By using the idea of the summability of rotational inertias prove that

$$I_1 = \frac{2mr^2 T_1^2}{T_2^2 - T_1^2}$$

4. Find a numerical value for the rotational inertia of the rod.

32.3. Assume, in Fig. 32.10 and Example 32.1, that all numerical factors remain the same except F_1, which is now supplied by an object of mass $m = 1.2$ kg, hung to the string wrapped round the drum. Let the system start from rest. The suspended object is at height $h = 2.7$ m above the floor.

1. Use kinetic-energy considerations alone to calculate the speed of the object just before it hits the floor by first deriving a relation for v^2 as a function of g, h, m, M, and R.

2. Find a numerical value for v by substituting values (except F_1) from Example 32.1.

32.4. A primitive cartwheel has a radius of 1.12 m and a mass of 200 kg. Started from rest, it reaches an angular velocity of 5 turns per second in 10 sec. Compute the magnitude of the applied torque in newton-meters. (Make the simplifying assumption that the wheel is a homogeneous solid disk.)

32.5. If the turntable in part A of Fig. 32.8 is spinning at the rate of 1 turn per second, how fast will it be spinning in part B if the separation between dumbbells changes from 2.2 m to 0.20 m? Assume that the rotational inertia of boy, stool, and turntable is constant at 2.1 kg-m² and that the mass of each dumbbell is 2.0 kg.

32.6. A meter stick whose mass is 0.23 kg has its zero end resting on a table. At the 25-cm mark we place a weight whose mass is 0.12 kg. The 100-cm end is held up by hand so that the stick is horizontal.

1. What upward force is exerted by the hand?

2. When the hand is removed, what is the instantaneous angular acceleration of the system? (The rotational inertia of a homogeneous stick of length L about an axis at one end is $mL^2/3$.)

32.7. A packed suitcase weighs more than 25 lb. The available spring scale reads only up to 25 lb, but the weight of the suitcase and its center of mass can be found as follows: One of the short edges of the suitcase is placed on the edge of a table. The vertical force needed at the other end of the suitcase to hold it horizontal, as measured with the scale, is 15 lb. When the experiment is repeated with the ends of the suitcase reversed, the scale reads 25 lb.

1. Calculate the weight of the suitcase.

2. Calculate the distance from the first edge to the center of mass if the suitcase is 0.9 m long.

32.8. 1. Perform an experiment like the one shown in Fig. 32.13, using four (instead of three) rubber-band chains, and prove, for any arrangement that produces equilibrium, (a) that the vector sum of the forces is zero and (b) that the algebraic sum of the torques is zero. (You will need a ruler to measure the lengths of the stretched rubber-band chains and weights to measure the force exerted by those chains when stretched. Iron washers or steel nuts of uniform size are good weights for home-made experiments.)

2. Prove experimentally that, whenever only three forces are used, the force vectors extended meet at a point.

3. Give a theoretical reason for the statement in part 2. (Hint: Extend any two vector lines until they meet; calculate torques about that point.)

33

Universal Gravitation

WHAT is so spectacular about an apple falling to the ground? Nothing! It is a common occurrence and is dismissed as such by common men. But Newton was far from common, and his thoughts about gravitation, possibly initiated by his seeing an apple fall from a tree, resulted in his theory of universal gravitation, which is considered one of the greatest achievements in the history of the human intellect.

33.1. The Meaning of Universal Gravitation

To appreciate that achievement, we must first understand the particular way in which the words "universal" and "gravitation" are used. Take "gravitation" first. We ordinarily associate the word with heaviness, and this is correct, for the word is derived from the Latin word for heavy. But that is only part of the story. If we shift our attention from heaviness to *attraction*, we shall be on the right track. The apple is heavy because the earth *attracts* it. It doesn't matter whether the apple tree is in Spain or China; the apples are attracted toward the center of the earth. Is this what we mean by "universality"—that objects anywhere near the surface of the earth fall toward its center? Yes, we mean this, but this is only a small part of what we mean. The universe that we have in mind is the universe of the astronomer—the universe in which the earth, the sun, the moon, the planets, and even all the stars of our own galaxy, the Milky Way, are just a small part. We mean universal in the broadest spatial sense you can imagine.

In the earth-apple example, the sequence of relevant ideas is this:

1. The earth attracts the apple with a force, **F**.
2. The apple attracts the earth with an equal and opposite force, $-\mathbf{F}$.
3. One apple, of mass m_1, will attract another apple, of mass m_2, with a force proportional to $(m_1 m_2)/r^2$ if r is the distance between their centers.

Everybody believes statement 1. Few people have ever thought about statement 2, and, when they do, they find it hard to believe. Most people have never thought about statement 3. When confronted with it, they may grant that the idea is conceivable but insist that it is not likely to be true, since they have never seen two apples rushing at each other under the influence of their mutual attraction. The idea that this weak kind of attraction can possibly act over 93 million miles to keep the earth in its orbit seems, at first, preposterous.

Newton was actually thinking, at first, not about the possibility that two small objects like apples attract each other, but about the force that keeps the moon in its orbit round the earth or the earth in its orbit round the sun. When the universality of his conclusions struck him, he was led to assert that *every particle attracts every other particle in the universe with a force that is directly proportional to the product of their masses and inversely proportional to the square of the distance between them.* Newton arrived at this conclusion after more than twenty years of intellectual effort, in the course of which he invented the differential calculus, the integral calculus, and the laws of dynamics, for any one of which he would have gone down in history as a great man.

It is tempting to approach this subject historically, for it is one of the most exciting episodes in the history of human thought. Here, however, having whetted your appetite, I shall do no more than refer you to some excellent books on the subject.† I shall now treat the subject as a logical continuation of our consideration of the dynamics of a particle, in which the laws of conservation and momentum hold sway.

33.2. A New Way to Write Torque and Angular Momentum

Before continuing our consideration of gravitation, we shall find it profitable to express torque and angular momentum as vectors. A force, **F**, acting at a point, A (Fig. 33.1.A), produces a torque, τ, which is equal to the lever arm about the point O multiplied by the force. The lever arm is exhibited as $r \sin \theta$. The magnitude of the torque is therefore $Fr \sin \theta$. Here r is the magnitude of the vector **r**, which localizes the point of application, A, of force **F** in relation to O. [Notice that, if **F** is decomposed into rectangular components one of which is along **r** (Fig. 33.1.B), it is only $F \sin \theta$ that exerts a torque about O. Its magnitude is still $Fr \sin \theta$.]

† Norman Feather, *An Introduction to the Physics of Mass, Length and Time* (Edinburgh University Press, 1959); Gerald Holton, *Introduction to Concepts and Theories in Physical Science* (Cambridge, Mass., 1952); I. Bernard Cohen, *The Birth of a New Physics* (Garden City, N.Y., 1960), a paperback (Anchor).

Let us invent a new form of multiplication called **vector multiplication, r × F**, to represent the torque due to **F**. This requires that the magnitude of **r × F** be $Fr \sin \theta$. How about the direction of the vector **r × F**? Since we pretend to be inventing (actually I am presenting the case for the accepted meaning of **vector product**), we are at liberty to choose any direction for **r × F** that makes sense dynamically. In Chapter 32 we saw that force **F** of Figure 33.1 produces a positive (counterclockwise) torque. It may, therefore, come as a shock for you to learn that we choose a direction for the vector **r × F** that is at right angles to both of them. We can justify this choice by observing, for example, how we can add torques to one another by using the laws of vector addition. You will have to take my word for it that a vector perpendicular to the plane determined by **r** and **F** (and coming out of the plane of the paper in the case of Fig. 33.1) has the correct direction for **r × F** in the sense that consistent physical results follow from this choice. Unlike the dot product **F·Δx**, which is a scalar and hence has no direction, the vector product that defines torque, **r × F**, has both magnitude and direction.

More generally, the vector product, **a × b**, of any two vectors **a** and **b** (which need not be a radius vector **r** and a force **F**) has the *magnitude* $ab \sin \theta$ (if θ is the angle between **a** and **b**). Its *direction* is perpendicular to the plane of **a** and **b** and points the way a right-handed screw would travel if turned through angle θ (Fig. 33.2.A). In Figure 33.2.B, for example, **a × b** points up out of the

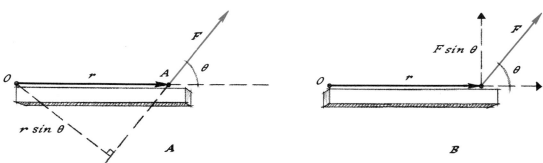

FIG. 33.1. *The torque due to a force, **F**, whose point of application is given by the displacement vector **r** is the vector product **r × F**. Its magnitude is $Fr \sin \theta$ (the magnitude of the force multiplied by the lever arm). Its direction is perpendicular to the plane of **r** and **F** and points the way a right-handed screw would travel if turned from **r** toward **F** through θ, the smallest possible angle between them.*

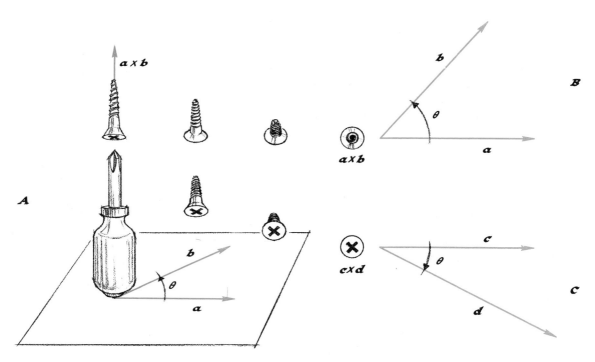

FIG. 33.2. (*A*) *The direction of* **a** $\times$ **b** *is perpendicular to the plane of* **a** *and* **b** *and points the way a right-handed screw would travel if turned from* **a** *toward* **b** *through* θ, *the smallest possible angle between them.* (*B*) *The vector* **a** $\times$ **b** *points up out of the paper; its direction is symbolized by a dot in a circle.* (*C*) *The vector* **c** $\times$ **d** *points down into the paper; its direction is symbolized by a cross in a circle.*

paper; for, if you rotated **a** toward **b** through the smaller of the two possible angles θ, a right-handed screw turning the same way would move up out of the paper. (This direction is usually symbolized by a dot inside a circle, suggesting that you are looking at the point of an approaching arrow or screw). In Figure 33.2.C, however, **c** $\times$ **d** points down into the paper; for, if you turned **c** toward **d** (which you must do clockwise to go through the smaller of the two possible angles), a right-handed screw would move down into the paper. (The symbol for this direction, a cross in a circle, can be remembered because of its similarity to the feathers of an arrow moving away from you or to the head of the type of screw shown in the figure.)

The magnitude of **a** $\times$ **b** has a simple geomet-

rical interpretation.† Consider the parallelogram *OABC* (Fig. 33.3), with its adjacent sides **a** and **b**. The altitude of this parallelogram is $BD = b \sin \theta$. Since the area of a parallelogram is equal to its base times its altitude, $ab \sin \theta$ is the area of the parallelogram *OABC*. We enclose **a** $\times$ **b** in vertical bars to indicate its magnitude:

$$|\mathbf{a} \times \mathbf{b}| = ab \sin \theta = \text{area of parallelogram } OABC$$

Under what circumstances does the vector prod-

† The area interpretation given here holds if the dimensions of **a** $\times$ **b** are L^2, as they are if **a** and **b** are both displacement vectors. In many examples of the vector product, however, this is not so. For example, $[\mathbf{r} \times \mathbf{F}] = ML^2T^{-2}$. Even in such a case we can draw lengths proportional to r and F, respectively, and obtain a parallelogram like that of Fig. 33.3, whose area is proportional to the magnitude of $\mathbf{r} \times \mathbf{F}$. Similar words of caution apply to angular momentum, $\mathbf{r} \times \mathbf{p}$, whose dimensions are ML^2T^{-1}.

uct of two vectors vanish? It is obvious that, if $\mathbf{a} = \mathbf{0}$ or $\mathbf{b} = \mathbf{0}$ or $\sin \theta = 0$, the product $ab \sin \theta$ vanishes. We can visualize this by imagining the effect of each of these quantities on the area of the parallelogram. Going back to Figure 33.1, we see that, when $\theta = 0$, the torque of magnitude $Fr \sin \theta$ also goes to zero.

We are now going to consider angular momentum as a vector. We begin by returning to a very simple example from § 32.3. We imagine a particle of mass m moving at constant angular velocity in a circle of radius r (Fig. 33.4). Its angular momentum is $I\omega$. Since $I = mr^2$ for a particle, $I\omega = mr^2\omega$. But $r\omega$ is v, the linear speed of the particle. Hence $I\omega = mrv$. Let us write this as

$$I\omega = r(mv)$$

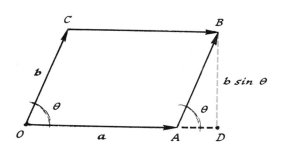

FIG. 33.3. *The magnitude of* $\mathbf{a} \times \mathbf{b}$ *is equal to the area of the parallelogram of which* $\mathbf{a}$ *and* $\mathbf{b}$ *are adjacent sides.*

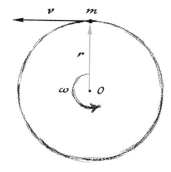

FIG. 33.4. *The angular momentum of a particle of mass* m *moving in a circle of radius* r *at constant angular velocity* ω *is* Iω = r(mv) = rp *if* v *is the linear speed of the particle and* p *is the magnitude of its linear momentum.*

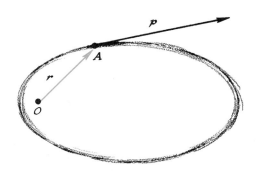

FIG. 33.5. *If the displacement of a particle is* r *and its linear momentum is* p, *its angular momentum is the vector* r × p.

or, rather, as

$$I\omega = rp \qquad [33.1$$

since p is, by definition, the magnitude of the linear momentum, mv.

Vectorially, $\mathbf{r}$ is the vector that localizes the particle in relation to O, and $\mathbf{p}$ is the linear-momentum vector. If we take the scalar product of $\mathbf{r}$ and $\mathbf{p}$, it comes out as zero ($\mathbf{r} \cdot \mathbf{p} = rp \cos \theta$), which is not what we want. We are thus led to consider the vector product, $\mathbf{r} \times \mathbf{p}$. In Figure 33.4, $\mathbf{r}$ and $\mathbf{p}$ are mutually perpendicular, and therefore $\sin \theta = 1$. The magnitude of $\mathbf{r} \times \mathbf{p}$ is simply rp, in agreement with equation 33.1. It is clear in this simple case that the angular momentum may be written as $\mathbf{r} \times \mathbf{p}$. It is not yet clear what advantage we have gained by writing it as a vector.

If the particle (Fig. 33.5) happens to be at A and is moving in a curved path, its location relative to point O can be given by the displacement vector $\mathbf{r}$. In this case $\mathbf{r}$ and $\mathbf{p}$ are not always mutually perpendicular. I assert without proof that $\mathbf{r} \times \mathbf{p}$ is still the angular momentum relative to O.

33.3. Torque, Central Force, and Conservation of Angular Momentum

We now inquire into the significance of the principle of the conservation of angular momentum in a case like that of Figure 33.5. (Remember that, when the sum of the external torques, $\Sigma\tau$,

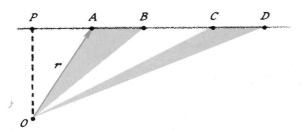

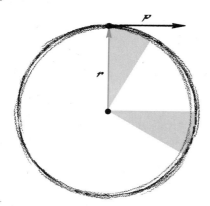

FIG. 33.6. *If* **F** *is zero, the torque* **r** × **F** *is also zero. This presents a special case of the conservation of angular momentum. It is obvious that even in this special case the radius vector sweeps out equal areas in equal times.*

FIG. 33.7. *A particle moving in a circle under the action of a central force of constant magnitude: Since* **F** *and* **r** *are parallel to each other,* **r** × **F** = 0. *In the absence of an external torque, the angular momentum,* **r** × **p**, *is constant. The radius vector sweeps out equal areas in equal times.*

acting on a body is zero, its angular momentum is constant. In particular, if only a single force acts on a particle in such a way that it exerts zero torque on it, the particle will conserve its angular momentum.) The reason why we are interested in this particular mode of motion will soon be clear. If a particle experiences a force, **F**, in the direction *AO* (Fig. 33.5), its torque, **r** × **F**, about *O* is zero, and it therefore conserves its angular momentum. The force acting on the particle is called a **central force** because it always points to a fixed spot. (It points, not along **r**, but in the opposite direction, toward *O*.) Hence we may state that *a particle moving under the action of a central force conserves angular momentum about*

an axis through the central point and perpendicular to the plane of motion. In Figure 33.5 angular momentum is conserved about an axis parallel to **r** × **p** and going through *O*.

But **r** × **F** is also zero if **F** is zero. This leads to a very special case of the conservation of angular momentum. If **F** = **0**, the particle conserves linear momentum as well as angular momentum about any point. A particle moving in obedience to the equation **F** = **0** travels in a straight line and covers equal distances in equal times (Fig. 33.6). In time Δt it goes from *A* to *B* or from *C* to *D*, and *AB* = *CD*. Observe that triangles *OAB* and *OCD* have equal areas. (Their bases, *AB* and *CD*, are equal, and they have a common altitude, *OP*.) Therefore **r**, the **radius vector** (a displacement vector from a fixed point, used to localize a moving point), sweeps out equal areas in equal times.

Another way in which a particle can conserve its angular momentum is to move in a circle at a constant speed (Fig. 33.7). In this case the force is centripetal, the torque **r** × **F** is zero, and the angular momentum is constant. Here the statement that **r** × **p** is a constant implies that $rp \sin 90° = rp = $ a constant. Since r is constant, p is constant, and so is v. Again it is intuitively apparent that r covers equal areas in equal times, wherever we start in the orbit.

We now consider a more general theorem.

33.4. The Law of Equal Areas in Equal Times

Finally, consider the consequence, for a particle moving in a plane, curved, but not circular, path (Fig. 33.8), of the condition that **r** × **p** is constant. This implies that

$$\mathbf{r}_1 \times \mathbf{p}_1 = \mathbf{r}_2 \times \mathbf{p}_2 \qquad [33.2$$

$$\mathbf{r}_1 \times m\mathbf{v}_1 = \mathbf{r}_2 \times m\mathbf{v}_2 \qquad [33.3$$

Since it can be proved that m comes out as a common factor on both sides of equation 33.3,

$$\mathbf{r}_1 \times \mathbf{v}_1 = \mathbf{r}_2 \times \mathbf{v}_2 \qquad [33.4$$

We can, in an analogous way, justify multiplying each velocity by time Δt. Using vertical bars to indicate numerical value, we get

$$|\mathbf{r}_1 \times \mathbf{v}_1(\Delta t)| = |\mathbf{r}_2 \times \mathbf{v}_2(\Delta t)| \qquad [33.5$$

This implies that the areas of triangles FAB and FCD are equal (Fig. 33.9), for the area of triangle FAB is $\frac{1}{2}|\mathbf{r}_1 \times \mathbf{v}_1(\Delta t)|$, and that of triangle FCD is $\frac{1}{2}|\mathbf{r}_2 \times \mathbf{v}_2(\Delta t)|$. Each is half of the parallelogram whose area defines a vector product of the type $\mathbf{r} \times \mathbf{v}(\Delta t)$. In Figure 33.9, it is true, points B and D are not on the curve; but an argument based on the limit concept (allowing Δt to approach zero) and on Fig. 33.9 leads to the idea that, when angular momentum is conserved, the exact *rate* at which the radius vector sweeps out area is a constant. Hence over a finite time interval, Δt, no matter how long, the total area, FAB, swept out by the radius vector starting at point A (Fig. 33.10) is the same as the total area, FCD, swept out in the same time, Δt, by the radius vector starting at some other point, C, on the curve. Points B and D *are* on the orbit in Figure 33.10.

We have now reached three interesting conclusions concerning a particle moving under the action of a central force:

1. If a particle moves under a central force, $\mathbf{F}$, the torque $\mathbf{r} \times \mathbf{F} = \mathbf{0}$.
2. Since the torque is zero, angular momentum is conserved; $I\omega = \mathbf{r} \times \mathbf{p} =$ a constant.
3. The conservation of angular momentum implies that the radius vector from the central point sweeps out equal areas in equal times.

Thus we have been led to the logical conclusion that a particle moving in obedience to the laws of dynamics under the action of a central force will describe a path whose radius vector sweeps out equal areas in equal times.

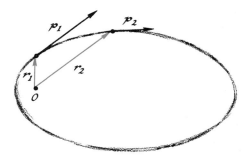

FIG. 33.8. *A particle moving in a curved path and conserving angular momentum: This implies that* $\mathbf{r}_1 \times \mathbf{p}_1 = \mathbf{r}_2 \times \mathbf{p}_2$.

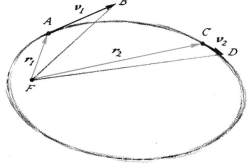

FIG. 33.9. *The conservation of angular momentum implies that the area of triangle* FAB *is the same as that of triangle* FCD.

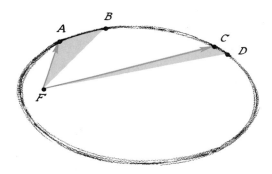

FIG. 33.10. *Applying an argument based upon the concept of limit to Fig. 33.9, one can prove that the radius vector sweeps out equal areas in equal times. The green area* FAB *is equal to the green area* FCD *if the time of travel from* A *to* B *is the same as that from* C *to* D.

The motion of an earth satellite (Fig. 33.10) is an example. When the satellite is in orbit, it is always being pulled toward the center of the earth; in other words, it experiences a central force. Its radius vector therefore sweeps out equal areas in equal times. The radar data received from such satellites amply confirm this fact. A satellite, obviously, moves more slowly when it is far from the earth than when it is near.

Is it possible for a particle to move under the influence of a force toward the *center* of an ellipse? Yes, but no particle has ever been observed to move in this way under the influence of a force that varies inversely as the square of the distance from particle to fixed point. Figure 33.11 shows

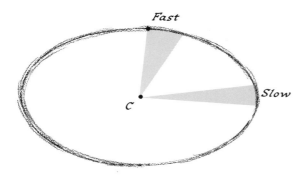

FIG. 33.11. *A particle moving in an elliptical path under the action of a force directed not toward the focus of the ellipse but toward its center.*

a particle obeying the rule of equal areas in equal times, but the force on it is $F = kr$ rather than $F = k/r^2$. The rule does not guarantee an inverse-square relation between force and distance unless the force is directed to a focus of the ellipse.

I have deduced the law of equal areas from the principles of dynamics. Historically, it was the other way round. Kinematics came before dynamics, and it was known that the planets obey the law of equal areas before it was known why. Without dwelling on the details, I shall now tell briefly how Newton was led to his discovery of the inverse-square law and how from it and his laws of motion he was able to deduce the law of equal areas, which Kepler had derived from the observational data of Tycho Brahe.

33.5. The Contributions of Brahe, Kepler, and Newton

The history of science shows clearly that even the greatest men have built on the groundwork left by their predecessors. Newton built his theory on the solid structure left by Copernicus, Brahe, Kepler, and Galileo. Here are Kepler's laws of motion of the planets, the first two stated by him in 1609 in *De motibus stellae Martis*, the third in 1619 in *Harmonice mundi*:

1. Each planet moves in an ellipse with the sun at one focus.

2. For each planet the line from the sun to the planet sweeps out equal areas in equal times.
3. The squares of the periodic times of the planets are as the cubes of their mean distances from the sun.

To feel Kepler's elation at these discoveries, one must read his enthusiastic comments on them.[†] And no wonder he was elated! He had been seeking these relations for twenty years and had finally hit upon them after an enormous amount of work. He had, to work with, the data compiled by his master, Tycho Brahe, who had assembled on the little island of Hveen, in Denmark, the instruments for the most elaborate observatory of his day. Brahe had, for example, a quadrant with a radius of nineteen feet, with which he made naked-eye observations (the telescope had not yet been invented) for twenty-one years. When Brahe died in 1601, he left to Kepler a vast accumulation of the most accurate astronomical data then in existence. Kepler set to work to discover the "music of the spheres"—that is, the laws governing the behavior of the planets, those "wanderers" among the stars whose course Brahe had traced so diligently for such a long time.

Observe that Kepler's laws are *kinematical* statements. They describe the motions of the planets but say nothing at all about the forces that produce these motions. Kinematical descriptions of the planets go back to the Chinese (2317 B.C.) and even to the Babylonians (about 3800 B.C.), but in all those thousands of years no one had discovered the relations stated so simply by Kepler. Kepler anticipated Newton's work in dynamics by more than fifty years. He was one of the giants on whose shoulders Newton stood, as he said, to "see farther than other men."[‡]

Let us consider what Kepler could have done

† "Finally I have brought to light and verified beyond all my hopes and expectations that the whole Nature of Harmonics permeates to the fullest extent, and in all its details, the motion of the heavenly bodies, not, it is true, in the manner in which I had earlier thought, but in a totally different, altogether complete way." (*Harmonice Mundi*, 1619.)
‡ A modern parody of Newton's famous remark says: "If I have seen *only a little bit farther* than other men, it is because I have stood on the shoulders of pygmies." This is possibly a biting commentary on the intellectual stature of some teachers.

in today's space age, with his pre-dynamical knowledge. To do this, we need to review the construction of an ellipse.

We can generate an **ellipse** by putting two pins at two points, F_1 and F_2, of a drawing board (Fig. 33.12), putting a loop of string round the pins, and then drawing with a pencil, P, the path traversed by the pencil as it keeps the string taut. That path is an ellipse with F_1 and F_2 as foci.

One property of the ellipse is apparent from the way we constructed it:

$$F_1P + PF_2 + F_2F_1 = \text{a constant}$$

But, since F_2F_1 is a constant,

$$F_1P + PF_2 = \text{a constant} \qquad [33.6$$

A verbal statement of equation 33.6 is, in fact, a definition of the ellipse. Another property, which may not be immediately apparent, is that, if F_1P is the direction of a beam of light, that beam can be specularly reflected by a curved mirror in the shape of this ellipse so that the reflected beam travels along PF_2. Sound waves, too, originating at F_1 in a so-called whispering gallery, which has an elliptical dome, are concentrated at F_2.

For a loop of fixed length, the ellipses drawn as F_1 and F_2 are placed closer and closer to each other are less and less eccentric and more and more like circles. The longest chord, AB, is called the **major axis.** The chord CD, which bisects AB, is called the **minor axis.** The length of the minor axis of the planet Mercury's orbit is 0.98 of that of the major axis; the length of the minor axis of Venus's orbit is 0.999977 of that of the major axis.

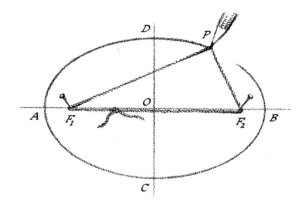

FIG. 33.12. *Drawing an ellipse.*

It is clear why circles are considered good approximations to planetary orbits. The very fact that the departure from perfect circles was noticed by Kepler speaks well for the accuracy of the data that Brahe had collected.

Kepler's third law is equivalent to the statement that $T^2 \propto s^3$ if s stands for semimajor axis and T for period. This implies that

$$\frac{T_1^2}{s_1^3} = \frac{T_2^2}{s_2^3}$$

Table 33.1 presents values of s and T for the first four planets. The ratio T^2/s^3, to four significant figures, is exhibited in the last column. The agreement is very good indeed.

If Kepler had wanted to compute the period of an earth satellite moving in an orbit very close to the earth (Fig. 33.13), he could have proceeded

TABLE 33.1

Some Modern Data on the Planetary Orbits

	s (semimajor axis; multiply by 10^6 for km)	T (period, or time for one revolution, in days)	s^3 (multiply by 10^{22} for km³)	T^2 (multiply by 10^4 for days²)	T^2/s^3 (multiply by 10^{-20} for days²/km³)
Mercury	57.91	87.97	19.42	0.7739	398.5
Venus	108.20	224.7	126.7	5.049	398.5
Earth	149.60	365.3	334.8	13.34	398.5
Mars	227.90	687.0	1,183.	47.19	398.7

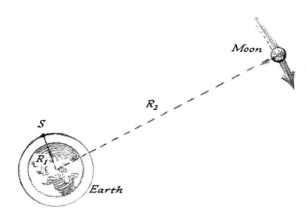

FIG. 33.13. *An earth satellite, S, and the moon moving in circles round the earth.*

as follows. (I shall use modern values for distances and periods.) Let R_1 be the radius of the earth and the approximate radius of the satellite orbit. Let T_1 be the period (the time in which it completes one revolution) of the satellite, S. Let R_2 and T_2 be the radius of the moon's orbit and the moon's period, respectively. Two of these quantities are commonly known:

$$R_1 = 6.37 \times 10^3 \text{ km (about 4,000 mi)}$$
$$T_2 = 27.3 \text{ days} = 3.94 \times 10^4 \text{ min}$$

The distance R_2 is also known:

$$R_2 = 3.84 \times 10^5 \text{ km}$$

Kepler's third law requires that

$$\frac{T_1^2}{R_1^3} = \frac{T_2^2}{R_2^3}$$

Solving for T_1^2, we get

$$T_1^2 = T_2^2 \frac{R_1^3}{R_2^3}$$

Substituting numerical values, we get

$$T_1^2 = \left(\frac{6.37 \times 10^3}{3.84 \times 10^5}\right)^3 \times (3.94 \times 10^4)^2 \text{ min}^2$$
$$= 70.8 \times 10^2 \text{ min}^2$$
$$T_1 = 84.2 \text{ min}$$

(See Prob. 33.15.)

Kepler could also have predicted how fast the earth satellite would have to move—

$$v = R_1 \omega = 2\pi R_1 / T_1$$

—in order to remain in a tight earthbound orbit.

33.6. The Case for an Inverse-square Law of Gravitation

As a kinematical description that applies to the planets, Kepler's laws work admirably. But with his statement of those laws the time was ripe for dynamical questions: *Why* do the planets move in elliptical paths? *Why* do they sweep out equal areas in equal times?

It is doubtful if Kepler suspected that man-made satellites would obey the same laws as the planets. But Newton, starting with the idea of the mutual attraction between bodies, not only deduced Kepler's laws but even suggested that man-made satellites could be put into orbit. Newton was not the first to conceive the idea of a strong pull exerted on the earth by the sun, or on the moon by the earth, but he was the first to have the data of Brahe, the laws of Kepler, the requisite intellectual curiosity, and the ability to concentrate on difficult mathematical problems for a sufficiently long time. He was the first to state the mathematical equation of universal gravitation.

Newton, as an old man, wrote, in retrospect of the year 1666, when he celebrated his twenty-fourth birthday: "In the same year I began to think of gravity extending to the orb of the moon; . . . from Kepler's rule of the periodical times of the planets . . . I deduced that the forces which keep the planets in their orbs must be reciprocally as the squares of their distances from the centers about which they revolve, and thereby compared the force requisite to keep the moon in her orb with the force of gravity at the surface of the earth, and found them to answer pretty nearly; . . . in those days I was in the prime of my age for invention, and minded mathematics and philosophy more than at any other time since."

Let us see how an inverse-square law accounts for the acceleration of a freely falling body. Suppose that S (Fig. 33.13) is not an orbiting satellite but a body near the surface of the earth and that R_1 is its distance from the earth's center. The body experiences an acceleration,

$$a_1 = g$$

The moon, considered as an object in circular motion, experiences the centripetal acceleration

$$a_2 = \frac{v^2}{R_2}$$

Now

$$v = \frac{2\pi R_2}{T}$$

and therefore

$$v^2 = \frac{4\pi^2 R_2{}^2}{T^2}$$

Hence

$$a_2 = \frac{4\pi^2 R_2}{T^2}$$

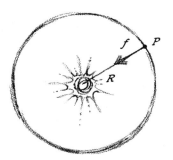

FIG. 33.14. *The special case of a circular orbit.*

Newton tried many different assumptions about the relation between a_1 and a_2, among them the assumption that acceleration is inversely proportional to the square of the distance:

$$\frac{a_1}{a_2} = \frac{R_2{}^2}{R_1{}^2} \qquad [33.7$$

This requires that

$$\frac{g}{4\pi^2 R_2/T^2} = \frac{R_2{}^2}{R_1{}^2} \qquad [33.8$$

Let us use the values of R_1, R_2, and T that are known today:

$$R_1 = 6.371 \times 10^3 \text{ km}$$
$$R_2 = 3.84 \times 10^5 \text{ km}$$
$$T = 28 \text{ days} = 236 \times 10^4 \text{ sec}$$

Solving equation 33.8 for g, we get

$$g = \frac{4\pi^2}{T^2} \frac{R_2{}^3}{R_1{}^2} = 9.81 \frac{\text{m}}{\text{sec}^2} \qquad [33.9$$

This value for the acceleration due to gravity is very close to the average values actually observed.

With these data we conclude that Newton's inverse-square guess "answers" much better than "pretty nearly."

With the data available to him in 1666, Newton would have obtained a value of g with an error of less than 4 percent. In 1680, when a better determination of the earth's radius had been made, he could have obtained g with an error of less than 1.3 percent.

In these calculations, you will notice, we measured distances from the center of the earth, as if all the mass of the earth were concentrated there. Newton himself surmised correctly that a homogeneous spherical body acts on external objects as if its mass were concentrated at its center, but it took him twenty years to prove this rigorously, and he held up publication of his results until he had done so. In the process he had to invent the technique that evolved into the modern differential and integral calculus!

For the special case of *circular orbits*, the fact that gravity obeys an inverse-square law can be deduced from Kepler's laws as follows (Fig. 33.14). The planet P, orbiting in a circle of radius R, experiences a force, f, pointing to the center of the sun. It must obey the equation $f = ma$, in which $a = \omega^2 R$ (centripetal acceleration). Using the formula $\omega = 2\pi/T$, we get

$$f = \frac{4\pi^2 mR}{T^2} \qquad [33.10$$

From Kepler's third law we know that $T^2 \propto R^3$, or that $T^2 = kR^3$. Putting this value into equation 33.10, we get

$$f = \frac{4\pi^2 mR}{kR^3} = \frac{4\pi^2 m}{kR^2} \qquad [33.11$$

We don't need to know the value of the constant k to see that the relation between f and R is an inverse-square relation.

It is not so easy to work backward and deduce that a planet obeying the inverse-square law and Newton's laws of motion can move in an elliptical path with the sun at one focus, but Newton did exactly that: he was eventually able to *deduce* Kepler's laws of motion from the inverse-square law and his own laws of motion. This was a tremendous triumph. It gave man analytical tools with which to predict the motions of all planetary bodies.

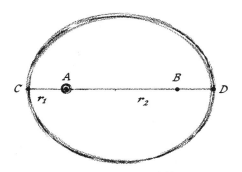

FIG. 33.15. *Round the earth, at focus A, a satellite moves in a very eccentric elliptic orbit. Because the instantaneous radius of curvature at point C is the same as that at point D, we can prove that the force of attraction varies inversely with the square of the distance from the center of the earth.*

An easy exercise that we can handle is to consider the forces acting on an earth satellite (Fig. 33.15) at the ends of the major axis, *CD*. Let us use the conservation of angular momentum:

$$\mathbf{r}_1 \times \mathbf{p}_1 = \mathbf{r}_2 \times \mathbf{p}_2$$

Dropping the vector notation, we have

$$r_1 m v_1 = r_2 m v_2 \qquad [33.12$$

Because the *instantaneous radii of curvature* at *C* and *D* are alike and equal to r_1, we can write the centripetal forces at *C* and *D*, respectively, as

$$f_C = \frac{m v_1{}^2}{r_1} \qquad [33.13$$

$$f_D = \frac{m v_2{}^2}{r_1} \qquad [33.14$$

Hence

$$\frac{f_C}{f_D} = \frac{v_1{}^2}{v_2{}^2} \qquad [33.15$$

Using equation 33.12, we get

$$\frac{f_C}{f_D} = \frac{r_2{}^2}{r_1{}^2} \qquad [33.16$$

Thus, for these particular points on the ellipse, we have proved that the force is inversely proportional to the square of the distance. To prove that rule more generally for other points on the ellipse requires the calculus. (A graphical demonstration of an approximate sort that does not require the calculus will be given in the next chapter.)

So far, considering only the force that the sun exerts on a planet, we have found that the mass of the planet enters into the formula (equation 33.11). Through his third law of motion (action equals reaction) Newton was led to believe that the mass of the sun had to enter in a reciprocal role. The final form of his law, stated here for particles but applicable by summation to aggregates of particles, is

$$F = G \frac{m_1 m_2}{r^2} \qquad [33.17$$

33.7. The Relation Between *g* and *G*

In the next chapter we shall see how the universal constant *G* can be found experimentally. Its value is

$$G = 6.670 \times 10^{-11} \frac{\text{nt-m}^2}{\text{kg}^2}$$

Table 33.2 presents the differences between *g* and *G*.

The force, *f*, that acts on a body of mass *m* near the surface of the earth (of mass *M* and radius *R*) can be expressed in two ways:

$$f = mg \qquad [33.18$$

$$f = \frac{GmM}{R^2} \qquad [33.19$$

TABLE 33.2

Comparison of *g* and *G*

g	*G*
The acceleration due to gravity at a point near the surface of the earth.	The constant of proportionality in the law of universal gravitation.
A vector.	A scalar.
Has dimensions LT^{-2}, MKS units m/sec².	Has dimensions $M^{-1}L^3T^{-2}$, MKS units m³/kg-sec².
Varies from place to place; approaches zero far from the earth.	Has the same constant value everywhere in the universe.

The effects of the earth's rotation require some corrections, which will be discussed later. We disregard these for the moment:

$$mg = \frac{GmM}{R^2} \qquad [33.20]$$

$$g = \frac{GM}{R^2} \qquad [33.21]$$

Thus g and G *are* related. Notice also that the mass of the earth appears in equation 33.21. If we knew g, G, and R, we could determine the mass of the earth. We shall take up problems of this sort in the next chapter.

33.8. Summary

Kepler described succinctly the kinematical behavior of the planets as they move in elliptic orbits with the sun at one focus. He discovered that their periods squared are proportional to the cubes of their semimajor axes and that a radius vector from the sun to a planet sweeps out equal areas in equal times.

It remained for Newton to show that all of this can be accounted for logically on the assumptions (1) that bodies attract one another with a force that is directly proportional to the product of their masses and inversely proportional to the square of the distance between them and (2) that they obey the formula $\mathbf{f} = m\mathbf{a}$. The law of equal areas, for example, is simply an illustration of the conservation of angular momentum.

Near the earth a body of mass m feels a pull of magnitude mg. This pull can also be expressed by the ratio GmM/R^2, in which G is the universal gravitational constant, M is the mass of the earth, and R is the radius of the earth. From this an obvious relation between g and G can be deduced.

Problems

33.1. 1. Use reasonable values to compute approximately (in MKS units) the force of gravitational attraction between two apples sitting close to each other.

2. What acceleration would one apple experience under the influence of this force alone?

33.2. 1. If r, in Fig. 33.5, is 3.5 m and p is 5.5 kg-m/sec, compute the angular momentum if the angle between them is 120°.

2. If the figure represents a body moving under the action of an inverse-square force that always points to O, what can be said about the value of $\mathbf{r} \times \mathbf{p}$ at any other time?

3. If the force always points to O but is not an inverse-square force, what can be said about the value of $\mathbf{r} \times \mathbf{p}$ at any other time?

33.3. A straight stick is stuck into flat horizontal ground at an angle of about 45° from the horizontal and leaning toward the north at a place where the sun is overhead at noon. Let $\mathbf{a}$ be a vector representing this stick, and let $\mathbf{b}$ be a vector representing its shadow, both originating where the stick enters the ground.

1. Discuss the way the magnitude of the vector $\mathbf{a} \times \mathbf{b}$ varies from dawn until sunset on a sunny day.

2. What is the direction of $\mathbf{a} \times \mathbf{b}$ at noon?

3. Draw $\mathbf{a} \times \mathbf{b}$ at other times of the day.

(This problem has no physical importance. It is just an exercise to help you visualize the vector $\mathbf{a} \times \mathbf{b}$.)

33.4. Let $\mathbf{r}$ be a vector from the center of the earth to the center of mass of a skyscraper in New York (latitude 40°N). The skyscraper has a mass of 10^6 kg.

1. Find the magnitude of the angular-momentum vector $\mathbf{r} \times \mathbf{p}$ in MKS units.

2. In what direction of the compass does $\mathbf{r} \times \mathbf{p}$ point?

3. Where are the points on the surface of the earth at which the angular-momentum vector is parallel to the earth's axis?

33.5. A single electron of mass 9.109×10^{-31} kg is revolving in a circle of radius 5.29×10^{-11} m with a speed of 2.18×10^6 m/sec.

1. Find the magnitude of the angular-momentum vector $\mathbf{r} \times \mathbf{p}$ calculated from the center of the circle.

2. What is the direction of this vector?

(Note: This is the angular momentum of an electron in a hydrogen atom according to the Bohr model discussed in Chap. 51.)

33.6. An athlete (Fig. 3.2.A) exerts a force of 250 nt to keep a ball of mass 5 kg moving in a circle of radius 1 m.

1. What is the torque of this force about the axis at the center of, and perpendicular to, the circle?

2. What is the magnitude of the angular momentum of the ball?

3. What is the direction of the angular-momentum vector in relation to the plane of the circular path?

33.7. Without resorting to the text, try to summarize the logical steps that begin with the statement "the force exerted by the earth on an earth satellite in orbit is a central force" and ending with "therefore the radius vector from the center of the earth to the center of the satellite sweeps out equal areas in equal times."

33.8. The orbits of the planets are ellipses, the most eccentric of which is that of Pluto. To see how nearly circular they all are, however, construct an ellipse, by the method of Fig. 33.12, as follows: Let the total length of the loop $F_1PF_2F_1$ be 8 units, and let the pins at F_1 and F_2 be 2 units apart. Such an ellipse has an eccentricity (OF_1/F_1D) of 0.333, whereas that of the orbit of Pluto is 0.247 and that of the earth's orbit is only 0.017.

33.9. The mass of the moon is approximately 1/80 of that of the earth, and its radius is about 0.27 of that of the earth. Compute the acceleration of a body on the surface of the moon in m/sec². (Hint: Deduce an algebraic expression for the acceleration

in each case, and divide one by the other. The constant factors will drop out, and the arithmetic will be greatly simplified.)

33.10. Find the location of a point between the moon and the earth where a body would feel equal and opposite pulls.

33.11. It is well known that the radius of the earth is about 4,000 miles and that the acceleration due to gravity on the earth's surface is about 9.8 m/sec². Compute from these data an approximate value for the mass of the earth in kg.

33.12. With what force does the moon pull on an object with a mass of 50 kg if that object rests on the surface of the earth at a distance of 384,000 km from the center of the moon? Can you name a well-known natural phenomenon that is governed by a force of this kind?

33.13. A pendulum has a period of 2 sec at a place on the surface of the earth where the distance to the center is 6.378×10^6 m. What will be the period of the same pendulum if it is taken to the top of a mountain 6,400 m high? (Hint: Write down two expressions for the period, and take their ratio. Simplify algebraically before substituting numerical values.)

33.14. A pendulum bob in a simple pendulum swings in a plane when released from rest. If it is initially given a push at right angles to this plane, however, it will move in an approximately elliptical path. Observe a pendulum in such motion, and give an argument to prove that the force acting on the bob is not an inverse-square force.

33.15. The TIROS III satellite, about 485 mi above the earth, orbits in 97 min. Calculate its period, using the procedure of the example in § 33.5 after adding 485 mi to R_1.

The Dynamical Requirements for Space Exploration

"We are living in the space age. Man has broken the tyrannical bounds of gravity that confined him so long to earth, only a tiny speck in the cosmos. Now man's machines and devices travel across the gravity barrier in the early exploration of a universe so vast that it defies comprehension. No longer are man's eyes and instruments blinded by the black curtain of atmosphere that closes out most of the incoming messages of radiation from outer space. Now vehicles shot beyond this atmosphere contain instruments that can 'see' the universe by the ultra-violet, x-rays, infra-red light, and radio emanations that could never penetrate our cloudy, opaque and tremulous atmosphere."

"Some may mourn that in our modern space age accurate measurements and clearer vision are dispelling many of the mystic veils and charming imagery of our past ignorance. In contrast, I feel that truth is beauty and that an understanding of space, time and the physical universe can only lead to a more interesting and captivating view of the universe. It may even lead to man's better understanding of himself."

F. L. WHIPPLE in his introduction to the *Larousse Encyclopedia of Astronomy*, by Lucien Rudaux and G. de Vaucouleurs (New York, Prometheus Press, 1959)

IF THE MONEY budgeted for an activity is any measure of its importance, the imminent exploration of space must seem of great consequence to some people. A spokesman for one of the rocket societies puts a price tag of 20 billion dollars on a trip to the moon, for example, and claims it is a bargain at that. Leaving aside the political, military, medical, and psychological problems that must be solved before we can sail off into space with the same assurance with which we now step onto an ocean liner and sail away in comfort over what was once the treacherous sea, I shall limit our attention to some of the simplest *physical* problems involved.

34.1. What We Need to Know Before We Can Leave the Earth

From the purely physical point of view, what does it take to leave the earth and travel in its gravitational field? The answer is *energy*. How much energy? This is the paramount quantitative question. To answer it precisely, we need to know the value of G in Newton's law of gravitation as accurately as possible:

$$F = \frac{GmM}{r^2} \qquad [34.1$$

An outline of a laboratory experiment that yields G is given below.

What other physical laws do we need to know in order to chart the course of a rocket ship or a satellite? The most important is $\mathbf{F} = m\mathbf{a}$,† the basic equation governing all motions. The others are (a) the principle of the conservation of linear momentum; (b) the principle of the conservation of energy; (c) the principle of the conservation of

---

† More accurately, $\mathbf{F} = \lim\limits_{\Delta t \to 0} \dfrac{\Delta \mathbf{p}}{\Delta t}$.

angular momentum. Fortunately for the continuity of my text, these principles will guide us also in the study of electricity and magnetism and atomic and nuclear physics. Now let us concentrate on G.

34.2. The Measurement of G

In 1797 and 1798 Henry Cavendish performed the pioneer experiment to measure G, the universal constant of gravitation. The accuracy of his work may be judged by the fact that the value he obtained, 6.754×10^{-11} nt-m/kg², is within 1.3 percent of the presently accepted value, 6.670×10^{-11} nt-m/kg².

Figure 34.1 illustrates the principle of the Cavendish experiment. The small lead balls, b and b',

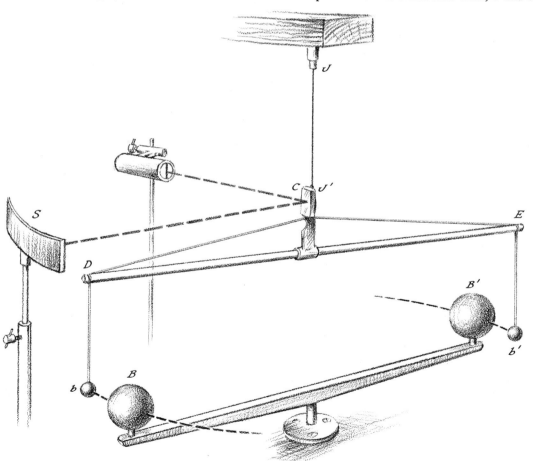

FIG. 34.1. *The principle of Cavendish's experiment to measure* **G**.

are attached to a rigid support, *DE*, which is suspended by a very long and fine but strong fiber, *JJ'*, made of fused quartz. The support is free to rotate under the force, *F*, of attraction of the larger balls, *B* and *B'*, for the smaller ones, *b* and *b'*. A beam of light, reflected by a mirror, *C*, attached to *DE*, indicates the twist of the fiber on the screen, *S*. Once we have determined the elasticity constant related to twist by timing the angular oscillation, the angle through which the fiber twists yields a measure of the gravitational attraction between each of the pairs of balls, *b-B* and *b'-B'*. Each of the balls *b* and *b'* has mass *m*, and each of the balls *B* and *B'* has mass *M*. With known or measurable values of *m*, *M*, *F*, and *r* (the distance between the centers of a pair of balls, *b* and *B* or *b'* and *B'*), we can solve the equation $F = GmM/r^2$ for *G*.

The experiment, a delicate one, requires considerable skill and some patience (the period of oscillation of the system may be about fifteen minutes, for example), but modern equipment makes it possible to perform it in a college laboratory.

Newton, although he died before Cavendish was born and never knew the measured value of *G*, was able, from astronomical data, to estimate that the density of the earth was between 5 and 6 gm/cm³—a range that includes the modern value, 5.517 gm/cm³. I have expressed the density in these units because it is customary to give the density of water as approximately 1 gm/cm³.

34.3. True Weight and Apparent Weight

We have seen (§ 5.4) that on or near the earth the weight of a body is the gravitational force with which the earth pulls on it. On or near the moon, however, the weight of the body would be the gravitational force with which the moon pulled on it. These approximate statements disregard the fact that the object is really subject, simultaneously, to the pull of both the earth and the moon. There is, for example, a point (Prob. 33.10) where the pulls of earth and moon cancel. At such a point, if we ignore the pull of other massive bodies, the weight of an object is practically zero. At each point in space there is a gravitational field

vector, **γ** (§ 4.8), produced by earth, moon, and other astronomical bodies. By definition this is the gravitational force per unit of mass at that point. The **true weight** of an object of mass *m* at that point is *m* times the gravitational field intensity there. Near the earth the pull of the earth alone is so much greater than other gravitational forces that the true weight of an object of mass *m* is very close to GmM/R_0^2 if *M* is the mass of the earth and R_0 is its radius.

But we have already seen (§ 25.3) that, when a man weighs himself in an elevator, the scale reading is higher than normal if the elevator is accelerating upward, lower than normal if it is accelerating downward, and normal if the acceleration is zero. In an accelerated frame of reference the weight of a body of mass *m* can be measured in two ways. One way is to measure the acceleration, **g'**, of the body in relation to the frame and to form the product *mg'*. Another way is to read the weight on a scale (Fig. 34.2) either placed on the floor of, or suspended from the ceiling of, the accelerated frame. The scale readings and *mg'* coincide, and we shall call the magnitude of either the **apparent weight** of the body. The force exerted by the scale on the object being weighed is a reaction force, which is equal and opposite to the apparent weight of the object.

Let us recapitulate. If you calculate the weight, *mg'*, of an object of mass *m* by measuring its acceleration, **g'**, relative to an accelerated frame, or if you obtain it from a reading on a scale attached to such a frame, the result is the *apparent* weight of the object. We should obtain the *true* weight of the object by adding vectorially all the gravitational forces acting on it whose magnitudes were calculated from Newton's law of gravitation in the form $F = GmM/r^2$.

We are now ready to consider the fact that a laboratory on the surface of the earth is actually an accelerated frame of reference. It is moving in a circle whose radius is the shortest distance between the laboratory and the axis of rotation of the earth. It has an acceleration that points centrally along such a radius. It is somewhat like the elevator with a downward acceleration. A scale reading taken on it is lower than it would be on an inertial frame of reference and should, strictly speaking, be called the apparent weight of

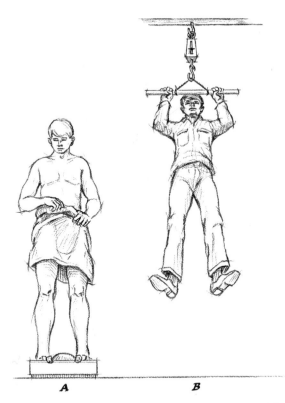

FIG. 34.2. *Two ways of finding your apparent weight.*

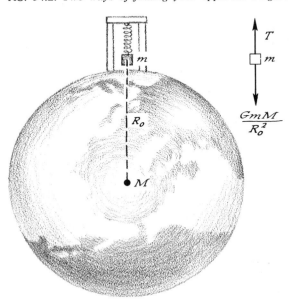

FIG. 34.3. *The tension, T, in the spring is a little less than the gravitational pull,* GmM/R_0^2. *The small net force toward the center of the earth is required to keep the body of mass* m *moving in a circular path.*

the object. The true weight of the object is a little greater than the apparent weight by an amount that we are about to calculate.

Consider a body of mass m suspended from the ceiling of a laboratory at the equator (Fig. 34.3). It is pulled upward by the tension, T, in the spring and downward by GmM/R_0^2 (the true weight for all practical purposes—we disregard the effect of all other astronomical bodies because of nearness to the earth). If T and GmM/R_0^2 were equal, the vector sum of the forces on the body would be zero, and it would move in a straight line. We know, however, that it moves in a circle of radius R_0 with angular velocity

$$\omega = 2\pi \text{ rad}/24 \text{ h} = 7.27 \times 10^{-5} \text{ rad/sec}$$

Therefore, GmM/R_0^2 must be a little larger than T to supply the needed centripetal force, $m\omega^2 R_0$. Hence

$$\frac{GmM}{R_0^2} - T = m\omega^2 R_0 \qquad [34.2]$$

Therefore

$$T = \frac{GmM}{R_0^2} - m\omega^2 R_0 \qquad [34.3]$$

Since the tension in the spring is numerically equal to the apparent weight, mg',

$$mg' = \frac{GmM}{R_0^2} - m\omega^2 R_0 \qquad [34.4]$$

or

$$g' = \frac{GM}{R_0^2} - \omega^2 R_0 \qquad [34.5]$$

I have been using the symbol g' in this argument to emphasize the usually neglected fact that the earth is an accelerated frame of reference. This value is, however, the actual acceleration that would be measured in such a laboratory. It is, therefore, what we normally find tabulated in handbooks as the local value of g. I shall hereafter drop the prime unless I want to stress the fact that the earth is a rotating, and hence an accelerated, frame of reference.

We know that g is about 9.8 m/sec². In comparison, $\omega^2 R_0$ is small. Let us calculate it:

$$\omega^2 R_0 = (7.27 \times 10^{-5} \text{ rad/sec})^2 \times 6.378 \times 10^6 \text{ m}$$
$$= 0.0339 \text{ m/sec}^2$$

At the poles $\omega^2 R_0$ is zero because the effective radius of rotation is zero there. In general, then, the difference between g and GM/R_0^2 is very small indeed.

At sea level on the equator g is 9.780524 m/sec²; at the poles it is 9.832329 m/sec². The difference is primarily due to the flattening of the poles, which are closer to the center of the earth than a point on the equator. These are facts that have interested geophysicists and astronomers in the past and are now of great importance to those who plan the travel of astronauts.

Notice that the negative sign preceding $m\omega^2 R_0$ in equation 34.4 implies that we can think of this quantity as a loss in weight due to the fact that the frame of reference is accelerated.

For an earth satellite in orbit the angular velocity, ω, is much greater than 7.27×10^{-5} rad/sec; in fact, $\omega^2 R_0$ is equal to GM/R_0^2. For the personnel in an orbiting laboratory g' is zero because the quantity $GM/R_0^2 - \omega^2 R_0$ vanishes. The apparent weight of objects in such a laboratory is zero.

34.4. Possible Trajectories for Earth Satellites

The trajectory of a bullet fired from the ground is approximately a parabola if the initial speed is not too great (Chap. 9). Over a portion of the earth small enough to be considered flat (Fig. 34.4), we can regard the acceleration due to gravity, g, as a constant. If there were no gravitational attraction, a bullet fired at O in the direction v_0 would be found at points A', B', C', and D' after

successive equal intervals of time. The bullet actually follows the path $OABCD$, which shows that it was a falling body every instant of the way. All satellites, too, are, in fact, falling bodies.

Observe also that, if gravity could have been turned off at A, the bullet would have traveled distance $v_1 t$, along the tangent to the parabola at A, in time t. Instead, it fell distance $\frac{1}{2}gt^2$, as shown by the small downward vector ending at B. A similar analysis at B shows that it fell distance $\frac{1}{2}gt^2$ in order to go through C. The important point is that, no matter where on the curve we begin a similar analysis, we can predict the subsequent motion of the bullet as the result of the addition of two vectors, vt and $\frac{1}{2}gt^2$. The equality of all the small downward vectors is a consequence of the facts that g is virtually constant during the bullet's movement and that we chose equal time intervals t.

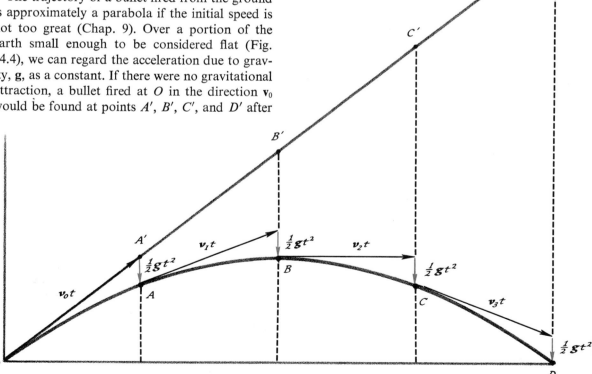

FIG. 34.4. *A bullet fired from the ground is a falling body.*

If the scale of our operation is considerably enlarged, the curvature of the earth becomes apparent (Fig. 34.5). An extremely fast bullet is shot off in the direction $\mathbf{v}_0$. Without gravity it would be at points A', B', C', and D' after successive equal intervals of time. It actually follows curve $ABCD$, but this is not a parabola; it is an ellipse with the center of the earth, O, as a focus. Since the central acceleration is no longer a constant, either in direction or in magnitude, we shall call it $\mathbf{a}$ instead of $\mathbf{g}$. We can use the sum $\mathbf{v}_0 t + \frac{1}{2}\mathbf{a}t^2$ to predict the bullet's trajectory only as an approximation that becomes better as we choose smaller values of t. It is, however, a good enough approximation to help us see how the fact that an earth satellite travels in an elliptical path with the earth at one focus and sweeps out equal areas in equal times *implies* an inverse-square force of attraction. We can demonstrate this as follows:

First we draw a large ellipse (Fig. 34.6) with foci at E and F_2 and determine two points, A and B, on it so that EB, or r_1, is three times EA, or r_0. If we can now locate points C and D so that areas AEC and BED are equal (for example, by filling the areas with equal numbers of lead pellets), the time intervals during which the satel-

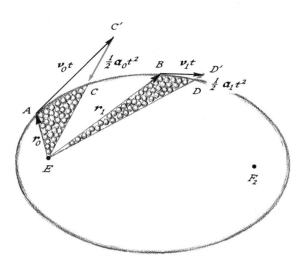

FIG. 34.6. *Graphical confirmation of the inverse-square law.*

lite moves from A to C and from B to D will be equal (Kepler's second law). Without gravity the satellite would go from A to C' in time t, but it falls distance $\frac{1}{2}\mathbf{a}_0 t^2$ to go through C. (We assume that t is small enough so that the variation in the central acceleration $\mathbf{a}_0$ is negligible in the passage from A to C. A similar remark applies to the central acceleration $\mathbf{a}_1$ between B and D.) Similarly, without gravity the satellite would go from B to D', but it falls distance $\frac{1}{2}\mathbf{a}_1 t^2$ to go through D.

Consider the ratio

$$\frac{\frac{1}{2}a_0 t^2}{\frac{1}{2}a_1 t^2}$$

Since the time intervals are equal (equal areas, equal times), it may be written simply as a_0/a_1. The ratio of the distances $\frac{1}{2}a_0 t^2$ and $\frac{1}{2}a_1 t^2$ is the same as that of the accelerations and *hence of the forces felt by the satellite at C and D respectively.* With a large, carefully drawn ellipse it is possible to confirm the fact that a_0 is close to four times a_1 if $r_1 = 2r_0$; that a_0 is close to nine times a_1 if $r_1 = 3r_0$; etc. In this way a graphical confirmation of the inverse-square law acting on a single satellite as it moves in its own orbit is possible.†

Newton seems to have been the first to suggest that one could put an earth satellite into orbit by

† This treatment was suggested by a 16-mm motion picture entitled "Elliptic Orbits," produced by the Physical Science Study Committee, Cambridge, Massachusetts.

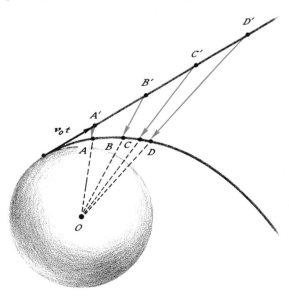

FIG. 34.5. *An extremely fast bullet, on a larger scale, is also a falling body.*

firing a projectile from a high mountain with sufficient speed, and he illustrated the idea by drawing the diagram reproduced as Figure 34.7—to which a few possible elliptic orbits for modern satellites have been added. If a muzzle speed of about five miles per second can be achieved, the projectile will circle the earth. At lower speeds it will fall as shown. Let us see how this approximate figure of five miles per second can be arrived at.

Once the projectile has left the gun at speed v in a horizontal direction, the only force acting on it is the centripetal force, mv^2/R_0, which in this case is equal to GmM/R_0^2; and, if g is the acceleration due to gravity, mg is approximately equal to GmM/R_0^2. We equate mg and mv^2/R_0 to obtain v:

$$\frac{mv^2}{R_0} = mg \qquad [34.6$$

$$v = \sqrt{R_0 g} \qquad [34.7$$

Figure 34.7 greatly exaggerates the height of the mountain. Actually we can use the mean radius of the earth for R_0. Using the metric values

$$R_0 = 6.378 \times 10^6 \text{ m}$$
$$g = 9.81 \text{ m/sec}^2$$

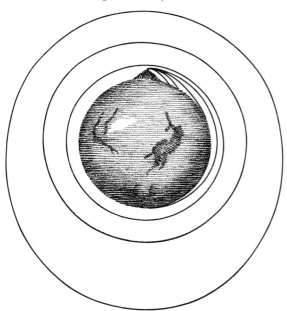

FIG. 34.7. A drawing (after Newton) suggesting that one could put an earth satellite into orbit by firing a projectile from a high mountain with sufficient speed.

we get

$$v = (6.378 \times 10^6 \text{ m} \times 9.81 \text{ m/sec}^2)^{1/2}$$
$$= (6.26 \times 10^7)^{1/2} \text{ m/sec}$$
$$= 7.91 \times 10^3 \text{ m/sec} \qquad [34.8$$

This is equivalent to 4.92 miles (roughly, 5 miles) per second.

How long would it take to travel 5,000 miles at 5 miles per second? The answer is 1,000 seconds, or about 17 minutes. If a missile of this speed, carrying a nuclear warhead, for example, were launched in a long, almost horizontally elliptical path and detected about halfway in its trajectory, the warning time would be about 8.5 minutes. A more detailed calculation could be made on the assumption that the missile was fired at an inclination of 45° to the horizontal (to increase its range), but the rough answer given here is pretty close to what may be expected of modern missiles. Since earth satellites have already been put into orbit, we know that velocities of about 5 miles per second have been achieved.

Since the circumference of the earth is about 25,000 miles, the time required for a satellite orbiting very close to the earth to complete one trip is about

$$\frac{25,000 \text{ mi}}{5 \text{ mi/sec}} = 5,000 \text{ sec} = \frac{5,000}{60} \text{ min} = 83 \text{ min}$$

Data on the existing earth satellites indicate that this estimate is very good.

A generalization known to Newton is that all the paths in which a body can move under the action of an inverse-square force of attraction are intersections of a plane with a right circular cone, or **conic sections**. In Figure 34.8 we see some of the possible curves: the circle, the ellipse, the parabola, and the hyperbola. Earth-satellite orbits are ellipses with the earth at one focus.

34.5. How Much Energy Does it Take to Escape from the Earth?

We have seen that, if $v = \sqrt{R_0 g}$, we can put a satellite into an almost circular elliptic orbit. Can we also shoot a missile vertically upward so that it never comes back? I shall show, by considering the energy involved, that at a speed only $\sqrt{2}$

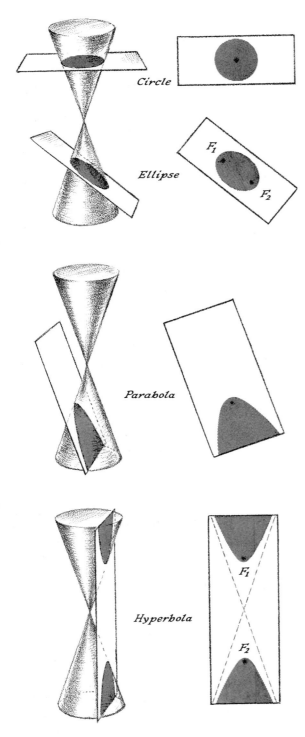

FIG. 34.8. *Conic sections.*

times larger than $\sqrt{R_0 g}$ (that is, about 7 miles per second) we can expect to lose the projectile in space. First we see (Fig. 34.9) that an external applied force, $\mathbf{F}_a$, pointing away from the center of the earth would do work in moving a body from r_0 to r_3. As a result of the conservation of energy (equation 28.15),

$$\mathbf{F}_a \cdot \Delta \mathbf{x} = \Delta U + \Delta K + \Delta Q$$

Here U is potential energy, K is kinetic energy, and Q is heat energy. (There are other forms of energy, but we consider them negligible.)

We next assume that we start and end with no kinetic energy; that is, $\Delta K = 0$. We assume also that no energy is lost to heat; that is, $\Delta Q = 0$. Hence the increment, ΔU, in potential energy is simply $\mathbf{F}_a \cdot \Delta \mathbf{x}$. The force needed for moving the body from r_0 to r_1 is somewhere between GmM/r_0^2 and GmM/r_1^2. Since the force $GmM/r_0 r_1$ certainly lies between those two values, let us use it as an approximation to the average force. The work done by this force in moving the body from r_0 to r_1 is

$$W_1 = \frac{GmM}{r_0 r_1}(r_1 - r_0) \qquad [34.9$$

Similarly, the increments of work performed by the (variable) force $\mathbf{F}_a$ in moving the body from r_1 to r_2 and from r_2 to r_3 are, respectively,

$$W_2 = \frac{GmM}{r_1 r_2}(r_2 - r_1) \qquad [34.10$$

$$W_3 = \frac{GmM}{r_2 r_3}(r_3 - r_2) \qquad [34.11$$

The total work done is

$$\Delta U = W_1 + W_2 + W_3$$
$$= GmM \left(\frac{r_1 - r_0}{r_0 r_1} + \frac{r_2 - r_1}{r_1 r_2} + \frac{r_3 - r_2}{r_2 r_3} \right)$$
$$= GmM \left(\frac{1}{r_0} - \frac{1}{r_3} \right) \qquad [34.12$$

The total increment in potential energy depends only on the initial and final radial distances. The result would be the same if we used a hundred or even a million subdivisions.

If we start at the earth's surface ($r_0 = R_0$) and move up to radial distance r, the increment in potential energy will be

$$\Delta U = GmM \left(\frac{1}{R_0} - \frac{1}{r} \right)$$

We can, in fact, simply call this the potential energy, U, since it is zero at $r = R_0$:

$$U = GmM\left(\frac{1}{R_0} - \frac{1}{r}\right) \qquad [34.13$$

Notice that this may be written as

$$U = GmM\left(\frac{r - R_0}{rR_0}\right) \qquad [34.14$$

For a point a small distance, h, above the earth's surface, we can write

$$r - R_0 = h$$
$$rR_0 \cong R_0{}^2$$

Substituting in equation 34.14, we get

$$U = \frac{GmMh}{R_0{}^2} \qquad [34.15$$

We recognize $GmM/R_0{}^2$ as approximately equal to the apparent weight, mg. Equation 34.15 may therefore be written for points near the surface of the earth as

$$U = mgh \qquad [34.16$$

We recognize our old potential-energy expression (§ 28.1) for what it is: a good approximation.

Now let us move to a point very far from the earth, at distance r'. We release a body of mass m from that point. What will its kinetic energy be when it lands on the earth? We use the fact that $\Delta U + \Delta K = 0$.

$$U_0 + K_0 = U + K$$

$$GmM\left(\frac{1}{R_0} - \frac{1}{r'}\right) + 0 = 0 + \frac{1}{2}mv^2$$

We can solve this for v^2; but, before we do that, let us assume that r' is so very distant that $1/r'$ is virtually zero. Then

$$\frac{1}{2}mv^2 = \frac{GmM}{R_0} \qquad [34.17$$

Let us write this as

$$\frac{1}{2}mv^2 = \left(\frac{GmM}{R_0{}^2}\right)R_0 \qquad [34.18$$

and then as

$$\frac{1}{2}mv^2 = mgR_0 \qquad [34.19$$

From this we get

$$v^2 = 2gR_0$$
$$v = \sqrt{2gR_0} \qquad [34.20$$

We say, speaking mathematically, that this is the speed with which the body would land if dropped from rest at infinity.

What would happen if we could reverse the procedure? Suppose we shot the body up vertically from the earth at speed $\sqrt{2gR_0}$. By the conservation of energy, we should expect it to reach "a point at infinity" with a zero speed. If we shot it off with any speed higher than this, it would still have kinetic energy at infinity. We therefore call this the escape speed:

$$v_e = \sqrt{2gR_0} \qquad [34.21$$

Observe that $v_e = \sqrt{2} \times \sqrt{gR_0}$. We have already calculated that $\sqrt{gR_0}$ is 4.92 miles per second. Therefore

$$v_e = 1.414 \times 4.92 \text{ mi/sec} = 6.96 \text{ mi/sec}$$
$$\text{(about 11.2 km/sec)}$$

To escape from the earth, then, you must leave at a speed a little less than 7 miles per second.

A study of the engines used to achieve such speeds is beyond the scope of this book. The tremendously intricate details of rocket motion and of the telemetering instruments that guide the rockets belong to a currently evolving technology, in which thousands of people are employed and billions of dollars per year are being expended.

Since the escape speed is 11.2 kilometers per second, the kinetic energy *per kilogram* is

$$\frac{1}{2}mv^2 = \frac{1}{2} \times 1 \text{ kg} \times (11.2 \times 10^3)^2 \frac{m^2}{\text{sec}^2} = 62.7 \times 10^6 \text{ J}$$

It takes this much energy for matter with a mass of one kilogram to escape from the earth.

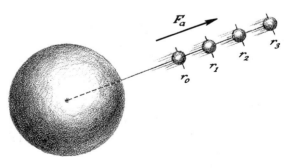

FIG. 34.9. *Illustrating the calculation of the potential energy of a system consisting of the earth and a projectile.*

34.6. The Total Energy in an Orbit

We shall consider the energy in an orbit a little further, not because we wish to go more deeply into the study of space, but because the solar system, with its family of planets revolving round the sun, has great similarity to a crude model of an atom, with its electrons revolving round the central nucleus and being held in their orbital paths, not by gravitational, but by electrical, forces, which, being inverse-square forces, have energy relations very similar to those, already discussed, of the sun and the planets. Keep in mind that we are getting ready for another kind of space exploration—a leap, figuratively speaking, into the atomic world.

What does a graph of potential energy against radial distance look like? The right member of equation

$$U = \frac{GmM}{R_0} - \frac{GmM}{r}$$

has two terms (see equation 34.13). The first is a constant. Since we are usually concerned with *differences* in energy, this constant does not play a very important role. (For earth-based operations, of course, in which we wish to calculate potential energies based on a value of zero at the earth's surface, the constant GmM/R_0 serves the purpose of making U equal to zero when r equals R_0.) When *differences* in energy are the most important thing, we can simply drop the constant term. The formula then has the form

$$U = -\frac{GmM}{r} \qquad [34.22$$

A negative potential energy may seem strange at first, but there is no great difficulty in imagining that to a person in a laboratory on the fiftieth floor of a skyscraper the gravitational potential energies of objects below him are negative if he arbitrarily takes the floor of his own laboratory as the zero for his potential-energy calculations. Objects on the fortieth floor still have a greater potential energy than those on the thirtieth floor even though both have negative potential energies in relation to the fiftieth floor.

Equation 34.22 demands that the zero of poten-

tial energy be at $r = \infty$. For all other values of r ($r > 0$) the potential energy is negative. The relation is an inverse one ($\backsim 1/r$), and the graph is therefore a hyperbola (Fig. 34.10).

For a circular orbit we can calculate also the kinetic energy, $\frac{1}{2}mv^2$. Consider first the centripetal force, mv^2/r. Since it must equal GmM/r^2, we write

$$\frac{mv^2}{r} = \frac{GmM}{r^2} \qquad [34.23$$

Hence

$$K = \frac{1}{2}mv^2 = \frac{GmM}{2r} \qquad [34.24$$

The total energy, $K + U$, is therefore

$$E = K + U = \frac{GmM}{2r} - \frac{GmM}{r}$$

$$= -\frac{GmM}{2r} \qquad [34.25$$

The shape of the total-energy ($K + U$) curve (Fig. 34.11) indicates that an orbit with a long radius (large r) has a greater total energy than one with a short radius. At r_1, for example, the total energy is -2 units; at the more distant point r_2 it is -1 unit, which is one unit *greater* than the energy at r_1.

An interesting point is that, if a body of mass m in a stable orbit with radius r_2 could lose some

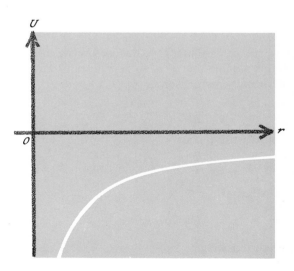

FIG. 34.10. *Graph of gravitational potential energy,* U, *against distance,* r.

energy and somehow get into an orbit with radius r_1, its kinetic energy (B) would be greater than it was at r_2 (A).

As I said earlier, the orbital-energy system just described bears a strong resemblance to the energy system associated with the electrons in an atom. It is, in fact, mathematically identical, and we shall utilize the derivation of this section, simply by changing symbols, when we come to study the hydrogen atom. (See § 37.1 and § 51.3.) We shall find, in the atom, something that would seem unusual for orbiting satellites: *not all orbital radii are permitted*. New rules begin to be important in the atomic realm. They are true in the macroscopic (or molar) realm also, but they do not become really observable until we enter the realm of very small particles. This we must soon do by way of the study of electricity.

34.7. Scientific Uses of the Exploration of Space

We are about to take leave of our study of mechanics. We were led, in a natural way, to a consideration of the problems of propulsion through space. We took that particular direction because the present great interest in the explora-

tion of space made it appropriate, but we must remember that the study of mechanics is basic to the study of all branches of physics. We shall presently begin the study of electricity, and it will not be long before we are studying the motion of particles that have both inertial mass and charge. Certain aspects of the study are called, in fact, *electrodynamics*.

What *scientific* value do we hope to gain from the study of space? It is not easy to answer this question except in a very general way. Political and military advantages are, to be sure, being sought by the powers engaged in the exploration of space. As scientific activity, however, the exploration is simply a continuation of the search for the relations, laws, and facts of nature. Some of these will be learned simply because we can now climb above the earth's atmosphere, which, until now, has kept us from receiving certain ultraviolet and x-ray signals from the sun and stars. Other facts will be learned because rockets can now carry robot laboratories that can send their messages to the earth, via radio waves, at the speed of light. Much has already been learned about the dangerous radiation surrounding our earth (Fig. 4.17), and this is undoubtedly only the beginning. The moon and the planets are bound to come next.

Theoretically, we need only Newton's laws of motion. Newton himself could have directed the firing of a modern missile, but the practical realization of his dreams had to wait until we had learned more about *microscopic space*—the atom. Only then could we venture forth. Our great power of communication stems mostly from electronics, an engineering offshoot of electricity, and our full technology is an outgrowth of atomic physics and chemistry.

We must therefore take leave of mechanics to embark on the study of electricity and atomic physics. The most interesting and challenging problems lie ahead!

34.8. Summary

It takes energy to leave the earth. The amount of energy can be calculated from the expression for gravitational potential energy,

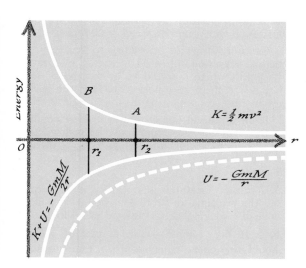

FIG. 34.11. *Three energy graphs.*

$$U = GmM \left(\frac{1}{R_0} - \frac{1}{r} \right)$$

At height h above the earth this expression becomes the well-known approximate formula $U = mgh$. It is often convenient to use, for potential energy, an expression that vanishes at infinity instead of at the earth's surface. The expression

$$U = -\frac{GmM}{r}$$

has this property, and, since it differs from the first expression for U by a constant, it yields the same measure of potential differences.

Calculations of energy require a knowledge of G, the universal constant of gravitation. We determine G in the laboratory by measuring the force of attraction between objects of known mass and shape separated by known distances.

Trajectories in space are computed from a knowledge of Newton's law of universal gravitation,

$$F = \frac{GmM}{r^2}$$

and his second law, $\mathbf{f} = m\mathbf{a}$. The trajectory of a body moving in an inverse-square field is a conic section.

The kinetic energy of a satellite in orbit is

$$K = \frac{GmM}{2r}$$

The potential energy is

$$U = -\frac{GmM}{r}$$

The total energy is therefore

$$E = -\frac{GmM}{2r}$$

The negative sign is a consequence of having chosen the zero of potential energy at infinity.

Problems

34.1. 1. From the fact that the mass of the moon is 7.35×10^{22} kg and its radius is 1,738 km prove that the approximate value of g on its surface is $(9.8)/6$ m/sec^2.

2. A man weighs 150 lb on the earth. What will he weigh, in pounds, on the surface of the moon?

3. If a man has enough energy to jump 1 m above the surface of the earth, how high should he be able to jump on the moon? (Hint: Gravitational potential energy is approximately mgh.)

34.2. Calculate the period of a moon satellite orbiting in a circular path very close to the moon's surface. (See the data of Prob. 34.1.)

34.3. Draw a diagram similar to that of Fig. 34.3, with the axis of the earth vertical, for an object suspended by a stretched spring at a place where the latitude is 40°.

1. The resultant of the vectors whose magnitudes are T and GmM/R_0^2 must now be a vector pointing from the object along a perpendicular to the earth's axis. Why?

2. Which has the greater magnitude, T or GmM/R_0^2?

3. Prove that the magnitude of the vector pointing toward the axis is $m\omega^2 R_0 \cos 40°$.

4. Will the spring be vertical? Explain.

34.4. A projectile is fired at an angle of 45° from the horizontal with a muzzle speed of 20 m/sec.

1. Carefully draw its trajectory to scale by the method suggested in Fig. 34.4—that is, by locating the points where it would be at the end of 1, 2, 3 . . . sec if there were no gravity and then taking gravity into account, using the formula $gt^2/2$.

2. Draw a tangent line at the point corresponding to the A of Fig. 34.4, and prove to yourself that by adding the vectors $v_1 t$ and $\frac{1}{2}gt^2$ you get the displacement vector AB. Repeat the argument for B and C.

34.5. Redraw carefully to scale the trajectory that the projectile of Prob. 34.4 would have if the value of g were 4.9 m/sec^2 instead of 9.8 m/sec^2.

34.6. 1. If Fig. 34.6 is drawn accurately, AE/EB should be approximately $\sqrt{a_1/a_0}$. Take measurements to confirm this.

2. Draw a large ellipse similar to that of Fig. 34.6

on a piece of graph paper. Choose any two equal areas $AEC = EBD$, preferably subtending smaller angles at E to increase the accuracy, by counting squares. In this way determine points corresponding to C and D. Repeat part 1 with new data from this ellipse.

34.7. 1. Compute the linear speed of an earth satellite of mass 100 kg in a circular orbit 1,600 km above the surface of the earth.

2. Compute its period.

3. Repeat for a satellite of mass 200 kg.

34.8. Calculate the work it would take to move a satellite whose mass is 100 kg from r_0 (Fig. 34.9), which is one earth radius from the earth's surface, to r_3, which is two earth radii from that surface.

34.9. 1. Calculate the total energy (kinetic plus potential) of an earth satellite of mass 95 kg at a distance of two earth radii from the surface of the earth.

2. If the satellite should lose total energy of the right amount, it would find itself in a stable orbit at a distance of one earth radius from the surface of the earth. (See, for example, r_1 of Fig. 34.11.) Prove that, even though it has lost energy, its new linear speed is greater than the old.

34.10. 1. Can a rocket with fuel leave the earth at much less than 11.2 km/sec and never return?

2. Devise, if possible, a way for a rocket to leave the earth, never to return, with a total expenditure of much less than 62.7 million J/kg.

IV

ELECTRICITY AND THE ELECTROMAGNETIC THEORY OF LIGHT

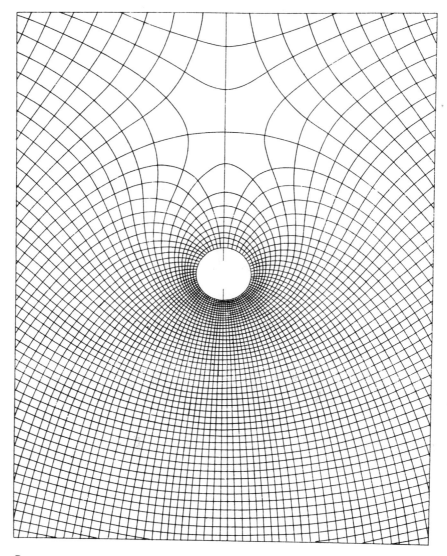

Representation of a Uniform Magnetic Field Disturbed by
an Electric Current in a Straight Conductor
(*From James Clerk Maxwell*, Treatise on Electricity and Magnetism, *1873.*)

Electricity and magnetism are intimately related, and Maxwell was the first to offer a comprehensive theory of their interrelations.

Electric Current
and Its Measurement

OLDER textbooks were usually divided into parts with such titles as Mechanics, Heat, Sound, Light, Electricity, and Magnetism. I have purposely avoided this division of the subject matter.

We have, of course, already covered a good deal of mechanics, for it is the basic branch of physics. You studied some aspects of sound and light in Part II, "Vibrations and Waves." We have done very little with heat, however, except to stress the fact that it is really the energy of the random motion of molecules.

And now we find that further progress toward our ultimate goal, an understanding of the atom, is impossible unless we master the elements of electricity and magnetism. Notice, however, that this part is entitled "Electricity and the Electromagnetic Theory of Light." Light is, somehow or other, related to electricity and magnetism, and we must understand this relation before we can proceed to the atom. Light comes from atoms. Atoms have moving electric charges in them. Accelerated electric charges send out waves—electromagnetic waves; and some of these are light waves. My treatment will be unconventional in that a desire to understand the electromagnetic nature of light is our basic motive for studying electricity.

35.1. Maxwell and Newton

For the sake of historical perspective I must state that James Clerk Maxwell (1831–1879) did

for electricity and magnetism what Sir Isaac Newton did for mechanics. Their great works were separated by almost 200 years: Newton published his *Principia Mathematica* in 1687; Maxwell published his *Treatise on Electricity and Magnetism* in 1873.

Newton has been called "the greatest of all natural philosophers." Besides his invention of the calculus and his contributions to mechanics and gravitation, he made significant contributions to the study of light, being the first to show that white light can be dispersed into the colors of the rainbow and to suggest a corpuscular theory of light. Maxwell has been called "the greatest theoretical physicist of the nineteenth century." Both Newton and Maxwell contributed in different ways to our understanding of light. They were able to condense a vast amount of knowledge into a small number of mathematical statements. We are already acquainted with Newton's formulas $F = m\mathbf{a}$ and $F = GmM/r^2$. Maxwell was able to condense descriptions of almost all electrical phenomena into four equations:

$$\nabla \cdot \mathbf{D} = \rho \qquad [35.1$$

$$\nabla \cdot \mathbf{B} = 0 \qquad [35.2$$

$$\nabla \times \mathbf{H} = \mathbf{J} + \frac{\partial \mathbf{D}}{\partial t} \qquad [35.3$$

$$\nabla \times \mathbf{E} = -\frac{\partial \mathbf{B}}{\partial t} \qquad [35.4$$

One other equation, called the Lorentz force law after H. A. Lorentz (1853–1928), is needed to complete the catalogue of basic formulas:

$$\mathbf{F} = q(\mathbf{E} + \mathbf{v} \times \mathbf{B}) \qquad [35.5$$

Do not be dismayed—we shall not pursue the subject mathematically to any great depth in this book. (Some of these equations, in a greatly simplified form, will be discussed in Chap. 43.) It is obvious at once that the equations 35.1–35.5 involve operators, such as ∇ and $\partial/\partial t$, that are foreign to us. We do recognize, however, that vectors and temporal rates of change are involved. We can, for example, think of $\partial\mathbf{D}/\partial t$ as the limit of $\Delta\mathbf{D}/\Delta t$. But, other than the symbols t (for time) and $\mathbf{E}$ (for electric field intensity), the variables ($\mathbf{D}$, $\mathbf{H}$, and $\mathbf{B}$) are new to us.

We shall not even get so far in the actual use of these equations as we got with the formula $\mathbf{F} = m\mathbf{a}$. It is my purpose, however, to clothe this skeleton of equations at least with the flesh and blood of *operational* meaning for some of their variables, and my purpose in exhibiting these equations here is to let you know at the outset that what may seem like many disconnected facts in electricity actually do fall into an ordered pattern, which we owe to Maxwell. I hope that this thought will be of some comfort to you and will offset the unpleasant effects of seeing so many new mathematical symbols all at once.

35.2. The Concept of Electric Current

In the two hundred years between Newton and Maxwell, a great deal of activity took place in physical science. With the aid of hindsight I shall pick out some experiments that will contribute to our understanding of electricity—not necessarily in historical order, but in one of the many possible logical arrangements.

One way to begin is to consider an experiment involving **electric current.** The very use of the term "current" presupposes that something flows. What flows is electric charge, and, since its flow—in a wire, for example—is invisible, we must begin by making its existence plausible.

Figure 35.1 shows the apparatus used in a simple experiment. (At first I shall show rather detailed drawings of such apparatus, but later I shall evolve a symbolic shorthand, called wiring diagrams, to replace these pictorial representations.) Let us follow the circuit and name the

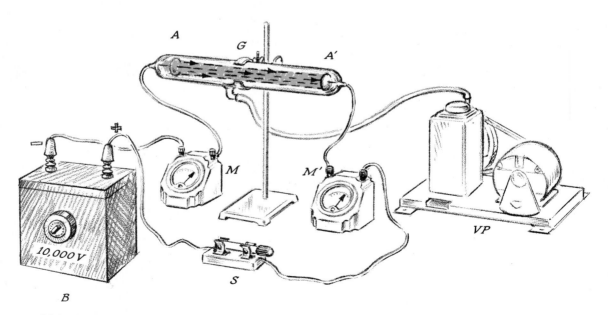

FIG. 35.1. *Apparatus to illustrate the concept of electric current.*

pieces of apparatus. (I shall explain how some of the pieces work; others I shall simply treat as "magic boxes," whose inner details are unknown to us but whose result we can depend upon— the way we depend upon a wristwatch, a portable transistor radio, or an automobile. No physicist is content to live forever, of course, in ignorance of the works of *any* magic box, but I cannot explain them all at once.) In the figure, then, is a closed glass tube, G. Sealed through its ends are wires ending in the parallel metal plates, A and A', called electrodes. The tube is connected to a vacuum pump, VP. Electrode A is connected by wire to a meter, M (called a galvanometer), which has a scale on its face. Electrode A' is connected by wire to a similar meter, M'. If we looked inside one of these meters, we should see a small permanent magnet and a coil of copper wire that can rotate within the field of the magnet. The coil rotates when there is a current in it (for reasons to be explained later). Its rotation is indicated by deflection of the needle on the face of the meter. Meter M' is connected by wire to a switch, S, which is essentially a copper blade, containing a gap, that assures the discontinuity of the metallic path from A' through M' to B when the gap is open and the continuity of that path when the gap is closed. After S comes the magic box marked B, a special kind of battery labeled 10,000 volts. (A car battery usually has 6 or 12 volts.) It has two terminals, marked, respectively, with a plus and a minus sign, which suggest that it is a source of electric charges. A wire from B to M and another from M to A seem to complete the circuit. But is the circuit really complete when the switch is closed? What is there between A and A'? No wires are there. At first, within G, there is air at atmospheric pressure.

We begin the experiment by closing the switch and watching the meters. Nothing happens. Leaving the switch closed, we start the vacuum pump. After a while we observe identical deflections on the meters: they both deflect *to the right*. If we reverse the connections on the battery, the meter needles both point *to the left*. If we open the switch, both meters read zero. We want a plausible explanation of what is going on.

If we ignore the rather complicated details of

what happens within the glass tube, the modern explanation is somewhat like this: When enough air molecules have been removed from G, it is possible for electrons to flow from A to A'. This experiment alone would, of course, only *suggest* that *something* flows; we wouldn't know just what. In the early days of such experimentation what flows was called *cathode rays*. The fact that the needle of each meter pointed first one way and then the other when the battery terminals were interchanged *suggests* that there is a definite direction of flow. When the switch is closed, both meters react simultaneously and instantaneously, regardless of the total length of the wire in the loop. (It could be a hundred miles long.) This suggests that whatever flows is already in the wire: the battery simply acts as a pump that can push a fluid along in pipes that are already full.

I have treated the space between A and A' as if it were completely empty except for electrons jumping from A to A'. The real situation is much more complicated than this, for the few molecules left inside G actually help in the liberation of electrons; but, in any case, it is right to think that electrons are being *accelerated* from A to A'.

This means that they must feel a *force*. This force is produced by the *electric field* that exists between A and A'. If G could be *completely* evacuated, the flow of electrons would cease, but the electric field, E, would still exist. In such a field any electric charge, q, experiences force $\mathbf{F} = q\mathbf{E}$. This follows from the definition of electric field (equation 4.1):

$$\mathbf{E} = \mathbf{F}/q \qquad [35.6$$

(You may have noticed the term $q\mathbf{E}$ in equation 35.5.) Electrons obey Newton's law, $\mathbf{F} = m\mathbf{a}$. They therefore experience acceleration $\mathbf{a} = \mathbf{F}/m = q\mathbf{E}/m$. (Relativistic speeds are encountered at very high voltages, and the formula

$$\mathbf{F} = \lim_{\Delta t \to 0} \frac{\Delta(m\mathbf{v})}{\Delta t}$$

is then used instead.)

The point of all this is, simply, that we are dealing with a new force, an *electric* force, rather than with a gravitational one. The electrons obey the formula $\mathbf{F} = q\mathbf{E}$ because they have the charge $q = 1.602 \times 10^{-19}$ coul, but they also obey the formula $\mathbf{F} = m\mathbf{a}$ because they have the inertial mass $m = 9.1091 \times 10^{-31}$ kg. (In making these assertions I am stating numerical facts that even Maxwell did not know. I shall have to explain later just how these quantities were measured.)

How about the electrons in the wire? Are they also accelerated? There is also an electric field, $\mathbf{E}'$, inside the wire, but there are very many electrons within the wire, some of which are free to move. All the electrons feel the force $\mathbf{F} = q\mathbf{E}'$ simultaneously, and the free ones start moving at the same time, but they meet opposition from the great number of atoms in the wire, the result being that their average behavior is a *constant flow*. [The fine sand in an hourglass runs through at a constant rate even though each particle of mass m feels pull $m\mathbf{g}$ downward. A retarding force keeps the average flow steady while the particles are passing through the constriction. The particles accelerate again after they get through. One can, by analogy, think of electrons flowing at a constant rate from B to A (Fig. 35.1); they are then

accelerated from A to A'.] The constant flow of charge is called electric current. Just how a galvanometer works to read this constant flow I shall explain later, and the precise details of how the battery works we shall never get to in this book. Except for a rather superficial description of how charges flow in liquids (§ 10.4), the battery will have to remain a magic box, but we can, nevertheless, still learn a great deal about electricity.

35.3. The Force on a Stream of Electrons

Before we move on to define a unit of current, let us consider a slight modification of the glass-tube apparatus. The electric field $\mathbf{E}$ is still established (Fig. 35.2.A) between A and A', but A' is now a cylinder with a hole, which some accelerated electrons get through. These electrons move at a *constant velocity* ($\mathbf{E} = 0$; therefore $\mathbf{F} = 0$) from A' to the fluorescent screen, F. They

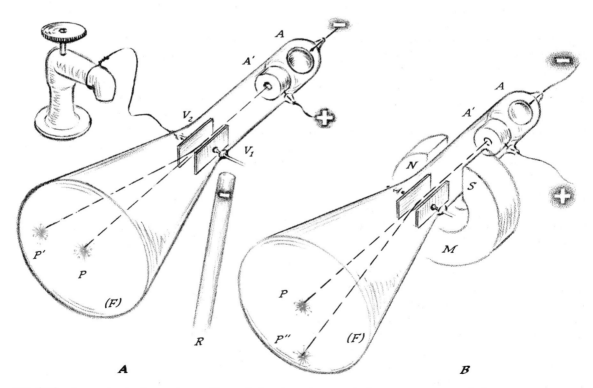

FIG. 35.2. *Apparatus to demonstrate effects of electric and magnetic forces on a stream of electrons.*

light up the screen at the point, P, where they hit. A negatively charged rod, R, brought near vertical plate V_1, deflects the spot from P to P', thereby proving that electrons carry a negative charge. When a magnet, M, is brought into position (Fig. 35.2.B) so that the electrons move through its magnetic field, they are deflected in a vertical direction. The spot originally at P moves to P'' when the magnet is moved in. In general, electrons moving at right angles to a magnetic field experience a force of which the direction is perpendicular both to the velocity of the electrons and to the direction of the magnetic field. [This part of the force appears in equation 35.5 as $q(\mathbf{v} \times \mathbf{B})$. We shall study it in Chap. 38.]

I have gone into considerable detail to present in advance the modern concept of **electric current** as a flow of electric charges. In many solids it is simply a flow of electrons. In gases and liquids the charged particles may be atoms and molecules. Let us now see how the unit of electric current, called the ampere, is defined.

35.4. The Force Between Two Wires Carrying Current; the Ampere

It is an experimental fact that two parallel wires carrying current either attract or repel each other. Since we have already seen that a stream of electrons is deflected by a magnetic field, we suspect that each wire carrying current produces a magnetic field that interacts with the current in the other wire.

In Figure 35.3 we have a picture with some of the characteristics of a schematic diagram. (Later we shall substitute for the battery a symbol that consists of one or more pairs of parallel line segments of unequal length. The long one represents the positive electrode and the short one the negative.) Without even knowing in what direction the electrons are flowing, we see at once that they must flow in opposite directions (A) in branches AB and CD and in the same direction (B) in branches EF and GH. The former repel each other; the latter attract each other.

The use of iron filings to explore a magnetic field confirms the fact that magnetic fields are in-

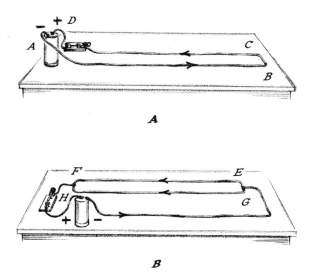

FIG. 35.3. *Illustrating direction of flow of current.*

volved here. Figure 35.4.A shows how filings arrange themselves round a current; Figure 35.5.A shows schematically how the field due to two currents having the same direction can be plotted with filings; Figure 35.6.A depicts the field due to two currents having opposite directions. Figures 35.4.B, 35.5.B, and 35.6.B are bird's-eye views of the cards on which the filings rest.

Parallel currents having a common direction attract each other; parallel currents having opposite directions repel each other.

The force of attraction or repulsion can be measured on specially designed balances. Figure 35.7 is a diagram of a balance designed by A. M. Ampère (1775–1836). He discovered that the force between the wires is directly proportional to the length, $l = CD$, that the parallel wires have in common and to the current, i, in each, and inversely proportional to the distance, r, between them:

$$F \propto \frac{i_1 i_2 l}{r} \qquad [35.7$$

The unit of current is called the **ampere.** Since l and r may both be measured in meters, it is apparent that $i_1 i_2 l/r$ has amperes² for units. The left side of the equation has newtons for units. We could replace the proportionality sign by an

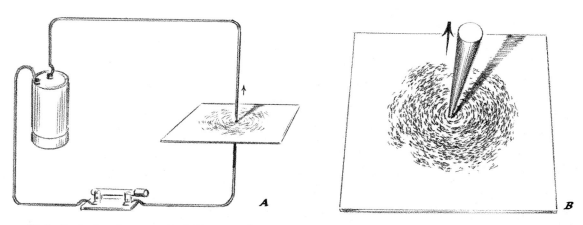

FIG. 35.4. *Exploring the magnetic field surrounding a wire carrying current.*

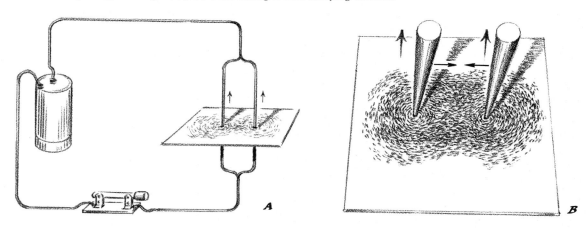

FIG. 35.5. *Exploring the magnetic fields surrounding parallel wires carrying currents in the same direction.*

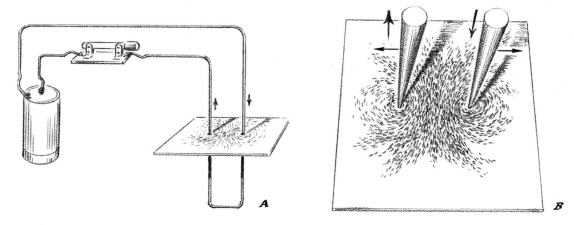

FIG. 35.6. *Exploring the magnetic fields surrounding parallel wires carrying currents in opposite directions.*

equality sign and a dimensionless constant, k, writing

$$F = \frac{k i_1 i_2 l}{r} \qquad [35.8$$

This would require amperes² to be equivalent to newtons. Another alternative is to allow the constant k to have nt/amp² as its unit. I shall adopt this convention in this book.† The choice of a value for k is arbitrary; for reasons that are partly historical and partly logical, the value is 2×10^{-7} nt/amp².

Equation 35.8 implies that two infinitely long parallel wires 1 meter apart and each carrying 1 ampere would experience a force of attraction (or repulsion) of 2×10^{-7} newton for every meter of their common length. This follows from the equation if we let $i_1 = i_2 = 1$ amp, $r = 1$ m, and $l = 1$ m.

In practical experiments we can use equation 35.8 for finite parallel lengths of wire that are very close to each other so that the effects at the ends are negligible.

EXAMPLE 35.1. In Fig. 35.7, current in AB is 5 amp, and current of the same direction in CD is 8 amp. We wish to know the force of attraction between the wires when $r = 1$ cm and $l = 80$ cm.

Having been given the values

$$i_1 = 5 \text{ amp}$$
$$i_2 = 8 \text{ amp}$$
$$l = 0.80 \text{ m}$$
$$r = 10^{-2} \text{ m}$$
$$k = 2 \times 10^{-7} \text{ nt/amp}^2$$

we use equation 35.8:

$$F = \frac{k i_1 i_2 l}{r}$$

$$= 2 \times 10^{-7} \frac{\text{nt}}{\text{amp}^2} \times \frac{5 \text{ amp} \times 8 \text{ amp} \times 0.80 \text{ m}}{10^{-2} \text{ m}}$$

$$= 6.4 \times 10^{-4} \text{ nt}$$

This is equivalent to the weight of an object whose mass, m, is such that $mg = 6.4 \times 10^{-4}$ nt:

$$m = \frac{6.4 \times 10^{-4} \text{ nt}}{9.8 \text{ nt/kg}}$$

$$= 6.53 \times 10^{-5} \text{ kg}$$
$$= 65.3 \text{ milligrams}$$

Observe that the *operation* of measuring a current involves the measurement of a force and some distances. We have gone back to mechanics, the solid base to which we return whenever possible. The current balances used in modern standards laboratories are far more complicated than the diagram of Ampère's original apparatus would indicate; but in principle they do the same thing: they measure a force that indirectly measures the current. Obviously, we now have a means of calibrating current meters, such as those of Fig. 35.1, and marking their scales in amperes. We shall assume that the galvanometers and ammeters we use have been so calibrated. In practice, the primary standards are usually current balances that exist only in government laboratories. Secondary standards of a less complicated sort are available for industrial and educational use.

35.5. The MKS Unit of Charge, the Coulomb

I have defined the basic unit of current in the MKS system, the ampere. I can now define the unit of charge in terms of the ampere. Let us say that the unit charge is the charge that flows by any point of a wire carrying one ampere for one

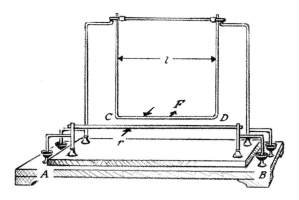

FIG. 35.7. *Highly simplified version of the apparatus used by Ampère to measure the force of attraction or repulsion between parallel wires carrying current.*

† Later, for reasons that are not apparent here, I shall assign the unit weber per ampere-meter to k. The weber/amp-m must, of course, be equivalent to nt/amp².

second (see § 10.4). This charge is called the **coulomb.** The defining equation is simply

$$q = it \qquad [35.9$$

in which q is the charge in coulombs, i is the current in amperes, and t is the time in seconds.†

EXAMPLE 35.2. A wire carries a current of 6 amp. We wish to know the total charge that flows by a given point in one hour.

We use equation 35.9, in which $i = 6$ amp and $t = 3,600$ sec:

$$q = 6 \frac{\text{coul}}{\text{sec}} \times 3,600 \text{ sec} = 21,600 \text{ coul}$$

Observe that we use coul/sec as the equivalent of amp.

The MKS units of electricity, such as the ampere, the volt, and the watt, are in common practical use. Most of the electrical equipment in the United States is designed to operate at 110–120 volts. A typical electric toaster, for example, might be labeled "110 volts, 500 watts." For everyday applications the ampere is a unit of reasonable size; there is a current of about 1 ampere in an ordinary 100-watt bulb connected to the 110-volt house line.

The coulomb is an extraordinarily large unit of charge to be applied to charges at rest. A piece of copper wire has a tremendous number of electrons in it, but the net charge in the wire is zero because each atom has as many positive as negative charges. If you could place a *net* negative charge of 1 coulomb on an insulated metal sphere, it would repel a similarly charged metal sphere 1 meter away with a force of 9×10^9 newtons. We must reconcile ourselves to the fact that, al-

---

† Notice that this assumes a constant current, i. More generally we can define i as a temporal rate of flow of charge; the average current is then $\bar{i} = \Delta q / \Delta t$, and the instantaneous current is

$$i = \lim_{t \to 0} \frac{\Delta q}{\Delta t}$$

though 1 coulomb per second can easily flow through a wire, it is very difficult to deposit 1 coulomb of charge on an insulated metal sphere!

The magnitude of the coulomb can also be appreciated in another way. One coulomb represents 6.242×10^{18} electrons. The mass of each electron, fortunately, is only 9.109×10^{-31} kg, and therefore the mass represented by 1 coulomb of charge in the form of electrons is only 6.242×10^{18} electrons $\times 9.109 \times 10^{-31}$ kg/electron, or 5.686×10^{-12} kg. This is just 0.005686 microgram.

I have defined the basic unit of charge in terms of electric current. Now we must examine the behavior of bodies when they have an excess of electric charge at rest. This branch of electricity is called **electrostatics.**

35.6. Summary

Many of the effects of electric and magnetic fields involving charges at rest and in motion were summarized by Maxwell in four equations introduced in this chapter but not to be pursued further except in a simplified form in Chapter 43.

Charges in motion constitute an electric current. Current is the rate of flow of charge. For a steady current $q = it$. In the MKS system charge q is measured in coulombs and current i in amperes. One ampere is one coulomb per second.

The ampere is defined in terms of the equation $F = ki_1i_2l/r$, which describes the force between the length l of two parallel wires carrying currents i_1 and i_2, separated by distance r. In the MKS system k is 2×10^{-7} nt/amp². The force on the wire is actually the force that a magnetic field exerts on the electrons in the wire.

More generally, the force on charge q moving with velocity $\mathbf{v}$ in electric field $\mathbf{E}$ and magnetic field $\mathbf{B}$ is $\mathbf{F} = q(\mathbf{E} + \mathbf{v} \times \mathbf{B})$. The first part, $\mathbf{F} = q\mathbf{E}$, has already been discussed in § 4.4, and the second, $\mathbf{F} = q(\mathbf{v} \times \mathbf{B})$, will be discussed in Chapter 38.

Problems

35.1. The electrodes within the evacuated glass tube of Fig. 35.1 are separated by a distance of 45 cm. Between them there is a uniform electric field whose intensity is 25×10^5 nt/coul. An electron leaves the cathode with an initial speed approaching zero.

1. What force on the electron is due to the field?

2. What is the initial acceleration of the electron?

3. If the acceleration remained constant, how long would it take the electron to reach the anode?

4. If its acceleration remained constant, what speed would the electron have at the anode?

5. Is your answer compatible with elementary relativity?

35.2. Between two large, horizontal, parallel plates there is a uniform vertical electric field, E, whose intensity is 95.0 nt/coul. An electron is fired horizontally into it with a speed of 5.0×10^6 m/sec. The electric field exerts a downward force on the electron. Plot the electron's trajectory carefully on graph paper for $t = 0, 1, 2, 3, 4 \times 10^{-7}$ sec. (Hint: The problem is very similar to that of the eraser pushed off a table, discussed in § 9.1. The acceleration is now Eq/m instead of g.)

35.3. If a large current is established in the circuit of Fig. 35.1 for a long time, the wires may become warm and one of the electrodes A and A' will be hotter than the other.

1. Which electrode will be hotter? Explain.

2. What might be an atomic explanation of the heat in the wires?

35.4. Draw a modification of Fig. 35.2 to show how the magnetic and electric fields might be oriented to produce opposite effects in the same straight line on the screen. (This idea is used in one form of a device called a mass spectrometer, which is used to "weigh" atoms.)

35.5. In Fig. 35.3.B the separation between wires EF and HG is 2 cm. The force of attraction between each centimeter of length in the wires is 3×10^{-5} nt. What is the current *in the battery*?

35.6. The current in an electric heater is 15 amp. It runs a whole day.

1. How many coulombs pass any given point of the heater coil?

2. How many electrons pass that point?

36

Electrostatics

"The fact that certain bodies after being rubbed appear to attract other bodies was known to the ancients. In modern times a great variety of other phenomena have been observed and have been found to be related to these phenomena of attraction."

"In the following Treatise, I propose to describe the most important of these phenomena to show how they may be subjected to measurement and to trace the mathematical connections of the quantities measured."

"In the application of mathematics to the calculation of electrical quantities I shall endeavor in the first place to deduce the most general conclusions from the data at our disposal and in the next place to apply the results to the simplest cases that can be chosen. I shall avoid as much as I can, those questions which though they have elicited the skill of mathematicians have not enlarged our knowledge of science."

JAMES CLERK MAXWELL, *Treatise on Electricity and Magnetism*

IN THE last chapter I found it convenient to define the basic unit of charge, the coulomb, by equation $q = it$ (coulombs equal amperes times seconds). This definition depends on the modern concept of electric current as a flow of charges, or electrons, but there are electrical effects that do not demand that the charges be in motion.

36.1. Static Electric Charges

A body with an excess of electrons is said to be negatively charged, and one with a dearth of electrons is said to be positively charged. If the charges are at rest (that is, if there is no current), the bodies are said to be *electrostatically charged*. **Electrostatics** deals with the electrical properties of bodies on which electric charges are at rest.

Currents of short duration are involved in the process of charging the bodies, but the electrostatic effects are due to charges that are at rest in relation to one another. Electrostatically charged bodies attract or repel one another. They must, therefore, exert forces on one another. This gives us a mechanical means of measuring electric forces, and we see again that mechanics is basic in our study of physics.

Consider first a qualitative experiment (Fig. 36.1). Two helium-filled rubber balloons (A) are moored to a common point, P. If each balloon is rubbed with a woolen cloth, they repel each other (B). If the woolen cloth is brought between them, they move closer together (C). If a plastic rod is rubbed with the woolen cloth and then brought between the balloons, it makes them move farther apart (D). If the cloth with which the rod was rubbed is brought between the balloons, they again move closer to each other (E).

The modern explanation of these effects goes somewhat like this: Like charges repel and unlike charges attract one another. Initially (A), the atoms of the balloon surfaces are electrically neutral, or uncharged; each atom has positive charges (protons) and negative charges (electrons) in equal numbers, and their effects cancel out. Rubbing the balloons with the woolen cloth removes electrons from the cloth and deposits them on the balloons. The balloons are then negatively charged, and they repel each other (B). The cloth was thereby left positively charged. When it is brought between the balloons, they are therefore attracted toward it (C). Rubbing the plastic rod with the woolen cloth takes electrons from the cloth and puts them on the rod. The negatively charged rod repels the balloons (D), but the positively charged cloth attracts them (E).

The law of attraction between charges is very similar to the universal law of gravitation. If a charge, q_1, is concentrated at a point at distance r from another point charge, q_2, the force on either charge has the magnitude

$$F = \frac{Kq_1q_2}{r^2} \qquad [36.1$$

This is called **Coulomb's law** after C. A. Coulomb (1736–1806), who used a torsion balance to measure such electrostatic forces.

Since all the quantities except the constant K have been defined, that constant can be determined experimentally. When MKS units are used, K comes out† as 9×10^9 nt-m²/coul².

A point charge of one coulomb separated by a distance of one meter from a similar point charge repels it with a force of 9×10^9 newtons. This is a tremendous force,‡ and one coulomb is, in fact, an extraordinarily large charge in electrostatics. [In current electricity, as we saw earlier, a flow of one coulomb per second (an ampere) is not at all uncommon.]

An electrostatic force is a vector whose direction is that of the line joining the two point charges.

---

† This value of K is an approximation but is adequate for most of our work. It can be shown theoretically that the magnitude of K is $c^2/10^7$ if c is the speed of light. This is a preview of the relation between electricity, magnetism, and light, which lay hidden until discovered by Maxwell.

‡ Remember that in gravitation

$$F = \frac{Gm_1m_2}{r^2}$$

in which expression

$$G = 6.67 \times 10^{-11} \frac{\text{nt-m}^2}{\text{kg}^2}$$

Observe that the constant G involves 10^{-11}, whereas K, in the electrostatical formula, involves 10^9; it follows that the ratio of the magnitudes of these constants is

$$\frac{K}{G} = \frac{9 \times 10^9}{6.67 \times 10^{-11}} \cong 10^{20}$$

Two unit charges (coulombs) separated by a distance of 1 m experience a force that is about 10^{20} times larger than the gravitational force between two bodies, each of 1-kg mass, placed 1 m apart.

Even 1 microcoulomb (a millionth of a coulomb; symbol, μcoul) separated by 1 m from another microcoulomb feels a force that is about 10^8 times larger than the gravitational force between two 1-kg bodies 1 m apart!

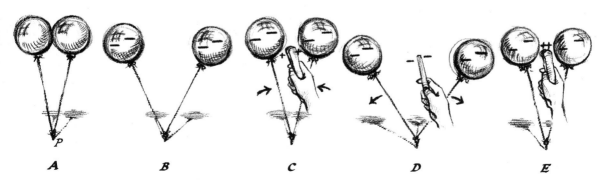

FIG. 36.1. *Experiment with two helium-filled rubber balloons moored to a common point.*

Large charged bodies are made up of many small charged bodies, and the net force between them can be figured out by vector addition. Fortunately, charges evenly spread over a spherical surface act—like gravitational forces—as if they were concentrated at the center of the sphere. Equation 36.1 may therefore be used to compute the force between two homogeneously charged spheres if r is the distance between their centers.

I can now show how Coulomb's law and elementary mechanics can help us estimate the charge on a body. Let us compute the charge on one of the balloons of Figure 36.2, using values from a real experiment for the physical dimensions involved. In this analysis we assume that each balloon has charge q. We further assume that the charge is homogeneously distributed over a spherical surface of radius R (this is unlikely unless we have conducting surfaces). A free-body diagram of the balloon on the left shows that it is in equilibrium under the action of three forces: the tension, OA, of the string; the net buoyant effect, OL, of the helium (lift minus weight); the electrostatic repulsion, OB. The force OL is balanced by OC, the vertical component of the tension, OA. The electrical force OB is balanced by the horizontal component, CA, of the tension, OA. The following approximate measurements were taken during the experiment, the last being estimated from the weight of a body that could be barely lifted by the balloon:

$$OD = 0.25 \text{ m}$$
$$DP = 1.00 \text{ m}$$
$$OC = OL = 0.5 \text{ nt}$$

Similar triangles show us that

$$\frac{OB}{OC} = \frac{OD}{DP}$$

Therefore

$$OB = \frac{0.25 \text{ m}}{1.00 \text{ m}} \times 0.5 \text{ nt}$$

$$OB = 0.125 \text{ nt}$$

But this is equal to the force of electrostatic repulsion,

$$\frac{Kq \times q}{r^2}$$

in which

$$K = 9 \times 10^9 \frac{\text{nt-m}^2}{\text{coul}^2}$$

$$r = 2(OD) = 0.5 \text{ m}$$

Therefore

$$OB = 9 \times 10^9 \frac{\text{nt-m}^2}{\text{coul}^2} \times \frac{q^2}{(0.5)^2} \frac{\text{coul}^2}{\text{m}^2}$$

Equating equal quantities, we get

$$0.125 \text{ nt} = \frac{9 \times 10^9}{0.25} \frac{\text{nt-m}^2}{\text{coul}^2} \times q^2 \frac{\text{coul}^2}{\text{m}^2}$$

$$q^2 = \frac{0.125}{9 \times 10^9} \times 0.25 \text{ coul}^2$$

$$= 3.48 \times 10^{-12} \text{ coul}^2$$

$$q = 1.87 \times 10^{-6} \text{ coul}$$

In words, the charge on one balloon is of the order of a microcoulomb.

Since the electronic charge is about 1.6×10^{-19} coul, there are

$$\frac{1}{1.6 \times 10^{-19}} = 6.24 \times 10^{18} \frac{\text{electrons}}{\text{coulomb}}$$

One microcoulomb therefore represents 6.24×10^{12} electrons. The woolen cloth gave up about 6.24×10^{12} electrons to the balloon. Since the mass of each electron is about 9.11×10^{-31} kg, the total mass added to the balloon was about

$$6.24 \times 10^{12} \text{ electrons} \times 9.11 \times 10^{-31} \frac{\text{kg}}{\text{electron}}$$

$$= 5.68 \times 10^{-19} \text{ kg}$$

No wonder the added weight is negligible!

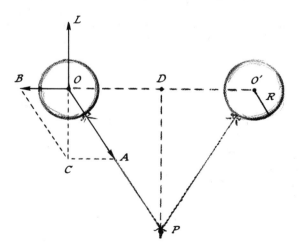

FIG. 36.2. *Diagram of the forces acting on one balloon of the pair shown in Fig. 36.1.*

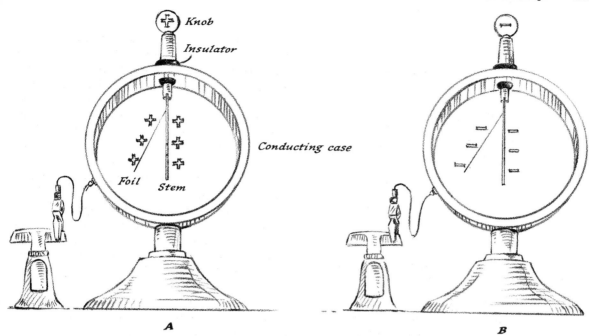

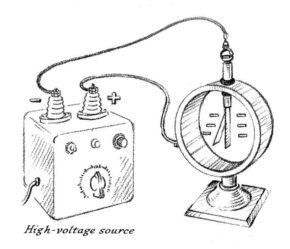

FIG. 36.3. *A typical electroscope: The essential part is a thin metal foil attached to a rigid metal stem, which is electrically insulated from the conducting case, shown here connected to ground.*

36.2. The Electroscope

The electroscope is a simple and sensitive device for detecting electric charges. One form of electroscope uses the force of repulsion between a strip of thin gold or aluminum foil and a rigid metal rod, the stem (Fig. 36.3). The rod is held in place by an **insulator,** which keeps the charge on the rod from flowing away. If electrons have been removed from the rod by some means, the rod and the foil share the positive charge (A); the angular deflection of the foil is a rough measure of the total charge. A negatively charged electroscope is also shown (B); the deflection of the foil indicates the presence of a charge, but tells us nothing about its sign. We shall soon see how to determine the sign of the charge.

A straightforward way to charge an electroscope would be to connect it to a battery—or to a special source of voltage, as shown in Figure 36.4. The only trouble with this procedure is that it would take a battery, or other source, of extremely high voltage to deflect the

High-voltage source

FIG. 36.4. *Connecting an electroscope to a high-voltage source as shown would leave a permanent charge on it.*

foil visibly. Unless proper precautions are taken, it is very dangerous to do experiments with a source of such high voltage. With a properly labeled source, however, the method would enable us to determine the sign of the charge put on the electroscope.

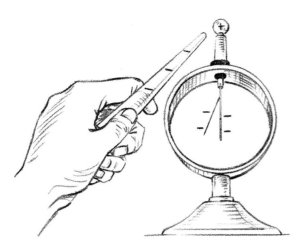

FIG. 36.5. *One way of temporarily charging an electroscope.*

trons in the knob down toward the stem and the foil. As the rod gets closer to the knob, the foil continues to rise. Since the forces on the foil can even cause it to break away from the stem, the rod must be brought in slowly and carefully. Usually a rod has to be fairly close (about 25 cm or less) to the knob before a deflection is visible. (Highly charged objects have stronger fields about them and hence are detectable at greater distances.) When the rod is moved away without touching, the foil falls. Without touching we have not left a charge on the electroscope; and even touching with the charged plastic rod often does not leave a sizable charge on the knob, for the non-conducting rod does not give up its charges readily. (A disadvantage of touching the electroscope knob with the charged rod has already been mentioned: the forces on the foil may tear it away from the stem. I shall describe a safer way of charging in § 36.3.)

The usual procedure (Fig. 36.5) is quite different. It consists simply in bringing a charged rod (for example, a plastic rod that has been rubbed with wool) near the knob of the electroscope. If the rod is negatively charged, it repels the elec-

If a long copper wire is attached to the knob (Fig. 36.6) and suspended by dry silk threads, T_1 and T_2, and a charged rod, R, is then brought

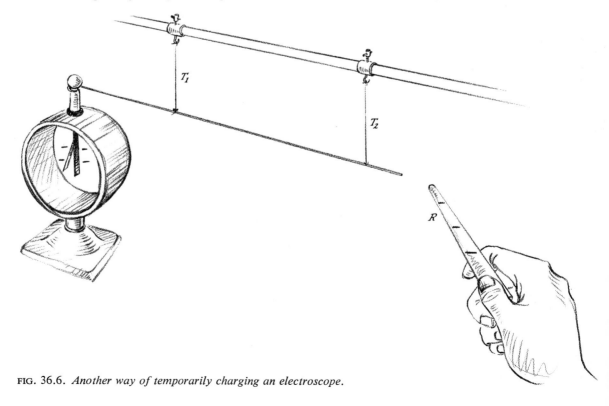

FIG. 36.6. *Another way of temporarily charging an electroscope.*

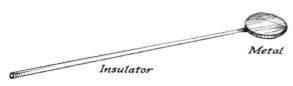

FIG. 36.7. *Metal paddle with an insulating handle, use-ful for sampling the charge on a body by touching it and bringing the paddle to an electroscope.*

near (but not touching) the distant end of the wire, the electroscope foil deflects even if the wire is more than 10 meters long. We say that the copper wire is a good **conductor** of electricity. Since no charge was transported from the rod to the wire, we conclude that charges that were already in the wire were repelled and made to migrate to the electroscope. But a charge, q, when it finds itself in an electric field whose intensity is E, experiences a force, F, according to the equation $F = qE$ (§ 4.4). Somehow the presence of the rod created in the wire a field that caused the migration of charges to the electroscope. But the charges do not continue to pile up on the foil. After a short while, when a sufficient number have accumulated, by mutual repulsion they keep others from approaching. In other words, the charges on the electroscope foil also create a field, which nullifies the effect of the distant rod. In a very short while the field intensity in the wire is zero. The migration of charges ceases. When the rod is removed, charges flow along the wire in the opposite direction and discharge the electroscope.

This was an experiment in electrostatics, but for a moment there was a current in the wire: at first electrons migrated toward the electroscope; when the rod was removed, electrons migrated away from the electroscope. Experiments in electrostatics are characterized by the fact that the currents involved in charging or discharging bodies are usually of very short duration. But the fact that we can use either a battery or a charged rod to produce a deflection in the electroscope indicates that charges of the same kind flow in both cases. Today, of course, we believe that these charges are electrons.

Since it is easy to damage the leaf of an electroscope, it is often desirable to use a small metal

paddle with an insulating handle (Fig. 36.7) to sample the charge on objects. The metal part of the paddle may then be allowed to touch the electroscope knob and charge it *by conduction*. The paddle simply shares its charges with the knob. But another method of charging the electroscope, called *charging by induction*, is preferable because it is even less likely to damage the leaf.

36.3. Charging an Electroscope by Induction

Figure 36.8 illustrates aspects of this process:

(A) We bring a negatively charged rod, R, near the knob of an electroscope. The leaf is deflected away from the stem by the mutual repulsion of negative charges.

(B) While the rod is held close to the knob (but not touching it), we *ground* the knob; that is, we supply a conducting path, such as a wire, from the knob to something like a water pipe, which, since we know it eventually penetrates the ground, we call our **ground**. In practice it is sufficient to touch the knob with a finger, for the human body is a sufficiently good conductor and an abundant source of charges for the quantities of charge involved here. We observe that the leaf falls. We have left a plus sign, however, at the knob itself, for we can think of some atoms in the knob, which had given up their electrons to the foil, as positively charged and as remaining that way as long as the negatively charged rod is nearby.

(C) When the ground wire (or the finger) is removed, the leaf remains down, even though the rod is still near the knob.

(D) When the rod is removed, the leaf flies up, indicating, as we say, that the positive charge has redistributed itself over the stem and the foil as well as the knob. This way of speaking does not really describe what we believe happens, but it is logically equivalent. We believe that the electrons, not the positively charged atoms, have the high mobility. When the rod is removed, electrons can flow from the stem and the foil up to the knob, redistributing the charge and leaving the stem and foil positively charged.

Notice that by this means we are able to ap-

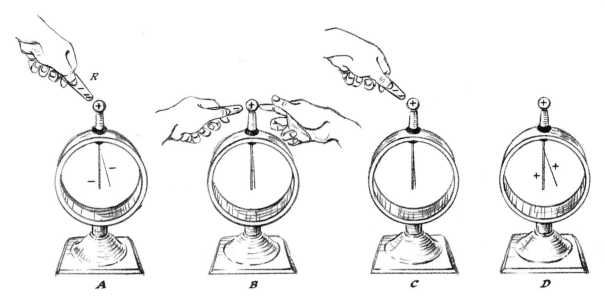

FIG. 36.8. *Charging an electroscope by induction: a permanent charge opposite in sign to that of the charging rod is left on the electroscope.*

proach the electroscope knob with caution, not allowing the rod to get so close that it damages the foil, whereas charging by conduction requires actual contact between the charged object, such as a paddle, and the knob of the electroscope; even before the two touch, the force on the leaf may become large enough to rip it off. We now see that the final charge on the electroscope has the sign that is *opposite* to that of the charging rod if we use the method of charging by induction illustrated in Figure 36.8.

The terms "positive" and "negative" were chosen before the details of electron flow were known.† Let us *arbitrarily* say that the charge on India rubber rubbed with rabbit's fur is negative. We can then use this as a standard with which to determine the signs of other charged bodies.

If, for example (Fig. 36.9), we leave, by induction, a permanent positive charge on an electroscope (A), as we did in Figure 36.8.D, any

† Benjamin Franklin was responsible for the introduction of the terms "positive" and "negative" to describe the different kinds of electric charge. The literature of electricity still treats current as a flow of positive charges although it is now known that it is the electrons that flow in wires.

negatively charged object near the knob will cause the leaf to fall (B), but a positively charged object brought near the knob will cause the leaf to rise (C). If the sign of the electroscope's initial charge is known, the electroscope can be used to determine the unknown signs of other charged objects. (Today a more conclusive test, since the basic unit of negative electricity is the electron, is to observe the effect of a charged body on a stream of electrons; see Fig. 35.2.) In this way, various materials have been arranged in a **triboelectric series** (Table 36.1). (*Tribo-* comes from the Greek word meaning "to rub.") Each substance in this list becomes more positive than any below it on contact under average conditions: glass in contact with wool becomes more positive than the wool, but India rubber in contact with the same wool becomes more negative. For electrostatic charges, non-conducting pairs of this series are rubbed against each other. Many of the modern plastic solids are among the most interesting, the most easily available, and the most triboelectric of triboelectric materials.

Table 36.1 suggests that electrostatic forces affect many substances. We can demonstrate this

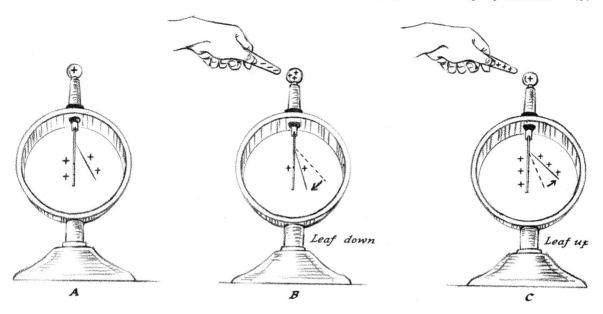

FIG. 36.9. *How to determine the sign of the charge on a body.*

with a simple holder for long thin objects, made out of string looped as in Figure 36.10. A pencil or even a ruler 2 meters long can easily be made to rotate when attracted by a comb rubbed on a woolen suit. Long objects made of metals or non-metals, either conductors or non-conductors, if substituted for the ruler, are attracted toward a charged rod held nearby. Such commonplace objects as a shoe, a banana, and a bottle move under the influence of something like a plastic coat-hanger that has been rubbed with wool.

Only charged objects attract or repel other charged objects. The reason why objects initially neutral can be attracted is that they become charged by induction. Suppose, for example, that a negatively charged rod is brought near one end of a suspended neutral metal bar (Fig. 36.11). The electrons in the bar are repelled to the far

TABLE 36.1

The Triboelectric Series†

Asbestos	Silk	Slate
Rabbit's fur	Al, Zn, Cd	Resins
Glass	Felt, Human skin	Cu, Ni, Co, Ag, Sn,
Mica	Cotton	Sb, Pd, C, brass
Wool	Rock salt	Para rubber
Quartz	Woods, iron	Sulfur
Calcite	Tinned iron	Pt, Au
Cat's fur	Cork, ebony	Celluloid
Ca, Mg, Pb	Amber	India rubber

† From *Smithsonian Tables*, 9th edition.

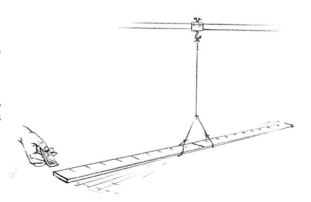

FIG. 36.10. *Demonstrating that electrostatic forces affect many substances.*

end. The attraction between the negative rod and the nearby positive end of the bar is therefore greater than the repulsion between the negative rod and the distant negative end of the bar, and attraction is the net result. If a positively charged rod is brought near, the result is still attraction, for all the signs on the metal bar are reversed. If the suspended bar is not metallic but is made of a so-called non-conductor (such as glass or a plastic), the effects are qualitatively similar, but the explanation has to be changed slightly, for charges do not migrate readily on non-conductors: a displacement of charge within each molecule would still produce the effect (if the charged rod is negative) of an excess of negative charges on the distant end of the bar. I shall discuss this in greater detail when we consider capacitors.

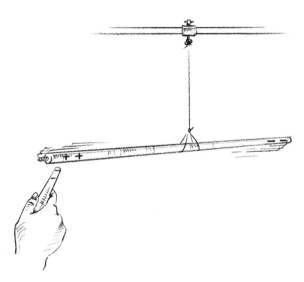

FIG. 36.11. *Attraction of an initially neutral metal bar by a charged rod.*

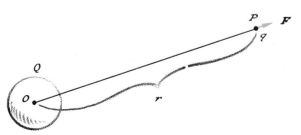

FIG. 36.12. *Illustrating the electric field due to a charge.*

36.4. The Electric Field Due to a Point Charge

We seek an expression (Fig. 36.12) for the field intensity, **E**, at point P, which is at distance r from charge Q, which is localized on a very small object at O (or on a metal sphere with its center at O). We sample the region at P by observing the force, **F**, felt by a small positive charge, q, placed there. The ratio of force **F** to charge q is,† by definition, the electric field intensity at P:

$$\mathbf{E} = \mathbf{F}/q \qquad [36.2$$

If q were a large charge, it would, of course, distort the field due to Q. We demand, therefore, that charge q be so small that its effect on the field of Q is negligible. As q gets smaller, **F** gets smaller in magnitude, but the ratio **F**/q approaches a limit, which is the value of **E** at the point. Since $F = KQq/r^2$, as we know from Coulomb's law,

$$E = \frac{F}{q} = \frac{KQq}{r^2}$$

The magnitude of the field intensity at P due to charge Q is therefore

$$E = \frac{KQ}{r^2} \qquad [36.3$$

We must remember that **E** is a vector, however, and the field due to several charges must be computed vectorially.

EXAMPLE 36.1. Let us compute the electric field intensity (Fig. 36.13) at point P on the perpendicular bisector of the line segment AB joining the two charges $+Q$ and $-Q$; point P is so located that PAB is an equilateral triangle. Imagine a *unit* positive charge at P. (In equation 36.2, if $q = 1$, E is numerically identical with **F**.) The unit charge experiences a repulsion in the direction AP, shown as the vector PC. Its magnitude is KQ/r^2. The effect of $-Q$ at B is a force of attraction pointing from P to B and shown as the vector PD. Its magnitude is also KQ/r^2 since $AP = BP$.

The field intensity at P is the vector sum of PC and PD. Its direction is parallel to AB. Its magni-

† See § 4.4. Division by q is equivalent to multiplication by $1/q$. In Chap. 3 I discussed multiplication of a vector by a scalar. **F**/q is equivalent to **F** $\times 1/q$.

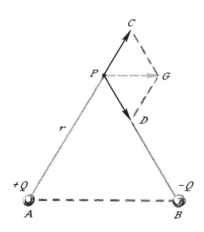

FIG. 36.13. *Illustrating Example 36.1.*

tude (in this special case, in which $AB = BP = PA$) is simply KQ/r^2.

If $Q = 10 \ \mu\text{coul}$ and $r = 0.25$ m,

$$E = \frac{KQ}{r^2} = 9 \times 10^9 \frac{\text{nt-m}^2}{\text{coul}^2} \times \frac{10^{-5} \text{ coul}}{0.0625 \text{ m}^2}$$

$$= \frac{9 \times 10^4}{6.25 \times 10^{-2}} \frac{\text{nt}}{\text{coul}}$$

$$= 1.44 \times 10^6 \frac{\text{nt}}{\text{coul}}$$

The field intensity at any other point can be computed in a similar way. The important thing to remember is that the field intensity is a vector and must be computed by vector addition.

The field lines for several configurations of charge are shown in Figure 36.14. Remember

from § 4.5 (a) that the line tangent to a field line gives the direction of the field intensity vector there; (b) that the density of lines (that is, the number of lines per unit area) is proportional to the magnitude of the field intensity at a point; (c) that the field-intensity vector at any point points in the direction in which a small positive test charge would accelerate if placed at the point.

36.5. The Production of Intense Electrostatic Fields

Machines that produce intense electric fields have always been a scientific curiosity. Today, in the form of Van de Graaff generators, for example, they also serve as useful research tools. I shall explain first the behavior of a much simpler device called the **electrophorus** (Fig. 36.15), for a thorough understanding of how it works can lead to an understanding of the more complicated machines.

The base, B, is a flat plate, made of hard rubber or some other non-conductor, which we charge by rubbing with wool or fur. A thin metal disk, D, to which is attached an insulating handle, H, is brought to rest (A) on B. Since B is a non-conductor, charges do not flow appreciably by conduction from B to D, but induced positive charges appear on the bottom of D, and negative charges appear on the top. (If we raised D by lifting H, the charges would rearrange themselves on D, which would return to its former state of

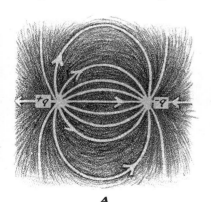

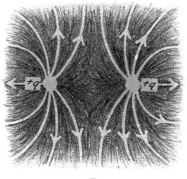

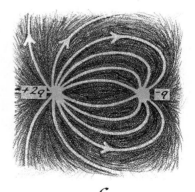

A   *B*   *C*

FIG. 36.14. *Electric field lines for different configurations of charge.*

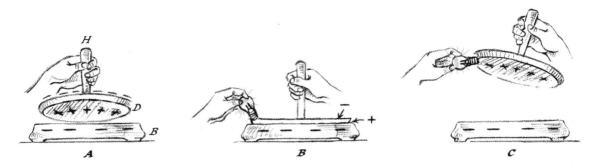

FIG. 36.15. *Charging and discharging an electrophorus through a neon bulb.*

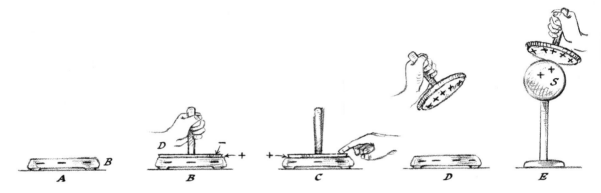

FIG. 36.16. *Charging a metal sphere with a charged electrophorus plate.*

neutrality. If D were then brought near an electroscope, it would not show any signs of being charged.) While D rests on B, we touch (B) one electrode of a neon glow lamp or a small fluorescent bulb to the top of D. We see an instantaneous flash of light in the lamp. We remove the lamp. We lift D, and, when it is several feet above B, we again (C) touch the lamp to the edge of D. The lamp lights up momentarily once more. Resting D again on B, we may repeat the cycle indefinitely, for no charge has been removed from B.

What happened the first time the lamp touched the top of D was that the negative charges flowed through the lamp, making it glow for an instant, and, by way of the operator's hand, to ground. (The electric field intensity between the hand and the electrode that touched D was great enough, even though glass intervened, to separate electrons from neon atoms and thus to make the neon gas a conductor.) That left the positive

charges on the bottom of D still bound by attraction to B. Then, when D was lifted high in the air, the residual positive charges distributed themselves all over it so that it had a net positive charge. The lamp lit up again when touched to D because electrons flowed from ground through the hand to D and in doing so produced a momentary flash of light in the lamp. This neutralized D, and the cycle could start again. The lamp was not needed to charge or discharge D. (Touching with a finger would have worked.) It simply showed that charges were flowing at two different times.

The usual way of employing the electrophorus is as follows (Fig. 36.16):

(A) We charge the base, B, by rubbing it with wool or fur.

(B) We bring disk D down on top of B.

(C) We touch the top of D momentarily.

(D) We lift D a good distance from B. It can

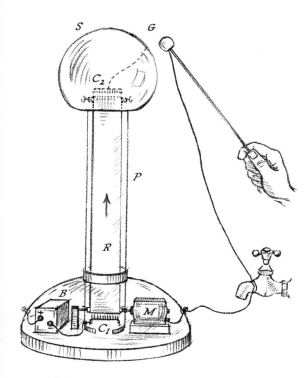

FIG. 36.17. *Schematic representation of a Van de Graaff demonstration generator.*

be brought close to a charged electroscope to show that it has a positive charge.

(E) With *D* we touch a metal sphere, *S*, mounted on an insulating stand. Sometimes we may see and hear a spark jump between *D* and *S*. (A better way to deposit a charge on a sphere, as we shall soon see, is to let the charged body enter the sphere through a hole and touch the interior.) Disk *D* shares its excess charge with *S* by conduction; that is, electrons rush from *S* to *D*, leaving *S* positively charged. Not all of the charge, but, if *S* is large, a great deal of the charge, passes from *D* to *S*.

The process can be repeated over and over again. More charge is deposited on *S* each time, but no charge is taken from *B*. Do we get something for nothing? No. Every time we lift *D* from *B*, we do *work* against electrical forces; we pay for the charge. Since *D* is *attracted* to *B* by electrical forces, we have to use an applied force,

F_a, pointing upward, to work against the electrical attraction. This suggests that the electrical potential energy of the system has been increased by our lifting of *D*. The gravitational potential energy has also been increased, of course, but the net increase in gravitational potential energy during the cycle is zero (see § 27.2).

If we repeat the process many times, the sphere will eventually be so highly charged (positively) that charges will no longer flow readily from *D* to *S*. Further repetitions of the cycle will not add charges to *S*. We can do better by depositing charges on the *interior* of a sphere as follows.

Figure 36.17 is a schematic cut-away view of a Van de Graaff demonstration generator. The interior of a metal sphere, *S*, is connected by wire to the metal comb, C_2, which has fine points on it. The comb collects charges from the conveyor belt, *R*, which, driven by a motor, *M*, runs up and down inside the insulating plastic tube, *P*. The battery, *B*, is not essential, but we can think of it as the source of the charges that are sprayed onto the conveyor belt by the fine points of the lower comb, C_1. As charges begin to accumulate on *S*, it takes work for *R* to move charges *of like sign* up to the region of *S* that is becoming densely populated with charge. The electrical potential energy of the system, therefore, increases as the motor does work by moving these charges up to *S*. By mutual repulsion the charges on *S* spread themselves over its exterior, a fact that we can easily prove by exploring the field around *S* with an electroscope. If a metal ball, *G*, connected to ground is brought near *S*, a large spark may jump between *S* and *G*. For a moment the motor may be heard to speed up. Now that charges have been removed from *S*, it is easy, for a short while, to transport more charges up to *S*; but soon it becomes again increasingly difficult.

Generators of this type are called Van de Graaff generators after their inventor, R. J. Van de Graaff (born in 1901). They are now used in research, within special enclosures, to produce very high voltages for the acceleration of charged atomic particles. "Voltage" is a word I have been using so far rather loosely. It is related to the concept of electrical potential, which I shall discuss in the next chapter.

36.6. Summary

Electrostatics deals with the effects of charges at rest. We can easily produce such charges by rubbing together certain objects, and we can detect them by means of an electroscope.

Atoms normally contain equal quantities of positive and negative charges. A body is therefore normally electrically neutral; but, if electrons are removed from it, it becomes positively charged. If a body possesses an excess of electrons, it is negatively charged.

Bodies with like charges repel and those with unlike charges attract one another. The force between point charges is given by the equation $F = Kq_1q_2/r^2$, known as Coulomb's law. If charge q is in coulombs and distance r is in meters, force F is in newtons if $K = 9 \times 10^9$ nt-m^2/coul^2.

A charged body is surrounded by an electric field whose intensity, $\mathbf{E}$, at a point is, by definition, the force felt by a unit positive charge at that point. The force on charge q is $\mathbf{F} = q\mathbf{E}$.

The field around point charge Q obeys the equation $F = KQ/r^2$. The field can be depicted by field lines. The direction of an electric field at a point is the direction of the field line at that point, and the magnitude of the field at a point can be shown by the density of field lines around the point. Strong electric fields are used in nuclear physics to accelerate charged atomic particles.

Problems

36.1. A charged metal sphere is supported by a vertical insulating rod on a heavy base. It is made to approach a similar but uncharged sphere.

1. Describe verbally and with several diagrams the changes in the charged status of both spheres as the first sphere approaches but does not touch the second.

2. What happens to the charges if the spheres touch and are then separated?

3. Starting as in part 1, suppose that while the spheres were almost touching you momentarily grounded the one that was originally uncharged; if they are subsequently separated, what is the state of charge of each sphere?

36.2. A very fine stream of water coming out of a metal faucet can be deflected by a charged comb. It is attracted whether the comb is positively or negatively charged.

1. Do you think that the stream of water became charged by friction in the pipe? What experiment would you perform to confirm your opinion?

2. Since charged bodies attract electrically only other charged bodies, how would you explain the attraction of the water stream by the comb?

36.3. Two small balls, each of mass 2.8×10^{-4} kg, are attached to opposite ends of a fine insulating thread 0.23 m long. When the thread is supported at its midpoint and the balls are charged with equal positive charges, the electric repulsion causes them to separate until their supporting threads are at right angles to each other. Find the magnitude of the charge on each ball. (Draw a figure.)

36.4. The charge on the balls of Prob. 36.3 leaks off slowly until the angle between the supporting threads is 30°. What fraction of the charge has leaked off?

36.5. A proton is massive and positive; an electron is light and negative. (See "Physical Constants" on the front flyleaf.) They have for each other the gravitational attraction of their masses and also the electrical attraction of their charges.

1. Find the electrical force on an electron at a distance of 5.29×10^{-11} m from a proton.

2. Find the gravitational force at the same distance, and compare it with the electrical force by taking the ratio of the two.

3. What should be the speed of the electron if it is to move in a circle of this radius round a proton under the action of the proton's attractive force? (This is discussed further in Chap. 51.)

36.6. The base, AB, of rectangle $ABCD$ is 4 cm, and the altitude, BC, is 3 cm. A tiny ball is placed at each corner. A positive charge of 1 μcoul is placed on each of the balls at A and B. What should be the magnitude and sign of the charges to be placed on the balls at C and D if the net force on the ball at A is to be zero?

36.7. Two small fixed spheres 15 cm apart bear positive charges in the ratio 2/1.

1. At what point between them would a positively charged sphere be in equilibrium?

2. Answer the same question if one of the fixed spheres is positive and the other negative.

36.8. An oil droplet weighs 2.8×10^{-14} nt and has a charge due to 8 extra electrons. It tends to fall, but an electric field is applied to keep it floating in air. What is the direction, and what is the magnitude in nt/coul, of the electric field?

36.9. The earth is a negatively charged sphere (about 5.7×10^5 coul). Near its surface there is an electric field whose magnitude is about 95 nt/coul. At hundercloud with a positive charge of 20 coul finds itself in this field. What is the direction, and what is the magnitude, of the electrical force on this cloud?

36.10. Electrons move in a metal wire under the action of an electric field, which, in typical cases, is about 0.25 nt/coul. What acceleration would this produce on an electron if it did not also feel some retarding forces?

36.11. In Fig. 36.13 let the line AB, extended, be an x axis with origin at B.

1. Derive a formula for the field intensity at a point, P, on this axis as a function of Q, x, and l (l being the length AB).

2. Derive mathematically the value of x for which the field intensity is zero. Does it check with common sense?

36.12. If, when a grain of puffed rice is resting on an uncharged horizontal metal plate, the disk from a charged electrophorus is brought down parallel to the plate, the rice will jump up and down between the plates. Explain. As a result of many such round trips, what would be the final state of charge of each plate?

Electric Potential
and Capacitance

I HAVE used the word "volt" as a label on mysterious magic boxes called batteries, and the time has come to explain what it means even if I don't explain what makes the batteries work. The volt is the unit of potential difference in the MKS system. To understand it, we must first consider the concept of electric potential energy.

37.1. Electric Potential Energy

If an external applied force has to do work to separate two objects that are under the influence of a conservative force, the potential energy of the system is greater when the objects are separated. In Figure 37.1, for example, two metal spheres on insulating supports at A and B have opposite electrical charges. It requires work to move one sphere from B to C against the electrical pull between the spheres. The electric potential energy of the system is therefore greater after the separation than before. The work in joules required for the separation is the increment in potential energy, ΔU.

Sometimes, when one of the objects is much smaller than the other, we speak of the potential energy of that object when we really mean the potential energy of the system. In Figure 37.2, for example, if Q and q are both positive charges on spherical objects, we say that the potential energy of q is greater at B than at A because it

takes work to move q from A to B while Q remains fixed. The force is $F = KQq/r^2$ if r is the distance between the centers of the spheres. The potential energy of q (more explicitly, of the system comprised of q and Q) is therefore

$$U = \frac{KQq}{r} \qquad [37.1$$

We obtain the result simply by analogy with gravitational potential energy, for which the force equation was $F = GmM/r^2$, the potential energy of m (more explicitly, of the system comprised of m and M) being $U = -GmM/r$ (equation 34.27). We use a positive sign in equation 37.1 because the force between two positive charges is repulsive, not, as with gravity, attractive.†

EXAMPLE 37.1. We wish to find how much work it takes to bring a positive point charge, q, of 1 μcoul from infinity to a point, P, that is 2 m away from a positive point charge, Q, of 100 μcoul.

The potential energy given by equation 37.1 is, *by definition*, the work it takes to bring q from infinity

† The expression KQq/r vanishes when $r = \infty$. I have arbitrarily chosen the point at infinity as the zero of our potential function. This is often convenient in theoretical electrostatics. For practical purposes, however, the surface of the earth is often taken as the arbitrary zero of potential, and electrical conductors are often put "at ground potential" by being connected to a metal pipe driven into the ground.

to a point at distance r from Q. We are given the quantities

$$K = 9 \times 10^9 \frac{\text{nt-m}^2}{\text{coul}^2}$$

$$Q = 100 \times 10^{-6} \text{ coul}$$
$$q = 10^{-6} \text{ coul}$$
$$r = 2 \text{ m}$$

Therefore

$$U = 9 \times 10^9 \frac{\text{nt-m}^2}{\text{coul}^2} \times 10^{-4} \text{ coul} \times \frac{10^{-6} \text{ coul}}{2 \text{ m}}$$

$$= \frac{9}{2} \times 10^{-1} \text{ nt-m}$$

$$= 0.45 \text{ J}$$

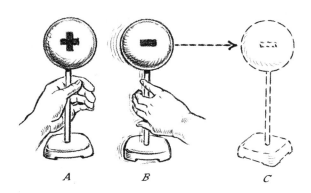

FIG. 37.1. *Illustrating electric potential energy.*

37.2. Electric Potential: Volts

Comparison with a gravitational field (Fig. 37.3) serves another useful purpose. As the force per unit mass is called the gravitational field intensity, $\gamma = \mathbf{F}/m$ (equation 4.9), so the force per unit charge is called the **electric field intensity,** $\mathbf{E} = \mathbf{F}/q$ (equation 4.1). It now becomes convenient to speak of the electric potential energy per unit charge, U/q, and to give it a name. We call it simply the **potential,** V. The potential of the charge q in Figure 37.3.A is therefore

$$V = \frac{U}{q} \qquad [37.2$$

The unit for electric potential is obviously the joule/coulomb, and this unit is called the **volt** (in honor of Alessandro Volta, Italian physicist, 1745–1827). *Volts are joules per coulomb.*

Differences in potential, as in gravitational problems, are of interest to us.

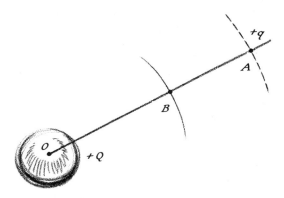

FIG. 37.2. *Illustrating electric potential energy.*

EXAMPLE 37.2. We wish to find the difference in potential, expressed in volts, between points A and B of Fig. 37.2 if $OA = 2$ m, $OB = 1.5$ m, and $Q = 100$ μcoul.

The potential at A is

$$V_A = \frac{U_A}{q} = \frac{KQ}{r_A} \qquad [37.3$$

Similarly, the potential at B is

$$V_B = \frac{KQ}{r_B}$$

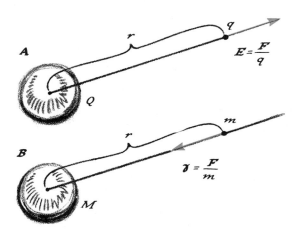

FIG. 37.3. *Comparison of electric (A) and gravitational (B) fields.*

The difference in potential, ΔV, is

$$\Delta V = V_B - V_A = \frac{KQ}{r_B} - \frac{KQ}{r_A}$$

$$= KQ\left(\frac{1}{r_B} - \frac{1}{r_A}\right)$$

$$= 9\times10^9 \frac{\text{nt-m}^2}{\text{coul}^2} \times 10^{-4}\ \text{coul} \times \left(\frac{1}{1.5} - \frac{1}{2.0}\right)\text{m}^{-1}$$

$$= 9(0.166)\frac{\text{nt-m}}{\text{coul}}$$

$$= 1.494\ \text{J/coul}$$

$$= 1.494\ \text{V}$$

A practical electrician carries a *voltmeter* around with him. To measure the potential difference between two wires, for example, he simply connects one terminal of his meter to one wire and the other terminal to the other wire; the needle on the meter then points to a number on a scale calibrated in volts. For him volts have operational meaning in terms of meter readings, and he would probably be surprised to learn of such an abstract definition of the volt as the one that led to equation 37.2. Whether he knows it or not, his voltmeter was calibrated against some standard that defined the volt by that equation.†

Notice that in the last example we sought the potential difference between two *points*. This is abstract indeed. The electrician could not connect his voltmeter to two mathematical points. Yet this abstraction permits the following definition of the **volt**: *There is a potential difference of one volt between the two points* A *and* B *if it requires one joule of work to transport one coulomb of electricity from* A *to* B *(or from* B *to* A*) against the force of an electric field.*

A practical criterion is this: if electric charges have a tendency to flow between two points, there is, very likely,‡ a difference in potential between them. In some cases a spark may jump between two points and thus indicate the existence of a potential difference. When (Fig. 37.4)

† It is also true that many voltmeters are calibrated against standard cells whose potential difference is *defined* as a certain voltage. How this numerical value of potential difference is chosen will not be explained here. The explanation would probably be just as perplexing to our practical electrician, although he would find it easier to start with a given cell as a standard of potential difference.
‡ For an exceptional case, see Fig. 41.12.

one end, *C*, of a stiff, curved, metal rod held by an insulating handle is allowed to touch the sphere, *B*, of a charged Van de Graaff generator (which has been turned off) while the other end, *D*, comes near a water faucet, *F*, a spark may be seen to jump between *D* and *F*. The fact that charges were able to flow between *D* and *F* is proof that *B* and *F* were initially at different potentials. The potential difference between them, in volts, is the work it takes to transport one coulomb from one to the other. If the Van de Graaff generator is not running, *B* and *F* will be at the same potential soon after *D* touches *F*. There will no longer be a tendency for charges to flow. This is characteristic of static charges residing on two different conductors. After they have been joined by a conductor, the potential difference between them vanishes.

Consider, now, an example of a different kind. A potential difference may be found (Fig. 37.5) between a house wire, *B*, and a cold-water pipe, *A*. A voltmeter connected across them may read

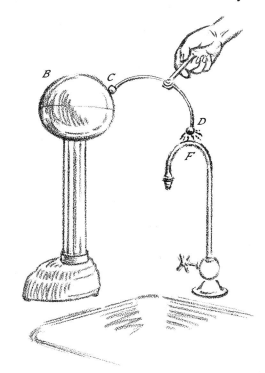

FIG. 37.4. *Demonstrating the presence of a potential difference.*

110 volts, a common potential difference in house wiring. You may discover that an electric light bulb, *L*, lights up if a wire connected to one of its terminals is connected (through a screwdriver with an insulating handle) to *A* while the other is connected to *B*. But this time the lamp stays lit, indicating that the flow of charges does not cease after the first contact. The light is proof that there is a difference in potential between *A* and *B*, but something must maintain that difference while charges flow. That something may be a battery or a generator. Whatever it is, it has to keep replenishing the charge.

It might be very dangerous—in fact, lethal—for you to touch points A *and* B *simultaneously with the hands.* Yet, though the potential difference between the sphere of the Van de Graaff generator and the faucet (Fig. 37.4) might be 10,000 volts or more, touching it and the faucet simultaneously, though it would shock you, would probably not be lethal, for the potential difference between *B* and *F* would be brought to zero so quickly that the total amount of charge carried through your body would not be very great.

Even within a wire there may be a potential difference. Charges will not ordinarily flow in the wire unless there is a potential difference between two different points in the wire. (We have already noted an exceptional case, illustrated in Fig. 41.12.) We can say something similar about electric fields: if there were no electric field within a wire, charges within the wire would not feel a force ($F = qE$). In a completely static case, however, the excess charge (if there is one) resides on the exterior of the wire, and there is no field within.

Whether two points are out in space or within a wire, the potential difference between them is one volt if one joule of work is done (by electrostatic forces) when one coulomb of charge flows from one point to the other. It is equally correct to say that the potential difference is one volt if it takes one joule of work to transport one coulomb from one point to the other against the direction of the electric force on the charge. The potential difference of equation 37.2 can cause work, *W*, to be done such that

$$W = qV \qquad [37.4$$

Here *W* is in joules if *q* is in coulombs and *V* is in volts.

EXAMPLE 37.3. An electric toaster operates for 10 min at its rated potential difference of 115 V, dissipating 500 W in the form of heat. We wish to know how many coulombs flow through it in this interval.

A watt is a joule per second. Therefore

$$W = 500 \, \frac{\text{J}}{\text{sec}} \times 600 \text{ sec} = 3 \times 10^5 \text{ J}$$

When a charge, *q*, is transported across potential difference *V*, the work done is *qV*. Therefore

$$qV = 3 \times 10^5 \text{ J}$$
$$q = \frac{3 \times 10^5 \text{ J}}{115 \text{ V}}$$
$$= \frac{3 \times 10^5 \text{ J}}{1.15 \times 10^2 \text{ J/coul}}$$
$$= 2.61 \times 10^3 \text{ coul}$$

37.3. Lines of Force

In Chapter 4 we saw that the electric field intensity, **E**, considered as a vector field, can be represented by lines of force; that the direction of **E** at a point is simply the direction of the straight line that is tangent to the line of force

FIG. 37.5. *The lighting of the lamp,* L, *demonstrates the presence of a potential difference between* B *and* A.

at the point; and that the strength of the field can be indicated by the density of the lines. Let us make this concept quantitative by assuming that the number of lines of force per unit area is numerically equal to the magnitude of the electric field intensity. If the number of lines of force that pass perpendicularly through area A (Fig. 37.6) is equal to the magnitude, Φ_E, of the **electric flux,** we write

$$E = \frac{\Phi_E}{A} \qquad [37.5$$

Let us now deduce how many lines to ascribe to one coulomb. Imagine a charge, Q, at the center of a sphere of radius r (Fig. 37.7). From Coulomb's law we know that $E = F/q = KQ/r^2$. Setting this equal to the E of equation 37.5, we have

$$\frac{\Phi_E}{A} = \frac{KQ}{r^2} \qquad [37.6$$

The total number of lines crossing the sphere is equal to the magnitude of $(KQ/r^2)A$. Since $A = 4\pi r^2$ (the surface area of a sphere),

$$\Phi_E = 4\pi KQ \qquad [37.7$$

This tells us that the number of lines of force we must associate with each coulomb is equal to $4\pi K$. An examination of the field lines of Figure 37.7 and an extension of the logic associated with equation 37.5 lead to the following useful rules for charged bodies of any shape or distribution of charge: (1) The total number of lines leaving a body of total charge Q is numerically equal to

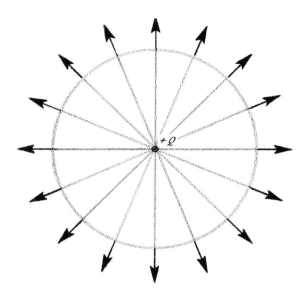

FIG. 37.7. *Field lines radiate in all directions from charge* Q. *We associate* 4πK *lines with each coulomb.*

$4\pi KQ$. (2) Lines of force are continuous; they start and stop only on charges (except in cases like that of Fig. 41.12), or else they travel to infinity. (3) If lines of force crossed, E would have two different directions at a point; therefore lines of force never cross. Let us use these rules to find the field intensity in three useful special cases.

First, consider a uniformly charged sphere with the total charge Q. At point P, which is at distance r from the center of the sphere, we find E by using the equation $E = \Phi_E/A$. If we take Φ_E as equal to $4\pi KQ$, by rule 1, and let A equal $4\pi r^2$, we get

$$E = \frac{KQ}{r^2}$$

This proves that the charged sphere behaves like a single charge concentrated at its center. This is the problem that took Newton twenty years to solve (for the gravitational case). What made our solution simple was that we assumed symmetry of the lines in all directions.

Second, to prove that the excess charge resides on the outside of a current-free conductor, we need to show that the field inside such a conductor is zero. If it were not zero, there would be a field, **E**, which would exert a force, $-e\mathbf{E}$, on each

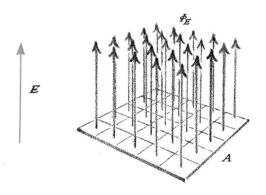

FIG. 37.6. *The number of lines of force per unit area,* Φ_E/A, *is numerically equal to the magnitude of the average electric field intensity,* E.

free electron, and then, contrary to our assumption, there would be current. If there were any excess charge, q, inside the conductor, there would be $4\pi Kq$ lines of force leaving it. But that would be a field, and we proved above that there is no field inside a current-free conductor. Hence any excess charge must reside on the outside of a conductor. This fact is used in the design of the Van de Graaff generator (§ 36.5). Charges are deposited on the inside of the sphere, but they quickly migrate by mutual repulsion to the outside of the sphere.

Third, suppose that a flat metal plate (Fig. 37.8) has a uniform surface-charge density, σ (measured in coul/m²). From each square meter emanate $4\pi K\sigma$ lines. Of these, $2\pi K\sigma$ go to the left, and $2\pi K\sigma$ go to the right. Since the field strength, E, is numerically equal to the number of lines per square meter, $E = 2\pi K\sigma$.

The field between two close and parallel uniformly charged plates of opposite sign (Fig. 37.9) can now be computed. In this case all the excess charges are to be found on the inside surfaces. If the charge density is σ, the number of lines per square meter leaving the positive plate is $4\pi K\sigma$ and is exactly equal to the number of lines per square meter landing on the negative plate. The total field intensity, E, at point P between the plates is therefore $4\pi K\sigma$.

The force felt by charge q between the plates is $F = qE$. The work done in carrying this charge from one plate to the other is Fd if d is the separation between the plates. Hence

$$W = Fd = q4\pi K\sigma d$$

The work per unit charge is therefore

$$\frac{W}{q} = 4\pi K\sigma d$$

This defines the **potential difference**, V, between the plates:

$$V = 4\pi K\sigma d \qquad [37.8$$

Let us now express σ as the total charge, Q, on one plate divided by the surface area, A; that is, $\sigma = Q/A$. Putting this into equation 37.8, we get

$$V = \frac{4\pi KQd}{A} \qquad [37.9$$

The ratio of charge to potential difference (soon to be called the capacitance) may be written as

$$\frac{Q}{V} = \frac{A}{4\pi Kd} \qquad [37.10$$

For the time being we observe that Q/V is a constant if A and d are constant. We can increase V by increasing the charge on the plates, but equation 37.10 says that the ratio Q/V is constant for a fixed pair of parallel plates.

Such a combination of plates is called a **capacitor**. Capacitors are used by the score in radio, television, and other electronic gear. Let us see why.

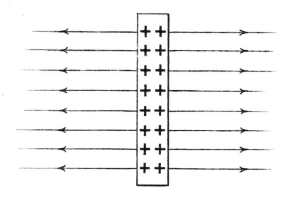

FIG. 37.8. *Electric field intensity in the vicinity of a flat metal plate with a charge of uniform density.*

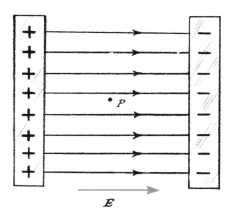

FIG. 37.9. *Electric field intensity between two parallel and uniformly charged plates of opposite sign.*

37.4. Capacitors, or Condensers

We can start with only one of two flat plates charged and end with a field between the two plates as follows (Fig. 37.10): Let *A* be a flat, positively charged metal plate with an insulating handle, and let a similar but uncharged plate, *B*, be connected to ground (A). When *A* is brought close to *B*, electrons migrate to *B* through the wire (B) by the attraction of the positive charges on *A*. A negative charge is thereby induced on *B*. The closer *A* is brought to *B*, the greater the number of negative charges that flow through the wire. The combination apparently has the ability to condense charges and was therefore originally called a **condenser.** The term has an instructive suggestiveness about it, but hereafter, in accordance with modern usage, we shall use the term **capacitor.** In the sense that it can store a greater charge, it becomes a better capacitor as the distance between the plates decreases and as the area of the plates increases.

A capacitor stores electricity somewhat as a pressure tank stores air. A capacitor whose plates are large or close together is said to have a large capacitance. It corresponds to a large tank. As air is pumped into a tank, the pressure goes up. If the tank is large, you can pump a lot of air into it without changing the pressure very much. A capacitor with great capacitance has an analogous property. You can add a large amount of charge to it without changing the potential difference between the plates very much. A small amount of charge can change appreciably the potential difference between the plates of a capacitor with a small capacitance. *The ratio of the quantity of electricity on one of the plates to the potential difference between the plates is called the* **capacitance** *of the capacitor.* The defining equa-

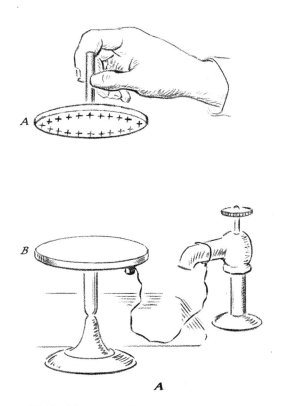

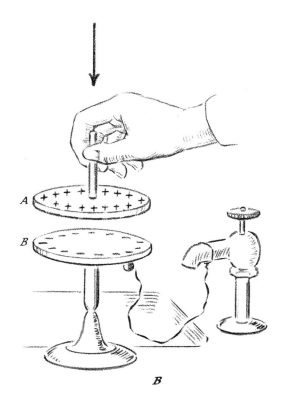

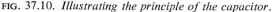

FIG. 37.10. *Illustrating the principle of the capacitor.*

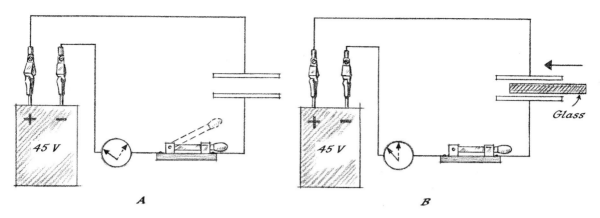

FIG. 37.11. *One way to increase the capacitance of a capacitor.*

tion for capacitance is, then,

$$C = \frac{Q}{V} \qquad [37.11$$

It can be shown that the charge on one plate of a parallel-plate capacitor with two plates is numerically equal to the charge (of opposite sign) on the other plate.

Equation 37.10, therefore, gives the capacitance of a parallel-plate capacitor:

$$C = \frac{Q}{V} = \frac{A}{4\pi Kd} \qquad [37.12$$

This confirms the qualitative statements about the effect of area and separation made in connection with Figure 37.10. The capacitance goes up linearly with the area and is inversely proportional to the distance between the plates.

The unit of capacitance is the **farad**, named after Michael Faraday (1791–1867).† *If a charge of one coulomb produces a potential difference of one volt across its plates, a capacitor is said to have a capacitance of one farad.* (It is customary not to abbreviate or symbolize "farad.")

EXAMPLE 37.4. A parallel-plate capacitor consists of two square plates, each 10 cm × 10 cm, separated by a distance of 1 mm. We wish to find its capacitance and to find the charge carried by one

---

† Faraday, one of ten children of a London blacksmith, began as an assistant in the Royal Institution and became its director. He discovered the laws of electrolysis and electromagnetism.

of the plates if the pair is connected to a 45-V battery. In this case the battery determines what the final potential difference will be, and charges will accumulate on the plates in accordance with equation 37.11.

Having tabulated what we know as

$$A = 0.1 \times 0.1 = 10^{-2}\,\text{m}^2$$
$$d = 1\,\text{mm} = 10^{-3}\,\text{m}$$
$$V = 45\,\text{V}$$

we see that

$$C = \frac{A}{4\pi Kd} = \frac{10^{-2}\,\text{m}^2}{4\pi \times 9\times10^9\,\text{nt-m}^2/\text{coul}^2 \times 10^{-3}\,\text{m}}$$

$$= 8.85\times10^{-10}\,\frac{\text{coul}^2}{\text{J}}$$

$$= 8.85\times10^{-10}\,\text{farad}$$

Our answer could also be written as

$$C = 885\,\mu\mu\text{farad}$$

The farad is a very large unit of capacitance. The microfarad (μfarad) and the micromicrofarad ($\mu\mu$farad) are used extensively in electronics.

To find the charge on one plate, we write

$$C = Q/V$$
$$Q = CV$$
$$= 8.85\times10^{-10}\,\text{farad} \times 45\,\text{V}$$
$$= 3.98\times10^{-8}\,\text{coul}$$

We can charge the capacitor of this example by connecting it to a 45-V battery through a sensitive galvanometer and a switch (Fig. 37.11). (A **galvanometer** is a very sensitive device for showing the presence of a current. If it were calibrated, it would be called an **ammeter** or a microam-

TABLE 37.1
Relative Dielectric Constants

Glass	from 4 to 9
Mica	5.8
Oiled paper	2.0
Paraffin	2.3
Quartz	4.4
Rutile (a form of titanium oxide)	100
Water	81
Alcohol	26
Oil	from 3 to 6
Polystyrene	2.6

meter.) If the capacitor was initially uncharged, the galvanometer, when the switch is closed (A), gives a momentary reading while charges flow through it to the capacitor. As soon as the capacitor is charged, the flow ceases. The total charge that flows is governed by the formula $Q = CV$. The only ways to get more charge to flow are to increase the capacitance, C, of the capacitor and to use a battery, or other source, of greater potential difference, V. It is an experimental fact that, if a piece of glass is slipped between the plates without touching either of them (B), the galvanometer indicates a flow while the glass is being moved in. Somehow, the glass increases the capacitance of the capacitor. With the glass in place, the same combination of plates at the same distance can store more charges at the same potential difference. (This will be explained in the next section.)

If the capacitance with the glass in place is C' and that without it is C, and if all other factors remain fixed, the ratio C'/C will be somewhere between 4 and 9. If mica is used instead of glass, to produce capacitance C'', the ratio C''/C is about 5.8. This number is called the relative dielectric constant of mica. In general, the **relative dielectric constant** of a substance is the factor by which we can increase the capacitance of a capacitor by substituting this substance for air—or, rather, strictly speaking, for empty space. (Air, which is easily ionized even in a weak field,

suffers a "breakdown" and lets sparks jump from one plate to the next as the voltage increases.)

Table 37.1 gives the relative dielectric constants of various materials. The materials listed are all **dielectrics.** They do not conduct electricity readily (distilled water becomes a conductor, however, as soon as impurities, even in minute quantity, enter it). In order to understand, at least qualitatively, why insulators have high dielectric constants, we must investigate the phenomenon of polarization.

37.5. Polarization

When a substance is placed in an electric field, E, every single electric charge, q, within it experiences the force $q\mathbf{E}$; positive charges are pulled in the direction of **E**, and negative charges are pulled in the opposite direction. Whether the charges move depends upon the substance, and the motion itself depends on the strength of the field and the time during which it acts. In metals there are many so-called free electrons that can travel over macroscopic distances within the sample. The atoms of dielectrics, compared with those of metals, have so few free electrons that they are virtually non-conductors, or insulators. The molecules of a dielectric bear positive and negative charges, of course, and each of these experiences a force when the dielectric is placed in a field, but only a slight separation of the charges within each molecule takes place. The effect is called **polarization.** Mobility is limited to molecular dimensions.

The relative ability of a material to conduct electricity is known as its **conductivity,** a quantity that will not be defined strictly until Chapter 40. For the present, all we need to know is that good conductors have high conductivity and that poor conductors have low conductivity, or—what amounts to the same thing—high resistivity. **Resistivity,** the inverse of conductivity, is also treated in Chapter 40. Table 37.2 lists the resistivities of a number of different substances for comparison.

When (Fig. 37.12) an uncharged slab of glass, G, is placed between the charged plates, A and B, of a capacitor, there is no migration of electrons, but the effect of the charge separation induced by the field is a net accumulation of polarization charges on the upper and lower faces of G.

Let us see how this works with the apparatus of Figure 37.13. When, the slab of glass being absent, the switch is closed (A), charges flow through the galvanometer and to the plates of the capacitor until the potential difference across the plates is the same as that of the charging battery. The galvanometer then reads zero. When the glass, G, is brought between the plates (B), polarization charges appear as shown. The appearance of positive polarization charges close to the negative charges on plate B weakens the resultant repulsive electrostatic force, and more electrons can therefore come from the battery to

reside on the plate. The capacitance of the combination has thereby been increased.

Another way to look at it is this: Consider the effect of the polarization charges on the field between the plates; they bring into existence a new component of field, E', but it points in the direction opposite to that of the original field, E. The vector resultant of these two fields is weaker than the original. Only if more charges flow onto the plates will the resultant field be brought up to the strength of the original field, a change that is required by the fact that the potential difference across the plates is kept unchanged. However you look at it, the capacitance of the capacitor, since $C = Q/V$, has been increased. The dielectric constant is therefore directly related to the polarizability of the dielectric substance.

Capacitors connected to one another possess a certain joint capacitance, which can be easily deduced for two special cases—capacitors in parallel and capacitors in series. The capacitance of a combination is just Q/V, as for a single capacitor. In this case Q is the total charge stored, and V is the potential difference across the terminals of the combination. Figure 37.14.A shows three capacitors connected in parallel with one another;

TABLE 37.2

Resistivity, ρ, in Ohm-meters† at 20°C

Aluminum	0.282×10^{-7}
Brass (Cu 66%, Zn 34%)	0.719×10^{-7}
Carbon at 0°C	349×10^{-7}
Carbon at 500°C	270×10^{-7}
Copper, annealed	0.172×10^{-7}
Lead	22.2×10^{-7}
Mercury	96.2×10^{-7}
Silver	0.162×10^{-7}
Sealing wax	8×10^{13}
Hard rubber	from about 10^{13} to 10^{16}
Glass	about 9×10^{11}
Paraffin oil	about 10^{14}
Distilled water	5×10^{3}
Aqueous sodium chloride solution, 10% by weight	8.33×10^{-2}

† The ohm is defined in § 40.3.

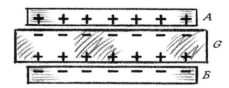

FIG. 37.12. *A flat glass plate, G, originally uncharged, is moved into the region between two charged metal plates, A and B. Induced charges appear on the surface of G.*

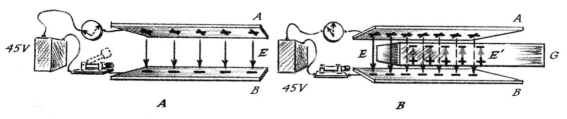

FIG. 37.13. *How glass, used as the dielectric, increases the capacitance of a capacitor.*

the potential differences of the different capacitors are the same, and the total charge is additive. Figure 37.14.B shows three capacitors in series; the charge on any one capacitor is the same as the charge on any other, but the potential differences are such that $V_1 + V_2 + V_3 = V$. From these facts it may be deduced that the capacitance of the capacitors in parallel is

$$C = C_1 + C_2 + C_3 \qquad [37.13$$

whereas that of the capacitors in series obeys the equation

$$\frac{1}{C} = \frac{1}{C_1} + \frac{1}{C_2} + \frac{1}{C_3} \qquad [37.14$$

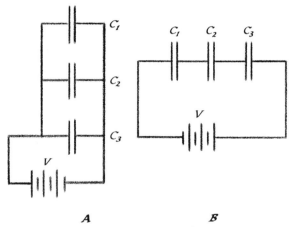

FIG. 37.14. (A) Three capacitors connected in parallel; the potential difference across C_1 is the same as that across C_2 and C_3. (B) The same capacitors connected in series; the charge on C_1 is the same as that on C_2 and C_3.

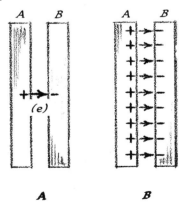

FIG. 37.15. Illustrating the storage of energy by a capacitor.

37.6. The Energy Stored in a Capacitor

Imagine two uncharged capacitor plates, A and B (Fig. 37.15). Since there is no field between them, it would take no work at first (A) to transport an electron from A to B; but, as more electrons are transported (B), making A positive and B negative, the developing field makes the transport harder. Suppose that a total charge, Q, eventually builds up a potential difference, V, across the plates. We know that it takes an amount of work equal to QV to carry charge Q across an established potential difference V; but, since the potential in the experiment started at zero and ended at V, its average value was $V/2$. Hence the work stored in a capacitor is $QV/2$. The units (equation 37.2) check:

$$\text{coul} \times \frac{J}{\text{coul}} = J$$

The basic formula is therefore

$$U = \tfrac{1}{2}QV \qquad [37.15$$

Since $C = Q/V$, this may also be written as

$$U = \frac{1}{2}\frac{Q^2}{C} \qquad [37.16$$

and

$$U = \tfrac{1}{2}CV^2 \qquad [37.17$$

Capacitors of many different kinds are used in electronic work today (Fig. 37.16).

37.7. Summary

The potential energy of a system consisting of charges Q and q, separated by distance r, is $U = KQq/r$. This is equal to the work required to bring charge q from infinity to a point at distance r from Q.

Electric potential energy per unit charge is called simply potential. It is measured in joules per coulomb, or volts. If a potential difference of one volt exists between two points, it takes one joule of work to transport one coulomb of electricity from one point to the other.

It is convenient to imagine $4\pi K$ lines emanating from each charge of one coulomb.

A capacitor is a device that can store electric

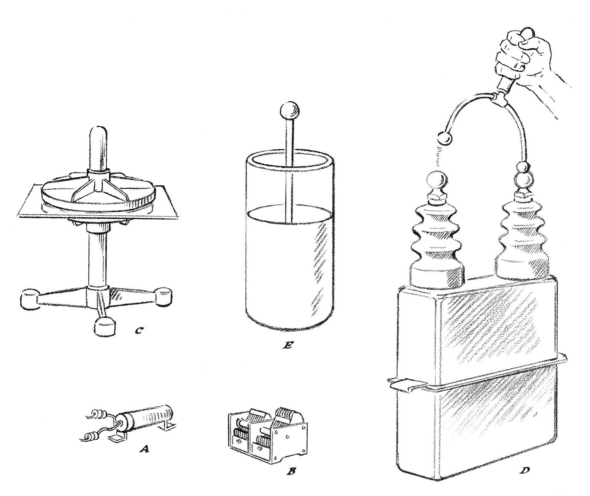

FIG. 37.16. *Capacitors: (A) A small capacitor, of a few μμfarads, made of metal foil and paper. (B) A variable capacitor (like those used in radios) in which the dielectric is air. (C) A laboratory capacitor consisting of two large disks, one on an insulating stand and the other with an insulating handle. (D) A large high-voltage capacitor, used in x-ray work and radio transmission. (E) A Leyden jar, consisting of two metal cylinders separated by glass (see Prob. 37.12).*

charges at rest. The capacitance of such a device is the ratio of the charge to the potential difference across it. The simplest capacitor consists of two parallel conducting plates separated by a dielectric. Its capacitance is proportional to the area of the plates and inversely proportional to the separation between them. If the dielectric is air or a vacuum, we can increase its capacitance by putting a dielectric like glass or mica between the plates. The increase in capacitance depends upon the fact that polarization charges appear on a dielectric when it is placed in an electric field.

The capacitance of several capacitors in parallel is simply the sum of the separate capacitances. The capacitance of several capacitors in series is always smaller than the smallest capacitance in the set; it is the reciprocal of the sum of their reciprocals.

Problems

37.1. An electron (charge $-e = 1.6 \times 10^{-19}$ coul) is released from rest close to the negative plate of a parallel-plate capacitor charged to a potential difference of 2×10^4 V. The distance between the two plates is 1 cm.

1. Compute the electric force to which the electron is subjected.

2. If the acceleration were constant, how much time would the electron take to reach the positive plate? (The mass of the electron is 0.9×10^{-30} kg.)

3. Does the assumption of constant acceleration lead to a final speed that exceeds the speed of light? Explain.

37.2. What is the intensity of the field between the two plates of a capacitor (dielectric: air) when the charge on it is 556×10^{-9} coul. The plates are two circular disks of radius 10 cm.

37.3. A parallel-plate capacitor (dielectric: air) is charged as in Fig. 37.11.A; the switch is then opened, and a sheet of paraffin that fits between but does not touch the plates is introduced as the glass is introduced in Fig. 37.11.B (but with the switch open). Find the ratio of the potential differences before and after this operation. The relative dielectric constant of paraffin is 2.3.

37.4. We have three identical capacitors (capacitance: C), for each of which the maximum supportable difference of potential is V.

1. Prove that, whether the capacitors are combined in series or in parallel, the maximum energy is constant.

2. Compute that maximum energy in terms of C and V.

37.5. Two capacitors of capacitance $C_1 = 2$ μfarads and $C_2 = 5$ μfarads are charged to potential differences of 200 V and 120 V, respectively.

1. Compute the charge on each and their total energy.

2. They are connected in parallel. Compute the new capacitance and (supposing that the total charge remains unmodified) the new potential difference between the plates.

3. Deduce the new energy of the system.

4. Account for the difference between the total energy preceding and that following the connection.

37.6. The separation between the plates of a parallel-plate capacitor is 1 mm. What must be the area of the plates if the dielectric between them is glass (relative dielectric constant: 5) and if we want a capacitance of 1 farad? Compare this area with that of a typical airport.

37.7. When two capacitors are connected in series with each other and with a battery, the charge on one is the same as the charge on the other. To make this plausible, draw a diagram and explain the distribution of charge that must take place at the plates that are connected to each other when the system is connected to a battery. (Where do these central plates get their charges?)

37.8. 1. Observing that the equation $U = KQq/r$ may be written as $U = (KQq/r^2)(r)$, prove that U has the dimensions ML^2T^{-2}, which are the dimensions of work or energy.

2. In Fig. 37.1 let the charges on the spheres be $+10$ μcoul and -10 μcoul. Compute U_1, the energy of the system composed of A and B separated by 10 cm, and U_2, the energy of the system composed of A and C separated by 15 cm. Find ΔU, the increment in the potential energy of the system.

3. Draw the field lines for both cases. Do you see why Faraday imagined that they behaved like rubber bands that it took work to stretch?

37.9. A metal sphere with a charge of 500 μcoul is placed with its center at one corner of a square whose side is 25 cm long. Going clockwise, little spheres with charges of 1, 2, and 3 μcoul are brought in and placed at the other corners. What is the potential energy of the system? (Hint: Work is a scalar. Potential energies may be added algebraically. Compute the work it takes to bring in one charge at a time from infinity.)

37.10. A lamp is marked 125 V, 50 W.

1. What do these marks mean?

2. How much work does it take to transport 1 coul of charge from one terminal of the lamp to the other when it is in operation?

3. How many joules will be transformed from electric potential energy into heat energy within such a lamp in 1 min?

Good

4. How many coulombs of charge pass through the lamp in this time?

5. Since amp = coul/sec, what is the current through the lamp?

37.11. Figure 36.17 illustrates the role of the belt in transporting charges within a Van de Graaff generator. In 1 min the motor performs 50 J of work lifting charge up to the already charged sphere. (This work is in addition to that done against friction.) The sphere is thus kept at an average potential of about 200,000 V above ground potential.

1. How much electric charge is delivered per minute (and lost by the sphere through leakage to the air)?

2. What is the current conveyed by the belt to the sphere?

37.12. Figure 37.16.E shows a modern version of a Leyden jar, an early type of capacitor. It consists of two cylindrical conductors separated by a glass cylinder. Compute the approximate capacitance of a Leyden jar whose inside metal cylinder has a radius of 6 cm and a height of 20 cm. Assume that the glass is 0.2 cm thick and has a relative dielectric constant of 5. (Hint: Imagine the cylinder cut and flattened out into a rectangle to compute its area. Use the formula for a parallel-plate capacitor. Don't forget to add the area of the base.)

37.13. The capacitor shown in Fig. 37.16.C is commonly used for laboratory and demonstration work. It can safely withstand a potential difference of 5,000 V. What is the charge stored at that voltage if the diameter of the disks is 18 cm and the mica between them is 0.4 mm thick?

37.14. A parallel-plate capacitor with air between the plates is charged to a potential difference of 750 V, after which both plates are left insulated. A flat plate of plastic, inserted so that it practically fills the gap, causes the potential difference across the capacitor to decrease to 125 V.

1. What is the dielectric constant of the plastic?

2. In a second experiment the first capacitor is connected to a battery across whose terminals there is a potential difference of 750 V. If the charge stored with air between the plates is 500 μcoul, what is the extra charge that moves onto one of the plates when the dielectric plate is moved in while the capacitor remains connected to the battery?

37.15. The capacitors of Fig. 37.14 have capacitance 1, 2, and 3 $\mu\mu$farads. They are connected to a 6-V battery.

1. Find the charge stored in each individual capacitor in both cases.

2. Find the total energy stored in each system.

37.16. If all the energy stored in a huge capacitor could be discharged through a special heating coil placed in a bathtub, the 150 kg of water in it could be raised in temperature by 30°C.

1. If the potential difference across the capacitor were 1,000 V, what would its capacitance have to be?

2. Does this seem like a reasonable way to heat a tub of water quickly?

38

Interactions Between Magnetic Fields and Moving Electric Charges

WE HAVE seen on several occasions (in § 35.3, for example) that a stream of electrons is deflected if it moves at right angles to a magnetic field. More generally, if the motion of the electrons has a component at right angles to the magnetic field, the electrons will be deflected. To deal with this effect quantitatively, we need to know the direction and magnitude of the deflecting force.

38.1. Effect of a Magnetic Field on a Stream of Electrons

The electrons in the cathode-ray tube of Figure 38.1.A land at P when the permanent magnet is not in place, at P' when the magnet is in place. The invisible magnetic field is here depicted by lines flowing from the N pole to the S pole of the magnet. Let us call the field intensity **B** It is a vector pointing from right to left. I have not yet defined **B** quantitatively; but, taking a hint from our experience with gravitational and elec-

tric fields, let us, for the time being, use the convention that the number of field lines perpendicular to a unit area is a measure of the magnitude of **B**. (A similar convention can be made for gravitational fields.) If Φ_B stands for the **magnetic flux** (Fig. 38.1.B), meaning the total number of **B** lines that cross area A perpendicularly, we shall assume that

$$B = \frac{\Phi_B}{A} \qquad [38.1$$

The unit for magnetic flux is called the weber after W. E. Weber, a German physicist (1804–1891). So far, then, **B** is in webers per square meter. In other words, a weber is a line. (I shall soon show that **B** can also be measured in newtons per ampere-meter.)

The direction of the force that acts on the stream of electrons in Figure 38.1.A can be remembered by reference to the hand in the figure. If the thumb of the left hand points in the direction of the electron flow (the right hand can be used for a flow of positive charges), and if the fingers of the left hand point in the direction of **B**, the thrust acting on the electrons points upward. This is easy to remember because the hand is in a position to push upward, as shown.

The force, **F**, acting on a body of charge q moving with velocity **v** is, as we know,

$$\mathbf{F} = q(\mathbf{v} \times \mathbf{B}) \qquad [38.2$$

This is the familiar vector product (§ 33.2 and § 35.3). The vectors **v** and **B** need not be perpendicular to each other, but **F** is perpendicular to the plane determined by **v** and **B**. If q is positive, a right-handed screw will move in the direction of **F** as **v** is turned through the smaller angle, θ, between **v** and **B**. If q is negative, as it is when the charged particles are electrons, the force has the direction of $-(\mathbf{v} \times \mathbf{B})$ (Fig. 38.1.C). As a reminder, Figure 38.2 shows a mason jar with a screw top. If this top is turned as shown, it moves *down*, the direction of $\mathbf{v} \times \mathbf{B}$ in Figure 38.1.C. Hence the electrons of this figure feel an *upward* force. So much for the direction.

The magnitude of the force acting on the stream of electrons is proportional to the speed of the electrons and to the intensity of the magnetic field. (I shall soon, in fact, *define* the intensity of a magnetic field accordingly.)

The magnitude of

$$\mathbf{F} = q(\mathbf{v} \times \mathbf{B})$$

is simply

$$qvB \sin \theta$$

Figure 38.1 illustrates a case in which $\theta = 90°$. For this case F reduces to qvB.

In Figure 38.1.A we disregarded the effect of the earth's magnetic field. This is justified if the axis of the tube is parallel to that field. In that case there is no component of electron motion at right angles to the earth's magnetic field and hence no force on the electron due to the earth's field. But, if we deliberately place the tube's axis at right angles to the earth's magnetic field, we can even determine the strength of that field by

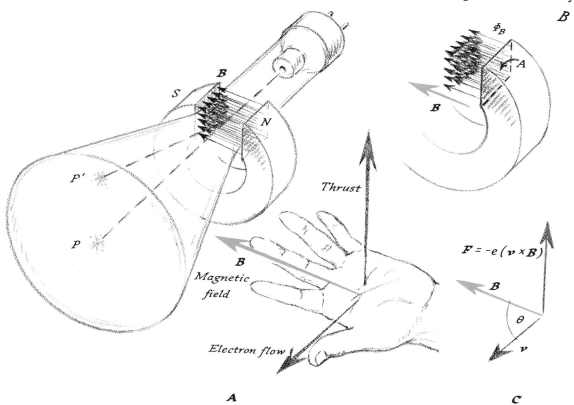

FIG. 38.1. *Illustrating the effect of a magnetic field on a stream of electrons.*

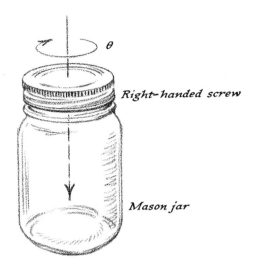

FIG. 38.2. *If the top of a mason jar is turned in a clockwise direction (as we look down on it), it moves down.*

measuring the deflection of the spot on the screen of such a cathode-ray tube. Imagine the magnetic field of the permanent magnet in Figure 38.1.A replaced by that of the earth. The earth's field will produce a small deflection. Next, if the tube

is pointed in a direction exactly opposite to that shown in the figure, the spot P will move down instead of up. A total deflection of about 2 cm, which is possible with simple equipment, makes this effect visible in an ordinary classroom.

Now we need units for B. Before getting them, let us observe the effect of a B field on electrons moving within a wire—that is, on an electric current.

38.2. Effect of a Magnetic Field on a Wire Carrying Current

1. *Magnetic Induction*

Electrons moving, in the direction shown (Fig. 38.3), inside a wire that passes between the poles of a magnet experience an upward thrust, which they communicate to the atoms of the wire. (The electrons can't jump out of the wire because they are subject to restraining forces at the boundary.)

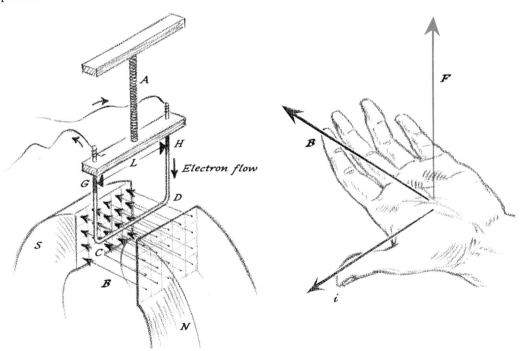

FIG. 38.3. *The thumb of the left hand points in the direction of electron flow, and the fingers point in the direction of* **B**; *segment* CD *of the wire therefore feels an upward force.*

Let n be the total number of electrons in the length, L, of the wire. The magnitude of the total charge is $q = ne$ (e being the charge in coulombs per electron). The total upward force on L is, therefore,

$$F = nevB \qquad [38.3$$

Suppose that the average speed of the electrons is such that an electron at D, moving at that speed, requires time t to get to C. Its average speed is $v = L/t$. In that time all n of the electrons in CD would file past C. The current, by definition, is $i = q/t = ne/t$. Substituting L/t for v and it for ne in equation 38.3, we get

$$F = it \left(\frac{L}{t}\right) B \qquad [38.4$$

$$= BiL \qquad [38.5$$

With this equation we can define B in terms of F, i, and L. The MKS units of B are obviously newtons per ampere-meter.

We can give B either in those units or in webers per square meter; they are equivalent units. The latter have the advantage of representing the field concept graphically; unfortunately, however, they are an extraordinarily large unit. One weber/m² is equivalent to 10,000 gauss, about as intense a fie!d as can be created in the laboratory. (Recently a field of 34,000 gauss has been reported around a faint star in the constellation of Lacerta.) The gauss, being a smaller unit, is convenient when we are dealing with weak fields. The horizontal component of the earth's magnetic field, for example, averages about 0.2 gauss, or 2×10^{-5} weber/m².

Having claimed a graphical advantage for the weber per square meter, we are confronted with the problem of visualizing even 1 weber/m² (let alone 2×10^{-5}). If, however, to each weber/m² we arbitrarily associate 10,000 lines, one for each square centimeter, our ability to visualize suddenly improves. The trick, then, is to use a unit (the gauss) such that one line per square centimeter adequately represents it. (If necessary, we could define another unit such that one line per square millimeter would represent it, and so on.) In other words, even though the weber/m² doesn't help visualization much if we associate only one

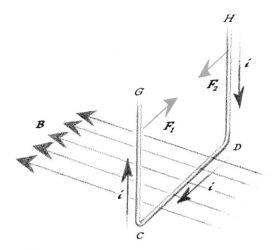

FIG. 38.4. *Illustrating Example 38.1.*

line to one weber, the concept of flux density (Φ_B/A) is still useful, for we can choose sub-units to help us visualize many lines per unit.

The proper name for **B** is **magnetic induction.**

EXAMPLE 38.1. We assume (Fig. 38.3) that, knowing the stiffness constant of the spring, A, we have found F. We are given the following data:

$$L = 5 \text{ cm}$$
$$i = 10 \text{ amp}$$
$$F = 0.2 \text{ nt}$$

We wish to find the magnitude, B, of the magnetic induction.

$$B = \frac{F}{iL}$$

$$= \frac{0.2 \text{ nt}}{10 \text{ amp} \times 0.05 \text{ m}} = 0.4 \frac{\text{nt}}{\text{amp-m}}$$

or

$$B = 0.4 \frac{\text{weber}}{\text{m}^2}$$

(If we write this as $B = 4,000$ gauss, we can imagine 4,000 lines per square meter instead of the visually meaningless 0.4 line/m².)

Why do we disregard parts CG and DH of the wire? If we use the rule of Fig. 38.1.C on CG, we see (Fig. 38.4) that force F_1 is in the direction CD. By the same rule force F_2 on HD is in the direction DC. These forces cancel each other.

It takes some imagination to realize that these

apparently weak forces can run the strong motors that supply mechanical forces for much of our industrialized society. We shall consider motors briefly in § 38.4.

2. *The Force Between Two Wires Carrying Currents*

We have already used the fact that a wire carrying current produces a magnetic field and that two parallel wires carrying current attract or repel each other (§ 35.4). If we replace the magnet of Figure 38.3 with a long wire (Fig. 38.5) carrying current i_1 and parallel to part L of the other wire, which carries current i_2, the force between them is

$$F = \frac{ki_1i_2L}{r} \qquad [38.6$$

(in which expression $k = 2 \times 10^{-7}$ nt/amp^2; see § 35.4). By separating the quantity ki_1/r we can rewrite this equation as follows:

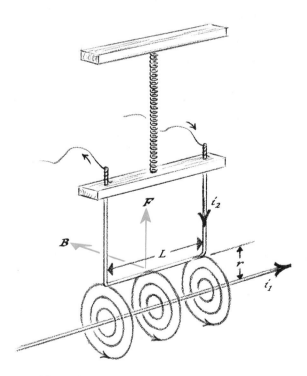

FIG. 38.5. *The magnetic field produced by current i_1 has the direction of vector* **B**. *The force,* **F**, *on the wire segment of length* L, *in which current* i_2 *is established, therefore points up.*

$$F = \frac{ki_1}{r} i_2L \qquad [38.7$$

But this becomes $F = BiL$ (equation 38.5) if we let

$$B = \frac{ki_1}{r} \qquad [38.8$$

and drop the subscript from i_2. Equation 38.8 is, in fact, the proper formula for the magnetic induction at distance r from a long wire carrying current i_1 (see equation 38.13). The field intensity gets weaker with distance but not by an inverse-square relation.

3. *Oersted's Discovery and the Concept of Magnetic Poles*

The fact that wires carrying current interact with magnetic fields was discovered accidentally by H. C. Oersted in 1820. Instead of having a large magnet push on a wire (as in our Fig. 38.3), he discovered what we, knowing Newton's third law, should foresee: that a wire carrying current can push on a magnet. A modern demonstration of this discovery can be done with a compass needle, a wire, and a battery (Fig. 38.6). The needle is first allowed to come to equilibrium in the earth's magnetic field. While the switch is open (A), the wire is placed above, close to, and parallel to the needle. When the switch is closed (B), an electric current is established in the wire by the battery, and the needle turns and remains almost at right angles to the wire. (Closing the switch constitutes a *short circuit*. If the battery is a storage battery, a huge current—more than 50 amperes—will flow, the wire will get hot, and the battery may be damaged. You should get some advice about protective resistance before trying this demonstration.) This effect can be explained as follows (Fig. 38.7): the N end of the needle feels a pull, **F**, in the direction of **B**, and the S end feels a pull, **F'**, in the opposite direction; these two forces exert torques about the axis of the needle, causing it to rotate.

It looks as if something like a magnetic charge, q_m, concentrated at the N end of the magnet, felt a force, q_mB, the way the electric charge q feels the force qE when placed in an electric field of intensity E. This idea, that magnets have *poles*

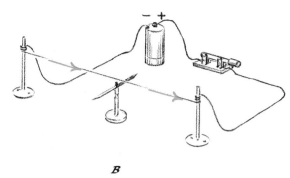

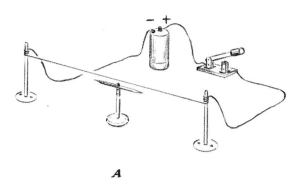

A   B

FIG. 38.6. *Oersted's discovery.*

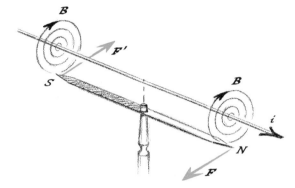

FIG. 38.7. *Explaining what Oersted discovered.*

at which something like magnetic charge exists, seemed very logical in the early days of the study of electricity. It is possible, in fact, to base a theory of magnetism on the idea of attraction and repulsion between such poles. In that theory the formula for the force of attraction (or repulsion) between two poles of strength p_1 and p_2, separated by distance r, is $F = cp_1p_2/r^2$ (in which expression c is a constant of proportionality). The similarity between this and the laws of gravitational attraction ($F = Gm_1m_2/r^2$) and electrostatic force ($F = Kq_1q_2/r^2$) suggests many fruitful analogies.

The regions around magnets where the field lines concentrate (see Fig. 4.13) are still called poles. The theory of magnetism based on poles is still used in advanced textbooks, for it summarizes many magnetic phenomena in a convenient mathematical way. But isolated N and S poles do not exist in the sense in which discrete negative and positive electric charges (the electron and the proton) exist, and it is not true that all the magnetic pole strength is concentrated at a mathematical point. All the known phenomena of magnetism can be explained, in fact, in terms of electric currents alone. The concept "pole" is not necessary for a logical explanation, and I shall develop some of the basic ideas about magnetism without recourse to that concept.

I shall not hesitate, however, to mention the poles of a magnet whenever they help us to visualize the magnetic field surrounding it. It is even useful to idealize the concept of pole and

say such things as "The direction of **B** at point P is the direction of the force felt by a small N pole at P." We can then mentally explore a magnetic field with an N pole as the probe, much as we explored an **E** field by observing its effect on a small positive test charge, q. A compass needle (Fig. 38.8) turns (A) until it aligns itself with the magnetic field, **B**, because the net torque produced by the field on its poles in this position (B) is zero. When we explore curved fields, the shorter the magnetic needle the better if we want its length to represent accurately the direction of the line tangent to the field at a point. In Figure 38.9, for example, the vector $\mathbf{F}_N$ is the strong repulsive force that would be exerted on a unit N pole at P by the pole marked N at the left end of the magnet, and the vector $\mathbf{F}_S$ is the weaker attractive force exerted on the unit pole at P by the pole marked S at the right end of the magnet. The vector, **B**, the vector sum of F_N and F_S, is the magnetic-induction vector at P; it is tangent to the field line that runs through P.

38.3. The Magnetic Fields Due to a Circular Loop, a Solenoid, and a Torus

A helpful rule for determining the direction of the magnetic field around a wire is illustrated in Figure 38.10. *If a wire is grasped with the left hand* (in imagination only, to be safe!) *so that*

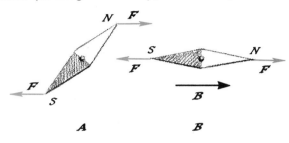

A   **B**

FIG. 38.8. *The torque on a compass needle in a magnetic field: (A) If* **B** *points to the right, the N pole is pushed to the right and the S pole to the left; the total torque is the product of* **F** *and the perpendicular distance between the two force vectors. (B) Eventually the needle aligns itself with the field, and the torque is zero.*

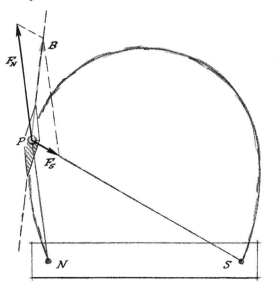

FIG. 38.9. *The needle aligns itself with the resultant magnetic field, which is the vector sum of attraction by the S pole and repulsion by the N pole.*

the thumb points in the direction of the electron flow, the fingers will encircle the wire in the direction of the magnetic field.

To check this against our knowledge that two parallel wires carrying current in the same direction attract each other, we can imagine two currents, i_1 and i_2, perpendicular to the plane of the paper (Fig. 38.11.A). As in Figure 33.2, let us use the symbol $\otimes$ to indicate electron flow away from you into the paper (remember that the cross looks like the tail of a departing arrow) and the symbol $\odot$ to indicate electron flow toward you out of the paper (the dot looks like the tip of an approaching arrow). We analyze the effects of i_1 on i_2 as follows: The circular arcs represent the magnetic field lines produced by the electron flow i_1, according to the rule of Figure 38.10. They go clockwise. A small N pole would feel a force in a direction tangent to one of these circles. At point P the magnetic induction due to i_1 is drawn as a vector, **B**, tangent to the circular field line at that point. The electron flow i_2 constitutes a current flowing in the same direction as i_1.

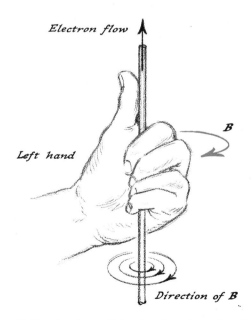

FIG. 38.10. *Another left-hand rule: when the thumb points in the direction of electron flow, the curled fingers point in the direction of the magnetic field associated with the current.*

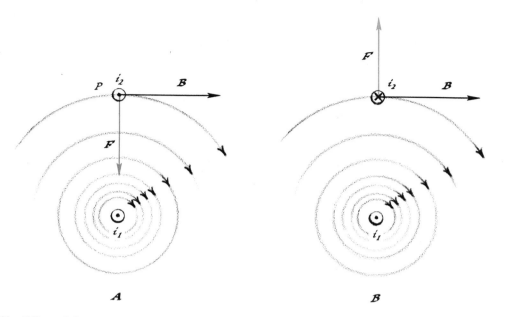

FIG. 38.11. *Effect of the magnetic field due to a current in one wire upon a parallel wire carrying current.*

The direction of force **F** on i_2 is given by the rule exemplified in Figure 38.1.A. Therefore i_2 is attracted toward i_1, in agreement with what we learned in § 35.4. A similar analysis applied to Figure 38.11.B indicates a repulsion between the wires when they carry currents in opposite directions. You should check this also by considering the effect of i_2 on i_1.

The left-hand rule of Figure 38.10 is handy when we visualize the effect of bending the wire into a circular loop (Fig. 38.12). The combined effect of many field lines at the center of the circle is a strong field whose magnetic induction is **B**. Notice that its direction is perpendicular to the plane of the loop. If the loop has N turns, it can be shown that $B = N\pi ki/R$ if R is the radius of the circle.

A solenoid, or cylindrical coil carrying a current, is approximately a sequence of circular loops. The cumulative effect of all the loops is a strong and fairly homogeneous field inside the coil, as shown in Figure 38.13, drawn from a photograph of iron filings lining up in such a field.

Using the idea that a field is a vector quantity, we expect a stronger effect when field lines going in the same direction meet and a weaker effect when lines going in opposite directions meet. The composite field can then be drawn with a high magnetic-flux density wherever the resultant field is strong and a low magnetic-flux density wherever the resultant field is weak. We owe to Faraday's pictorial and non-mathematical imagination the idea that the magnetic field lines traced by iron filings around magnets and current-carrying coils are real. He introduced, in fact, the picture of the universe as consisting of fields of various types

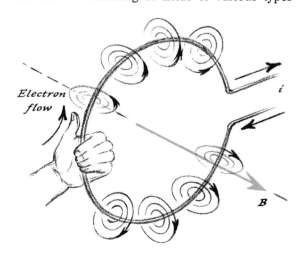

FIG. 38.12. *Predicting the direction of the magnetic field due to current in a circular wire.*

FIG. 38.13. *Magnetic field lines due to current in a solenoid as shown by iron filings.*

(see Chap. 4)—a picture that is very important in modern physics.

Figure 35.5 shows field lines for two parallel conductors with currents going in the same direction, and Figure 35.6 shows them for currents going in opposite directions. It is easy to see why magnetic lines seemed so real to Faraday. If you imagine them to be rubber bands, they would pull the wires closer in Figure 35.5 and, by their resistance to crowding, push them apart in Figure 35.6. James Clerk Maxwell, who was later to put electromagnetic theory on a sound mathematical basis, had great respect for the intuitive grasp of electric and magnetic fields that Faraday had acquired through the field-line concept. Maxwell said this about the work of Faraday:

". . . before I began the study of electricity I resolved to read no mathematics on the subject till I had first read through Faraday's *Experimental Researches in Electricity*. I was aware that there was supposed to be a difference between Faraday's way of conceiving phenomena and that of the mathematicians, so that neither he nor they were satisfied with each other's language. I had also the conviction that this discrepancy did not arise from either party being wrong.

"As I proceeded with the study of Faraday I perceived that his method of conceiving the phenomena was also a mathematical one, though not exhibited in the conventional form of mathematical symbols. I also found that these methods were capable of being expressed in the ordinary mathematical forms, and thus compared with those of the professed mathematicians.

"When I had translated what I considered to be Faraday's ideas into a mathematical form, I found that in general the results of the two methods coincided, so that the same phenomena were accounted for, and the same laws of action deduced by both methods, but that Faraday's methods resembled those in which we begin with the whole and arrive at the parts by analysis, while the ordinary mathematical methods were founded on the principle of beginning with the parts and building up the whole by synthesis. . . . I also found that several of the most fertile methods of research discovered by the mathematicians could be expressed much better in terms of ideas derived from Faraday than in their original form."

The problem of finding quantitative expressions for the magnetic field intensity at the center of a circular loop such as that of Figure 38.12 or along the axis of a solenoid such as that of Figure 38.13 was solved by Ampère. The method consists of adding vectorially, at a point, all the contributions of the different sections of a current-carrying conductor. Ampère discovered that he could find the magnitude, B, of the resultant field intensity at point P of Figure 38.14 by assuming that each little length, Δl, of the conductor contributed $\Delta B = (\Delta l) i / R^2$ to that magnitude. The problem (one for the integral calculus) was to add all the contributions from all the Δl's that made up the wire. The result was, of course, $B = ki/r$, in accord with equation 38.8. (For the loop, of radius R, of Fig. 38.12 the magnetic induction at the center is $B = \pi ki/R$.)

It was later shown that the field could be calculated in a different but equivalent way. Imag-

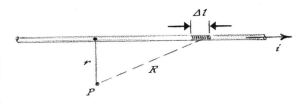

FIG. 38.14. *Ampère's method of computing the magnetic field at a point near a current-carrying wire.*

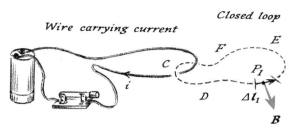

FIG. 38.15. *Another way of computing the magnetic field near a current-carrying wire.*

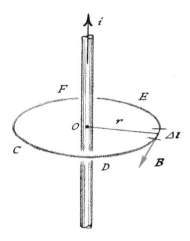

FIG. 38.16. *Illustrating the use of equation 38.9.*

ine (Fig. 38.15) a closed loop, *CDEFC* (a mathematical curve, not a wire), of arbitrary shape that completely encircles (links with) a wire carrying current. The magnetic field intensity due to this current has a certain magnitude, B, at point P_1, where there is an element of length that is expressed in vector form as Δl_1. We form the scalar product, $\mathbf{B}_1 \cdot \Delta l_1$, and do the same at another point, P_2, of the loop to obtain $\mathbf{B}_2 \cdot \Delta l_2$. We repeat the operation until the Δl's cover the whole path *CDEFC*. Now we add up all these scalar quantities:

$$\underset{\substack{\text{closed} \\ \text{loop}}}{\Sigma \mathbf{B} \cdot \Delta l} = \mathbf{B}_1 \cdot \Delta l_1 + \mathbf{B}_2 \cdot \Delta l_2 + \mathbf{B}_3 \cdot \Delta l_3 + \dots$$

The sum round a complete loop is equal to $2\pi k$ times the current in the wire:

$$\underset{\substack{\text{closed} \\ \text{loop}}}{\Sigma \mathbf{B} \cdot \Delta l} = 2\pi ki \qquad [38.9$$

The power of this expression stems, in part, from the fact that it holds for any complete loop, regardless of the shape. Let us see if it works in a special case. Consider, for example, an infinitely long conductor carrying current i (Fig. 38.16). Draw a circle, *CDEF*, of radius r, in a plane perpendicular to the direction of i, with its center, O, in the center of the wire. Because of symmetry, the magnitude of **B** is constant all along this path; and, since in this example **B** always has the same direction as Δl,

$$\mathbf{B} \cdot \Delta l = B(\Delta l) \cos 0° = B(\Delta l)$$

Hence

$$\underset{\substack{\text{closed} \\ \text{loop}}}{\Sigma \mathbf{B} \cdot \Delta l} = B(\Delta l_1) + B(\Delta l_2) + B(\Delta l_3) + \dots \quad [38.10$$

or

$$\underset{\substack{\text{closed} \\ \text{loop}}}{\Sigma \mathbf{B} \cdot \Delta l} = B(\Delta l_1 + \Delta l_2 + \Delta l_3 + \dots) \qquad [38.11$$

$$= 2\pi rB \qquad [38.12$$

Now let us use equation 38.9:

$$2\pi rB = 2\pi ki$$

$$B = \frac{ki}{r} \qquad [38.13$$

This is identical with equation 38.8; so the closed-loop method works in this case. We seem to be using our magic-box approach with equation 38.9: we don't know how it was derived, but we see that it works in a special case.

The closed-loop method works also with another shape of great symmetry, the toroidal coil. A torus is a doughnut-shaped surface. Imagine N evenly spaced turns of wire wrapped round such a torus (Fig. 38.17.A). Current in this wire will produce a magnetic field inside the toroidal surface. The magnetic field along the closed loop consisting of the circle of radius r is of constant magnitude, again from considerations of symmetry. (A cutaway view is shown for convenience in Fig. 38.17.B, but the magnetic field we are considering is that due to all the turns shown in Fig. 38.17.A.) This time the closed loop would encircle N turns, each with current i. The application of equation 38.9 therefore yields

$$\underset{\substack{\text{closed} \\ \text{loop}}}{\Sigma \mathbf{B} \cdot \Delta l} = N2\pi ki \qquad [38.14$$

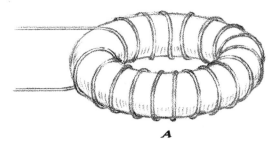
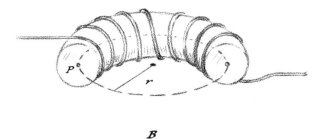

FIG. 38.17. *Magnetic induction in a toroidal coil.*

Hence

$$B2\pi r = N2\pi ki$$

$$B = \frac{Nki}{r} \qquad [38.15$$

This is the formula for the magnetic induction in a toroidal coil at a point like P (Fig. 38.17.B).

EXAMPLE 38.2. A toroidal coil (Fig. 38.17) whose radius, r, is 15 cm has 1,000 evenly spaced turns. It carries a current of 5 amp. We wish to find the magnetic induction, in webers/m², within this coil. We use equation 38.15:

$$B = \frac{Nki}{r}$$

$$= 1{,}000 \times \frac{2 \times 10^{-7}\ \mathrm{nt}}{\mathrm{amp}^2} \times \frac{5\ \mathrm{amp}}{0.15\ \mathrm{m}}$$

$$= 6.66 \times 10^{-3}\ \frac{\mathrm{nt}}{\mathrm{amp\text{-}m}}$$

or

$$B = 6.66 \times 10^{-3}\ \mathrm{weber/m^2}$$

or

$$B = 66.6\ \mathrm{gauss}$$

To find the magnetic induction, B, inside a very long solenoid with n turns per meter, carrying current i, we form a loop, $CDEF$ (Fig. 38.18), such that one side is very far away from the coil.

$$\underset{\substack{\text{closed}\\ \text{loop}}}{\Sigma \mathbf{B} \cdot \Delta \mathbf{l}} = \mathbf{B} \cdot \Delta \mathbf{l} + (\Sigma\ \text{terms like } \mathbf{B}_1 \cdot \Delta \mathbf{l}_1) + \mathbf{B}_2 \cdot \Delta \mathbf{l}_2$$

$$+ (\Sigma\ \text{terms like } \mathbf{B}_3 \cdot \Delta \mathbf{l}_3) \quad [38.16$$

All the terms on the right-hand side of this equation vanish except $\mathbf{B} \cdot \Delta \mathbf{l}$. For example, $\mathbf{B}_2 \cdot \Delta \mathbf{l}_2$ vanishes because $\Delta \mathbf{l}_2$ is so far away that B_2 is virtually zero; $\mathbf{B}_1 \cdot \Delta \mathbf{l}_1$ vanishes because $\mathbf{B}_1$ is perpendicular to $\Delta \mathbf{l}_1$. (The magnetic-flux lines run-

ning through $\Delta \mathbf{l}_1$ are approximately perpendicular to $\Delta \mathbf{l}_1$, and this is true for all points along CD if $\Delta \mathbf{l}$ is very small and is near the center of the coil.) For similar reasons all the contributions along EF and CD vanish. We are therefore left† with

$$B(\Delta l) = 2\pi[n(\Delta l)]ki \qquad [38.17$$

The magnetic induction along the axis of a long solenoid is therefore

$$B = 2\pi nki \qquad [38.18$$

Equations 38.13, 38.15, and 38.18 are of great practical use as formulas. In our theoretical development of the subject, however, the so-called circuital form of Ampère's law (equation 38.9,

---

† Observe that

$$n\,\frac{\mathrm{turns}}{\mathrm{meter}} \times \Delta l\ \mathrm{meters}$$

is simply the total number of turns encircled by the loop in going from F to C.

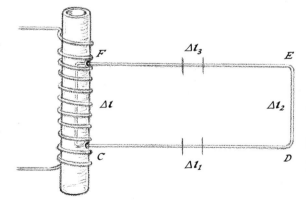

FIG. 38.18. *Magnetic induction in a solenoid.*

which says that the sum of $\mathbf{B} \cdot \Delta \mathbf{l}$ round a closed loop is $2\pi k$ times the total current enclosed by the loop) will play a more important role when we try to exhibit the links between electricity, magnetism, and light.

38.4. The Electric Motor and the Galvanometer

I shall describe only the essentials of the electric motor and the galvanometer. If we use the rule of Figure 38.3, the portion EF of the coil $CDEF$ in Figure 38.19 experiences an upward force, and CD experiences a downward force. This produces a counterclockwise torque that turns the coil. The coil is connected to a split-ring commutator so that part EF, when it finds itself where CD is now, will experience a downward thrust; hence the coil will continue to turn. The maximum torque occurs when the coil is in the position shown. If EF is L and the radius is r, the magnitude of the torque is then

$$\tau = 2rF = 2rBiL$$

A real motor is a very complicated device in which coils with many turns are used, but the basic idea is that the force $F = Bil$ acts on the wires and produces a torque.

In a galvanometer (Fig. 38.20) the torque produced in a coil is allowed to turn the coil against the counter-torque produced by a spring. If rotation through angle θ produces counter-torque $c\theta$, the relation

$$\tau = 2rBiL = c\theta$$

must hold; that is,

$$i = \frac{c}{2rBL} \theta$$

If the galvanometer is designed so that B is constant for different positions of the coil, the last equation says that the current is directly proportional to the angle of deflection, θ. A current meter based on this principle is called a *d'Arsonval galvanometer*. It is easy to convert a galvanometer requiring a few microamperes for full deflection into an ammeter requiring several amperes for full deflection or into a voltmeter, as we shall see in Chapter 40.

38.5. A Stream of Charged Particles Moving in a Circular Path

The formula $\mathbf{F} = q(\mathbf{v} \times \mathbf{B})$, which we used to derive several of the other formulas in this chapter, such as $F = BiL$, says that a charged particle moving in a magnetic field experiences a force that is perpendicular both to the velocity of the particle and to the magnetic field. A force perpendicular to the velocity can do no work on the

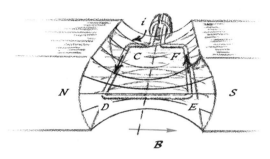

FIG. 38.19. *The essential elements of an electric motor are a current-carrying coil that can rotate and a magnetic field. If i is electron flow, the coil will experience a counterclockwise torque. The coil is connected to a split-ring commutator, which permits the torque to remain counterclockwise even after rotation through 180°.*

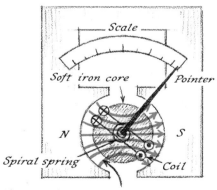

FIG. 38.20. *A galvanometer is, in principle, very much like an electric motor. The main difference is that the torque produced by the magnetic field on its coil turns against a restoring torque produced by a spring. The angular movement of the coil is thus limited to about 90°.*

particle. Under those circumstances the magnitude of **v** cannot increase.

If a stream of charged particles is injected into a homogeneous magnetic field at right angles to it, the particles will move in a circular path, as shown in Figure 38.21 (negatively charged particles, A; positively charged particles, B). The magnitude of the force is equal to the magnitude of $q(\mathbf{v} \times \mathbf{B})$, which equals

$$Bqv \sin 90° = Bqv$$

in which expression q is the magnitude of the charge in coulombs. Because **F** is a centripetal force, we may write $F = mv^2/R$ if m is the mass of each particle and R is the radius of the circular path. Therefore

$$\frac{mv^2}{R} = Bqv \qquad [38.19$$

$$R = \frac{mv}{qB} \qquad [38.20$$

It is instructive to consider qualitatively the effect of each term on the right side of this equation. A large m, for example, means a great inertia. Since a body with great inertia will not be deflected as readily as one with little inertia, the radius, R, of its path will be long. You are urged to think out for yourself the effect of the other

factors in equation 38.20 if you wish to understand its physical significance. Let us consider a numerical example.

EXAMPLE 38.3. A proton is injected normally into a homogeneous field of intensity $B = 0.15$ weber/m² at a speed of 10^6 m/sec. We wish to find the radius of curvature of its path.

We use the formula

$$R = \frac{mv}{qB}$$

The mass of a proton is roughly 1,840 times the mass of an electron. The correct values to three significant figures are

$$m = 1.67 \times 10^{-27} \text{ kg}$$
$$v = 10^6 \text{ m/sec}$$
$$q = 1.60 \times 10^{-19} \text{ coul}$$
$$B = 0.15 \text{ weber/m}^2$$

Therefore

$$R = \frac{1.67 \times 10^{-27} \text{ kg} \times 10^6 \text{ m/sec}}{1.60 \times 10^{-19} \text{ coul} \times 0.15 \text{ weber/m}^2}$$

$$= 6.96 \times 10^{-2} \text{ m} = 6.96 \text{ cm}$$

Our knowledge of how moving electric charges interact with magnetic fields is going to be very useful when we begin to study the details of the

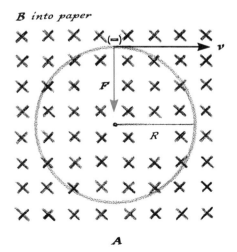

A

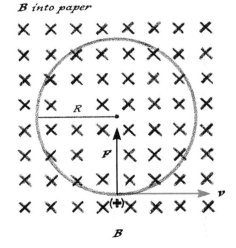

B

FIG. 38.21. *Streams of charged particles moving at right angles to a magnetic field.*

atom. There are several different ways to make the paths of charged atomic particles visible, and we shall consider them in Chapter 56. As a preview, the photograph on page 662 shows the tracks of a number of such particles in a device called a bubble chamber. The radius of curvature of the tracks can be measured in such pictures. Equation 38.20 suggests that a knowledge of some of the factors—such as magnetic induction, mass, charge, velocity, and radius—may make possible a determination of the unknown factors.

38.6. Summary

The direction and magnitude of magnetic induction can be visualized as the direction and flux density of magnetic field lines.

An electric charge moving in a magnetic field experiences a force whose direction is perpendicular both to the field and to the velocity of the charge. The magnitude of the force is proportional to the speed and to the magnitude of the magnetic induction. This force acts on charges within wires as well as on free charges. An example of this is afforded by the force acting on a wire carrying current in a magnetic field.

Oersted discovered what we should expect from Newton's third law: that a wire carrying a current can affect a compass needle.

All magnetic effects can be explained in terms of electric currents, but it is often convenient to speak of the poles of a magnet even though, unlike electric charges, they cannot be isolated.

The sum of terms like $\mathbf{B}\cdot\Delta\mathbf{l}$ round a closed loop is equal to $2\pi k$ times the current enclosed by the loop. Many experimental facts can be explained by this relation, which predicts accurately the magnetic induction due to configurations of wires carrying current. It implies—and this is of even greater importance—the intimate connection between electric and magnetic fields that will appear when we study the electromagnetic nature of light.

Problems

38.1. In a television receiver a stream of electrons moves horizontally with a speed of 10^8 m/sec in a room where the horizontal intensity of the earth's magnetic field is 2×10^{-5} weber/m². (The **B** vector points from south to north; see § 39.1.)

1. If the electrons' initial direction points west, what are the direction and the magnitude of the force on them that is due to the earth's magnetic field?

2. Answer the same question if their initial direction points southeast. (Assume that geographic north and magnetic north coincide.)

38.2. 1. What are the magnitude and the direction of the force on a straight wire 2 m long if it carries a current of 100 amp in the magnetic field of the earth, whose horizontal intensity is 2×10^{-5} weber/m²? The direction of electron flow is from east to west.

2. Answer the same question if the electrons flow from south to north.

38.3. In Fig. 38.5, i_1 is 30 amp, i_2 is 50 amp, and r is 2 cm when equilibrium has been reached. The length L is 10 cm. The force constant of the spring is 0.03 nt/cm. What stretch, in centimeters, is produced in the spring by the force of attraction between the wires?

38.4. A long straight wire carries a current of 10 amp. What are the direction and the magnitude of the magnetic induction at a point 5 cm from the wire?

38.5. What is the current in a long straight wire that produces, at a distance of 5 cm from the wire, a magnetic induction whose magnitude equals that of the horizontal component of the earth's field (2×10^{-5} weber/m²)?

38.6. A long straight wire carries 20 amp.

1. Find the magnetic induction at points, in a plane perpendicular to the wire, whose distances are 0.5, 1.0, 2.0, and 4.0 cm.

2. Plot magnetic induction, B, against distance, r, from the center of the wire.

38.7. A long straight wire carries 15 amp. Another wire, parallel to the first and 10 cm away, carries 5 amp in the opposite direction. Locate a point between them where the resultant magnetic induction has a magnitude of zero.

38.8. Two long straight wires at right angles to each other cross without electrical contact. Each carries a current of 1 amp.

1. Find a formula for the magnetic induction at a point on the angle bisector at distance x from the intersection.

2. What happens at such a point if you reverse the direction of one of the currents?

38.9. A thin solenoid 40 cm long consists of 800 turns of wire wrapped on a cylinder of short radius. What current, in amperes, will produce a magnetic induction of 2 gauss (2×10^{-4} weber/m²) at its center?

38.10. Suppose that you have a piece of wire (enamel-covered for insulation) 2 m long and 2 mm thick. It carries a current of 20 amp.

1. If the wire is kept straight, what is the maximum magnitude of the magnetic induction at any point in the space around it?

2. If the wire is wrapped on a cylinder whose diameter is 5 cm, find the maximum number of turns per meter and the magnetic induction at the center of the resulting solenoid.

3. With the same length of wire and the same current, how would you create a greater magnetic induction at the center of a circle of diameter 5 cm?

38.11. A circular coil of radius 5 cm has 50 turns of wire and carries a current at a place where the horizontal component of the earth's magnetic induction is 2×10^{-5} weber/m². The plane of the

circle is that of the magnetic meridian. A magnetic compass is placed at the center of the coil so that its needle can rotate in a horizontal plane. When there is no current, the needle points north; when there is a current, it points northwest. What is the strength of the current in amperes?

38.12. The torque applicable in Fig. 38.19 is $2rBiL$. Notice that $2rL$ is the area of the coil.

1. If r were increased and L decreased so that the area remained the same, would the torque for a given current be the same? Explain.

2. What is the maximum torque that can be produced in a coil whose area is 8 cm² with 40 turns placed in a field whose magnetic induction is 0.05 weber/m² when the current in the coil is 1 milli-ampere?

38.13. If, when a simple pendulum has reached the end of its swing, the bob is given a sudden push at right angles to the plane of its motion, it will move with speed v in a horizontal circle of radius r and complete one revolution in time T, the natural period of the pendulum (that is, $T = 2\pi\sqrt{l/g}$). Hence $vT = 2\pi r$. Since only v and r are variable, this says that r is proportional to v. If you increase v by a series of impulses, r will increase proportionally. The bob will move faster in a larger circle in order to complete its cycle in the same time. The pendulum in circular motion will become a useful model when we consider how the radius of the curved path of a charged particle in a cyclotron (§ 56.3) increases with speed.

A charged body in a homogeneous magnetic field also moves in a circle of fixed radius if its speed is constant. According to equation 38.20, that radius is proportional to speed, as it was for the bob: if the speed is suddenly increased, the charged body will move faster in a larger circle. What is the speed of a proton moving in a circle of radius 15 cm in a homogeneous field where the magnetic induction has a magnitude of 0.12 weber/m²?

The Nature
of Magnetism

THE EARTH is a huge natural magnet. We live immersed in its magnetic field with even less apparent concern for that field than for the equally invisible sea of air called the atmosphere, which also engulfs us. Yet both are subject to intense exploration today because they affect the particles and waves that come to us from outer space. In this chapter, by studying magnets, we hope to learn something that will give us at least a clue to the cause of the earth's magnetism.

39.1. Magnets

The exact origin of the earth's magnetic field is still unknown. The magnetic field lines exterior to the earth behave as if they originated in a huge permanent magnet within it (Fig. 39.1).

Sampling of the earth's magnetic field is going on today by way of rockets and satellites equipped with delicate sensing and transmitting devices. The horizontal intensity of the earth's magnetic induction (in New York City, for example) is about 1.77×10^{-5} weber/m². (Compare this with the huge value 3.4 webers/m² recently discovered around a distant star by spectroscopic examination of its light.) Other natural magnets are the lodestones known since ancient times—usually samples of iron ore that are found in a magnetized state.

One modern man-made magnet is illustrated here. The Alnico permanent magnet (Fig. 39.2) produces a magnetic induction of about 0.1 weber/m² between its poles. A laboratory **electromagnet** (that is, one that is magnetized only when electricity is flowing through its windings) can produce a magnetic induction of about 1 weber/m².

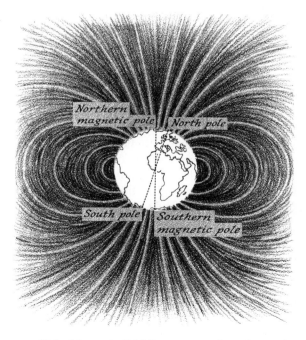

FIG. 39.1. *Magnetic field lines surrounding the earth.*

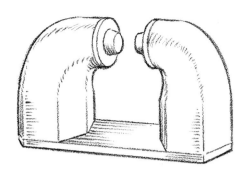

FIG. 39.2. *Alnico permanent magnet.*

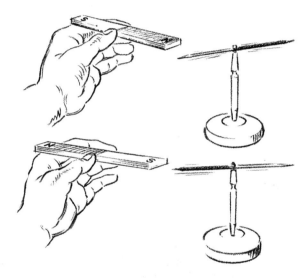

FIG. 39.3. *A bar magnet and a compass needle.*

One form of magnetic indicator consists of a thin magnetized needle free to rotate about a vertical axis. In the absence of other magnetic fields it aligns itself with the horizontal component of the earth's field (all magnetic compasses work on this principle). The end of the needle that points in the general direction of the geographic north is called the north, or north-seeking, pole of the needle. (The earth's magnetic-induction lines run from the southern to the northern hemisphere.)

A magnetic needle may be affected by gravitational, electric, and magnetic attractions all at once. The fact that a magnetic needle falls to the

ground when you release it proves that gravitational force acts on it. Similarly, the fact that *either* end of a magnetic needle on an insulated support is attracted by an electrostatically charged rod shows that electrostatic forces also act on the needle as a whole. In this chapter, however, we are concerned only with the needle's response to the field of a permanent magnet or an electromagnet or to an electric current.

One end of a bar magnet attracts one end of the compass needle and repels the other (Fig. 39.3). The magnetic field lines around the magnet crowd into the regions we have called poles (§ 38.2.3). Like poles repel and unlike poles attract each other. There is, however, an important difference between magnetism and electricity: it is not possible to isolate magnetic poles. You cannot create a north pole without creating a south pole simultaneously.

39.2. Poles and Dipoles

If you put an electric charge, q, on a small metal sphere, its field will be represented as in Figure 39.4.A. This single concentration of charge may be called an **electric pole.** If you put charge $-q$ on another sphere, the combined field of the pair will be represented as in Figure 39.4.B. This combination is called an **electric dipole,** and its field is called an **electric dipole field.** The field around a bar magnet, as exhibited by iron filings, is shown in Figure 39.4.C. It resembles the electric dipole field and is called a **magnetic dipole field.** No magnetic field exactly like that of Figure 39.4.A has ever been found. A long steel needle with a sphere at each end can be magnetized so that the field around one sphere looks *almost* like that of the figure, but the presence of the other pole keeps the pattern from being that of a perfectly isolated pole. In other words, magnetic dipoles are common, but isolated magnetic poles are non-existent.

Let us see how we can measure something about a dipole even though we cannot isolate the poles. We begin with an electric dipole by imagining an insulating rod (Fig. 39.5), with charge $+q$ concentrated at one end and charge $-q$ concen-

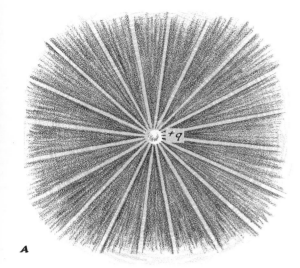

trated at the other end, suspended at its center, C, by a fine insulating string, CD. If this dipole is brought into a uniform electric field, **E** (shown by the field lines), the positive charge will feel force $+qE$ in the direction of **E**, and the negative charge will feel force $-qE$ in the opposite direction. The combined effect is a torque whose magnitude, τ, is $2(qE)(d/2)$ if **d** is perpendicular to **E** and is, by definition, the vector from the negative pole to the positive pole. This may be written as $\tau = (qd)E$. The product qd is, in fact, the magnitude of a vector called the **electric dipole moment,** to which the symbol **p** is assigned (not to be confused with the **p** for linear momentum); that is, $p = qd$. The torque can therefore be considered the product of the dipole moment and the electric field intensity. More generally it can be written vectorially in the equation

$$\tau = \mathbf{p} \times \mathbf{E} \qquad [39.1$$

in which $\mathbf{p} = q\mathbf{d}$ (**d**, as we have seen, is a vector from the negative to the positive pole). Remember that the vector product τ is a vector perpendicular to both **p** and **E**. You should check Figure 39.5 to see if you agree that $\mathbf{p} \times \mathbf{E}$ points along CD as shown, indicating that the torque will tend to produce a rotation in the sense indicated by the

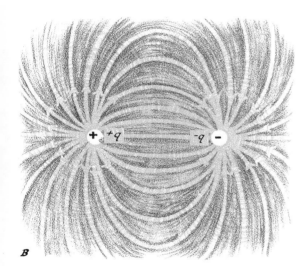

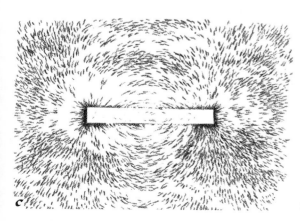

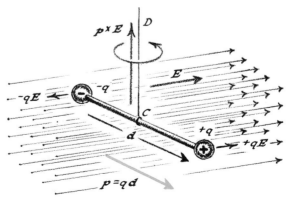

FIG. 39.5. *An electric dipole in an electric field.*

curved arrow. The magnitude of τ is

$$\tau = pE \sin \theta \qquad [39.2$$

if θ is the angle between **p** (or **d**) and **E**.

The reason for introducing the topic of dipole moment by way of electrostatics is that electric charges can be isolated. Notice that we can measure τ if we know the torsion characteristics of the suspending string. We can also measure E and θ separately, thus leaving the dipole moment to be solved for in equation 39.2. We can, in other words, give operational instructions on how to measure the dipole moment of an electric dipole without specifying the pole strength (the charge in this case) or the distance between poles. Those instructions give us a clue to a way of measuring a magnetic dipole moment by means of the measurable torque that a magnetic dipole feels in a magnetic field, even though there are no isolated poles.

What do we mean by "dipole moment of a magnetic dipole"? We can define it by analogy with equation 39.1. If we put a magnetic needle (our test dipole) into a magnetic field of known magnetic induction, **B**, it experiences a torque, τ, which we can measure (for example, by the angle of twist in a fiber). The **magnetic dipole moment, μ,** can then be defined abstractly as the vector that satisfies the equation

$$\tau = \mu \times \mathbf{B} \qquad [39.3$$

or the related scalar equation

$$\tau = \mu B \sin \theta \qquad [39.4$$

in which τ, B, and θ are all experimentally measurable quantities.

Let me show how I can arrive at the same result by starting with the concept of poles—that is, by assuming (Fig. 39.6) that a positive (N) magnetic pole of strength $+q_m$ exists at point D and a negative (S) magnetic pole of strength $-q_m$ exists at point C. The force acting on D is $q_m B$ to the right when the compass is placed in a field whose magnetic induction has magnitude B; the force acting on C is $-q_m B$ to the left. The torque exerted by these forces is $\tau = 2(q_m B)(d/2)$ if **d** is the vector from the negative pole to the positive pole and is perpendicular to B. This torque may be written as $\tau = \mu B$ if we let μ equal $q d_m$. The

torque depends on the product of d and q_m. We do not need to know either d or q_m separately; we may lump them together into one quantity, $\mu = q_m d$, and call this the magnitude of the dipole moment. This takes us back to equations 39.3 and 39.4, the defining equations for magnetic dipole moment, in which pole strength no longer appears explicitly.

Let us summarize these remarks in this way: Suppose you have a torsion device that can measure torques by giving you a reading on a dial. Suppose you connect this to some object and discover that this object, when you carry it into a room where the magnetic induction, **B**, is known to exist, feels a torque of magnitude τ. Whatever the object is, we say it has a magnetic dipole moment simply because it feels a torque when placed in a magnetic field. We have two numbers, τ and B. To find μ, we still need a direction. In the case of the magnetic needle, its longer axis provides us with a direction, and we can use the angle, θ, between it and **B** to solve the equation $\tau = \mu B \sin \theta$ for the magnitude, μ, of the magnetic dipole moment.

Consider now the behavior of a long, current-carrying helical coil in a magnetic field (Fig. 39.7). The coil has the axis CD. The reasoning used for Figure 38.13 indicates that, when electrons flow in the wire in the direction shown, D behaves like the N pole of a magnet. The coil feels a torque tending to produce rotation in the direc-

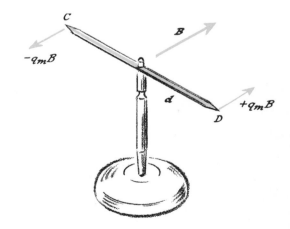

FIG. 39.6. *The torque exerted on a compass needle by a magnetic field.*

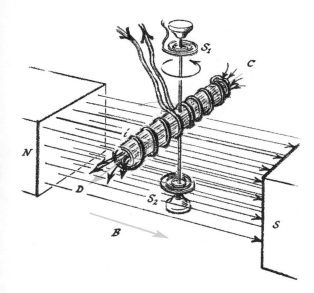

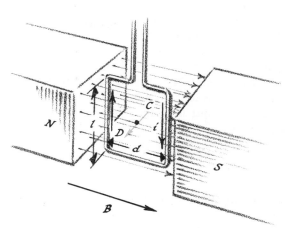

FIG. 39.7. *A current-carrying helical coil in a magnetic field.*

FIG. 39.8. *Even a current going round a single loop has a measurable dipole moment, whose direction is perpendicular to the plane of the loop.*

tion of the curved arrow. We can measure the torque by calibrating the springs, S_1 and S_2; we can measure the angle between CD and **B**; and we can, therefore, if **B** is known, compute the magnetic dipole moment of the coil from the equation $\tau = \mu B \sin \theta$.

This introduction now permits us to associate the direction CD with a single rectangular loop (Fig. 39.8). If the angle between CD and B is θ, we can easily show, by an extension of the argument used in § 38.4, that the torque acting on the loop is

$$\tau = 2(Bil)\left(\frac{d}{2}\right)\sin \theta \qquad [39.5$$

This may be written as the equation

$$\tau = BiA \sin \theta \qquad [39.6$$

in which A is the area, ld, of the loop. We see at once that, if we let μ equal iA, equation 39.6 can be written in the form

$$\tau = \mu B \sin \theta$$

which is identical with equation 39.4. In other words, even a current going round a single loop has a measurable dipole moment. It may be written as a vector in the equation

$$\mu = iA \qquad [39.7$$

in which the direction of the vector **A**, chosen to

represent the area A, is that of CD in Fig. 39.8—that is, is perpendicular to the plane of **A**. (It is an accepted convention to represent an elementary area by a vector perpendicular to it. It certainly makes good sense in this case.) It can be shown that equation 39.7 holds for a circular loop just as well.

We are now ready to consider an electron revolving about a nucleus (Fig. 39.9). Suppose it is moving in a circular path of radius r at speed v. We imagine, near point P, an observer capable of

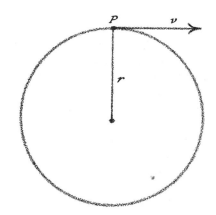

FIG. 39.9. *An electron bearing charge* e *and moving with speed* v *in a circle of radius* r *has the dipole moment* $\mu = evr/2$.

counting the passages of this electron. Since $v = 2\pi r/T$, the time, T, for one complete revolution is $2\pi r/v$. Hence $v/2\pi r$ is the number of times the electron passes P per second. Since the magnitude in coulombs of the electronic charge is e, the number of coulombs that pass point P per second is $ev/2\pi r$. This is, by definition, the current in this loop. Using equation 39.7, we see that the magnitude of the dipole moment of this current is

$$\mu = \frac{ev}{2\pi r} \times \pi r^2 = \frac{evr}{2} \qquad [39.8$$

EXAMPLE 39.1. We wish to find the magnetic dipole moment due to the orbital motion of an electron if its speed is 2.19×10^6 m/sec and the radius of its orbit is 5.29×10^{-11} m. (These values of v and r are consistent with the simple Bohr theory of the hydrogen atom.)

We know that

$$e = 1.60 \times 10^{-19} \text{ coul}$$
$$v = 2.19 \times 10^6 \text{ m/sec}$$
$$r = 5.29 \times 10^{-11} \text{ m}$$

Therefore

$$\mu = \frac{evr}{2} = 9.27 \times 10^{-24} \frac{\text{coul-m}^2}{\text{sec}}$$

The units for the dipole moment come out as (coul/sec) $\times$ m^2, or amp-m^2, in agreement with equation 39.7.

An electron moving in a circular orbit has an angular momentum,

$$I\omega = mr^2 \times \frac{v}{r} = mrv$$

It also has a magnetic dipole moment, $\mu = evr/2$, which, as we have just seen, is due to orbital motion. Since both expressions have rv in them, it seems that an electron, whenever it has an angular momentum, also has a magnetic dipole moment.

Although the modern concept of the atom does not permit us to say that an electron within an atom actually moves in a circular path, the model is a good first approximation and has the great advantage that it is easy to visualize. Less easy to visualize, but very important, is the fact that an electron also has a dipole moment that is due to its *spin;* see the next section.

The modern theory of magnetism rests on the idea that an electron behaves like a little magnet— that is, that an electron within an atom has a dipole moment, μ. When you place such an electron in a magnetic field, $\mathbf{B}$, it experiences a torque, $\tau = \mu \times \mathbf{B}$. The ability of a bar magnet to align itself with an external magnetic field is related to the torque felt by electrons within it because of their dipole moments.

39.3. Amperian Currents

Ampère was the first to suggest that the properties of magnets could be attributed to electric currents due to charges circulating within the magnetic material. In 1836, more than fifty years before the discovery of the electron, he practically staked his scientific reputation on the assertion that "currents that never die" exist within a magnet and are responsible for its magnetic properties. This culminated a series of brilliant experiments, which had been sparked by Oersted's discovery (1820) that a wire carrying current could affect a magnetic needle. Just one week after Oersted's work was reported to the French Academy of Sciences, Ampère read his first paper, refining Oersted's original observation into the left-hand rule illustrated in Figure 38.10, and for the following four months nearly all the weekly meetings of the Academy were devoted to the implications of Oersted's discovery, with Ampère as the main contributor.

Today there is evidence not only that an electron has angular momentum and a dipole moment because of its orbital motion but also that it has both an intrinsic angular momentum, a **spin** (as if it rotated on its own axis as the earth rotates on its axis), and, associated with this spin in iron and a few other elements and certain alloys, a dipole moment that is the main contribution to **ferromagnetism** (see the next section), the kind of magnetic phenomenon associated with those substances. Although Ampère knew nothing about these electron properties, he was able, using a very elementary idea of circulating currents, to fit the basic facts of magnetism into a plausible theory. Let us examine a very simple, partly fictional, but highly visual account of the behavior of magnets in terms of circulating currents.

We first assume that magnetizable materials, such as iron and steel, have within them circulating currents, oriented at random. There is good evidence that, when electricity flows in a coil wrapped round a U-shaped piece of steel, such as that of Figure 39.10, sitting on a flat slab of soft iron, the lines of magnetic induction, **B**, follow a pattern somewhat like that shown. What effect will **B** have upon the circulating currents? Each little loop is a little dipole; we therefore suspect that they turn so that their magnetic-moment axes run parallel to **B** and thus increase the total magnetic induction. This effect is indeed observed with iron and steel. Both the U-shaped piece of steel and the flat piece of iron become magnetized; their circulating currents are oriented so as to add to the field lines. For reasons offered

today by quantum mechanics, certain kinds of steel retain their new internal orientations, but certain kinds of iron do not. When the current is turned off (Fig. 39.11), the steel will keep its magnetism, and the iron, once separated from the steel, will lose it. The former becomes a permanent magnet.

Next let us consider the effect of adjacent current loops. For simplicity in description, let us draw them as rectangles (Fig. 39.12.A). We think of a current in each loop. At a point not on a loop the effects of portions such as *a* and *b* of adjacent loops cancel. (That is, their external magnetic fields are zero.) So do the effects of portions such as *c* and *d*. The net result of all of these small currents is that only the contribution along the edges of *ABCD* (Fig. 39.12.B) survive. We say that the single loop *ABCD*, with current *i* in it, can represent or replace the individual loops.

On one end of a bar magnet (Fig. 39.13) we

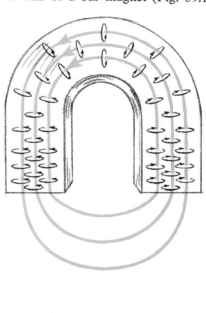

FIG. 39.10. *Magnetization of steel and soft iron by a magnetic field due to an electric current.*

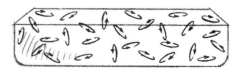

FIG. 39.11. *After the current of Fig. 39.10 is turned off and the iron is separated from the steel: the steel remains a magnet; the iron does not.*

draw (A) a current loop, *ABCD*, that symbolizes the effect of many loops. Nearby is a wire carrying a current as shown. Looking at this configuration from above (B), we indicate a current going down into the paper at *C* and a current coming out of the paper at *B* and at *P*. Since the currents at *B* and *P* go in the same direction, they exert an attractive force on each other (as in Fig. 35.5), as shown by vector *PD*. But the currents at *C* and *P* go in opposite directions, producing a repulsion on *P*, as shown by vector *PE*. The vector sum of these forces is vector **F**.

Let us check the consistency of this result with

previously stated rules. We use the reasoning of Figure 38.13 to arrive at another way of remembering the effect of a circular current. If the fingers of the left hand point in the direction of the circulating electron current, the thumb will point in the direction of the resulting magnetic induction. Figure 39.14 shows (A) how the **B** due to the magnet is related to the circulation of current in its elementary loops (and also to electron flow in a circular coil) and (B) how the direction of thrust **F** is determined from the rule of § 38.1, with **B** pointing from left to right and *i* pointing up. Thrust **F** points toward the reader. The idea of Amperian currents permits us to explain the force between a magnet and a wire as a force between currents.

The attraction between two magnets can also be visualized (Fig. 39.15) as an attraction between currents. Side *AB* of one loop, for example, would attract side *HG* of the other loop. The fact that a permanent magnet, after being broken, still has N and S poles is explainable in terms of current loops. An alternation of the poles (S, N, S, N) in two such pieces of magnet seems inevitable in view of the current loops of the figure. An easy way to demonstrate this is to

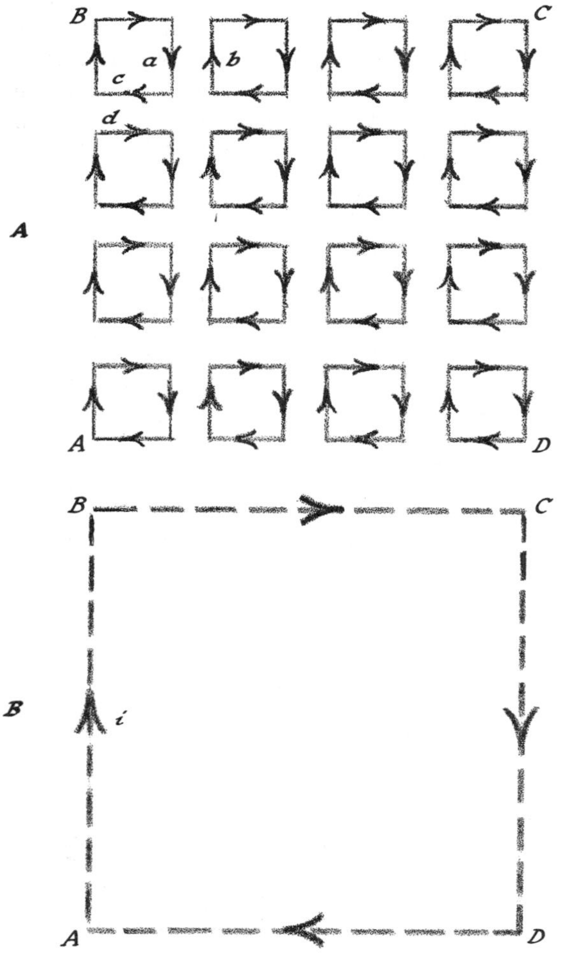

FIG. 39.12. *How one current loop can represent a number of current loops.*

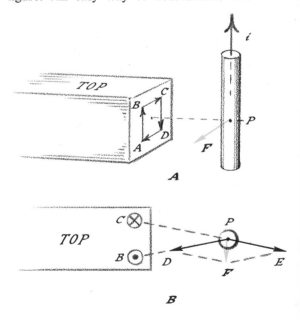

FIG. 39.13. *The force between a magnet and a current-carrying wire.*

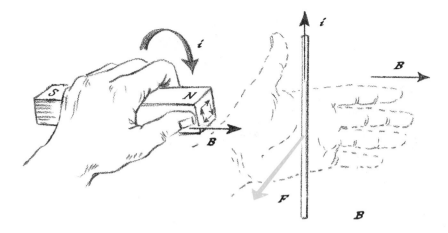

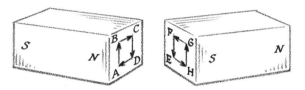

FIG. 39.14. *The idea of amperian currents permits us to explain the force between a magnet and a wire as a force between currents: (A) The current loops in the magnet are responsible for* **B.** *(B) The left-hand rule predicts that thrust* **F** *on current* i *will point out of the paper as shown.*

magnetize a piece of thin piano wire by drawing it across the poles of a strong permanent magnet or electromagnet. (There is a trick to doing this, but let us assume that you get just two poles, one at each end of the wire.) Test the polarity of the ends by bringing them close to a magnetic needle. Now cut the wire with a pair of heavy shears. The polarity of the ends of the pieces will be found to agree with that of Figure 39.15. The process may be repeated many times, and each piece will always exhibit both N and S polarities, confirming experimentally the fact that poles cannot be isolated.

An unmagnetized iron nail, *A*, behaves like a magnet (Fig. 39.16) when brought near a strong magnet. It can pick up another nail, *B*, as long as it is near the magnet. Try to explain this effect, called *magnetization by induction*, by the effect the field of the bar magnet has on the elementary current elements of *A*. You can demonstrate the effect of temperature by heating nail *B* with a Bunsen flame. When the nail reaches a certain temperature, it loses its induced magnetism and falls. The exact temperature at which a body loses its magnetism because of heat, known as the Curie point, can be predicted by modern physics. In a qualitative way you can conceive that the molecular agitation due to heating would disturb the alignment of dipole moments and thereby weaken the magnetization.

FIG. 39.15. *The attraction between magnets visualized as an attraction between currents.*

39.4. Ferromagnetism, Paramagnetism, and Diamagnetism

In a more advanced textbook of 634 pages on the physics of electricity and magnetism I find the following statement: "The explanation of the properties of magnetic materials is a complicated subject, involving atomic physics, physics of the solid state, physical chemistry and some nuclear physics. In a textbook on electricity and magnetism we can only consider certain limited aspects of this complicated problem."[†] It goes without saying that my treatment of the subject is very limited indeed in comparison. But I shall mention some well-known qualitative facts even though I cannot go into the theory behind them.

At first glance it looks as if there were only

† William Taussig Scott, *The Physics of Electricity and Magnetism* (John Wiley & Sons, 1959), p. 371.

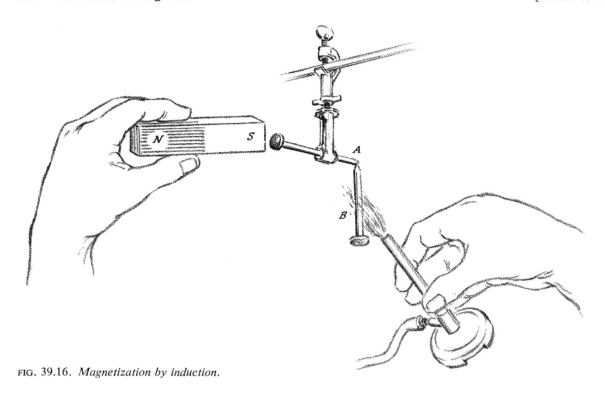

FIG. 39.16. *Magnetization by induction.*

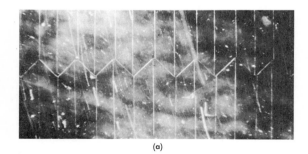

(a)

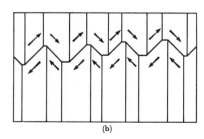

(b)

FIG. 39.17. (*a*) *Photograph of a domain pattern of a single crystal with a zigzag boundary.* (*b*) *Sketch showing directions of magnetization.* (*From the Bell Telephone Laboratories.*)

one material, iron, that exhibited strong magnetic effects, but experimental and theoretical investigation shows that in iron, cobalt, and nickel, and in certain alloys, adjacent atoms are locked into parallel alignment by especially strong coupling between their magnetic moments. These substances are said to exhibit **ferromagnetism** (see also § 39.3). In most substances, the orbital and spin magnetic moments have random orientation, which cancels out their effects; in the ferromagnetic substances, however, the forces between atoms are such that the magnetic moments line up and add constructively to the total field. Today it is known that macroscopic domains containing many atoms with their current loops all lined up constitute the basic magnetic regions (Fig. 39.17). It is also known that the electron spin rather than the orbital magnetic moment is mainly responsible for the ferromagnetic effect.

Two weaker magnetic effects, paramagnetism and diamagnetism, are of great theoretical importance. **Paramagnetism** is somewhat similar to ferromagnetism in that the magnetic moments of the electrons in an atom do not average out to zero but have a resultant magnetic dipole moment that causes the atomic dipole to line up with the field. Aluminum, neodymium, oxygen, palladium, platinum, and air have paramagnetic properties. **Diamagnetism** is exhibited by substances whose magnetic moments do add up to zero; by the application of a magnetic field their atoms or molecules are given a magnetic moment whose direction is opposite to that of the field. It is a very weak effect, but it is the one effect that is felt by all atoms. It is completely masked, of course, by the much stronger ferromagnetism.

In conclusion, magnetism is of great theoretical interest today for two reasons. First, it has been discovered that even the basic uncharged particle, the **neutron,** has a magnetic moment. Because it is uncharged, the neutron can penetrate solid matter with ease; and, because it has a magnetic moment, it can relay signals about the magnetic state of the regions it explores. Second, we can achieve extremely low temperatures by utilizing certain transformations of magnetic energy. The low temperatures make possible the creation of large currents without production of heat. Such currents make very strong magnetic fields possible. We need such fields to contain by magnetic deflection the rarified populations of charged particles known today as **plasma.** Certain nuclear processes that take place in the sun cannot be simulated in man-made laboratories until sufficiently strong magnetic fluxes are available.

I have barely introduced the subject of magnetism; but, if you carry with you the concepts of Amperian current and dipole moment, you will have two basic ideas on which to build the logical structure that follows.

39.5. Summary

Magnetic poles cannot be isolated. A pair of equal and opposite poles, called a dipole, has a magnetic dipole moment, μ, such that, when the dipole is placed in a field of magnetic induction **B**, it experiences a torque, $\mu \times \mathbf{B}$. A coil carrying an electric current, an isolated circulating electric charge, and a spinning electron also have magnetic dipole moments. An external magnetic field produces on them a torque that tends to line up the magnetic dipole moments with the field. An adequate theory of magnetism, first proposed by Ampère, can be built on the idea of currents circulating within matter. Their magnetic dipole moments account for the torques that act on individual circulating electrons and on the gross matter in which they are embedded. A refinement of this theory indicates that the dipole moment due to electron spin rather than that due to orbital motion is responsible for ferromagnetism.

Problems

39.1. Units for electric dipole moment, **p**, in the MKS system are coul-m. Electric field intensity is measured in nt/coul. The vector product $\mathbf{p} \times \mathbf{E}$ has the units of a torque, nt-m.

1. An electric dipole consists of opposite charges each of magnitude 5 μcoul. The separation between them is 0.02 m. What is the magnitude of the dipole moment in coul-m?

2. A potential difference of 1,000 V is placed across parallel metal plates 0.15 m apart. What is the electric field intensity between them in nt/coul? (Remember: V/m = nt/coul.)

3. What is the *maximum* torque (in nt-m) that could be experienced by the electric dipole of part 1 placed in the field of part 2?

39.2. 1. Two bar magnets are placed on the same straight line with the S pole of one near the N pole of the other. Draw the field lines between the nearby poles.

2. The same two magnets are placed on the line with the N pole of one near the N pole of the other. Draw the field lines between the nearby poles.

3. Explain the attraction and the repulsion in terms of the properties of field lines.

39.3. Repeating Oersted's experiment (§ 38.2.3), we find that, when a current is established in a wire 2 cm away, the compass needle comes to rest at an angle of 75° from the earth's magnetic field, which has a horizontal intensity of 1.77×10^{-5} weber/m² at that point. Calculate, in amperes, the magnitude of the current in the wire. (Remember that the field intensity at distance r from a wire carrying current i is $B = ki/r$.)

The following information will be useful in Probs. 39.4, 39.5, 39.6, and 39.7: Units for magnetic dipole moment, μ, in the MKS system are amp-m², as may be seen from equation 39.7. Magnetic induction, **B**, can be measured in webers/m² or in the equivalent nt/amp-m. The vector product $\mu \times \mathbf{B}$ has the units of a torque, nt-m.

39.4. A bar magnet set in a uniform magnetic field whose strength is 10^{-3} weber/m² feels a maximum torque of 4 nt-m.

1. What is the position of the magnet in relation to the field direction corresponding to this maximum torque?

2. Compute the dipole moment of the magnet.

39.5. 1. A magnetic needle experiences a maximum torque of 2×10^{-3} nt-m in a homogeneous magnetic field whose intensity is 3 webers/m². What is the magnetic dipole moment of the needle?

2. In Example 39.1 the magnetic dipole moment of a circulating electron was computed to be 9.27×10^{-24} amp-m². What maximum torque would such a circulating electron feel in a magnetic field of intensity 0.3 weber/m²?

39.6. Compute the torque exerted on a magnet whose dipole moment is $\mu = 20$ amp-m² set in a magnetic field of 0.2 gauss when the angle between the direction of the field and that of the line joining the poles of the magnet is 60°.

39.7. Suppose that the dimensions of the rectangular coil in Fig. 39.8 are 3 cm × 2 cm.

1. If the current, i, is 8 amp and the magnitude of the magnetic induction is 1,500 gauss, what is the maximum torque (in nt-m) that could act on the coil?

2. In what direction will the coil turn under the influence of this torque?

3. In what direction will the magnetic field of the current-carrying coil itself point after the coil has turned to minimize the torque acting on it?

4. Will the coil's magnetic field tend to augment or diminish the field of the magnet?

39.8. Explain magnetization by induction, as exemplified in Fig. 39.16, by describing the effect that the magnetic field of the bar magnet has on the magnetic dipole moments of the electrons of nail A.

A Simple Electric Circuit: Ohm's Law

WE BEGIN this chapter by considering the operational steps we might take, in an elementary laboratory, in order to learn more about electric current. We shall then try to build up a theory that accounts for our observations.

40.1. A Simple Series Circuit: Measurement of Potential Difference

Figure 40.1 shows what our apparatus looks like: *A*, a six-volt storage battery; *B*, a lamp in a socket; *C*, a knife switch; *D*, a voltmeter; *E*, an ammeter; *F*, some connecting wires. From now on

we shall, as much as possible, use the shorthand of conventional diagrams, as in Figure 40.2, which shows battery *A*, lamp *B* (the zigzag line is actually the symbol for an element with resistance), and switch *C* connected in series. When the switch is closed, the lamp lights up. We say that there is an electric current or that there is a flow of electric charge, but we don't, of course, see anything flowing. The fact that the bulb lights up when the switch is closed is the only outward sign that anything flows.

It is not uncommon to begin such an experiment with little or no knowledge of what is inside the magic boxes *A*, *B*, *D*, and *E* (Fig. 40.1). All we

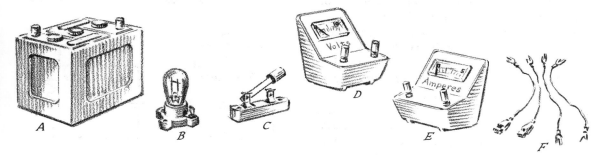

FIG. 40.1. *Apparatus needed for a simple experiment with electric circuits:* A, *a 6-V battery;* B, *a lamp in a socket;* C, *a knife switch;* D, *a voltmeter;* E, *an ammeter;* F, *typical connecting wires, two of the clips on which are called alligator clips.*

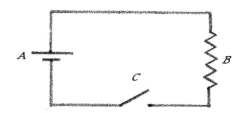

FIG. 40.2. *Schematic diagram of a series circuit including a battery*, A, *connected to a lamp*, B (*shown here as a resistor*), *through a switch*, C.

know is that *D* measures potential difference and that *E* measures current. In this chapter we shall look inside *B*, *D*, and *E*. The battery, *A*, however, will have to remain just an electron pump; I shall leave its inner details out of the discussion because they involve the complicated molecular mechanism by which chemical energy is converted into electrical energy.

We want to understand why the voltmeter readings of Figure 40.3 are what they are at different places. We are going to limit ourselves in this chapter to an understanding of the simple circuit of Figure 40.2. We shall move more slowly than is customary in a chapter on electric circuits, and only when we peek inside the voltmeter and the ammeter shall we see slightly more complicated circuits in series and in parallel. Our immediate objective is limited; but, if you understand all the details of this discussion, you will have a firm grasp of fundamentals.

We first notice, as we consider the reading of the voltmeter in different parts of Figure 40.3, *that we do not need to disturb the circuit when we take a voltmeter reading.* We simply connect the voltmeter to two points of the circuit.

Next we observe and record the data, and then we try to explain them by theory. When the voltmeter (Fig. 40.3) is connected across the battery (A), it reads 6 volts if the switch is open; with the switch closed (B) it reads 5.45 volts. Connected across the lamp, it reads 0 if the switch is open (C) and 5.45 volts if the switch is closed (D). Connected across one of the connecting wires, it reads 0 whether the switch is open (E) or closed (F).

If the voltmeter is telling the truth, the potential

difference across the terminals of the battery is 6 volts when there is no current in the circuit (A). The potential difference across the battery drops when there is current (B). There is no potential difference across the terminals of the lamp (C) until the switch is closed (D), and there is never a measurable potential difference across one of the connecting wires. Our theory of what is going on must account for all these readings (and a lot more).

Let's begin our description of what we think is going on. We have already encountered a momentary flow of charge in electrostatic experiments, but something different is obviously happening here, for this current can flow for a long time. Something replenishes the charge; something maintains a potential difference that produces a steady flow of charge. This something, in our experiment, is the battery. The terminals of the battery are *charged* in the very sense in which we used the word in electrostatics. If our battery has only two terminals, an electric field surrounds

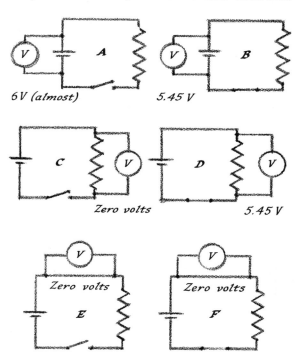

FIG. 40.3. *Readings on a voltmeter as it is connected to different parts of a series circuit that is sometimes open and sometimes closed.*

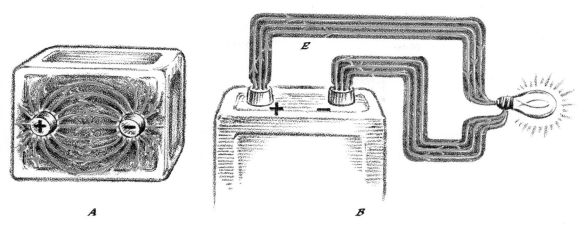

FIG. 40.4. (A) *The electric field lines in air surrounding the terminals of a battery.* (B) *The electric field lines within a wire connecting the two terminals of a battery through a lamp.*

them as if they constituted an electric dipole. Figure 40.4.A shows the electric field between the two battery terminals. It looks very much like the electric field between two charged metal balls on insulating stands; but there is a difference in what happens to these fields if the terminals are connected with a wire. A wire connecting one charged ball to the other would carry current only for an instant, for the potential difference between them would soon be zero, and the field would vanish. If the terminals of the battery are connected, a large current can exist in the wire for a much longer time, and the field between the terminals will still be like that of Figure 40.4.A after the wire is removed. In Figure 40.4.B we see the electric field lines (**E**) that come into existence *within* the wire that runs from one terminal through the lamp to the other terminal. I said earlier that there can be no electric field within a conductor, but that is true only in the electrostatic case. Charges move in the wire of Figure 40.4.B *because* there is an electric field within it.

Since the lamp gets hot, it is obvious that energy is involved. It looks very much as if something were playing the role that friction plays in mechanics. Something *is* playing that role; it is called *resistance* (defined in § 40.3), and we shall soon consider it in some detail.

Let us now recall the definition of electric field, **E**, as **F**/q, the force per unit charge (§ 4.4). An electron finding itself in electric field **E** experiences the force $\mathbf{F} = -e\mathbf{E}$. It should experience the acceleration $\mathbf{a} = \mathbf{F}/m$, and it does, but it cannot pick up much speed, for it collides with other electrons. The average behavior of many electrons, starting and stopping, is, nevertheless, a general drift in the direction of $-e\mathbf{E}$. Statistically, the free electrons drift at an average speed determined by the magnitude of the force $-e\mathbf{E}$.

The idea of motion at a constant speed under the action of balanced forces can be perfectly illustrated by the falling of small spheres (such as marbles) through a tall glass beaker containing glycerin (Fig. 40.5.A); balls of the right weight and dimensions achieve a terminal velocity. The force of gravity, $m\mathbf{g}$, pulls them downward, but a viscous frictional force, **f**, pushes them upward. When $m\mathbf{g} = \mathbf{f}$, the acceleration is zero (see § 5.2).

A positive charge, q, in electric field **E** feels the force $q\mathbf{E}$ (Fig. 40.5.B). If it also feels an equal retarding force, **f**, it can move at a constant speed. What happens in a wire is somewhat like this. For two reasons, however, you must not take any such picture literally. First, no electron travels for long without hitting another, and the concept of drift velocity is therefore purely statistical. (It takes a lot of kinetic energy to carry an electron into contact with another, even when the other is anchored to an atom. What I have called hitting just means being decelerated by a force

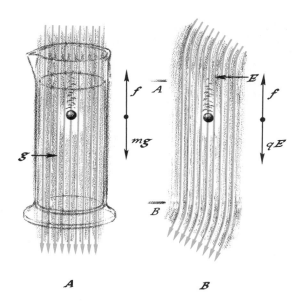

FIG. 40.5. (A) The gravitational field lines running through a tall glass beaker containing glycerin; little spheres fall through it at a constant speed. (B) The electric field lines in a wire; electric charges move with a constant average speed within the wire.

field. Here it would pay you to re-read § 3.7, dealing with the concept of contact.) Second, electrons have a negative charge and move opposite to E, but this does not damage the model of Figure 40.5.

Traditionally, the direction of current in a wire has been taken as from the positive to the negative pole (in the part of the circuit outside the battery). In this book, since it is now known that in a wire the electrons do the moving, I have broken with tradition by assigning to i the direction of electron flow. But I shall use the symbol $I (= -i)$ for the conventional direction (from positive to negative) whenever it can simplify the wording of statements. All the left-hand rules I gave in the study of magnetism relate to i. If we associate the *right hand* with I, similar rules apply. In other words, I is the direction in which positive charges would move in a wire. Since positive charges tend to move from a region of high electric potential to one of low potential, it is con-

venient to use the traditional symbol for current, I, in these cases. (We simply need to remember that the electrons in metallic conductors move in the opposite direction; in liquids, however, positive as well as negative charged bodies move.) Whenever we use the symbol q without any further specification, it will represent a positive charge. The electronic charge will, of course, be written as $-e$.

There are two ways of expressing the reason why a ball moves downward through the beaker of glycerin. One is to say that it moves down because mg points downward; the other is to say that it has a tendency to move from a region of high potential to one of low potential. The same language applies to *positive* charges in an electric field: they move from A to B in Figure 40.5.B because qE points that way, or (since an applied force would do work in moving a positive charge from B to A) they move from a region of high potential to one of low potential.

Potential difference, V, is measured in volts, which we identified earlier (§ 37.2) with joules per coulomb. The work that will move charge Δq through distance x from B to A is (by the formula "work equals force times distance") $\Delta U = (\Delta q)Ex$. The work per unit charge is $\Delta U/\Delta q = Ex$. The left-hand side has the units joules per coulomb, or volts. The right-hand side has newtons per coulomb times meters for units. This equivalence is worth remembering. We may write

$$V = Ex \qquad [40.1$$

or

$$E = V/x \qquad [40.2$$

Now we are getting somewhere. The quantities on the right-hand side of the second equation are measurable, V with a voltmeter (we'd better find out how it works), x with a meter stick.

If we connected a voltmeter across points A and B of Figure 40.5.B, would it show a reading? I said earlier (Fig. 40.3.F) that there is no detectable reading across a wire carrying current. You will have to take my word for it that a certain very sensitive kind of voltmeter would indicate a small potential difference between points A and B if there were a current in the wire.

EXAMPLE 40.1. A sensitive voltmeter indicates a potential difference of 10^{-6} V between points A and B of Fig. 40.5.B. The distance between the points is $x = 2$ m. We wish to know (1) what force, in newtons, an electron feels within the wire; (2) what acceleration it experiences; (3) what the increment in its speed is if it travels for 10^{-7} sec.

1. The force on a charge, q, is $F = Eq$. Since, by equation 40.2, $E = V/x$, we know that $F = Vq/x$. We are given that

$$V = 10^{-6} \text{ V}$$
$$q = -e = -1.60 \times 10^{-19} \text{ coul}$$
$$x = 2 \text{ m}$$

Therefore, if we drop the minus sign,

$$F = \frac{10^{-6} \times 1.60 \times 10^{-19}}{2} \text{ nt}$$
$$= 8 \times 10^{-26} \text{ nt}$$

2. The acceleration is $a = F/m$. We know that

$$F = 8 \times 10^{-26} \text{ nt}$$
$$m = 9.11 \times 10^{-31} \text{ kg}$$

Therefore

$$a = \frac{8 \times 10^{-26} \text{ nt}}{9.11 \times 10^{-31} \text{ kg}}$$
$$= 8.78 \times 10^{4} \text{ m/sec}^2$$

3. We know that

$$\Delta v/\Delta t = a$$

Therefore

$$\Delta v = a(\Delta t)$$
$$= 8.78 \times 10^{4} \text{ m/sec}^2 \times 10^{-7} \text{ sec}$$
$$= 8.78 \times 10^{-3} \text{ m/sec}$$

There are experimental reasons for believing that this is of the right order of magnitude for the average speed of electrons in a wire.

40.2. Electromotive Force

We can extend the analogy of balls falling through glycerin to a simple electric circuit.

In Figure 40.6.A we see balls rolling and falling under the action of the earth's gravitational field, **g**. If the balls are to keep moving at a constant rate, work has to be done against gravitational force as each ball is lifted from D to A. The energy is supplied by the man, who acquires it by the complicated chemical process that transforms food energy into mechanical energy. Notice that there is a small difference in gravitational potential, $g(\Delta h_1)$, between points A and B, a large differ-

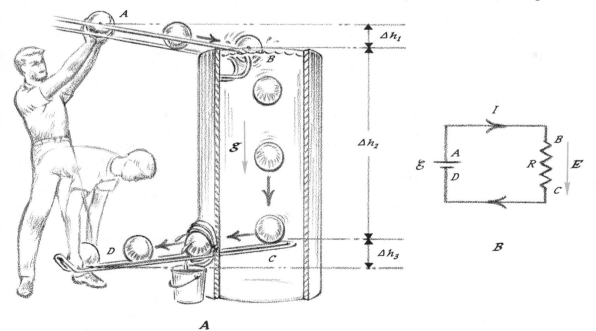

FIG. 40.6. *Analogy between the effect of the earth's gravitational field and that of an electric field.*

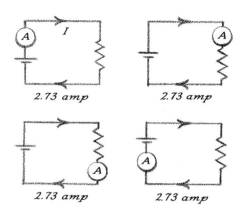

FIG. 40.7. *How an ammeter will read when connected in different parts of a circuit.*

ence, $g(\Delta h_2)$, between points B and C, and a small difference again, $g(\Delta h_3)$, between points C and D. In this arrangement a "potential-difference meter" (analogous to a voltmeter) could consist of an ordinary meter stick.

The frictional force on each ball as it falls in the glycerin from B to C is equal to its weight. This makes the resultant force zero, which is what is required for descent at a constant speed. The frictional force on each ball in AB and CD is much smaller than its weight. This is suggested by the small slope of the inclined planes in these regions. The man has to do work mgh ($h = \Delta h_1 + \Delta h_2 + \Delta h_3$) on each ball to move it from D back to A so that it can start the cycle again.

In Figure 40.6.B we have the electrical counterpart of Figure 40.6.A, a complete electric circuit, $ABCD$. Electric charges are moving under the influence of the electric field, $\mathbf{E}$. The potential difference between points A and B is very small because the charges encounter only a slight resistance to their motion in this region. The potential difference between points B and C is great because the resistance there is great; the letter R signifies, in fact, that this portion of the circuit, like the lamp in Figure 40.2, is a **resistor** (a conductor with relatively large resistance). There is only a small potential difference between C and D. The charges have a low potential at D, and it takes energy, which is supplied by the battery, to lift them to a high potential at A. The battery transforms chemical into electrical energy by a complicated process, which I shall not analyze

any more than I analyzed the internal workings of the man of Figure 40.6.A.

The ability of the battery to raise positive charges from a low potential at D to a high potential at A is measured by the number of joules per coulomb, $\Delta W/\Delta q$, it needs in order to do this. (It is actually electrons, with negative charges, that are moving—and the other way round; but this poses only semantic problems. We could talk the whole thing out by using different words, but we are here adhering to the classical idea that current consists of positive charges whose potential is *raised* in going from D to A.) The ratio $\Delta W/\Delta q$ is called the **electromotive force** (abbreviated as emf) of the battery and is symbolized as $\mathcal{E}$. It is the work per unit charge done by the battery in moving positive charges against the electric field within the battery. It is not, of course, a force in the Newtonian sense; it is measured in joules per coulomb, or volts, not in newtons; but the word "force" has become firmly established in the vocabulary of electricity. Since $\Delta W/\Delta q$ is measured in volts, you might ask why we do not simply say that $\mathcal{E}$ is the difference in potential between points D and A. The answer is that the battery itself may have internal resistance, and that the potential difference between points D and A may therefore be somewhat less than $\mathcal{E}$, depending on how much internal resistance there is. Ideally, with no internal resistance, $\mathcal{E}$, measured in volts, would be equal to the difference in potential between points D and A.

Let us return, for illustration, to Figure 40.3. The voltmeter showed (B) a potential difference of 5.45 volts between D and A *when there was electric current in the circuit*. This was not, however, the emf of the battery. *The potential difference across the terminals of a battery is never exactly equal to its emf when there is current through the battery.* When the switch is open (A), the potential difference is *almost* 6 volts. We have to hedge here because some charges flow even when the voltmeter alone is connected across the battery; the potential difference is not quite equal to the emf unless the resistance of the voltmeter is infinite—that is, unless the voltmeter draws no current. *A good voltmeter, obviously, has a very high resistance.*

I have been using the term "resistance" in a qualitative way. In order to define it precisely, I have to measure current. Notice that the argument so far has not depended upon current. I have talked only of potential difference ("voltage" in the vernacular of the electrician). But perhaps our rolling-ball analogy (Fig. 40.6) has shown why the reading of the voltmeter in Figure 40.3.F was zero. (It corresponded to a vanishingly small Δh_1.) The *potential rise* ($\mathcal{E} = \Delta W/\Delta q$) within the battery—that is, the emf—must equal the sum of the *potential drops* (ΔV) in the complete circuit or loop. We let V_{AB} mean "the potential difference between points A and B." Since V_{AB} and V_{CD} (Fig. 40.6.B) are both practically zero, the voltmeter readings of Figure 40.3.B,D are practically identical. We now imagine (Fig. 40.6) connecting one terminal of the voltmeter to point A. We then touch points B, C, and D with a wire connected to the other terminal of the voltmeter. We read that $V_{AB} = 0$, that $V_{AC} = 5.45$ volts, and that $V_{AD} = 5.45$ volts. The reason for this is that

$$V_{AD} = V_{AB} + V_{BC} + V_{CD}$$
$$= 0 + 5.45 \text{ V} + 0 = 5.45 \text{ V}$$

Before we can proceed, we need to define resistance in terms of potential difference and current.

40.3. Ohm's Law

We shall now use the ammeter in the circuit of Figure 40.3. *To use an ammeter, you must break into the circuit at some point and allow the current to pass through the ammeter.*† Figure 40.7 shows that the ammeter reads 2.73 amperes in each of four different positions. This simply means that charges are conserved. The number of charges flowing per second past any point in the circuit must be the same as the number flowing per second past any other point; otherwise charges would be either accumulating or leaking away. If, for

† Two interesting exceptions to this statement are: (1) a special alternating-current ammeter that just clamps its coil round the current-carrying wire; (2) a special direct-current meter, used by automobile electricians, that works essentially like Oersted's experiment; it is simply clipped onto the battery-charging line.

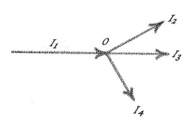

FIG. 40.8. *The sum of inward currents at a junction is equal to the sum of outward currents.*

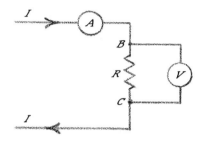

FIG. 40.9. *One way to connect an ammeter and a voltmeter to measure the resistance of a resistor.*

example (Fig. 40.8), we have a junction, O, where the currents are I_1, I_2, I_3, and I_4, it must be true that $\Sigma I = 0$—that is, that $I_1 + I_2 + I_3 + I_4 = 0$—if we consider "coming into O" as positive and "leaving O" as negative.

So far Figure 40.7 simply confirms the fact that the current in a single loop is the same everywhere, including the battery. Outside the battery, positive charges tend to flow from regions of high to regions of low potential; inside the battery, the energy supplied by the battery makes it possible for positive charges to flow against the electric field that is naturally there (compare DA in the rolling-ball analogy, Figure 40.6.A).

We now need an experimental fact about metallic conductors. If such a conductor (labeled BC) is connected as in Figure 40.9, the ammeter will show the current in it, and the voltmeter will show the voltage across it. If different currents, I, are made to flow through it, different voltages, V, will appear across it. A plot of V against I is a straight line going through the origin (Fig. 40.10); that is, the ratio of V to I is constant. (This is not true of all kinds of conductors; it is not true, for example, of vacuum tubes or of certain types of crystals.) I shall now *define*, by the following equation, the quantity called the **resistance, R,** of the conductor *BC*:

$$R = \frac{V}{I} \qquad [40.3$$

For some materials (for many different kinds of metallic wires, for example) and under certain conditions (at constant temperature, for example) the resistance defined in this way is a constant, independent of *I*. For other kinds of conductors (vacuum tubes, for example) the *R* defined in this way is not independent of *I*. In all cases the resistance defined by equation 40.3 is measured in **ohms**. Obviously, "volts divided by amperes" is equivalent to ohms. Equation 40.3 is known as **Ohm's law** after Georg Simon Ohm, a German physicist (1787–1854).

If the current is *I* and the cross-sectional area

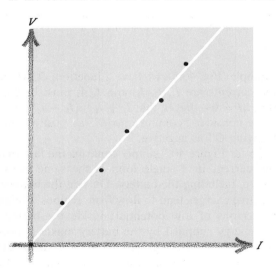

FIG. 40.10. *A plot of voltage against current in an ohmic conductor.*

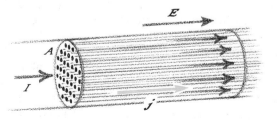

FIG. 40.11. *Illustrating the definition of current density.*

FIG. 40.12. *The voltage drop between* P_1 *and* P_2 *is so small that the bird feels no shock.*

of the wire is *A*, the **current density, j,** has the magnitude

$$j = \frac{I}{A} \qquad [40.4$$

and is measured in amperes per square meter. For the class of conductors I have been talking about (called **ohmic conductors**) it is an experimental fact that the electric field intensity, **E**, established inside the wire (Fig. 40.11) is proportional to the current density in the wire. In other words, experiments show that

$$\mathbf{E} \propto \mathbf{j} \qquad [40.5$$

(I have written **j** as a vector because **E** is a vector.) There must be a constant of proportionality, ρ, such that

$$\mathbf{E} = \rho\mathbf{j} \qquad [40.6$$

Remembering that **E** is measured in volts per meter (equation 40.2), let us find the potential difference, *V*, across a length, *l*, of wire as follows. Dropping the vector notation, we have

$$El = \rho jl \qquad [40.7$$

Using equation 40.4, we get

$$El = \rho \frac{I}{A} l \qquad [40.8$$

But, according to equation 40.2, *El* = *V*. Therefore

$$V = \rho \frac{I}{A} l \qquad [40.9$$

FIG. 40.13. *The voltage drop between* Q_1 *and* Q_2 *might be great enough to kill the bird.*

or

$$\frac{V}{I} = \frac{\rho l}{A} \qquad [40.10$$

But this is the ratio that defines resistance, R (equation 40.3). Hence

$$R = \frac{\rho l}{A} \qquad [40.11$$

That is, the resistance of a wire is directly proportional to its length and inversely proportional to its cross-sectional area. [I could have introduced ρ by means of equation 40.11, but I wanted to emphasize, once again (equation 40.6), the existence of an electric field within a wire carrying a current.] The constant of proportionality, ρ, is called the **resistivity** of the material. Resistivity is the inverse of conductivity. Table 37.2 lists the resistivities of some common substances.

EXAMPLE 40.2. We wish to find the resistance of a piece of copper wire 1 km long and 1 mm in diameter.

We know that

$$\rho = 0.172 \times 10^{-7} \text{ ohm-meter}$$
$$l = 10^3 \text{ m}$$
$$d = 10^{-3} \text{ m}$$

Therefore

$$A = \frac{\pi d^2}{4} = 7.85 \times 10^{-7} \text{ m}^2$$

and (equation 40.11)

$$R = \frac{0.172 \times 10^{-7} \text{ ohm-meter} \times 10^3 \text{ m}}{7.85 \times 10^{-7} \text{ m}^2}$$
$$= 21.9 \text{ ohms}$$

(The filament of an ordinary 100-W light bulb has a resistance of about 100 ohms.)

We can now consider the *voltage drop* in wires carrying current. You have seen birds perched on such wires without being killed and apparently without feeling any shock. Now, one of the harmful things in electric shock, to birds or to people, is the current through the body. This current obeys, approximately, Ohm's law, which implies that we get big currents through the body if we touch points with large potential differences.

There *is* a voltage drop, $V = IR$ (see equation 40.3), in a wire, but the potential difference (Fig. 40.12) between points P_1 and P_2, where the bird's feet rest on the wire, is exceedingly small. In Example 40.2 we saw that the resistance of 1,000 meters of a certain copper wire was 21.9 ohms. The resistance of 10 centimeters would be only 21.9×10^{-4} ohm. Even if the wire carried a current of 100 amperes (very unlikely), the potential drop from P_1 to P_2 would be only 0.219 volt. Such a small potential difference could not send enough current through the bird to do much harm.

A great potential drop might occur (Fig. 40.13) across some distant load—a motor, M, perhaps.

Hence the potential difference between points Q_1 and Q_2 on wires carrying the same current might be very great indeed. If the bird could put one foot at Q_1 and the other at Q_2, it might be killed.

We can now consider our original circuit symbolically. In Figure 40.14 the battery, B, with its internal resistance, r, is enclosed in a dashed line; the lamp, L, has resistance R. The current, I, is the same in both B and L. The potential drop in L is IR (equation 40.3); the potential drop in B is Ir. The charges leave point P at the same potential at which they arrive there. The work per unit charge done by the battery, $\varepsilon = \Delta W/\Delta q$, must therefore exactly equal the drop in potential, $IR + Ir$. Hence

$$\varepsilon - Ir = IR \qquad [40.12$$

Now Figure 40.3 indicates (D) that $IR = 5.45$ volts and (B) that $\varepsilon - Ir = 5.45$ volts. From Figure 40.7 we see that $I = 2.73$ amperes. Therefore

$$R = \frac{5.45 \text{ V}}{2.73 \text{ amp}} = 2 \text{ ohms} \qquad [40.13$$

From Figure 40.3.A we know that ε is almost 6 volts. Therefore, using the equation

$$\varepsilon - Ir = 5.45 \text{ V} \qquad [40.14$$

we get

$$Ir = (6 - 5.45) \text{ V}$$
$$= 0.55 \text{ V} \qquad [40.15$$

But $I = 2.73$ amperes. Therefore

$$r = \frac{0.55 \text{ V}}{2.73 \text{ amp}}$$

$$= 0.2 \text{ ohm}$$

We have now accounted for the voltage readings of Figure 40.3, and we have learned something about electric circuits in the process.

40.4. How the Ammeter and the Voltmeter Work

I have already told how a galvanometer works; it is a coil, mounted between the poles of a magnet, whose dipole moment experiences a torque when it carries current (§ 38.4). If (Fig. 40.15.A,C) a low-resistance conductor, S (called a shunt), is connected across the coil, C, in parallel with it, most of the current flows through S, and we have

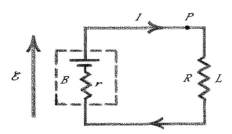

FIG. 40.14. *Our original series circuit treated symbolically. The internal resistance of the battery is shown as* r. *If* ε *is the emf of the battery,* ε − Ir = IR.

an **ammeter**. The combination, which has a low resistance, can be designed to measure even a large current, for very little of the current flows through the coil.

The same galvanometer can be converted into a **voltmeter** (Fig. 40.15.B,D). If the coil, C, is connected in series with a resistor, M, of high resistance (called a multiplier), even a large potential difference, V, across the terminals A and B will produce only a small current through the coil, C, since $I = V/R$ and R here includes the resistance of both M and C. The whole device has, as a good voltmeter must have, a high resistance. The details may be clarified by reference to Problems 40.15, 40.16, and 40.17.

It is also left for Problem 40.14 to prove that, when two resistors are connected in series, the resistance of the combination is simply the sum of the two resistances, but that, when they are connected in parallel, the reciprocal of the combination is the sum of the reciprocals of the individual resistors. For resistors in series (as in Fig. 40.15.B,D)

$$R = R_1 + R_2 \qquad [40.16$$

For resistors in parallel (as in Fig. 40.15.A,C)

$$\frac{1}{R} = \frac{1}{R_1} + \frac{1}{R_2} \qquad [40.17$$

40.5. Electric Power Dissipated as Heat

The analogy of balls falling through glycerin (Fig. 40.6.A) is useful, for we see immediately that the loss in potential energy must appear as heat. Similarly, the loss in potential energy of charges moving in the resistor, R, of Figure 40.6.B can appear in the form of heat. The work required to lift a ball in Figure 40.6.A is $W = mgh$. The work per unit mass is $W/m = gh$. Similarly, the work required to move the positive charge Δq from B to A is

$$\Delta W = (\Delta q)V_{BA} = \text{coulombs} \times \text{volts}$$

$$= \text{coulombs} \times \frac{\text{joules}}{\text{coulomb}} = \text{joules}$$

The rate of doing work, P (for power), is

$$P = \frac{\Delta W}{\Delta t} = \frac{\Delta q}{\Delta t} V_{BA} \qquad [40.18$$

But $\Delta q/\Delta t$ is the current, I, in amperes. Hence $P = IV_{BA}$. This must be in joules per second, or watts. If all this power goes into heating the resistor, we may write

$$P_J = IV \qquad [40.19$$

The subscript J is for "joule," to remind us that heat is being generated. Thus "amperes times volts" is equivalent to "watts." Since 4.184 joules = 1 calorie, we may use the expression $IV/4.184$ to compute the calories per second generated in a resistor.

From Ohm's law (equation 40.3) we know that $V = IR$; so we may write

$$P_J = I(IR) = I^2R \qquad [40.20$$

Since, if several resistors are connected in series, they all carry the same I, this form of the equation ($P_J = I^2R$) is useful.

On the other hand, since $I = V/R$, we may write

$$P_J = \frac{V}{R} V = \frac{V^2}{R} \qquad [40.21$$

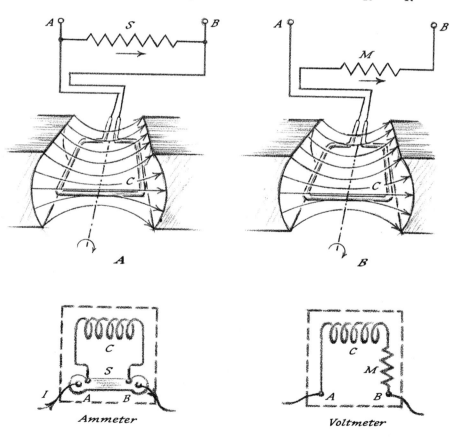

FIG. 40.15. *Symbolic representation of the components (A, C) of an ammeter and (B, D) of a voltmeter.*

Since, if several resistors are connected in parallel, each has the same potential drop as the others, this form ($P_J = V^2/R$) is applicable to such combinations.

40.6. Summary

A battery has the ability to raise positive charges from a low potential to a high potential. Positive charges in an external electric circuit connected to this battery tend to flow from the region of high potential to that of low potential. This flow is called current. Actually, in wires, negative charges (electrons) flow in the opposite direction, but the logic is not affected.

The work per unit charge done by the battery is called its electromotive force, ε; it is the ratio $\Delta W/\Delta q$, measured in joules per coulomb, or volts.

The potential rise in the battery must equal the sum of all the potential drops, ΔV, in the whole circuit. The potential drop across an ohmic resistor of resistance R in which there is current I is $V = IR$ (Ohm's law). The resistance of a wire is directly proportional to the product of its length and its resistivity and is inversely proportional to its cross-sectional area.

The flow of charges in a wire is very similar to the flow of a liquid in a pipe. When several wires meet at a point, for example, the sum of the inward currents is equal to the sum of the outward currents.

In both pipes and wires energy can be dissipated in the form of heat. If the potential drop in a wire is V, the work it takes to move charge q across it is qV, and the rate of doing work, or power, is $P = IV$. The power that goes into heating a resistor may be written as I^2R or as V^2/R.

Problems

40.1. Two solid metal spheres, without touching each other, are supported by thick copper wires connected to the terminals of a battery. A third sphere, large enough to touch both of the other spheres simultaneously, is supported by an insulating handle and brought in slowly from a distance. Draw electric field lines both in air and within the thick copper wires for various static positions of the third sphere. Finally let it touch the other two, and draw the new fields as you imagine them both inside and outside all the conductors.

40.2. In Example 40.1 we concluded that the average speed of electrons in a wire was only a few mm/sec. We all know, however, that a telephone wire carries information electrically at a very great speed. How do you reconcile the two facts?

40.3. If a thick wire 5 m long were connected to the terminals of a 6-V storage battery, a strong electric field would be established within it. (It would also ruin the battery.)

1. What would be the electric field intensity within the wire in V/m and in nt/coul?

2. What would be the average force on an electron within the wire?

40.4. A wire has a diameter of 2.3 mm. The current in the wire is 3.5 amp.

1. Find the current density in the wire in amp/m².

2. Find the electric field intensity in the wire if its resistivity is 0.286×10^{-7} ohm-m.

3. What would be the force on an electron in the wire?

40.5. Another way of measuring current, alternative to that of Fig. 40.9, is to insert the ammeter between B and C, in series with the resistor, leaving the voltmeter across B and C.

1. If the ammeter had no resistance and the voltmeter had infinite resistance, would the change make any difference in their readings?

2. Suppose, in a possible but somewhat exaggerated case, that a good ammeter has very little resistance and that a good voltmeter has very high resistance. If resistance R is about the same as that of A, is it preferable to have A placed as in Fig. 40.9 or between B and C? Explain.

40.6. Consider a circuit like that of Fig. 40.3, but with different elements. The internal resistance of the battery is 0.25 ohm. When the voltmeter is connected across the battery with the switch open, as in part A, it reads 12 V; the current in the circuit with the switch closed is 3.2 amp.

1. What is the resistance of the external resistor?

2. What is the voltmeter's reading across the battery when the switch is closed?

40.7. Electrons are accelerated in a cathode-ray tube to a terminal speed of 40,000 km/sec.

1. Compute the potential difference across the electrodes that can impart this speed to an electron that starts from rest. (Hint: Treat the problem non-relativistically, and equate the electron's final kinetic energy with the work done by the electric field on its charge.)

2. If the electrons are focused on a rectangular sheet of platinum 1 mm thick and of area 1 cm², the temperature of the platinum rises from 20°C to 1,770°C (its melting point) in 1 min. The density of platinum is 21.4 gm/cm³, and its specific heat is 0.032 cal/gm/°C. Compute the current represented by the moving electrons.

40.8. The density of mercury is 13.6 gm/cm³, and that of copper is 8.9 gm/cm³. What is the length of a copper wire whose resistance is the same as that of a column of mercury 1 m high and of the same cross-sectional area?

40.9. A copper wire has a cross-sectional area of 0.8 mm². We replace it by an aluminum wire of the same length and same resistance. The density of copper is 8.9 gm/cm³, and that of aluminum is 2.7 gm/cm³.

1. What is the cross-sectional area of the aluminum wire?

2. What is the ratio of the masses of the two wires?

40.10. A 50-ohm resistor is connected in parallel with one of variable resistance, x. The system is connected through a 3-amp fuse to a source of potential difference of 110 V. For what value of x will the fuse blow out?

40.11. A 110-V line is fused to carry no more than 5 amp. How many 110-V 40-W incandescent lamps can be connected in parallel before the fuse blows out?

40.12. An electric toaster is rated at 1,000 W for use on 110 V. If it were accidentally connected to 220 V, what power would it momentarily dissipate before it burned out? (Assume that the resistance does not change, although in reality it does.)

40.13. One electric light bulb (A) is designed for 110 V and 50 W, another (B) for 110 V and 75 W. (You may make the simplifying assumption, not strictly justified when charges flow, that the bulbs have the same resistance when connected in series as when connected in parallel.)

1. In a normal house circuit they are connected in parallel. Which is brighter?

2. If they are connected in series to a 110-V line, find the potential drop across each lamp, and

3. Find the power dissipated in each.

4. Which lamp is now brighter?

40.14. 1. Two resistors are connected in series. Their resistances are r_1 and r_2. The current entering one is i. Prove that the potential difference across the system is $i(r_1) + i(r_2)$ and that the total resistance is therefore $r_1 + r_2$.

2. The same two resistors are connected in parallel to a source across whose terminals the potential difference is V. Current i enters the system and breaks up into i_1 and i_2. Prove that the potential difference across one resistor is the same as that across the other resistor and that i therefore equals $V/r_1 + V/r_2$. Prove that the resistance, r, of the combination is given by the equation $1/r = 1/r_1 + 1/r_2$.

40.15. In the text I say, "A good voltmeter, obviously, has a very high resistance."

1. Would it be correct to add "and the higher the better"?

2. How much current would there be in a voltmeter of infinite resistance connected to a 6-V battery?

3. Try to "invent" a voltmeter that works without current. (Such a voltmeter exists.)

40.16. The coil of a galvanometer has a resistance of 50 ohms and requires 0.001 amp for full-scale deflection.

1. What potential difference across the meter will produce full-scale deflection?

2. A resistance multiplier of 9,950 ohms is placed in series with the coil (Fig. 40.15.B,D). What is the ratio of the total resistance to that of the coil?

3. What is the potential difference across the combination when the current in the coil (and hence in the multiplier) is great enough to produce full-scale deflection?

4. We now have a voltmeter. What is the ratio of the maximum voltage readable on the voltmeter to that required for full-scale deflection of the galvanometer's needle? Compare with the ratio in part 2.

40.17. Describe how the basic galvanometer of Prob. 40.16 can be modified by the use of a shunt (Fig. 40.15.A,C) to become an ammeter whose full-scale deflection is 1 amp. What is the resistance of the shunt in ohms?

40.18. A 3-ohm resistor is connected in parallel with a 5-ohm resistor. This combination is connected in series with a 6-ohm resistor and a battery whose emf is 12 V and whose internal resistance is 1 ohm. Calculate the current in each resistor.

41

Electromagnetic Induction

WITHOUT getting out of your seat, look around you, and count how many of the following you can see: an electric light, a radio, a television set, an electric typewriter, an electric heater, a toaster, a refrigerator, an electric phonograph, a tape recorder, a washing machine, a vacuum cleaner, an electric shaver. The list could be extended without much effort. The chances are pretty good that most of these operate on electric charges that are pushed around inside wires, not by batteries but by electromagnetic induction. Most of them are connected to a distant generator that produces an electromotive force by moving conducting wires across magnetic fields. Let us see how this can come about.

41.1. Electromotive Force Without Batteries

I have described at length (§ 38.1) how a beam of electrons is deflected when it enters a magnetic field. Any particle bearing charge q and moving with velocity $\mathbf{v}$ experiences, we saw, force $\mathbf{F} = q(\mathbf{v} \times \mathbf{B})$. An electron feels force $\mathbf{F} = -e(\mathbf{v} \times \mathbf{B})$. It doesn't make any difference, we found, whether the electron is outside a wire (Fig. 38.1.A) or inside it (Fig. 38.3); it feels the force just the same.

Looking now at the open loop of thick copper wire being pulled through magnetic field $\mathbf{B}$ with velocity $\mathbf{v}$ in Figure 41.1, we concentrate our attention for a moment on a single electron at P.

It shares velocity $\mathbf{v}$ (pointing to the left) with every other part of the loop, and it therefore feels the force $\mathbf{F} = -e(\mathbf{v} \times \mathbf{B})$. Forming the vector product $\mathbf{v} \times \mathbf{B}$ and taking the direction opposite to this vector (§ 38.1), we conclude that the force, $\mathbf{F}$, acting on the electron points away from us along GH. Since every electron in section GH of the wire feels a similar force, electrons are pushed from G to H. The result of this is a migration of charges from H to C and from D to G just as if G and H were electrodes of a battery. Obviously, sphere C becomes negatively charged, and D becomes positively charged. An electric field, $\mathbf{E}$, would be found in the air between C and D. It is apparent that we have created an

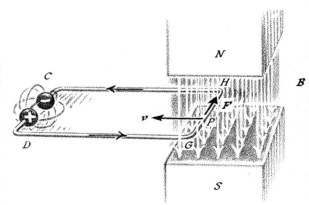

FIG. 41.1. *Creation of an electric field by relative motion between a conductor and a magnetic field.*

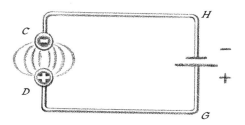

FIG. 41.2. *A battery connected between* G *and* H *would also produce a potential difference and an electric field between* C *and* D.

electric field by producing relative motion between a conductor (*GH*) and a magnetic field— that is, by **electromagnetic induction.**

Have we produced an electric current? Only an instantaneous one; electrons moved out of *D* and into *C*, but the flow then stopped even though the motion of the loop continued. But we did establish a potential difference. The situation is analogous (Fig. 41.2) to connecting *C* and *D* to a battery with the wires *CH* and *DG*. Except for an instant, there is no current in the circuit, but there is a potential difference across *GH*. This is produced by the emf of the battery and is measured by the work that it takes to move a unit positive charge from *H* to *G*. As we saw earlier (§ 40.3), the electromotive force of the battery, $\varepsilon = \Delta W/\Delta q$, is the work per unit charge done by the battery in moving positive charges from a region of low to one of high potential. Analogously, in Figure 41.1, the work that it takes to move positive charge Δq from *H* to *G* is simply the magnitude of the force times the distance. The force is $F = (\Delta q)vB$, and the distance, *HG*, is *l*. The work is $\Delta W = (\Delta q)vBl$. The work per unit charge, $\Delta W/\Delta q$, is *Blv*. If MKS units are used for *B*, *l*, and *v*, the potential difference across *HG*, in volts, is

$$\varepsilon = Blv \qquad [41.1$$

The charges flow as if driven by a battery of electromotive force ε. Any device that produces an emf in this way is called a **generator.** The large and complicated generators that send current through the electric appliances of a whole city depend, basically, on the principle of equation 41.1.

That is about as far as I shall go in describing how a generator works. It is, however, at least one step further than I got in describing how a battery works. A battery, as we saw, can *maintain* a potential difference and produce a current of some duration. Can electromagnetic induction do the same? Let's see.

41.2. Electric Current Without Batteries

Figure 41.3 is a partly schematic diagram in which the loop of Figure 41.1 is closed by a galvanometer between *C* and *D*. I have also added a variable resistor, *EF*, called a **rheostat,** in series with the loop, and I have mounted the magnet on a rolling platform so we can move it back and forth instead of moving the wire.

Here is what we observe: (1) If we move the magnet from left to right at constant velocity, the needle of the galvanometer indicates a steady current. (2) As soon as the magnet stops, the current stops. (3) When the velocity of the magnet is great, the current is great. (4) When the magnet moves in the opposite direction, the current reverses its direction. (5) If the resistance (*EF*) is increased and the velocity of the magnet is kept the same, the current diminishes; in other words, the circuit behaves somewhat as if the loop were cut, and connected to a battery, at *G* and *H*. (6) If *N* turns of wire are used instead of one, the current is *N* times as large.

Experiments of this sort were first conducted by Michael Faraday, in England, in 1831 and by Joseph Henry, in the United States, at about the same time. Neither they nor anyone else suspected that the electromotive forces generated in this way would some day provide light and power for whole cities and states. By shifting from a stationary magnet and a movable coil (Fig. 41.1) to a stationary coil and movable magnet (Fig. 41.3), we have already illustrated a basic principle—that under the conditions described what is important is the *relative motion* between the current loop and the magnetic field.

Under other conditions, however, an electromotive force can be produced without such relative motion. In Figure 41.4 two coils, *E* and *F*,

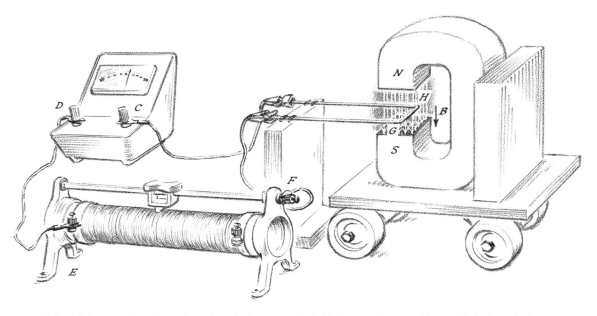

FIG. 41.3. *If the wire loop is stationary and the magnetic field is moved, an emf is established in the loop.*

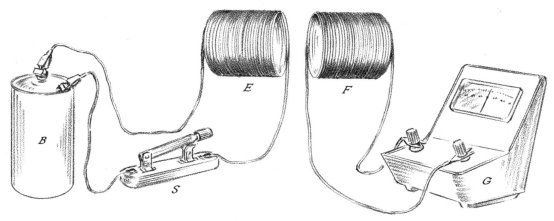

FIG. 41.4. *Without relative motion between coils* E *and* F, *an emf is produced in* F *as switch* S *is either closed or opened.*

are near each other but not touching. Coil *E* is connected to a battery, *B*, when the switch, *S*, is closed. Coil *F* is connected directly to a galvanometer, *G*; there is no battery in this circuit. Yet, even without relative motion between *E* and *F*, the galvanometer shows a momentary current as the switch is closed and a momentary current in the opposite direction as the switch is opened. Even without relative motion, we see, a *changing* magnetic field induces an electromotive force in coil *F*. As soon as the magnetic field ceases to change, the force vanishes. *It is the change of magnetic flux in a circuit that produces an electromotive force.* Let us examine this effect—another example of **electromagnetic induction.**

41.3. The Rate of Change of Flux

The flux, Φ, of the magnetic induction **B**, running perpendicularly to the plane of a coil of area A (Fig. 41.5), was defined in § 38.1 as $\Phi = BA$.

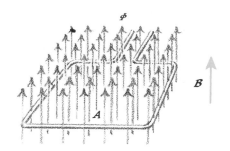

FIG. 41.5. *The flux of the magnetic induction* B, *running perpendicularly to the plane of a coil of area* A, *is* $\Phi = BA$.

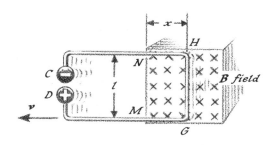

FIG. 41.6. *The flux that is linked by the loop is equal to the area* xl *multiplied by the magnetic induction* B.

(We shall drop the subscript B from Φ_B in this chapter.) Since B is in webers/m² and A is in m², Φ is measured in webers. (If the vector **B** is not perpendicular to the plane of A, then $\Phi = B_\perp A$, in which formula $B_\perp$ is the component of **B** that is perpendicular to the plane of A.) We can change the flux through the coil in any of three ways: by changing the magnitude of **B**, by changing the area of the coil, or by changing **B**'s orientation to the plane of the coil. No matter how we do it, if we effect the change $\Delta\Phi = \Phi_2 - \Phi_1$ in time Δt, we produce in the coil an electromotive force such that

$$\mathcal{E} = -\frac{\Delta\Phi}{\Delta t} \qquad [41.2$$

This is **Faraday's law of induction.**

Let us apply the law to the loop of Figure 41.1, which I have redrawn schematically in Figure 41.6. At any instant the flux that goes through (is *linked* by) the loop $DGHC$ is

$$\Phi = B \times \text{area} = Blx$$

if x is the distance NH. The rate of change of the flux is

$$\frac{\Delta\Phi}{\Delta t} = \frac{\Delta(Blx)}{\Delta t}$$

but, since B and l are constant,

$$\mathcal{E} = -\frac{\Delta\Phi}{\Delta t} = -Bl\frac{\Delta x}{\Delta t}$$

and, since $\Delta x/\Delta t = v$,

$$\mathcal{E} = -Blv$$

In this illustration x decreases with time; hence $\mathcal{E}$ is essentially positive. The minus sign will play

a more important role later. For the time being, observe that this *magnitude* (Blv) of the emf, predicted by Faraday's law of induction (equation 41.2), agrees with the value derived in equation 41.1. Of the two expressions $-Blv$ and $-\Delta\Phi/\Delta t$, the latter is the more general; it applies to all cases of electromagnetic induction, as we shall see when we consider cases in which there is no relative motion that we can measure.

41.4. Which Way Will the Charges Move? Lenz's Law

We know that it takes energy to move electrons through a wire. We feel pretty certain by now that we can't get something for nothing. Where does the energy come from?

I have given arguments that support the idea that an electromotive force is established in a loop of wire when it is pulled through a magnetic field (Fig. 41.7), whether the loop is closed (A) or open (B). If the loop is closed, electrons flow in the circuit. If the resistance in the circuit is low (if, for example, the wire is made of a highly conductive material such as copper·and has a large cross-section), the current will be large. The (electron) current, i, flows as shown. But a wire of length l carrying current i experiences the force $F = Bil$. A careful check (using the left-hand rule of Fig. 38.3) reveals that the force acting on GH points from left to right in Figure 41.7.A. In order to move the loop from right to left we *have to do work;* that is how we pay for the

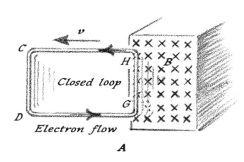 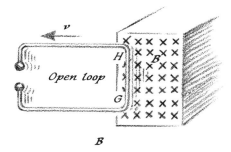

FIG. 41.7. *Motion through the magnetic field sets up an electromotive force in the loop of wire whether the loop is closed (A) or open (B).*

emf. In Figure 41.7.B we have to pay very little because the current lasts only a fraction of a second. We can feel the difference. (If a generator is turned by hand, it is easy to turn when the circuit is open; as soon as we connect a lamp or other load into the circuit, we can feel that it takes more work to turn the crank.)

Let us compute the rate at which the work is done. We let the applied force, F, move the loop through distance Δx in time Δt. The work done is $F(\Delta x)$. The rate of doing work is

$$\frac{\Delta W}{\Delta t} = F \frac{\Delta x}{\Delta t}$$

Since F is equal to Bil, and since $\Delta x/\Delta t = v$,

$$\frac{\Delta W}{\Delta t} = Bilv$$

The emf, $\mathcal{E}$, that drives current round the circuit is measured in joules per coulomb. Hence $\mathcal{E}i$ has the units

$$\frac{J}{coul} \times \frac{coul}{sec} = \frac{J}{sec}$$

This is the rate at which work is done on the charges. Therefore $\mathcal{E}i = Bilv$. Dividing through by i, we get, once again, $\mathcal{E} = Blv$. We have now derived this expression in three different ways. Perhaps you now feel convinced that the formula is correct and that the emf is there whether the loop is open or closed.

Observe that the current established in the loop sets up a force that *opposes* the motion of the outside agency moving the loop. This is a special case of a principle known as **Lenz's law:** *The induced current will appear in such a direction as to oppose the cause that produced it.* In Figure 41.8,

for example, if a bar magnet is moved toward the coil with its north pole facing an end of the coil, the electron current, i, flows in the coil as shown by the arrows; in that way a north pole is set up at the right-hand end of the coil (Fig. 39.14), and the motion of the magnet is opposed. If the magnet, in the same orientation, is moved away from the coil, electrons in the coil flow in the opposite direction. This produces a magnetic field that attracts the bar magnet and hence, again, opposes its motion.

Lenz's law does not depend on the idea of poles: it is true in general. If the opposite of Lenz's law were true, the induced current would help rather than hinder the motion, and then we should really be getting something for nothing.

41.5. Two Ways to Change Magnetic Flux

Since $\Phi = B_\perp A$, we can change Φ either by changing A or by changing $B_\perp$. Imagine (Fig. 41.9) a loop of insulated wire loosely held by a small ring, R (we want the wire insulated so that the circuit will not be completed at the ring); the crosses represent lines of magnetic induction, **B**, running into the paper. The area of the loop decreases from A_1 to A_2 and then to A_3. If we assume a homogeneous magnetic field, $\Phi_1 = A_1 B$ and $\Phi_2 = A_2 B$. If the change takes place in time Δt, the emf in the loop is simply

$$\mathcal{E} = -\frac{\Phi_2 - \Phi_1}{\Delta t} = -\frac{\Delta \Phi}{\Delta t} \qquad [41.3$$

It becomes zero as soon as the area ceases to change. If the area were to *increase* in a sequence from A_3 through A_2 to A_1, an emf in the opposite direction would be generated. In this example we have relative motion between a conductor and a magnetic field.

Suppose, however, that the area of the loop remains the same while B changes. Since B can be produced by an electromagnet, it is easy to change B by changing the current through the coil of the magnet. In Figure 41.10 the crosses again indicate lines of magnetic induction, and it is clear that B_2 is greater than B_1 and that B_3 is greater than B_2. The fluxes are $\Phi_1 = B_1 A$, $\Phi_2 = B_2 A$, and $\Phi_3 = B_3 A$. If the change from Φ_1 to Φ_2 occurred in time Δt, the average emf in the loop would be

$$\mathcal{E} = -\frac{\Phi_2 - \Phi_1}{\Delta t} = -\frac{\Delta\Phi}{\Delta t}$$

An experimental arrangement for producing such a change is shown in Figure 41.11. The current i_1 produces the magnetic induction **B**. To change this current we can vary the resistance in its circuit by sliding the contact C along the rheostat, R. While this current is changing, B is changing; hence Φ is changing, and hence an emf is induced in the circuit containing the galvanometer, G.

An interesting variation of this idea is shown in Figure 41.12. The flux, concentrated between the two parts of a cylindrical shaft, passes through the center of a circular coil, D, which is connected

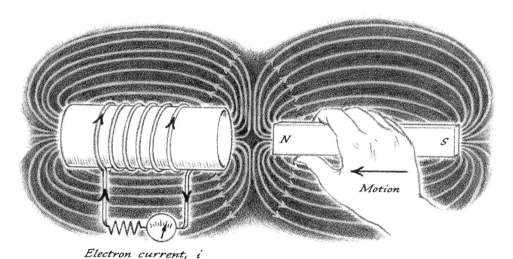

Electron current, i

FIG. 41.8. *An example of the operation of Lenz's law.*

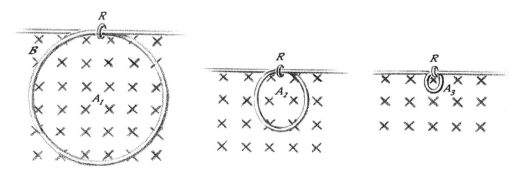

FIG. 41.9. *One way to change the magnetic flux through a loop is to vary the area of the loop while the magnetic induction remains constant.*

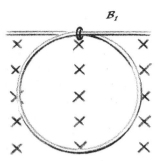
B_1

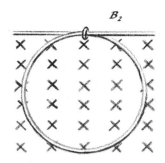
B_2

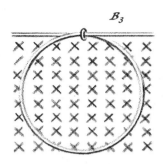
B_3

FIG. 41.10. *Another way to change the magnetic flux through a loop is to vary the magnetic induction while the area of the loop remains constant.*

to a galvanometer, *G*. We say that the total flux *linked* by the coil is $N\Phi$ if N is the number of turns in the coil. (Observe that we count the flux once for each complete turn.) If we vary the flux by moving the sliding contact, *C*, an induced emf, $\mathcal{E} = -N(\Delta\Phi/\Delta t)$, will produce a current through *G* even though no part of *D* is in contact with any of the flux lines at all. As long as $\Delta\Phi/\Delta t$ is not zero, there will be an induced emf in *D*. The electrons in the wire of *D* feel a force that drives them through the wire. This is exactly what would happen if a battery were connected in series with *G* and *D*. We say, therefore, that an electric field,

E, has been created in the wire by the changing flux in the center of the coil.

The analogy with the magnetic field that surrounds a wire is notable. We know that a wire carrying a current has a circular magnetic field around it, and in Figure 41.13.A. a (positive) current, *I*, is shown along with a few lines of the circular field of magnetic induction, **B**, that surrounds it. In Figure 41.13.B a *constantly changing flux*, $-\Delta\Phi/\Delta t$, is shown along with the circular electric field lines associated with it. This is something new indeed—electric field lines that neither originate nor end on electric charges!

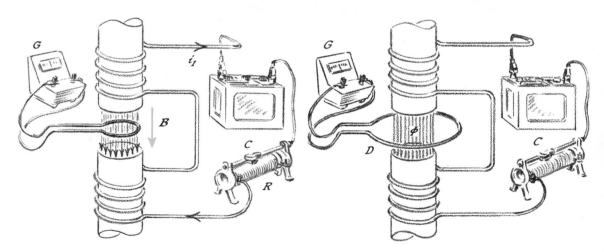

FIG. 41.11. *If we vary* B *by changing current* i_1, *an emf is induced in the circuit containing the galvanometer.*

FIG. 41.12. *In this arrangement the magnetic field lines link loop* D *without touching it. A changing flux nevertheless induces an emf in the loop circuit.*

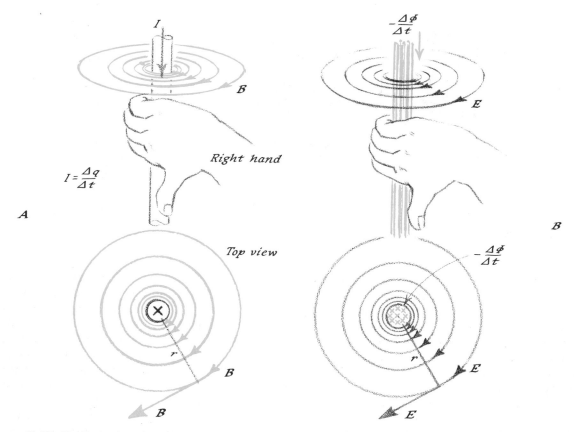

FIG. 41.13. *Similarity between the magnetic field lines of* **B** *that surround* **I** *and the electric field lines of* **E** *that surround* $-\Delta\Phi/\Delta t$.

Let us choose a line at distance r from the center. The electric field intensity, symmetrically, has the same magnitude, E, at every point of that circle. Hence E, the force per unit charge, is equal to F/q. The work that it takes to carry a charge once round the circle is $W = F2\pi r = Eq2\pi r$. The work per unit charge is $W/q = E2\pi r$. But this, by definition, is $\mathcal{E}$. Hence $\mathcal{E} = 2\pi r E$. From Faraday's law of induction we get

$$-\frac{\Delta\Phi}{\Delta t} = 2\pi r E \qquad [41.4$$

From this we can get

$$E = -\frac{1}{2\pi r}\frac{\Delta\Phi}{\Delta t} \qquad [41.5$$

The electric field intensity is inversely proportional to the radial distance, r. This is just like the dependence of B on r in Fig. 41.13.A. Compare equation 38.13, $B = ki/r$, from which it follows that

$$B = k\frac{\Delta q}{\Delta t}\frac{1}{r}$$

There are various fruitful ways of comparing the electric and magnetic effects. When we moved the magnet in Figure 41.3, we induced an electric field in the wire. We may, therefore, say: *When the source of a magnetic field is moved, it creates an electric field.* We also know that an electron is a source of electric field, and that, when it moves (for example, along a wire), a magnetic field is produced around the wire (Fig. 41.13.A). Hence we may also say: *When the source of an electric field (a charge) is moved, it creates a magnetic field.*

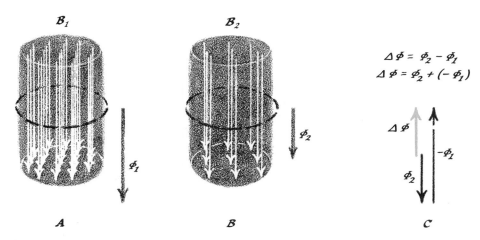

$$\Delta \Phi = \Phi_2 - \Phi_1$$
$$\Delta \Phi = \Phi_2 + (-\Phi_1)$$

FIG. 41.14. *Illustrating how to calculate* $\Delta\Phi$.

The two italicized statements exhibit a certain duality between electric and magnetic fields. An even more general statement, apparent from Figure 41.13.B, in which we need not *move* anything (since a change in flux can be produced without motion, as, for example, in an electromagnet), is this: *When a magnetic field changes, an associated electric field is produced.*

The idea of duality might lead us to ask the next logical question: When an electric field changes, is an associated magnetic field produced? The search for the answer to this question led Maxwell to his greatest contribution and to his prediction of electromagnetic waves. Today we know that light and radio waves belong in that category. (We shall explore this topic further in Chap. 43.)

One last thought: In Figure 41.13, we assume that the magnetic field, **B**, exists whether anything is there to feel it or not, and that the electric field, **E**, surrounding the changing flux, $-\Delta\Phi/\Delta t$, is there whether a wire is there or not. The strength of an electric field at a point is the force that *would be felt* by a unit charge placed there. Free charges can actually be accelerated in the circular field, **E**, of Figure 41.13.B. An electron accelerator called the **betatron** works on this principle.

To take signs into consideration, let us treat Φ as if it were a vector with the direction of **B**. Suppose that the flux through a coil is diminishing (Fig. 41.14). At first (A) the flux has the value Φ_1; later (B) it has the smaller value Φ_2. Now $\Delta\Phi = \Phi_2 - \Phi_1 = \Phi_2 + (-\Phi_1)$. Part C shows how $\Delta\Phi$ is found: $-\Delta\Phi/\Delta t$ points downward in this case. This is how it is shown in Figure 41.13.B. The direction of **E** is, by definition, the direction of the force felt by a small *positive* test charge. In Figure 41.13 the *right hand* must be used for both parts: A, you grasp the wire with the thumb pointing the way the positive current, I, points, and the fingers will then curve in the direction of **B**; B, you let the thumb of the right hand point in the direction of $-\Delta\Phi/\Delta t$, and the fingers will then point in the direction of **E**.

41.6. Summary

If the magnetic flux linked by a coil of wire varies with time, an electromotive force is induced in the coil, which produces a current if the coil circuit is closed. The electromotive force is associated with an electric field produced by the variation of the magnetic field. The magnitude of the electromotive force is $\mathcal{E} = -\Delta\Phi/\Delta t$. The charges flow in the direction that opposes the cause that induced them. A duality between electric and magnetic fields therefore begins to appear in the following form: when the source of a magnetic field is moved, it creates an electric field; when the source of an electric field is moved, it creates a magnetic field. This leads to the deeper duality discovered later by Maxwell.

Problems

41.1. Instead of spheres at C and D, in Fig. 41.1, imagine the two parallel plates of a capacitor connected to the wire loop. $B = 950$ gauss, $v = 0.25$ m/sec, and $l = GH = 15$ cm.

1. What is the emf in the wire loop?

2. While the loop is in motion, what is the electric field intensity in nt/coul between the capacitor plates if their separation is 0.75 cm? (Hint: nt/coul = V/m.)

41.2. 1. What happens to the charges on the plates of Prob. 41.1 if the loop is pulled twice as fast as it was before?

2. What happens to the charges on the plates if the loop is stopped?

3. How could you create an alternating electric field between the plates of the capacitor?

41.3. Let the experiment illustrated by Fig. 41.3 start with the magnet to the left of where it is shown. Move it to the right at constant speed until its field no longer links the loop. Sketch a plot of the emf in the loop as a function of time.

41.4. 1. Could you, in principle, heat the rheostat wire of Fig. 41.3 by moving the magnet from left to right and back several times?

2. If so, and if the resistance of the rheostat, though variable, is always much greater than the resistance of the rest of the circuit, describe by what physical means you would maximize the heat produced in the rheostat within a given time. List all the relevant variables you can imagine.

41.5. Two identical helical coils with many turns are connected in series and placed far from each other. A bar magnet is suspended vertically from a fixed helical spring with one of its poles inside the empty vertical core of one coil. An identical bar magnet is similarly suspended within the core of the second coil. Both magnets have the same natural period of oscillation.

1. What do you think will happen to the second

magnet and spring if, when they are at rest, the first magnet is started and allowed to oscillate?

2. What do you think will happen if the wires to the terminals of one of the coils are interchanged?

3. What will a galvanometer in series with the two coils show? (If in doubt, *do the experiment!*)

41.6. Check to see if the direction of electron flow in Figs. 41.1 and 41.6 follows Lenz's law.

41.7. Suppose, in Fig. 41.3, that a rectangular coil of 1,000 turns is being pulled out of a homogeneous field of intensity 0.5 weber/m² at a constant speed of 0.25 m/sec. The edge corresponding to GH is 15 cm long. Compute the emf in the coil.

41.8. Redraw Fig. 41.8 carefully for the case in which the permanent magnet is being pulled away from the coil. Indicate the proper directions on all field lines and of the current in the coil.

41.9. In Fig. 41.9 let B be homogeneous and constant at 0.25 weber/m². Let A_1 be 100 cm² and A_2 be 30 cm². If the change takes place continuously within 0.1 sec, compute the average emf in the wire loop.

41.10. Assume, for Fig. 41.10, that the area is 100 cm² in all three cases. Let B_1 be 0.10 weber/m² and B_2 be 0.55 weber/m². If the change takes place in 0.25 sec, what is the average emf in the loop?

41.11. In Fig. 41.12 the cross-sectional area of the cylindrical coils is 400 cm². At one instant, in the pole pieces between the coils, the magnetic induction, **B**, associated with flux Φ has the magnitude $B_1 = 0.10$ weber/m², and 0.25 sec later the magnitude $B_2 = 0.55$ weber/m². During this interval, at a point like D, 0.35 m from the center of the coil's axis, what is the average electric field intensity in nt/coul?

41.12. Assuming that $\mathbf{B}_1$ and $\mathbf{B}_2$ point as in Fig. 41.14, use Figs. 41.13 and 41.14 to determine the direction of the electric field intensity E in Prob. 41.11.

Alternating Current and Oscillating Circuits

WHY do I discuss alternating currents in this course? I have two reasons, one practical and the other theoretical.

The practical reason is that most electrical appliances for the home and for industry use alternating current. (Some, it is true, will operate on either alternating or direct current.) Electrical energy can be carried through wires more economically at high voltage than at low voltage. Alternating current, by means of a transformer, can easily be stepped up in voltage at the source and stepped down near the point of consumption. This is not true of direct current. Hence most of our appliances are designed to utilize the alternating current generated at some distant power plant.

But I shall not dwell on the practical applications of alternating current, for I have what is possibly a more valid reason for discussing it: alternating currents of high frequency are the source of *electromagnetic waves*. These include not only the waves used in television, radio, and radar, but also all forms of light, visible and invisible. We shall culminate our study of electricity and magnetism by seeing how Maxwell came to the conclusion that electromagnetic waves must exist and how he even predicted that they would

travel with a speed of 3×10^8 m/sec, which, we know, is the speed of light. This will lead us to consider light as an electromagnetic phenomenon. The synthesis between light and electricity and magnetism effected by Maxwell's equations was the most brilliant theoretical work of the nineteenth century.

First let us compare alternating current with direct current and consider a few fundamental facts about alternating current: how it is generated and how it is measured.

42.1. Alternating Current Compared with Direct Current

The current supplied by an automobile battery (Fig. 42.1.A) is **direct current** (DC). It goes in one direction and can remain fairly constant for hours; the plot of current, i, against time, t, is a horizontal line. Figure 42.1.B includes a schematic representation of a hand-driven generator and a graph of the current it produces in a lamp. That current (in accordance with the principles presented in § 41.1 and § 41.2) moves first in one direction and then in the other; that is, it alternates. If the crank is turned with a constant angular velocity, the current varies as shown in the graph. This is an **alternating current** (AC).

The principle of the AC generator is illustrated in Fig. 42.2. If the coil $CDFE$ is rotated (A), an emf will be established across its ends and will be picked up by a conductor making contact with the slip-rings S_1 and S_2. In part B the coil is shown against a background of crosses symbolizing the magnetic induction, **B**, between the magnetic poles of part A. We can calculate ε from the equation $\varepsilon = -\Delta\Phi/\Delta t$. An equivalent derivation uses equation 41.1, $\varepsilon = Blv$, in which $l = CD$. In Figure 42.3 we see that, since **v** is not perpendicular to **B** (except when $\theta = 90°$ and $\alpha = 0°$), we should use the formula $Blv \sin \alpha$ (α is the angle between **v** and **B**) or the equivalent formula $Blv \cos \theta$ (θ is the complement of α; therefore $\cos \theta = \sin \alpha$). But θ is being generated by the rotation of the coil at the constant angular velocity

ω (in radians/sec); so $\theta = \omega t$. This leads to the equation

$$\varepsilon = Blv \cos \omega t \qquad [42.1$$

The speed, v, may be written as $v = r\omega$. Hence, since the effective length of the coil is $2l$,

$$\varepsilon = 2Blr\omega \cos \omega t \qquad [42.2$$

The factor 2 enters because both CD and EF (Fig. 42.2) contribute to the emf.†

If the quantities $2B$, l, r, and ω are all constant, we can lump them together into a single constant, ε_0. Hence

$$\varepsilon = \varepsilon_0 \cos \omega t \qquad [42.3$$

Here ωt is an angle, as it should be, since we are going to take the cosine of it, and ε_0 and ε are

† Observe that $l(2r)$ is the area of the coil. The product of this area and B is the maximum flux linked by the coil. It may be shown that the ε of equation 42.2 is equal to

$$-\lim_{\Delta t \to 0} \frac{\Delta\Phi}{\Delta t}$$

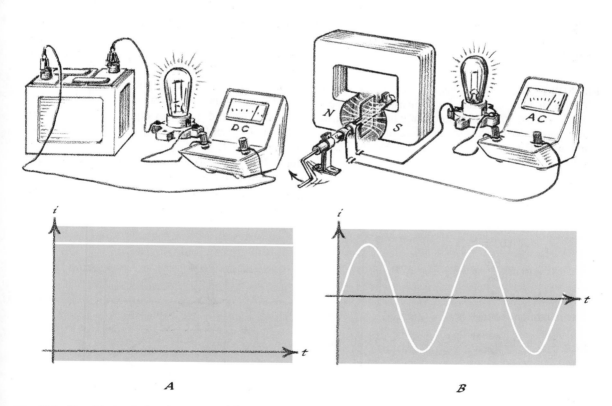

A

B

FIG. 42.1. *Two kinds of electric current: (A) one source of direct current and a plot of the current against time; (B) one source of alternating current and a plot of the current against time.*

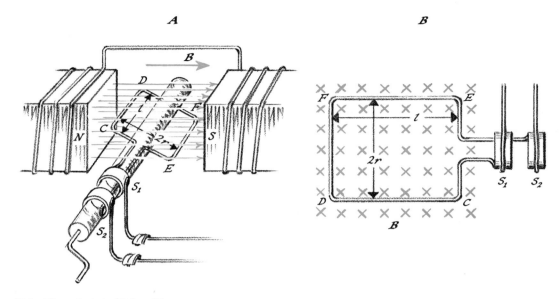

FIG. 42.2. *The principle of the AC generator.*

both in volts. The symbol $\mathcal{E}_0$ represents the maximum voltage. If the coil has N turns, $\mathcal{E}_0$ is $2Blr\omega N$.

EXAMPLE 42.1. A rectangular coil, such as the $CDFE$ of Fig. 42.2, has the dimensions $l = 5$ cm and $r = 2$ cm. We wish to know, if it has 1,000 turns and makes 60 revolutions per second, what maximum voltage is generated in a field of 0.216 weber/m².

We know that

$$B = 0.216 \frac{\text{weber}}{\text{m}^2}$$

$$l = 0.05 \text{ m}$$

$$r = 0.02 \text{ m}$$

$$\omega = 60 \frac{\text{rev}}{\text{sec}} \times \frac{2\pi \text{ rad}}{\text{rev}} = 377 \frac{\text{rad}}{\text{sec}}$$

$$N = 1{,}000$$

The maximum voltage is $\mathcal{E}_0 = 2Blr\omega N$.

$$\mathcal{E}_0 = 2 \times 0.216 \frac{\text{weber}}{\text{m}^2} \times 5 \times 10^{-2} \text{ m} \times 2 \times 10^{-2} \text{ m}$$
$$\times 3.77 \times 10^2 \frac{\text{rad}}{\text{sec}} \times 10^3$$

$$= 164 \frac{\text{webers}}{\text{sec}}$$

$$= 164 \text{ V}$$

The generator described in this example produces an alternating current of 60 cycles per second. This is called its frequency. A cycle is completed in 1/60 second.

Figure 42.4 represents the generator coil in several positions and shows a graph of the emf against time, the graph of equation 42.3. If such a fluctuating emf is applied to a lamp like that of Figure 42.1, why doesn't the lamp flicker? It does! But in 1/120 second, the time between the maximum voltage in one direction and the maximum voltage in the opposite direction, the tungsten filament of the lamp does not have a chance

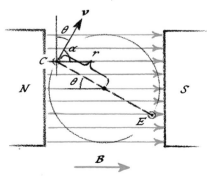

FIG. 42.3

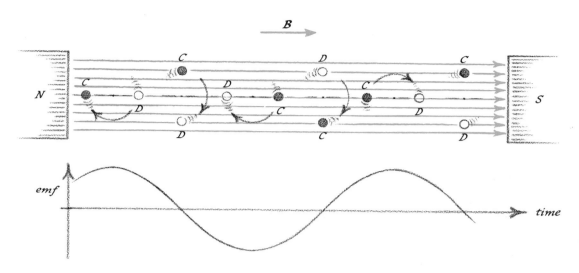

FIG. 42.4. *Schematic diagram showing a generator coil in several positions and the corresponding graph of the emf against time.*

to cool very much; so the flicker is almost imperceptible. (The retentiveness of the eye also helps to create the illusion of continuity.)

Another question: Shouldn't the ammeter needle of Figure 42.1.B make 120 reversals per second? If its basic movement were of the d'Arsonval type (§ 38.4), it would try to, but the inertia of the coil suspension would prevent it from doing so. Meters for alternating current are not of the d'Arsonval type. They utilize, instead, the repulsion between the currents in two coils. The direction of the current doesn't matter. If the current produces repulsion during one half of a cycle, it will produce repulsion during the other half also.

42.2. Amperes, Volts, and Watts of Alternating Current

Many electrical appliances for the home have a label saying, "Use only on 115 volts AC." What does "115 volts AC" mean? Since alternating current varies in magnitude with time, "115 volts" must mean some kind of average. This, however, cannot be the ordinary arithmetic mean, which would be zero since the graph of voltage, like that of current (Fig. 42.1.B), is a sine curve;

every positive ordinate is matched by an equal negative ordinate in the next half cycle, and the sum of all the ordinates in a cycle is therefore zero.

But, since power, as we know, is being dissipated in the form of heat in a lamp operated on alternating current, this power cannot average out to zero. This fact suggests how to calibrate an AC ammeter. The dial on such a meter is marked "1 ampere (AC)" for the current through it that produces, in a resistor, the same amount of heat per second as 1 ampere of direct current would.

Consider the formula for power in the form $P_J = i^2 R$ (§ 40.5). The fact that i is squared and is therefore always positive or zero suggests that we examine the graph of i^2 against t. In Figure 42.5 (where the vertical axis is used for both i and i^2 and therefore is not labeled) the black curve represents i, the green curve i^2. The ordinate of every point on the i^2 curve is the square of the ordinate of the corresponding point on the i curve. Since negative values of i produce positive values of i^2, all the ordinates of i^2 (see the green curve) are either zero or positive. The average value of i^2 is clearly not zero.

In the special case shown, where the maximum value of i is 1 ampere, the maximum value of i^2

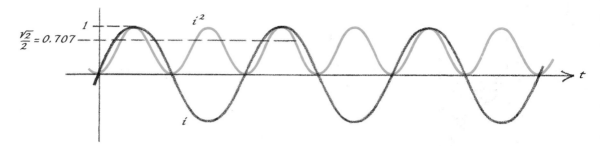

FIG. 42.5. *The black curve represents* i, *the green curve* i².

is also 1 (amp²). (Remember that we are dealing with two different graphs. Imagine having drawn them on transparent paper and then superimposed them.) The ordinary average of i^2 is $1/2$ (which seems plausible on inspection of Fig. 42.5 and can be proved with the definition of mean value of a function given in § 6.6). The kind of average to be used here for i, however, is called the **root-mean-square**. It is the square root of the mean value of i^2. Hence

$$i_{\text{rms}} = \sqrt{\overline{i^2}} \qquad [42.4$$

The bar above i^2 signifies the mean. It can be shown quite generally that

$$\overline{i^2} = \tfrac{1}{2}(i_{\text{max}})^2$$

Therefore, if the graph of i is a sine or a cosine curve,

$$i_{\text{rms}} = \sqrt{\tfrac{1}{2}(i_{\text{max}})^2} \qquad [42.5$$

$$= i_{\text{max}} \sqrt{\tfrac{1}{2}} = i_{\text{max}} \left(\frac{\sqrt{2}}{2}\right) \qquad [42.6$$

$$= 0.707 \, i_{\text{max}} \qquad [42.7$$

Ammeters for AC are calibrated to read i_{rms}. The reason is simple. Observe that

$$(i_{\text{rms}})^2 = \tfrac{1}{2}(i_{\text{max}})^2 = \overline{i^2}$$

Therefore

$$(i_{\text{rms}})^2 R = \overline{i^2} R$$

That is, the use of i_{rms} in the formula $P_J = i^2 R$ yields the correct value of the average power. An alternating current of 1 ampere rms will produce in a resistor the same heat per second as a direct current of 1 ampere in the same resistor.

Similar reasoning leads to an equation for AC voltage:

$$V_{\text{rms}} = 0.707 \, V_{\text{max}} \qquad [42.8$$

Even though AC measuring instruments often do not say "rms," the scales do show rms values. As far as heating is concerned, 100 volts AC rms across a resistor will produce the same heat per second as 100 volts DC across the same resistor.

This can be confirmed with an error of 5 percent or less by means of a simple paraffin photometer and two identical light bulbs (Fig. 42.6). We first find a location, O, such that the illumination (as judged when we view the light scattered at right angles to the beam) produced by one bulb is identical with that produced by the other *when both are connected to the same DC voltage.* We next connect one bulb to an AC source of variable voltage (the one illustrated, called an autotransformer, is diagramed in Fig. 42.7.B) and put an arbitrary DC voltage, V_1, on the other. (If a fixed DC voltage is put across the ends of a wire-wound resistor, a fraction of that voltage can be obtained through connections across part of the resistor, as diagramed in Fig. 42.7.A.) Having adjusted the AC voltage until photometric balance is achieved, we label the scale of the AC voltmeter V_1 at this point. By repeating this procedure at many different voltages we can establish the scale of the AC voltmeter or compare an existing scale with that of the DC voltmeter.

Another simple and instructive experiment utilizes an ordinary neon glow lamp (Fig. 42.7). After connecting the lamp to a variable source of direct current (A), we increase the voltage from

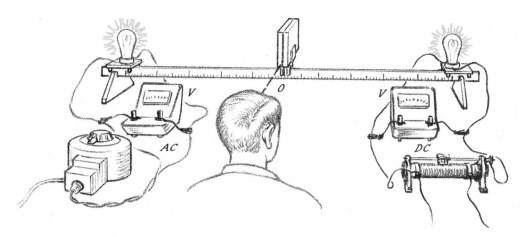

FIG. 42.6. *The definition of AC volts is such that, when the reading of the AC voltmeter is identical with that of the DC voltmeter, the lamps will be equally hot and hence equally brilliant. This can be confirmed with a simple photometer.*

zero up to the point where the lamp first glows, repeating several times and recording the average voltage, V_{DC}. We now connect the lamp to a variable source of alternating current (B) and let V_{AC} represent the lowest voltage reading, on the AC meter, at which the lamp lights up. The ratio V_{AC}/V_{DC} will come out close to $0.707 = \sqrt{2}/2$. The reason, of course, is that, when the AC meter reads a certain value, V, the maxima reach $\sqrt{2}V$, and it is the maximum voltages that ionize the neon and cause the lamp to glow.

EXAMPLE 42.2. The alternating current in an electric toaster reads 5 amp on an AC meter. The voltage *across* the toaster reads 115 volts AC. We

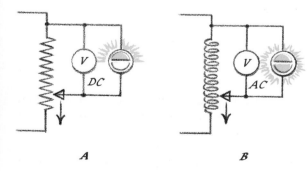

FIG. 42.7. *Comparing the lowest DC and AC voltages at which a neon glow lamp will light.*

wish to know what power is being dissipated in the form of heat and what the maximum voltage across the toaster is.

Since we know that AC meters give the correct answers for power in ordinary DC formulas, we may use the formula

$$P_J = i^2R = iV = \frac{V^2}{R}$$

Since we know i and V, we have

$$P_J = iV = 5 \text{ amp} \times 115 \text{ V} = 757 \text{ W}$$

We know that the maximum voltage is always $\sqrt{2}$ times as great as the rms voltage. Therefore

$$V_{\max} = \sqrt{2} \times 115 \text{ V} = 1.414 \times 115 \text{ V} = 163 \text{ V}$$

42.3. The Transformer

An iron-core transformer is shown schematically in Figure 42.8. A coil with N_P turns is wound on one side of the core. If there is current in this circuit, marked P for *primary*, a magnetic flux, Φ, will be established in the core. The *secondary* coil, S, with N_S turns, links the same flux N_S times. If the flux changes by amount $\Delta\Phi$ in time Δt, the induced emf in the primary coil is $N_P(\Delta\Phi/\Delta t)$, and the induced emf in the secondary coil is $N_S(\Delta\Phi/\Delta t)$. If the resistance of the primary coil can be made extremely low, the voltage applied across it will be numerically the same as the

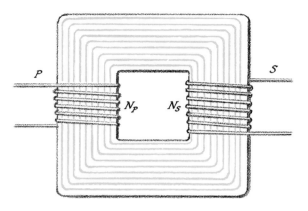

FIG. 42.8. *Schematic diagram of a transformer.*

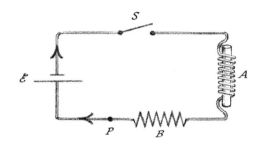

FIG. 42.9. *A coil with an iron core connected in series with a resistor.*

induced emf. Therefore

$$\frac{\text{voltage applied across primary}}{\text{voltage induced in secondary}} = \frac{N_P(\Delta\Phi/\Delta t)}{N_S(\Delta\Phi/\Delta t)} \quad [42.9$$

If the applied voltage is sinusoidal (that is, if its graph is a sine or a cosine curve), the rms voltages in the two coils will be in this same ratio; that is, if V_P and V_S stand for AC rms voltages,

$$\frac{V_P}{V_S} = \frac{N_P}{N_S} \quad [42.10$$

This equation explains how AC voltages can be stepped up or stepped down with a transformer by proper choice of the ratio N_P/N_S.

42.4. Self-inductance

Suppose you put a DC voltage of 100 volts across a coil of wire with an iron core and find that the current in it is 2 amperes. If you connect the same coil to an AC generator of 60 cycles per second whose output voltage is 100 volts AC, will 2 amperes (AC) flow in the coil? Probably not. Just as the changing flux induced an emf in the secondary coil of the transformer, so the changing flux, even in the single coil, induces in it an emf $[-N(\Delta\Phi/\Delta t)]$, which, according to Lenz's law, opposes the cause of the change in the flux. In other words, the effect of the self-induced emf in the coil is to oppose both the rise and the fall of the current in the circuit. The over-all effect is to reduce the rms current in the circuit. This gives rise to the concept of **impedance,** which plays in AC circuits the role that resistance plays in DC circuits. (We have considered only the contribution of inductance to the impedance. Resistance and capacitance also contribute to the impedance in a circuit.)

We shall not pursue the study of impedance here, but, since we do need the concept of **self-inductance** in order to study oscillating electric circuits, we shall consider a simple experiment, one that is basically simpler than connecting a coil to an AC generator. Let us simply connect a coil with a core to a DC battery and discuss the *transient* effects of the coil in the circuit. When the switch, S, is first closed in the circuit of Figure 42.9, charges begin to flow through the coil, A, and the resistor, B, simultaneously. The change in magnetic flux in the coil induces an emf, equal to $-N(\Delta\Phi/\Delta t)$. Since the flux at any instant is directly proportional to the current ($\Phi \propto i$), there is a constant, L, such that the induced emf may also be written as $-L(\Delta i/\Delta t)$. If we start at point P in the circuit and go round the loop once, we may write

$$\mathcal{E} - L\frac{\Delta i}{\Delta t} - iR = 0$$

or

$$\mathcal{E} - L\frac{\Delta i}{\Delta t} = iR \quad [42.11$$

If there were no self-induced emf, we could obtain the current from equation 42.11 by dropping $L(\Delta i/\Delta t)$. This would yield $i = \mathcal{E}/R$. The effect of $-L(\Delta i/\Delta t)$ is to reduce the effective emf, and hence the current, in the circuit. When the switch is closed, the current rises (Fig. 42.10) to its asymptotic value, $\mathcal{E}/R$, along curve C. If the

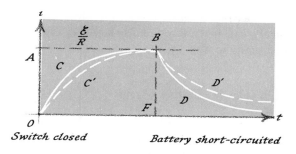

FIG. 42.10. *Curves illustrating self-inductance.*

battery is short-circuited with the switch closed, the current drops to zero, not instantaneously, but along curve D. A larger value of L would cause the current to take longer, when the switch is first closed, to reach its final value (see C') and, when the battery is short-circuited, to reach zero (see D'). The quantity L is called the **coefficient of self-inductance.** Self-inductance is somewhat analogous to inertia in mechanics: it opposes change in current just as inertia opposes change in the velocity of a massive body. We shall find this analogy useful.

If L equaled zero, the current would rise instantaneously (OA) when the switch was closed and would drop suddenly to zero (BF) when the battery was short-circuited. Not being zero, L kept the current from increasing rapidly when the battery was first introduced into the circuit and opposed its sudden vanishing when the effect of the battery was nullified by a short circuit.

The unit of inductance is called the **henry** in honor of Joseph Henry (1797–1878), an American scientist, first Director of the Smithsonian Institution, who investigated this and several of the other effects also discovered by Faraday. From the formula $\varepsilon = -L(\Delta i/\Delta t)$ we see that volts equal henries times amperes per second or that henries equal volt-seconds per ampere.

A coil carrying current has energy associated with the magnetic field around it. One way to demonstrate this is to connect a 6-volt automobile lamp across two cells (4 volts) of an automobile battery (Fig. 42.11). The coil, C, consists of many turns of copper wire round an iron core. Both the high number of turns and the core increase

the inductance of the coil. When the switch is first closed, charges flow rapidly through the lamp, but the maximum voltage across it (4 volts) is not enough to make it glow brightly. When the switch is then opened, the flux in the coil diminishes rapidly to zero, producing a large emf [$\varepsilon = -N(\Delta\Phi)/\Delta t$], which, driving a sudden burst of current through the lamp at high voltage, produces a sudden flash.

The work that it takes to carry charge Δq across an emf of magnitude $L(\Delta i/\Delta t)$ is

$$(\Delta q)L\frac{\Delta i}{\Delta t}$$

Since this is an incremental amount of energy, let us write it as

$$\Delta U = (\Delta q)L\frac{\Delta i}{\Delta t} \qquad [42.12$$

or

$$\Delta U = L\frac{\Delta q}{\Delta t}\Delta i \qquad [42.13$$

And, since current i is, by definition, $\Delta q/\Delta t$, we may write

$$\Delta U = Li(\Delta i) \qquad [42.14$$

This is reminiscent of the increment in potential energy in a spring having the force constant k: $\Delta U = (kx)\Delta x$. The kx is a force; the Δx is a distance. The product is work or energy. The result of stretching such a spring from $x = 0$ to $x = X$ is (§ 28.6)

$$U = \tfrac{1}{2}kX^2$$

An identical mathematical analysis based on equation 42.14 leads to

$$U = \tfrac{1}{2}Li^2 \qquad [42.15$$

This is the energy stored in the magnetic field of a coil that carries current i and whose inductance is L.

EXAMPLE 42.3. A coil with an iron core has a coefficient of self-inductance, L, of 30 henries. It has a resistance of 2 ohms. It is connected across a 6-V storage battery. We wish to know the maximum energy stored in the magnetic field of this coil.

First we observe that the *final* value of the current will be

$$i = \frac{\varepsilon}{R} = \frac{6 \text{ V}}{2 \text{ ohms}} = 3 \text{ amp}$$

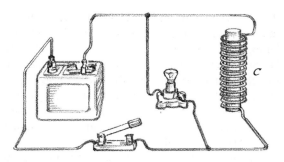

FIG. 42.11. *Demonstration that a current-carrying coil has energy associated with its magnetic field.*

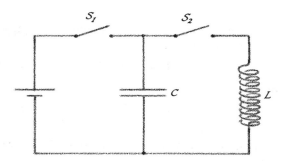

FIG. 42.12. *An* LC *circuit (right), consisting of a coil with inductance* L *and a capacitor with capacitance* C. *The circuit (left) containing the battery is used only for charging the capacitor.*

The energy formula (equation 42.15) gives us

$$U = \tfrac{1}{2}Li^2$$
$$= \tfrac{1}{2} \times 30 \text{ henries} \times 9 \text{ amp}^2$$
$$= 15 \frac{\text{V-sec}}{\text{amp}} \times 9 \text{ amp}^2$$
$$= 135 \text{ V-amp-sec}$$
$$= 135 \text{ V-coul}$$
$$= 135 \text{ J}$$

We have already run across the idea that energy can be stored in the electric field of a capacitor. In § 37.6 we derived the formula

$$U = \frac{qV}{2} = \frac{q^2}{2C}$$

for the energy in a capacitor of capacitance C when charge q is stored on one of its plates. Since both a coil with inductance and a capacitor with capacitance can store energy, we now seek the energy relations of a circuit that has both

inductance and capacitance. We shall see how energy can be transferred from one to the other in a periodic way.

42.5. The Oscillating Circuit

A series circuit with inductance L and capacitance C is sometimes called an LC circuit. We are going to think through an experiment with one (Fig. 42.12). First we charge the capacitor by closing switch S_1 momentarily. This establishes across the capacitor a potential difference, V, equal to the emf of the cell, and deposits charge $q = CV$ on the capacitor. Switch S_1 is left open after the capacitor has been charged. Then, by closing switch S_2, we connect in series the coil, of inductance L, and the capacitor, of capacitance C. The subsequent changes in q, i, and $\mathcal{E}$ [$\mathcal{E}$, the emf induced in the coil, equals $-L(\Delta i/\Delta t)$] will be followed with the aid of Figure 42.13.

The capacitor begins to discharge (see circuit O in the lowest line of Fig. 42.13) as charges flow from it through the coil; in other words, the charge on the capacitor begins to decrease (line A, curve OP). This means that the current through the coil begins to increase negatively (line B) as the charge (and hence the voltage) across the capacitor begins to decrease. Consistently with the definition $i = \Delta q/\Delta t$, the current in the coil starts at zero and increases initially in a negative direction (line B). (Observe, in line A, that the slope, $\Delta q/\Delta t$, starts at zero and becomes negative.)

The inertial characteristics of L retard the flow of charge initially; but, when the capacitor has been completely discharged (points P, associated with circuit P), the effect of the inductance is to prolong the current. This sends charges to the capacitor while the current in the coil diminishes in magnitude (from P to Q). Eventually there is no current in the coil (points Q, associated with circuit Q), but the capacitor is fully charged. The polarity of its plates is opposite to its initial polarity. Now charges begin to flow in the opposite direction. When the capacitor is fully discharged (points R, associated with circuit R), the current in the coil is at its maximum in a direction opposite to that associated with point P. Soon

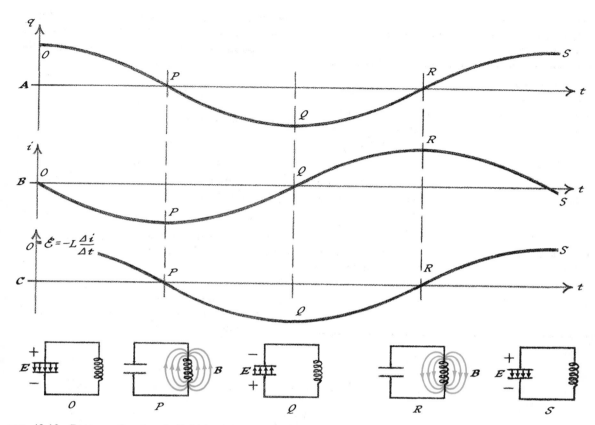

FIG. 42.13. *Bottom: the electric field in the capacitor and the magnetic field round the coil of an* LC *circuit at each of successive stages in time, O, P, Q, R, S. Lines A, B, and C: the corresponding graphical descriptions; charge, current, and voltage are shown at points O, P, Q, R, and S of each t axis.*

after that (*S*) the capacitor is fully charged, as it was at the start, and the cycle is ready to begin again. The emf induced in the coil is $\mathcal{E} = -L(\Delta i/\Delta t)$. This is plotted in line C.

Notice that initially there was energy $(q^2/2C)$ in the electric field, **E**, of the capacitor. Later there was energy $(Li^2/2)$ in the magnetic field, **B**, of the coil. There was a continuous interchange from one to the other.

The analogous mechanical experiment consists in stretching a spring with a weight attached to it and then releasing it (Fig. 42.14). The steps are labeled like those of the corresponding steps of Figure 42.13. In step *O*, the energy is stored in the spring $(kx^2/2)$. In step *P*, the potential energy of the spring is zero, but the kinetic en-

ergy, $mv^2/2$, of the weight is at its maximum. Later (*Q*), the kinetic energy is zero, and the potential energy is at a maximum. In step *R*, all the energy is kinetic again, and in step *S* we are back where we started. There has been a continuous interchange of energy from the kinetic form to the potential form.

For the sake of comparison, I tabulate energy in the mechanical case next to that of the corresponding electrical case (Table 42.1). I have put $\frac{1}{2}Li^2$ beside $\frac{1}{2}mv^2$ because I have already suggested that L is analogous to inertia (measured by m). To pursue our analogy further, we may pair off the other quantities (Table 42.2). Since $i = \Delta q/\Delta t$ and $v = \Delta x/\Delta t$, and since the stiffness, k, of a spring can be written as the inverse of the **com-**

TABLE 42.1

Comparison of Energy Formulas for Two Vibrating Systems

Mechanical	Electrical
Vibrating spring, of stiffness constant k, with object of mass m attached	Electrical oscillation in a series LC circuit, of capacitance C and inductance L
Kinetic energy: $\frac{1}{2}mv^2$	Energy stored in magnetic field of coil of inductance L: $\frac{1}{2}Li^2$
Potential energy: $\frac{1}{2}kx^2$	Energy stored in electric field of capacitor of capacitance C: $\frac{1}{2}\frac{q^2}{C}$

pliance, c (defined by the equation $k = 1/c$), I have included them in Table 42.2 to make the similarities more striking. We know (§ 25.6) that the period of a vibrating spring is

$$T = 2\pi \sqrt{\frac{m}{k}} \qquad [42.16$$

We can now write this as

$$T = 2\pi\sqrt{mc} \qquad [42.17$$

This suggests that the natural period of oscillation of the LC circuit, if we put L in place of m and C in place of c, might be

$$T = 2\pi\sqrt{LC} \qquad [42.18$$

A more detailed mathematical analysis proves that it is.

EXAMPLE 42.4. We wish to find the natural period and the frequency of an LC circuit if $L = 10$ millihenries and $C = 2$ $\mu\mu$farads.

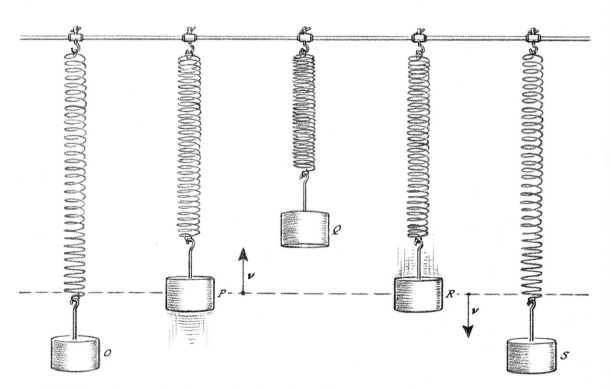

FIG. 42.14. *Successive transitions between kinetic and potential energy in a vibrating spring.*

TABLE 42.2

Analogous Quantities in Vibrating Systems

Mechanical	Electrical
m	L
$v = \dfrac{\Delta x}{\Delta t}$	$i = \dfrac{\Delta q}{\Delta t}$
$k = \dfrac{1}{c}$	$\dfrac{1}{C}$
x	q

$$T = 2\pi\sqrt{10\times 10^{-3}\text{ henry} \times 2\times 10^{-12}\text{ farad}}$$
$$= 2\pi\sqrt{2\times 10^{-14}\text{ sec}^2}$$
$$= 2\pi \times 10^{-7}\sqrt{2}\text{ sec}$$
$$= 8.88\times 10^{-7}\text{ sec}$$

The frequency, ν, is, by definition, $1/T$. Therefore

$$\nu = \frac{1}{T} = \frac{1}{8.88\times 10^{-7}}\text{ sec}^{-1}$$
$$= 1.13\times 10^{6}\text{ sec}^{-1}$$

This frequency, of about a million cycles, or a thousand kilocycles, per second, is within the range of frequencies used in some radio work.

We can explore our analogy a bit further. We know that the equation $f = ma$ must hold for the spring. Since $f = -kx$ and $a = \Delta v/\Delta t$, this may be written as

$$-kx = m\frac{\Delta v}{\Delta t}$$

Looking back at Table 42.2 and substituting i for v, L for m, etc., we might ask whether the equation

$$\frac{q}{C} = -L\frac{\Delta i}{\Delta t}$$

holds in the electrical case. We see immediately that it does, for q/c is the voltage across the capacitor. (The definition of capacitance is $C = q/V$.) And $-L(\Delta i/\Delta t)$ we recognize as the emf induced across the coil. As we go round the loop of the LC circuit, we must have, since there is no battery to supply an emf,

$$\frac{q}{C} + L\frac{\Delta i}{\Delta t} = 0$$

Finally, consider an LC circuit that includes resistance R (Fig. 42.15.A). When the switch, S, is first closed, charges start to flow through R and to be deposited on the upper plate of C. Simultaneously, charges leave the lower plate of C and flow through L. If there is a battery with emf in the circuit, we can start at P and go once round the loop, observing the rise and fall in potential. We get

$$\mathcal{E} - iR - \frac{q}{C} + \mathcal{E}_2 = 0 \qquad [42.19$$

Here $\mathcal{E}_2$ is the emf induced in L; it acts like a

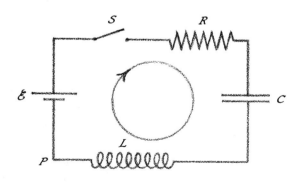

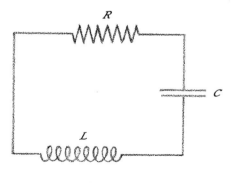

FIG. 42.15. (*A*) *A series circuit with resistance, capacitance, inductance, and a battery.* (*B*) *A similar series circuit without a battery.*

battery in opposing $\mathcal{E}$. Therefore

$$\mathcal{E}_2 = -L\frac{\Delta i}{\Delta t}$$

Hence

$$\mathcal{E} - iR - \frac{q}{C} - L\frac{\Delta i}{\Delta t} = 0$$

$$\mathcal{E} = iR + \frac{q}{C} + L\frac{\Delta i}{\Delta t} \qquad [42.20$$

In a circuit without a battery (Fig. 42.15.B)

$$0 = iR + \frac{q}{C} + L\frac{\Delta i}{\Delta t} \qquad [42.21$$

The analogous equation in the mechanical experiment (Fig. 42.16) is

$$0 = vr + \frac{x}{c} + m\frac{\Delta v}{\Delta t} \qquad [42.22$$

of which all the symbols except r have been defined. Notice that an object of mass m sus-

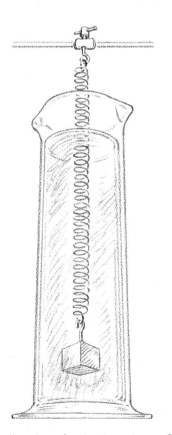

FIG. 42.16. *A spring vibrating in a viscous fluid.*

pended from a spring of force constant k experiences the net restoring force $-kx$ when displaced through distance x from its equilibrium position. Let us assume that it also experiences a frictional force proportional to its velocity, v. The force on the object is therefore $-vr - kx$ if r is the appropriate constant of proportionality. This force must equal the mass times the acceleration. Hence $-vr - kx = ma$. If we set a equal to $\Delta v/\Delta t$ and k equal to $1/c$, we get

$$-vr - \frac{x}{c} - m\frac{\Delta v}{\Delta t} = 0$$

or

$$vr + \frac{x}{c} + m\frac{\Delta v}{\Delta t} = 0 \qquad [42.23$$

If we compare this with the equation (42.21)

$$iR + \frac{q}{C} + L\frac{\Delta i}{\Delta t} = 0$$

we see that electrical resistance, R, plays the role of the frictional constant, r. If we displace the suspended object and then release it, we shall begin an oscillation whose period is $T = 2\pi\sqrt{mc}$ if r is small. The oscillation will eventually die out because the energy will be converted, through friction, into heat. Similarly, an electrical oscillation started by our giving a capacitor an initial charge will have the period $T = 2\pi\sqrt{LC}$ if R is small, and it too will die out because the energy will be dissipated as heat ($\propto i^2R$).

This analogy between electrical and mechanical oscillations serves us in the study of both types of oscillation.

42.6. Summary

Alternating current oscillates. Charges flow first in one direction and then in the other.

The emf associated with AC obeys the equation

$$\mathcal{E} = \mathcal{E}_0 \cos \omega t$$

if $\mathcal{E}_0$ is the maximum value of $\mathcal{E}$, ν is the frequency, and T is the period of the oscillation ($\omega = 2\pi\nu = 2\pi/T$).

Ammeters and voltmeters for AC are designed to read the root mean square of the variable current and voltage, respectively. The relations are and

$$i_{rms} = (\sqrt{2}/2)i_{max}$$

$$V_{rms} = (\sqrt{2}/2)V_{max}$$

When it clearly does not stand for the instantaneous value, the symbol i, used with AC, means i_{rms}. This value of i in the formula i^2R gives accurately the power converted to heat in a resistor.

Similar remarks apply to V and V_{rms}.

A coil of wire has—besides resistance—self-inductance, which, in an AC circuit, has an iner-

tia-like characteristic—it tends to oppose changes in current the way mass tends to oppose changes in velocity in mechanical systems. There is, in fact, a perfect analogy between the quantities displacement, velocity, mass, and compliance, in mechanics, and charge, current, inductance, and capacitance, respectively, in a series AC circuit. This analogy is very useful when we wish to solve certain mechanical problems electrically and certain electrical problems mechanically.

Problems

42.1. 1. Redraw the curve of Fig. 42.1.B, and on the same set of axes plot the curve of i vs t for a coil with two turns instead of one, keeping the rate of rotation fixed.

2. Plot the curve corresponding to a coil with one turn turning twice as fast as shown in the figure.

42.2. Consider, in the set-up of Fig. 42.2, a coil with 100 turns making 5 rev/sec where $B = 500$ gauss. If $l = 3$ cm and $r = 1.2$ cm, find the maximum value of the emf.

42.3. The formula for heating in a resistor is either i^2R or V^2/R. Does the presence of a square term for i and for V suggest that the heating effect is always positive for AC? Explain.

42.4. The neon bulb of Fig. 42.7 begins to glow at 44 V when the DC voltage is raised gradually from zero. The same bulb begins to glow on AC when the AC meter reads 62.22 V. If the DC voltmeter's reading is correct, is the AC voltmeter's reading correct at this point?

42.5. Power may be written as iV, i^2R, or V^2/R for AC, as it was for DC, provided i and V are rms values. Suppose that a power of 100 kilowatts is to be carried over an AC line whose total resistance is 2 ohms.

1. What current is needed at 10,000 V?

2. What power is lost as heat in the wires?

3. What current is needed at 100 V?

4. What power is lost as heat in the wires?

5. Comment on the power delivered, compared with the power lost in the wires, in part 4.

42.6. Transformers to reduce AC of 220 V and 50 cycles/sec to AC of 110 V and 50 cycles/sec are common.

1. If such a transformer is connected backward (that is, if the 220-V line is connected to the secondary coil), what voltage will appear on the primary coil?

2. What happens to the frequency in this case?

42.7. A common value of self-inductance for a special coil (called a *choke coil*) in amplifying circuits is 30 henries.

1. How much energy is stored in such a coil when the AC through it has the rms value of 100 milliamperes?

2. There are peak intervals when the rms current reaches 1.00 amp. What is the energy stored in the choke coil then?

42.8. 1. What is the natural period of oscillation of a series circuit with capacitance $C = 2.5 \times 10^{-12}$ farad and inductance $L = 1.25 \times 10^{-1}$ henry?

2. What is the corresponding natural frequency in kilocycles/sec?

3. Is this the correct order of magnitude for the frequency of a radio station on the amplitude-modulation (AM) band? (Consult a newspaper.)

42.9. The circuit of Fig. 42.13 has no resistance in it. A real circuit always has some resistance.

1. What will be the effect of this resistance on the amplitude of the electrical oscillation as a function of time? To answer this, consider the effect of friction in the analogous case of an oscillating spring with a weight on it (Fig. 42.16).

2. Imagine releasing the spring in a fluid so viscous that the weight simply moves toward its equilibrium position without overshooting it. What would be the analogous electrical experiment? Draw a circuit that is a modified form of Fig. 42.12, and tell how to perform an experiment that would illustrate this case of extreme viscous damping.

42.10. The current in a series circuit with capacitance C, inductance L, and resistance R, driven by a generator whose emf is ε and whose period is T, is

$$i = \frac{\varepsilon}{\sqrt{R^2 + \left(\dfrac{2\pi C}{T} - \dfrac{T}{2\pi L}\right)^2}}$$

It is obvious that, when

$$2\pi C/T = T/2\pi L$$

the current has its maximum value. Solve this equation for the period of the generator that produces the greatest current. Prove that this is equal to $2\pi\sqrt{LC}$ (see equation 42.18).

43

Maxwell's Equations and the Electromagnetic Nature of Light

"There are certain summits of achievement in the history of science, the formulation of certain general laws, which command the profound respect of all following generations. Newton's laws of motion together with his law of gravitation are one such an eminence. Newton's work makes it possible to unravel all the phenomena associated with mechanical motions. After Newton's day, a knowledge of physics which did not include an understanding of Newton's work was inconceivable.

"Maxwell's equations are for electric and magnetic phenomena what Newton's laws are for mechanical phenomena. While later advances such as relativity and quantum mechanics have followed, an understanding of this newer knowledge of the universe presupposes an understanding of Newton's laws and of Maxwell's equations. Maxwell's equations are fundamental not only to electronics but to all of physics. To anyone who is motivated by anything beyond the most narrowly practical, it is worth while to understand Maxwell's equations simply for the good of his soul."

From *Electrons, Waves and Messages* by JOHN R. PIERCE. Copyright © 1956 by John R. Pierce. Reprinted by permission of Doubleday & Company, Inc.

IN 1873 James Clerk Maxwell deduced the existence of electromagnetic waves (see Table 17.1). He even predicted that they would be found to travel at the speed of light. In 1888 Heinrich Hertz demonstrated how to generate such waves and also convinced himself, by testing them for the usual wave properties (reflection, refraction, diffraction, and interference), that they *were* waves. In 1894 Guglielmo Marconi demonstrated transmission of intelligence by radio waves over a distance of one and a half miles. In 1959 radio signals were being received on the earth from a

50-watt transmitter on the Pioneer V space probe eight million miles away.

I cite this sequence of events to illustrate only one—electromagnetic waves—of the many electrical phenomena that are implicit in Maxwell's famous equations. The purpose of this chapter is to make the existence of electromagnetic waves plausible and to show how their speed was predicted.

43.1. Maxwell's Equations

We are not prepared to study those equations in their usual form (§ 35.1), but we have progressed sufficiently to discuss the two equations (35.3 and 35.4) that contain the information about waves. (See equations 43.1 and 43.2.)

The information conveyed by Maxwell's equations can be stated in different ways. The first equation (35.1), for example, implies that $4\pi K$ lines of electric flux emanate from each point charge of 1 coulomb (§ 37.3). Since the charge carried by a single electron is very small when measured in coulombs, we may assign some large multiple of $4\pi K$ to each coulomb in order to imagine many lines of electric flux emanating from the one electron. (Since $K = 9 \times 10^9$, and since $e = 1.6 \times 10^{-19}$ coulomb, only $1.13 \times 10^{11} \times 1.6 \times 10^{-19} = 1.81 \times 10^{-8}$ line emanates from a single electron. If we arbitrarily assigned $10^{11} \times 4\pi K$ lines to one coulomb, we might assign 1,810 lines to one electron as an aid to visualization.) The important thing is that we imagine these lines as connected to the electron and moving along with it. Maxwell's second equation (35.2) implies that isolated *magnetic* charges (poles) do not exist. We may not, therefore, imagine an isolated pole with lines emanating from it.

I shall not write the first two equations in this section. Instead, I shall concentrate on Maxwell's third and fourth equations (35.3 and 35.4), the essence of which I write, tentatively, as

$$\underset{\substack{\text{closed} \\ \text{loop}}}{\Sigma \mathbf{B} \cdot \Delta \mathbf{l}} = 2\pi k i \qquad [43.1$$

$$\underset{\substack{\text{closed} \\ \text{loop}}}{\Sigma \mathbf{E} \cdot \Delta \mathbf{l}} = -\frac{\Delta \Phi_B}{\Delta t} \qquad [43.2$$

(Equation 43.1 appeared for the first time as equation 38.9.) I say "tentatively" because I must modify equation 43.1 slightly in order to exhibit the perfectly equivalent roles that electric fields and magnetic fields play in free space. Equations 43.1 and 43.2, on their left side, exhibit this equivalence: one has **B** in it where the other has **E**. On the right side, however, they differ: one has Φ_B (magnetic flux) in it, but the other does not have Φ_E (electric flux).

Let us review the meaning of equation 43.1. In a region where a magnetic field, **B**, exists, we draw a closed curve (Fig. 43.1.A). We break it up into small elements of length, $\Delta \mathbf{l}_1, \Delta \mathbf{l}_2, \ldots$, and we form the scalar product $\mathbf{B}_1 \cdot \Delta \mathbf{l}_1$. Repeating this for $\Delta \mathbf{l}_2, \Delta \mathbf{l}_3, \ldots$, we form the sum $\mathbf{B}_1 \cdot \Delta \mathbf{l}_1 + \mathbf{B}_2 \cdot \Delta \mathbf{l}_2 + \mathbf{B}_3 \cdot \Delta \mathbf{l}_3 + \ldots$. If the $\Delta \mathbf{l}$'s cover the whole loop, we write the sum as

$$\underset{\substack{\text{closed} \\ \text{loop}}}{\Sigma \mathbf{B} \cdot \Delta \mathbf{l}}$$

This sum is equal to $2\pi k$ times the current, in amperes, enclosed by the loop. (Positive current is shown in the figure. Since $I = -i$, it corresponds to a downward flow of electrons.)

Equation 43.1 was used in § 38.3 to determine the magnetic induction around a long wire carrying current. Since, for example, **B** and the element of length $\Delta \mathbf{l}$ (Fig. 43.1.A) are vectors and are always in the same direction, that equation, if the loop is a circle of radius r, yields

$$B \times 2\pi r = 2\pi k i$$

or

$$B = \frac{ki}{r}$$

which is the formula for the magnetic induction at distance r from an infinitely long wire carrying current i (equation 38.13). Equation 43.2, in a similar way, yields the electric field (Fig. 43.1.B) that accompanies the changing magnetic flux Φ_B (equation 41.4). If we follow a circular loop of radius r, it yields

$$E \times 2\pi r = -\frac{\Delta \Phi_B}{\Delta t}$$

$$E = -\frac{1}{2\pi r} \frac{\Delta \Phi_B}{\Delta t}$$

It is sometimes called the "transformer equation"

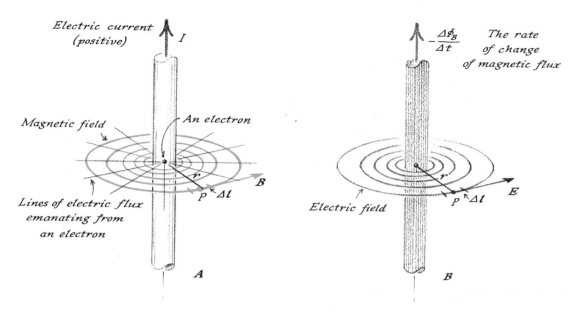

FIG. 43.1. (A) *The magnetic field associated with a moving electric field.* (B) *The electric field associated with a changing magnetic field.*

because the emf in a transformer is induced by $\Delta\Phi_B/\Delta t$ (equation 41.2).

Equation 43.2 states very clearly that a *changing* magnetic field is accompanied by an electric field. The idea that a *moving* electric field is accompanied by a magnetic field is implicit in equation 43.1, but it needs a bit of explaining.

An electric current consists of moving charges. In Figure 43.1.A one of these charges (an electron) is shown with some radial lines coming out of it. These are *electric field lines* since the electron is an electric charge. If you imagine the electron moving down in the wire and *carrying its electric field with it,* you can attribute the existence of magnetic field **B** at a point like P to the *motion* of this electric field.

But the symmetry of equations 43.1 and 43.2, as we have seen, is not perfect. Since we must take nature as we find it, not as we might wish it to be, we must explore the consequences of equation 43.1. (We cannot, however, hide the fact that, for the sake of symmetry, we wish equation 43.1 contained a term like $\Delta\Phi_E/\Delta t$ instead of $2\pi ki$.)

It is easy to show that a *moving* or *changing* magnetic field is accompanied by an electric field. In Figure 43.2.A, for example, we know that charges in the wire CD feel the effects of an electric field when the magnet is moved transversely as shown. But we also know, from experiments, that a varying current in wire QR (Fig. 43.2.B) is accompanied by a current in wire ST, thus proving that a changing magnetic field (that produced at P by i in QR) is accompanied by an electric field, **E** (the one that pushes charges in ST).

Let us summarize all of this as follows: (1) a *moving* or *changing* magnetic field is accompanied by an electric field; (2) a *moving* (or *changing*) electric field is accompanied by a magnetic field. I have discussed experiments designed to confirm all but the parenthetical part of statement 2. Maxwell, in order to avoid contradictions with his other equations, asserted that a changing electric field is accompanied by a magnetic field. This idea, his most important contribution, led to the prediction of electromagnetic waves.

We now consider the contradiction discovered by Maxwell and the way he resolved it.

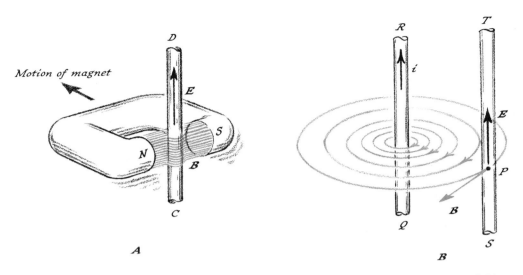

FIG. 43.2. *Induction of current: (A) by a moving magnetic field; (B) by the changing magnetic field associated with a changing current.*

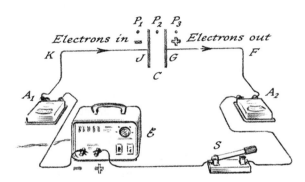

FIG. 43.3. *The charging of a capacitor.*

43.2. The Displacement Current

When a capacitor is being charged, electrons flow from the battery to one of its plates and to the battery from the other. In Figure 43.3, for example, electrons flow from K to J and from G to F while the capacitor, C, is being charged, even though *there is no transport of electrons from plate* J *to plate* G *across the space between them;* sensitive current meters, A_1 and A_2, show a current and read alike. While the current lasts, a magnetic field surrounds the wires, and we

should find the magnetic fields at points P_1 and P_3 to be alike at the same time.

How about the magnetic field at point P_2, right above the empty region of the capacitor? Using Ampère's ideas, one would expect the different parts of the wire from K to J and also from G to F to contribute to a magnetic field at P_2. For the moment, therefore, let us *assume* that the magnetic induction at P_2 is the same as that at P_1. In Figure 43.4, where the capacitor is drawn with parallel circular plates to simplify the analysis, we take a closed loop consisting of the four-sided figure whose opposite sides of lengths Δl_1 and Δl_2 are arcs of circles with their centers on the axis of the wire beneath them. We form the sum

$$\Sigma \mathbf{B} \cdot \Delta \mathbf{l}$$
closed
loop

for this loop. We then take $\mathbf{B}_1$ as the value of $\mathbf{B}$ over Δl_1 and $\mathbf{B}_2$ as the value of $\mathbf{B}$ over Δl_2. Since the effects of $\mathbf{B} \cdot \Delta \mathbf{l}$ cancel out over the unnamed sides of the loop, and since no current is enclosed by this loop, we get (equation 43.1), after dropping the vector notation and using the equation $\Delta l_2 = -\Delta l_1$,

$$B_1 \Delta l_1 - B_2 \Delta l_1 = 0 \quad \text{or} \quad B_1 = B_2$$

So far, there is no contradiction with the assumption that the magnetic field is the same at points P_1 and P_2.

We now consider a circular loop (in a plane parallel to the plates of the capacitor), of radius r, between the capacitor plates, and starting at P_2. Here all the elements Δl of the loop run in the same direction as the *assumed* field, $\mathbf{B}_2$. It follows that

$$\underset{\substack{\text{closed} \\ \text{loop}}}{\Sigma \mathbf{B} \cdot \Delta \mathbf{l}} = 2\pi r B_2 = 0$$

since no current—there is only an electric field, $\mathbf{E}$, between the plates—is enclosed by this loop. This implies that B_2 is zero, and now we *do* have a contradiction. Maxwell resolved it by amending the formula

$$\underset{\substack{\text{closed} \\ \text{loop}}}{\Sigma \mathbf{B} \cdot \Delta \mathbf{l}} = 2\pi k i$$

to

$$\underset{\substack{\text{closed} \\ \text{loop}}}{\Sigma \mathbf{B} \cdot \Delta \mathbf{l}} = 2\pi k \left[i + \frac{1}{4\pi K} \left(\frac{\Delta \Phi_E}{\Delta t} \right) \right] \qquad [43.3$$

In other words, he postulated the phenomenon represented by the term

$$\frac{1}{4\pi K} \left(\frac{\Delta \Phi_E}{\Delta t} \right)$$

and gave it the name **displacement current,** which, for pedagogical reasons, is unfortunate. No transport of charge occurs, and there is no displacement of the kind introduced in § 3.4.

Observe that $\Delta \Phi_E / \Delta t$ is the rate of change of electric field intensity. We are requiring that a change in electric field be associated with a magnetic field. Let us examine the consequences of this assertion for the capacitor of Figure 43.4. In the region between the plates, $i = 0$, and only

$$\frac{1}{4\pi K} \left(\frac{\Delta \Phi_E}{\Delta t} \right)$$

survives within the brackets of equation 43.3. In the wires leading to the capacitor, on the other hand, $\Delta \Phi_E / \Delta t$ is virtually zero, and only i survives. We now examine in detail what is happening at the capacitor.

The capacitance of a capacitor is, by definition, $C = Q/V$ (equation 37.11). The capacitance of a capacitor with parallel plates of area A separated by distance d is $C = A/4\pi Kd$ (equation 37.12). Multiplying by V, we get

$$VC = \frac{AV}{4\pi Kd}$$

Using the fact (equation 40.2) that V/d

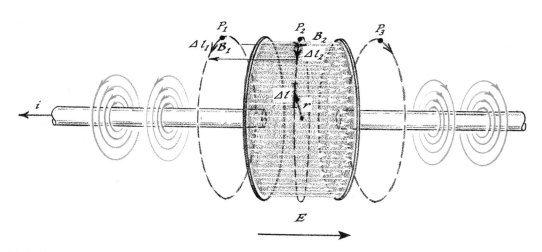

FIG. 43.4. *One of the loops chosen for computation of $\Sigma \mathbf{B} \cdot \Delta \mathbf{l}$ has for boundaries circular arcs at P_1 and P_2 and two straight line segments parallel to the wire. No current is enclosed by this loop; so $\Sigma \mathbf{B} \cdot \Delta \mathbf{l} = \mathbf{0}$. The logical consequence of this is that $\mathbf{B}_1 = \mathbf{B}_2$. Another loop consists of a circle through P_2, of radius r, in a plane parallel to the capacitor plates. The logical consequence of the equation $\Sigma \mathbf{B} \cdot \Delta \mathbf{l} = \mathbf{0}$ is now, however, that $B_2 = 0$.*

(volts/meter) is the equivalent of E (joules/coulomb) and that $VC = Q$, we get

$$Q = \frac{AE}{4\pi K} \qquad [43.4$$

(The constant K occurs in equation 36.1.) The electric flux, Φ_E, is, by definition, exactly AE (A in m² and E in lines/m²) since **E** is perpendicular to the capacitor plate. Hence

$$Q = \frac{\Phi_E}{4\pi K} \qquad [43.5$$

This implies that

$$\frac{\Delta Q}{\Delta t} = \frac{1}{4\pi K}\left(\frac{\Delta\Phi_E}{\Delta t}\right) \qquad [43.6$$

But $\Delta Q/\Delta t$ (coul/sec) is the rate at which charges are accumulating on the plates and *hence must be the current in the wires leading to the plates.* The term

$$\frac{1}{4\pi K}\left(\frac{\Delta\Phi_E}{\Delta t}\right)$$

therefore has the physical dimensions of a current.

Now let us call

$$i + \frac{1}{4\pi K}\left(\frac{\Delta\Phi_E}{\Delta t}\right)$$

the *total* current postulated by Maxwell. In the wire,

$$\frac{\Delta\Phi_E}{\Delta t} = 0$$

and only i contributes to the term in the brackets of equation 43.3. In the space between the plates, $i = 0$, and only

$$\frac{1}{4\pi K}\left(\frac{\Delta\Phi_E}{\Delta t}\right)$$

contributes. From equations 43.1 and 43.3 we see that

AROUND THE WIRE: $\displaystyle\sum_{\substack{\text{closed}\\\text{loop}}} \mathbf{B}\cdot\Delta\mathbf{l} = 2\pi ki$

BETWEEN THE PLATES: $\displaystyle\sum_{\substack{\text{closed}\\\text{loop}}} \mathbf{B}\cdot\Delta\mathbf{l} = \frac{2\pi k}{4\pi K}\left(\frac{\Delta\Phi_E}{\Delta t}\right)$

Since, according to equation 43.6,

$$\frac{1}{4\pi K}\left(\frac{\Delta\Phi_E}{\Delta t}\right)$$

is numerically equal to i, the right-hand sides of these equations are equal. Hence the left-hand sides are equal. If we take the sum

$$\sum_{\substack{\text{closed}\\\text{loop}}} \mathbf{B}\cdot\Delta\mathbf{l}$$

round a circle containing P_2 (Fig. 43.4), we get the same answer as when we take that sum round a circle containing either P_1 or P_3. In other words, the magnetic field *is* the same at points P_1, P_2, and P_3 of Figure 43.4 if the total current postulated by Maxwell is taken into account.†

We are now ready to write Maxwell's equations for free space (where $i = 0$). We take equations 43.2 and 43.3 and write them for this special case:

IN FREE SPACE: $\displaystyle\sum_{\substack{\text{closed}\\\text{loop}}} \mathbf{E}\cdot\Delta\mathbf{l} = -\frac{\Delta\Phi_B}{\Delta t} \qquad [43.7$

IN FREE SPACE: $\displaystyle\sum_{\substack{\text{closed}\\\text{loop}}} \mathbf{B}\cdot\Delta\mathbf{l} = \frac{k}{2K}\left(\frac{\Delta\Phi_E}{\Delta t}\right) \qquad [43.8$

Except for a constant of proportionality, they are now perfectly symmetrical. We can replace E by B and B by E and get a valid statement (except for the constant). We can now assert (equation 43.7) that *a changing magnetic field* ($\Delta\Phi_B/\Delta t$) *is accompanied by an electric field* (**E**) *and that* (equation 43.8) *a changing electric field* ($\Delta\Phi_E/\Delta t$) *is accompanied by a magnetic field* (**B**). It therefore seems that, if we got a changing electric field, it would have a changing magnetic field associated with it; but a changing magnetic field has a changing electric field associated with it; and so on, in space. We are now ready to consider the generation of electromagnetic waves.

43.3. Electromagnetic Waves

In Chapter 13 we considered the basic characteristics of waves. Using a long spiral spring, for example, we showed that the activity at one point of a wave is copied identically (except, perhaps, for a reduction in amplitude) at subsequent points and at subsequent instants of time. Even the simplest pulse of the falling dominoes

---

† I may have left the impression that the changing field alone causes the magnetic field at P_2. This is wrong—for the current in the wires produces a magnetic field at P_2. We do not need the displacement current to save the magnetic field at P_2, but we do need it to get rid of the incomplete equation 43.1 and substitute one that always works.

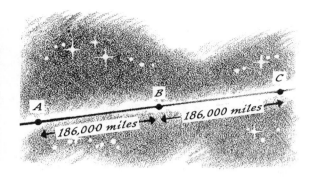

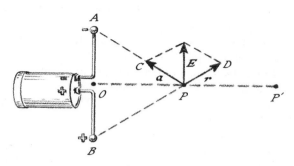

FIG. 43.5. *Three points in interstellar space.*

FIG. 43.6. *Simple (but not very practical) way to produce an electric disturbance.*

obeyed the pattern "what *now* happens *here* (near the source) happens *there* (far from the source) *later*." The events at one point of a transverse wave in a rope are motions at right angles to the rope. The events at a point of a sound wave traveling from a tuning fork to an ear are vibrations of the air molecules in the direction of the line from fork to ear; if we removed the air with a vacuum pump, there would be no molecules to vibrate, and there would be no wave. All the waves we have considered so far have required material particles. Now we are about to consider waves that can travel in a vacuum.

We know that electric and magnetic fields can exist in a vacuum. Let us see if we can imagine an electric wave and then try to conceive a way of generating it. A good laboratory for imagined experiments requiring a vacuum is interstellar space. We take three points (Fig. 43.5), A, B, and C, in a straight line. Point B is 186,000 miles from A and from C. We imagine an electron at rest at each point. (A body at rest remains at rest unless acted upon by an external force.) At time $t = 0$ we observe that the electron at A undergoes one cycle of a transverse motion and comes to rest again. We observe a similar motion of the electron at B at $t = 1$ sec and of the electron at C at $t = 2$ sec. It certainly looks as if a wave of electric force had passed by at 186,000 mi/sec. We have not seen the wave, but we have seen its effects. ("Who has seen the wind? / Neither you nor I. / But when the leaves bow down their heads / The wind is passing by.")

How could we generate such an electric dis-

turbance? A simple (but not very practical) way would be to connect a pair of wires to a battery as shown in Figure 43.6. The wires end in spheres A and B. When the wires touch the positive and negative terminals of the battery, the spheres become charged. (Electrons migrate from B to the positive terminal and from the negative terminal to A.) A small positive charge, q, placed at point P on the line OP, which is the perpendicular bisector of AB, feels an attraction, **a**, to A and a repulsion, **r**, from B. The resultant of these vectors is the vector **E**, parallel to BA. If q were a unit charge, the force, **F**, felt by it at P would be the field intensity there. Since, in the MKS system, the unit charge, the coulomb, is exceedingly large, let us assume that **E** represents

$$\lim_{q \to 0} \frac{\mathbf{F}}{q}$$

We now imagine another point, P', 186,000 miles away from P on the line OP. Will a charge, q, placed there feel an electric force at the same time that the charge at P does? When the wires first touch the terminals of the battery, is the field due to the charges at A and B established simultaneously all over space? Do the charges at P and P' feel a push at the same instant? We have good reason to believe that the answer is "no"; the effect occurs first at P, one second later at P', two seconds later another 186,000 miles farther along the line, and so on.

This is getting interesting! It's like the pulse of falling dominoes *without the dominoes*! The charges at P and P' are not, in fact, necessary to our conception of a wave. They were put there to reveal the wave's passage, but the wave did not depend on their presence.

When the wires are first touched to the battery, we imagine a pulse of electric field strength traveling outward in all directions, reaching the moon in about 1.3 seconds, the sun in 8.3 minutes, and Alpha Centauri in 4.3 years. (The pulse gets weaker, of course.)

What happens if the two wires are short-circuited at O and the battery is removed? The charges rearrange themselves on the wire so that electrical neutrality results. The field intensity drops to zero at P, and another second later it drops to zero at P'. The pulse of extinction reaches the moon in 1.3 seconds, the sun in 8.3 minutes, and Alpha Centauri in 4.3 years.

Before Maxwell's work, it was not known that electric effects were propagated *at this particular speed*. As soon as it was granted that the speed of propagation is not infinite, waves began to be plausible. Let us consider this plausibility a little further, and then I shall show how Maxwell arrived at his prediction of 186,000 miles per second as the speed of propagation.

When (Fig. 43.7) the wires are connected to the battery (A), an electric field, E, pointing upward, is produced at point P. If the wires are short-circuited (B), the electric field intensity goes to zero at P as soon as the wave of destruction reaches it. If the position of the battery, with its connected wires, is reversed (C), the electric field that reaches P points downward. The pulse of destruction never catches up with the previous

pulse of field creation because they both travel at the same speed.

If the wires (Fig. 43.8) are connected to a coil, D, that is magnetically coupled to a coil of inductance L that is in series with a capacitor of capacitance C, an alternating emf induced in D can drive electrons alternately from B to A and from A to B. We do not show what is in chamber I of the magic box, but let us suppose that it can feed electrical energy to the LC circuit (chamber II) to sustain oscillations at its natural frequency. If that frequency is, for example, 100 kilocycles per second, the electric field at P will complete a cycle 100,000 times every second. During half of each cycle, the field will point down (as at E'), and during the other half it will point up. At a point 186,000 miles beyond P, the field will mimic the effects at P, but one second later. Points nearer P will feel the effects sooner.

This phenomenon has all the earmarks of a wave. At every point, as at P, there is a *changing electric field*. According to Maxwell's equations, we should find also a magnetic field.

We can go back to the wire in search of its cause (Fig. 43.8). During the part of the cycle when electrons are moving from B to A, a magnetic field surrounds the wire. But it is not created simultaneously throughout all of space: it takes one second to travel 186,000 miles.

Let us consider the magnetic effect at the nearby point P. Electrons moving up the wire (BA) produce the magnetic induction **B**; a half cycle later the magnetic induction **B'** will point in the op-

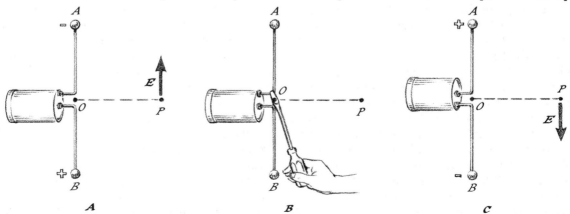

FIG. 43.7. *Illustrating the propagation of electromagnetic waves.*

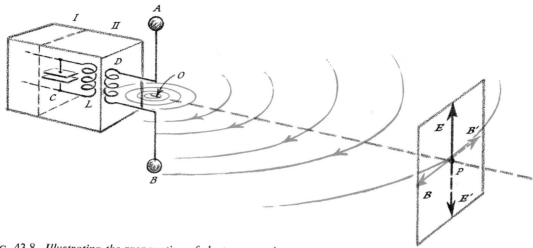

FIG. 43.8. *Illustrating the propagation of electromagnetic waves.*

posite direction; and so on. This makes it plausible that the **B** vectors are perpendicular to the **E** vectors and in the same plane. Since that plane is perpendicular to *OP*, transverse waves seem to be called for. (I shall show later how it was demonstrated experimentally that the waves are indeed transverse.)

If a transverse pulse is traveling along a long rope, we don't have to go all the way back to the source to find the plausibility of its continued propagation. A wave ensues from the vibration in any region of the rope. The propagation of an electromagnetic wave is analogous. The very fact that there is a changing electric field in a region means that we can expect to find a magnetic field there; and, if it turns out that the magnetic field is changing (and it *will* change if the electric field is generated by an alternating current at the source), Maxwell's equations demand that it have an associated electric field. So the variation of the electric and magnetic fields implies the propagation of an electromagnetic wave.

Consider, for example, the meaning of

$$\sum_{\substack{\text{closed} \\ \text{loop}}} \mathbf{E} \cdot \Delta \mathbf{l} = -\frac{\Delta \Phi_B}{\Delta t}$$

(equation 43.2) for a loop drawn round point *P* of Figure 43.8, as shown diagrammatically in Figure 43.9. (The square of Fig. 43.9 is at right angles to that of Fig. 43.8.) The plane of the rectangular loop *GHJK* is perpendicular to **B**

(shown going perpendicularly into the plane of the paper). The **E** field is labeled $\mathbf{E}_1$ at *H*, $\mathbf{E}_2$ at *J*. Along *HJ* and *GK* that field is perpendicular to the loop element and contributes nothing to $\sum \mathbf{E} \cdot \Delta \mathbf{l}$. Notice that $\Delta \mathbf{l}_2 = -\Delta \mathbf{l}_1$. What survives in the summation may be written, without vectors, as

$$-E_1 \Delta l_1 + E_2 \Delta l_1 = -\frac{\Delta \Phi_B}{\Delta t}$$

Suppose that **B** is a constant. Then $\Delta \Phi_B / \Delta t$ is zero at *P*, and

$$E_1 \Delta l_1 - E_2 \Delta l_1 = 0$$

This implies that $E_2 = E_1$; in other words, there is no *spatial* change in **E**. But, if $\Delta \Phi_B / \Delta t$ is not

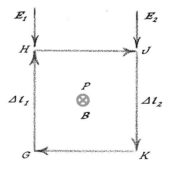

FIG. 43.9. *A loop, GHJK, at right angles to* **B**, *chosen for evaluation of* $\sum \mathbf{E} \cdot \Delta \mathbf{l}$. *The direction HJ is the same as that of OP in Fig. 43.8.*

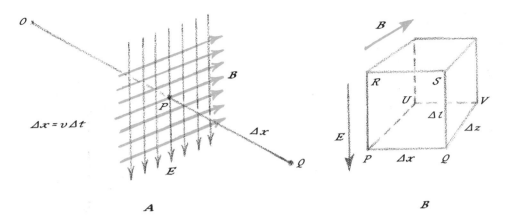

FIG. 43.10. *Illustrating the propagation of electromagnetic waves.*

zero (Fig. 43.8)—that is, if the magnetic field at P is changing *in time*—then $E_2 \neq E_1$; that is, the electric field is changing *in space*. This is the explanation of the propagation of the **E** wave. Because of the equivalence of **E** and **B** in Maxwell's equations, a similar argument explains the propagation of the **B** wave. With more sophisticated mathematical tools (partial differential equations) the mathematical demonstration becomes precise and rigorous.

So much for the possibility of electromagnetic waves. How fast would they travel? Does the theory predict what experiment reveals: that they would travel at the rate of 186,000 miles per second? Let us see.

43.4. The Speed of Propagation of Electromagnetic Waves

Even if the shape of a stone dropped into a pond is very irregular, the shape of the wave front produced by the stone on the pond's surface is always circular far from the source. When the circles get large enough, portions of them look like straight lines. The electromagnetic waves originating in the dipole BA (Fig. 43.8) are never quite spherical; along a line such as OP and at great distances they are approximately plane waves. In the subsequent analysis we shall make the simplifying assumption that we are dealing with a plane wave front.

Imagine, then, a pulse of **E** and **B** fields originating at point O (Fig. 43.10.A). At the distant point P the lines of **E** and **B** that mark the passage of the pulse lie on a plane perpendicular to the direction of propagation, OP. The wave front has reached P but has not yet reached Q, which is at distance Δx beyond P. If the speed of propagation is v, then $v(\Delta t) = \Delta x$. In Figure 43.10.B a cube is drawn to help us visualize the direction of the **E** vectors (pointing down) and the **B** vectors (pointing at right angles to **E**).

Now let us imagine the lines of **B** going into the paper (Fig. 43.11) and denote them by the symbol ×. At first (A) the wave front has just crossed the boundary PR; at time Δt later (B) it has not quite reached the boundary SQ. For this reason

$$(\Phi_B)_1 = 0 \quad \text{at} \quad t = 0$$

$$(\Phi_B)_2 = (\text{area } PQSR) \times B \quad \text{at} \quad t = \Delta t$$

$$(\Phi_B)_2 - (\Phi_B)_1 = (\text{area } PQSR) \times B = (\Delta x)(\Delta l)B$$

The increment $(\Delta \Phi_B)$ in magnetic flux (Φ_B) is $(\Delta x)(\Delta l)B$. The rate of change of flux is

$$\frac{\Delta \Phi_B}{\Delta t} = \frac{(\Delta x)(\Delta l)B}{\Delta t} \qquad [43.9$$

We know, since $v(\Delta t) = \Delta x$, that $\Delta t = \Delta x/v$. Putting this value of Δt into equation 43.9, we obtain

$$\frac{\Delta \Phi_B}{\Delta t} = \frac{(\Delta x)(\Delta l)B}{\Delta x/v} = (\Delta l)Bv \qquad [43.10$$

According to equation 43.7,

$$-\frac{\Delta \Phi_B}{\Delta t} = \Sigma \mathbf{E} \cdot \Delta \mathbf{l}$$
$$\text{closed} \atop \text{loop}$$

Now observe that **E** runs parallel to PR, runs

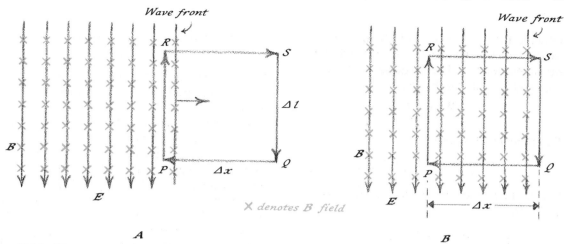

FIG. 43.11. *Illustrating the propagation of electromagnetic waves.*

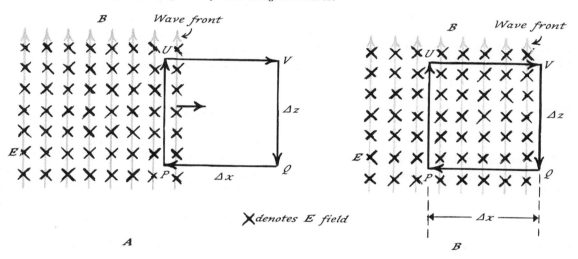

FIG. 43.12. *Illustrating the propagation of electromagnetic waves.*

perpendicular to RS and PQ, and never reaches SQ. Therefore

$$\underset{\substack{\text{closed}\\\text{loop}}}{\Sigma \mathbf{E} \cdot \Delta \mathbf{l}}$$

is simply $-E(\Delta l)$; and therefore, using equations 43.10 and 43.7, we get

$$(\Delta l)Bv = E(\Delta l) \qquad [43.11$$

or

$$Bv = E \qquad [43.12$$

That gives us one expression with the velocity in it. We shall now obtain another by repeating the argument for the $\mathbf{E}$ field. By looking at the field lines of Fig. 43.10.B from another direction, looking down on face $UVQP$, you can see E lines

going away from you and $\mathbf{B}$ lines pointing up. They are drawn this way in Figure 43.12.A. The equation analogous to equation 43.9 (obtainable by a similar argument) is

$$\frac{\Delta \Phi_E}{\Delta t} = \frac{(\Delta x)(\Delta z)E}{\Delta t} \qquad [43.13$$

Using again the value $\Delta t = \Delta x/v$, we obtain

$$\frac{\Delta \Phi_E}{\Delta t} = (\Delta z)Ev \qquad [43.14$$

This time we use the fact (equation 43.8) that

$$\underset{\substack{\text{closed}\\\text{loop}}}{\Sigma \mathbf{B} \cdot \Delta \mathbf{l}} = \frac{k}{2K}\left(\frac{\Delta \Phi_E}{\Delta t}\right)$$

Observe that, in Figure 43.12.B, **B** runs parallel to *PU*, runs perpendicular to *UV* and *PQ*, and never reaches *QV*. The products **B**·Δ**l** along *UV*, *VQ*, and *QP* all vanish; hence

$$\sum_{\substack{\text{closed} \\ \text{loop}}} \mathbf{B} \cdot \Delta \mathbf{l} = B(\Delta z)$$

Equation 43.8 becomes

$$B(\Delta z) = \frac{k}{2K} \left(\frac{\Delta \Phi_E}{\Delta t} \right) \qquad [43.15$$

Substituting into this equation from equation 43.14, we get

$$B(\Delta z) = \frac{k}{2K} (\Delta z) E v \qquad [43.16$$

$$B = \frac{k}{2K} E v \qquad [43.17$$

Dividing equation 43.17 by equation 43.12 ($Bv = E$), we get

$$\frac{1}{v} = \frac{k}{2K} v \qquad [43.18$$

Hence

$$v^2 = \frac{2K}{k} \qquad [43.19$$

Now we must substitute the proper values of K and k. The quantity K appeared in Coulomb's law of electric charges,

$$F = \frac{K q_1 q_2}{r^2}$$

(equation 36.1), and has the value

$$K = 9 \times 10^9 \frac{\text{nt-m}^2}{\text{coul}^2}$$

The quantity k first appeared in the definition of the ampere,

$$F = \frac{k i_1 i_2 L}{r}$$

(equation 35.8), and has the value

$$k = 2 \times 10^{-7} \text{ nt/amp}^2$$

Therefore

$$2 \frac{K}{k} = \frac{2 \times 9 \times 10^9}{2 \times 10^{-7}} \frac{\text{nt-m}^2}{\text{coul}^2} \times \frac{\text{amp}^2}{\text{nt}}$$

$$= 9 \times 10^{16} \frac{\text{m}^2}{\text{coul}^2} \times \frac{\text{coul}^2}{\text{sec}^2}$$

$$= 9 \times 10^{16} \frac{\text{m}^2}{\text{sec}^2} \qquad [43.20$$

Putting this value into equation 43.19, we get

$$v = 3 \times 10^8 \text{ m/sec} \qquad [43.21$$

We recognize this as the speed of light (for which we have been using the approximate value 186,000 mi/sec).

Maxwell observed that the value of v predicted by his equations came out close to the then known value for the speed of light. The conjecture that light itself was an electromagnetic wave then seemed inevitable.

It was not long after Maxwell's theoretical discovery that Hertz produced and detected electromagnetic waves in the laboratory by techniques that were the forerunners of modern radio; but this is a separate and fascinating story, which we do not have time to cover here. We must use Maxwell's results to pursue the idea that light is an electromagnetic wave and has the properties that the electromagnetic theory predicts for it.

43.5. Summary

A moving or changing magnetic field is always accompanied by an electric field. A moving or changing electric field is always accompanied by a magnetic field. In free space all this is summarized mathematically, if the summation is taken round a closed loop, by the equations

$$\sum \mathbf{E} \cdot \Delta \mathbf{l} = -\frac{\Delta \Phi_B}{\Delta t}$$

$$\sum \mathbf{B} \cdot \Delta \mathbf{l} = \frac{k}{2K} \left(\frac{\Delta \Phi_E}{\Delta t} \right)$$

in which the duality between electric field **E** and magnetic field **B** is apparent. The precise differential equations of which these are approximate statements lead directly to the prediction of electromagnetic waves and to the value $\sqrt{2K/k}$ for their speed. Substitution of the proper MKS values for K and k yields 3×10^8 m/sec (with the accuracy with which we have given K) for the predicted speed of electromagnetic waves. This value corresponds very closely to the experimental value of the speed of light in a vacuum and gives strong support to the idea that light is an electromagnetic wave.

Problems

43.1. 1. What are the MKS units for $\mathbf{B} \cdot \Delta \mathbf{l}$? (Hint: From the equation $F = Bil$ you can get units for B.)

2. Prove that ki has the same units. (Hint: Obtain units for k by considering the equation $F = ki_1i_2l/r$.)

43.2. 1. Six wires each carrying 2 amp in the same direction run parallel to one another. A closed loop is considered in space as surrounding all of the wires. What is the value of $\Sigma \mathbf{B} \cdot \Delta \mathbf{l}$, in MKS units, round such a loop?

2. Two parallel wires run close to each other. They carry 2 amp each in opposite directions. What is $\Sigma \mathbf{B} \cdot \Delta \mathbf{l}$ for a closed loop round such a combination?

43.3. In a small region of space where there are no charges, a small closed loop links an electric flux that is 20 nt-m²/coul at one instant and 35 nt-m²/coul 0.0015 sec later. Compute the value of $\Sigma \mathbf{B} \cdot \Delta \mathbf{l}$ in MKS units round the closed loop.

43.4. Prove that the significant figures for $2K/k$ and hence for K alone are those of c^2 if c is the speed of light.

43.5. Prove carefully that $\Sigma \mathbf{E} \cdot \Delta \mathbf{l}$ did not vary round the closed loop $PRSQ$ (Fig. 43.11) during the interval of time Δt used in equation 43.9. Do this by considering $\Sigma \mathbf{E} \cdot \Delta \mathbf{l}$ round $PRSQ$ at the beginning of the interval and once again at the end of the interval.

43.6. Within the region between the plates of Fig. 43.4, would you expect the momentary magnetic field that exists when the switch is first closed to be strong near the center of the plates or near an edge? Explain.

The Polarization of Light and Other Electromagnetic Waves

ONE quality of a good theory is that it explains many phenomena that seem, without the theory, to be unrelated. The electromagnetic theory of light is such a theory. The purpose of this chapter is to exhibit some properties of light that we can easily understand if we assume that light is an electromagnetic wave.

In our study of optics we saw that light, in common with other waves, can be reflected, refracted, and diffracted, and that it obeys the principle of superposition, which is clearly demonstrated by interference. But we did not specify what kind of wave light is. We now seek to prove that light is an electromagnetic wave and that its vibrations are transverse rather than longitudinal. The experimental proof of the latter property depends on polarization. I shall explain what polarization is after I have shown that the propagation of electromagnetic waves depends on *accelerated* electric charges.

44.1. The Radiation Produced by Accelerated Charges

We have now accumulated considerable evidence to support the following two statements: (1) *electric fields are associated with charges and with changing magnetic fields;* (2) *magnetic fields are associated with currents and with changing electric fields.*

An accelerated charge can produce the combination of changing electric and magnetic fields that we associate with electromagnetic waves. Imagine (Fig. 44.1) an isolated charge, q, at O. (It could be in a wire, but that is not necessary.) If it is at rest, it produces at P an electric field in the direction OPQ; but this is not the electric field we are interested in at the moment. If q is moving with constant speed along OC, it produces at P a constant magnetic field at right angles to OP because it constitutes a constant current; but such a constant magnetic field is not of interest to us right now. If the charge experiences an acceleration, $\mathbf{a}$, in the direction OC, it produces at P a *changing* magnetic field, $\mathbf{B}$, which has an associated changing electric field, $\mathbf{E}$ (in obedience to Maxwell's equations), parallel to $\mathbf{a}$. An electric field in this direction (parallel to $\mathbf{a}$) does not exist when the charge at O is either at rest or moving with constant velocity. A charge at O, accelerated as shown, produces an electromagnetic wave with $\mathbf{E}$ and $\mathbf{B}$ fields oriented as in Figure 44.1.

We learned earlier that a charge has electric field lines emanating radially from it. The simple coulomb field ($E = Kq/r^2$) associated with the charge at O points along OPQ, but the transverse **E** field associated with the accelerated charge q points parallel to **a** and obeys the relation

$$E = \frac{Kqa}{rc^2} \qquad [44.1$$

in which a is the magnitude of the acceleration of the charge, r is the distance to it, and c is the speed of light. The significant characteristics of this field are the following: (1) The field is transverse rather than longitudinal. (2) It varies inversely with distance and not inversely with the square of the distance; at great distances, therefore, it can be many times larger than the coulomb inverse-square field. (3) It vanishes if the acceleration is zero: *only accelerated charges produce a transverse field.*

Some of these ideas can be remembered by analogy with a stretched rope. If one end of such a rope (Fig. 44.2.A) is given a transverse acceleration, a transverse pulse will be transmitted along the rope. Similarly (Fig. 44.2.B), if charge q at O is given a transverse acceleration, **a**, a transverse pulse of electric intensity is propagated along the otherwise undisturbed electric field line OP. (One

important difference between the two parts of the figure is that in part A the pulse can travel only along the single rope shown, whereas in part B the field line shown is only one of many that emanate from q. The pulse travels along every line whose direction has a component normal to **a**.) There is no propagation of energy in the perpendicular direction, OC. So far I have been speaking of pulses. If the charge q executes simple harmonic motion, it will produce a traveling sine wave of electric fields (Fig. 44.3). It will also, of course, generate magnetic fields at right angles to the electric fields, as shown in Figure 44.4.

We can summarize all this as follows: *An accelerated charge radiates electromagnetic energy in all directions perpendicular to the acceleration.* Some energy is radiated in directions that are not perpendicular to the acceleration, but the intensity of the radiation diminishes gradually to zero as we move away (Fig. 44.2.B) from the perpendicular direction OP toward the parallel direction OC.

We have ample proof that energy can be transported in this way, for most of the energy that comes to the earth from the sun is in the form of electromagnetic waves. Some of it we call light

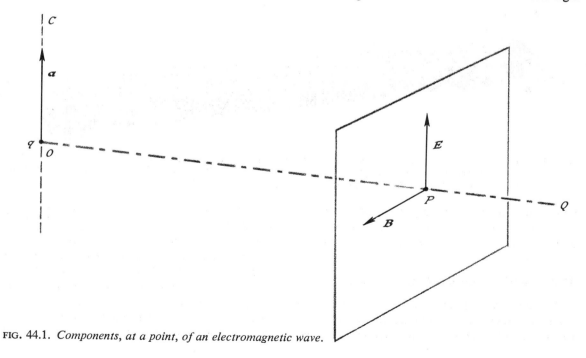

FIG. 44.1. *Components, at a point, of an electromagnetic wave.*

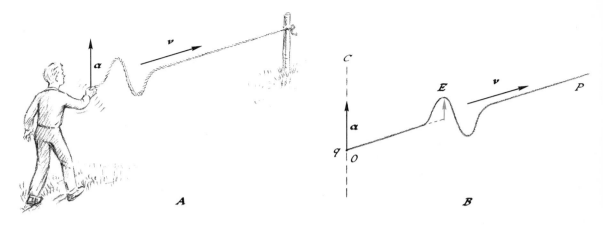

FIG. 44.2. *Analogy between a transverse pulse in a rope (A) and a transverse pulse along an electric field line (B).*

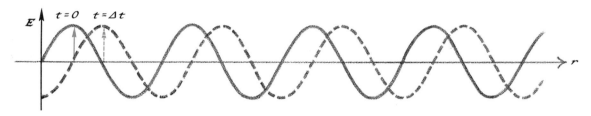

FIG. 44.3. *A wave of electric intensity produced by a charge oscillating in simple harmonic motion. The solid curve represents the wave at one instant. The dashed curve represents the wave at a time Δt later. The green vectors represent the E field at different times and places.*

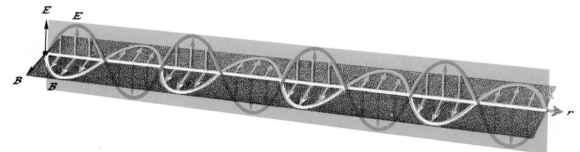

FIG. 44.4. *A simple polarized electromagnetic wave emanating from an accelerated charge and moving in the r direction. The E vectors (green) lie in a vertical plane, and the B vectors (white) lie in a horizontal plane. Both are perpendicular to the direction of propagation of the wave.*

and some heat, but a good portion of it is ultra-violet radiation, radio waves, and x-rays. (A table of electromagnetic radiations appears in § 17.3.)

44.2. The Polarization of Radio Waves

Before we take up light let us clarify the meaning of **polarization** by reference to radio waves. In Figure 44.5, *CD* is a linear antenna connected to a transmitter, *T*, that generates alternating current of high frequency. The coupling device is symbolized by induction coil *L*. Electric charges, *q*, within wire *CD* are accelerated in direction **a** and set up an electric field wave in space. All the E vectors lie in a plane containing **a**—in our drawing the plane of the paper. The wave depicted is said to be a **plane-polarized wave.** (Observe, in Fig. 44.4, that the E wave and the B

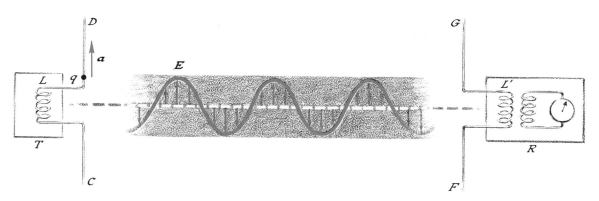

FIG. 44.5. *A plane-polarized* **E** *wave produced by accelerated charges in the antenna,* CD, *of a transmitter,* T. *The* **E** *field, when it reaches the receiver,* R, *accelerates charges in its antenna,* FG, *and produces a current in* L'.

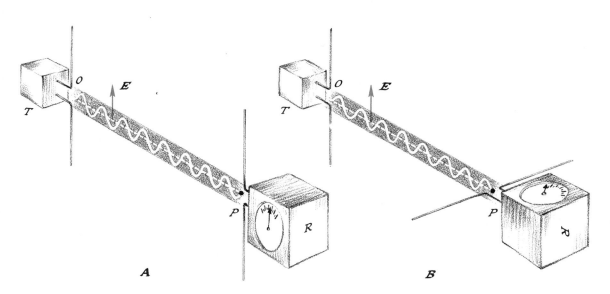

FIG. 44.6. *Proof of polarization: (A) Receiver antenna is parallel to transmitter antenna; signal picked up is at a maximum. (B) Receiver antenna is perpendicular to transmitter antenna; signal picked up is at a minimum.*

wave are polarized in mutually perpendicular planes. I shall stress the **E** vector in subsequent work because it is responsible for many of the observable effects of light. Henceforth I shall not draw the **B** vectors, but they are always present when **E** varies with time.) The receiver, *R*, also has a linear antenna. The electric field, **E**, pushes charges up and down its length and through the receiver's coupling coil, L'. The electric signal thus received (Fig. 44.6) is amplified electronically and displayed (A) as a reading on a meter. If the receiving antenna were perpendicular (B) to the plane of field **E**, its electrons could not be pushed along its length, and the signal picked up would drop to zero. We can show that the wave is polarized by rotating the receiving antenna about line *OP*, which joins the transmitter and the receiver.

To prove that radio signals are waves, you may demonstrate that they can produce diffraction and interference (see § 13.7). To prove that they are electromagnetic, you simply show that they exert force on electric charges (as they do in the receiving antenna). Finally, their transverse nature is confirmed by the fact that they can be plane-polarized. We shall now see that light has similar properties.

44.3. The Evidence for the Electromagnetic Nature of Light

I have already taken pains to show (§ 23.1 and § 23.2) that light has wave-like characteristics. How do we know it is an electromagnetic wave? We should like to be able to show, in a simple and direct way, that light has an E field capable of exerting force on electric charges, but we cannot pick up a light wave with an ordinary antenna attached to a radio receiver, for, as we shall see presently, the frequency is too high. We do have plenty of other evidence of an E field in light, but it is somewhat indirect.

The first clue to the electromagnetic character of light waves is their speed. The presently accepted experimental value for the speed of light is

$$c = 299{,}792.5 \pm 3 \frac{km}{sec}$$

Precise measurements of the speed of radio waves about 1 centimeter long give values that lie between

$$c = 299{,}789.3 \pm 0.8 \frac{km}{sec}$$

and

$$c = 299{,}792.7 \pm 0.25 \frac{km}{sec}$$

How about theoretical values? The speed of electromagnetic waves predicted by Maxwell's equations is $\sqrt{2K/k}$. The constant k is from the formula (equation 35.8) for magnetic forces,

$$F = k \frac{i_1 i_2 l}{r}$$

and K is from the formula (equation 36.1) for electric forces,

$$F = \frac{Kq_1 q_2}{r}$$

Using the latest laboratory value of the ratio K/k, we get

$$\sqrt{\frac{2K}{k}} = 299{,}784 \pm 10 \frac{km}{sec}$$

The agreement between this and the measured values of c for both light and radio waves lends great weight to the idea that light is an electromagnetic wave.

Since light waves obey the formula $c = \nu\lambda$, we can determine the frequency, ν, if we know the speed, c, and the wavelength, λ. The wavelength of the green line of the mercury spectrum, as measured with a diffraction grating, is 5.461×10^{-7} m. This yields the frequency

$$\nu = \frac{3 \times 10^8 \text{ m/sec}}{5.461 \times 10^{-7} \text{ m}}$$

(When we write that $c = 3.0 \times 10^8$ m/sec, we are in error by less than 0.04 percent.) That is,

$$\nu = 5.5 \times 10^{14} \text{ sec}^{-1}$$

This frequency is sufficiently high to suggest that electrons accelerated within an atom are responsible for the electromagnetic wave called light.

Is this order of magnitude (10^{14}) reasonable? Imagine an electron moving with constant angular velocity ω in a circular path with a radius, r, of 0.5×10^{-10} m. (This is compatible with our knowledge of atomic radii; see Chap. 51.) Assume that it is acted upon by an electrical centripetal force,

$$F = \frac{Kq_1 q_2}{r^2}$$

which is due to a massive positive nucleus. Using the expression $m\omega^2 r$ for centripetal force, we have

$$\frac{Kq_1 q_2}{r^2} = m\omega^2 r \qquad [44.2$$

Here q_1 is the electronic charge, e, of -1.6×10^{-19} coul; q_2 is the positive charge on the nucleus. If we assume that q_2 is numerically equal to e, the magnitude of ω^2 is

$$\omega^2 = \frac{Ke^2}{mr^3} \qquad [44.3$$

Putting in the known values of the quantities K, e, m, and r, we get

$$\omega = 4.5 \times 10^{16} \text{ sec}^{-1} \qquad [44.4$$

Since ν is related to ω as in the equation $\nu = \omega/2\pi$,

$$\nu \cong 7.21 \times 10^{15} \text{ sec}^{-1} \qquad [44.5$$

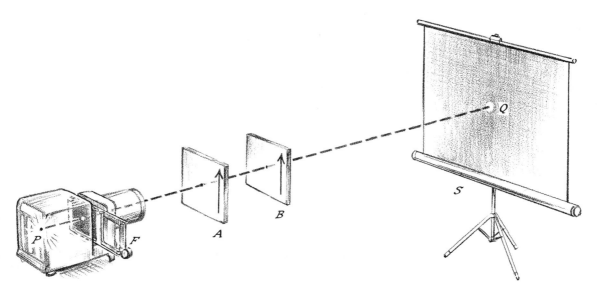

FIG. 44.7. *Simple demonstration of polarization.*

The order of magnitude is almost right. The idea that accelerated electrons within atoms are responsible for light is at least plausible. We shall soon see that the idea will have to be greatly modified before it can be reconciled with our present knowledge of the atom, but in the rest of this chapter we shall assume that accelerated electrons can account for the electromagnetic effects associated with light.

44.4. The Polarization of Light

How do we prove *experimentally* that light can be polarized? Although some of the manifestations of the polarization of light were discovered before the electromagnetic theory was accepted, we shall review some experiments in polarization from the vantage point that the electromagnetic theory gives us. Our purpose is to support the electromagnetic theory of light, not to explore such experiments exhaustively.

Polarizing film, sold under the name Polaroid, makes the following simple demonstration possible. If two sheets of such film, *A* and *B* (Fig. 44.7), are placed in the beam of a projector, the image of a circular hole in the projector's film plane, *F*, appears at *Q*, on screen *S*, only slightly dimmed by sheets *A* and *B* if they have the same orientation. (The arrows drawn along the edges of the sheets indicate the same orientation. Later we shall associate such an arrow with the direction of the **E** vector that passes through the polarizer.) We now rotate sheet *B* on the axis *PQ* while keeping its plane perpendicular to the axis. When the arrow of *B* is perpendicular to that of *A*, the intensity of the beam reaching *Q* is reduced nearly to zero. If we rotate *B* further until its arrow points down (while that of *A* still points up), we bring the intensity back to its maximum. If the angle between the two arrows is θ, the intensity at *Q* is proportional to $\cos^2 \theta$. If we leave *B* fixed and rotate *A*, we get the same result: the intensity at *Q* is at its maximum when $\theta = 0°$ and $180°$, at its minimum when $\theta = 90°$ and $270°$. If we remove sheet *B*, so that the beam passes only through *A*, rotation of *A* does not affect the beam's intensity. Rotation of the projector on the axis *PQ* does not affect the intensity at *Q* in any case.

The polarizing film, or any other device that takes unpolarized light and renders it plane-polarized, is called a **polarizer**. Even if we do not know how a polarizer works, this simple experiment proves that two orientations of the polarizers, in relation to each other, allow the maximum

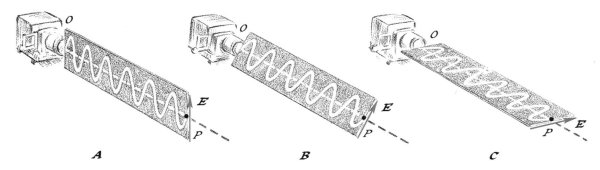

FIG. 44.8. *Three plane-polarized waves.*

transmission. The transverse character of light waves is already strongly suggested. All the results of experiment are compatible with the assumption that the light from the projector is unpolarized, that *A* plane-polarizes it, and that *B* lets the polarized light through fully only when *B*'s direction of polarization coincides with that of *A*. Let us consider carefully what all this means.

In Figure 44.8 let *OP* be the axis of the beam coming out of a projector. A piece of cardboard with a sketch of a sine curve symbolizing the wave of electric intensity, **E**, is shown (A) in a vertical position. A single electron vibrating parallel to **E** could produce such a plane-polarized wave. Another electron, vibrating parallel to the **E** vector of part B, would produce a wave with the plane of polarization shown there. Still another electron could have produced the **E** wave

of part C. Imagine waves, started by many different accelerated electrons, coming out in all possible planes containing the axis *OP*. A beam consisting of such waves is said to be unpolarized. Actually it is randomly polarized in many different planes; it contains waves polarized in all the possible planes about *OP*. Looking (Fig. 44.9) toward point *O* from *P* (A), we can represent all these planes by radial lines (B) or, schematically, by vectors in two mutually perpendicular directions (C), as if we had resolved all the vectors of part B into *x* and *y* components. The schematic representation serves as a useful shorthand if we don't confuse its vectors with the mutually perpendicular **E** and **B** vectors. We shall be dealing exclusively with **E** vectors in diagrams like Figure 44.9.

Let us return to Figure 44.7. The light polarized

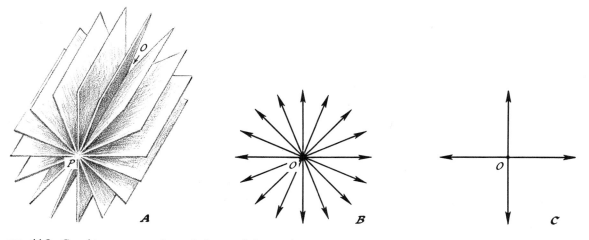

FIG. 44.9. *Graphic representations of planes of plane-polarized waves.*

by sheet A does not look different from ordinary light. We tell it is polarized by trying to send it through a second polarizer, B. In this capacity B is sometimes called an **analyzer.** A combination of polarizer and analyzer does not allow light to pass through if they are crossed—that is, if their planes of polarization are perpendicular to each other. This is represented schematically in Figure 44.10. The light coming out of the projector is unpolarized, as symbolized first by arrows in many directions (C) and then by two plane-polarized waves (D). The waves with components parallel to a vertical plane get through both sheets, A and B, because something about the orientation

of these sheets (A) permits light plane-polarized in this way to get through. If sheet B is turned (B) through 90°, however, the plane-polarized beam from A does not get through it.

A vivid analogy is that of a transverse wave on a rope going through a narrow slit (Fig. 44.11). If the wave produced by the source has a component parallel to the slit of A, it gets through A and (A) if the slit of B is parallel to that of A, through B also. If the slit of B is at right angles (B) to that of A, the plane-polarized wave from A does not get through B.

Light can be polarized in several different ways: by reflection, by scattering, and by passing through

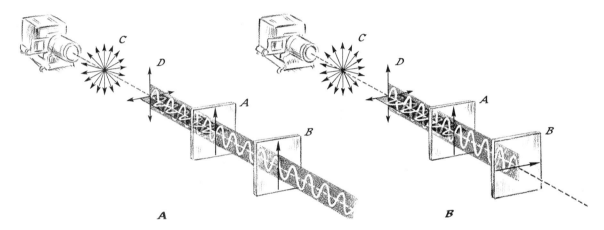

FIG. 44.10. *Schematic representation of the action of a polarizer,* A, *and an analyzer,* B.

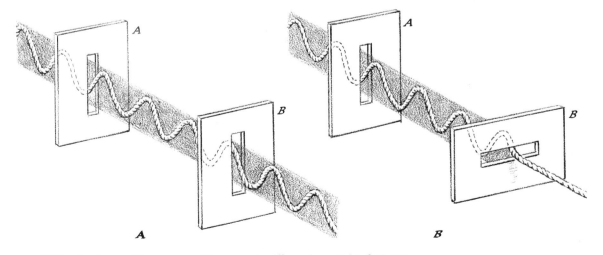

FIG. 44.11. *Analogy, with a rope, to illustrate the effect of crossed polarizers.*

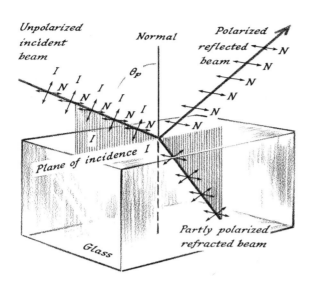

FIG. 44.12. *Polarization at a flat, transparent, non-metallic interface (air-glass). When the angle of incidence is the angle of polarization, θ_p, the reflected beam is completely polarized, the refracted beam is partly polarized, and reflected and refracted beams are normal to each other.*

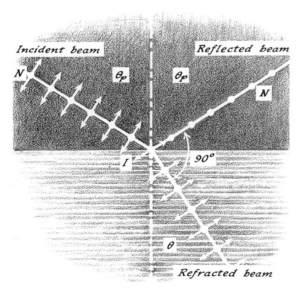

FIG. 44.13. *When the angle of incidence is the angle of polarization, θ_p, the I components of the refracted beam are parallel to the reflected beam.*

special crystals in which it travels at different speeds in different directions. We shall consider each of these briefly.

44.5. Polarization by Reflection

When a beam of unpolarized light hits a plane glass surface at other than normal incidence, the reflected beam is always more or less polarized; it is a mixture of unpolarized light and plane-polarized light. At a certain special angle of incidence, called the **angle of polarization,** which occurs when the reflected and refracted beams are perpendicular to each other (Fig. 44.12), the reflected beam is completely polarized (for a reason to be described presently). This is true not only for glass but for water and for many transparent non-metallic substances that reflect and refract light. The plane of incidence, *I*, is the plane determined by the incident beam and the normal to the surface. Normals to this plane are labeled *N*, and the **E** vectors in the reflected beam are all parallel to *N*. The **E** vectors in the incident beam have some components (labeled *I*) in the plane of incidence and others (labeled *N*) in a plane normal to both *I* and the incident beam. The refracted beam is partly polarized and contains both *I* and *N* components.

From Snell's law (equation 20.2) it follows (Fig. 44.13) that, for the special value θ_p of the angle of incidence,

$$\frac{\sin \theta_p}{\sin \theta} = n \qquad [44.6$$

if *n* is the index of refraction of the medium. Since θ_p and θ are complementary angles ($\theta + \theta_p = 90°$), $\sin \theta = \cos \theta_p$. Hence

$$\frac{\sin \theta_p}{\cos \theta_p} = \tan \theta_p = n \qquad [44.7$$

That is, the tangent of the angle of polarization is equal to the index of refraction of the refracting material. This rule, known as **Brewster's law,** follows from the fact that the reflected and the refracted beam are normal to each other when the angle of incidence equals the angle of polarization. Since the index of refraction varies slightly with wavelength, the angle of polarization does too. If, for example, $n = 1.5$, then $\tan \theta_p = 1.5$, and $\theta_p = 57°$.

Notice that the I components of the refracted beam in Figure 44.13 are parallel to the reflected beam. Charged bodies within the medium, accelerated in the I directions by an **E** field, would not radiate in the direction of the reflected beam. This gives us at least a qualitative explanation of the complete polarization of the reflected beam when the angle of incidence is the angle of polarization.

Polarized light is detected, as we have seen, by means of an analyzer. In part A of Figure 44.14 light reflected and polarized by a black glass sheet, A, attached to a wedge, is reflected again at B, a sheet of the same kind as A, because the plane of polarization produced by A is parallel to the N plane direction of B. (The prismatic shapes have no optical function. They are drawn this way to make the geometry evident.) In part B the second reflector, B, has been turned so that the plane of polarization produced by A is parallel to the I plane of B. The intensity of light reflected from B is now at its minimum.

One can demonstrate a similar effect (Fig. 44.15) in the classroom, polarizing a beam of light from

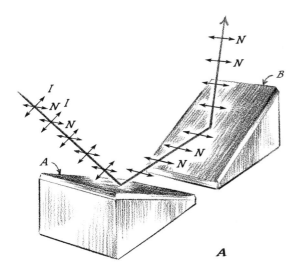
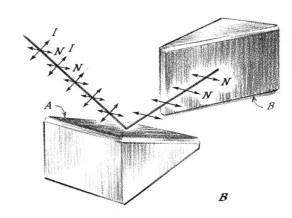

A **B**

FIG. 44.14. *Polarization of light by reflection.*

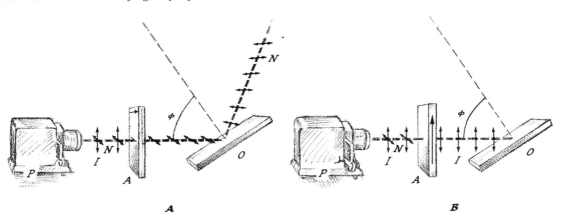

A **B**

FIG. 44.15. *Classroom demonstration, using polarized light, of the variation of reflectivity with the angle of incidence.*

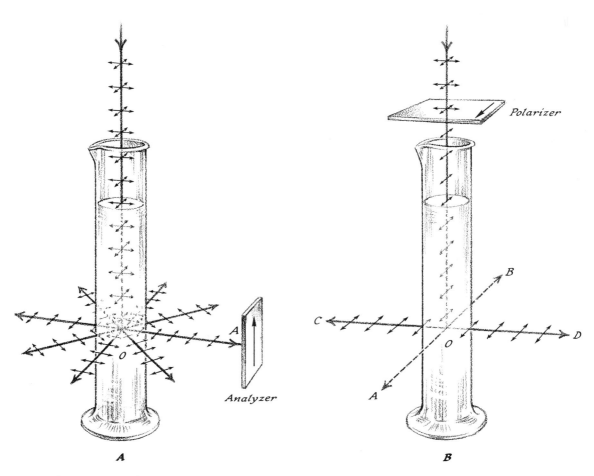

FIG. 44.16. *Polarization by scattering.*

a projector, *P*, by sending it through a sheet polarizer. If the sheet, *A*, is oriented (A) so that the emergent beam is polarized in a plane that is perpendicular to the *I* plane of an ordinary piece of glass at *O*, the light reflected from the glass varies gradually in intensity but never goes to zero as angle ϕ is varied. If *A* is oriented (B) to produce light polarized in the *I* plane of the glass, the intensity of the reflected beam goes to zero when the glass is tilted so that ϕ equals the angle of polarization; the sheet polarizer and the reflecting glass form a crossed pair of polarizers. (The second polarizer is used as an analyzer.)

44.6. Polarization by Scattering

A beam of unpolarized light, entering, from above, a tall cylinder full of slightly soapy water (Fig. 44.16.A), is polarized by the molecules of the scattering material (the soap in this case). When the cylinder is viewed through an analyzer along a line such as *AO*, the analyzer, if its plane of polarization is vertical, blocks the scattered light. This result is easy to reconcile with the idea that the electrical vibrations induced by the incident light radiate at right angles to the vibrations that induced them. Suppose, however, that the incident beam has been polarized (Fig. 44.16.B) by a sheet polarizer. An electron at point O is accelerated in the directions OA and OB; it can therefore radiate in the perpendicular directions OC and OD but not in the directions OA and OB. Without further analyzers (the liquid is acting as one) it will be seen that light is scattered better in the directions OC and OD than in the directions OA and OB. (When, in a classroom demonstration, the instructor rotates the polarizer about the vertical axis, the class can observe the rotation of the scattered beam.)

The light from the sky on a clear day is polarized by scattering. The transverse electric fields in a beam of sunlight accelerate the electrons of the air molecules, causing them to radiate. To understand the relation between this statement and Figure 44.16.A, imagine the sun to be directly overhead. As you look at the horizon, you are looking at air molecules that are radiating toward you, polarized in a horizontal plane—a statement that you can verify by looking through an analyzer whose plane of polarization is marked. An analogous argument can be applied when the sun is in any other position. If the sun is setting in the west and you look horizontally toward the north, the light scattered by the air molecules comes toward you polarized in a vertical plane.

44.7. Polarization by Double Refraction

If we produce a very narrow circular beam of light (Fig. 44.17) by putting a small circular aperture, A, in the film plane of a projector, and then send the beam through a calcite crystal, C, it will produce two circular images, I_1 and I_2, instead of one, on the screen, S, if the crystal is oriented in a special way—which may be found experimentally. If the crystal is rotated on the axis of the projection lens, one of the images will remain fixed while the other revolves round it. If a sheet polarizer, P, is placed in the beams and rotated, it extinguishes one beam and leaves the other at maximum brightness; if it is then turned through 90°, the spot that was invisible before is now bright, and the spot that was bright is now invisible. In other words, the beams emerging from C are polarized, and the planes of polarization of the two emergent beams are at right angles to each other. I shall not attempt to explain this effect. Some crystals—tourmaline, for example—absorb one of the beams, and only one emerges.

The sheet polarizer manufactured by the Polaroid Corporation has this ability to absorb one of the polarized beams produced by double refraction and transmit the other. It is available in large sheets, is quite transparent, and is not costly.

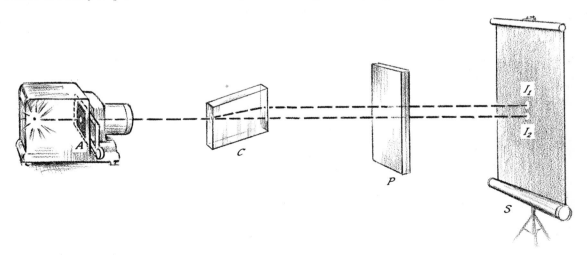

FIG. 44.17. *Double refraction by a calcite crystal.*

An early type of this polarizer consisted of a large number of parallel crystals embedded in a transparent plastic sheet. A later type, not consisting of crystals, is made of a plastic material, called polyvinyl alcohol, whose molecules are very long. When a sheet of this material is stretched in one direction, its molecules align themselves in that direction. Iodine is added in the process to enable the material to absorb one of the polarized beams. It is probably the most important polarizing material. It is mass-produced for sunglasses that reduce the glare of polarized reflected light and for photographic filters that darken the blue sky, utilizing the fact that the light of the sky is polarized in certain directions. A polarizing filter placed in front of the camera lens and properly oriented can stop the polarized light from entering the camera. It works well with colored film because it does not introduce color of its own.

Double refraction can be brilliantly demonstrated by projection through transparent materials and crossed polarizers; the strains within the materials are thereby exhibited. A plastic tape-dispenser (Fig. 44.18), tape-recorder reel, or

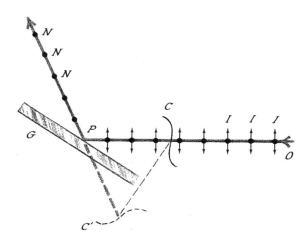

FIG. 44.19. *How a piece of ordinary cellophane may show the color effects of double refraction.*

coat-hanger, viewed through crossed polarizers, exhibits a pattern of lines that is intimately related to the strains within the material. If you wish to see the beautiful colors exhibited under crossed polarizers by ordinary transparent cellophane, the polarized light from the sky can substitute for the polarizer, and an ordinary sheet of window glass can serve as the analyzer. Suppose, for example, that the light scattered from the setting sun (Fig. 44.19), polarized in plane I, approaches glass plate G along line OP. The glass polarizes the light by reflection, and its plane of polarization, normal to I, is indicated by the dots marked N. Hence glass and sky constitute a pair of crossed polarizers. The image of a sheet of cellophane at C will be seen at C'; but, since it is, in effect, between polarizer and analyzer, the color effects of double refraction will be visible.

This concludes our brief study of light as electromagnetic radiation. We are, however, not yet through with light. The "century of the atom" was to follow Maxwell's theory, and that theory alone did not offer sufficient explanation of spectral phenomena. We must move on to the great discoveries made in the twentieth century and associated with the names of Röntgen, Bohr, Planck, Rutherford, J. J. Thomson, Einstein, Schrödinger, Heisenberg, de Broglie, Fermi, and many others. We are at last ready to begin the study of atomic and nuclear physics.

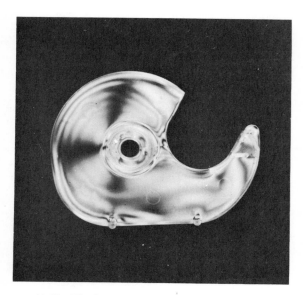

FIG. 44.18. *Black-and-white photograph, taken through crossed polarizers, of a plastic tape-dispenser. The streaks and curves are really of various colors.*

44.8. Summary

An accelerated charge radiates transverse electromagnetic waves in all directions that have a component normal to the acceleration. The waves are polarized in a plane containing both the acceleration vector and the line of propagation of the wave.

Because light waves travel at the same speed as radio waves and because they also can be polarized, it is reasonable to assume that light waves are electromagnetic. An electromagnetic theory of light accounts, in fact, for many of light's observed characteristics.

Light from most sources is unpolarized, but it can be polarized by reflection from non-metallic surfaces, by scattering from small particles or even molecules of a transparent medium, and by double refraction. Polarized light has many practical applications and is of growing theoretical interest, giving weight to the view that light waves are transverse waves.

Problems

44.1. Discuss the following statements: (1) Longitudinal waves are unpolarizable. (2) Since light can be polarized, light waves must be transverse.

44.2. 1. Charge q, at rest, produces a field, E, at point P, at distance r from q, exhibiting a $1/r^2$ relation. What is the direction of such a field?

2. An accelerated charge produces an E field at distance r, exhibiting a $1/r$ relation. What is the direction of the field?

3. When r is large, which field predominates?

4. Plot $1/r$ and $1/r^2$ against r on the same paper for the values $r = 2, 4, 6, 8, 10$.

44.3. A beam of light from an unknown source enters a laboratory.

1. Describe several methods of determining whether the light is polarized.

2. Which method requires the least expensive apparatus?

3. Which method do you think will be most sensitive in measuring the angle of orientation of the plane of polarization?

44.4. Compute the angle of polarization for yellow light, of wavelength 5,893 A, reflected from diamond (2.42) and from ice (1.31). The number in parentheses is the index of refraction.

44.5. Sunlight reflected from a still surface of water is more or less polarized.

1. What is the position of the sun when the polarization is greatest?

2. Is the E vector of the reflected light then predominantly horizontal or vertical?

44.6. Prove or disprove the following statement: All angles of polarization by reflection are greater than 45°.

44.7. If a plastic tape-recorder reel is placed between crossed polarizing sheets, it will exhibit colors that are due to double refraction. Now explain the following: Even without polarizers the same plastic reel will exhibit colors if viewed in the light coming from the sky on a clear day. Are the colors of a thin oil film on water due to the same cause?

44.8. 1. The sun is overhead; the sky is clear; you face the horizon in any direction you choose. Will the E vector of the scattered light from the sky be vertical or horizontal?

2. The sun is setting in the west, and you face the south. Will the E vector of the scattered light be horizontal or vertical?

44.9. Verify the arithmetic leading to equations 44.4 and 44.5.

V

INTRODUCTION TO ATOMIC PHYSICS

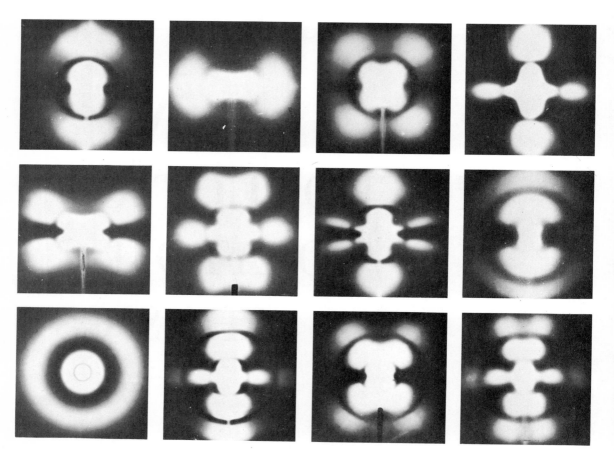

Electron-wave Patterns of the Successive Quantum States
of an Electron Confined by a Nucleus
(From Harvey E. White.)

Although it is impossible to see atoms, it is possible to construct mathematical and visible models that predict the behavior of an electron bound to a nucleus. Such models suggest the dual nature of particles and waves.

The New Physics: Atoms and Electrons

"The universe is composed of substances (forms of matter) and radiant energy. . . . The existence of atoms is now accepted as a fact. . . . All ordinary matter consists of atoms. The exceptional kinds of matter are the elementary particles from which the atoms are made (electrons, protons, neutrons), and other subatomic particles. . . . The evidence for the existence of atoms is now overwhelming."

LINUS PAULING, *General Chemistry*, Second Edition

WE ARE now ready to begin in earnest our study of atomic physics. The quotation from Linus Pauling about matter, radiant energy, and atoms serves as the point of departure for Part V of this book. We begin with the assertion that the existence of atoms is now an accepted fact, and we seek to build up an elementary atomic theory.

This is what we have been preparing for. Our detailed knowledge of mechanics, waves, and electricity is now about to be focused on the atom. There is good reason for this concentration. By understanding matter at the atomic level we can bring together, in a coherent whole, facts that seemed to be unrelated.

In this chapter I shall simply make some assertions about atoms. The remaining chapters of Part V will be devoted to the experimental and theoretical proof of these assertions.

45.1. Atomic Models

What does an atom really look like? The question sounds reasonable enough until we analyze it. Looking usually requires that light hit the thing we are talking about and then bounce off it to our eyes, aided, if necessary, by a microscope or a telescope. Atoms, however, present several difficulties. One is that they are extremely small—so small that the light hitting an atom may give it an impulse or may even cause drastic changes in it. The very act of illuminating the thing we want to look at can change its location and its structure. This immediately gives us a clue to one of the roles that light plays in atomic physics.

Nothing has stopped us, however, from *imagining* how atoms may look. In this way we have created different atomic models. Some have explained a few of the observed phenomena. The perfect model would explain all of them, but we have no perfect model. Some of those we have are reviewed here, with their successes and their limitations.

1. *The Elastic Sphere of Elementary Kinetic Theory*

By assuming that a gas consists of molecules—in some cases individual atoms—that are small, perfectly elastic spheres, we are able to evolve a kinetic theory that explains very well the behavior of ideal gases and clarifies the macroscopic concept of temperature. The theory fails to explain the behavior of real gases when the pressure is so high that short-range interactions between molecules must be taken into account, but it explains beautifully the behavior of all gases at low pressure.

The mean kinetic energy of translation of a gas molecule is given by the expression $3kT/2$ (equation 31.44), in which k is the Boltzmann constant and T is the Kelvin temperature. At 300°K (a typical room temperature on a hot day) this comes out as 3.88×10^{-2} electron volt (1 ev $\cong$ 1.6×10^{-19} J; see § 6.2).

Consider another numerical example. It takes about 540 calories to convert 1 gram of water at 100°C into steam. Knowing that there are 18 grams in a mole of water, 6.02×10^{23} molecules in a mole, and 1.6×10^{-19} joule in an electron volt, we can deduce that it takes 4.22×10^{-1} electron volt per molecule to make this transition.

In both examples the result is less than 1 electron volt per molecule. The electron volt is a useful unit of energy in atomic physics. When the energy involved per molecule is considerably less than 1 electron volt, we can safely treat the molecules (or the atoms—in case each molecule consists of a single atom) as impenetrable spheres. This suggests that 1 electron volt, more or less, is an energy limit above which the theory of impenetrable spheres should fail—and it does. When you reach the region of 1 electron volt per atom or molecule, you can begin to remove electrons from the atoms or the molecules.

2. *The Electronic Atom*

In our study of electricity we learned that, if we treat atoms as impenetrable spheres, we cannot account for the experimental fact that electrons can be removed from atoms by contact with other atoms, by heat, by electric fields, and by light. All these phenomena force us to believe that electrons are a basic part of atoms. It takes work to pull an electron away from an atom. This work can be measured in different ways. Using, for example, the relation

$$E = h\nu = hc/\lambda$$

(§ 19.4 and § 49.3), we can determine the energy it takes to eject a photoelectron from a substance by means of light. Experiments yield values between 1 and 5 electron volts per atom. This seems to confirm the idea that some atoms are not impenetrable to energy greater than about one electron volt per atom.

The chemical properties of atoms are associated with energies of the same magnitude. The heat of combustion of coal, for example, is about 7,000 calories per gram. Using the atomic weight of carbon, the Avogadro constant, and the conversion from calories through joules to electron volts, we may write this as 3.7 electron volts per atom. This illustrates the fact that an ordinary chemical change (oxidation in this case) involves energy transformations of the order of a few electron volts per atom.

What I have called the electronic atom could also be called the *chemical atom*, for the outer electrons of an atom determine its chemical behavior. (Chemists are usually concerned with how atoms combine with one another to form molecules. We shall not consider this interesting and important topic at all.)

3. *The Spectral Atom*

Chemists have shown that more than ninety different kinds of atoms exist in nature, but a tool developed by physicists, the spectroscope, has given us our most detailed information about the *structure* of atoms. This information comes from the characteristic frequencies of the light emitted by all atoms of the same kind. The characteristic spectrum associated with each atom not only is like a complex fingerprint, permitting identification, but also carries numerical data in the form of wavelengths. The relation

$$E = h\nu = hc/\lambda$$

tells us that there is an intimate correlation between the wavelengths emitted by an atom and the energy levels of that atom. It has been discovered that energies between 1 and 100,000 electron volts are required to disturb the electrons in the different energy levels of atoms. The most loosely bound electrons of the light atoms require the least energy, and the most tightly bound electrons of the heavy atoms require the most energy. The atom not only ceases to behave like an impenetrable sphere but can be stripped even of its innermost electrons when energy of the order of 100,000 electron volts per atom is applied.

The light produced when neon gas is excited by energy of the order of 100 electron volts per atom gives us the characteristic reddish glow of neon signs. The invisible radiation produced when accelerated electrons bombard tungsten with an energy of about 100,000 electron volts per atom is called x-rays, and the deepest electrons within the tungsten atom are affected in its production.

4. *The Nuclear Atom*

As long as the energy applied to it does not exceed about 100,000 electron volts, the *nucleus* of an atom behaves like an impenetrable core. If the energy does exceed a quantity of that order of magnitude, the solid nuclear core begins to break down, and we find that the nucleus has structure. Radioactivity, fission, fusion, and transmutation of elements are examples of the nuclear changes associated with energy considerably higher than 100,000 electron volts per nucleus. Today we have machines that can accelerate individual nuclei to energies of a million electron volts (Mev = 10^6 electron volts) and even a billion electron volts (Bev = 10^9 electron volts). (A notation equivalent to "Bev" is "Gev." The prefix "giga" stands for 10^9. Since "billion" means 10^9

in the United States but 10^{12} throughout Europe, "Gev" is replacing "Bev" in the literature.)

Which atomic model should we use? One way to answer this question is to say that we should use the simplest model that provides good agreement between theory and experiment. In general, the more sophisticated models give results that are not inconsistent with those given by the simpler models.

45.2. Survey of Atomic Physics

Here is a brief statement of what is known about atoms. The details will be developed gradually in subsequent chapters.

All ordinary matter consists of atoms. Atoms are the basic building blocks that keep their identity when chemical reactions take place. They are very small—from about 2 to 5 A in diameter.† Every atom consists of a nucleus and *n* electrons. The **nucleus** is a small, heavy particle containing almost all the mass of the atom. It has a positive charge that is equal in magnitude to the charge of *Z* electrons, *Z* being a positive integer representing the number of electrons in the neutral atom. The simplest atom is that of hydrogen, for which $Z = 1$; another simple one is helium, for which $Z = 2$; and so on.

Ordinary matter is electrically neutral. Its individual atoms are electrically neutral; that is, each atom contains equal amounts of positive and negative charge.

The atomic nucleus occupies a very small part of the whole atom. Nuclei have diameters of about 10^{-12} cm, or 10^{-4} A. It would take more than 10,000 nuclei lined up next to one another to cover an atomic diameter. The volume of an atom is therefore more than $(10^4)^3 = 10^{12}$ times the volume of a nucleus. It has been said—and correctly—that a nucleus inside its atom is, in relative size, like a fly inside a cathedral. If nuclei could be packed together closely, the resulting aggregate would have a density of about 10^{12}

---

† The symbol A stands for *angstrom*, a unit named after the Swedish physicist A. J. Ångström (1814–1874): 1 A = 10^{-8} cm; 1 cm = 10^8 A.

gm/cm³. (Ordinary matter has a density of about 1 gm/cm³.) A heaping tablespoonful of nuclei would weigh as much as a million automobiles.

The **electron** is a particle with a small mass, $1/1,836$ of the mass of the lightest nucleus. It has a negative charge, $e = -1.60210 \times 10^{-19}$ coulomb. The electron is about as large as a nucleus, its diameter being about 10^{-12} cm. The electrons in an atom are attracted to the positive nucleus, but they move around rapidly in the space surrounding the nucleus and extending over a diam-

eter of a few angstroms. The effective size of an atom is the space filled by these rapidly whirling electrons. You may have seen a mother surrounded by very active children who run circles around her; she cannot be reached because the cloud of children shields her from outer contacts. In a similar way, the cloud of electrons whirling round a nucleus repels any other atom that approaches this not clearly defined diameter.

Figure 45.1 shows an artist's conception, based upon modern calculations, of the distribution of

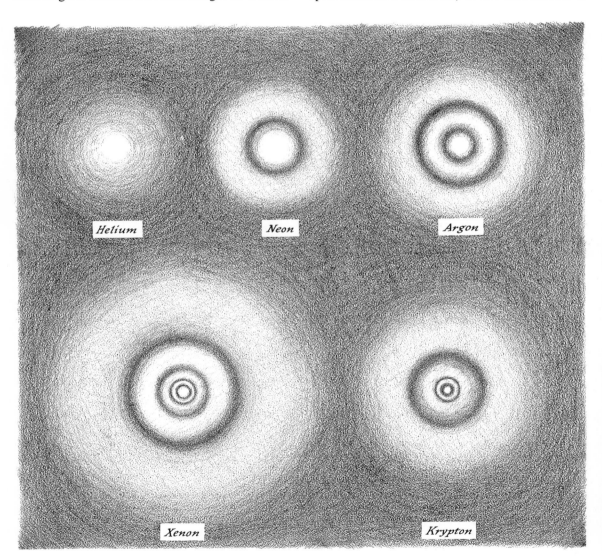

FIG. 45.1. *An artist's conception, based upon modern calculations, of the distribution of electrons in five atoms.*

electrons in five noble-gas atoms, which were chosen for their simple spherical shells. The light areas represent regions where the probability of finding an electron is high.

In the study of chemistry it is necessary to distinguish (see § 10.3) between the substances called *compounds*, which can be decomposed into two or more other substances, and those called *elements*, which cannot be further decomposed by the application of energy less than about 100,000 electron volts per atom. Here, again, a tool developed by the physicists—*x*-rays—supplies the means of proving a substance to be an element. In this book we shall be concerned primarily with the elements, not with the great array of useful and interesting compounds studied by the chemists, nor with the complicated theory of chemical bonding, which explains the forces that bind atoms together in molecules.

The first atom for which a successful theory was evolved was the hydrogen atom. In discussing it briefly, I shall bring out some of the essential concepts of general atomic theory.

The nucleus of the hydrogen atom is a **proton.** It carries a positive charge numerically equal to the charge of an electron. A proton and an electron, combined in a certain way, make up the hydrogen atom. In 1913 the Danish theoretical physicist Niels Bohr developed a theory in which the electron moved in a circular orbit about the massive proton. The atom was held together by the coulombic electrical force somewhat as the sun and a planet in its orbit are held together by the inverse-square gravitational attraction.

Bohr's picture is now thought to be incorrect, but we shall study it in some detail because it successfully predicted the frequencies of the spectral lines of hydrogen. A marvelous synthesis of concepts from classical mechanics and the then current ideas about waves, electricity, and light, it is one of the great milestones of modern physics. We shall use Bohr's theory to test our own understanding of basic physical principles.

Before we can consider the atom of helium, one of the next elements in the order of increasing complexity, I have to introduce still another particle, the **neutron.** The neutron was not discovered until 1932, but it is now believed to be,

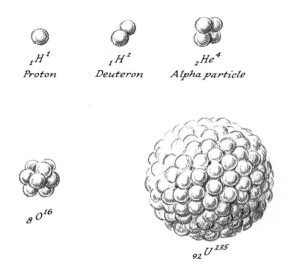

FIG. 45.2. *An artist's conception of the hypothetical structure of some atomic nuclei.*

along with the electron and the proton, one of the building blocks out of which atoms are made. It has a mass of 1.0087 (on a scale where the proton has 1.0728 units) and is electrically neutral. The helium nucleus is composed of two protons and two neutrons, its total positive charge being $2e$ and its total mass being about four times as great as that of a hydrogen atom.

The proton and the neutron are almost alike in mass. All nuclei (except that of hydrogen) seem to be made of protons and neutrons (Fig. 45.2), and the total number of such almost equally massive particles in the nucleus is known as the **mass number** (A) of that kind of nucleus. The **atomic number** (Z) is the number of protons in the nucleus. A **nucleon** is any constituent of a nucleus, either proton or neutron. Hence the mass number of a nucleus is the number of its nucleons. In equations for nuclear reactions, the atomic number is often used as a left subscript and the mass number as a right superscript to the chemical symbol for the element. For example, $_1H^1$, $_1H^2$, $_2He^4$, $_8O^{16}$, and $_{92}U^{235}$ represent hydrogen, deuterium (heavy hydrogen), helium, oxygen, and uranium nuclei, respectively. Figure 45.2 shows diagrammatic representations of these nuclei. No one asserts that nuclei, if we could see them, would really look like these diagrams.

The nucleus is the control room of the atom.

Its atomic number, as we have seen, indicates both the number of protons in it and its positive charge. Since a neutral atom must have as many electrons as its nucleus has protons, the atomic number, Z, also represents the total number of electrons in the neutral atom. The chemical behavior of an atom is determined by its electronic structure, and this is governed by the total number of protons in the nucleus. The atomic number therefore determines how an atom will behave chemically. Atoms with the same atomic number but different mass numbers are called **isotopes** of the same element.

The symbol Z stands for a variable that can take on only positive integral values from 1 to about 103. Atoms with Z equal to 1, 2, 3, . . . 92 can be found in nature; atoms with Z equal to 93 . . . 103 have been artificially produced.

The chemist, in dealing with the species of matter called elements, weighs them as he finds them in nature and tabulates their relative **atomic weights.** He is aware, however, that elements have isotopes of different masses and that his atomic weight for a given element is the average weight of the isotopes of the element found in nature. The physicist, on the other hand, has instruments admirably suited for measuring the mass of the nuclides. A **nuclide** is a species of matter characterized by the constitution of its nucleus—that is, by the number of neutrons and protons it contains. In this view an isotope is one of a group of two or more nuclides having the same atomic number. The physicist measures the masses of nuclides and refers to their **atomic masses.** The terms "atomic mass" and "atomic weight" do not, therefore, have the same meaning, although the *numerical expressions* for these two properties of an atom are often the same, since relative atomic weights are always measured in a common gravitational field. We shall, to avoid confusion, use "atomic mass" for the nuclides and "atomic weight," in its traditional sense, for the elements. Since 1961 the international unions of chemistry and physics have agreed on a single scale of weights and masses, in which the reference standard is the carbon isotope $_6C^{12}$, to which is assigned the mass of exactly 12.

If the atoms are arranged in the order of in-

TABLE 45.1

Relative Atomic Weights Based on the Atomic Mass $_6C^{12} = 12$

Element	Atomic Number, Z	Atomic Weight
Hydrogen	1	1.00797[a]
Helium	2	4.0026
Lithium	3	6.939
Beryllium	4	9.0122
Boron	5	10.811[a]
Carbon	6	12.01115[a]
Nitrogen	7	14.0067
Oxygen	8	15.9994[a]

[a] Atomic weights known to be variable because of natural variation in isotopic composition.

creasing Z, certain periodicities in their properties become apparent. These will be discussed in § 53.5. The first eight elements are tabulated in Table 45.1. Notice that, if they had been arranged in the order of increasing atomic weight, the order would have been identical with the one shown; the correspondence does not hold, however, for all subsequent values of Z. Not until the discovery of x-ray spectra (§ 53.3) was firm proof found that the atomic numbers, not the atomic weights, order the elements so that their periodic properties become apparent throughout the whole range of Z.

This completes my preliminary assertions about atoms. My task now is to show how we gained the information that culminated in this picture of the atom. I begin with the particle that one would meet first in approaching any atom—namely, the electron.

45.3. Millikan's Determination of the Electronic Charge

The latest experimental values for the electronic rest mass and the electronic charge are

$$m_e = (9.1091 \pm 0.0004) \times 10^{-31} \text{ kg}$$

and

$$e = (1.60210 \pm 0.00007) \times 10^{-19} \text{ coul}$$

(In slide-rule computations the figures 9.11×10^{-31} kg and 1.60×10^{-19} coul are adequate.) How can the mass and the charge of an electron be measured so accurately? It is really extraordinary that we can write the electronic charge with an uncertainty of no more than 2 parts in 100,000. (It would certainly be difficult to find your own height or weight with such accuracy!)

R. A. Millikan (1868–1953), by 1909, had measured e with an uncertainty of about 1 percent. The basic idea underlying his method will be clear if the following simple example is first understood.

You are given four paper bags with iron washers in them and are told to consider whether all the washers are alike in weight, and to determine the most probable weight per washer, without opening the bags. You weigh the bags and their contents and set down the results as in Table 45.2.

Examination of the figures discloses that bag III is twice as heavy as bag IV ($15.2 = 2 \times 7.6$) and that bag II is three times as heavy as bag IV ($22.8 = 3 \times 7.6$). We may wish to assume that bag IV has 1 washer, bag III has 2 washers, and bag II has 3 washers; but the fact remains that the weight of bag I is not an integral multiple of the weight of bag IV. Let us next suppose that bag IV contains 2 washers. That makes the weight of one washer 3.8 grams; and, since $19.0 = 5 \times 3.8$, we come to the tentative conclusion that there are 5 washers in bag I, and 6, 4, and 2 washers in bags II, III, and IV, respectively. It is possible, of course, that the right numbers are 10, 12, 8, and 4; that would make the weight of one washer 1.9 grams. Our confidence in the identity of all washers and in 3.8 grams as the

TABLE 45.2

Weights of Paper Bags Containing Washers

Bag	Weight of Washers	Supposed Number of Washers
I	19.0 gm	5
II	22.8 gm	6
III	15.2 gm	4
IV	7.6 gm	2

weight of each washer increases if further experiments along the same line do not produce contradictory results.

Millikan, improving on experiments first performed by J. J. Thomson, succeeded in measuring the charges on very small objects and from them deduced the charge on the individual electron by an analysis similar to that used with the paper bags and the washers. For this work he received the Nobel Prize for Physics in 1923. The experiment was crucial: it established the quantitative atomicity of charge.

Over a period of years (1906–1916) Millikan and his co-workers carried out experiments with the apparatus shown schematically in Figure 45.3. A battery, B, connected as shown across a resistor, R, supplies a high and variable DC voltage, which is connected to the plates, P_1 and P_2, of a capacitor through a reversing switch, S. An atomizer sprays small oil drops into the chamber. The larger drops fall rapidly, and the smaller ones fall slowly. (A flat piece of paper falls slower than an identical one that has been crumpled. This illustrates how the force of air friction retards the fall of objects that have a relatively large area. You can demonstrate this variation of speed with size by emptying an ashtray from a height and observing the behavior of the ashes and other particles. The largest objects plummet down with acceleration g, but the smallest bits of ash descend slowly at an almost constant speed.)

Some of the droplets acquire an electric charge in the process of being sprayed. Some of these get through the hole, H, and can be observed through the microscope under proper illumination. If P_1 is made positive, the negatively charged droplets move up and the positively charged droplets move down. Reversing the switch reverses their direction of motion. Occasionally one can hold a falling droplet in place by supplying the upward electric force neE, in which E is the electric field strength between the plates and n is an integer. When the drop is in equilibrium, the downward force, mg, must equal the upward force, neE. (The drop can also be in motion at constant velocity under the action of viscous, electrical, and gravitational forces whose vector sum is zero.) The mass of the droplet is deduced

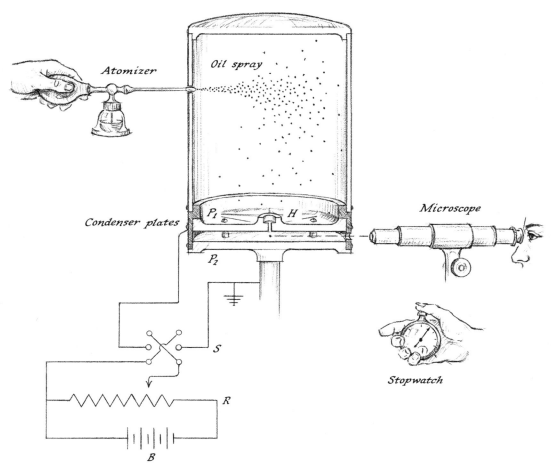

FIG. 45.3. *Highly schematic version of the apparatus used by R. A. Millikan in determining the charge of the electron by the oil-drop method.*

from its terminal velocity when the field is turned off. This computation requires a knowledge of the viscosity of air. It was discovered in 1935 that Millikan's value of e was off by about 1 percent because the viscosity of air was not known accurately enough when the experiment was first done.

Values of ne are obtained from the equation $ne = mg/E$. Values such as the following, in coulombs, were obtained:

$$ne = 8.01 \times 10^{-19} = 5 \times 1.59 \times 10^{-19}$$
$$ne = 6.41 \times 10^{-19} = 4 \times 1.59 \times 10^{-19}$$
$$ne = 9.71 \times 10^{-19} = 6 \times 1.59 \times 10^{-19}$$
$$ne = 3.20 \times 10^{-19} = 2 \times 1.59 \times 10^{-19}$$

All these values of ne have 1.59×10^{-19} as a common factor. Millikan concluded that this is the value of the basic electric charge. By shining x-rays on the droplets he found that occasionally a droplet under observation changed its velocity suddenly. He concluded that one or more electron charges had been added to or subtracted from the droplet: the droplet had been ionized with the help of x-rays. Nevertheless, the basic common factor always came out as 1.59×10^{-19} coulomb.

Although the results of this experiment are not now considered precise (the presently accepted value being closer to 1.602×10^{-19} coul), Millikan had succeeded in showing, for charges on oil drops, what has now been confirmed by many different kinds of experiments: that, whenever matter of different kinds is electrically charged, its charge is always an integral multiple of the basic electronic charge, e. Electrons isolated in any other way also always carry a charge that is very nearly 1.602×10^{-19} coulomb.

45.4. J. J. Thomson's Method of Finding e/m

Let us now look briefly at one method of finding the mass of the electron. In the absence of electric and magnetic fields the electrons from the cathode of Figure 45.4 land at point P_1 of the fluorescent screen. Under the influence of an electric field alone they land at P_2. Under the influence of a magnetic field alone they land at P_3. With both electric and magnetic fields acting, the strength of the electric field, E, is adjusted so that the electric and magnetic effects cancel and the electrons again land at P_1. Under these circumstances the electric force, eE (§ 36.4), and the magnetic force, Bev (§ 38.1), are equal. Since $eE = Bev$,

$$v = \frac{E}{B} \qquad [45.1$$

If the magnetic field alone is used, the electrons (while in a uniform field of intensity B) move in an arc, of radius R, such that $mv^2/R = Bev$ (§ 38.5). Therefore

$$\frac{e}{m} = \frac{v}{BR} \qquad [45.2$$

Knowing v and B and deducing R from the geometry of the landing position, P_3, J. J. Thomson (1856–1940) first measured e/m. The accepted value of e/m today is $(1.758897 \pm 0.000032) \times 10^{11}$ coul/kg.

Thomson's experiments, for which he was awarded the Nobel Prize for Physics in 1906, were done in 1897 at the Cavendish Laboratory at Cambridge University, and thus preceded those of Millikan. As soon as Millikan (1909) had found e to be nearly 1.60×10^{-19} coulomb, m could be solved for. To three significant figures, $m = 9.11 \times 10^{-31}$ kg.

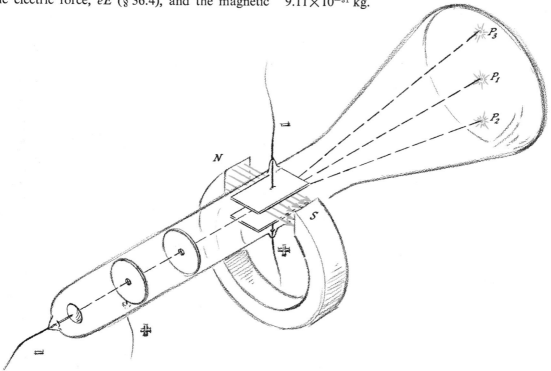

FIG. 45.4. *Schematic drawing of the apparatus used by J. J. Thomson to measure the ratio of the charge to the mass of an electron.*

We can only begin to imagine the excitement produced by these new discoveries, which heralded the birth of a new physics. The existence of the electron had been established by measurement of two of its basic characteristics, its mass and its charge. (We shall learn later about its angular momentum and magnetic moment.)

45.5. Summary

No perfect atomic model exists. You may decide which to use, of the several models discussed, by employing, as a rough criterion, the amount of energy involved. If energies considerably less than one electron volt per atom are involved, the elastic-sphere model of kinetic theory will probably work well. For energies of a few electron volts per atom you have to remember that atoms have electrons that may be stripped off; this is the range of energies involved in many common chemical reactions. Atoms as the source of electromagnetic radiation require energies all the way from a few electron volts for visible light to many thousands of electron volts per atom for x-rays. When you reach a billion electron volts, you are in a realm where even the hard core of the atom—the nucleus—can be made to disintegrate and exhibit structure.

The three most important constituents of atoms are electrons, protons, and neutrons. They are unbelievably small and light, but their charge and mass have been measured with great accuracy. Atomic physics begins with a knowledge of the measurable characteristics of these constituents. The methods by which those characteristics have been measured are among the cleverest and most delicate in the history of science.

Problems

45.1. 1. It takes about 80 cal to convert 1 gm of ice into water. Calculate approximately how many electron volts per molecule it takes to make this transition.

2. With energies of this order of magnitude, should it be possible to remove electrons from the atoms involved?

45.2. It is found that the ultraviolet spectral line of mercury with a wavelength of 2,537 A can eject photoelectrons from zinc. What energy, in electron volts, is associated with this wavelength? (See § 19.4. The Planck constant is $h = 6.6256 \times 10^{-34}$ J-sec.)

45.3. A certain nuclear reaction releases 10^9 ev (1 Bev or 1 Gev) per particle. If all of this energy could have been used to remove one of the outer electrons from each of several atoms, approximately (order of magnitude only) how many electrons could have been released?

45.4. To ionize an atom of sodium, potassium, or rubidium requires an energy of 5.14, 4.34, or 4.16 ev, respectively. To ionize an atom of helium, neon, or argon requires an energy of 24.5, 21.5, or 15.7 ev, respectively. Which of the atoms named readily combine chemically with other atoms, and which

do not? (Look this up in a chemistry text if necessary.) Try to give a qualitative explanation of chemical activity in terms of ionization energies.

45.5. Tabulate in separate columns the following information for each of the nuclides $_1H^1$, $_2He^4$, $_8O^{16}$, $_{20}Ca^{40}$, $_{28}Ni^{58}$, $_{47}Ag^{107}$, $_{80}Hg^{202}$, and $_{92}U^{203}$: (A) the total number of nucleons; (B) the total number of protons; (C) the total number of neutrons; (D) the atomic number, Z; (E) the mass number, A.

45.6. In an experiment with apparatus similar to that of Fig. 45.3 the plates P_1 and P_2 were 0.728 cm apart, and the potential difference was 756 V. An oil drop with 3 electrons is at rest in this field. What is the mass of the drop?

45.7. In an oil-drop experiment (Fig. 45.3) a student's observations led to the conclusion that four drops carried charges of 1.59, 3.15, 4.81, and 6.31 × 10^{-19} coul, respectively. What average value of e can be deduced from these data?

45.8. With the apparatus of Fig. 45.4 it is found that, if a potential difference of 740 V is applied across parallel plates whose separation is 0.82 cm in a magnetic field whose intensity is 0.0950 weber/m², the electron beam lands at the undeviated position, P_1. What is the speed of the electrons?

46

Elementary Relativity

"Energy, at any rate kinetic energy, resists motion in the same way as ponderable masses. Is this also true of all kinds of energy?

"The theory of relativity deduces, from its fundamental assumption, a clear and convincing answer to this question, an answer again of a quantitative character: all energy resists change of motion; all energy behaves like matter; a piece of iron weighs more when red-hot than when cool; radiation traveling through space and emitted from the sun contains energy and therefore has mass; the sun and all radiating stars lose mass by emitting radiation. This conclusion, quite general in character, is an important achievement of the theory of relativity and fits all facts upon which it has been tested."

ALBERT EINSTEIN and LEOPOLD INFELD, *The Evolution of Physics* (Simon and Schuster, New York, 1938), p. 208

THE atom bomb, the nuclear electric generating plant, and the nuclear-powered submarine are dramatic proof that atomic energy can be released and harnessed. This energy is derived from losses of mass within the nuclei of atoms. The fact that energy has mass ($E = mc^2$), as revealed by the theory of relativity, is alone a practical reason for studying relativity, but it was not what motivated Albert Einstein (1879–1955). His real motive was the desire to find new ways of looking at space, time, and matter—ways that would avoid the contradictions into which classical physics had fallen by the end of the nineteenth century.

The reason why many of these contradictions had escaped notice until then is that the classical formulas agree with experiments to a high degree of accuracy for bodies that move much more slowly than light. When you consider that light travels 2×10^5 times as fast as a bomber moving five times as fast as sound waves in air, you re-

alize that most of the moving objects we encounter in our daily experience are moving very slowly indeed in comparison with the speed of light.

46.1. The New Physics: Relativity

Certain aspects of relativity are not new. They were known to Galileo and Newton and are accepted by most people today as intuitively obvious. If, for example, a car going east at 40 mph approached another car going west at 50 mph, most people would grant that their relative speed of approach was 90 mph, and they would be right in adding the two speeds (actually, subtracting vectors). If the speeds were close to the speed of light, however, adding them would give the wrong result for the relative speed of approach.

Such speeds, impossible for cars on a road, are not impossible for electrons. In some television picture tubes, for example, electrons can be made to move at speeds about one-tenth that of light. Experiments with similar tubes in the laboratory indicate that the old formulas of Galilean relativity don't work for speeds close to that of light. Einstein found a way to reconcile the old and the new experiments, but he had to abandon some of the intuitively obvious notions of space, time, and matter.

In order to follow even the barest outline of his thinking, we need the concept **frame of reference,** which we shall abbreviate as FR (see § 7.7). I illustrate it with the example of a jeep moving along the deck of an aircraft carrier (Fig. 46.1). For the jeep, the deck is a frame of reference. In

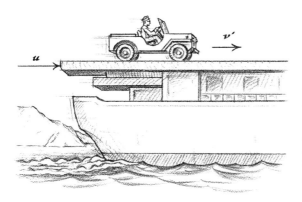

FIG. 46.1. *An example of Galilean relativity.*

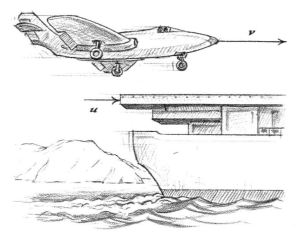

FIG. 46.2. *Another example of Galilean relativity.*

relation to the deck, the jeep is moving at 20 mph. In relation to the shore, the carrier is moving at 30 mph in the same direction. Galilean relativity says that the speed of the jeep in relation to the shore is 50 mph. These considerations are important to a pilot landing his aircraft on the deck of a moving carrier. If he comes in for a deck landing (Fig. 46.2) with a ground speed of 90 mph in the direction of the carrier's motion, he knows that his speed in relation to the carrier is only 60 mph.

We can dramatize the special problem encountered at very high speeds by imagining an experiment involving light itself (Fig. 46.3). A searchlight on the shore sends a beam of light to the aircraft carrier, which is moving away from the shore at constant velocity, $\mathbf{u}$. In transit the beam activates two photoelectric cells, P_1 and P_2, whose signals are used to measure the speed of light, c, in a shore-based laboratory. If light behaved the way aircraft do, we should expect the speed on the carrier, measured by means of photoelectric cells P_3 and P_4, to be $c - u$; but the result comes out as c, just as it did on the shore! The crucial experiments that confirmed this prediction utilized, not the speed of a ship in relation to the shore (that would be much too low), but the orbital speed of the earth (about 30,000 meters per second) in relation to a frame of reference with its origin fixed in the sun and with axes pointing in directions fixed in relation to certain stars. The conclusion drawn from this and other experiments is that the speed of light, when measured by any two observers in uniform relative motion, is always the same. This clearly calls for a modification of the simple law of combination of velocities, which we associate with Galilean relativity.

Before we can modify it, we have to express the concept mathematically. Let the frame of reference F′R′ (printed green) move with velocity $\mathbf{u}$, in relation to FR (printed black), in the positive x direction (Fig. 46.4; see also Fig. 15.9). Let the x' axis slide along the x axis with velocity $\mathbf{u}$, and let y' be parallel to y. If the origins O and O' coincide at $t = 0$, the distance $OO' = ut$. If the x coordinate of point P is x' in relation to F′R′ and x in relation to FR, the relation between x, x', and ut is

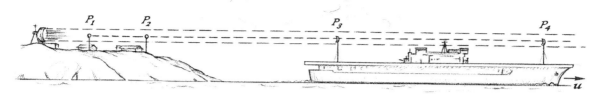

FIG. 46.3. *Demonstration that the speed of light is the same whether measured between two fixed points on the ground or measured between two points on a moving aircraft carrier.*

$$x = x' + ut \qquad [46.1$$

(See equations 7.1 and 15.5, where v was used instead of u.) This is called the transformation of Galilean relativity. Let Δx be the increment in x, and $\Delta x'$ be the increment in x', during the interval Δt. This yields

$$\Delta x = \Delta x' + u(\Delta t) \qquad [46.2$$

Dividing by Δt, we get

$$\frac{\Delta x}{\Delta t} = \frac{\Delta x'}{\Delta t} + u \qquad [46.3$$

Taking the limit as Δt approaches zero leads to

$$v = v' + u \qquad [46.4$$

which is simply the Galilean law of addition of velocities: the jeep's velocity (Fig. 46.1) relative to the shore (v) equals the jeep's velocity relative to the carrier (v') plus the carrier's velocity relative to the shore (u); the plane's velocity (Fig. 46.2) relative to the shore (v) equals the plane's velocity relative to the carrier (v') plus the carrier's velocity relative to the shore (u).

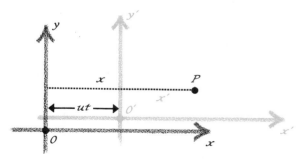

FIG. 46.4. *The frame of reference x'y' moving (parallel to the x axis) with constant velocity **u** in relation to the frame xy.*

If the velocity of light is to come out the same when measured in either FR or F′R′, equations 46.1 and 46.4 must be basically wrong, and yet they can't be very much wrong when the velocities are much lower than c. Einstein discovered that a slight modification makes them correct. This involves two factors, γ (not to be confused with gravitational field intensity) and δ, which are each very close to 1 when $u/c \ll 1$ (when u/c is much smaller than 1). I rewrite equations 46.1 and 46.4, and put next to them the corresponding equations of Einstein's relativity, in Table 46.1.

TABLE 46.1

Modification of Galilean Relativity

Galilean Relativity		Einstein's Relativity	
$x' = x - ut$	[46.5	$x' = \gamma(x - ut)$	[46.7
$v' = v - u$	[46.6	$v' = \delta(v - u)$	[46.8

Before I stress the differences, let us consider the similarities. If speeds u and v are like that of the supersonic bomber, or lower, both γ and δ are practically 1. There is therefore no contradiction between the two kinds of relativity at low speeds. When u approaches the speed of light, however, γ tends toward infinity. The correct expressions are:

$$\gamma = \frac{1}{\sqrt{1 - u^2/c^2}} \qquad [46.9$$

$$\delta = \frac{1}{1 - uv/c^2} \qquad [46.10$$

I shall show later how H. A. Lorentz ran across the factor γ even before Einstein did, but I shall do no more with δ than show that it leads to consistent results.

Another idea connected with Galilean relativity deserves mention because it was not discarded or modified by Einstein. It concerns the laws of physics in two frames moving uniformly with respect to each other. The *acceleration* of the jeep on the carrier would come out the same whether measured in the carrier frame of reference or in the shore-based frame of reference. The reason is apparent if we apply equation 46.6:

$$v_2' - v_1' = (v_2 - u) - (v_1 - u) = v_2 - v_1 \quad [46.11$$

The *difference* between velocities v_2' and v_1' in one frame comes out the same as the difference between velocities v_2 and v_1 in the other frame because the common velocity drops out. Since the change in velocity occurs in the same increment of time in both systems, the acceleration is the same in both systems. Since forces obey the equation $f = ma$, they also, if the mass were constant, would come out the same in both frames. Galilean relativity postulates, in fact, that the laws of mechanics are the same in both frames. This persuaded Einstein to postulate in his sytem that *all* the laws of physics (not only of mechanics but also, for example, of electromagnetism) hold identically in all frames of reference moving with uniform motion in relation to one another.

46.2. The Michelson-Morley Experiment

The crucial experiment that forced physicists to face the problem of the constancy of the speed of light was performed by A. A. Michelson and E. W. Morley in 1887. One of the unresolved problems of classical electromagnetic field theory was that of the ether—the hypothetical medium in which electromagnetic waves were propagated. If the ether pervaded the universe, the earth moving through it at speed u ($\cong$ 30,000 m/sec in relation to the frame of reference mentioned earlier) was logically equivalent to a stationary earth with the ether drifting past it at speed u in the opposite direction.

Imagine a boat capable of moving at speed c in still water. (The letter c is used here to suggest the role that the speed of light will play in later experiments, but it does not stand for the speed

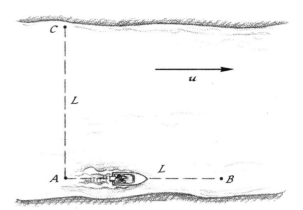

FIG. 46.5. *Analogy with the Michelson-Morley experiment.*

of light here.) If it makes the round trip ABA (Fig. 46.5), parallel to the stream, which moves with speed u, the time taken by the round trip is

$$T_1 = \frac{L}{c+u} + \frac{L}{c-u} \quad [46.12$$

After combining terms and dividing both the numerator and the denominator by c^2, we write this as

$$T_1 = \frac{2L/c}{1 - u^2/c^2} \quad [46.13$$

If the boat makes the round trip ACA, normal to the stream, it has to head slightly into the stream as it crosses the stream on both legs of the trip, and the magnitude of the resultant velocity is $\sqrt{c^2 - u^2}$. The total time for the round trip is therefore

$$T_2 = \frac{2L}{\sqrt{c^2 - u^2}} \quad [46.14$$

Dividing numerator and denominator by c, we write this as

$$T_2 = \frac{2L/c}{\sqrt{1 - u^2/c^2}} \quad [46.15$$

Notice that we used Galilean relativity (we used the vector addition of velocities) and that it clearly predicts *different* times for the two round trips.

What Michelson and Morley did was to make one light beam follow a path like ABA, in the direction of the earth's motion and back, and to make another beam follow a path like ACA, at right angles to that motion ($AB = AC = L$). Light went from A to equidistant mirrors at points B

and C and was reflected back to A. They were prepared, by very delicate interference techniques, to detect, on the light's arrival at A, any difference in time $(T_2 - T_1)$ by measuring a corresponding difference in phase. The differences in phase observed by them and other investigators implied only very small fractions of the difference in time expected from classical considerations based on equations 46.13 and 46.15 (with u equal to 30,000 m/sec) and were statistically explainable. They concluded that it took light the *same* time to travel a path like ABA as to travel a path like ACA. As a result of this and subsequent experiments the scientific community felt confident that there was no measurable difference between the times T_1 and T_2. (A test made in 1964, using infrared laser light, showed that the effect of "ether drift" is less than 1/1,000 of what might be produced by the earth's orbital velocity.)

And now began a search for an explanation. There are many ways of explaining away the result of the Michelson-Morley experiment. We shall consider only two.

Lorentz took this view: The ether exists, but the length of the arm AB, in the direction of **u**, shrank from L to $L' = L/\gamma$; the arm AC, at right angles to **u**, did not shrink.

If we put L' in place of L in equation 46.13, we get

$$T_1' = \frac{2L'/c}{1 - u^2/c^2} = 1/\gamma \, \frac{2L/c}{1 - u^2/c^2}$$

$$= \frac{2L/c\sqrt{1 - u^2/c^2}}{1 - u^2/c^2} = \frac{2L/c}{\sqrt{1 - u^2/c^2}} \quad [46.16$$

This makes T_1' come out the same as T_2 (equation 46.15) if we assume that the velocity of light combines with the ether-drift velocity according to the Galilean relativistic formulas (equations 46.5 and 46.6).

Einstein took a different view: There is no ether. The time of round-trip travel must be the same in both cases. If the ether existed, there would be a preferred frame of reference in the universe (the one in which the ether was at rest). The negative result of the Michelson-Morley experiment is simply due to the fact that there is no ether.

Eventually Einstein was led to state the basic postulates on which the new physics could be founded: (1) the velocity of light in a vacuum is the same in all frames of reference moving uniformly in relation to one another; (2) all laws of nature are the same in all frames of reference moving uniformly in relation to one another. It can also be shown as a corollary that (3) positions and velocities are transformed from one frame of reference to a second that is in uniform motion relative to the first according to the equations (46.21–46.24) of Einstein's relativity (see Table 46.2).

When I wrote equation 46.7, I did not state explicitly the formulas for y', z', and t'. They are now stated in Table 46.2.

Equations 46.20 and 46.24 relate to time. Equation 46.20 says what we assumed before without stating it explicitly—that in Galilean relativity two identical clocks will keep the same time even though one is moving in relation to the other. Equation 46.24, on the other hand, says that the time (t') measured by a clock in F'R' can be different from the time (t) measured by an identical clock in FR. This opens up the whole subject of the relativity of time (first introduced in § 7.7), but we cannot consider it further here.

The remarkable thing is that the factor γ that Lorentz deduced from his explanation of the Michelson-Morley experiment (while keeping the ether concept) is the same factor γ that appears in the Einstein relativistic formulas; in each case

$$\gamma = \frac{1}{\sqrt{1 - u^2/c^2}}$$

A graph of γ against u/c appears in Figure 46.6. Lorentz was even able to prove that the formulas of electromagnetism hold in F'R' in the identical

TABLE 46.2

Transformation Equations: Galilean Relativity and Einstein's Relativity Compared

$$\gamma = \frac{1}{\sqrt{1 - u^2/c^2}}$$

Galilean Relativity		Einstein's Relativity	
$x' = x - ut$	[46.17	$x' = \gamma(x - ut)$	[46.21
$y' = y$	[46.18	$y' = y$	[46.22
$z' = z$	[46.19	$z' = z$	[46.23
$t' = t$	[46.20	$t' = \gamma(t - ux/c^2)$	[46.24

form that they have in FR only if the equations of transformation are exactly equations 46.21–46.24. Hence those equations are still called the Lorentz transformation even though Einstein's derivation and interpretation of them are quite different from Lorentz's. We see here an example of convergence on an idea from different directions. The presently accepted interpretation is that of Einstein: *There is no ether; the speed of light as measured by an observer at rest in one frame of reference is the same as that measured by an observer at rest in any other frame of reference moving with constant velocity relative to the first; the laws of physics are the same in all such frames of reference.*

I assert without proof that the law of combination of velocities, equation 46.8, follows directly from equations 46.21–46.24. Let us examine one of its implications. We suppose that the speed, v', of the jeep relative to the carrier in Figure 46.1 approaches the speed of light. What will be its speed, v, relative to the shore? We use equations 46.8 and 46.10:

$$v' = \delta(v - u)$$

$$\delta = \frac{1}{1 - uv/c^2}$$

$$v' = \frac{v - u}{1 - uv/c^2} \qquad [46.25$$

If we now substitute c for v' in the last equation

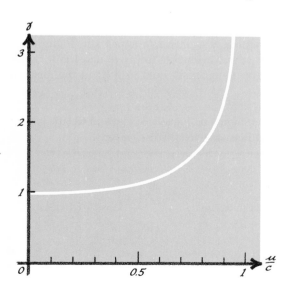

FIG. 46.6. *Graph of* γ *against* u/c.

above and manipulate algebraically, we get the equation

$$c(c^2 - uv) = c^2(v - u) \qquad [46.26$$

from which we get the equation

$$v(u + c) = c(u + c)$$

or

$$v = c \qquad [46.27$$

That is, if the jeep's velocity relative to the carrier were equal to the speed of light, c, its velocity relative to the shore would also be c; its velocity cannot differ from c in another frame of reference that has a uniform velocity in relation to the first frame.

46.3. Implications of the Relativistic Equations

Hereafter, when I use the adjective "relativistic," I shall mean "according to Einstein" unless some other meaning is specified.

Let us see how the new formulas are used. We suppose that the ends of a stick are at x_1' and x_2' in F'R'. The length of the stick, measured by an observer in F'R', is $x_2' - x_1'$. In FR the ends have coordinates x_1 and x_2 such that

$$x_2' = \gamma(x_2 - ut) \qquad [46.28$$

$$x_1' = \gamma(x_1 - ut) \qquad [46.29$$

The length of the stick, measured by an observer in FR, is $x_2 - x_1$. If the observations of x_1 and x_2 are made at the same time t (by the clock in FR), we can get $x_2 - x_1$ by subtracting equation 46.29 from equation 46.28:

$$x_2' - x_1' = \gamma(x_2 - x_1) - 0 \qquad [46.30$$

$$x_2 - x_1 = \frac{x_2' - x_1'}{\gamma} \qquad [46.31$$

The variable γ, we remember, is always equal to or greater than one.

Suppose that the stick used is a meter stick; that is, suppose that, when F'R' is coincident with and at rest in relation to FR, the stick is found to be equal in length to a standard meter. To an observer in F'R' it is always a meter long; to an observer in FR, however, its length when F'R' is moving with speed $0.8c$ in relation to FR is (equation 46.31 and Fig. 46.6)

$$x_2 - x_1 = \frac{1}{\gamma} = \frac{1}{1.66} = 0.60 \text{ m}$$

The length of the meter stick as measured by an observer in FR is 60 centimeters.

Now consider the effect of the constancy of the speed of light. If the speed of light for observers in both FR and F'R' is c, a flash at $t = 0$ should produce a spherical wave front, of radius $r = ct$ to the observer in FR, of radius $r' = ct'$ to the observer in F'R'. Let us imagine that F'R' is moving with speed u in the positive x direction. At time $t = 0$, O and O' coincide, and at that instant a light flashes at the common origin. At the later time t' the wave front, as noted by the observer in F'R', is a sphere of radius ct'. The equation of such a sphere is

$$(x')^2 + (y')^2 + (z')^2 = c^2(t')^2 \qquad [46.32$$

You can prove (Prob. 46.11), as an exercise in algebra, that, if you replace all the primed quantities of equation 46.32 by their equivalents from equations 46.21–46.24, you will get

$$x^2 + y^2 + z^2 = c^2 t^2$$

The interpretation of this result is that the observer in FR also notes a spherical wave front traveling with speed c away from the origin. This is exactly what the observer in F'R' observes with his clocks and measuring sticks!

I can now summarize the conclusions that can be deduced from equations 46.21–46.24. They have all received ample experimental confirmation. They apply only when the relative velocity between two frames of reference is constant.

Length: The length of a body as measured by an observer traveling with it is greater than the length of the same body as measured by an observer whom it is passing at speed u. The ratio of the larger to the smaller is

$$\gamma = \frac{1}{\sqrt{1 - u^2/c^2}}$$

An observer traveling with an electron through the tube of a linear accelerator two miles long at speed $0.999c$ would measure the tube's length as 0.089 mile. In general, the length, L', of an object measured by an observer on the moving frame, F'R', is longer than the length, L, of the same object measured by a stationary observer: $L' = \gamma L$.

Time: The time interval, $t_2' - t_1' = \Delta t'$, between two events is shorter for an observer traveling with the events than the time interval,

$t_2 - t_1 = \Delta t$, between the same events recorded by the observer whom the events are passing: $\Delta t = \gamma(\Delta t')$.

Mass: A body's mass, m', is less for an observer moving with the body than the mass, m, of the same body, for an observer in relation to whom the motion takes place: $m = \gamma m'$. This idea leads to the concept of **rest mass,** m_0, which is the mass of an object at rest in relation to the observer. When the object has speed u, relative to the observer, its mass is

$$m = \gamma m_0 = \frac{m_0}{\sqrt{1 - u^2/c^2}}$$

Momentum: The momentum of a body of mass m moving with velocity v is $p = mv$. The mass varies with the velocity: $m = \gamma m_0$. Hence

$$p = \frac{m_0 v}{\sqrt{1 - v^2/c^2}}$$

The graph of momentum against velocity is therefore not linear except approximately for very low velocities; it is shown in Figure 46.7. The law of the conservation of momentum holds for relativistic momentum.

Force: Force is the rate of change of momentum,

$$\lim_{\Delta t \to 0} \frac{\Delta p}{\Delta t}$$

This definition of force is identical with Newton's, but we must use the relativistic formula for momentum.

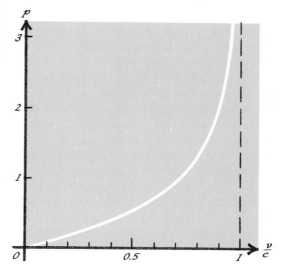

FIG. 46.7. *Graph of momentum,* p, *against* v/c.

Kinetic energy: The relativistic formula for kinetic energy is not $K = mv^2/2$ but

$$K = m_0c^2(\gamma - 1) \qquad [46.33$$

There is no contradiction with classical mechanics at low velocities, for in the limit as v/c approaches zero equation 46.33 becomes $m_0v^2/2$ (see Prob. 46.8). Figure 46.8 is a graphical comparison of the relativistic kinetic energy with $m_0v^2/2$. It shows clearly that it would require an infinite amount of energy to impart speed c to any material body.

46.4. Mass and Energy

To atomic physicists, the most important conclusion to be drawn from the theory of relativity is, probably, that matter (one of whose measurable properties is mass) has energy and that energy has the attribute mass. The first hint of this conclusion comes from equation 46.33, which can be written as

$$K = m_0c^2\gamma - m_0c^2 \qquad [46.34$$

Now $m_0\gamma$ is simply m; so we may write

$$K = mc^2 - m_0c^2$$

$$K = (m - m_0)c^2 \qquad [46.35$$

This equation asserts that the increment in mass $(m - m_0)$ is directly proportional to the kinetic energy of the body, the constant of proportionality being c^2. This idea has been broadened in the general theory of relativity, according to which not only kinetic energy but all kinds of energy have mass. In general, then, $E = mc^2$ is the total energy of matter of mass m. If the difference in mass due to motion, $m - m_0$, accounts for the kinetic energy of the body, then $K = (m - m_0)c^2$.

Are mass and energy synonymous? Since their physical dimensions are M and ML^2T^{-2}, respectively, we conclude that they are not; but matter (measurable by its mass) has energy, and energy has the attributes (inertia and weight, for example) of mass. If the total mass of matter in the universe is M, the total energy in the universe is Mc^2.

It is apparent, since c^2 is extremely large, that a portion of matter whose mass is one kilogram has a tremendous amount of energy:

$$E = 1 \text{ kg} \times (3 \times 10^8 \text{ m/sec})^2 = 9 \times 10^{16} \text{ J}$$

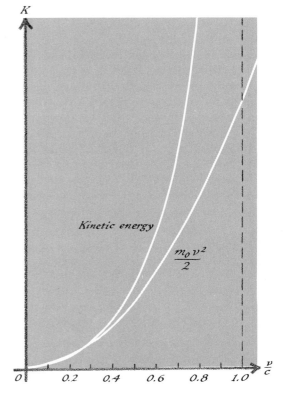

FIG. 46.8. *Graph of kinetic energy compared with that of* $m_0v^2/2$, *both against* v/c.

This amount of energy could lift a platform bearing all the people in the world (about 3×10^9 persons) to a height of more than 30 miles.

It is clear that, if even only a small fraction of the energy that resides in matter can be harvested, it will add appreciably to our available resources. Most of the mass of an atom is in its nucleus, and it is to the nucleus of the atom that we must eventually look for the energy of the future.

46.5. Summary

The values of many of the measurable quantities of physics depend on the frame of reference from which they are measured. A certain kind of relativity was known even to Galileo, but the precise equations that apply to two frames of reference moving uniformly in relation to each other were deduced by Einstein in his special theory of relativity. In his theory the speed of light is invariant for all such frames. The resulting equations predict interesting and apparently paradoxical conclusions regarding length, mass, and time as measured in two such frames. Of far-reaching importance is the connection, implicit in his equations, between energy and mass. The well-known formula $E = mc^2$ was suggested by the special theory, but its validity for all forms of energy is discussed in Einstein's general theory of relativity, which is beyond the scope of this book. This formula has been amply confirmed by many experiments, especially those in nuclear physics.

Problems

46.1. You are riding at a constant speed in a specially designed rubber-tired monorail car whose ride is smooth and silent. The track is straight. You cannot see out. Your speed is 300 mph. What experiment can you perform within the car to prove that you are moving? (Would a ball, some string, a meter stick, a spring balance, and a watch help?)

46.2. Suppose that during the night, while you were asleep, *everything* in the universe became a thousand times smaller than it had been. What experiment could you perform the following morning to prove that you had altered in size? (Hint: In a well-known joke a shipwrecked sailor, encountering a king-sized Coca-Cola bottle for the first time, exclaims: "I've shrunk!")

46.3. 1. A top is spinning at the rate of 500 rev/sec. A microscopic bug sits on its surface. What is the apparent speed, of that bug, of the Large Magellanic Cloud, which is 3×10^{19} m away?

2. How does that speed compare with the speed of light?

3. Is the frame of reference on the top moving with uniform motion in relation to the stars?

46.4. A truck is moving with a speed of 50 mph on a straight road behind another truck moving at 40 mph in the same direction. A boy who can throw a baseball with a speed of 60 mph, standing in the following truck, pitches a ball to a boy on the leading truck. What is the speed of the ball in relation to the latter boy?

46.5. A constant force applied to a rocket in the direction of its straight-line motion keeps increasing its speed. If the force were applied long enough, the speed of the rocket should exceed that of light. According to Einstein, this does not happen. Explain why not.

46.6. 1. A watch has a certain mass when the spring has run down. It is then wound by hand as far as possible. Is the mass of the watch different after being wound?

2. If you think it is, estimate by how much.

46.7. Calculate, from Fig. 46.8, the approximate speed of a body for which the kinetic-energy formula $m_0 v^2 / 2$ is in error by 20 percent.

46.8. Prove that the quantity

$$K = m_0 c^2 (\gamma - 1)$$

approaches $m_0 v^2 / 2$ as v/c approaches zero. Hint: Remembering that ϵ stands for a small quantity, use the formula

$$\sqrt{1 - \epsilon^2} \cong 1 - \epsilon^2/2$$

Another useful approximation, for small δ, is

$$\frac{1}{1 - \delta} \cong 1 + \delta$$

46.9. Electrons can be accelerated to a speed that is 0.999999999 of the speed of light. What is the ratio of the mass of such an electron to its rest mass? Hint: Use the formula

$$(1 - \epsilon)^2 \cong 1 - 2\epsilon$$

in which $\epsilon = 10^{-9}$.

46.10. Prove the statement (made in § 46.4) that matter of mass 1 kg has enough energy to lift a platform bearing the world's population to a height of more than 30 mi.

46.11. Begin with the equation

$$(x')^2 + (y')^2 + (z')^2 = c^2 (t')^2$$

Substitute values of x', y', z', and t' from equations 46.21–46.24. Prove that

$$x^2 + y^2 + z^2 = c^2 t^2$$

Detecting and Weighing Molecules, Atoms, and Atomic Particles

MOLECULES, atoms, and atomic particles are much too small to be weighed individually on any kind of balance or scale. Scientists have weighed them individually, however, by measuring the deflection of charged particles in electric and magnetic fields.

The average atomic weights of the different elements, as they occur in nature, have also been determined and tabulated (Appendix F). They have been extremely useful to the chemist, whose computations are based on the assumption that mass is conserved, but the intimate correspondence between mass and energy now requires that we know the masses of individual atoms with much greater accuracy than ever before.

47.1. Three Ways of Weighing Things

I shall describe three different methods of weighing things and then show how those methods are applied at the atomic level.

1. *Relative Weights*

You separate the couples at a dance, let us suppose, and put all the men on a huge scale of the kind used to weigh vehicles; their total weight is W_1. Then you weigh all the women together; their total weight is W_2. You don't need to know the total number of couples to conclude that the ratio of the weight of one man to that of one woman is W_1/W_2. This is, of course, an average. You do need to know that the number of men is the same as the number of women; but you don't need to count them to know that.

2. *Weighing a Known Number of Identical Objects*

It is difficult to weigh a single sheet of writing paper on a postal scale, but it is easy to weigh a thousand sheets and divide the result by 1,000. This time you do have to know the number of objects, and you assume that they are identical.

3. *Weighing by Deflection*

If you tie a stone to a string, the tension in the string as you whirl the stone at constant angular velocity in a circle of constant radius is directly proportional to the mass of the stone. The string deflects the stone from a straight path. Electric and magnetic forces can deflect charged particles. The inertial mass of such a particle can be determined from the kinematical effect of the deflecting force on the particle.

We use the word "weighing" loosely to mean the determination of mass by any of the methods described. Now let us see how those methods are applied to molecules, atoms, and atomic particles.

47.2. Atomic Weight and Atomic Mass

If you fill a vessel with oxygen at a certain pressure and temperature and later fill the same vessel with hydrogen at the same pressure and temperature, the ratio of the weights of the contents of the vessel in the two cases gives the ratio of the molecular weight of oxygen to that of hydrogen.

$$\frac{\text{weight of O}_2 \text{ in vessel}}{\text{weight of H}_2 \text{ in vessel}} = \frac{\text{weight of O}_2 \text{ molecule}}{\text{weight of H}_2 \text{ molecule}}$$

Here we have used Avogadro's hypothesis that equal volumes of different gases at the same pressure and temperature contain the same number of molecules. In this particular example we also had to use the fact that both oxygen and hydrogen molecules contain two atoms each (observe that we specified O_2 and H_2), a fact that has to be deduced from the chemical evidence. The point, however, is simply this: you don't have to know the number of particles to get relative weights. All you have to know is that the number of particles is the same in both samples. This illustrates one of the methods used by chemists to arrive at their table of atomic weights (Appendix F).

As we saw earlier (§ 45.2), the term "atomic weight," as used by the chemist, means the average weight of the atoms of the element, as it is found in nature, on a scale on which the mass of the carbon isotope $_6C^{12}$ is set arbitrarily at exactly 12. On this scale the atomic weight of hydrogen comes out as 1.00797.

Historically, oxygen was first chosen as the base because it combines with most elements. The chemists could evaluate the atomic weights of such elements by weighing their oxygen compounds. With oxygen at exactly 16, moreover, a large number of elements have nearly integral atomic weights (carbon, 12.011; nitrogen, 14.007;

sodium, 22.910; etc.), and none has an atomic weight less than 1 (hydrogen, 1.0080; helium, 4.0026; lithium, 6.939). In 1961 a compromise between the international unions of chemistry and physics led to the acceptance of the mass of the isotope $_6C^{12}$ as exactly 12. This change did not disturb very much the old chemical tabulations (based on oxygen set at 16); so it was acceptable to the chemists. Being based on the mass of a nuclide, $_6C^{12}$, and not on a mixture of isotopes, the new scale was acceptable to the physicists.

William Prout (1785–1850), a physician of Edinburgh and London, suggested in 1816 that all atoms are built of hydrogen. The atomic weights then available to him showed no serious disagreement with this hypothesis (and he is said to have disregarded, as erroneous, those that showed slight disagreement). Later, when it was discovered that chlorine has an atomic weight of 35.453, Prout's hypothesis seemed to be clearly contradicted by the facts.

Today, however, using refined mass spectrometers, we know that some chlorine atoms have an atomic mass of 34.968855 (very close to 35) and others an atomic mass of 36.965896 (very close to 37), the abundance of the former being 75.7 percent and that of the latter being 24.23 percent. The weighted average of these ($36.965896 \times 0.2423 + 34.96885 \times 0.7577$) is (rounded out to five significant figures) 35.453. It is clear that the isotopic constitution of chlorine explains why the atomic weight is not more nearly integral. There is now ample evidence that the samples of this and other elements used by chemists are actually mixtures of the different isotopes that an element may have. It looks as if Prout may have been on the right track after all.

In modern nuclear physics we do not say that all other atoms are compounded of hydrogen atoms, but we do say that all nuclei except that of hydrogen are made up of protons and neutrons. (The hydrogen nucleus is a proton.) The atomic mass of a proton is 1.007277, and that of a neutron is 1.008665.

The notation used can be illustrated by the isotopes of oxygen. All the isotopes in Table 47.1 behave alike, chemically, and all have the same atomic number, 8.

47.3. Weighing Molecules by Weighing a Sample Containing a Known Number of Molecules

The next illustration is analogous to weighing the thousand sheets of paper. We know that M grams of a homogeneous substance whose molecular weight is M (in other words, a *mole* of the substance) contains N_A molecules, N_A being the Avogadro constant. The weight of one molecule in grams is therefore M/N_A. Our success depends on having an accurate value of the Avogadro constant.

A mole of carbon weighs 12.01115 grams. The accepted value of the Avogadro constant is 6.02252×10^{23}. The weight of a single molecule of carbon (in this case a single atom) is therefore

$$\frac{12.01115}{6.02252} \times 10^{-23} \text{ gm} = 1.99437 \times 10^{-23} \text{ gm}$$

(The mass of the earth is 5.983×10^{21} gm. One gram is heavier in relation to a molecule of oxygen than the earth is in relation to one gram.)

The Avogadro constant, N_A, leads us, we see, to specific numerical information about the mass of individual molecules. As a means of introducing the topic of x-rays I shall now outline one of the many different methods of determining N_A.

47.4. X-ray Determination of the Avogadro Constant

In 1895, Wilhelm Konrad Röntgen (1845–1923), professor of physics at the University of Würzburg, reported the discovery of a new kind of radiation, which, because its nature was still unknown, he called *X-Strahlen*, or x-rays. The discovery was accidental; but it is an example of the kind of accident that can be exploited only by one who is well prepared. He had enough curiosity and physical knowledge to pursue the consequences of his discovery rapidly.

There were glass tubes of the kind called *Crookes tubes* and *Hittorf tubes* in many European laboratories, including Röntgen's. He had discovered that, even if he covered an operating

Hittorf tube with a mantle of thin black cardboard, a fluorescent screen lit up when brought near the tube. He immediately began a series of experiments, which showed that x-rays penetrate matter that is opaque to ordinary light, that they expose photographic film and discharge electroscopes, and that they originate wherever cathode rays strike matter. (The effect is very noticeable when they strike certain metals.)

Within a few weeks after the announcement of his discovery, x-rays were being used for medical investigations. Hardly any other event in the history of science matches Röntgen's discovery in impact upon scientists and laymen alike. It heralded an era of great scientific activity: radioactivity was discovered in 1896; the electron was discovered in 1897; Planck's quantum theory was announced in 1900; the light quantum (or photon) was discovered by Einstein in 1905, and his special theory of relativity was developed in the same year.

Today the Geiger-Müller counter is a common tool for detecting x-rays. If we use it instead of the slow photographic technique, we can repeat in the classroom some of Röntgen's exciting experiments, using, as sources of x-rays, cathode-ray tubes very similar to his (Fig. 47.1). Such tubes are still available at scientific supply houses.

Röntgen discovered many of the properties of x-rays, but their basic nature remained a mystery until 1912, when Max von Laue (1879–1960) suggested that a crystal used as a three-dimensional

TABLE 47.1

Isotopes of Oxygen

Symbol	Atomic Number	Mass Number	Atomic Mass	Abundance
$_8O^{14}$	8	14	14.008597	trace
$_8O^{15}$	8	15	15.003072	trace
$_8O^{16}$	8	16	15.994915	99.76%
$_8O^{17}$	8	17	16.999133	0.037%
$_8O^{18}$	8	18	17.999160	0.204%
$_8O^{19}$	8	19	19.003577	trace
$_8O^{20}$	8	20	20.004071	trace

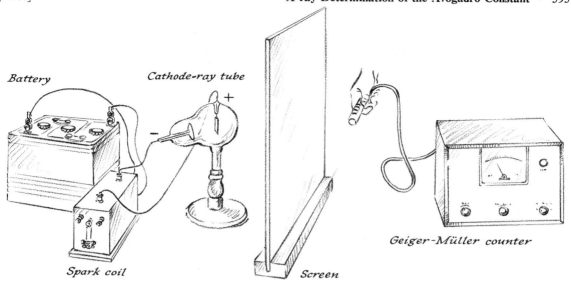

FIG. 47.1. *Use of a modern Geiger-Müller counter to detect* x-rays *produced by a Hittorf tube (a simple cathode-ray tube) similar to the one that Röntgen used.*

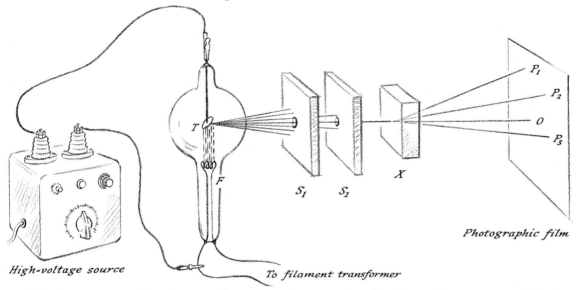

FIG. 47.2. *An arrangement for using a modern* x-ray *tube to reproduce Laue's experiment on* x-ray *diffraction.*

diffraction grating might show whether *x*-rays have wave properties. Experiments performed during the first decade after Röntgen's discovery indicated that *x*-rays, if they are waves, must have wavelengths several thousand times as short as those of visible light. No man-made device could rule a grating with lines so close, but Laue knew that the atoms in a crystal are separated by distances of the order of one angstrom, and he had

the idea that the crystal could serve as a grating. The experiment, performed by W. Friedrich and P. Knipping, proved that *x*-rays do indeed behave like waves of extremely short wavelength—about 1 A.

An arrangement for reproducing Laue's experiment—but with a modern *x*-ray tube—is shown in Figure 47.2. Electrons from a hot filament, *F*, are attracted to the target, *T*, by a strong electric field. The deceleration of the electrons as they hit the target produces the electromagnetic radiation called x-rays. Small circular openings in the lead screens S_1 and S_2 determine a fine beam, which is allowed to hit a crystal, X. Most of the beam, continuing through the crystal in the same direction, lands at O, on the photographic film; but, if the exposure is long enough, other spots appear around O at points like P_1, P_2, and P_3. Figure 47.3 reproduces a photograph made in this way with a crystal of the mineral rutile. This experiment shows at once that x-rays are waves and that their wavelength is of the order of 1 A. The locations of the spots on the film correspond to diffraction maxima produced by the constructive interference of waves diffracted by the regularly spaced atoms in the crystal.

In principle, the mathematical calculation of

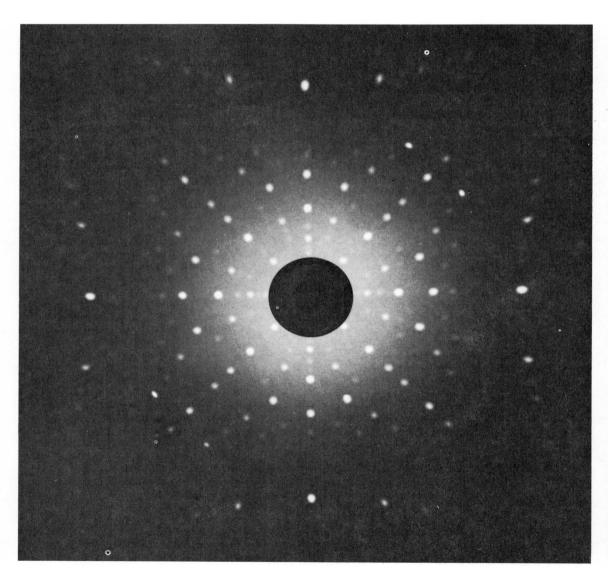

FIG. 47.3. *Laue spots made with apparatus similar to that of Fig. 47.2. (Photograph from the General Electric Research Laboratory.)*

the beam directions that give rise to the spots (called Laue spots) is simple: they are the directions in which beams arrive in phase at the film; in practice, the calculation could be very complicated. A great simplification, due to Sir Lawrence Bragg (born in 1890), is based upon the fact that within a crystal there are planes containing many atoms. These planes, Sir Lawrence showed, behave like mirrors for x-rays. We therefore call the phenomenon **Bragg reflection** although we know that it is actually the constructive interference of the radiation scattered by the atoms that is involved.

A plane containing many atoms need not be parallel to a crystal surface (formed either by cutting or by cleaving). An analogy is a cornfield, in which a line containing many corn stalks need not be parallel to the edge of the field. Sighting along a diagonal of a large rectangular cornfield, where stalks are planted in equally spaced and mutually perpendicular rows and columns, for example, one may find many stalks standing on a straight line that is neither on a row nor on a column. In fact, many such parallel lines may be found, each containing numerous stalks.

In a similar way, in a crystal, many parallel planes may be found, each containing many atoms. For these planes, Bragg proved, the incident and outgoing beams obey the ordinary law of reflection (angle of incidence equals angle of reflection). The effect is the same as if each such plane were a mirror, but the theory requires that the radiation from atoms in parallel planes interfere constructively. Bragg showed (Fig. 47.4), that for two such planes, π_1 and π_2, separated by distance d (A) the total path difference for rays obeying the law of reflection (B) is $2d \sin \theta$. (Angle θ is the complement of the angle of incidence.) For constructive interference this difference must be an integral number, n, of wavelengths. This led to the expression known as **Bragg's law**[†]:

$$n\lambda = 2d \sin \theta \qquad [47.i$$

The integer n is called the **order** of the reflection (reflections for which $n = 1$, for example, are called first-order reflections), λ is the wavelength of the radiation, and d is the distance between the crystal planes, which, as we saw earlier, need not be parallel to a crystal face.

Figure 47.5 shows schematically an arrangement for Bragg reflection. Notice that the angle θ in x-ray work is measured from the surface rather than from the normal to the surface. The apparatus must be designed so that, as the angle (θ_1) between the incident beam and surface is changed, the ionization chamber that detects the reflected beam is shifted so that θ_2 is always equal to θ_1. A graph of the intensity (observed with an arrangement like this but using a tube with a palladium target), plotted against the incident angle, θ, is shown in Figure 47.6. The highest peak is found at the reflection that occurs when $n = 1$.

[†] Both Sir William Bragg (1862–1942) and his son Sir Lawrence Bragg worked in the field of x-ray analysis and spectroscopy, but Bragg's law is attributed to Sir Lawrence.

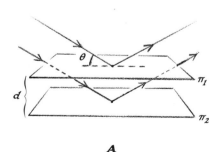

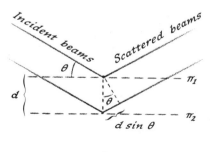

A   **B**

FIG. 47.4. (*A*) *Atoms in two different planes, π_1 and π_2, contributing constructively to a scattered beam.* (*B*) *Two-dimensional analysis of the geometric conditions required for constructive interference from atoms in two different planes separated by distance* d.

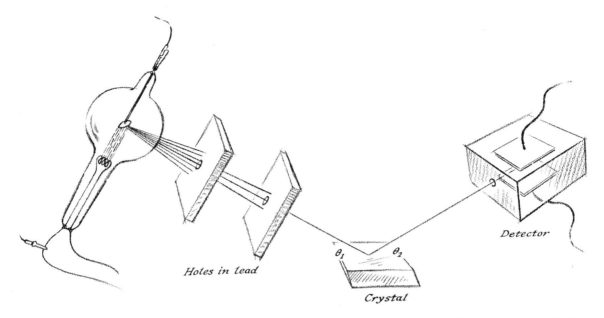

FIG. 47.5. *Experimental set-up for detection of Bragg reflection of x-rays by a crystal. The ordinary law of reflection is obeyed, but the reflections are strong only for angles obeying the equation* $n\lambda = 2d \sin \theta$.

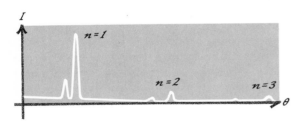

FIG. 47.6. *The intensity,* I, *of Bragg reflection of x-rays (emitted from a tube with a palladium target) from certain faces, known technically as (100), of a rocksalt crystal, as a function of the incident angle,* θ.

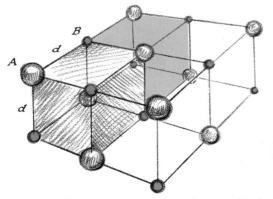

FIG. 47.7. *Schematic representation of atoms of sodium and chlorine in sodium chloride.*

It is apparent that, if the radiation has only one wavelength and that wavelength is known, the crystal-lattice space, d, can be determined from equation 47.1. And vice versa: in some early experiments, values of d, obtained independently, were used in the equation to determine wavelengths.

Wavelengths can be independently measured today. Man-made ruled diffraction gratings can be used in reflection, for, at grazing incidence, the *effective* separation of the rulings is smaller than the actual separation. This permits an evaluation of λ from another laboratory-measured distance (the ruling interval). Using λ as a known quantity, we can, of course, get the lattice space, d, from equation 47.1. The separation of atoms in thousands of crystals has been obtained in this way. For the atomic planes parallel to the natural faces of a rock-salt crystal, for example, this method gives $d = 2.814$ A.

Let us see how this value of d permits a determination of the Avogadro constant. First we must know that the atoms in rock salt are arranged in a cubic lattice like that of Figure 47.7, the sodium and chlorine atoms alternating along any line. To a single atom, such as A, we can associate the space of one cube of side d (and volume d^3), as shown by the shaded volume. To another atom, such as B, we can associate the green volume. We can account for the whole volume of the crystal in this way by associating the volume d^3 to each sodium and to each chlorine atom.

Consider a sample of salt weighing 58.4428 grams. Call this mass M (units: grams/mole). This is a mole of salt, for the atomic weight of sodium is 22.9898 and that of chlorine is 35.453. Since density, ρ, is mass per unit volume, we may write that $\rho = M/V$. The total volume in this case is $2N_A d^3$, for there are exactly N_A molecules in a mole and two atoms per molecule. (Remember that N_A is a pure number whose units are those of a pure number per mole.) Therefore

$$\rho = \frac{M}{2N_A d^3} \qquad [47.2$$

Solving for the Avogadro constant, we get

$$N_A = \frac{M}{2\rho d^3} \qquad [47.3$$

We know that, to three significant figures,

$$M = 58.4 \text{ gm/mole}$$

We can easily find out that

$$\rho = 2.18 \text{ gm/cm}^3$$

and (from x-ray determinations with a ruled grating) that

$$d = 2.81 \times 10^{-8} \text{ cm}$$

Therefore, to three significant figures,

$$N_A = 6.02 \times 10^{23}$$

It would be difficult to exaggerate the importance of the Avogadro constant. It has been determined by more than fourteen different and interrelated methods. The presently accepted value, obtained by appropriate weighting of these methods, is $N_A = 6.02252 \times 10^{23}$.

47.5. Weighing Atoms by the Use of Electric and Magnetic Fields: J. J. Thomson's Method

The first successful attempt to weigh atoms by the use of deflecting forces was carried out by J. J. Thomson with a technique similar to that used to find e/m for the electron.

Figure 47.8 shows, in a highly schematic man-

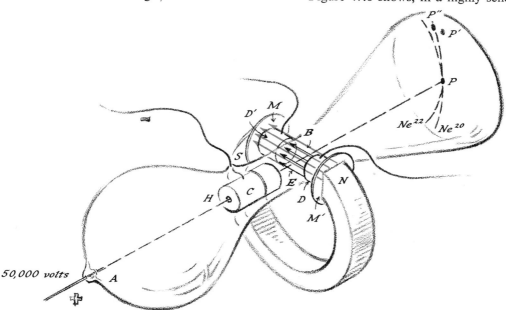

FIG. 47.8. *Schematic diagram of J. J. Thomson's apparatus for measuring the ratio of the charge to the mass of atomic particles.*

ner, how electric (**E**) and magnetic (**B**) fields running *in the same direction* were produced. The pole pieces, D and D', are electrically insulated from the large magnet by thin mica sheets, M and M'. In the chamber at the left are neon atoms, some of which have become positively charged by the loss of one electron each. A potential of about 50,000 volts accelerates the charged atoms from the anode, A, toward the cathode, C, and some enter the latter's aperture, H. These move on at high speed and land at P on the fluorescent screen when neither the electric nor the magnetic field deflects them. When the magnetic field, **B**, acts alone in the direction indicated, it exerts an upward force on positive ions, causing them to land at point P'. An electric field, **E**, produced by use of the pole pieces, D and D', as electrodes, deflects the ions to the left, causing them to land at point P''. It can be proved that all particles, regardless of speed, with the same ratio of charge to mass, q/m, will, under the simultaneous action of **E** and **B** fields, land on a parabola of which P'' is a point.

J. J. Thomson observed the predicted parabolic traces on the screen. By similar techniques, greatly refined, it has been found that the mass of a positively charged hydrogen ion (that is, of a hydrogen nucleus) is $(1,836.13 \pm 0.01)$ times the mass of an electron.

Another spectacular discovery was that several different parabolas appeared. Thomson deduced, and subsequent experiments have confirmed, that each parabola is due to a different value of q/m. If you examine particles having the same charge, different parabolas mean different nuclear masses. It was the first time that the isotopes of neon had been thus separated from one another. The lighter atoms landed on the flatter parabola. The isotopes Ne^{20} and Ne^{22} were definitely identified in this way. Here was the beginning of **mass spectroscopy,** by means of which the masses of thousands of isotopes have been measured with great accuracy.

47.6. Natural Radioactivity

In March 1896, less than a year after Röntgen's discovery of x-rays, A. H. Becquerel (1852–1908) announced another startling discovery: the phe-

nomenon now called **natural radioactivity.** The glass of a Crookes tube used in the production of x-rays fluoresces where the x-rays impinge, and Becquerel knew also that certain uranium salts are phosphorescent after being exposed to sunlight. He found that such a salt, when placed near a photographic plate covered with opaque black paper, exposed the plate. The similarity to x-rays was obvious. It was soon discovered, however, that previous exposure to the sun was not necessary. Certain salts that had been carefully hidden from the sun for months worked just as well. The cause was unknown, but the activity was called **radioactivity.**

One of the most inspiring episodes in the history of modern science is told in the biography of Marie Sklodowska Curie (1867–1934). She and her husband, Pierre Curie (1859–1906), succeeded in isolating two new elements after patiently separating bismuth and barium chemically from pitchblende, a uranium-bearing ore. Since neither barium nor bismuth is radioactive when pure, they deduced and proved that two new elements, which they named polonium ($Z = 84$) and radium ($Z = 88$), were responsible for the tremendous increase of radioactivity found in these chemically separated samples. These were the first of a long line of elements to be discovered through radioactivity.

Some measure of the Curies' labors is given by the fact that only 1/5 gram of radium was extracted from a ton of pitchblende. Pure polonium is 10 billion times, pure radium 20 million times, as radioactive as uranium.

The results of subsequent experiments are summarized schematically in Figure 47.9. In 1899 Ernest Rutherford, then a newly appointed professor of physics at McGill University, continued experiments that he had begun while working under J. J. Thomson at the Cavendish Laboratory in Cambridge, England. He had discovered that a magnetic field could separate the radioactive rays (Fig. 47.9) into two components, which he named *alpha* (α) and *beta* (β) *rays*. The deflections indicated that the alpha rays were positive and the beta rays negative. (The gamma rays were discovered later.)

Radioactive rays can ionize air and can therefore discharge a charged electroscope. The rate of

such discharge soon became a quantitative measure of the intensity of radioactivity. Using such
simple equipment as fluorescent screens to observe
scintillations (the short flashes of light produced
by the impact of alpha, beta, and gamma parti-
cles† on a fluorescent screen) and electroscopes,
Rutherford and his students deduced that the
charge on the alpha particle was numerically
about twice as large as that on the beta particle.
Since the deflection of the alpha particles was
much less than that of the beta particles, he deduced that the former were more massive. Today
we know that alpha particles are helium nuclei
($_2He^4$) and that beta particles are fast electrons.
In 1900, Paul Villard (1860–1934) discovered a
third set of rays, which were not deflected by the
magnetic field. They are called *gamma* (γ) *rays*.
We know today that they are a form of electromagnetic radiation similar to *x*-rays, but more
energetic; they have wavelengths in the range

† It is customary to speak of alpha *particles* and of
gamma *rays*. We shall see later (Chaps. 49 and 50) that
massive particles in motion have wave-like characteristics
and that electromagnetic (and other) waves have particle-
like characteristics. Because of this wave-particle duality,
we may speak of alpha, beta, and gamma radiations as
particles or as waves.

TABLE 47.2
Natural Radioactivity

Particle	Charge ($-e$ is the electronic charge)	Mass on atomic-mass scale (u^a)	Nature
α	$+2e$	4.00151	Helium nucleus ($_2He^4$)
β	$-e$	0.000549	Fast electron
γ	0	0	Similar to *x*-ray

^{a} Unified atomic mass units.

from 10^{-4} to 1 A. Table 47.2 shows the basic
properties of the particles (rays) found in natural
radioactivity.

The source of these new radiations was the
subject of much speculation, but one thing was
certain: the atomic changes involved were drastic.
Rutherford actually collected alpha particles by
allowing them to enter a glass chamber through a
thin foil for a long time. When he examined the
spectrum of the electrical discharge produced in
this particle gas, he found the spectrum of helium,
thus proving conclusively that alpha particles are

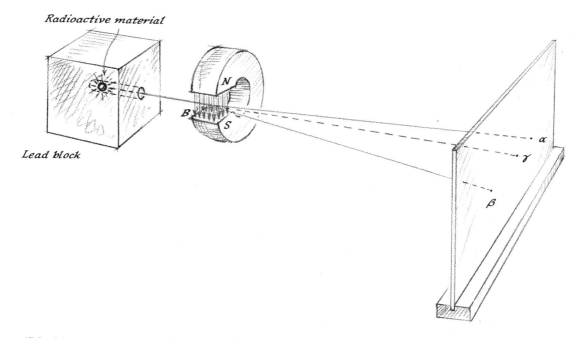

FIG. 47.9. *Magnetic separation of alpha and beta rays; the gamma rays are not deflected by the magnetic field.*

helium nuclei. The parent atoms had disintegrated and produced helium nuclei as offspring.

Transmutation takes place when an atom disintegrates, or—as we also say—undergoes **radioactive decay.** An atom emits a radioactive product *once* and thereby becomes an atom of a different species. Before an atom disintegrates, there is nothing about it to suggest that it is abnormal. It behaves chemically and otherwise like all other atoms of its kind. Its death is a spontaneous and unpredictable event; statistically, however, one can predict the average behavior of a large aggregate of radioactive atoms.

The discrete nature of disintegrations can be seen in a simple way. The luminous quality of some watch dials is due to spontaneous disintegration. To see it, you need to let your eyes become adapted to darkness by waiting in a very dark room for about ten minutes. A luminous watch dial (of the proper kind), viewed under tenfold magnification, then looks like a field of stars each of which gives one single flash and dies.

It is significant that all elements with atomic numbers greater than 83 are radioactive. We shall study them later.

47.7. Summary

Relative atomic weights of the elements found in nature were first measured by the chemists, who actually weighed known samples very carefully. Much later the absolute mass of atomic particles was measured by deflection of charged particles in electric and magnetic fields. In this way it was discovered that some atoms (isotopes) of the same chemical species have different weights.

In 1961 the international unions of physics and chemistry agreed to use the carbon isotope $_6C^{12}$ as a standard and gave it, arbitrarily, the mass 12.

Radioactivity was discovered soon after the discovery of x-rays, and both have played important practical and theoretical roles ever since. X-rays, for example, when used to measure the distance between atoms in crystals, made it possible to determine the Avogadro constant.

Nuclear physicists are concerned with precise values of the masses of atomic nuclei and their constituents. This knowledge is fundamental both in the practical applications of nuclear energy and in the development of a theory of nuclear structure.

Problems

47.1. Compute, in kilograms, the mass of a single molecule of water to as many significant figures as possible from a knowledge of atomic weights and the Avogadro constant. (See Appendix F.)

47.2. An x-ray tube with a copper target puts out a very strong monochromatic line of wavelength λ. When x-rays are reflected from parallel planes of a rock salt crystal for which $d = 2.814$ A, the first-order ($n = 1$) Bragg reflection is observed at 14° 10′.

1. What is the wavelength, λ, in angstroms?

2. At what angle will the second-order reflection take place?

47.3. With the apparatus of Fig. 47.8 the speed of the neon ions depends on where ionization takes place. If it occurs near the anode, *A*, the ion picks up a lot of speed before entering *H*. If the ion is formed near *H*, it can't pick up as much speed before entering *H*.

1. Will all positive ions, fast and slow, land at the same point, *P*, when both **E** and **B** are zero?

2. Let **B** = 0; **E** is constant but not zero. Where will slow (fast) positive ions land?

3. Let **E** = 0; **B** is constant but not zero. Where will slow (fast) positive ions land?

4. Let both **E** and **B** be constant but not zero. Where will slow (fast) positive ions land?

47.4. 1. The ions of Prob. 47.3 land on a parabola whose equation is

$$y^2 = \frac{eB^2}{2mE} x$$

Describe the effect of a small value of *m* on the shape of the parabola.

2. Reconcile part 1 with Fig. 47.8.

47.5. In Fig. 47.8 we drew curves for neon atoms that had each lost one electron. What kind of curves would have resulted for neon atoms that had each lost two electrons? Using the equation of Prob. 47.4, try to sketch both sets of curves roughly.

48

Rutherford's Nuclear Atom

THE KIND of mental picture you have of atoms and molecules depends on the kind of experiments you have done or read about. To explain the gas laws, for example, you imagine molecules as hard elastic spheres moving about at random. To explain crystal structure, you imagine the atoms, no longer as moving about with complete freedom, but as more or less fixed in relation to one another. To explain electrolysis, electrostatic effects, and electric current, you imagine that atoms can be deprived of their electrons and that these can travel right through the empty spaces in solids, liquids, and gases under the action of an electric field.

With the discovery of natural radioactivity (1896) and the identification of alpha particles as helium nuclei by Lord Rutherford (1909), the time was ripe for speculation about atomic structure. The striking consequence of the atomic disintegrations that produced alpha particles was that one element had been transmuted into another: helium, though quite different from radium, had been produced by radium's natural disintegration.

The hazy picture of an atom that had emerged by 1910 was something like this: An atom was small (about 1 A in radius) and behaved, up to a certain point, like a hard, impenetrable, elastic body. It was electrically neutral, but electrons could be removed from it, leaving it positive. Some atoms were unstable and disintegrated spontaneously, giving off positively charged alpha and negatively charged beta particles.

What kind of atom do you have to imagine to explain all these facts? One important question, in particular, confronted Rutherford: How is charge distributed within the atom? Since the atom is electrically neutral, positive and negative charges must somehow be in equilibrium within it, but what are their relative positions?

48.1. The Distribution of Charge Within the Atom

J. J. Thomson, whose ingenious experiments with electric and magnetic fields had revealed the ratio of charge to mass, both for electrons and for charged atoms, proposed the hypothesis that positive and negative charges were more or less evenly distributed throughout the body of the atom. The electrons were like plums distributed throughout an otherwise positive plum pudding (Fig. 48.1.A). Rutherford held a different view, which stemmed from his observations on the scattering of alpha particles.† He was led to conceive the atom as mostly empty space except for

† A nuclear-atom model was proposed by O. O. Nagaoka seven years before Rutherford's historic paper of 1911. He even discussed its application to atomic phenomena, but Rutherford gets all the credit in the literature because, being in the main stream of advancing atomic science, he stimulated other scientists to follow up his ideas.

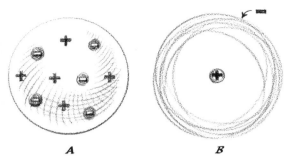

FIG. 48.1. *J. J. Thomson's model (A), and Rutherford's model (B), of the atom.*

a hard core containing almost all of the mass and all of the positive charge, with electrons distributed outside (Fig. 48.1.B).

Let us go back to our early consideration of particles and waves used as probes. In a dark cave you can pick up a stone and throw it into the unknown space ahead. If by chance you hit a stalactite, the stone may bounce back, indicating that something hard lies ahead. The return speed of the stone tells you something about the nature of what it hit; after all, stones thrown into a sand pile don't bounce back. Or you may yell into the darkness and hear an echo. In either case, the nature of the unknown region is revealed, in part, by the way it interacts with the particles and waves thrown into it.

The atomic particles that Rutherford had at his command for exploration were the fast alpha particles expelled in radioactive disintegrations. He had observed that alpha particles can darken a photographic film. He noticed, in fact, that a beam of alpha particles going through a rectangular slit would expose a rectangular area on a photographic plate; unless the experiment was done in a good vacuum, however, the edges of the image were blurred. Even with a good vacuum, the blurring appeared if a thin sheet of mica was placed over the aperture, suggesting that the mica made the alpha particles swerve away from a straight line as they went through it. Knowing that the alpha particles, compared with other atomic particles, had tremendous momentum, Rutherford began to wonder what kind of force could possibly deviate them in the slight thickness

of a mica sheet. Inasmuch as alpha particles are electrically charged and can be deflected by an electric field, the idea that the force was due to an electric field of extraordinary strength was probably born right there.

48.2. The Experiments of Geiger and Marsden

With Hans Geiger, then one of his students, Rutherford set out to find a way to count alpha particles. About this time, Erich Regener, at the University of Berlin, had discovered that an alpha particle, when it lands on a zinc sulphide screen, produces a momentary flash of light—a scintillation that can be clearly observed under a microscope by dark-adapted eyes.

The spectacular aspect of this phenomenon is that it makes visible a single, isolated, atomic event. If the rate at which alpha particles hit the screen is low enough, you can count the number of arrivals per unit of time. Because the scintillation can be seen under a microscope, it can be localized not only in time but in space as well. You know both when and where the alpha particle lands on the screen. Its arrival there is truly an *event* in the operational sense (see § 7.2).

Rutherford was quick to exploit this method for his investigations. He set Geiger to doing the experiment shown schematically in Figure 48.2.A. A radioactive source at *A* produced a beam of alpha particles, which traveled approximately along the axis of an evacuated glass tube and whose divergence was limited by a slit at the exit of the cylinder holding the source and by a rectangular slit in a metallic plate, *B*. Ignoring *C* for the moment, we see that the alpha particles that got through *B* would cause a zinc sulphide screen, *D*, to fluoresce. The fluorescence was intermittent, consisting of scintillations. They were viewed by a dark-adapted eye through a low-power microscope, *E*. From the data on frequency and position a graph of intensity (scintillations per second per unit interval on the *x* axis) was plotted (Fig. 48.2.B). The result was like curve I. The insertion of a very thin gold (or silver or copper) foil, *C*, made some of the alpha particles swerve from their straight path. Those

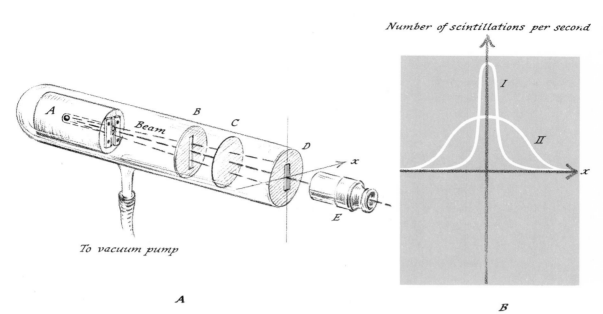

FIG. 48.2. *The Rutherford-Geiger experiment.*

that swerved to the left and to the right broadened the base of the graph as shown (exaggerated) by curve II. The deflections due to the presence of foil *C* were small (less than a degree), and many of the particles were deflected.

Ernest Marsden, then an undergraduate at Cambridge, was asked to arrange an experiment that would show if alpha particles could bounce off thin foils. The apparatus he set up under Geiger's direction is shown schematically in Figure 48.3. Most of the alpha particles originating in a radioactive source at *A* went through the foil, *B*, but some were deflected (the term "scattered" is also used) through a large angle and produced scintillations, *C*, on the fluorescent coating of a glass plate, *F*, which was observed through a microscope. The lead block, *P*, prevented alpha particles from going directly from the source to the screen. Note that what was observed was *not* a specular reflection of particles.

Because he had observed only a slight deflection of particles going through the foil of Figure 48.2.A, Geiger did not really expect to observe any wide deflection; but, when he and Marsden turned out the lights and looked at the fluorescent screen (Fig. 48.3), they saw, to their great surprise, an occasional scintillation. They later calculated that about one in every 8,000 alpha particles hitting the foil was widely deflected. They tried many variations of the experiment, and they found, for example, that the number of alpha particles widely deflected increased as they added to the number of foils placed one behind another. The probability of deflection was increased by an increase in the thickness of foil; alpha particles that penetrated one foil had some chance of being deflected by the next.

All these observations were reported to Rutherford, who, of course, sought to explain the apparent contradiction posed by the very slight deflections of Figure 48.2 and the much greater deflections observed for the first time in the experiment of Figure 48.3. His surprise at the wide-angle deflection, or "back scattering," of alpha particles from gold foils can be summarized in his own words: "It is just as surprising as if a gunner fired a shell at a single piece of paper and for some reason or other the projectile bounded back again." His idea of a nuclear atom emerged from this study.

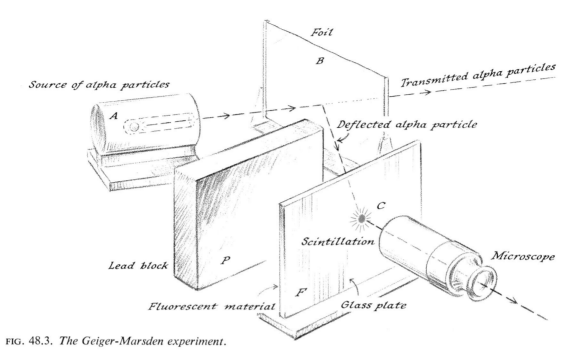

FIG. 48.3. *The Geiger-Marsden experiment.*

48.3. Rutherford's Explanation of the Scattering of Alpha Particles

Rutherford came to the conclusion that the space within the atoms of the foil was mostly empty. Hence most of the alpha particles went through without deviation. Within each atom, however, was a small, dense core, the positively charged nucleus, which had most of the mass of the atom. It was so small that a direct hit was very rare.

Alpha particles that happen to come close to this positively charged nucleus experience a strong repulsive force. The charge on the alpha particle is $+2e$, and the charge on the nucleus of the atom in the foil is $+Ze$ (Z being the atomic number and e the electronic charge). The coulombic repulsive force is therefore given by the expression

$$F = K\frac{(2e)(Ze)}{r^2} \qquad [48.1$$

in which r is the distance between the alpha particle and the nucleus, and K is the constant of proportionality that appears in equation 36.1.

If the nucleus of the foil atom is much more massive than the alpha particle, it can be considered as remaining at rest during the collision. The alpha particle then moves in a hyperbolic path with the nucleus at one focus. Except for the fact that the electrical force is repulsive instead of attractive, the situation is very similar to that of a comet moving in the gravitational field of the sun.

Since the days of Newton it has been known that the path of a particle moving under the influence of a central inverse-square force is a conic section (parabola, hyperbola, ellipse, or circle; see Fig. 34.8). The planets move in elliptical paths round the sun. A comet, however, may have a hyperbolic path with the sun at one focus; and, similarly, even though the force is repulsive, an alpha particle follows a hyperbolic path with the nucleus of the target atom at one focus. If the paths of several different alpha particles repelled by a heavy nucleus are all drawn in the same picture, the result is somewhat like Figure 48.4. The particles that approach the center of repulsion closely are scattered vigorously, but many more are scattered forward than backward.

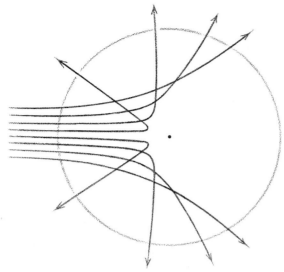

FIG. 48.4. *A set of hyperbolic paths for alpha particles approaching the center of a nucleus at different distances.*

A hyperbola is characterized by a pair of lines called the *asymptotes*, to which the curve gets closer and closer as the distance from the focus increases. In all three parts of Figure 48.5 the lines AB and CD are the asymptotes of a hyperbola, one branch of which is shown (PQR). Imagine the nucleus of the target atom at focus F_2. The alpha particle, while still far away, approaches

the nucleus along the line AB. Since AB does not pass through F_2, the alpha particle, as it approaches the nucleus, feels a repulsive force that pushes it to one side and away. Point Q marks its nearest approach to the nucleus. The distance from Q to F_2 depends on the distance, b (the **impact parameter**), between AB and F_2. (For a well-aimed alpha particle b has a very small value.) The alpha particle departs along side QR of the branch, becoming more and more nearly parallel to CD. Since the distance QF_2 turns out to be much less than the distance between the detector and the source of the alpha particles, the particle behaves as if it had come in on line AB and departed on line CD, having been deflected in its direction through angle θ. As b gets smaller, θ approaches 180°, but head-on collisions are very rare. The fact that alpha particles can move in different hyperbolic paths, which depend on their original aim (smaller b means better aim), is illustrated in Figure 48.5.

The calculations for a head-on collision are simple and very instructive. In this case the alpha particle is slowed down until it comes to rest at distance d from the nucleus, and then it starts going back. Its initial kinetic energy, $\frac{1}{2}mv^2$, is all converted to electrical potential energy (Kq_1q_2/d, equation 37.1), at the point of closest approach. (Compare the expression for force, equation 48.1.)

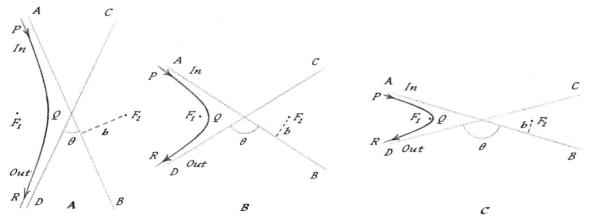

FIG. 48.5. *Three of the hyperbolic paths of Fig. 48.4 drawn with their asymptotes. The nucleus is at focus F_2 of the hyperbola. The deflection increases as the impact parameter, b, gets smaller.*

Hence

$$\frac{1}{2} mv^2 = \frac{K(2e)(Ze)}{d} \qquad [48.2$$

$$d = \frac{4KZe^2}{mv^2} \qquad [48.3$$

Rutherford knew that alpha particles from the particular radioactive source he was using had a speed of about 2.0×10^7 m/sec. Tabulating this and other quantities to put into equation 48.3, we have

$$K = 9 \times 10^9 \text{ nt-m}^2/\text{coul}^2$$

$$Z = 79 \text{ (atomic number of gold)}$$

$$e = 1.602 \times 10^{-19} \text{ coul}$$

$$m = 6.65 \times 10^{-27} \text{ kg}$$

$$v^2 = 4 \times 10^{14} \text{ m}^2/\text{sec}^2$$

It follows that

$$d = \frac{4 \times 9 \times 10^9 \times 79 \times 2.56 \times 10^{-38}}{6.65 \times 10^{-27} \times 4 \times 10^{14}} \text{ m}$$

$$= 2.74 \times 10^{-14} \text{ m}$$

This result is noteworthy, for it is about 3×10^{-4} times the estimated diameter of an atom (10^{-10} m). Before being deflected through 180°, an alpha particle can get as close as d to the center of a nucleus! It would be tempting to conclude that the radius of a nucleus is shorter than 2.74×10^{-14} m; but, for all we know, the nucleus is made of soft repulsive stuff, and the alpha particle sinks into it, gets slowed down, stops, and comes bouncing out again. All we may really conclude is that the alpha particle runs into an adverse field that is conservative in nature. Like a comet going inside the solar system, the alpha particle, if it does get inside a nucleus, does not bump into anything that takes away its energy. If, on the other hand, we draw conclusions from the whole range of angular distribution of alpha particles, as Rutherford did, we are on safer ground in considering 2.7×10^{-14} m the upper limit of the nuclear radius, for it is unlikely that the observed results could mean anything but free and unimpeded flight under inverse-square repulsion.

Rutherford concentrated his attention on the mathematical formulation of the general problem of the particles that are not deflected through 180°. First (Fig. 48.6) he arrived at a mathemat-

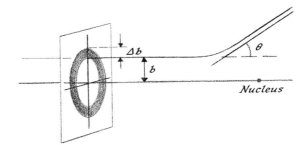

FIG. 48.6. *All the alpha particles with impact parameters* b *experience deflection* θ. *In practice, all those having impact parameters between* b *and* b + Δb *experience deflections between* θ *and* θ + Δθ. *See also Fig. 48.7.*

ical expression connecting the variable b and the angle, θ, through which the alpha particle is deflected. His analysis next involved consideration of the fraction of particles that approached with impact parameters between b and $b + \Delta b$. From this he deduced a formula showing what fraction of the incoming alpha particles would be deflected between two angles, $\theta' = \theta + \Delta\theta$ and θ.

The confirming experiment set up a detector by which one could count scintillations and thus determine what fraction of the incoming alpha particles were deflected through angles between θ and θ' (Fig. 48.7). The initial results of Geiger and Marsden convinced Rutherford that his analysis was essentially correct. He had *proved* that the atom has a small positive nucleus that is thousands of times smaller than the whole atom. He wrote a theoretical paper summarizing his views, sent it to the *Philosophical Magazine*, and went about other investigations.

After their initial report, Geiger and Marsden conscientiously set about checking every detail of Rutherford's scattering formula. James Chadwick did similar experiments later and was able to deduce experimental values of Z for different foils:

PLATINUM	SILVER	COPPER
77.4	46.3	29.3

For these the periodic table now lists the atomic numbers

78	47	29

The agreement between experimental results and tabular values confirms in a striking way the validity of Rutherford's mathematical analysis. The circumstantial evidence soon reached such proportions that for physicists everywhere the nuclear atom became a reality.

In our discussion the interactions between alpha particles and electrons have been neglected because the energy losses involved are negligible. (See Prob. 48.5.)

48.4. Chadwick's Discovery of the Neutron

Perhaps by now you are reconciled to accepting, on circumstantial evidence, the reality of atomic particles. The mass of an alpha particle is only about 6.65×10^{-27} kg, but fast alpha particles can ionize gases, darken a photographic film, trip Geiger counters, produce scintillations on a fluorescent screen, and generate visible tracks in a cloud chamber. Electrons are 1,800 times less massive, but they too can do all these things. If you were in search of an atomic particle that could not do any of these things, how could you prove it existed?

The neutron is such a particle, and the story of its discovery has some of the excitement of a mystery novel.† It was not found until 1932, but I shall tell something about it here for two rea-

† For a good account of this discovery see Donald J. Hughes, *The Neutron Story* (Garden City, N.Y., 1959), an Anchor paperback.

sons. One is that the discoverer, James Chadwick, has already been mentioned among those who followed Rutherford's lead in using alpha particles to bombard matter and learn its secrets. The other is that, though we can account for the nucleus of the simplest atom, hydrogen, by saying it is simply a proton, the very next atom (except for isotopes of hydrogen such as deuterium) in the order of increasing complexity, helium, has a positive charge of two units but a mass of four units. Two protons would explain the charge of the helium nucleus, or alpha particle, but not its mass of four units.

For a while a combination of four protons and two electrons was imagined. It would have a positive charge of two units, and its mass would be right; but, for reasons yet to be stated, the electron is now thought to be too large to reside in any nucleus. The existence of a neutral particle about as massive as a proton was considered a possibility as soon as the charge and mass of the alpha particle were known, but the very fact that it was uncharged would make it difficult to detect. All the methods of detecting electrons and alpha particles work because those particles are charged. They interact with the electric fields that surround the constituents of atoms. An uncharged body like the neutron, on the other hand, can go right through matter because it is unaffected by the electric fields surrounding electrons and protons.

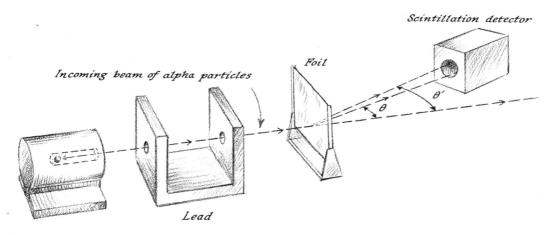

FIG. 48.7. *Schematic diagram of a typical Rutherford scattering experiment. The counter is able to pick up particles scattered through angles between θ and θ'.*

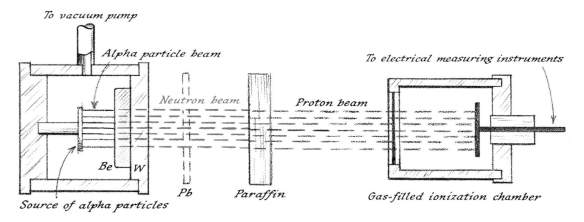

FIG. 48.8. *Chadwick's discovery of the neutron.*

The situation of the neutron just after Rutherford was somewhat analogous to the situation of the x-ray just before Röntgen. As we have seen, many investigators had Crookes tubes and had unwittingly generated x-rays with them, but it took Röntgen to follow the clues and give the right explanations. Similarly, there must have been many investigators playing with alpha particles and unwittingly producing neutrons after Rutherford's discovery, but it took Chadwick to trace the elusive neutron to its source.

One of the reasons why many investigators were engaged in bombarding matter with alpha particles was the idea of **transmutation,** the changing of one element into another. Not only do transmutations take place spontaneously, as in natural radioactivity, but by 1919 Rutherford had bombarded nitrogen with alpha particles and converted it into oxygen. Protons ($_1H^1$) were knocked out and detected by magnetic deflection. The reaction may be written as

$$_2He^4 + {_7}N^{14} \longrightarrow (_9F^{18}) \longrightarrow {_8}O^{17} + {_1}H^1$$

The bombardment of nitrogen ($_7N^{14}$) with alpha particles ($_2He^4$) yields fluorine, which disintegrates at once into an intermediate, unstable isotope of oxygen ($_8O^{17}$) and a proton ($_1H^1$).

In 1930, in Germany, W. Bothe and H. Becker discovered that, when alpha particles were allowed to hit the metal beryllium, a very penetrating radiation was produced, which manifested itself by ejecting high-energy protons from paraffin. It could go right through several inches of lead. If the new rays were gamma rays, as was at first thought, they were more penetrating than the most penetrating gamma rays known until then. Bothe and Becker were unable to identify the radiation. It was left for Chadwick to discover the neutron.

The experimental set-up developed by Chadwick is shown schematically in Figure 48.8. He proposed this explanation: The alpha particles hit the beryllium nuclei and produce a neutral particle—the neutron—of atomic mass 1 and zero charge. Being neutral, the neutron can pass through the wall, W, and even through a sheet of lead, *Pb*. The neutron, upon hitting a proton (hydrogen nucleus) in the paraffin, transfers all of its kinetic energy to it. The protons emerging from the paraffin, being charged particles, are detected in the ionization chamber. This explanation accounted for all the observed facts. The effect of the alpha particles on the beryllium may be written as

$$_4Be^9 + {_2}He^4 \longrightarrow {_6}C^{12} + {_0}n^1$$

Here $_0n^1$ stands for the neutron, a particle of mass number 1 and zero charge (and hence atomic number zero). The fact that it is uncharged gives the neutron its great penetrating power. The fact that its atomic mass is 1 means that in a collision with a proton it can give the proton its kinetic energy. (When two billiard balls collide elastically, the first ball stops dead and transmits all its momentum to the second ball *if the masses of the two balls are identical.* See § 31.6.)

Observe that the sum of the subscripts 4 and 2 on the left side is equal to the sum of the subscripts 6 and 0 on the right. This simply says that charge is conserved. Similarly, the sum of the superscripts 9 and 4 on the left equals the sum of 12 and 1 on the right. This says that mass is conserved, but the statement is only approximate; slight deviations from these integral values account for the observed energy changes, which, considered along with the energy associated with mass, must yield a perfect balance.

A curious aspect of Chadwick's solution is that, by resorting to the crudest model imaginable for the hydrogen nucleus, an elastic sphere, he got the right answers.

When we first considered the atom, in our study of kinetic theory, we regarded it as an elastic sphere, and we got reasonable results as long as the energy involved did not disrupt the atom—and it did not if it was less than a few electron volts per atom. Now in our first look at the nucleus we may regard it too as an elastic sphere—but with a radius almost 10,000 times as short as that of the atom. Instead of the few electron volts per atom that it takes to disrupt (ionize)

atoms, it takes energy of almost a million electron volts per nucleus to disrupt nuclei. The first hint of such great energy came from analysis of the kinetic energies of the alpha and beta particles ejected by radioactive atoms.

For his discovery Chadwick was awarded the Nobel Prize for Physics in 1935. Many other atomic particles have been discovered since, but no one now doubts that the main constituents of the nucleus are protons and neutrons.

48.5. Summary

The results of experiments on the scattering of alpha particles by thin metal foils convinced Rutherford that the nucleus of the atom is a positively charged hard core whose diameter is approximately 1/10,000 of that of the atom.

Chadwick's discovery of the neutron, an electrically neutral particle whose mass is about that of a proton, added the missing link to an explanation of the mass and the charge of nuclei. Their charge comes from protons, but both protons and neutrons contribute to their mass.

The way was now clear to accounting for the over-all neutrality of the atom by imagining enough electrons surrounding the nucleus to balance its positive charge.

Problems

48.1. Copy the table below on a sheet of paper. In column 1 are listed some of the properties that particles may have. By writing YES or NO in each of the empty spaces, indicate whether the particle named does, in fact, have the property mentioned. If you know a formula and a numerical value, insert them. If in doubt, enter a question mark now, and amend the table later.

	PROTON	ELECTRON	NEUTRON	PHOTON
Rest mass				
Charge				
Energy				
Linear momentum				
Angular momentum				
Size				

48.2. Gold has the atomic number 79 and the mass number 197. How many protons and how many neutrons comprise the gold nucleus?

48.3. 1. Could alpha-particle experiments of the type illustrated in Fig. 48.7 work with tungsten instead of gold? Name some practical difficulty that might be encountered.

2. What would be the closest approach to a head-on collision for alpha particles whose speed was 2.0×10^7 m/sec?

3. If, on very close approach, the coulombic repulsion were weakened by a short-range attractive force, would you expect your calculated answer to be more or less than the actual value? Explain.

48.4. 1. An alpha particle is fired at a gold nucleus with a speed of 1.9×10^7 m/sec and an impact parameter of 2×10^{-14} m. Calculate the angular momentum of the particle with respect to an axis through the gold nucleus. [Hint: See § 33.2. Note that $\mathbf{r} \times \mathbf{p} = (r \sin \theta)mv = bmv$.]

2. Does the hyperbolic orbit allow conservation of angular momentum? Assume the gold nucleus to be fixed in position. (Hint: Observe that both asymptotes are at distance b from the focus.)

3. The actual distance of closest approach of this alpha particle is d. From the conservation of angular momentum find an expression for the speed, v', of the particle at this point in terms of b, d, m, and v. A good diagram will be helpful.

48.5. 1. In a precise analysis of alpha-particle scattering, the recoil of the nucleus ought to be considered. If the alpha particle has an incident speed of 2×10^7 m/sec, what will be its final speed after a head-on elastic collision (see § 31.6) if you assume that the gold nucleus was initially at rest? Use the fact that

$$\frac{\text{mass of gold nucleus}}{\text{mass of helium nucleus}} = \frac{197}{4}$$

2. What fraction of its initial kinetic energy will the alpha particle have lost after impact? [Hint: The argument that leads to equation 31.33 yields $4m_1m_2/(m_1 + m_2)^2$ for the fractional loss.]

3. Is the assumption (made for the purpose of simplification) that the gold nucleus remains at rest a good one?

4. Estimate, in a similar way, what fraction of its original energy an alpha particle would have lost after elastic impact with an electron. (The mass of the alpha particle is about 7,200 times that of an electron.)

48.6. The use of areas in certain computations of probability is illustrated in the following.

1. A circular target has a diameter of 80 cm. The bull's-eye has a diameter of 15 cm. A thousand projectiles, traveling in a straight line normal to the target, are thrown at random to different parts of the target. How many of them, on the average, will hit the bull's-eye? (Hint: Consider the ratio of the area of the bull's-eye to the total area.)

2. In a similar experiment, in which the total number of projectiles is not known, 10 projectiles, on the average, land between two circles of radii 20 and 21 cm. How many, on the average, will land between two circles of radii 70 and 71 cm? [Hint:

$$\pi r_2{}^2 - \pi r_1{}^2 = \pi (r_2 - r_1)(r_2 + r_1) = 2\pi \bar{r}(r_2 - r_1)$$

or, roughly, $2\pi r_1 \Delta r$.]

3. In Rutherford's experiment, the quantity b, known as the impact parameter, measures the distance by which the alpha particle would miss the nucleus if it were undeflected. Obviously, b is a random quantity that may have any value. If, in Fig. 48.6, ten particles per second, on the average, have impact parameters between 1.00×10^{-13} m and 1.01×10^{-13} m, how many per second, on the average, will have impact parameters in the range from 2.00×10^{-13} m to 2.01×10^{-13} m? How many per second in the range from 0.50×10^{-13} m to 0.51×10^{-13} m?

4. If the radius of the gold nucleus is R_N and the radius of the gold atom is R_A, calculate the probability (a fraction less than 1) that an alpha particle entering the atom will have an impact parameter less than R_N. Use the approximate values $R_A = 10^{-10}$ m, $R_N = 10^{-14}$ m.

Particles of Light

WE HAVE considered a lot of evidence to prove that light is a wave: light waves can be reflected, refracted, diffracted, and polarized, and they obey the principle of superposition, as shown by interference. All this was known even before Maxwell demonstrated the electromagnetic character of the waves. And we know that even gamma rays and x-rays are electromagnetic radiations (the Laue experiment proves that they can be diffracted by crystals). As such, they are a form of light and have all the characteristics we attribute to waves. In this chapter, nevertheless, we shall examine some evidence for the *particulate* nature of electromagnetic radiation.

49.1. Particles Without Mass or Charge?

Now that we have met the neutron, a particle with mass but without charge, and the electron, a particle with as much charge as a proton but with very little mass, we are ready to ask: Is there a particle without charge and without mass? If there is such a particle, it will obviously raise semantic problems: after all, can you keep stripping particles of their measurable properties and still claim that they exist as particles?

What is a particle, anyway? So far, it's been something small. That means you can localize it; you can tell where it is and say that it occupies very little space. But the localization has usually involved its interactions with electric and magnetic fields (as in experiments to determine e/m) or its ability to impart momentum to particles that are readily detectable (as when neutrons

give up their momentum to protons, which can be detected because their charge can be measured in an ionization chamber).

In considering the products of natural radioactivity, we came across something that was not deflected by electric or magnetic fields. I called it a gamma ray and said that it was like an energetic x-ray. All attempts to associate charge with gamma rays have failed, but such rays are capable of ejecting electrons from matter, and in doing so they behave like particles. Do gamma rays consist of particles? They do have some of the properties of electrons, alpha particles, and beta particles: they can darken photographic plates, produce fluorescence on a zinc sulphide screen, and discharge an electroscope. We shall see that gamma rays, x-rays, and, in fact, all forms of light, visible and invisible, can transfer momentum as if they consisted of particles; but their charge is zero.

49.2. The Pressure of Light

One of the interesting implications of the electromagnetic theory is that light has *momentum*, which sounds more like the characteristic of a particle than that of a wave. When we think of the classical formula for momentum, mass times velocity, it seems contradictory to say that light has no mass but does have momentum. If you fire bullets at a pendulum in bursts that are in rhythm with its natural frequency, you can start it swinging. Can you push something by shining light on it? Can you impart momentum to a material body by illuminating it? The answer is "Yes." The effect is very small and difficult to detect, but P. N. Lebedev (1900) in Europe and E. F. Nichols and G. F. Hull (1903) in America demonstrated experimentally that you can impart momentum to a body by shining light on it.

The idea that light behaves like a stream of particles is not new in physics. More than three hundred years ago Kepler pointed out that the tails of some comets swerve away from the sun as if the sunlight were pushing them.† Newton's conception of light as corpuscles, or particles, was maintained by his followers until the wave theory's success in explaining diffraction and interference made a corpuscular theory untenable. The severest blow to Newton's corpuscles was delivered by experiments proving that light *slows down* in passing from air to water. (Newton's concept required a *speeding up* if it was to explain

† It is now believed that another stream of particles emitted by the sun, known as the "solar wind," contributes appreciably to this effect.

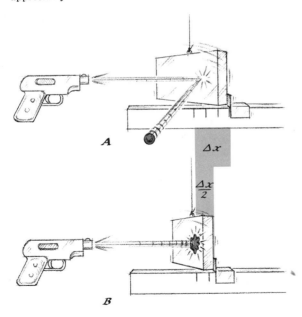

FIG. 49.1. (*A*) *Elastic impact: the block, pushing on the ball, first stops it and then speeds it up on its return flight; the ball, pushing back on the block, produces displacement* Δx *at one edge.* (*B*) *Inelastic impact: the block pushes on the ball enough to stop it; the ball, pushing back on the block, produces displacement* $(\Delta x)/2$ *at one edge.*

the bending of a beam *toward the normal* in passing from air to water (§ 18.3). Although the pressure of light is confirmed by experiment and explained by electromagnetic theory, some other experiments, to be described, will demand a return to the idea of particles.

As an introduction to an experiment that demonstrates the pressure of light, consider first a simple experiment with a toy gun that shoots marbles at a metal block suspended as a torsion pendulum (Fig. 49.1). The impact of a marble causes the edge of the block to move a certain distance, Δx (measured by the displacement of an aluminum rider on a meter stick) when the collision is elastic (A). If we make the collision inelastic by putting a bit of plasticene on the block, so that the marble sticks to it (B), the deflection of the block will be approximately $(\Delta x)/2$. The push exerted by the marble is greater when reflection takes place than when absorption takes place.

This suggests that, if particles of light behave the way marbles do, a very delicate torsion balance in which the block of Figure 49.1 is replaced by a light transverse rod bearing vanes of very light metal foil (Fig. 49.2) will show greater twist when the light hits only the highly reflective shiny-light surface, S, than when the same light hits only the highly absorbent dull-black surface, B. The idea turns out to be experimentally demonstrable, but there are several serious experimental obstacles to be overcome. The most serious is the requirement of an extremely high vacuum,† but modern vacuum technique makes it possible to reach the extremely low pressure needed. The pressure of light can be demonstrated with equipment assembled by an industrious and clever student.‡ If we let light hit one vane of the torsion

† If the vacuum is poor, as it is in the little radiometers that have a pinwheel with vanes that are light-shiny on one side and dull-black on the other (available in optical shops and toy stores), turning takes place when light hits the vanes, but in the sense opposite to that expected with a very high vacuum. The reason is that the air molecules left in the radiometer chamber rebound faster off the dull-black side than off the cooler shiny-light side.

‡ A demonstration of the effect has been filmed. See the motion picture entitled *The Pressure of Light*, produced by Educational Services Incorporated, 104 Main Street, Watertown, Mass.

pendulum in flashes that are timed to reinforce the vane's oscillation, we can build up the amplitude to a magnitude that we can easily measure by observing the deflection of another light beam as it is reflected from a mirror, M, attached to the transverse rod supporting the vanes.

The concept of **energy density** in a region through which light is passing is sometimes useful. If inside a box of volume V there is the amount of energy W, the average energy density is $\overline{w} = W/V$. In MKS units it would be measured in joules per cubic meter. Observe that the units of pressure are equivalent to these. Pressure is force per unit area: $P = F/A$. Multiplying both numerator and denominator by distance Δx, we get

$$P = \frac{F(\Delta x)}{A(\Delta x)}$$

The numerator is work (joules); the denominator is a volume (meters cubed). It is not surprising, therefore (although I have not proved it), that the pressure exerted by a beam of parallel rays is simply

$$P = w \qquad [49.1$$

The pressure is equal to the energy density. This equation was derived in the electromagnetic theory of light, in which light is considered as waves, of course, not as particles, but it is, nevertheless, correct also for particles of light.

In electromagnetic theory it is proved that the total momentum associated with the energy, W, that fills the box mentioned above when a plane wave is going through it is given by the expression W/c, in which c is the speed of light. I shall not prove this, either, but we see that it makes sense dimensionally:

$$[W] = ML^2T^{-2}$$
$$[c] = LT^{-1}$$

Therefore

$$\left[\frac{W}{c}\right] = \frac{ML^2T^{-2}}{LT^{-1}} = MLT^{-1}$$

These are the physical dimensions of momentum. The formulas are correct whether light is a wave or a particle. We pass now to Planck's discovery of the quantum, which revived the idea of light as a particle.

49.3. Planck's Quantum

The most revolutionary idea of modern physics was proposed by a theoretical physicist who was trying to explain the wavelength and intensity of the glow given off by hot bodies. Max Karl Ernst Ludwig Planck (1858–1947) was interested

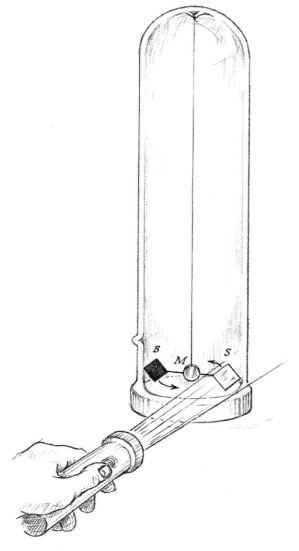

FIG. 49.2. *A delicate torsion balance, in a highly evacuated glass tube, for detecting the pressure of light.*

in the distribution of the energy produced by a hot blackbody. A **blackbody** is a body that absorbs all the radiation that falls on it and therefore looks black when cold. The same body, when heated, can glow. If you were to look through a tiny hole into a large, fiery furnace, the reddish glow you would see would be a pretty good approximation to the visible portion of what is called **blackbody radiation.** In 1900 Planck suggested that radiant energy, instead of being continuous, comes in little bundles, which he called **quanta.** (If the energy is electromagnetic radiation, the quanta are also called **photons;** they are the particles of light we have been seeking.) He had found that, in order to work out a theory that would fit the experimental facts, he had to adopt the radical idea that radiant energy of frequency ν comes in bundles of magnitude $h\nu$—h being a constant of nature now called the **Planck constant** (6.6256×10^{-34} J-sec). For this work Planck was awarded the Nobel Prize for Physics in 1918.

Planck's ideas stimulated other physicists who won the Nobel Prize. Albert Einstein, for example, received the prize in 1921, in part, for his discovery of a quantum explanation of the photoelectric effect, and Arthur Holly Compton received it in 1923 for proving that x-ray photons have momentum. The modern concept of the atom would have been impossible without Planck's quantum. Let us see how the idea of the quantum was developed.

A single-filament electric-light bulb connected to a variable source of potential difference (an autotransformer, for example) exhibits some of the characteristics of a radiating blackbody. As the filament's temperature rises, the filament not only gets brighter but also gets whiter; as the temperature falls, the filament first gets redder, but below a certain temperature no glow is visible: the spectral composition changes with temperature.

The spectrum of the filament can be viewed through a diffraction grating held in the hand. Several graphs of the energy spectrum† are shown in Figure 49.3; the wavelengths involved are

† It is possible to choose units for J_λ so that the areas under the curves of J_λ against λ are proportional to joules per square meter per second.

mostly in the invisible infrared region of the spectrum. Notice that the peaks occur at shorter wavelengths as the temperature rises. At the still higher temperature associated with solar radiation (about 6,000°K), a good portion of the energy is in the visible part of the spectrum, and some of it is in the ultraviolet and x-ray regions (Fig. 49.4), but most of it is in the infrared region beyond 7,000 A. One of the theoretical problems at the beginning of this century was to account for such empirical curves as those of Figures 49.3 and 49.4.

If λ_m is the wavelength at which the greatest amount of radiation is emitted by a blackbody at absolute temperature T, the product $\lambda_m T$ is a constant, A:

$$\lambda_m T = A \qquad [49.2$$

This statement is called **Wien's displacement law** (after Wilhelm Wien, 1864–1928). The term "displacement" refers to the fact that the value of λ at which a maximum occurs is *displaced* toward shorter wavelengths (Figs. 49.3 and 49.4) by a rise in temperature. The symbol A stands for the Wien displacement constant, the value of which is approximately 2.88×10^{-3} m-°K.

Both experiment and theory likewise confirmed the idea that the total power, E, emitted per unit area by a blackbody is proportional to the fourth power of its absolute temperature. We may write, therefore, that

$$E = \sigma T^4 \qquad [49.3$$

This is called the **Stefan-Boltzmann law,** and σ stands for the Stefan-Boltzmann constant, a modern value for which is 5.6687×10^{-8} W-m^{-2}-°K^{-4}. Note that E is measured in joules per square meter per second.

The search for a theoretical formula that would fit the experimental facts of Figure 49.3 was carried on earnestly by Wien and by Lord Rayleigh (John William Strutt, 1842–1919) and Sir James Jeans (1877–1946). They were only partially successful, as shown in Figure 49.5. Wien's formula fit the facts fairly well on the long-wavelength side of the curve. The Rayleigh-Jeans formula was a good approximation only for the very long wavelengths. But the formula evolved by Planck fit all the points very closely.

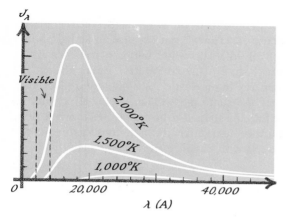

FIG. 49.3. *Graph of radiant energy as a function of wavelength for a blackbody at temperatures corresponding to the infrared.*

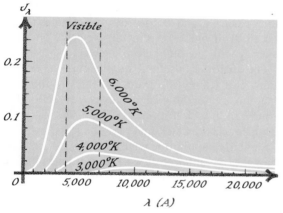

FIG. 49.4. *Graph of radiant energy as a function of wavelength for a blackbody at higher temperatures, including those associated with solar radiation. Some of the wavelengths are in the ultraviolet and x-ray regions.*

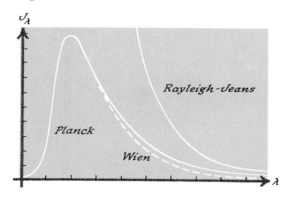

FIG. 49.5. *Graphs of three blackbody-radiation formulas.*

I shall only state Planck's final result and tell briefly what he did to get a formula that worked. Planck's radiation law is stated by the expression

$$J_\lambda = \frac{2\pi c^2 h}{\lambda^5}\left[\frac{1}{e^{ch/\lambda kT}-1}\right] \qquad [49.4$$

in which J_λ is measured in joules per second per square meter per unit wavelength interval. Consider only the dimensionless quantity within brackets. If we use the relation $c/\lambda = \nu$, it becomes

$$\left[\frac{1}{e^{h\nu/kT}-1}\right]$$

If we examine the exponent of e dimensionally, we first notice that kT is a term we encountered in the kinetic theory of gases (§ 29.5 and § 31.7). It is proportional to the average kinetic energy per particle. Therefore $h\nu$ must have units of energy since $h\nu/kT$ must be a pure number.

The revolutionary idea that Planck had to introduce was, as we have seen, that radiant energy of frequency ν comes in the units $h\nu$ and *never* in some fraction of $h\nu$ such as $0.3h\nu$. By introducing this idea he was able to derive equation 49.4, which fits the experimental facts. Planck did not observe particles of light experimentally, but he laid the groundwork for future experiments, and those proved that quanta of radiation must exist.

The Planck constant, h, is approximately 6.63×10^{-34} J-sec. The smallness of this number accounts for the fact that quantum effects show up principally at the atomic level. Let us compute $h\nu$ for light with a wavelength of 5,000 A (which is in the green portion of the visible spectrum). Since $\nu = c/\lambda$, we get

$$\nu = 3\times 10^8 \text{ m/sec} \div 5\times 10^{-7} \text{ m} = 6\times 10^{14} \text{ sec}^{-1}$$

The product $h\nu$ comes out as 3.98×10^{-19} J. Recalling that 1 electron volt is 1.602×10^{-19} J, we see that one photon *of this particular frequency* has an energy of about 2.5 electron volts, which is enough energy to ionize certain atoms. In other words, a photon of green light (about 5,000 A) has enough energy to dislodge a single electron from some kinds of atoms. On a macroscopic scale this is a very small amount of energy (see the inside of the back cover).

Here is how the new words are used: we say that radiant energy is *quantized*; a particle of light (visible or invisible) is called a *photon*; a photon of light of frequency ν carries a quantum of energy of magnitude $h\nu$. It is both interesting and slightly bewildering to find that the formula for the energy of this new particle explicitly exhibits a frequency, ν, which is a characteristic of waves. Similarly, the momentum of the photon, if we use the idea at the end of § 49.2, is $h\nu/c$, which equals h/λ. The momentum of this photon is $(6.63 \times 10^{-34})/(5 \times 10^{-7}) = 1.33 \times 10^{-27}$ kg-m/sec. An investigation of some other experiments may help us to give operational meaning to these new concepts.

49.4. Einstein's Photoelectric Equation

The most direct confirmation of the quantum hypothesis is found in the photoelectric effect. Light shining on metals and other materials is capable of ejecting electrons from them. (It would be good to review § 19.4 at this point.) The ejected electrons come off with energies that depend only on the frequency of the radiation and not on its intensity; the electromagnetic theory, however, states that the energy in a wave depends on its intensity. The experimental facts are, therefore, impossible to reconcile with the electromagnetic theory of light but easy to explain if we assume that light consists of photons—particles that carry energy $h\nu$. Einstein suggested that a photon is capable of giving up all its energy, $h\nu$, to a single electron in the metal. Some of this energy is used in the work, W_0, that it takes to pull the electron out of the metal, and what's left over appears as kinetic energy of the electron. For non-relativistic speeds we may write that

$$h\nu = W_0 + \tfrac{1}{2}mv^2 \qquad [49.5$$

This simple equation explained the rather meager experimental data available to Einstein and was confirmed with great care by Millikan in 1916. (We shall soon see how it made possible an independent determination of the Planck constant, h.)

Consider an analogy to supplement that of the bell-ringer of § 19.4. The spring of a pinball machine (Fig. 49.6) can impart energy $h\nu$ to a white ball, A. (We call it $h\nu$ only in order to carry

over the results of the argument to the real photoelectric experiment, not because an actual photon is involved.) The white ball can roll—ideally, it should slide to avoid rotation—and give up all its energy in an elastic collision with a black ball, B, of the same mass. The black ball climbs up the hill and loses kinetic energy W_0 in work done against conservative and non-conservative forces. It is left with kinetic energy $mv^2/2$ such that

$$h\nu - W_0 = \tfrac{1}{2}mv^2 \qquad [49.6$$

If $h\nu$ is less than W_0, the black ball never gets to the top of the ledge. All energy in excess of $h\nu - W_0$, however, goes into the kinetic energy of the black ball. The equation we have evolved (49.6) is the same as equation 49.5. If we think of the white ball as a photon, the black ball as a photoelectron, and W_0 as the work it takes to get the electron out of the metal, we have a useful analogy with the photoelectric effect.

The analogy is useful if we recognize its limitations. It certainly illustrates graphically the idea that, no matter how many times you shoot the white ball, it will, if its energy, $h\nu$, is less than W_0, *never* knock the black ball over the ledge.

Similarly, a photon whose energy, $h\nu$, is less than W_0 (the amount of work that it takes to free an electron from the forces that bind it to the material) will not eject an electron; and, if $h\nu$ exceeds W_0, the excess, $h\nu - W_0$, appears as kinetic energy, $mv^2/2$, of the ejected photoelectron.

With apparatus such as that shown very schematically in Figure 49.7, the photoelectric properties of an emitter of photoelectrons can be studied. Through a quartz window, Q, visible and ultraviolet light from a source, S, outside

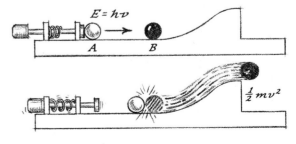

FIG. 49.6. *A pinball model for the photoelectric effect.*

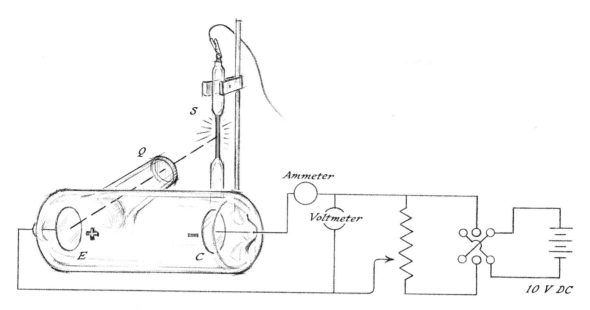

FIG. 49.7. *Apparatus for studying photoelectric properties.*

the evacuated chamber can reach the emitter, E. If electrode C is at a negative potential in relation to E, it will repel the photoelectrons emitted by E. If the voltage across EC is V, the work done on an electron moving from E to C is eV. If we increase the magnitude of V (for a fixed frequency, ν), we reach a value (measured with a voltmeter) at which the fastest electrons are halted, and the current through the ammeter therefore approaches zero. Let us call this value the stopping potential, V_s. The work done in bringing such an electron to a halt is eV_s. This must be equal to the kinetic energy of the most energetic photoelectron emitted at that frequency. The photoelectric equation therefore becomes

$$h\nu - W_0 = eV_s \qquad [49.7$$

This is a first-degree equation in ν and V_s. Its plot is a straight line (Fig. 49.8). Experiments have shown that the data obtained from repetitions of the experiment for different values of ν, and hence of V_s, do lie on such a line. Note that, when V_s is zero, $h\nu = W_0$. The slope of this line is h/e. (In analytic geometry the equation $y = mx + b$ represents a line whose slope is m. Writing equation 49.7 in the form

$$V_s = \frac{h}{e}\nu + \frac{-W_0}{e}$$

we recognize that h/e plays the role of the slope, m.) Therefore, knowing e and the experimental value of the slope, we can solve for h. By this means investigators have got values of h that agree with other determinations of the Planck constant.

Thus, by making the bold assumption that light comes in particles each of which is capable

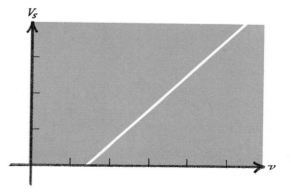

FIG. 49.8. *Plot of stopping potential, V_s, against frequency, ν, of the light.*

of giving up its entire energy to a single electron, Einstein was able to explain quantitatively all the then observed characteristics of the photoelectric effect.

As we might expect, moving S farther away (Fig. 49.7) reduces the intensity of the light at E. This means that the number of photons landing on E each second is reduced and hence that the number of electrons emitted by E each second is reduced also. But, even in very weak light, the graph of Figure 49.8 remains the same. In other words, the energy, $h\nu$, of the individual photons is not altered by a change in the intensity of the beam.

Now a word of warning: do not take the analogy of Figure 49.6 literally. It gives some of the right qualitative and quantitative answers, but you should not imagine a photon as a little ball that preserves its identity after it gives up its energy. Photons are a strange kind of particle. They are created easily in large numbers (when you light a candle, for example), and they vanish when their energy is absorbed (when they land on dull black paper, for example). You would have to imagine that the white ball disappeared when it struck the black ball in Figure 49.6.

I began § 49.1 by asking: Is there a particle without charge and without mass? I have just been talking about one—the photon. The energy and momentum relations cited in § 49.2 are, in fact, true only for particles of zero rest mass.

This is only the beginning of the new world of particles that atomic physics forces upon us. Don't be dismayed by the apparent contradiction in the statement "Waves are particles." A reconciliation will be effected when we explore the evidence for the statement "Particles are waves."

49.5. Summary

In the development of a successful theory of blackbody radiation, Planck was led to the extraordinary conclusion that light comes in discrete quanta whose value is $h\nu$—ν being the frequency of the light and h the constant that now bears his name.

Einstein later explained the ability of light to eject electrons from metals by treating light as a stream of particles each carrying energy $h\nu$. Since then many experiments have confirmed the belief that light consists of particles, called photons, whose rest mass and charge are zero. They carry energy and momentum, which they can share in collisions with other particles.

The extremely small numerical value of the Planck constant, 6.6256×10^{-34} J-sec, helps to explain why the granularity of light usually passes unnoticed. Light of ordinary intensities involves so many photons that their effects seem continuous.

Problems

49.1. 1. List all of the evidence you can think of for the wave nature of light.

2. List the evidence presented in this chapter for the particle nature of light.

49.2. Compare the energy and momentum of a quantum of yellow-green light ($\lambda = 5,500$ A) with the energy and momentum of (A) a raindrop that has fallen freely for 3 m, (B) of a hard-thrown baseball.

49.3. 1. The wavelength at which the sun emits the most energy is about 5,000 A. Using Wien's displacement law, calculate the temperature of the sun, assuming it to radiate like a blackbody (actually a fairly good assumption).

2. The star Pleione has a temperature of about 10,000°K. At what wavelength does it emit the most energy?

3. If a star is hot enough, most of its radiation lies in the ultraviolet region and beyond, and so it is not visible through the earth's atmosphere. At what temperature must a star be if it emits the most energy at 2,000 A?

49.4. 1. The intensity of sunlight on the earth (the solar constant) is 495 J/m²/sec. Calculate the pressure of sunlight (in nt/m²) on the earth at a point where the sun is overhead, assuming that all the sunlight is absorbed.

2. What is the total force exerted on the earth by sunlight? (For this calculation it is satisfactory to replace the earth by a disk of the same radius, the plane of which is at right angles to the direction of the sun.)

49.5. 1. The temperature of the sun is 5,785° K, and its radius is 6.96×10^8 m. Calculate from the Stefan-Boltzmann law the total amount of energe radiated per second by the sun.

2. All of the energy emitted by the sun per unit time interval must cross an imaginary sphere, the radius of which is that of the earth's orbit. Calculate how far the sun is from the earth if the power that reaches the earth before absorption by the atmosphere is 1,374 W/m².

49.6. Light incident on an aluminum surface ejects photoelectrons. The energy of the photoelectrons is then measured by means of a stopping potential, as described in the text illustrated by Fig. 49.7. In a typical experiment the following data are obtained:

Stopping Potential, V_s	Frequency of Light
0.90 V	9.57×10^{14} sec⁻¹
1.30	11.22
1.50	11.82
1.90	13.05
2.30	15.00

Draw a graph of these data, and use it to obtain (A) a value for the Planck constant, h; (B) the binding energy, W_0, of an electron in metallic aluminum.

49.7. 1. Give the MKS units for each physical quantity in equation 49.4.

2. Deduce the MKS units for J_λ.

49.8. The function

$$y = \left(\frac{1}{x^5}\right)\left(\frac{1}{8^{1/x} - 1}\right)$$

has many of the features of equation 49.4. Plot y against x for $x = 0.125, 0.25, 0.5, 1.0, 2.0, 3.0$. Tabulate values of x, $1/x^5$, $1/(8^{1/x} - 1)$, and y in four separate columns. Compare your results with those of the graphs of Figs. 49.3 and 49.4.

49.9. A laser can generate light whose power for a short time is 1 megawatt. It can be focused on a spot whose area is 10^{-12} m² (1 micron × 1 micron). What is the radiation pressure at such a spot? (Hint: In 1 sec all the energy in a rectangular box with a base of area A and an altitude of magnitude c will pass through the base.)

49.10. Using the method of Prob. 49.4, calculate the total force due to sunlight on the Echo II satellite, which is a sphere of diameter 33 m. Assuming that the mass of the satellite is 100 kg and its altitude 100 mi, calculate also the gravitational force on it, and compare this with the force due to sunlight. Does the latter contribute an appreciable effect? (Use the value for the sun's power that applies outside the earth's atmosphere, 1,374 W/m².)

Waves or Particles? Waves of Matter

THE TURN of the century was the dawn of a new era in physics. It was a time of bold departures from old ways. New experimental facts called for new explanations. The photoelectric effect, as we have seen, could be easily explained as due to particles of light but not as due to a wave; for, though an electromagnetic theory could explain the shaking loose of electrons by the E field of a wave, calculations of intensity, based on the energy spread out on a whole wave front, did not account for what actually happened. Yet the bold assumption that *all* the energy of a photon could be concentrated on a single electron accounted for experimental observations very nicely.

The pioneering had begun with Planck and his quantum. The pattern was set. The thing to do was to see if the new concept worked in a situation other than the one for which it was invented. Einstein took the expression $h\nu$ seriously and, instead of confining the idea to the radiation within an enclosure, as Planck had done, applied it to light particles traveling over great distances. He conceived of bullets of light that could knock electrons out of matter. His theory combined boldness and simplicity. It worked. He proved that photons do carry energy $h\nu$.

50.1. The Crucial Experiment: the Compton Effect

The electromagnetic theory showed that light has momentum and that we can compute the amount by dividing the energy contained in a volume full of electromagnetic radiation by the speed of light (§ 49.2). If you divided the energy of a photon, $h\nu$, by the speed of light, c, would you have the correct value for the momentum of a photon?

A. H. Compton, in 1923, discovered that x-ray wavelengths get longer after the rays are scattered. In working out a theoretical explanation of his experimental findings, he found that, if he used the formula

$$p = \frac{h\nu}{c} \qquad [50.1$$

for the momentum of an x-ray photon, he got a consistent explanation. Since $c = \nu\lambda$, the formula can also be written as

$$p = \frac{h}{\lambda} \qquad [50.2$$

which indicates that short wavelength is associated with great momentum.

Compton chose to use x-ray photons, which have a wavelength about 5,000 times as short as those of visible light and a correspondingly greater momentum. He also assumed that, in an interaction between a photon and an electron, *both momentum and energy are conserved.* In other words, he, like Einstein, decided to take Planck's quantum idea seriously and see if it really worked in a new situation.

A simplified and modern version of his experiment is shown in Figure 50.1. An x-ray tube, X, is operated at such a voltage that it emits a good portion of its energy at a wavelength, λ, that is characteristic of its target. The metal of the foil, F, is chosen to act as a filter in order to decrease as much as possible the relative intensity of wavelengths other than λ. A narrow beam is formed as the radiation passes through small holes in two thick lead sheets, L. The beam strikes a carbon block, C. Part of the beam goes right through, undeflected; part interacts with the carbon atoms and ejects photoelectrons from them. In this interaction the beam is deflected through an angle, α, that may vary up to 180°. The wavelength of the deflected beam is measured with a crystal spectrometer, whose main components are a crys-

tal, A, and an ionization chamber, D. Compton found that the deflected beam had a longer wavelength than the incident beam. There was this difference between Compton's experiment and earlier experiments on the photoelectric effect: he was interested in observing and explaining not only the effect on the ejected electron but any effect the interaction had on the photon itself.

If a photon of energy $h\nu$ gives up part of its energy to an electron (Fig. 50.2), its energy, $h\nu'$, after collision is less than the original energy. This change implies that its frequency is lower and its wavelength longer. The electron of the carbon atom in the block is not really free. It has a binding energy of the order of one electron volt. In Compton's collision the energy transferred to the electron is about 25,000 electron volts. We can therefore neglect the binding energy and treat the electron as if it were free.

By treating the collision as elastic, conserving both energy and momentum, Compton derived for the increase in wavelength, $\Delta\lambda$, the formula

$$\Delta\lambda = \lambda' - \lambda = \frac{h}{m_0 c}(1 - \cos\alpha) \qquad [50.3$$

in which m_0 is the rest mass of the ejected elec-

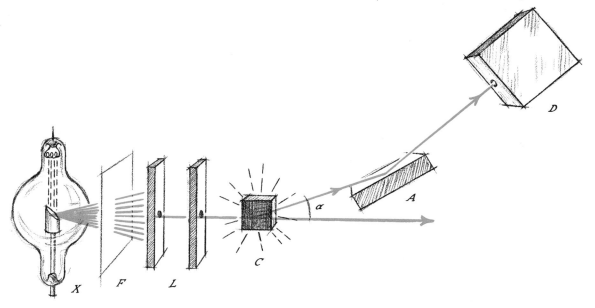

FIG. 50.1. *Compton's scattering experiment.*

tron. It accounted very well for the experimental results. Notice that $\Delta\lambda$ is a function of the scattering angle, α. Since the largest possible value of $(1 - \cos\alpha)$ is 2 (see Prob. 50.4), the largest value of $\Delta\lambda$ is $2h/m_0c$. This experiment was a resounding triumph for the quantum ideas: it proved, once again, that they worked.

EXAMPLE 50.1. We wish to find the numerical value of $2h/m_0c$.

We know that

$$h = 6.63 \times 10^{-34} \text{ J-sec}$$
$$m_0 = 9.11 \times 10^{-31} \text{ kg}$$
$$c = 3.00 \times 10^8 \text{ m/sec}$$

Therefore

$$\frac{2h}{m_0c} = \frac{2 \times 6.63 \times 10^{-34}}{9.11 \times 10^{-31} \times 3 \times 10^8} \frac{\text{joule-sec}}{\text{kg-m sec}^{-1}}$$

$$= 4.85 \times 10^{-12} \text{ m}$$
$$= 4.85 \times 10^{-2} \text{ A}$$

The shift in wavelength is, *at most*, 0.0485 A, whatever the initial wavelength. If $\lambda = 1$ A, a change in wavelength of 0.0485 A is readily detectable.

In the observation of the Compton shift, as the change in wavelength is called, another crucial experiment had been performed with simple equipment. Rutherford's experiments with alpha particles, Millikan's confirmation of Einstein's photoelectric equation, and now Compton's proof that photons have momentum—these were all accomplished with equipment that would look infantile compared with today's huge accelerators.†

50.2. Is Light a Particle or a Wave?

If you ask nature this question with a photoelectric cell, the answer seems to be "It's a particle." If you ask the question with a diffraction grating, the answer seems to be "It's a wave." The answer you get depends upon your experimental apparatus!

The incredulous attitude of physicists of the old school, about 1910, is expressed by the story of

† A wavelength of 1 A corresponds to an energy of about 12.3×10^3 electron volts. The Compton effect has been verified at energies as high as 250 million electron volts with the Berkeley electron-synchrotron.

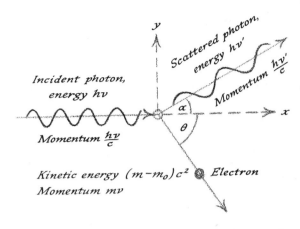

FIG. 50.2. *Collision between a photon of energy* $h\nu$ *and an electron at rest.*

the quantum diver. This diver jumps off a diving board at one end of a magic quantum pool. Instead of forming water waves, all the energy is concentrated on another swimmer at the other end of the pool, who is suddenly ejected out of the water and up onto the diving board at that end! The concentration of the energy of a photon ejecting a photoelectron is something like this and just as hard to believe in if you've seen the evidence for light waves all your life.

The dilemma—wave or particle—arises only if you assume that light, if it is one thing, cannot be the other. The modern view is that light has the properties of both. Let us consider some experiments to see the reasons for this view.

Imagine a pipe from which milk flows at the rate of one quart per minute when the valve is opened (Fig. 50.3). You have to wait a minute for the milk to fill a quart container. Now imagine a conveyor belt on which quart containers of milk have been placed irregularly but in such a way that, *on the average*, one container per minute passes a certain point. You are told that you may pick up a container if it passes that point during a random *half minute:* a bell rings at $t = 0$ and again at $t = 0.5$ minute, and you are permitted to pick up any container that goes by during that time. How many containers will you pick up? You can't predict the answer! You may pick up none; but there is a chance that you will pick up one, and there is even a chance that you will pick up two. On the other hand, the probability of collecting a full quart from the pipe in 0.5 minute is zero. The apparent continuity associated with waves is like that of the flow in the pipe, and the discontinuity associated with particles is like that of the containers.

Analogous experiments, in which we collect light instead of milk, indicate that light comes in quanta. No matter how short a time interval you choose or how weak the source of light, there is some chance of picking up a photon from that source. Light exhibits its quantized character

when its brightness is greatly reduced. If you put a lighted flashlight bulb (Fig. 50.4) 1 meter away from a photoelectric cell with a photo-emissive area of 1 square centimeter (A), a constant electric current is produced in the cell circuit because the number of photoelectrons released per second is huge (about 10^{10}). If you move the bulb to a distance of 10^5 meters (B), the light intensity at the photoelectric cell goes down by the factor $(10^5)^2 = 10^{10}$ (§ 19.3). The number of photoelectrons released *averages* about one per second. If you look for photoelectrons for only half-second

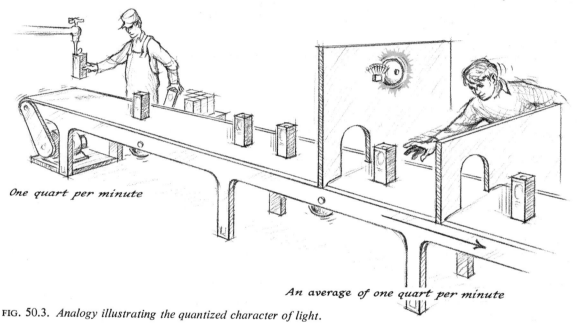

One quart per minute

An average of one quart per minute

FIG. 50.3. *Analogy illustrating the quantized character of light.*

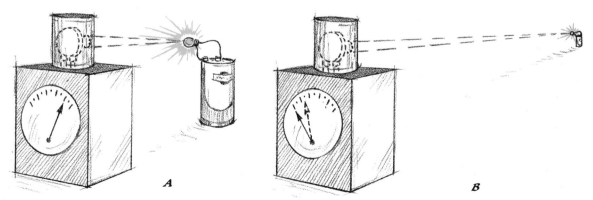

A

B

FIG. 50.4. *Experiment illustrating the quantized character of light.*

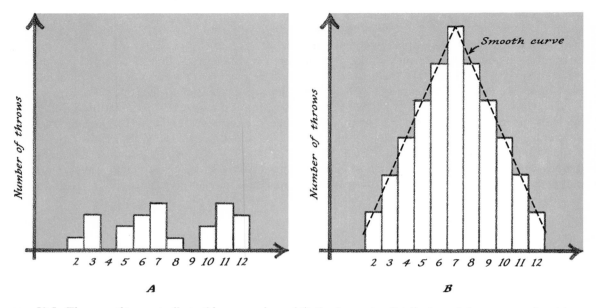

FIG. 50.5. *The smoothing-out effect of large numbers: (A) the frequency distribution of the sums produced by a few throws of dice; (B) the frequency distribution of the sums produced by many throws.*

intervals, you will occasionally pick one up. This can happen, as in the case of milk in containers, only if light comes in quantized packages.

Such experiments have actually been performed. (The light is picked up by a very sensitive photoelectric cell called a *photomultiplier*. The signals appear on a cathode-ray oscilloscope.) They confirm the idea that light exhibits particle-like characteristics when the intensity is low. A low intensity simply means that the *average number* of photons hitting the photoelectric cell per second is small.

The effect of large numbers on events that occur at random is to smooth out the statistical fluctuations and create the illusion of continuity. A simple way to prove this is to take a pair of dice and tabulate the number of times a 2 or a 3 or any other possible sum is thrown (Fig. 50.5). So long as the number of throws is small, the graph of frequency against sum exhibits discontinuities (A); you cannot predict what number will turn up at the next throw, and there seems to be no order at all in the events. After thousands of throws have been tabulated, however, the frequency curve looks quite smooth (B), with a maximum at 7, the most probable combination.

When great numbers of photons participate in an experiment, the wave character of light is apt to predominate. In Figure 50.6, for example, which illustrates the double-slit experiment (§ 23.2) performed with a distant monochromatic source, *S*, the intensity pattern (continuous curve, *F*) on the screen *CD* is predicted correctly by the wave theory. We can actually see the interference pattern through a magnifier. We don't see individual photons landing. What would happen if the source

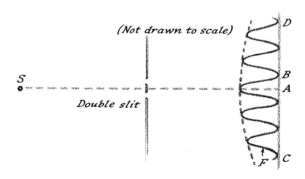

FIG. 50.6. *Distribution of intensity produced by many photons going through a double slit. Since the number of photons is very large, the plot of intensity against displacement on the line* CAD *is a smooth curve with maxima and minima as shown.*

were made so weak that only one photon per second (on the average) left it? Most of the time only one photon would be somewhere in the region between S and CD. Would an interference pattern result? About fifty years ago, G. I. Taylor, then a student at Cambridge University, performed such an experiment. (He used a needle instead of a double slit, and his interference pattern was different from that of Fig. 50.6, but the principle was the same.) He put a photographic plate at CD and made the light source so weak that it required an exposure time of several months (during which he went sailing, so the story goes), but the interference pattern was there when he developed the film. He calculated that most of the time there was only one photon between S and CD. How, then, could interference take place? The point is that it did, and we must reconcile our thinking to the experimental facts. If he had been able to count photons as they landed and had quit while the total number of photons was still small, his graph might have had the chaotic appearance of the bar graph of Figure 50.5.A. As the total number of photons was large, the statistical fluctuations were smoothed out, and the pattern predicted by the wave theory emerged.

If we persist in applying our ideas of Newtonian mechanics to photons and atomic particles, we shall be continually frustrated. We have to learn to say that the *probability* of having a photon land (Fig. 50.6) at a point like A (an interference maximum) is high and that the probability of having it land at a point like B (an interference minimum) is low. You *cannot* predict whether any given photon will land at A or at B (or anywhere else), but the interference pattern predicted by the wave theory does yield the *probability* of collecting photons within a given region of CD. We can, by using the wave theory as a calculating device for probabilities, predict what fraction of the photons, *on the average*, will land within any given region of CD. Wherever the wave theory predicts a great intensity, the probability of finding a photon is high. If the photons arrive one at a time, they will appear to land in great disorder, at random times and in random places; but the cumulative effect of many photons, even arriving singly, is the same as the pattern produced when

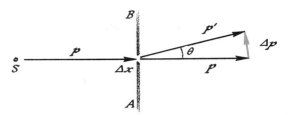

FIG. 50.7. *Illustrating Heisenberg's uncertainty principle.*

many arrive together. Even single photons are governed in their *average* behavior by the wave properties of light. The wave theory gives the probability curve that applies to each single photon. *We must conclude, then, that wave behavior, in this sense, applies even to individual photons.*

50.3. The Heisenberg Uncertainty Principle

A mechanistic philosophy, in the classical sense, assumes that, if you know the velocity and momentum of all the particles in the universe at any instant, you should, in principle, be able, by applying to them the laws of mechanics, to calculate where each of them will be at any later time. We consider now whether the idea of knowing both the velocity and the momentum of a particle at one instant has operational meaning.

We can attempt to localize a beam of photons conceptually into what we might call a single ray as follows: We let the monochromatic light from a very distant point source, S, illuminate a screen, AB, with a slit of width Δx (Fig. 50.7). The smaller we make Δx, the more accurately we localize the beam. We can give its x coordinate (along AB) with the uncertainty Δx.

Suppose the momentum of an entering photon is **p**. Diffraction experiments tell us that there is some probability that the emerging photon will have a new direction. The new momentum is, therefore, a new vector, **p′**. It can be conceived as the vector sum

$$\mathbf{p}' = \mathbf{p} + \Delta\mathbf{p} \qquad [50.4$$

in which $\Delta\mathbf{p}$ is an increment in momentum approximately in the x direction. If the energy of the photon remains unchanged, the magnitude of the new momentum, **p'**, is the same as that of **p**. Dropping the vector notation, we see that

$$\frac{\Delta p}{p'} = \frac{\Delta p}{p}$$

Hence, approximately,

$$\frac{\Delta p}{p} = \sin \theta \qquad [50.5$$

if θ is the angle of deviation. Diffraction experiments also tell us that the maximum deviation, θ_m (for the photons headed for the first diffraction minimum), obeys the equation

$$\sin \theta_m = \frac{\lambda}{\Delta x} \qquad [50.6$$

(See equation 23.5.) Using the equality $\theta = \theta_m$ in equation 50.5 and combining it with equation 50.6, we get

$$\frac{\Delta p}{p} = \frac{\lambda}{\Delta x} \qquad [50.7$$

or

$$(\Delta p)(\Delta x) = p\lambda \qquad [50.8$$

Now we recall that the momentum of a photon may be written as $p = h/\lambda$. Putting this into equation 50.8, we obtain

$$(\Delta p)(\Delta x) \gtreqless h \qquad [50.9$$

(The sign > is included because values of θ less than θ_m are possible.) Equation 50.9, although derived here for a special experiment, is the essence of **Heisenberg's uncertainty principle** (after Werner Heisenberg, born in 1901). Its consequences are far-reaching. The constant h, as Planck discovered, is very small, *but it is not zero*. Therefore, if we attempt to get better information on the location of the photon by narrowing the slit, equation 50.9 demands that the uncertainty in momentum, Δp, become very large. And the only way to get better information on momentum is to allow greater uncertainty in location.

You cannot have perfect knowledge simultaneously of both the location and the momentum of a particle. Nature does not seem to be built to permit us this luxury! "Knowing both the velocity and the momentum of a particle" does not seem to have operational meaning. It is now believed that the principle involved in equation 50.9 is quite general and universally applicable to all

kinds of particles. It can be derived in other ways. It has been confirmed experimentally in the sense that no exception to it has been found.

50.4. Waves of Matter (de Broglie Waves)

In 1924, Prince Louis-Victor de Broglie (born in 1892) introduced the concept of waves associated with matter. This was the beginning of the wave theory of matter. He was awarded the Nobel Prize for Physics in 1929.

Having observed that light waves have particle-like characteristics, de Broglie suggested that matter should have wave-like characteristics. When he made this suggestion, there was no experimental evidence for it: de Broglie argued simply from a symmetry that he felt should exist in nature.

Consider the formula for the momentum, p, of a photon: $p = h/\lambda$. Solving this for λ, we get $\lambda = h/p$; we obtained the wavelength by dividing Planck's constant by the momentum of the photon. De Broglie suggested, by analogy, that a particle of mass m moving with speed v should have associated with it a wave of wavelength

$$\lambda = \frac{h}{mv} \qquad [50.10$$

which would govern its behavior in a probabilistic sense.

Consider, first, a baseball with a mass of 0.15 kg moving with a speed of 20 m/sec. Its momentum is 3 kg-m/sec. The wavelength to be associated with this ball, according to equation 50.10, is

$$\lambda = \frac{h}{mv} = \frac{6.63 \times 10^{-34} \text{ J-sec}}{3 \text{ m/sec}}$$
$$= 2.21 \times 10^{-34} \text{ m} \qquad [50.11$$

The diameter of an atom is about 10^{-10} m. The diameter of an atomic nucleus is about 10^{-14} m. Surely we are not talking about an observable length when we consider 10^{-14} m. Now consider a lazy microbe (mass about 10^{-15} kg) moving only 1 cm a day (about 10^{-7} m/sec). Its de Broglie wavelength is

$$\lambda = \frac{6.63 \times 10^{-34} \text{ J-sec}}{(10^{-15} \text{ kg})(10^{-7} \text{ m/sec})}$$
$$= 6 \times 10^{-12} \text{ m} = 6 \times 10^{-2} \text{ A}$$

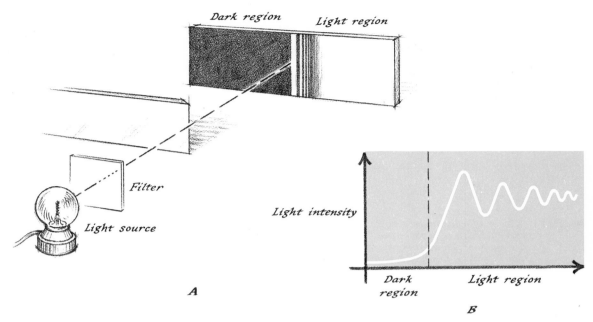

Dark region   *Light region*

Filter

Light intensity

Light source

Dark region   *Light region*

A

B

FIG. 50.8. (A) *Experimental arrangement for observing the diffraction of light round a sharp straight edge and the effects of interference in the light region. (B) Theoretically expected pattern of light intensity in the light region.*

This is still a very short wavelength but comparable to that of x-rays. If we are to succeed in observing de Broglie wavelengths, our particles must have very little mass and not too much energy.

That takes us back into the atomic realm. It looks as if these new ideas of quantum mechanics were ideally suited to the atomic domain. De Broglie waves have actually been observed for electrons, atomic beams, and neutrons. De Broglie was right: all of them exhibit wavelengths given by equation 50.10.

In the chapters on waves I pointed out that diffraction and interference are the crucial tests of a wave. The shadow made by a sharp straight edge in monochromatic light from a line source (Fig. 50.8.A) exhibits the familiar interference pattern (see Fig. 23.25) and produces (Fig. 50.8.B) the familiar curve of intensity against displacement. Compare the pattern with the greatly enlarged shadow made by a sharp edge in a beam of electrons (Fig. 50.9). A beam of electrons certainly seems to have wave-like characteristics.

As another example, consider the behavior of a beam of helium atoms hitting the freshly cut surface of a lithium fluoride crystal (Fig. 50.10). The crystal diffracts the beam of atoms as crystals diffract x-rays and as gratings diffract light. The first-order reflections at C and D obey the equation $\sin \theta = \lambda/d$, in which θ is the angle

FIG. 50.9. *Interference bands produced by a beam of electrons at the edge of a shadow region. (Drawn from an electron micrograph.)*

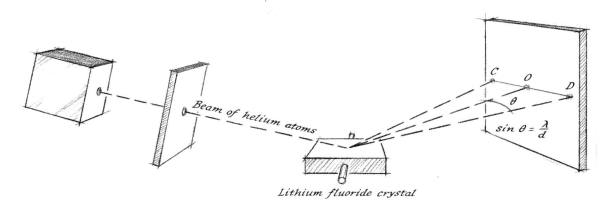

FIG. 50.10. *A beam of helium atoms strikes a lithium fluoride crystal. The main reflected beam lands at* O, *but the regular spacings in the crystal produce maxima at symmetrical points such as* C *and* D. *The effects are easily explained if the beam of atoms is treated as a wave whose wavelength is given by the expression* $\lambda = h/p$, *in which* p *is the momentum of a helium atom.*

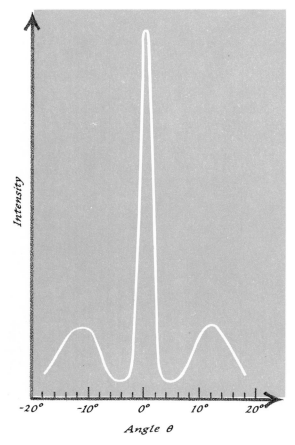

FIG. 50.11. *Graph of the intensity of the reflected beam of Fig. 50.10.*

shown, λ is the de Broglie wavelength of the beam, and d is the crystal-lattice spacing. The experiment is conducted in an evacuated chamber. The helium comes from a sample of gas that is close to room temperature. From the crystal lattice spacing, 2.85 A, and the measured diffraction angle, about 12°, the de Broglie wavelength is calculated to be about 0.57 A. If we use the mean velocity corresponding to room temperature in the equation $\lambda = h/mv$, the de Broglie wavelength again comes out as 0.57 A. Figure 50.11 shows the graph of the reflected-beam intensity produced by the experiment. The scanning takes place on the line CD (Fig. 50.10).

Experiments with beams of neutrons indicate that they too can be diffracted as if they were waves.†

To sum up: ever since C. J. Davisson and L. H. Germer discovered, in 1927, that the beam of electrons reflected from a nickel surface exhibits maxima and minima that can be well accounted for on de Broglie's hypothesis, a great deal of evidence has accumulated for the idea that moving particles of matter have wave-like characteristics. In 1937 C. J. Davisson and G. P. Thomson shared the Nobel Prize for Physics for their work on electron diffraction.

† See Donald J. Hughes, *The Neutron Story* (Garden City, N.Y.), an Anchor paperback.

50.5. Summary

Compton observed that x-ray wavelengths get longer when the rays are scattered. He was able to account for what happened by assuming that, when an x-ray photon strikes an electron, and the electron recoils, conserving both energy and momentum, some energy is subtracted from the photon, thereby increasing its wavelength. This was a resounding triumph for the particle theory of light (x-rays in his experiment).

Photons—the particles associated with light and other electromagnetic radiations—are, as we saw in Chapter 49, a strange kind of particle. Though they have many of the properties of matter, such as momentum, they differ in at least two important respects: they have no rest mass, and they are easily created and easily destroyed. Electrons, neutrons, and atoms are much more durable.

The momentum of a photon being h/λ, de Broglie suggested that, if symmetry prevailed, particles might behave like waves, with a wavelength equal to h/mv. Experiments with electrons, atoms, neutrons, and other particles have confirmed this relation. The dual nature of particles and waves has therefore been established. In particular, light has been demonstrated to behave both like a particle and like a wave.

An important corollary to all this is Heisenberg's uncertainty principle, one form of which implies that you cannot know simultaneously, with high precision, both the location and the momentum of a particle. It sets important limitations on all measurements at the atomic level.

With this brief introduction we have entered the world of the new physics. At first its discoveries seem paradoxical and contradictory, but all subsequent examination of these strange new ideas confirms their validity without overthrowing the validity, in a limited sense, of all the old classical knowledge. (I borrow a phrase from Edward Kasner and James R. Newman's *Mathematics and the Imagination:* "Paradox Lost and Paradox Regained.")

When must we use these new concepts of light in preference to the old? Whenever we have the combination of few photons and high energies, the concept of particles will predominate; whenever we have the combination of many photons (their fluctuations are statistically smoothed out) and low energy per photon (for example, in visible light, infrared light, and radio waves), the concept of waves is preferable. But we no longer speak of an either-or. The particle and the wave are two aspects of the same thing.

Problems

50.1. We saw earlier that modern concepts imply that the electron is too large to be contained in a nucleus.

1. Calculate the de Broglie wavelength of an electron with energy of about 1 ev, and compare it with nuclear dimensions. (For non-relativistic speeds, kinetic energy may be written as $E = mv^2/2$; from this you can prove that momentum, mv, equals $\sqrt{2mE}$.)

2. If an electron were somehow confined to a volume of the size of a nucleus, what would be the minimum uncertainty in its momentum? What energy would be associated with a momentum of that magnitude? Compare this result with the approximate figure of 1 Mev for the energy that it takes to knock a particle out of a nucleus.

3. Calculate the de Broglie wavelength of a proton with energy of 1 Mev. (The mass of a proton is about 1,840 times the mass of an electron.) Is this length of the right order of magnitude to fit into a nucleus?

50.2. This problem illustrates the value of approximations made by use of the uncertainty principle. The orbit of the electron in a hydrogen atom is known to have a radius of $r_0 = 5 \times 10^{-11}$ m. The momentum of the electron is uncertain because, although we know the radius of the orbit and the speed, v, we don't know where in the orbit the electron is at any instant, and we therefore don't know which way, at any instant, the momentum vector is pointed. In these circumstances the uncertainty in momentum is $2mv$.

1. From the uncertainty in the electron's position $(2r_0)$ calculate the uncertainty in its momentum, and set it equal to $2mv$. Prove, from this, that the electron's speed in its orbit is $h/4mr_0$.

2. Calculate the kinetic energy of the electron in its orbit from the equation

$$E = \frac{(mv)^2}{2m}$$

and prove that it is equal to $h^2/32mr_0^2$.

3. Calculate the frequency, v, with which the electron goes round the nucleus, and prove that it is equal to $h/8mr_0^2\pi$.

4. Calculate the energy of a photon having that frequency, and prove that it is equal to $h^2/8mr_0^2\pi$. Is this of the same order of magnitude as the kinetic energy of the electron in its orbit?

50.3. 1. What is the de Broglie wavelength of an electron that has been accelerated to a final speed of $0.0001\ c$ (c being the speed of light)?

2. Use the formula for single-slit diffraction (§ 23.4) to estimate the approximate angular spread that is produced if you send the electron beam through a slit 1 micron (10^{-4} cm) wide.

3. How wide will the beam be 3 m from the slit?

50.4. A photon with energy hv and momentum hv/c approaches a particle, of mass m, that is at rest. A head-on collision sends the photon directly back-ward with new energy hv' and new momentum hv'/c as the particle goes forward with energy $mv^2/2$ and momentum mv.

1. Derive a formula for the photon's change in wavelength, and compare it with the value given by equation 50.3 when $\alpha = 180°$. Remember that $\cos 180° = -1$. [Hint: Prove that, if $mv^2/2$ is written as E and if $mv = \sqrt{2mE}$, then

$$v = \frac{E + c\sqrt{2mE}}{2h}$$

and

$$v' = \frac{c\sqrt{2mE} - E}{2h}$$

Prove, from this, that

$$\lambda' - \lambda = \frac{4ch}{2mc^2 - E}$$

If $2mc^2 \gg E$, the result checks with equation 50.3.]

2. If the particle struck by the photon were a free proton, what would be the photon's change in wavelength?

50.5. In § 48.4 we saw that very energetic gamma rays would have been needed to eject high-energy protons from the paraffin in Chadwick's experiment. Use the formula

$$\lambda = \frac{2ch}{E + c\sqrt{2mE}}$$

which is derivable from the formula of Prob. 50.4.1, to compute the wavelength of a gamma ray that could give a proton a kinetic energy of 5 Mev.

51

The Bohr Atom

THE SPECTROSCOPE is the tool with which we have analyzed into its component frequencies the light emitted by excited atoms. Since the light is passed through a slit in the spectroscope, it forms images of that slit—fine lines, in different colors, which we call the **spectral lines** of the element being investigated.

Our task in learning what an atom is like from a study of its atomic spectrum has been likened to that of a blind man who must infer the structure of a piano by listening to the tones it produces—of different pitches—as its different keys are struck. But this analogy presupposes spectral analysis: the different pitches have already been separated. Without spectral analysis the problem is much more difficult. To infer what a neon atom, for example, is like by looking at a lighted neon bulb without a spectrometer is more like trying to figure out the appearance of a piano by hearing the sounds it makes as it falls down a flight of stairs!

The latter analogy attempts, in a very crude way, to convey something of what we think happens in an atom. An atom may be raised to a state of high energy. In falling back to its normal state, it may produce visible light, of a single color or of many colors, and invisible light. Seen without a spectroscope, the colors are hopelessly mixed; seen with a spectroscope, they become orderly lines that tell a great deal about the atom.

The purpose of this chapter is to relate how Niels Bohr evolved a theory of the hydrogen atom that accounted for all the visible spectral lines of hydrogen—and for many invisible ones that were observed later.

51.1. The Experiment of Franck and Hertz

An experiment first performed by James Franck and Gustav Hertz in 1913 showed that atoms absorb energy from electrons in quanta. (It is necessary to understand this experiment before we consider the absorption and emission of light in quanta.) Figure 51.1 illustrates the basic idea of the experiment but is highly schematic.

Electrons, produced in an evacuated chamber, by a hot filament, F, are accelerated by a potential difference, V, toward the metal box surrounding regions II and III. Some electrons enter, through hole B, chamber II, containing mercury gas. The energy of an electron going through the hole is eV, which can be expressed in joules or in electron volts. The pumps connected with chambers I and III work fast enough to keep the pressure low in those chambers despite the leakage of mercury molecules from chamber II. In chamber II the electrons collide with the molecules of the mercury vapor. After many random collisions some electrons emerge from hole C into chamber III. Imagine now some device that measures the speed (and hence the energy) of those electrons. The figure indicates a curved path of shorter radius for slower electrons and a curved path of longer radius for faster electrons, as if they were affected by a magnetic field (pointing into the plane of the paper). This is only a schematic representation of something like a mass spectrograph or an apparatus for determining e/m (§ 47.5). There are several ways in which the energy of the electrons can be measured. The details need not

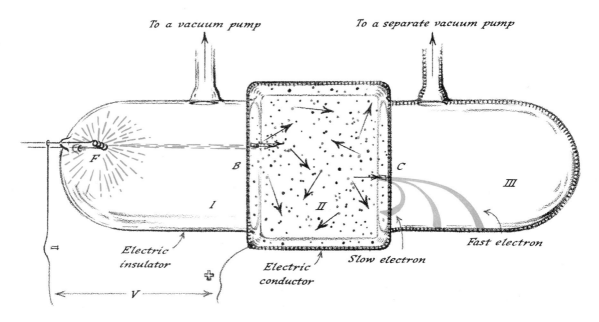

To a vacuum pump

To a separate vacuum pump

F

B

C

I

II

III

Electric
insulator

Electric
conductor

Slow electron

Fast electron

V

FIG. 51.1. *The experiment of Franck and Hertz.*

concern us here. Let's concentrate on what happens to the electrons.

Franck and Hertz could control the energy of the electrons entering chamber II at *B* by varying the potential, *V*. They found that, when *V* had a certain value, the electrons coming out at *C* had practically no energy at all; apparently they had given it up to the gas molecules. More specifically (if the gas in the chamber is mercury), when *V* is 1 V, and the energy of the electrons entering at *B* is therefore 1 ev, the electrons that come out at *C* also have an energy of 1 ev; when the entering electrons have an energy of 2 ev, the emerging electrons also have an energy of 2 ev; and so on, up to a point, as the voltage is raised: most of the electrons coming out of *C* have the same energy as those entering at *B* as long as *V* is less than 4.9 V. At about 4.9 V, however, an interesting change takes place: some of the electrons that enter *B* with an energy of 4.9 ev emerge from *C* with practically zero energy. As long as the energy of the incoming electrons is less than 4.9 ev, the molecules of mercury are incapable of accepting any energy from them; as soon as 4.9 ev is reached, they may accept this bundle of energy (4.9 ev) quite readily. If electrons enter

chamber II with 5.9 ev, they leave it with 1 ev; if they enter with 6.5 ev, they leave with 6.5 − 4.9 = 1.6 ev; if they enter with 6.7 ev, they leave again with almost zero energy.

Thus Franck and Hertz discovered these and the other thresholds of energy at which atoms of mercury are willing to accept bundles of energy. (For this achievement they were awarded the Nobel Prize for Physics in 1925.) Their conclusion was that atoms can change their internal energy but only in sharply defined steps. These steps are shown in the energy-level diagram of Figure 51.2. The energy levels correspond to the **excited states** of the mercury atom. All mercury atoms have identical excited states. Atoms of other kinds have different sets of excited states. The state in which an atom is normally found is called its **ground state.**

Quantum jumps such as those just described are so small that they are not noticeable in the ordinary scale of things. A baseball, for example, moving at a speed of 30 mph has a kinetic energy of about 10 J, or close to 6×10^{19} ev. A change in its kinetic energy of only 4.9 ev would be a change of approximately 1 part in 10^{19} (1 part in 10,000,000,000,000,000,000) and would be imperceptible. Even if the ball lost energy at a rate a million times greater than 4.9 ev per second, experiments would lead us to think that it was losing energy continuously. It wasn't, of course, but no experiment would ever detect quantum jumps even of a million times 4.9 ev in a baseball.

The ordinary mechanics of Newton, in which gradual and continuous changes of energy are conceivable, works well for events on the ordinary laboratory scale, but it fails at the atomic level. The atomic realm, like the realm of very high speeds encountered in relativity, is really outside our normal experience, and it should not surprise us that Newtonian mechanics fails in both realms. We do have a right to expect, however, that any new mechanics will reduce to Newtonian mechanics in the proper situation.

51.2. Atomic Excitation and Emission and Atomic Spectra

What do excited atoms do with their extra energy? They can lose it in the form of radiation. If we use the formula $E = h\nu$ with E equal to

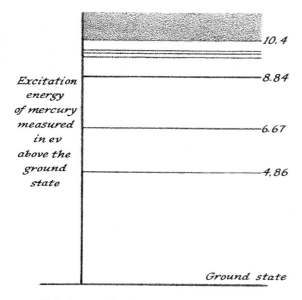

FIG. 51.2. *Energy levels corresponding to the excited states of the mercury atom. There is an infinite number of discrete levels between 8.84 ev and 10.4 ev, but only three are drawn. The continuum of states above 10.4 ev is drawn as a shaded area.*

4.9 ev, we can solve for ν. We choose 4.9 ev because it is the lowest excitation energy above the ground state for mercury atoms. We get

$$\nu = \frac{E}{h} = \frac{4.9 \text{ ev}}{6.63 \times 10^{-34} \text{ J-sec}}$$

After converting electron volts into joules, we may write this as

$$\nu = 1.18 \times 10^{15} \text{ sec}^{-1}$$

If we convert from frequency to wavelength, using the formula $\lambda = c/\nu$ and numerical values of greater precision, we get

$$\lambda = 2,537 \text{ A}$$

Any spectroscopist familiar with ultraviolet spectra would recognize this as the strong invisible line of mercury, which is detectable with special photoelectric cells. (It is the wavelength commonly used in germicidal lamps. It is also responsible for exciting the fluorescence in ordinary fluorescent lights.)

This calculation suggests that the very same jumps by which the mercury atom gains energy from electron bombardment are those exhibited by its spectrum when it loses energy by radiation. In other words, excited atoms can radiate energy in going from a state of high excitation to one of low excitation. The formula is

$$h\nu = E_{\text{initial state}} - E_{\text{final state}} \qquad [51.1$$

The energy is emitted in the form of photons. Each photon emitted means that some individual atom has dropped from a higher to a lower state of excitation. Emitting energy as light, as well as accepting energy from electron bombardment, the atom jumps from one energy state to another.

An atom can absorb as well as emit light. It can be raised to a higher state of excitation by accepting energy from light of the proper frequency. Light of wavelength 2,537 A, for example, can be absorbed by mercury atoms. In general, the absorption is strong at the frequencies determined by equation 51.1. Some of the dark lines in the solar spectrum, for example (see the color plate facing p. 270), occur where the prominent emission lines of sodium occur and have been ascribed to absorption by sodium atoms in the cooler outer shell of gas around the sun.

At the end of the nineteenth century a great

$$\lambda = \frac{3{,}645.1n^2}{n^2 - 4} \qquad [51.2$$

This gives the wavelength in angstroms. Each integer, starting with $n = 3$, gives a different line of the hydrogen spectrum. Balmer's was the first successful attempt to fit a formula to the spectral lines of an element. His method was elaborated by J. R. Rydberg for the spectra of heavier elements, and W. Ritz contributed a form that exhibited each term of the series (sequence) as the difference between two energy levels. (This was important because later, as we shall see, Bohr found that the frequency of any spectral line is derivable from a difference between energy levels.)

Balmer's triumph is reminiscent of Kepler's successful attempt to find a formula for the period of the planets revolving round the sun. Period is, after all, the inverse of frequency. The final formula resulted, in each case, from an attempt to put into mathematical form the results of many observations of frequencies; and in each case a question immediately followed: "Why?" The answer for the planets was eventually given by Newton, who showed that he could derive Kepler's laws by assuming a gravitational attractive force depending on the inverse square of the distance between the sun and the planets. And now Bohr showed that, starting with the electric force of attraction between a massive, positively charged nucleus and a light, negatively charged electron, he could derive, at least for hydrogen, the sequence of Balmer and obtain a first clue to those of Rydberg and Ritz from basic physical principles. Newtonian mechanics was not adequate for that task, but Bohr's genius found a way to modify Newton—a way that served as the basis of a new mechanics. Kepler had his Newton, and Balmer had his Bohr. But the stories are not completely parallel; and they couldn't be, for laws of mechanics that are adequate for planets are far from adequate for atoms. Bohr's theory was, in part, a fortuitous mixture of classical and modern ideas. That it is basically wrong is demonstrated by its failure to explain even the spectrum of helium. Yet it is so suggestive and ingenious that it bears examination. Albert Einstein called Niels Bohr "one of the great creative geniuses of our generation."

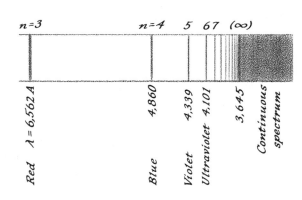

FIG. 51.3. *The lines in the Balmer series of the hydrogen spectrum.*

wealth of spectroscopic information was available in the form of tabulated wavelengths of many spectral lines. These wavelengths, or their associated frequencies, are, of course, just numbers. The problem was to find some order in this apparent jumble of numbers. In 1885, Johann Jakob Balmer, a Swiss high-school teacher of mathematics, took up the study of the spectral lines of hydrogen as a problem in numbers. A plot of the lines on a wavelength scale (Fig. 51.3) exhibits the regularity associated with a *sequence* (§ 1.6). The crowding near 3,645 suggests that this is the limit of the sequence. The problem is to find an expression for the nth term. (See Prob. 1.5.G.)

Balmer found a formula that gave the wavelengths of a certain set of spectral lines of hydrogen very accurately. (They are now called the *Balmer series*. The word "series" is still used although the word "sequence" is preferable if we wish to avoid confusion between the terms as they are used in mathematics, where "series" usually implies a sum. I shall defer to usage and speak of series of spectral lines, but I shall use the term "sequence" when I wish to emphasize the strict meaning of the word "limit.") The formula is

51.3. Bohr's Planetary Model of an Atom

Once Rutherford had discovered that there is a massive nucleus within each atom, it was inevitable that the electrons whirling round the nucleus be likened to the planets moving round the sun. Bohr imagined the electron in an orbit very much like those of the planets. The force of attraction in the atomic case was the electrical coulombic force.

At this point it would pay you to review § 34.6 very carefully. I stated there (and in parts of § 34.5) that the *gravitational* force of attraction between two bodies of masses m and M is $F = GmM/r^2$, and that the potential energy of the system is $U = -GmM/r$. I also proved that we can write the kinetic energy, $mv^2/2$, of the small mass as $K = GmM/2r$, making the total energy

$$E = K + U = -\frac{GmM}{2r}$$

From this I inferred that a body making a transition from a stable orbit of radius r_2 to one of shorter radius r_1 would lose energy.

Much of this argument has its parallel in the atomic case, as I shall presently show; but, whereas a planetary system, viewed classically, can change continuously from one configuration to another, atomic configurations change only by finite energy jumps. Bohr considered the total energy of the hydrogen atom in a manner very similar to that just followed for planetary motion, but he had to depart from classical ideas at several points: he assumed (1) that certain orbits are stable; (2) that an electron can make quantum jumps according to the formula $\Delta E = h\nu$; (3) that angular momentum is quantized.

The first assumption demonstrated boldness; Bohr knew full well that, classically, an accelerated electron in an orbit would radiate and fall into the nucleus in about 10^{-8} sec. The second accounted for the observed wavelengths of spectral lines; it demonstrated ingenuity in adapting an idea from classical physics—in a vibrating string, for example, only certain frequencies are permitted—to an analogous situation in the atom. The third, the quantization of angular momentum, gave the right results according to the corre-

spondence principle (§ 52.4); so Bohr accepted it. (Only after the invention of wave mechanics was it rationally explained.) By using the formula

$$E_{\text{initial state}} - E_{\text{final state}} = h\nu$$

he derived for the spectral lines of hydrogen a formula that coincided with Balmer's formula and hence with the experimental facts.

We shall now go through the calculations. What follows is probably the longest and most important derivation in the book. Keep in mind that our first goal is to express the permitted orbital radii, r_n, in terms of n and of physical constants. (It would pay you to restudy § 37.1 before proceeding.)

Bohr began by taking Rutherford's concept of a nucleus with the positive charge Ze, in which Z is the atomic number (it is 1 for hydrogen, but we shall keep on using Z for the sake of generality) and e is the magnitude of the electronic charge (a positive number). The coulombic force on a single planetary electron is

$$F = \frac{K(Ze)e}{r^2}$$

The potential energy of the system is

$$U = -\frac{K(Ze)e}{r}$$

(This is identical with equation 37.1 except for the minus sign, which we use because the force between the nucleus and the electron is an attractive one. Compare this with equation 34.22 for the case of gravitational attraction.)

Let us assume that the nucleus is at rest and that the electron moves round it in a circular path of radius r. The mathematical argument, except for constants, is identical with that for planetary motion (§ 34.6).

The electron experiences a centripetal force, mv^2/r, which we equate with the coulombic force:

$$\frac{mv^2}{r} = \frac{K(Ze)e}{r^2} \qquad [51.3$$

From this we get immediately the kinetic energy:

$$\tfrac{1}{2}mv^2 = \frac{KZe^2}{2r} \qquad [51.4$$

The potential energy is

$$U = -\frac{KZe^2}{r} \qquad [51.5$$

The total energy, $U + mv^2/2$, becomes, therefore,

$$E = -\frac{KZe^2}{2r} \qquad [51.6$$

The results of the Franck-Hertz experiment and the evidence of spectral lines both suggest that atoms can absorb and emit energy only in discrete bundles, or quanta. Since E can take on only discrete values, r can take on only discrete values. To cope with this problem, Bohr found, he had to postulate the quantization of angular momentum; that is, he had to postulate that angular momentum also comes in discrete units. The quantization that gives the correct answer may be written as

$$I\omega = n\frac{h}{2\pi} \qquad [51.7$$

Here n can take on only integral values: $n = 1$, 2, 3, ... Bohr was led to this equation by the correspondence principle (§ 52.4), which demands agreement between quantum and classical formulas in certain limiting cases.

Since $I = mr^2$ and $\omega = v/r$, we may write that

$$mr_nv = n\frac{h}{2\pi} \qquad [51.8$$

The subscript n has been attached to r to indicate the particular value of r associated with the integer n. After dividing by r_n and squaring, we may write this equation as

$$m^2v^2 = \frac{n^2h^2}{4\pi^2r_n^2} \qquad [51.9$$

Multiplying both sides of equation 51.4 by $2m$, we get

$$m^2v^2 = \frac{KZe^2m}{r} \qquad [51.10$$

Equating the right-hand sides of equations 51.9 and 51.10, we get

$$\frac{n^2h^2}{4\pi^2r_n^2} = \frac{KZe^2m}{r_n} \qquad [51.11$$

from which we obtain the equation we have been seeking

$$r_n = \frac{n^2h^2}{4\pi^2KZe^2m} \qquad [51.12$$

Let's pause for a moment to examine the implications of this result. It says that the permitted radii are proportional to the squares of the inte-

gers (n^2). Except for the constants in equation 51.12, the radii are like the numbers of the sequence 1, 4, 9, 16, . . . n^2. The shortest radius is that for which $n = 1$. For that we have the equation

$$r_1 = \frac{h^2}{4\pi^2KZe^2m} \qquad [51.13$$

Putting in the known numerical values, of slide-rule accuracy, we get

$$r_1 = \frac{(6.63\times10^{-34}\ \text{J-sec})^2}{4 \times (3.14)^2 \times 9\times10^9\ \frac{\text{nt-m}^2}{\text{coul}^2}}$$
$$\times (1.60\times10^{-19})^2\ \text{coul}^2 \times 9.11\times10^{-31}\ \text{kg}$$
$$= 5.27\times10^{-11}\ \text{m} \qquad [51.14$$

This makes the diameter almost exactly one angstrom (10^{-10} m), which puts us in the right order of magnitude for atoms. Figure 51.4 shows Bohr's permitted radii schematically. The other data of the figure are discussed later.

Our next goal is to express the discrete energies E_n as a function of n. To do this, let us put the r_n of equation 51.12 into the energy expression, 51.6, using the subscript n on E to indicate the energy associated with the nth permitted radius:

$$E_n = -\frac{2\pi^2K^2Z^2e^4m}{n^2h^2} \qquad [51.15$$

The energies an electron can have are represented by E_n for $n = 1, 2, 3, ...$ The integer n is called

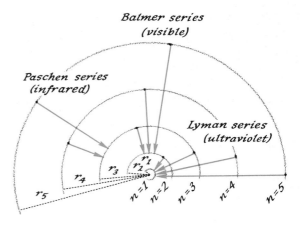

FIG. 51.4. *The permitted radii of the Bohr orbits for hydrogen. The transitions indicated by arrows between circles correspond to lines of the spectral series whose name is given. See also Fig. 51.6.*

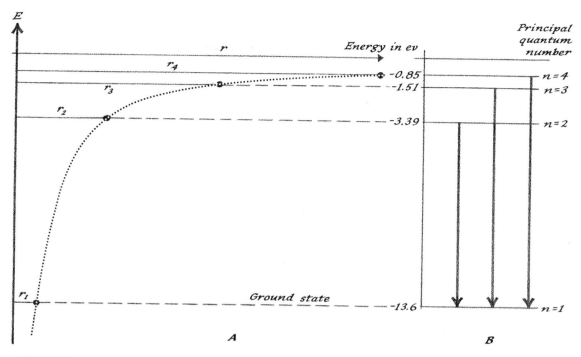

FIG. 51.5. (A) A plot of E_n against r_n. The round dots on the curve mark permitted values of E_n and r_n. (B) Energy-level diagram for the excited states of hydrogen.

(for reasons to be explained later) the **principal** (or **total**) **quantum number.** A plot of equation 51.15, showing E_n as a function of r_n, appears in Figure 51.5.A. The values of E_n are also carried over to Figure 51.5.B, an energy-level diagram for hydrogen with energies expressed in electron volts. (Values up to $n = 4$ are shown.)

Let the quantum number n_2 be associated with a higher energy state and n_1 with a lower energy state ($n_1 < n_2$). Bohr postulated that, when an electron drops from a state of the higher energy E_{n_2} to a state of the lower energy E_{n_1}, it radiates a photon of energy $h\nu$:

$$h\nu = E_{n_2} - E_{n_1} \qquad [51.16$$

Substituting for the energies from equation 51.15 and solving for ν, we get

$$\nu = \frac{2\pi^2 K^2 m e^4 Z^2}{h^3}\left(\frac{1}{n_1^2} - \frac{1}{n_2^2}\right) \qquad [51.17$$

Using the relation $1/\lambda = \nu/c$, we write

$$\frac{1}{\lambda} = \frac{2\pi^2 K^2 m e^4 Z^2}{h^3 c}\left(\frac{1}{n_1^2} - \frac{1}{n_2^2}\right) \qquad [51.18$$

The constant preceding the parentheses (with Z equal to 1) is called the *Rydberg constant:*

$$R = \frac{2\pi^2 K^2 m e^4 Z^2}{h^3 c} = 1.09737 \times 10^7 \text{ m}^{-1}$$

For the Balmer series, therefore, with transitions down to $n_1 = 2$ and with $n_2 = n$:

$$\lambda = \frac{4n^2}{R(n^2 - 4)} \qquad [51.19$$

Putting in the value $R = 1.09737 \times 10^7$ m^{-1}, we get

$$\lambda = \frac{3,645.1 n^2}{n^2 - 4}$$

which is the Balmer formula (equation 51.2), valid for n equal to or greater than 3. We can imagine the elation with which Bohr greeted this spectacular result.

Not only was the Balmer series accurately accounted for; many other series of hydrogen lines fit into the Bohr formula as well (Fig. 51.6). Transitions down to $n_1 = 2$ are the Balmer series; those down to $n_1 = 3$ are the Paschen (infrared)

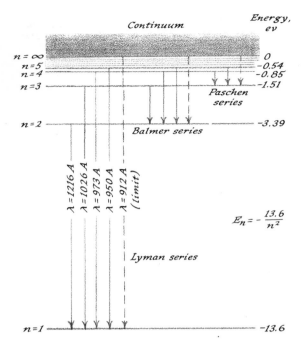

Continuum

Energy, ev

$n = \infty$ ——————————————— 0
$n = 5$ ——————————————— -0.54
$n = 4$ ——————————————— -0.85
$n = 3$ ——————————————— -1.51

Paschen series

$n = 2$ ——————————————— -3.39

Balmer series

$\lambda = 1216\,A$
$\lambda = 1026\,A$
$\lambda = 973\,A$
$\lambda = 950\,A$
$\lambda = 912\,A$ *(limit)*

$E_n = -\dfrac{13.6}{n^2}$

Lyman series

$n = 1$ ——————————————— -13.6

FIG. 51.6. *The Lyman, Balmer, and Paschen series in the spectrum of hydrogen. Because the other lines would be too close together to be visible, only a few lines are shown in each series.*

series; those down to $n_1 = 1$ are the Lyman (ultra-violet) series. The Balmer and Paschen series were accounted for, the Lyman series predicted, by Bohr's theory. It was a great triumph, although not a complete one, as we shall see in the next chapter. Despite its strange assumptions, the theory pointed the way to a new understanding of the atom.

Let us take note of one more similarity, and one difference, between atoms and gravitational planetary systems.

In § 34.5 we considered the concept of escape velocity. As it is possible to give a rocket so much energy that it will not return to the earth, so it is possible to raise an electron to such an energy level that it is no longer bound to its nucleus. The energy of that level is called the **ionization energy.** The lowest energy state of the hydrogen atom ($n_1 = 1$, Fig. 51.6) is -13.6 ev below the ionization level; it takes 13.6 ev of energy to lift an electron out of the ground state to the ionization level, which corresponds mathematically to $n_2 = \infty$.

An important difference between an atom and a planetary system is that, with respect to their energy levels, all atoms of hydrogen are alike, all atoms of mercury are alike, and so on. All atoms of each kind have the same energy levels. Planetary systems do not exhibit discontinuities in energy levels. One can therefore conceive of many different planetary systems; unlike atoms, planetary systems are all different.

51.4. Summary

Bohr made three assumptions about the electron in a hydrogen atom: (1) it has stable orbits; (2) its angular momentum is quantized in units of $h/2\pi$; (3) transitions between one stable orbit and another are accompanied by the emission or absorption of electromagnetic waves whose frequency, ν, is given by the equation $\Delta E = h\nu$, in which ΔE is the change in energy and h is the Planck constant. He obtained, for the wavelengths of the spectral lines of hydrogen, values that agreed very well with experiment, and he predicted spectral lines that were later found experimentally.

Problems

51.1. Go through the derivation of Bohr's formula (§ 51.3), noting carefully the words whose meaning had had to be clarified by operational means in previous chapters. Make a list of the physical concepts (in § 51.3) that must be clear before the Bohr model of the atom can be understood. (In the very first paragraph, for example, the following terms appear: massive, nucleus, atom, electron, planet, force, electrical coulombic force.) Look at the chapter titles, especially in Part I, for suggestions.

51.2. The following steps may help you discover for yourself an interesting and important interpretation of one of Bohr's ideas. Consider a hydrogen atom in an excited state given by the principal quantum number n.

1. Write expressions for the following in terms only of n and physical and mathematical constants: (A) the orbital radius; (B) the momentum of the electron; (C) the de Broglie wavelength of the electron; (D) the circumference of the orbit.

2. Divide the circumference by the wavelength. The result should be a function of n.

3. What physical interpretation of n does this afford? (It would pay to reread § 17.3.)

4. Is this the interpretation of n given when it was first introduced in § 51.3? Explain.

51.3. Singly ionized helium (a helium atom from which one electron has been removed) may be thought of as a hydrogen atom for which $Z = 2$. Notice that, in the approximation used in our derivation, the mass of the nucleus does not enter.

1. Write down the general expression, similar to equation 51.19, for the wavelengths of the Balmer series of singly ionized helium. (Hint: Use the value 2 for Z in equation 51.18.)

2. Do any of these wavelengths coincide with the Balmer lines of ordinary hydrogen? You may find it instructive to draw a sketch of the Balmer spectrum of hydrogen and under it the Balmer spectrum of singly ionized helium. This is how helium was first discovered in the spectrum of the sun.

51.4. Hydrogen-like atoms can be formed with a proton for a nucleus and a particle called the μ-meson (mu-meson) taking the place of the electron. (Such atoms are called **muonium**. They are important because a study of them gives us some

details about the structure of protons.) The μ-meson has a mass about 300 times the mass of an electron, but in all other respects is similar to the electron (except that it is short-lived, which is not important to this problem).

1. What is the binding energy (ev) of a μ-meson in the ground state of muonium?

2. What is the smallest permitted radius of its orbit?

3. In what part of the electromagnetic spectrum would its emitted radiation fall?

51.5. 1. The so-called H_α line of hydrogen is emitted during the transition from $n_2 = 3$ to $n_1 = 2$. Calculate the wavelength of H_α light. Is it in the visible part of the spectrum?

2. The Ly_α line is the first of the Lyman series, corresponding to the transition from $n_2 = 2$ to $n_1 = 1$. Calculate the wavelength of the Ly_α line. What portion of the spectrum does the Ly_α line fall in? Stars emit copious amounts of Ly_α; try to find out if this radiation can penetrate the earth's atmosphere.

51.6. 1. What is the energy of a photon capable of ionizing hydrogen?

2. What is the wavelength of such a photon?

3. One way to produce many such photons is to raise the temperature of hydrogen gas in an enclosure to such a value that its blackbody radiation has a peak at that wavelength. What is this temperature? (See equation 49.2.)

4. Explain why an external beam of Ly_α photons should go through hydrogen more readily when it is above this temperature than when it is considerably below it.

Wave Packets
and Wave Mechanics

TODAY it is known that Bohr's picture of the hydrogen atom is wrong. Some features of the Bohr model survive, however, in all subsequent atomic models: (1) the ratios of the orbital radii; (2) the idea that only certain discrete energy levels are permitted for the electrons of an atom; (3) the idea that photons of energy $h\nu = \Delta E$ are emitted or absorbed when a transition takes place from a higher energy level to a lower one or vice versa. The model of the hydrogen atom based on wave mechanics succeeded where the simple Bohr theory had failed. It is, however, a mathematical model, and harder to visualize. I shall try to describe it in outline, without going deeply into mathematics.

52.1. The Failure of Bohr's Theory

According to Heisenberg, we cannot specify both the position and the momentum of an electron in an atom. Conceptually, Bohr's model requires that we do so, and to this extent it violates Heisenberg's uncertainty principle. Yet Bohr's theory correctly predicted the energy levels permitted to an electron in a hydrogen atom, and the prediction was confirmed later by wave mechanics; it succeeded in spite of having arrived at those levels by way of orbits. It succeeded, however, only for hydrogen; it failed for ordinary atoms of higher atomic number.

The wave model that has superseded Bohr's model does not violate the uncertainty principle.

It offers, instead of the definite orbits imagined by Bohr, regions of probability of finding an electron. These are fuzzy three-dimensional regions somewhat like clouds of smoke surrounding the nucleus. The probability of finding an electron is high where the smoke is dense. Instead of imagining an electron whirling round alone, we imagine a three-dimensional wave associated with an electron. If the amplitude of the wave is great, the square of the amplitude—which is proportional to the intensity—is also great, and the probability of finding the electron is high (and we imagine a high density of smoke in our cloud). If you visualized a hydrogen atom with this interpretation in mind, it would look like Figure 52.1.A in the ground state ($n = 1$) and like Figure 52.1.B in a state of greater excitation ($n = 3$). (The three-dimensional pictures would be obtained by rotation of these figures round a central axis.)

The whiteness of a ring represents the probability of finding an electron there; the fact that the outer rings are gray and the inner one is white means that you are more likely to find an electron in the inner one. These diagrams were drawn according to the modern wave theory named after Erwin Schrödinger. Although the radius of the first circle in Figure 52.1.B. agrees well with Bohr's orbital radius (0.53 A), there is an important difference: in following the wave interpretation we don't say that an electron *is* anywhere in particular; we only say that it has a certain probability of being found there.

Another reason for dissatisfaction with Bohr's picture was that the quantization of angular momentum was assumed *ad hoc* and did not allow for a state with zero angular momentum. In the wave theory this quantization is a natural consequence of the properties of waves, and a state with zero angular momentum is predicted.

Since a purely mathematical treatment is beyond the scope of this book, my task in the rest of this chapter is to make certain aspects of the wave theory plausible. I shall first try to show that, if you allow some uncertainty in the momentum of a particle, and hence in its wavelength, it is possible to localize the particle within certain limits. You may find the following derivation somewhat lengthy; but, if you succeed in grasping its meaning, you will have reached a rewarding summit of understanding.

52.2. Wave Packets Associated with Particles

With a particle of mass m moving at speed v a wave of length $\lambda = h/mv$ is associated (equation 50.10). A perfect knowledge of λ implies a perfect knowledge of momentum and hence, by the uncertainty principle $[(\Delta p)(\Delta x) \geqq h]$, a great uncertainty in location. We can say the same thing in another way: to have a single wavelength, a wave train† has to be infinitely long. A

† If the end of a very long, stretched, horizontal rope is given a few shakes, a series of pulses will travel along the rope. At a certain instant all points of the rope will have zero displacement except those within limits such as $x = x_0 \pm \Delta x$. Within these limits the instantaneous displacement varies smoothly with distance, having negative as well as positive values. Such a disturbance (not limited to waves on a rope) will be called a **wave train.**

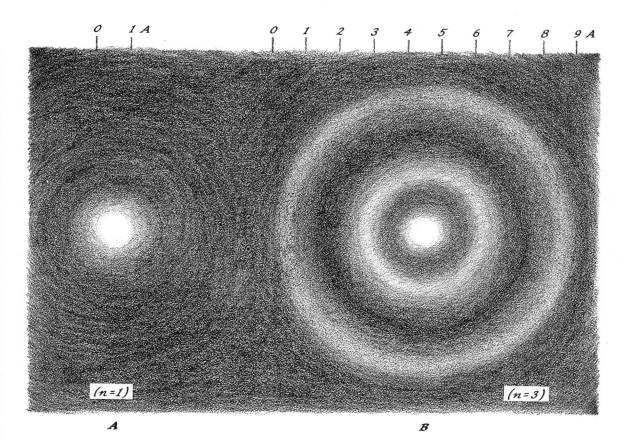

FIG. 52.1. *Visualization (in two dimensions only) of the probability of finding an electron in a hydrogen atom in two states of excitation.*

FIG. 52.2. *A wave train, of wavelength* λ = h/p, *associated with a particle.*

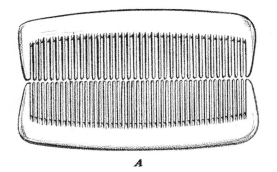

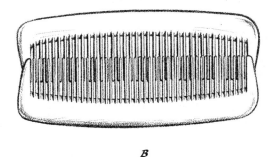

A   *B*

FIG. 52.3. *Illustration for analogy with wave packets and group velocity.*

mathematical analysis invented in 1822, long before Bohr and Heisenberg, by the French mathematician Jean Baptiste Joseph Fourier (1768–1830) shows that a finite wave train is equivalent to the sum of many wave trains of different wavelengths, each of infinite extent.

The same type of analysis applied to sound shows that a vibration of short duration is equivalent to the sum of many vibrations of different frequencies and long duration. Enthusiasts for the high-fidelity reproduction of music know that they need an amplifier capable of amplifying a very wide range of frequencies to reproduce accurately a sound of short duration such as the clash of two cymbals.

We return to the problem of a wave with space as a variable (rather than a single vibration with time as a variable). It can be shown that a wave train of limited extent in space is the equivalent of many wave trains, of different wavelengths, each of infinite extent. All this can be proved mathematically. I shall describe a model to show that it is reasonable.

Imagine a wave train of wavelength λ, and infinite in extent, associated with a particle traveling along the x axis (Fig. 52.2). The amplitude, and hence the intensity, which is proportional to the square of the amplitude, are constant all along the x axis. The probability of finding the particle associated with this wave is therefore the same

everywhere on the x axis. Thus, by assigning a definite wavelength, λ, to the particle, we have made $\Delta\lambda$ equal to 0 and hence Δp equal to 0. By the uncertainty principle, therefore, $\Delta x = \infty$. The uncertainty of location is infinite. We cannot specify where the particle is if we have given its associated wavelength with perfect accuracy.

Let's see what the effect would be of having just two slightly different wavelengths (λ_1 and λ_2) associated with the same particle. A simple way to visualize this is to take two combs (Fig. 52.3) with slightly different spacings between their teeth (A). If we put one comb on top of the other and hold them up between the light and our eyes (B), there will be some dark and some light regions. The lightest regions are found where the teeth have almost identical x coordinates, the darkest where the teeth of one comb lie halfway between the teeth of the other comb. If the teeth represent the crests of waves, the light areas are regions where the waves have almost identical phase; in the dark regions the waves are more or less out of phase. Similarly, the amplitudes of two sinusoidal waves can be combined by addition, as in Figure 52.4. Let us call regions such as *A*, *B*, and *C* **wave packets.** If the difference between the two wavelengths is very small, the size of each wave packet and hence the distance between their centers get large. (If—as an extreme case—the difference in wavelength is zero, the wave packet

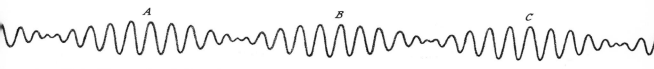

FIG. 52.4. *Wave packets A, B, and C, formed by two waves with wavelengths in the ratio 9:10. With infinite wave trains the wave-packet pattern would repeat itself without end.*

is infinite in extent.) Conversely, if the difference between wavelengths is great, the size of each packet and hence the distance between their centers get small. The resultant amplitude is great at the center of a wave packet. The probability of finding the associated particle is high at *A*, *B*, and *C*.

We now move the two combs in the same direction, perpendicular to the teeth, one at speed v_1 and the other at speed v_2. (For the purpose of the demonstration we may hold one of the combs still.) The group of packets corresponding to *A*, *B*, *C*, etc., can be made to move, with a speed called the **group velocity**, more slowly (in relation to a fixed frame of reference) than either comb. (It is easier to do this than to describe it, and I urge you to try it, in place of mathematical analysis, as the moving comb moves forward. If one comb is held still as suggested, the packets may move backward as the moving comb moves forward.) Let us consider just one such packet, which contains only two wavelengths, λ_1 and λ_2, each associated with a particle.

In the distance Δx (Fig. 52.5), wave 2 has *n* complete cycles and wave 1 has $n + 1$ complete cycles ($n = 4$ in the figure). Therefore

$$\frac{\Delta x}{\lambda_1} = n + 1 \quad \text{and} \quad \frac{\Delta x}{\lambda_2} = n$$

Hence

$$\frac{\Delta x}{\lambda_1} - \frac{\Delta x}{\lambda_2} = 1 \qquad [52.1$$

Using the formula $p = h/\lambda$ in this equation, we get

$$\Delta x \left(\frac{p_1}{h} - \frac{p_2}{h} \right) = 1 \qquad [52.2$$

$$(\Delta x)(\Delta p) = h \qquad [52.3$$

This looks very much like the uncertainty principle, but, of course, we have not yet associated this Δx with the uncertainty in the position of the particle. We can, nevertheless, begin to get some useful information out of it. If we divide both

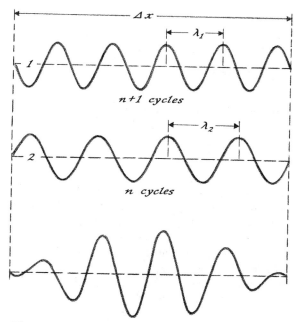

The sum of the displacements of waves 1 and 2

FIG. 52.5. *Wave packet formed by superposition of two waves whose wavelengths are in the ratio 8:10.*

sides of equation 52.3 by *p*, we obtain the equation

$$\Delta x \frac{\Delta p}{p} = \frac{h}{p} = \lambda$$

It can be shown mathematically that $\Delta p/p = \Delta\lambda/\lambda$ except for sign. Hence, for magnitudes only,

$$\Delta x \frac{\Delta\lambda}{\lambda} = \lambda$$

This says that for $\Delta\lambda/\lambda$ of the order of 1, Δx is of the order of λ. If $\Delta\lambda/\lambda = 10$, for example, $\Delta x = 0.1\lambda$; if $\Delta\lambda/\lambda = 0.1$, $\Delta x = 10\lambda$. This confirms what I said earlier: if λ_1 and λ_2 are far apart, the distance Δx (the size of the packet) is short;

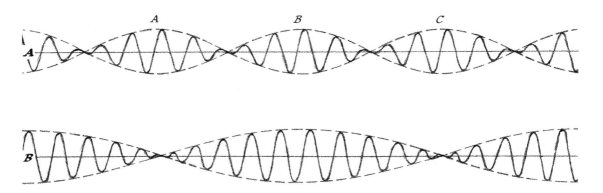

FIG. 52.6. *Wave packets formed by combination (A) of waves with wavelengths of 10 and 8 units (see Fig. 52.5) and (B) of waves with wavelengths of 10 and 9 units (see Fig. 52.4). Observe that packets at the center, B, will always be superposed constructively.*

if λ_1 and λ_2 are close, the distance Δx is long. It is possible to choose a value of $\Delta\lambda/\lambda$ for which Δx is of the order of λ. We know, however, that we have not yet localized the particle to a single wave packet, such as B (Fig. 52.4). There are still many others like those at A and C, but we have made a start in the right direction.

Consider waves with wavelengths $\lambda_1 = 10$, $\lambda_2 = 8$, and $\lambda_3 = 9$, in arbitrary units. The result of combining waves with wavelengths λ_1 and λ_2 is shown in line A of Figure 52.6. The result of combining waves with wavelengths λ_1 and λ_3 (λ_3 lies between λ_1 and λ_2) is shown in line B. The separation between packets is greater because the difference $\lambda_1 - \lambda_3$ is smaller than $\lambda_1 - \lambda_2$. The effect (not shown) of combining waves with wavelengths λ_1 and λ_4 if λ_4 lay between λ_1 and λ_3 would be like line B but with the wave packets even farther apart. The waves in these illustrations have been chosen so that they have a crest at the central point, B. The resultant amplitude at B increases with the addition of each successive wave; but at other points, especially those far from B, the effects of positive and negative contributions tend to cancel, with the result that a single wave packet of large maximum amplitude survives at B and the amplitude approaches zero everywhere else. It can be shown that, if *all* wavelengths between λ_1 and λ_2 are combined in this way, a very well-localized wave packet results at B, and the resultant of the superposition approaches zero at points that are many wavelengths away from B.

Think of the matter in this way: Take a wave that has a crest at B and wavelength λ_1. Now add to it waves of which all have a crest at B but different wavelengths. At B, all the amplitudes must add up to a large total amplitude. At point A or C, well removed from B, we are adding together numbers that are equally likely to be positive or negative. Hence they must add up to something small. If you add enough waves, you can make the amplitude at points like A and C as much smaller as you like than the amplitude at B. Imagine, then, waves with *all* the wavelengths between λ_1 and λ_2 combined by superposition. The result is a single, well-defined packet at B for which equation 52.3 is true. The significance of this argument is as follows: For a particle whose momentum is $p \pm \Delta p$ one may construct a wave packet whose length, Δx, is of the order of magnitude of the wavelength, λ, associated with the momentum, p—namely, $\lambda = h/p$ if $\Delta p/p$ is roughly 1. Under these circumstances the wavelength, λ, associated with a particle of momentum p is a rough estimate of the uncertainty in the localization of the particle.

To summarize: A moving particle has associated with it a wave packet that determines its behavior in a probabilistic sense. In order to describe the behavior of the particle in a physical situation, one needs only to replace it conceptually by the wave packet.

52.3. The Wave Explanation of Quantized Energy States

In our study of waves we found that standing waves, unlike progressive waves, can be confined within two fixed ends if they have a node-antinode-node (abbreviated as *NAN*) configuration (Fig. 17.1). We also found (§ 17.1) that a standing wave can be regarded as the superposition of two waves of the same frequency moving in opposite directions. To generate such a wave, you don't need an operator at each end of the rope. A single operator to vibrate one end suffices if reflection is permitted at the other end. We found, furthermore, that, besides the fundamental frequency (for the *NAN* mode), only certain other frequencies occur [producing patterns *NANAN*, *NANANAN*, etc. (Fig. 17.2)]. No frequency lower than the fundamental frequency occurs; standing waves of lower frequencies simply cannot be formed. Suppose we required that, regardless of the frequency, the amplitude always be less than a certain maximum for each frequency: a discrete energy corresponding to each frequency would be implied. (This artificial condition that we impose on the rope has an analogue in wave mechanics for the following reason: since the wave amplitude is a measure of probability and the total probability must be 1, it is clear that amplitudes of arbitrary magnitude are not allowed for probability waves.)

Consider now an atom or an atomic particle (there is no use in considering macroscopic particles, for their de Broglie waves are too short) moving in a cubical box with perfectly reflecting walls. It bounces back and forth between two walls. It has a definite amount of energy. Looked at classically, it seems to be able to change its energy continuously (for example, by losing a little at a time through friction with the air). Classically, therefore, all energy levels seem possible.

Now let us look at the particle from de Broglie's point of view. Conceptually, we shift our attention to the associated wave. We conceive of a wave moving from left to right and producing a reflected wave, moving from right to left, with which it can interfere (Fig. 52.7). For a particular wavelength, obviously, the pattern *NAN* will be established; for another wavelength the pattern *NANAN* will be established; and so on.

A unique energy level corresponds to the wavelength that produces the fundamental pattern. Let's compute it. Figure 52.7 shows that, in general, if the width of the box is d, the wavelength, λ_n, that will establish a standing wave with n loops obeys the equation

$$n\frac{\lambda}{2} = d \qquad [52.4$$

in which d is the width of the box. From the de Broglie relation we obtain the equation

$$p_n{}^2 = \frac{h^2}{\lambda_n{}^2} \qquad [52.5$$

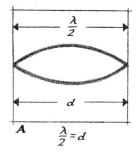

$A \quad \frac{\lambda}{2}=d$

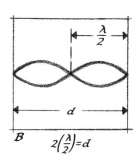

$B \quad 2\left(\frac{\lambda}{2}\right)=d$

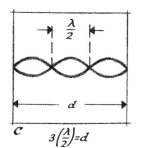

$C \quad 3\left(\frac{\lambda}{2}\right)=d$

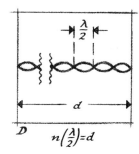

$D \quad n\left(\frac{\lambda}{2}\right)=d$

FIG. 52.7. *Standing-wave patterns associated with a particle bouncing back and forth between the walls of a box.*

From the formula

$$E_n = \tfrac{1}{2}mv_n{}^2$$

(in which v_n is the velocity that will produce λ_n) we obtain the equation

$$2E_nm = m^2v_n{}^2 = p_n{}^2 \qquad [52.6$$

From equations 52.5 and 52.6 we get

$$E_n = \frac{h^2}{2m\lambda_n{}^2} \qquad [52.7$$

Using equation 52.4 in equation 52.7, we get

$$E_n = \frac{h^2n^2}{8md^2} \qquad [52.8$$

This example illustrates how a wave implies the existence of discrete energy levels. (This time they are proportional to n^2 rather than, as in the Bohr atom, to $1/n^2$. The reason for the difference is that the restoring force in the case of the box is quite different from the simple inverse-square force of the Coulomb field.)

It is obvious from equation 52.8 (since $h = 6.63 \times 10^{-34}$ J-sec) that E_n is an extremely small number ($\sim 10^{-68}$) for values of $n^2/8md^2$ close to 1. No wonder, then, that wave mechanics is useful primarily for objects of atomic and subatomic size! An atom, of course, is not a box with rigid walls. The restoring force does not act abruptly at a certain distance from the nucleus.

The precise values of the discrete energy levels in the hydrogen atom were calculated by Schrödinger by means of a wave equation that yielded the amplitude of a wave as a function of the electron's radial distance, r, from the nucleus and of two other variables, θ and ϕ (instead of the usual rectangular coordinates x, y, and z). The value of the square of Schrödinger's wave function, Ψ, at a point gives the probability of finding an electron there. Without going into the mathematical details, I shall summarize by saying that this complicated wave is characterized by three quantum numbers (integers), usually called n, l, and m, which arise from quantizations very similar to the simple one associating the n of equation 52.8 with the box. In the hydrogen atom the principal quantum number, n, can take on the values 1, 2, 3, etc.; the integer l, which represents the quantization of angular momentum (rather than n as in the Bohr theory discussed in Chap. 51), can take on only the values 0, 1, 2, . . .

up to $(n - 1)$; and m, called the magnetic quantum number, can take on positive, zero, and negative integral values: l, $l - 1$, $l - 2$, . . . 0, -1, -2, . . . $-l$. All this may sound as mysterious and as unfounded as numerology, but these rules actually evolve quite naturally from the mathematics of the Schrödinger equation. We shall consider all this more thoroughly in Chapter 53.

52.4. Bohr's Correspondence Principle

The concepts of the new quantum physics replace the clear picture of an electron moving in circular orbits of definite radius by a fuzzy picture representing only the abstract concept of the probability of finding an electron. We may lament the loss of the old graphic representation, but the new theory really works for all particles of atomic size, and the old theory does not.

For objects of macroscopic size, moreover, the new theory does not contradict classical theory; the two correspond perfectly. We had an example of this fusing of modern and classical ideas in considering Einstein's relativity. Galileo's relativity can be deduced as a special case of Einstein's relativity, but not vice versa. Einstein's relativity is the more general. Both theories give the same answer for classical problems; for these, we say, the correspondence is perfect. Similarly, the classical concepts of motion can be deduced from the quantum-mechanical concepts; the converse is not true. Quantum mechanics is fundamental.

The idea that the new and the old physics must give the same results for classical problems was raised by Bohr to the level of a fundamental principle—his **correspondence principle.**

As an illustration consider first the great difference between classical and quantum answers when we ask about the frequency of the light given out by a revolving electron in a low energy state.

The number, ν^*, of revolutions per second made by the electron in the nth permissible orbit can be computed as follows. From the fact that the kinetic energy, $\tfrac{1}{2}mv_n{}^2$, is numerically equal to the E_n given by equation 51.15 we can get v_n in terms of r_n. Using r_n from equation 51.12 we get

$$\nu^* = \frac{4\pi^2mK^2Z^2e^4}{n^3h^3} \qquad [52.9$$

Classically, this should be the frequency of the emitted radiation. According to quantum mechanics, the frequency, ν, is obtained differently. It comes from the formula $h\nu = \Delta E$ (equation 51.17) and may be written as

$$\nu = \frac{2\pi^2 mK^2 Z^2 e^4}{h^3}\left[\frac{(n_2 - n_1)(n_2 + n_1)}{n_2{}^2 n_1{}^2}\right] \quad [52.10$$

For very large values of n, the term in the brackets, when $n_2 - n_1 = 1$ (a jump from one orbit to the next lower one), becomes approximately $2/n^3$, making the quantum-mechanical frequency, ν, identical with the classical frequency, ν^*. This result shows that, for large quantum numbers, transitions between adjacent energy levels emit or absorb radiation of the same frequencies as those calculated by classical means. This is an illustration of the correspondence principle. In the mind of Bohr, the correspondence principle became a powerful tool. By means of it he was able to choose the quantization condition (equation 51.7) that would give the right result.

To see how the principle applies to the hydrogen atom, consider the values of Table 52.1. From equation 52.9 the classical frequencies of hydrogen were calculated for six values of n and $(n + 1)$. From equation 52.10 the quantum-theory frequency was calculated for an energy jump from E_{n+1} to E_n. As n increases, there is an increasingly closer correspondence between classical and quantum-theory frequencies; by the time n reaches 500, the agreement between the mean ν^* and ν is very good. In classical problems the values of n are very much greater than 500, and the correspondence is accordingly better.

52.5. Summary

A moving particle has associated with it a wave packet that determines its behavior in a probabilistic sense. In order to describe the behavior of the particle in a physical situation, one need only replace it, conceptually, by the wave packet.

The probability of finding the particle at a point is associated with the square of the amplitude, or the intensity, of the wave at that point. A very slight uncertainty in the momentum, and hence in the wavelength associated with the particle, implies, by the Heisenberg uncertainty principle, a great uncertainty in localization of the particle, and hence a long wave packet. Conversely, a great uncertainty in the momentum, and hence in the wavelength associated with the particle, implies only a slight uncertainty in localization and hence a short wave packet.

These ideas have led to a wave mechanics that is applicable to all atomic particles and that gives results consistent with classical mechanics. The existence of discrete energy states follows in wave mechanics in a manner analogous to the existence of standing waves in macroscopic vibrating systems. The idea that the new and the old physics must give the same results for phenomena of laboratory size is the essence of Bohr's correspondence principle.

TABLE 52.1

Classical and Quantum-theory Frequencies of the Hydrogen Atom

n	ν^* Orbit Frequency $(n + 1)$	ν^* Orbit Frequency (n)	ν Quantum Theory $(\nu = \Delta E/h)$
1	0.823×10^{15} sec^{-1}	6.58×10^{15} sec^{-1}	2.47×10^{15} sec^{-1}
5	3.04×10^{13}	5.27×10^{13}	4.03×10^{13}
9	6.58×10^{12}	9.04×10^{12}	7.72×10^{12}
24	4.22×10^{11}	4.77×10^{11}	4.48×10^{11}
100	6.38×10^{9}	6.58×10^{9}	6.52×10^{9}
500	5.22×10^{7}	5.27×10^{7}	5.25×10^{7}

Problems

52.1. 1. Using either equation 52.9 or 52.10, confirm the statement that ν, if $n = 500$, is about 5.3×10^7 cycles/sec.

2. Express ν in megacycles per second. How does this compare with the frequency of a typical FM station? with that of a typical AM station?

52.2. In the helium atom, two electrons can be placed in the ground state ($n = 1$). The radius of the $n = 1$ orbit is approximately that given by the Bohr theory for $Z = 2$, and, on the average, the two electrons will be about a radius apart. Compare the magnitude of the force holding an electron in its orbit with the magnitude of the average force between the two electrons. Does the answer suggest to you a reason why the Bohr theory is not very good for a two-electron atom?

52.3. 1. Suppose that the electron of the hydrogen atom were kept in its orbit by the gravitational attraction between it and the proton instead of by the electric attraction. If the orbit were, nevertheless, of the same size (1 A in diameter), what would be the frequency with which the electron completed its orbit?

2. The heaviest naturally occurring nucleus is $_{92}U^{238}$. If calculations of force are to be made to six significant figures, does the gravitational force have to be taken into account?

52.4. Consider the atom $_{92}U^{238}$. Calculate the kinetic energy of an electron in the state $n = 1$ by using the expression for E_n (equation 51.5) to which it is numerically equivalent. Is the result much less than 0.5 Mev? If the kinetic energy comes out as much less than the rest energy of an electron (0.5 Mev),

the Bohr formula, which is non-relativistic, may be used as a rough approximation.

52.5. 1. The wave packet of Fig. 52.5 has about 4.5 complete cycles in it; that is, $\Delta x \cong 4.5\bar{\lambda}$. Note that this agrees with the equation

$$\Delta x \frac{\Delta\lambda}{\bar{\lambda}} = \lambda$$

of § 52.2 if we write it as the equation

$$\Delta x = \frac{\bar{\lambda}}{\Delta\lambda}\bar{\lambda}$$

in which

$$\Delta\lambda = \lambda_2 - \lambda_1 \quad \text{and} \quad \bar{\lambda} = \frac{\lambda_1 + \lambda_2}{2}$$

with λ_1 equal to 8 units and λ_2 equal to 10 units.

2. In a similar way, derive the approximate number of cycles expected in a wave packet for which $\lambda_1 = 9$ units and $\lambda_2 = 10$ units, and check the result by consulting Fig. 52.6.

3. Using only rough sketches of

$$y_1 = \cos 45x$$
$$y_2 = \cos 40x$$
$$y_3 = \cos 36x$$

(waves of wavelengths 8, 9, and 10 units, respectively), confirm that

$$y = y_1 + y_2 + y_3$$

would have a peak at $x = 0$ and that the addition of more and more waves of the same type ($y = \cos kx$) with wavelengths between 8 and 10 will strengthen the maximum at $x = 0$ and make the sum at points far from x relatively small.

Atomic Structure

WE HAVE reached the last chapter of Part V, on atomic physics. Part VI will be devoted to the nucleus. In our study of atoms we have already considered their nuclei, of course, for you can't have atoms without nuclei; and it must be apparent that the division of subject matter into "atomic" and "nuclear" is arbitrary. It simply suits our convenience to put the characteristics of the outer electronic structure of atoms into a part called "atomic physics." (The part could also be called "the theoretical basis of chemistry," for the quantum-mechanical theory of the atom now makes it possible to account for the chemical properties of atoms—valence, ionization potential, chemical activity, etc.) We have done no more than scratch the surface of the vast topic called "atomic physics." Yet we must soon drop it; we must then focus our attention on the nucleus if we are to get more than a glimpse of that fundamental storehouse of energy.

I have said on several occasions that Bohr's picture of the atom is wrong and that the wave-mechanical picture is right. Bohr's picture, with its well-defined orbits, violates the uncertainty principle; the wave theory, with its fuzzy probability regions, does not. Bohr's assumption that angular momentum is an integral multiple of $h/2\pi$ is correct, but his assumption that it is $nh/2\pi$ (n being the principal quantum number) is wrong. His theory does not account for the spectral lines of neutral helium; the wave theory does account for them accurately. Indeed, all the facts of atomic structure and much of chemistry seem to be explained by modern quantum

theory. The great success of the Bohr model in accounting for the spectral frequencies of hydrogen begins to look like a happy accident. Nevertheless, as we follow the evolution of atomic theory, guided by the inspired guesses of men of genius like Einstein and Bohr, we study that model, among other reasons, for the insight it gives us into the methods used by scientists.

The ultimate goals of the study we have been pursuing are a good theory of the electronic structure of all the atoms and an explanation of the periodicity of their chemical properties when they are arranged in the order of increasing atomic number. These goals would require a complete textbook. In this concluding chapter I shall confine myself to selected topics that show (1) the limited result of extending Bohr's picture to atoms other than hydrogen and (2) how one cornerstone of the modern wave theory, Pauli's exclusion principle, makes possible a systematic explanation of how complex atoms can be built up around the cores of simple ones. Then we shall stop abruptly and move on to a closer look at the nucleus and its structure.

53.1. Extension of Bohr's Theory to Other One-electron Atoms

The normal hydrogen atom is neutral because the negative charge of its electron is balanced by the equal positive charge of its nucleus. The nucleus of deuterium, the heavy hydrogen isotope ($_1H^2$), though it is twice as heavy as that of ordi-

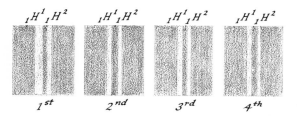

$_1H^1$ $_1H^2$ $_1H^1$ $_1H^2$ $_1H^1$ $_1H^2$ $_1H^1$ $_1H^2$

1st   *2nd*   *3rd*   *4th*

FIG. 53.1. *High-resolution spectra of hydrogen ($_1H^1$) and deuterium ($_1H^2$) compared. The first four members of the Lyman series of the two hydrogen atoms are shown for the first-order spectrum. (Drawn from a photograph by Harvey E. White.)*

nary hydrogen ($_1H^1$), has, like that of ordinary hydrogen, a single positive charge. Hence deuterium is a neutral atom with one electron. Its spectrum can be accounted for by the simple Bohr theory.

A different kind of one-electron atom is the singly ionized helium atom, He$^+$. This is a helium atom that has lost one of its electrons by ionization. Its spectrum also can be accounted for by the simple Bohr theory. Let us consider these cases in detail.

The spectral frequencies of deuterium may be derived from Bohr's equation (51.17), written in the form

$$h\nu = \frac{2\pi^2 K^2 Z^2 e^4 m}{h^2}\left(\frac{1}{n_1^2} - \frac{1}{n_2^2}\right) \qquad [53.1$$

According to this equation, the spectral lines of deuterium should be identical with those of ordinary hydrogen, for *the mass of the nucleus does not appear.* The value of the nuclear charge, Z (§ 45.2), is still 1, and m is the mass of the electron. The expression is identical with the one used for the lines of ordinary hydrogen. But a high-resolution spectrograph shows a slight difference between the spectra of $_1H^1$ and $_1H^2$ (Fig. 53.1), a shift in frequency of about 3 parts in 10,000. It is owing to the experimental skill of the spectroscopists who built and used these instruments that such a small difference is observable.

If we seek the reason for the difference, it is natural to consider how the mass of the nucleus enters into the calculations. Bohr assumed an infinite mass for the nucleus, and it fails to appear in his calculations because only the electron was assumed to move. It simplified calculations considerably to make this assumption. Actually, however, nucleus and electron form a system rotating about their common center of mass (see § 26.4). Mathematical analysis based upon the fact that the center of mass does not move shows that, if the mass of the electron is m and that of the nucleus is M, we can get the correct value of $h\nu$ by writing the **reduced mass** of the system,

$$\frac{m}{1 + m/M}$$

instead of m in equation 53.1. This substitution accounts readily for the slight difference between the spectra of $_1H^1$ and $_1H^2$ ($m/M \cong 1/1,840$ for $_1H^1$ and half of that for $_1H^2$). The isotope $_1H^2$ was first detected, in fact, by spectroscopic means.

Next consider singly ionized helium, He$^+$, as another one-electron atom. Its spectral lines are obtainable from equation 53.1, but notice that now $Z = 2$. The factor Z^2 is now 4 instead of 1. The atom's frequencies should be 4 times the corresponding frequencies of hydrogen, an inference that has been amply confirmed by experiment. Similar remarks can be made about doubly ionized lithium and triply ionized beryllium. They are both one-electron atoms, and the Bohr theory accounts for their spectral frequencies as accurately as for those of hydrogen.

Thus far the Bohr theory succeeds; but the most sensitive spectroscopes also show some fine structure in the spectrum of hydrogen—that is, some lines very close to those predicted by Bohr but different enough to demand explanation. The numerical details of this fine structure and of other subtle effects were ultimately explained by the wave theory, but some were accounted for even earlier by Arnold Sommerfeld, who extended Bohr's concept to elliptic orbits. His theory achieved some success but was bound to fail for the more complex atoms because its well-defined orbits violated the uncertainty principle. I shall discuss Sommerfeld's theory briefly because it illustrates how groping, even with imperfect concepts, evolves new ideas that point the way to deeper insights.

53.2. Elliptic Orbits: the One-electron Atom According to Sommerfeld

It is a well-known fact of classical mechanics that a very light body revolving round a very massive one, under the influence of an attractive inverse-square law of force of either gravitational or electrical origin, can follow an elliptical path with the massive body at one focus. It was only natural, therefore, that one of the earliest extensions of Bohr's theory should have involved the consideration of elliptic orbits.

Sommerfeld, undertaking the mathematical analysis of elliptic orbits, found that their description required more than one quantization condition—that is, more than the single quantum number n. Although he too quantized angular momentum in integral multiples of $h/2\pi$, he symbolized it by l, reserving the symbol n for the integer that characterized the total energy of the electron in the elliptic orbit. His expression for the total energy, using the non-relativistic mass of the electron, is

$$E_n = \frac{-2\pi^2 K^2 Z^2 e^4 m}{n^2 h^2}$$ [53.2]

which is, of course, the same function of n that Bohr had arrived at, fortuitously, in spite of having erroneously adopted $n(h/2\pi)$ as the permitted values of angular momentum. Since the frequency of the emitted light is $h\nu = E_{n_1} - E_{n_2}$, the new theory leads to the same spectral lines as the Bohr theory. A more refined analysis, using the relativistic mass of the electron, reveals that the second quantization condition imposes slight variations on the energy terms—variations that predict lines not predicted by equation 53.2 alone. These lines were observed and thus lent support to Sommerfeld's model. Finally, in order to explain the behavior of the atom in a homogeneous magnetic field, he introduced a third quantum number. This also led to modifications of the energy levels and to the prediction of spectral lines produced in transitions from one energy level to another.

The theories of both Sommerfeld and Bohr suffered from the same basic weakness: they assumed, in principle, that both the momentum and the location of the electron could be stated precisely. Yet they pointed the way toward the quantization conditions that eventually appeared as logical deductions in the wave mechanics invented by Erwin Schrödinger (born in 1887).

The graphical representation of Figure 53.2 shows (we know now not to take this literally) four possible orbits corresponding to $n = 2$. One is a circle, and three are ellipses. Although each corresponds to $n = 2$, the energy associated with each orbit is slightly different from that associated with the others. In the wave-mechanical treatment there are, of course, no such definite orbits. We mention them in passing because they represent a partially successful attempt to extend Bohr's classical ideas. It, too, suffered from not permitting zero angular momentum for the electron. The classical explanation was that this would require the electron to go through the nucleus—an impossibility for classical particles but, as we shall see, not inconceivable when a wave replaces the particle conceptually.

Before going on to summarize some of the gains introduced by the wave-mechanical atom, let us consider one more way in which Bohr's model has served well as an approximation: in explaining the gross details of x-ray spectra.

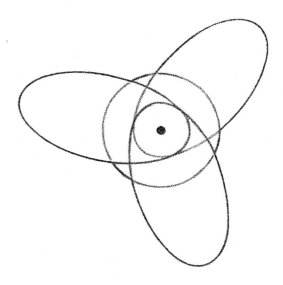

FIG. 53.2. *Sommerfeld's electron orbits, one circular and three elliptic, associated with* n = 2.

53.3. Application of Bohr's Theory to the X-ray Spectra of Atoms with More than One Electron

One idea in Bohr's theory has withstood the test of time and has been incorporated into all successive atomic theories, including the wave theory—the idea that spectral frequencies, ν, are obtainable from a knowledge of energy levels, E_{n_1}, E_{n_2}, etc., according to the formula

$$h\nu = E_{n_1} - E_{n_2} \qquad [53.3$$

The answers to the old questions "Why does an atom give off only certain definite frequencies?" and "Why doesn't the atom collapse?" are intimately connected with the discrete energy levels of the atom's electrons. The main difference between the Bohr theory and the wave theory is in the way the energy levels are calculated.

A crude extension of Bohr's theory is useful in explaining the x-ray spectra of many-electron atoms. Even before wave mechanics there were reasons (based upon the periodicity of the chemical properties of the atoms, for example) for believing that in such atoms there are, at most, 2 electrons in the $n = 1$ energy state, 8 electrons in the $n = 2$ state, 18 electrons in the $n = 3$ state, and so on. The energies associated with the orbits would, according to equation 51.15, be

$$E_n = \frac{-2\pi^2 K^2 Z^2 e^4 m}{n^2 h^2} \qquad [53.4$$

This formula was derived, of course, for the hydrogen atom ($Z = 1$), but we may consider it a valid first approximation even for the energy levels of more complex atoms. Observe that, if $n = 1$, the formula gives the ionization potential of an electron in the ground state, or, as we say figuratively, in the innermost shell. For hydrogen we found it to be -13.6 ev. We may therefore write, more generally,

$$E_1 = -13.6Z^2 \text{ ev} \qquad [53.5$$

Now consider a heavy atom, such as tungsten ($Z = 74$). Substitution into equation 53.5 yields

$$E_1 = -74{,}473 \text{ ev}$$

which means that it takes 74,473 electron volts of energy to remove an electron from the $n = 1$ shell of tungsten.

One way to remove such an electron from a piece of tungsten is to bombard the piece with accelerated external electrons, as is done in x-ray tubes (Fig. 47.3). When an electron has been removed from the $n = 1$ shell, the tungsten atom is in an excited state. An electron from an outer shell can fall into the inner shell. In the process, a high-energy photon is emitted. Such photons are known as x-ray photons. The study of x-ray spectra permits us to check the validity of equation 53.4.

The frequency, ν, of a photon produced as an electron from the nth shell falls into the $n = 1$ shell is obtainable from the equation

$$h\nu = 13.6Z^2 \left(\frac{1}{1^2} - \frac{1}{n^2} \right) \text{ ev} \qquad [53.6$$

(Since the energy is expressed in electron volts, h is in electron-volt–seconds.) It is obvious at a glance that, if all other quantities remain fixed, ν is proportional to Z^2. A plot of the square root of the x-ray frequency, $\sqrt{\nu}$, against the atomic number, Z, should therefore be a straight line going through the origin.

H. G. Moseley first tested this idea experimentally (1914) by studying the x-ray spectra of many of the known elements. When he plotted the experimental values of $\sqrt{\nu}$ for the transition from $n = 2$ to $n = 1$ (the frequency, ν, is obtainable from the wavelength, which is determined by an x-ray spectrograph) against Z, he found that the points did lie on a smooth curve that was very nearly straight (Fig. 53.3). That line did not, however, go exactly through the origin. Moseley found that it did go through the origin if Z was replaced by $Z - \sigma$ in the equation. When the final state corresponds to $n = 1$ and the atom has many electrons, it is found that σ is fairly constant at 0.5. The effective value of Z in this transition is therefore $Z - 0.5$. (When Z is large, the error resulting from the use of $\sigma = 1$ instead of $\sigma = 0.5$ is not great, and $\sigma = 1$, though incorrect, has the advantage of being intuitively reasonable—at least for operations taking place entirely outside the first orbit and not too close to it—for the following physical reason:

the one electron left in the $n = 1$ state shields the nucleus and makes the effective net charge on it $Z - 1$ rather than Z.) For molybdenum ($Z = 42$), for example, we may write, for the energy of the photon radiated by a transition from $n = 2$ to $n = 1$,

$$hv = 13.6 \left(\frac{1}{1^2} - \frac{1}{2^2}\right)(42 - 0.5)^2 \text{ ev} \quad [53.7$$

$$= 17,500 \text{ ev} \quad [53.8$$

which is close to the experimental value, 17,400 ev.

What Moseley discovered was that the experimental x-ray data fit well an expression of the form

$$hv = 13.6 \left(\frac{1}{1^2} - \frac{1}{2^2}\right)(Z - \sigma)^2 \text{ ev} \quad [53.9$$

But the expression for hv in the simple Bohr theory is

$$hv = 13.6 \left(\frac{1}{1^2} - \frac{1}{2^2}\right) Z^2 \text{ ev} \quad [53.10$$

for the same set of lines. This suggests very strongly that the Bohr picture, with the slight modification of Z to $Z - \sigma$, actually gives a good explanation of the mechanism of x-ray production and hence is at least a very good rough model, even of complex atoms.

Moseley's discovery was important for the fol-

lowing reason: The order of the elements in the periodic table (Table 53.1) and hence the number (1, 2, 3, . . .) assigned to each were first established by the chemists' technique of determining atomic weights. No one realized at first what we now know: that such a number also represents the integral number of charges on the nucleus; but the successful correlation of Moseley's x-ray spectra with Bohr's theory of the atom proved conclusively that a more generally useful order of the atoms is given by their atomic numbers, Z, than by their atomic weights. Cobalt and nickel, for example, which had been erroneously assigned numbers based on their atomic weights, were put into the proper order of atomic number as a result of Moseley's experiments. When the elements are tabulated in the order of ascending atomic numbers (Table 53.1), the earlier apparent exceptions to periodic behavior disappear. Although an explanation of the fine details of the spectra of light elements like helium and argon had to wait for the wave theory, Bohr's theory, with good accuracy, accounted for at least the gross details of the x-ray spectra of heavy elements.

To proceed with our study of the structure of atoms, we must now drop the Bohr model and return to the wave theory associated with the name of Schrödinger; but first we need an important idea that was proposed by Pauli.

53.4. Pauli's Exclusion Principle

Among the giants of "the revolution of 1926" Wolfgang Pauli (1900–1958) must always be counted. The contribution for which he will be longest remembered is probably that called **Pauli's exclusion principle**. I shall state it first in terms of the circular and elliptic orbits of Sommerfeld's theory, but later we shall see that it is essential to the general wave formulation, in which such orbits are no longer considered to exist. Pauli discovered that no orbit can have more than two electrons. With this rule we can determine the total population of each of the various energy states. If, for example, to the picture we have for the $n = 2$ state (Fig. 53.2) we add dots represent-

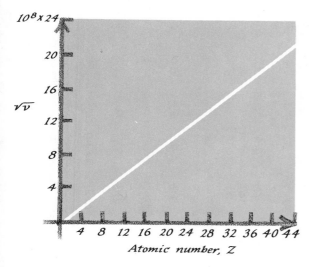

FIG. 53.3. Moseley's law: the square root of the x-ray frequency plotted against atomic number is a straight line.

TABLE 53.1

Periodic Table of the Elements†

1																	2
H 1.008																	He 4.00
3 Li 6.94	4 Be 9.01											5 B 10.8	6 C 12.01	7 N 14.01	8 O 16.00	9 F 19.0	10 Ne 20.2
11 Na 23.0	12 Mg 24.3											13 Al 27.0	14 Si 28.1	15 P 31.0	16 S 32.1	17 Cl 35.5	18 Ar 39.9
19 K 39.1	20 Ca 40.1	21 Sc 45.0	22 Ti 47.9	23 V 50.9	24 Cr 52.0	25 Mn 54.9	26 Fe 55.8	27 Co 58.9	28 Ni 58.7	29 Cu 63.5	30 Zn 65.4	31 Ga 69.7	32 Ge 72.6	33 As 74.9	34 Se 79.0	35 Br 79.9	36 Kr 83.8
37 Rb 85.5	38 Sr 87.6	39 Y 88.9	40 Zr 91.2	41 Nb 92.9	42 Mo 95.9	43 Tc (99)	44 Ru 101.1	45 Rh 102.9	46 Pd 106.4	47 Ag 107.9	48 Cd 112.4	49 In 114.8	50 Sn 118.7	51 Sb 121.8	52 Te 127.6	53 I 126.9	54 Xe 131.3
55 Cs 132.9	56 Ba 137.3	57–71 See below	72 Hf 178.5	73 Ta 180.9	74 W 183.9	75 Re 186.2	76 Os 190.2	77 Ir 192.2	78 Pt 195.1	79 Au 197.0	80 Hg 200.6	81 Tl 204.4	82 Pb 207.2	83 Bi 209.0	84 Po (209)	85 At (210)	86 Rn (222)
87 Fr (223)	88 Ra (226)	89– See below															

57 La 138.9	58 Ce 140.1	59 Pr 140.9	60 Nd 144.2	61 Pm (147)	62 Sm 150.4	63 Eu 152.0	64 Gd 157.3	65 Tb 158.9	66 Dy 162.5	67 Ho 164.9	68 Er 167.3	69 Tm 168.9	70 Yb 173.0	71 Lu 175.0
89 Ac (227)	90 Th 232.0	91 Pa (231)	92 U 238.0	93 Np (237)	94 Pu (242)	95 Am (243)	96 Cm (247)	97 Bk (245)	98 Cf (251)	99 Es (254)	100 Fm (253)	101 Md (256)	102 No (254)	103 Lw (257)

† Parenthetical values are the mass numbers of the isotopes with the longest half-lives.

ing electrons in orbit, and no more than two in each orbit, we obtain the picture shown in Figure 53.4. We shouldn't take this representation literally, but it does account for at most eight electrons, corresponding to the $n = 2$ state.

In Schrödinger's wave mechanics, in which there are no orbits, the equivalent statement of Pauli's exclusion principle is that no two electrons in an atom can be in the same state. I shall now show what is meant by the term "state." The **state** of an electron in an atom is characterized, not by a single integer, n, which is the principal quantum number, but by four quantum numbers, n, l, m, and s. The restrictions on the first three of these numbers appear as natural consequences of Schrödinger's theory. I can do no more than set them down as a set of rules that can be justified by theory. Even treating them like rules of a game, however, may prove instructive. For example: n is a positive integer (it cannot be zero); l, the quantum number associated with angular momentum, is either zero or a positive integer that cannot exceed $n - 1$; m, the magnetic quantum number, related to the splitting of energy levels that occurs when the atom is put into a homogeneous magnetic field, is a

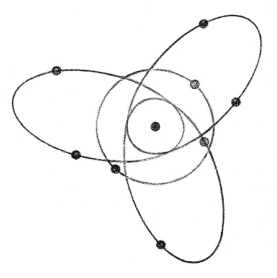

FIG. 53.4. *If, by Pauli's exclusion principle, we assign, at most, two electrons to each orbit for the* $n = 2$ *state, eight electrons are accounted for.*

positive or negative integer or zero [it may equal l or $-l$ or any integer in between, including zero $(-l \leq m \leq l)$]. Notice that I am not giving reasons for these restrictions, but let me illustrate how they work for the $n = 2$ state. (I defer, for the moment, a description of the spin quantum number, s.)

If the principal quantum number is $n = 2$, we may have, in accordance with the restrictions stated above,

$$n = 2 \qquad l = 1 \qquad m = 1$$
$$l = 1 \qquad m = 0$$
$$l = 1 \qquad m = -1$$
$$l = 0 \qquad m = 0$$

If we consider the three integers in the order n, l, m, the possible triplets (each is called a configuration) are

$$2, 1, 1$$
$$2, 1, 0$$
$$2, 1, -1$$
$$2, 0, 0$$

Each leads to an energy state associated with $n = 2$. Instead of the single energy level E_2, as in the Bohr theory, we have four choices of $E_{n,l,m}$. In the hydrogen atom, if we consider at first only the effects of n and l, the energy of the electron depends, to a first approximation, only on n. All configurations with the same n have the same energy, and the energy levels are those predicted by the Bohr theory. In atoms having more than one electron, however, the situation is more complicated, and the energies may depend on both n and l. Finally, in the presence of a magnetic field, which may be due either to external magnets or to the magnetic properties of the nucleus, the situation becomes even more complicated, and the energy depends on all three numbers, n, l, and m.

What Pauli's exclusion principle tells us, once we have characterized the states by configurations involving the quantum numbers n, l, and m according to the given rules, is that for each of these we can have, at most, two electrons. We are now ready to count up the total number of possible states for a single electron for $n = 2$ and hence, in a multiple-electron atom, the total number of electrons that can be characterized by the expression $n = 2$:

$$
\begin{array}{llll}
n = 2 & l = 1 & m = 1 & \text{2 electrons} \\
n = 2 & l = 1 & m = 0 & \text{2 electrons} \\
n = 2 & l = 1 & m = -1 & \text{2 electrons} \\
n = 2 & l = 0 & m = 0 & \underline{\text{2 electrons}} \\
& & \text{Total} & \text{8 electrons}
\end{array}
$$

The rule works for $n = 1$, too. In this case the restriction that l be not more than $n - 1$ means that $l = 0$. The restriction that the absolute value of m be no greater than l means that $m = 0$. The $n = 1$ shell is therefore characterized by the expressions $n = 1$, $l = 0$, and $m = 0$. According to Pauli, it takes two electrons to fill it.

The rules, which are logical deductions from wave mechanics, also work for larger values of n (see Probs. 53.2 and 53.3) and are worth remembering even though I have presented them as if they had been discovered by the trial-and-error technique used by Balmer in finding the formula for the sequence of numbers proportional to the wavelengths of the hydrogen atom.

What is the physical significance of Pauli's exclusion principle? What operational facts can it be related to? At this point I shall be painfully brief. It turns out that an electron has not only an angular momentum that is due to its orbital motion but also one that is due to spin—as if it rotated about an axis the way the earth does; we say, then, that it has a spin quantum number, s. This number is either $+\frac{1}{2}$ or $-\frac{1}{2}$; it cannot be anything else. [It is not within the scope of this book to explain why it comes only in multiples of $\frac{1}{2}(h/2\pi)$.] The state of an electron is therefore completely characterized by a set of four numbers: n, l, m, and s. They are all integers except s, which is either $+\frac{1}{2}$ or $-\frac{1}{2}$. The two electrons in the neutral helium atom, for example, are characterized by the sets

$$
\begin{array}{l}
1, 0, 0, +\tfrac{1}{2} \\
1, 0, 0, -\tfrac{1}{2}
\end{array}
$$

Without any pictures of orbits, elliptic, circular, or other, **Pauli's exclusion principle** can be stated simply: *No two electrons in an atom can have the same set of quantum numbers; that is, no two electrons in an atom can be in the same state.*

53.5. Wave Mechanics and the Structure of the Atom

We have reached the point where I can be only descriptive and not at all analytical, for Schrödinger's equation requires, for its solution, certain mathematical tools (partial differential equations) that we are not prepared to handle. It is enough to say that the solutions of the equation represent the possible energy states not only of the hydrogen atom but of all other atoms. So much information is packed into them that with this equation one can correctly predict the chemical properties of atoms even before doing experiments. The equation implies, for example, that the ionization potential of helium is 24.6 ev, the highest ionization potential among the elements. Since chemical forces generally cannot produce energies much greater than a few electron volts, no ordinary chemical force is strong enough to disturb the electrons in the shell of the helium atom. The Schrödinger equation thus implies that helium is chemically inert under normal circumstances, and we know that it is. The chemical inactivity of the other noble gases, and, indeed, all the basic chemical properties of all the other atoms, can likewise be predicted by means of the equation—if you understand how to use it.

We are not in a position to derive the numerical values of the energy states that come out of the solutions of Schrödinger's equation. We can, however, as an illustration, at least characterize the states of the electrons for the atoms starting with $Z = 1$ and going up as far as $Z = 18$.

First observe, in Table 53.2, how the permitted sets of states are established in terms of their quantum numbers without going further than 2 for the principal quantum number. It takes two electrons with $n = 1$ to fill the first shell; it takes eight electrons with $n = 2$ to fill the next shell; and so on. Next consider Table 53.3 which shows the n and l quantum numbers associated with the different electrons in the different atoms up to $Z = 18$ and gives the total number of electrons in each atom. Beyond $Z = 18$ the very simple order of formation shown here breaks down somewhat, but the possibility of describing the structure of the atoms by means of the wave equation does not. Notice how the ionization potential drops from helium to lithium and rises (except for two small drops) from lithium to neon, drops from neon to sodium and rises (except for two small drops) from sodium to argon.

The pioneer work on the periodic table was done by the Russian chemist Dmitri Mendeleev (1834–1907). His organization of the elements led him to propose such a table and to use it in predicting the existence and properties of a number of additional elements. When some of those that he predicted in 1869 were discovered a few years later, Mendeleev was hailed as a prophet. All of this occurred long before the structure and the ionization potentials of atoms were known.

May this brief account whet your appetite for further study of this subject! It is obvious, however, that the detailed numerical secrets of the atom cannot be calculated by those who are unable to use the mathematical tools that are necessary for the solution of Schrödinger's equation.

53.6. Concluding Remarks on Atomic Physics

As new theories replace the old, we must remember that some parts of the old theory survive · the test of time. As we pass from the Bohr theory to the more mathematically sophisticated wave theory, the concept of well-defined circular orbits vanishes, but the idea that spectral frequencies are deducible from the equation $h\nu = E_{n_1} - E_{n_2}$ survives. What is new is the mathematical and physical structure that yields the correct numerical values of the energy states E_{n_1} and E_{n_2}.

Despite the great power of wave mechanics, it does not now seem probable that we shall stop using Bohr's highly visual ideas as the basis of an introduction to atomic structure, especially since fairly good values for the energy levels of x-rays can be deduced from his theory. We saw, in

TABLE 53.2

Permitted States in Terms of Their Quantum Numbers

n	l	m	s
1	0	0	½
1	0	0	−½
2	0	0	½
2	0	0	−½
2	1	1	½
2	1	1	−½
2	1	0	½
2	1	0	−½
2	1	−1	½
2	1	−1	−½

TABLE 53.3

Electronic Structure and Ionization Potential of Elements with Atomic Numbers 1–18

			Principal quantum number, n = 1		n = 2			n = 3		
Z		Element	Ionization Potential (ev)	l=0	l=0	l=1		l=0	l=1	l=2
1	H	Hydrogen	13.60	1						
2	He	Helium	24.58	2						
3	Li	Lithium	5.39	2	1					
4	Be	Beryllium	9.32	2	2					
5	B	Boron	8.30	2	2	1				
6	C	Carbon	11.26	2	2	2				
7	N	Nitrogen	14.54	2	2	3				
8	O	Oxygen	13.61	2	2	4				
9	F	Fluorine	17.42	2	2	5				
10	Ne	Neon	21.56	2	2	6				
11	Na	Sodium	5.14	2	2	6	1			
12	Mg	Magnesium	7.64	2	2	6	2			
13	Al	Aluminum	5.98	2	2	6	2	1		
14	Si	Silicon	8.15	2	2	6	2	2		
15	P	Phosphorus	10.55	2	2	6	2	3		
16	S	Sulphur	10.36	2	2	6	2	4		
17	Cl	Chlorine	13.01	2	2	6	2	5		
18	Ar	Argon	15.76	2	2	6	2	6		

particular, that, as Z approaches 100 (in round numbers, about as high as Z can go), the factor Z^2 of the energy formula (equation 53.5) approaches 10,000; that is, the innermost electrons of the atoms of highest atomic number have energies about 10,000 times as great as the ionization potential of hydrogen. In general, the closer you get to the nucleus of an atom of high atomic number, the more energy you need to disturb it. We are now ready to consider what it takes to disturb that nucleus.

53.7. Summary

Sommerfeld achieved a limited improvement on Bohr's theory by considering elliptic orbits, the relativistic mass of the electron, and the quantization effects of a magnetic field. His formula for E_n (n being the principal quantum number) was the same as Bohr's; but his refined formula for energy levels, which took two additional quantization conditions into account, explained the fine structure of spectral lines, which was not explained by Bohr's theory.

The quantization rules imposed *ad hoc* by Sommerfeld are accounted for today as a mathematical consequence of Schrödinger's wave mechanics. Besides the principal quantum number n, it takes three other quantum numbers to specify the state of an electron in an atom: the angular-momentum quantum number l, the magnetic quantum number m, and the spin quantum number s.

The fact that s can take on only two values is important in Pauli's exclusion principle, which states that no two electrons in an atom can be in the same state.

Despite the success of wave mechanics, the simple Bohr picture will probably continue to be used for an approximate description of one-electron atoms and x-ray spectra.

Problems

53.1. Taking m/M into account, calculate the ratio of the wavelength of a line in the hydrogen spectrum and that of the corresponding line in the deuterium spectrum.

53.2. Build up a table of permitted values of l and m for the $n = 3$ state. Remember that $0 \leq l \leq (n - 1)$ and that $-l \leq m \leq l$.

53.3. Using the result of Prob. 53.2, prove that nine different orbits are possible and hence that eighteen electrons can fit into the $n = 3$ shell.

53.4. It is known (from advanced versions of the theory of radiation) that a photon always carries one unit of angular momentum. When an atom emits radiation, therefore, it obeys a selection rule—arising from the conservation of angular momentum—that can be written as $\Delta l = \pm 1$. Consider an electron in a hydrogen atom, in the excited state $n = 3$, $l = 2$.

1. Can such an electron fall directly into the ground state with the emission of a single photon?

2. Indicate a possible set of intermediate states by which the electron can reach the ground state.

3. What (minimum) number of photons must be emitted in order that the electron reach the ground state?

53.5. 1. Compute to three significant figures the x-ray wavelength predicted by equation 53.9, with σ equal to 0.5, for a copper target in which an electron jumps from the level $n = 2$ to $n = 1$.

2. What is the percentage error in your calculated value (the experimental value being 1.54 A)?

53.6. Tungsten, gold, and lead have high atomic numbers. Discuss their relative merits as possible targets for x-ray rubes if the purpose is to produce highly penetrating radiation (large ν). Consult equation 53.9 and tables of physical properties (such as those found in the *Handbook of Chemistry and Physics* published by the Chemical Rubber Company of Cleveland). Consider the atomic number, heat conductivity (the impact of electrons heats the target), electrical conductivity (the target must conduct electricity), melting point, and cost.

53.7. A short-lived system called **positronium**, which is suggestive of an atom, consists of a positron (a particle with the mass of an electron and a positive charge numerically equal to that of an electron) and an electron. Using the formula for the reduced mass (§ 53.1) of the system, calculate its binding energy in electron volts. (Hint: Calculate the ionization potential—that is, the work that it takes to separate the oppositely charged particles.)

VI

ELEMENTARY
CONCEPTS OF
NUCLEAR PHYSICS

Events in a Bubble Chamber
(*Photograph from CERN.*)

It is possible to smash the nucleus, the hard core of an atom, with extremely powerful electromagnetic sledgehammers—the particle accelerators. Some of the events, fortunately, can make themselves visible by the tracks they produce in a bubble chamber. Such events are controlled nuclear explosions on a subatomic scale.

IN JULY 1945 an explosive event of historic importance took place: an atomic bomb was successfully detonated in New Mexico. The accelerated pace of events in those disturbing times may be gauged by the fact that only three weeks later the first atomic bomb used on a military objective was dropped on Hiroshima (Japan). Since that instant world affairs have taken a new direction.

The construction of the bomb was a scientific and technical feat of fantastic proportions. The work was done in secret at a cost of about two billion dollars. When Niels Bohr was brought over from Europe as a consultant on the feasibility of the bomb, he said, in effect: "You will have to turn the United States into a huge factory to do it." When he came back after the war and surveyed the tremendous installations at Hanford (Washington) and Oak Ridge (Tennessee), where the different methods of separating isotopes were developed, he commented, "You see—you *did* turn the United States into a factory."

The relevance of all this to physics is that the bomb was conceived, promoted, designed, and built by physicists. Unlike the more recent missiles and satellites, which are primarily triumphs of engineering, based, for the most part, on old and well-tested physical principles, the success of the bomb depended upon the newest developments in pure physics.

The decision to build the bomb, however, and the decision to drop it, were made not for scientific but for political and military reasons. Other grave decisions, since that historic moment, have been forced upon us. The new responsibilities of the leaders of men are obviously very great.

The physical effect of the bomb was immediate and devastating. The social effect, it is becoming clear, is an era of new responsibility, a kind of social fall-out whose effects will be felt for a long time. Chapters on nuclear physics have been included in this text because the new responsibility must be shared by scientists and laymen alike. The scientist must communicate the basic ideas of his science so that they may be widely understood. The layman must learn the elements of nuclear physics in order to shoulder his new responsibility more intelligently.

I might have ended this book right after the discussion of the Bohr model of the atom. That was the first milestone in modern atomic physics, and I could have justified stopping there. Why have I pushed further, into a region where research is still being pursued at a feverish pace and where the basic facts, in many cases, have not yet been put together into a simple and coherent theory? The answer is that nuclear physics has suddenly thrust upon all mankind a tremendous new source of energy, and that no responsible person can act intelligently in guiding the future development of this energy without knowing at least the elements of its physical mechanism. I propose, therefore, to give an elementary account of nuclear physics.

I have tried so far to develop the basic concepts of physics in such a way that their application to the nucleus will be a logical extension. Important operational quantities—energy, angular momentum, magnetic moment—and the basic concept of quantization, which, together with that of the wave nature of matter, led to success in atomic theory, will find immediate application as we consider the nucleus.

The development of this part of the book will differ from that of the earlier parts for several reasons: (1) We shall be dealing with the still evolving physics of the second quarter of the twentieth century rather than with such well-established topics as the mechanics of the seventeenth century (Newton), the electrostatics of the eighteenth (Coulomb), and the electromagnetism of the nineteenth (Faraday and Maxwell). (2) The force that binds an electron to its nucleus is known; it is the coulombic attraction. Basing our work on it, we can deduce the energy levels of an atom. The force that holds together the protons and the neutrons within nuclei, however, is not yet accurately known, and we therefore do not yet have a mathematical theory of the energy levels within the nucleus. (3) The basic concepts of nuclear physics need mathematics if they are to be *precisely expressed*, and that mathematics is difficult. I maintain that they can be *understood*, however, without full mathematical precision and rigor. They are, after all, physical concepts.

In this part of the book I shall continue to limit the treatment to the clear development of a few topics for the sake of their physical relevance; it may occasionally be apparent, however, that I am resisting the understandable temptation to dwell on the overwhelming social implications of nuclear physics, for it may be true, as someone has said, that the human importance of developments in nuclear physics transcends even their physical importance. The peaceful uses of nuclear physics may conceivably outweigh its destructive potentialities. Judgment of the facts needed for intelligent decisions on these subjects will demand a certain amount of knowledge of the physical facts. It is the purpose of this part to provide that knowledge.

The Atomic Nucleus

I HAVE already (Chap. 45) presented some evidence to show that atomic nuclei are extremely small, their diameter being about 10^{-4} times the diameter of an atom, or about 10^{-7} times the wavelength of visible light. Even with high-energy photons, such as those of x-rays, therefore, diffraction would prevent us from seeing nuclei. In this sense, nuclei can never be seen. Nevertheless, nuclear events have been made dramatically visible by use of cloud and bubble chambers. Some of the techniques will be described in § 56.4.

54.1. Elementary Characteristics of Nuclei

For the time being it is enough to know that charged particles moving rapidly through a gas can leave a trail of ions on which visible condensation can take place. Figure 54.1 shows the tracks made by alpha particles (helium nuclei) passing through oxygen. Each fork in a track represents a collision between an alpha particle and an oxygen nucleus. Impressed by the feeling of seeing the invisible by means of this technique, Rutherford once referred to the invention of the cloud chamber as "the most original and wonderful in scientific history."

Since we can't see nuclei, we invent models of them that do not contradict the experimental facts. Pictures made with the modern bubble chamber (which has superseded the cloud chamber) and data from an even newer device called the spark chamber indicate that nuclei behave somewhat like highly elastic billiard balls: like the

molecules of kinetic theory, they obey, in their collisions, the law of the conservation of linear momentum. The billiard-ball model tells us nothing, however, about the internal structure of the nucleus. The same was true in the elementary kinetic theory of gases at low pressure, you will remember—the collisions between gas molecules

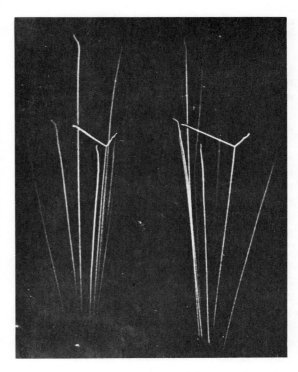

FIG. 54.1. *Collision between an alpha particle and an oxygen nucleus. (Photograph from P. M. S. Blackett and the Royal Society.)*

were calculated without recourse to knowledge of the internal structure of the molecule. We shall begin our consideration of the nucleus in the same way; when we speak of its radius, however, we must remember that the more refined wave-mechanical picture will not permit us to conceive of it so naively.

If we assume that a nucleus is a hard little sphere of volume proportional to A (the mass number), its radius would be proportional to $A^{1/3}$. The following formula does, in fact, give the nuclear radius (in meters) in terms of the mass number:

$$R = 1.2 \times 10^{-15} \times A^{1/3} \qquad [54.1$$

The evidence to support this formula comes from several different sources. Some of it comes from particles bouncing off nuclei (§ 1.2). Fast neutrons, for example, have a short enough de Broglie wavelength (§ 50.4) to permit us to calculate, with simple geometrical optics, the diameter of the shadow of a nucleus upon which they impinge. Experiments using fast electrons as missiles also show that equation 54.1 holds well except for the very smallest nuclei.

Since the nuclear mass is proportional to A and the volume of a sphere of radius R is $(4/3)\pi R^3$, we may write the nuclear density, ρ, in arbitrary units as

$$\rho = \frac{mass}{volume} = \frac{kA}{\frac{4\pi}{3}R^3} = \frac{kA}{\frac{4\pi}{3}(1.2)^3 \times 10^{-45} \times A} \qquad [54.2$$

in which k is the mass of one nucleon. Observe that the A's cancel out, making ρ independent of the mass number. In other words, nuclear density is constant to a first approximation. (See Prob. 54.1.)

For atoms and molecules the billiard-ball model, without inner structure, worked well as long as the energy of interaction was low. Higher energies (a few ev), however, produced ionization; that is, they stripped electrons off the atoms, thus proving that atoms have constituent parts (electrons and nuclei). Similarly, cloud-chamber photographs of nuclear collisions at very high energies (in the Mev range) have demonstrated that nuclei also have constituent parts.

Figure 54.2 shows what happens when an alpha

particle hits a nitrogen nucleus. The particle (a helium nucleus) disappears, a proton (a hydrogen nucleus) appears, and the resulting oxygen nucleus recoils.

Here we are no longer dealing with simple, impenetrable, ball-like nuclei. This transmutation of elements is symbolized by the equation involving the corresponding nuclides.

$$_2He^4 + {}_7N^{14} \longrightarrow {}_8O^{17} + {}_1H^1 \qquad [54.3$$

It is not obvious, of course, how Figure 54.2 confirms the idea that the alpha particle enters the nitrogen nucleus and disappears. The point I am making here, however, is that the evidence of many similar experiments has led to the belief that nuclei have component parts, and a detailed analysis of cloud-chamber pictures shows that in nuclear collisions the principles of the conservation of energy and momentum account for the observed phenomena.

We now proceed to consider the component parts of nuclei and the forces that hold them together.

54.2. Nucleons, the Basic Constituents of the Nucleus

Since parts of this topic have been covered before (Chaps. 45 and 47), we shall move along rapidly. Each atomic nucleus has the charge Ze. (Z is the atomic number, a positive integer, and e is the charge of the proton; we shall symbolize the electronic charge by $-e$.) The mass of the atom corresponding to a given nuclide is given the symbol M. It is called the atomic mass and is expressible in unified atomic mass units (u). Unless otherwise specified, the atomic mass includes the mass of the electrons of the neutral atom. In the system $_6C^{12} = 12$ (see § 45.2) the mass numbers of the nuclides are very close to integers. The integer closest to M is the mass number A (the total number of neutrons and protons in the nucleus). The nuclei of two simple atoms are, for example, those of hydrogen and helium. In Table 54.1 we tabulate for them the quantities Z, A, and M. Notice that A is very close to M in value. The values of M, however, are, according to custom, for neutral atoms, not

FIG. 54.2. *Collision between an alpha particle and a nitrogen nucleus. (Photograph from P. M. S. Blackett and the Royal Society.)*

for nuclei. We can obtain the mass of the nucleus alone, if it is needed, by subtracting from M the mass of the planetary electrons. Since there are Z planetary electrons in a neutral atom, Zm is the quantity we must subtract from M, if m is the mass of the electron, to get the nuclear mass. Although there is no atom for which $M = 1.00000$, it is convenient to assume one, for one gram of such atoms would contain N_A atoms ($N_A = 6.02252 \times 10^{23}$ being the Avogadro constant). The mass (M_1) of such a hypothetical atom defines the **unified atomic mass unit** (u).† One u is $(6.0225 \times 10^{23})^{-1}$ gm or 1.6605×10^{-27} kg.

With this relation we can always transform masses from unified atomic mass units to kilograms and vice versa, but this is seldom neces-

† The unified atomic mass unit (u) is 1/12 of the mass of the atom of the $_6C^{12}$ nuclide. In the old system ($_8O^{16} = 16$) the atomic mass unit (amu) was 1/16 of the mass of the atom of the $_8O^{16}$ nuclide.

TABLE 54.1

Name of Atom	Symbol for Corresponding Nuclide of Greatest Abundance	Z	A	M $_6O^{12} = 12$ (in u)
Hydrogen	$_1H^1$	1	1	1.007 8252[a]
Helium	$_2He^4$	2	4	4.002 6036

[a] A space is left between the third and the fourth decimal place to facilitate reading. The almost unbelievable precision found in the table illustrates the desirability of having tables of relative values for atomic masses.

TABLE 54.2

Particle	Mass		Rest Energy (Mev)
	u	kg	
M_1 (hypothetical)	1	1.6605×10^{-27}	931.478
Electron	5.48597×10^{-4}	9.1091×10^{-31}	0.511 006

sary in nuclear physics; the u turns out to be the natural unit of mass. The convenient unit of energy in nuclear physics is the Mev (million electron volts). In Table 54.2 the masses of the hypothetical atom M_1 and the electron, and their corresponding rest energies, are compared. It will be useful in subsequent work to remember that the energy of the rest mass of the electron is about one-half Mev and that of a hydrogen atom is close to a thousand Mev (one Bev). These conversions are effected by means of the equation $E = mc^2$. Small differences in mass are important because of the enormous magnitude of c^2. Another useful conversion factor is 1 Mev = 1.60210×10^{-13} J.

The two nucleons, or basic constituents of nuclei, are the proton ($_1p^1$) and the neutron ($_0n^1$). They are very similar in mass. The mass of the proton is 1.007277 u, and that of the neutron is 1.008665 u. These values are so close that on first approximation it is correct to say that the mass of a nucleus is the mass of a nucleon times the total number (A) of nucleons. A nucleus is composed of Z protons and N neutrons. The mass number, A, therefore equals $Z + N$. Atoms having nuclei with the same Z are called *isotopes* (§ 45.2), those with the same A are called *isobars*, and those with the same N are called *isotones*. (The names are of little consequence in what follows. I shall later discuss only isotopes.)

Having stressed the similarity between protons and neutrons, we now consider some differences. The fact that the neutron is slightly heavier than the proton tells us that it has more available energy. I am speaking here of free neutrons and protons. A free neutron is unstable; it has a half-life (§ 57.2) of ten minutes and disintegrates into a proton and an electron and a third particle called a *neutrino*. Such disintegration suggests complications that we shall temporarily avoid. We shall see later that there is no operational way to account for electrons residing within a nucleus (Prob. 57.7). It is also possible for a proton to disintegrate into a positive electron (a positron; § 56.3), a neutron, and a neutrino. When neutrons and protons are within a nucleus, we say that they are *bound* rather than *free*. Bound neutrons are very much like bound protons in stability. The basic difference between neutron and proton is, of course, that the proton is positively charged while the neutron is neutral.†

To summarize: Outside the nucleus, the neutron's lack of charge permits it to travel unhindered by the strong coulombic forces that would act on a proton. Within the nucleus, where the coulombic interaction is not the important one, proton and neutron are very much alike, and it will be their similarities that interest us. Some useful facts are listed in Table 54.3 for use in the examples that follow.

Since the mass of the electrons is included when we write the mass of an atom, it seems reasonable to find that the mass of the hydrogen atom (1.00782522 u) is greater than the mass of a proton, which is the bare nucleus (1.00727663 u). But adding the mass of an electron (0.000548597 u) to that of a proton yields 1.007825227 u, which is slightly greater than the actual mass of the hydrogen atom. We shall presently pursue the significance of this and similar discrepancies because they turn out to be of great importance.

54.3. Deuterium: Forces Between Nucleons

Consider the arithmetic for a deuterium atom (with nuclide $_1$H^2):

One proton	1.00728 u
One neutron	1.00867 u
One electron	0.000549 u
	2.016499 u
Deuterium atom	2.014102 u
Difference	0.002397 u

In bringing together the component parts, we have lost mass of 0.002397 u. (Notice that the mass of the electron drops out when we subtract.) Using Einstein's mass-energy relation, $E = mc^2$, we attribute the decrease in mass to a loss of energy of 0.002397 × 931 Mev ≅ 2.23 Mev. Since it would require 2.23 Mev of work to separate

---

† There is another operationally meaningful property of nucleons—their spin. Protons and neutrons have the same spin (1/2 in the unit $h/2\pi$). Although this property plays an important theoretical role, we shall seldom have occasion to use it in our elementary consideration of nucleons.

TABLE 54.3

Name of Particle	Symbol for Particle or Nuclide of Atom	Mass (in u)
Electron	$_{-1}e^0$	0.000548597
Proton	$_1p^1$	1.00727663
Hydrogen atom	$_1$H^1	1.00782522
Neutron	$_0n^1$	1.0086654
Deuterium atom	$_1$H^2	2.01410219
Helium atom	$_2$He^4	4.00260361

the components, we call this the binding energy of the atom. Since the electron masses cancel out, it is really the binding energy of the deuterium nucleus.

In general, if the total mass of the nucleus is less than the sum of the masses of its component nucleons, the combination is stable. Now that we are confronted with binding energies of a few Mev, we realize that we are dealing with energies that are several orders of magnitude greater than the 13.6 ev that it takes to join a proton and an electron into the stable combination known as a hydrogen atom. The basic principle is the same, however. (See Prob. 54.3.)

Now consider the problem of bringing two protons close to each other. In the helium nucleus, as we know, there are two protons separated by a distance of about 10^{-15} m. If the coulombic repulsion held in this region, the two protons would repel each other with a tremendous force. This can be computed with Coulomb's law:

$$F = \frac{Ke^2}{r^2} \qquad [54.4$$

The magnitude of the force, F, comes out as 230 newtons. Such a force acting on a proton (mass ≅ 1.7×10^{-27} kg) would produce the acceleration

$$a = \frac{230 \text{ nt}}{1.7 \times 10^{-27} \text{ kg}} = 1.35 \times 10^{29} \text{ m/sec}^2 \qquad [54.5$$

(Remember that the acceleration due to gravity is only 9.8 m/sec^2.) If this were the only force acting on the protons, they could never be held together in the helium nucleus. We are led to the conclusion that in that nucleus, which contains two protons and two neutrons, the repulsive coulombic force normally acting on the two protons must be balanced by a different and very strong attractive force that takes over when the protons get as close to each other as $\sim 10^{-14}$ m. More generally,

as we shall see, protons attract protons, protons attract neutrons, and neutrons attract neutrons, when they are so close.

In preparation for a later discussion of the concept of potential energy, consider a ball rolling up the hill of Figure 54.3. If its kinetic energy at P is great enough, it may reach a point like Q, come to rest, and start rolling back. The ball feels a force repelling it away from the axis of symmetry, OA, at each point of its path.

If the hill has a cavity, as in Figure 54.4, the ball may roll into it. At a point like R the ball experiences a force attracting it toward the axis of symmetry, OA. From a classical point of view, of course, if the ball had enough kinetic energy to enter the cavity, it would also have enough to roll past the second summit, S, and into the region T. Classically, a ball could not enter the cavity and be trapped unless it had lost some energy. Such a loss could be caused by friction. We shall see (if we neglect the tunneling effect, to be discussed later) that the trapping of a nuclear particle in a potential cavity is possible, wave-mechanically. The force that acts on a proton approaching another proton has *some* of the characteristics suggested by Figure 54.4. A repulsion (outside the cavity) that increases sharply as the distance decreases changes suddenly to a very strong attraction (inside the cavity).

In Figure 54.5 a ball rolling on a horizontal table feels neither attraction nor repulsion, but at points like Q and R it feels an attraction toward OA. This illustrates how a neutron reacts to the presence of a proton: at close range, the neutron feels a strong attraction; at great distances it feels neither attraction nor repulsion.

There is a great deal of evidence today to support the contention that the proton-proton (p-p) force is very similar in kind and in magnitude to the proton-neutron (p-n) force and to the neutron-neutron (n-n) force at very short distances. We therefore lump them all together as *strong, short-range, nucleon-nucleon interactions.*

Fortunately for the stability of the material world of things around us, the forces binding the fundamental particles of the universe are very great indeed.

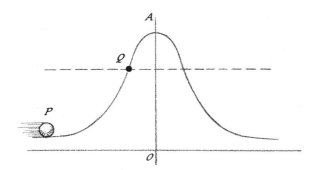

FIG. 54.3. *A ball with enough initial kinetic energy to reach point* Q.

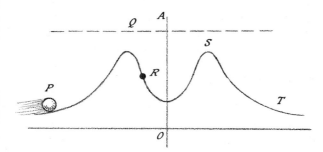

FIG. 54.4. *A crude model for proton forces.*

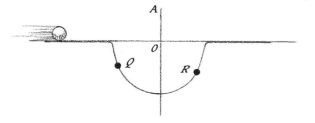

FIG. 54.5. *A crude model for close-range attraction of neutron by proton.*

54.4. Summary

Nuclei have nucleons (neutrons and protons) as their basic constituents. Since nuclear diameters are of the order of 10^{-14} m, there must be a strong force of attraction between two protons at very close range. This is contrary to what would be expected from the law of coulombic repulsion. Approximately similar attractive forces, in fact, must be postulated between all nucleons at ranges of the order of nuclear diameters.

If the sum of the masses of the constituent particles of a nucleus, when they are outside the nucleus, exceeds the mass of the nucleus, it takes work to pull the nucleus apart, and the nucleus is stable. The difference in mass is a measure of the binding energy of the nucleus. Typical nuclear binding energies are in the Mev range, whereas the ionization energies of electrons in atoms are in the electron-volt range.

Problems

54.1. The mass of one nucleon is 1.67×10^{-24} gm.

1. Show that nuclear density is about 2.3×10^{14} gm/cm³.

2. Convert this to tons/cm³.

54.2. Find the mass of a hydrogen nucleus in unified atomic mass units. Express this, to five significant figures, in grams.

54.3. The binding energy of the electron in the hydrogen atom is 13.6 ev.

1. Convert this to Mev and then to unified atomic mass units (u).

2. Would the mass found in part 1 be detectable in the electronic mass given in Table 54.3?

The Structure and Stability of Nuclei

THE FIRST problem concerning the atomic nucleus is "What is in it?" The second is "What holds it together?" The answer to the first (although, strictly speaking, we know operationally only what comes out of it when it is hit in different ways) is "neutrons and protons." We may answer the second by saying "nuclear forces," but it is at once apparent that we don't learn anything about nuclear forces simply by naming them. We must, rather, be able to measure them and then theorize about them.

It is instructive to remember how we answered similar questions about the atom: "What is in an atom?" and "What holds it together?" The first question is somewhat like "What is in the solar system?" The solar system is not like a bag containing marbles. We may, indeed, say that the sun and the planets are in the solar system; but that system is a dynamic entity, and its constituents are in it, not like seeds in an apple or plums in a pie, but more like dancers in a ballet. They belong together even while they move in relation to one another. We may likewise say that electrons and nuclei are in an atom, but their relations are dynamic, whether we consider the inaccurate but visually clear model of Bohr or the mathematically precise but visually fuzzy model of wave mechanics. We have a similar problem in describing the nucleus. We may say that it is composed of neutrons and protons, but their relation to one another is not static.

The force binding an electron to its nucleus is known. It is the coulombic electrical attraction, and its magnitude can be given by a mathematical formula; but there is no straightforward law of force describing what keeps protons and neutrons together in the nucleus. We have, therefore, no complete theory of nuclear structure. We nevertheless know a great deal about nuclei and how they are held together. The purpose of this chapter is to present some of this information.

55.1. The Measurable Properties of Nuclei

The most easily measured quantity involved in a classroom full of boys and girls is their number. How many boys are there, and how many girls? The answer, in each case, is an integer and is a result of simple counting.

For statistics on health we might also want the weight of each pupil. To measure this we need a scale. This time we get a set of numbers that are probably not integers and the statistical information, for example, that the average weight of boys is greater than the average weight of girls of the same age.

We can begin with nuclei in a similar way. First we can tabulate the facts that involve whole numbers. How many protons and how many neutrons are there in the different nuclei? What is the ratio of neutrons to protons? These questions can be answered even before nuclear masses are known very accurately. Next we can seek regularities or peculiarities as we plot the information against some such variable as the atomic mass number. Finally we can measure accurately the masses of the nuclei and their constituents and the energy levels associated with them. These will generally not be whole numbers.†

The atomic mass number (A), the atomic number (Z), and the number of neutrons (N) are all positive integers or zero; and they are not independent, for $N + Z = A$. Values of Z, although they represent nuclear properties, were known from chemistry and x-ray spectra. The atomic mass, M (§ 54.2), is not an integer except for $_6C^{12}$, for which it is 12 by definition. The analytical balance first used by chemists made it possible to determine, to four or five significant figures, the atomic weights of the different chemical elements. The mass spectrometer (§ 47.5) has made it possible to determine, to seven or eight significant figures, the relative masses of the individual isotopes of any element. Without the information obtained from such measurements, much of the basic work in nuclear physics would have been impossible.

For the neutron, $Z = 0$ and $A = 1$; for the proton, $Z = 1$ and $A = 1$; for the deuterium nucleus ($_1H^2$), $Z = 1$ and $A = 2$; for the helium nucleus ($_2He^4$), $Z = 2$ and $A = 4$; and so on. Each particular species of nucleus, with specific values of A and Z, is called a **nuclide**. Not all nuclides are found in nature, and not all nuclides are stable.

The present range (§ 1.4) of the variable Z is the set of integers from 0 to 103, inclusive. Some of these nuclei have not been observed in nature: $Z = 43, 61, 85, 87$, and 97–103. The value of A rises, with only a few drops, from 1 (proton or neutron) to 257 (lawrencium).

The stable nuclides start at the light end with $N/Z = 1$ and end at the heavy end with $N/Z \cong 1.6$. In other words, in the light nuclides the number of neutrons is the same as the number of

protons (with some exceptions), but in the heavier nuclides there are more neutrons than protons. This statement is summarized schematically in Figure 55.1; each dot in the figure represents a stable nuclide, and a continuous curve running very close to many of the dots can be drawn. The dashed line goes through the points for which $N = Z$.

Information such as this is the beginning of knowledge about nuclear forces. Let us assume, for example, that the nucleon-nucleon attractive forces act only at very short distances (see Prob. 55.3). At short range the *n-p*, *n-n*, and *p-p* forces, as they are called, are all attractive, but at longer range the coulombic repulsion between protons tends to disrupt the nucleus. As the number of nucleons increases, the nucleus becomes larger. In a large nucleus, some protons, being relatively distant from others, feel the long-range repulsion of the coulombic forces. If the nucleus is not to fall apart, more neutrons must be added. Hence in large nuclei there are more neutrons than protons. In this simple explanation I have made some assumptions that need investigation (for example, that nucleons attract only nucleons that are very close), but it illustrates how theorizing about nuclear forces can begin with a very modest amount of experimental information on the relative numbers of protons and neutrons.

Another interesting fact is that a nuclide with x protons and y neutrons is, in general, very similar in stability and other properties to a nuclide having exactly y protons and x neutrons. A study of several such pairs of nuclides, in which the protons are replaced by neutrons and vice versa, indicates that we can account for their similarities by assuming that the *p-p* force is very similar to the *n-n* force. Examples of such pairs are: $_2He^3$ and $_1H^3$; $_4Be^7$ and $_3Li^7$; $_5B^9$ and $_4Be^9$; $_6C^{14}$ and $_8O^{14}$. (In a large nucleus, containing many more neutrons than protons, the replacement of neutrons by protons would produce instability because of the long-range coulombic repulsion between protons.) Interchange of *n* and *p* in the three force pairs, *n-p*, *n-n*, and *p-p*, yields *p-n*, *p-p*, and *n-n*, respectively. Since the *n-p* force is the same as the *p-n* force, the similarities between the two nuclides of a pair seems

---

† Among the other nuclear properties that have operational significance are *angular momentum*, both orbital and spin, and *parity*. These are beyond the scope of this book.

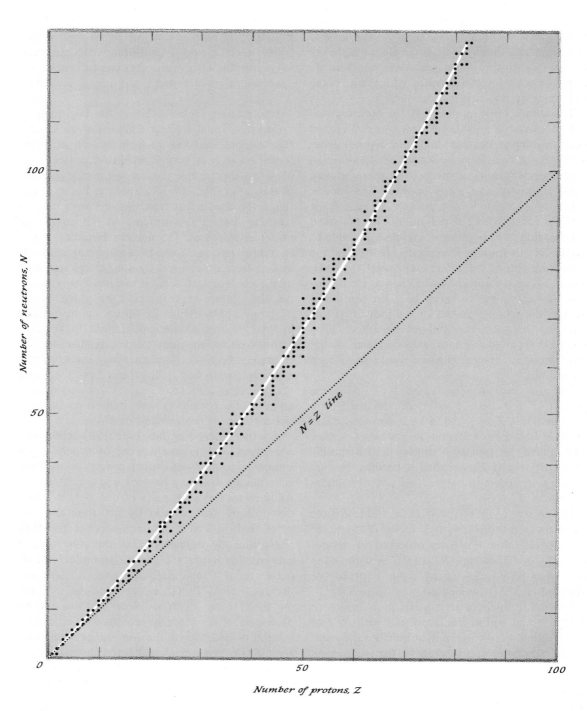

FIG. 55.1. *The number of neutrons plotted against the number of protons. Each dot represents a stable nuclide.*

to depend on the similarities between the *p-p* and *n-n* interactions.

Other regularities have been observed: the nuclides with even Z are much more numerous than those with odd Z; the nuclides with even A are more numerous than those with odd A; and nearly all nuclei with even A have even Z. Table 55.1 illustrates these points. This kind of numerology reminds us of the early attempts to find simple relations among the radii of the sun's planetary orbits and of the much later attempts by Balmer and others to find a formula that would explain the spectral lines of hydrogen. The astronomical problem was solved by the discoveries of Kepler and Newton, the atomic

problem by those of Bohr and his followers. No general solution of the nuclear problem has yet been found.

Among the triumphs of atomic theory was its ability to explain theoretically a fact known experimentally to chemists: that neutral atoms with $Z = 2, 8, 18$, etc. (the inert, or noble, gases) are exceptionally stable. For nuclei it turns out that nuclides with 2, 8, 20, 50, 82, and 126 *nucleons of the same kind* are particularly stable. (These numbers are called the magic numbers.) Although we do not have a mathematical expression for the force between nucleons, we can confirm the magic numbers theoretically with an approximate law and a few assumptions.

But let us come quickly now to the measurable nuclear quantity that has produced some of the most useful results—the atomic mass of the nucleus. One way to illustrate the present state of the art of measuring mass is to extract the first three entries from a current nuclear table. We observe (Table 55.2) that the isotopic masses are expressed to seven significant figures. It is at once apparent that, just as the atomic weights to four or five significant figures obtained by chemists with the analytical balance were the beginning of *atomic* chemistry, these masses, obtained with the most refined mass spectrometers, are the foun-

TABLE 55.1

Z	Number of Stable Isotopes	Number with Odd A	Number with Even A
48	8	2	6
49	2	2	0
50	10	3	7
51	2	2	0

TABLE 55.2

Short Table of Isotopic Masses ($_6C^{12} = 12$)†

Atomic Number Z	Name	Symbol	Mass Number A	Isotopic Mass (unified atomic mass units) u	Relative Abundance %
0	Neutron	n	1	1.008665	
1	Hydrogen	H	1	1.007825	99.985
1	Deuterium	D	2	2.014102	0.015
1	Tritium	T	3	3.016049	
2	Helium	He	3	3.016030	1.3×10^{-4}
2	Helium	He	4	4.002604	99.9999

† First five columns from L. A. König, J. H. E. Mattauch, and A. H. Wapstra, "1961 Nuclidic Mass Table," *Nuclear Physics*, 31 (1962). The figures on relative abundance are from the *Trilinear Chart of Nuclides* by William H. Sullivan of the Oak Ridge National Laboratory.

Some heavy elements—for which Z ranges from 96 to 103, inclusive—are curium, berkelium, californium, einsteinium, fermium, mendelevium, nobelium, and lawrencium, in that order.

dation of a modern *nuclear* chemistry. These data have facilitated the application of nuclear physics even though the theoretical structure is incomplete.

55.2. Binding Energy and Stability

It is observed that the mass of a stable nucleus is less than that of its separated parts. The excess mass found when the nucleons are separated indicates an excess of energy in that state. This implies that it takes energy to pull the nucleons apart. The most important relation here is Einstein's famous $E = (\Delta m)c^2$.

Consider a *purely fictitious* example to drive home the point that mass and energy are inseparable and interconvertible. A pair of horseshoe magnets, held together by their mutual attraction, forms a unit whose mass is 1.8 kg (Fig. 55.2). When they are then pulled apart and weighed separately, each has a mass of 1 kg; that is, their total mass is 2 kg after they have been pulled apart. Since it takes work to pull them apart, we conclude that the increase of 0.2 kg in the mass represents the increase in the energy of the system. If the increase in mass

were really as great as this, it would have been discovered long ago; it is actually about 10^{-17} kg, and no balance is sensitive enough to detect it. At the atomic level, however, there are special techniques for detecting even smaller differences in mass.

The difference in mass is actually measured by mass-spectrometric techniques (§ 47.5). In this way we can determine not the *force* holding nucleons together, but the *energy* it takes to pull them apart—that is, the binding energy (expressed in mass units). This is numerically equal to the mass that is apparently lost when the same nuclear particles unite to form a stable nucleus.

Let us derive a simple expression for the binding energy and the binding energy per nucleon. We let m_p be the mass of a proton and m_n the mass of a neutron. Since there are Z protons and $A - Z$ neutrons in a nucleus, the total mass of the separate nucleons is $Zm_p + (A - Z)m_n$. If the mass of the nucleus is M', the difference in mass is

$$\Delta m = Zm_p + (A - Z)m_n - M' \qquad [55.1$$

(In practice, the atomic mass of the neutral atom $_1\text{H}^1$ can be used in place of m_p if the mass of the neutral atom is used instead of M'. See Example

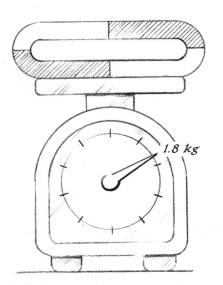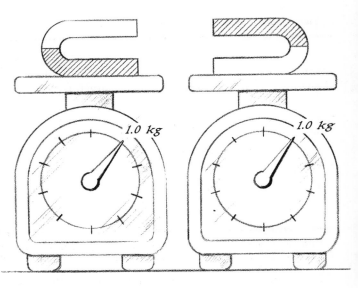

FIG. 55.2. *Fictitious example: the magnets weigh more when apart than when together.*

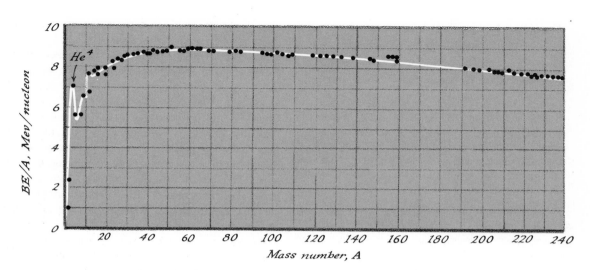

FIG. 55.3. *Binding energy per nucleon plotted against mass number.*

55.1 and Prob. 55.2.2.) Equation 55.1 may be expressed in unified atomic mass units or in grams or may be converted to Mev with the conversion factor 931.5 Mev for each u (§ 54.2). This mass difference is a measure of the binding energy. Hence the *binding energy per nucleon*, BE/A is

$$\text{BE}/A = \frac{Zm_p + (A - Z)m_n - M'}{A} \qquad [55.2$$

The plot of this equation in Figure 55.3 has three important features: (1) The binding energy per nucleon is fairly constant at a little more than 8 Mev over a large part of the curve. (2) The binding energy per nucleon is at its maximum near $A = 60$; we conclude that the nuclei in the middle range are the most stable, that the heavy nuclei are less stable. (3) Among the light nuclei, those with A equal to 4, 8, and 12 have peaks of higher binding energy than their immediate neighbors; this seems to indicate that the combination of two protons and two neutrons is particularly stable among the light elements.

The fact that BE/A is fairly constant over a large region means that BE is proportional to A, at least approximately. Now A is the total number of nucleons in the nucleus. If a short line segment were drawn from each nucleon inside a nucleus to every other nucleon, the total number of segments would be

$$\frac{A(A - 1)}{2} = \frac{A^2 - A}{2}$$

[This follows from the law of *combinations*, which is applicable, for example, to committees: the number of two-member committees that can be formed from a group of n people is $n(n - 1)/2$.] If each nucleon felt bound to every other nucleon, and if the number of nucleons were large, the binding energy would be approximately proportional to A^2. The experimental fact that it depends on A rather than on A^2 supports, instead, the idea of short-range forces. No nucleon can feel bound to all the other nucleons; for, if any nucleon did, the binding energy would be proportional to A^2. Hence it is likely that each nucleon feels bound only to its nearest neighbors. (We shall return to this situation, which is reminiscent of the forces that give rise to surface tension in liquids, in the next section.)

EXAMPLE 55.1. Let us consider the binding energy of the oxygen nucleus, made up of eight protons and eight neutrons. We make the calculation in terms of mass, but we know very well that we can convert to energy units easily:

BE = 8 (mass of $_1\text{H}^1$) + 8 (mass of neutron)
− 15.994915

This comes out as

$$BE = 0.13701 \text{ u}$$
$$BE = 127.6 \text{ Mev}$$

The binding energy per nucleon is therefore

$$\frac{BE}{A} = \frac{127.6}{16} = 7.98 \text{ Mev}$$

The justification for using the mass of the hydrogen atom, $_1H^1$, instead of the mass of the proton is that the eight electron masses counted there are subtracted later since the atomic mass of oxygen includes that of eight electrons.

A nucleus is stable if its mass is less than the combined masses of any pair of nuclei made by its subdivision. For example, $_3Li^7$ is stable against the subdivision

$$_3Li^7 \longrightarrow {_2He^4} + {_1H^3}$$

because the mass relations are

$_2He^4$		4.002604 u
$_1H^3$		3.016049 u
	Sum	7.018653 u
$_3Li^7$		7.016005 u

But $_2He^5$ is unstable against the decomposition

$$_2He^5 \longrightarrow {_2He^4} + {_0n^1}$$

The mass of $_2He^5$ is 5.012296 u; the other masses are

$_2He^4$		4.002604 u
$_0n^1$		1.008665 u
	Sum	5.011269 u

The energy surplus of $_2He^5$ comes out as

$$5.011269 \text{ u} - 5.012296 \text{ u} = -0.001027 \text{ u}$$

A negative energy surplus indicates instability.

All known nuclidic masses have been measured accurately and systematically, for both practical and theoretical reasons; the data are needed for a theoretical model of nuclear forces.

55.3. Nuclear Models

We have already learned that models are useful in our theorizing, especially in theorizing about things that cannot be seen. Some models are very easy to visualize. The Bohr model of the atom is easy to visualize because of its similarity to the planetary system of the sun. It is not cor-rect, however, and must therefore be used with caution as a guide to our thinking.

Another type of model is the purely mathematical one. The Schrödinger wave equation leads to atomic models that cannot be easily visualized. The density of the fuzzy clouds in Figure 52.1, for example, is proportional to the intensity of the wave functions obtained from Schrödinger's equation: a high density corresponds to a high probability of finding an electron. The clean-cut orbits of the Bohr picture are gone. The model is no longer simple and easy to visualize, but it makes up for that lack by its greater accuracy.

In dealing with the nucleus, we run into the same kind of trouble. To explain some nuclear experiments, we need only imagine the nucleus as a solid ball in which the neutrons and protons are embedded. To explain others, we need to imagine the nucleus as a drop of liquid, capable of holding itself together by forces similar to those of surface tension, yet also capable of adding other droplets to make a new and larger droplet.

Nuclei, like atoms, have excited states. In explaining them, we are forced by the wave-mechanical picture to a more abstract concept, which we can summarize by drawing hypothetical graphs of potential energy against nucleon separation and ascribing the experimentally discovered excited states within the nucleus to the wave properties of moving particles. In this view the nucleons within the nucleus possess tremendous kinetic energy. There is no way to specify location and momentum simultaneously for these particles (the principle of uncertainty), but it is possible to conceive a hypothetical potential energy whose characteristics explain the possible energy levels, which are very similar, in principle, to those we associated with orbits in Bohr's picture of the atom.

We shall consider briefly only the liquid-drop model and some consequences of the model associated with what is called a potential well.

1. *The Liquid-drop Model*

Some of the points of similarity between a nucleus and a liquid drop are as follows: (a) As

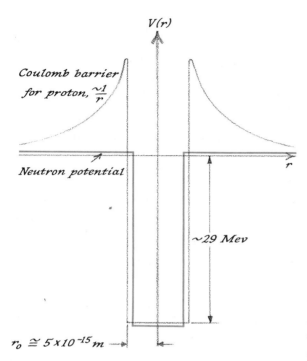

FIG. 55.4. *Graph of potential against radial distance for a proton and a neutron.*

the molecules in a droplet interact with only a small number of their closest neighbors, so do the nucleons in a nucleus; the interaction forces are short-range. (b) The nucleus and the droplet both show effects of surface tension. (c) The kinetic energy of nucleons is akin to the thermal agitation of molecules. (d) The loss of nucleons during nuclear reactions is like the evaporation of molecules from a liquid. (e) The nuclear instability that leads to fission (§ 58.1) is somewhat like the instability of a vibrating droplet.

There are also important differences. The density of the common liquids is of the order of 1 gm/cm³; the density of nucleons is about 2.4×10^{14} gm/cm³. The surface tension of water is 75 dynes/cm (I shall not define surface tension precisely, but the preceding statement means that a single surface of water film pulls on a neighboring one with which it shares a common linear boundary 1 cm long with a force of 75 dynes); the surface tension of the hypothetical nuclear fluid is 9.3×10^{19} dynes/cm. The liquid-drop model works best for heavy nuclei.

2. *The Potential Well*

The behavior of a nucleon within a nucleus is roughly expressible by a curve of potential, which, because of its shape (Fig. 55.4), is often called a **potential well.** The potential well represents the average effect of all the other nucleons.

The ground state of a nucleon is at an energy level about 8 Mev below zero; that is, it takes a net energy of about 8 Mev to remove a nucleon to a place where the radial distance, r, is infinite. If the nucleon is a proton trying to enter the nucleus, it encounters a barrier in the form of the coulombic repulsion, which takes over if r becomes greater than about 5×10^{-15} m. Classically, it could not get out of the nucleus without having great excess energy to get it over the hump; wave-mechanically, this is not necessarily so.

The precise behavior of the nucleons within the nucleus is not specified at all by the model. The nucleons can be thought of as independent particles, such as we find in a gas. The kinetic energy of the protons inside a nucleus, as computed from this model, is about 21 Mev. The total potential depth is $21 + 8 = 29$ Mev, the 8 Mev being the figure we computed earlier as the average binding energy per nucleon. The black curve of Figure 55.4 is for a proton, and the green line represents the neutron potential, which, for reasons that are beyond the scope of this book, dips slightly lower than the proton potential.

The exact shape of the potential well is not known; if it were, we should know the law of force that applies to nucleons. The depth of the hypothetical square-well potential has, however, been estimated. Hence we are not in complete ignorance about nucleons within a nucleus, although the picture is even less definite than the fuzzy wave picture of the electrons in an atom.

55.4. Structure of the Nucleus

Our knowledge of atomic nuclei has progressed along lines that run somewhat parallel to those that led to our knowledge of atoms. First came the evidence for the *existence* of atoms; then the *external* properties of atoms and combinations of atoms were investigated; then the *inner* structure of atoms was investigated experimentally (spectroscopically) and finally was adequately explained theoretically (wave mechanics). The nucleus as an entity has gone through similar stages. First came the evidence for the *existence* of a nucleus (Rutherford alpha-particle scattering experiments); next came a study of the *external* properties of nuclei (size, mass, and charge) and of their interactions with electric and magnetic fields (mass spectrograph) and with one another (nuclear collisions and reactions); finally the problem of the *inner* structure of the nucleus led to the discovery that the basic constituents of nuclei are protons and neutrons. Experiments also seemed to show that wave mechanics is applicable to the nucleus and its nucleons. Excited energy states were discovered, and transitions from one state to another were found to be accompanied by radiation in agreement with the basic formula $\Delta E = h\nu$.

But there are two basic differences between the atomic and the nuclear problems. One is in the order of magnitude of the energies involved: atomic energies are properly expressible in electron volts, but nuclear energies are better measured in millions of electron volts. The other difference is that, though the theoretical problem of the atom is basically solved, that of the nucleus is not: the force acting between electrons and nuclei is known as a function of their separation, but the force acting between nucleons is not known in similar detail. It is therefore not yet possible to predict the properties of nuclei theoretically.

All the chemical properties of atoms depend on the single variable Z, which is the number of planetary electrons in a neutral atom (or the number of protons in its nucleus). In principle you could build a computing machine, supply it with the necessary instructions and numerical constants, and then, if you fed $Z = 2$ into it, for example, you could read out from it the chemical properties of helium. In a similar way it could also give the chemical properties of the other elements from $Z = 1$ all the way to $Z = 92$ (uranium) and beyond.

The problem of the nucleus is more complicated. We need to know not only Z, but A as well, for, since Z is the number of its protons, $A - Z$ is the number of its neutrons, and we need both to determine its properties. But it is not yet possible, even in principle, to construct a computing machine that would yield the properties of the helium nucleus if fed the numbers $Z = 2$ and $A = 4$; for we cannot yet describe the forces between nucleons in a definite and clear-cut way. Although it is not yet possible to predict accurately the properties of nuclei, a great deal is known about them.

Just as the spectroscopists of the nineteenth century continued, despite the lack of a unifying theory, to amass a tremendous number of factual data concerning atoms, so today, with the aid of the mass spectrometer and other very sophisticated instruments, we are accumulating a great many operational nuclear data in the hope that an adequate theory will eventually fit them into a coherent whole.

55.5. Summary

The first and possibly the most important measurable quantity associated with a nucleus is its mass. The binding energy of nucleons in a nucleus can be calculated from very accurate measurements of mass.

The great precision with which one can measure nuclear masses by means of the mass spectrometer has made it possible to accumulate a wealth of information, from which imperfect but extremely useful theories concerning the forces that bind nucleons together within nuclei have been constructed.

With a knowledge of the number of protons and neutrons in the nucleus and of its atomic mass, the binding energy has been calculated.

Although the mathematical relation that represents the force of attraction between nucleons has not been discovered, sufficient data have been collected to make possible significant practical and theoretical advances in nuclear physics.

Problems

55.1. In a table of nuclides with more than 750 entries [L. A. König, J. H. E. Mattauch, and A. H. Wapstra in *Nuclear Physics*, 31: 18 (1962)] we find the data presented here in Table 55.3. Observe that three isotopes of copper appear. (There are seven others as well, but we can gain some important information from this sample.)

1. Fill in the column for N, which stands for the number of neutrons in the nuclide.

2. Find the atomic mass of the copper nuclides with A equal to 64 and 65. (Example: For copper with A equal to 63, take $63.000000 - 0.070406 = 62.929594$.)

TABLE 55.3

Selected Nuclides ($_6C^{12} = 12$)

Z	A	N	Symbol	Mass Excess for Neutral Atom (multiply by 10^{-6})
28	63		Ni	-70334 u
29	63		Cu	-70406
30	63		Zn	-66792
28	64		Ni	-72041
29	64		Cu	-70239
30	64		Zn	-70855
31	64		Ga	-63262
28	65		Ni	-69959
29	65		Cu	-72214
30	65		Zn	-70766
31	65		Ga	-67267
32	65		Ge	-62200

3. Observe that the atomic mass is given to eight significant figures. In the table of atomic weights given in Appendix F, however, the atomic weight of copper is given as 63.54—to only four significant figures. Explain the apparent discrepancy in the precision to which these numbers are given. (Hint: What kinds of experiments do we need to determine each of them?)

55.2. 1. It can be determined that 69.1 percent of all copper atoms have A equal to 63 and that 30.9 percent have A equal to 65. Calculate, to three significant figures, the weighted average of their isotopic masses. Does it come out as 63.5?

2. Using an atomic mass of 1.00783 u for neutral $_1H^1$ and m_n equal to 1.00867 u, calculate from equation 55.1 the binding energy of $_{29}Cu^{63}$ in Mev. The source of Table 55.3 gives a binding energy of 551.378 Mev for $_{29}Cu^{63}$.

55.3. 1. Imagine A beads on a string. If a bond of attraction exists only between a bead and its nearest neighbor, prove that exactly A bonds exist. (Assume, for simplicity's sake, that the ends of the string are tied together.)

2. If, on the other hand, a bond exists between each of A beads and every other one, prove that there are exactly $(A^2 - A)/2$ bonds. If you cannot prove it, confirm it by actual counting for $A = 4$, 5, and 6.

3. For large values of A a good approximation to the function $A^2 - A$ is simply A^2. Confirm this by tabulating A, A^2, and $(A^2 - A)$ for $A = 1$, 5, 10, 100, and 250. Are all of these permissible values for the atomic mass number A?

55.4. If the potential energy, U, is known as a function of distance, x, the force is numerically equal to $\Delta U/\Delta x$, which is the slope of the potential-energy curve (§ 27.4). The steeper the curve, the greater the slope.

1. What is wrong with a nuclear model that uses a square well for a potential curve? (Hint: What is the slope of the curve at the edges of the well?)

2. How could we modify this curve slightly to avoid this error?

Nuclear Reactions

CHEMICAL reactions, which occur when substances are converted into other substances by a rearrangement of atoms, can be described symbolically, experimentally, and theoretically. Let's consider this example:

$$3Fe + 4H_2O \longrightarrow Fe_3O_4 + 4H_2$$

This *symbolic* representation of a chemical reaction tells us that molecules of iron and of water may yield iron oxide and hydrogen molecules, but it tells us nothing about how the experiment is performed. Could you collect hydrogen molecules by putting an iron nail, for example, into a glass of water? An *experimental* description of the reaction tells us that steam is passed over iron filings heated to a temperature of about 600°C, a fact that could hardly be learned from the symbolic representation. A *theoretical* description would involve the electronic chemical bonds that tie iron to oxygen in this particular combination.

56.1. What is a Nuclear Reaction?

Unlike chemical reactions, which occur when substances are converted into other substances by a rearrangement of atoms, nuclear reactions occur when nuclei are converted into other nuclei by a rearrangement of their nucleons. Like chemical reactions, they can be described *symbolically*, *experimentally*, and *theoretically*.

Let's consider this example:

$$_2He^4 + {_7}N^{14} \longrightarrow {_8}O^{17} + {_1}H^1 \qquad [56.1$$

This says that helium nuclei combine with nitro-

gen nuclei to yield oxygen nuclei (of a kind rarely found in nature) and hydrogen nuclei. What the bare symbols leave unsaid is that the helium nuclei are fast alpha particles ejected from a naturally radioactive substance and bombarding a nitrogen target.

Equation 56.1 describes the first recorded artificial nuclear modification, performed by Rutherford in 1919. Like the chemical equation, it fails to explain how the experiment is performed. It leaves many questions unanswered. For example: In what form is the nitrogen used, as a gas, as a solid, or as a liquid? Or is it joined to other atoms in a compound? By what experimental means do we detect the presence of oxygen and hydrogen nuclei in the final product? Do we have to use a mass spectrograph, or can we use an ordinary optical spectrograph, to determine whether the final product contains oxygen and hydrogen nuclei? It is apparent that, to answer some of these questions, we shall at least have to tell how to *generate* and how to *detect* nuclear particles.

To explain equation 56.1 theoretically, we need a theory of the forces that bind nucleons together and a good model to show how a nucleus can capture a nucleon from the outside and become a new, stable nucleus of a different nuclide.

In both chemical and nuclear reactions the concept of energy plays an important part: in the first case, the iron filings and the water had to be heated; in the second case, the alpha particles had to move at very high speed.

We know that the energies required for chemical reactions are of the order of a few electron volts per molecule (§ 45.1). It is not surprising, therefore, that elementary chemistry can begin with do-it-yourself experiments such as burning sugar (an example of oxidation) and collecting the products (which include water). Many chemical experiments can be done with simple apparatus, some chemicals, and a flame.

In nuclear reactions, however, energies of a few million electron volts per particle are often involved. Since the early experiments of Rutherford and others, who used naturally radioactive substances as atomic bullets to initiate reactions, the modern machinery for nuclear physics has included accelerating machines such as the cyclotron and the linear accelerator, which are far from being either simple or natural. The symbolic representation of a nuclear reaction does not announce that the artillery required is an accelerator costing a million dollars.

Equation 56.1 permits a simple check on the conservation of charge (the sum of the subscripts on either side is the total number of protons) and on the conservation of the total number of nucleons (the sum of the superscripts on either side is the total number of protons and neutrons); unless the figures agree, the equation is wrong. But, as it now stands, the equation does not mention the conservation of energy. Since the binding energy and the kinetic energy of the ejected particles can all be expressed in atomic mass units, a special energy term, Q, which stands for the energy released, is often included to indicate the conservation of energy in a nuclear reaction.

56.2. The Q Value: Disintegration Energy

Consider a very general kind of nuclear reaction involving two nuclear particles and a photon. Let m_1 and m_2 be the rest masses and E_{k_1} and E_{k_2} the kinetic energies of the initial particles; let m_3 and m_4 be the rest masses and E_{k_3} and E_{k_4} the kinetic energies of the final particles; let $h\nu_0$ be the initial photon energy and $h\nu$ the final photon energy. Equating energy before and after the reaction, we obtain

$$m_1c^2 + E_{k_1} + m_2c^2 + E_{k_2} + h\nu_0$$
$$= m_3c^2 + E_{k_3} + m_4c^2 + E_{k_4} + h\nu \quad [56.2$$

Transposing and collecting terms, we get

$$[(m_1 + m_2) - (m_3 + m_4)]c^2$$
$$= [(E_{k_3} + E_{k_4}) - (E_{k_1} + E_{k_2})] + h(\nu - \nu_0) \quad [56.3$$

On the right side of the equation we see (1) the new kinetic energy minus the old plus (2) the new photon energy minus the old—in other words, the *change* in kinetic and photon energies resulting from the reaction. This energy, which is the energy transformed from mass energy to energy of other kinds in a nuclear reaction, is called the **Q value** or the **disintegration energy** of the reaction. It is obvious that

$$Q = [(E_{k_3} + E_{k_4}) - (E_{k_1} + E_{k_2})] + h(\nu - \nu_0) \quad [56.4$$

and that an equivalent expression is

$$Q = [(m_1 + m_2) - (m_3 + m_4)]c^2 \quad [56.5$$

If the masses are in kilograms and c is in meters per second, equation 56.5 gives Q in joules. If the masses are expressed in unified atomic mass units, a more convenient unit in nuclear work, the disintegration energy, Q', may now be written as

$$Q' = (m_1 + m_2) - (m_3 + m_4) \quad [56.6$$

As an example let us analyze the reaction of equation 56.1. First we must justify the use of *atomic* masses in this case rather than the nuclear masses of equation 56.6. Let the chemical symbols stand for the corresponding masses of the neutral atoms and m_e for the mass of one electron; let m_1, m_2, m_3, and m_4 represent the nuclear masses of the nuclides $_2He^4$, $_7N^{14}$, $_9F^{18}$, and $_1H^1$, respectively.

$$(He + N) - (O + H)$$
$$= (m_1 + 2m_e + m_2 + 7m_e)$$
$$- (m_3 + 8m_e + m_4 + m_e) \quad [56.7$$
$$= (m_1 + m_2) - (m_3 + m_4) \quad [56.8$$

By using the atomic masses instead of the nuclear masses, we get the correct result for Q because the electronic masses cancel out. [Warning: If positrons (positive electrons) are emitted, the electronic masses do *not* cancel out.] After tabulating the atomic masses (Table 56.1), we see that

$$Q = 18.005678 - 18.006958 \quad [56.9$$
$$= -0.001280 \text{ u} \quad [56.10$$

TABLE 56.1

Atomic Masses (u) Involved in Equation 56.1
($_6C^{12} = 12$)

$_2He^4$	4.002604	$_8O^{17}$	16.999133
$_7N^{14}$	14.003074	$_1H^1$	1.007825
He + N	18.005678	O + H	18.006958

Since the potential energy of 1 u of mass is 931.5 Mev, we get

$$Q = -0.001280 \times 931.5 = -1.192 \text{ Mev} \quad [56.11$$

We shall understand the physical significance of the negative Q if we consider equation 56.4 when $h(\nu - \nu_0) = 0$. It is that the kinetic energy of the particles after the reaction is less than the kinetic energy of the particles before the reaction. The fact that the sum of the rest masses is greater after the reaction than before indicates (equation 56.5), if the target nucleus is at rest, that the reaction will take place only if the alpha particle has a kinetic energy of at least 1.192 Mev.

A special kind of reaction, requiring no outside starter, is the spontaneous emission of alpha particles by certain nuclei. We call such emission **alpha decay.** It occurs, for example, with radium:

$$_{88}Ra^{226} \longrightarrow {}_{86}Rn^{222} + {}_2He^4 + Q \quad [56.12$$

Using the atomic masses, we get

$$226.025360 = 222.017530 + 4.002604 + Q \quad [56.13$$

$$Q = +0.00523 \text{ u or } +4.87 \text{ Mev} \quad [56.14$$

The positive Q shows that radium is unstable; we say that it *alpha-decays.* Since no photon energy is involved, the 4.87 Mev of energy is the total kinetic energy of the products, radon and the alpha particle. The kinetic energy of such alpha particles can be used, in fact, to start such reactions as that of equation 56.1.

In the two examples given, a **transmutation** takes place. In the first, nitrogen is changed to oxygen, but it requires an energy (1.192 Mev) millions of times greater than that found in ordinary chemical reactions. It is no wonder, then, that nitrogen and oxygen, along with the other ordinary elements, were long considered indestructible and unchangeable building blocks of

nature. In the second example, radium spontaneously becoming radon, we have a natural transmutation of elements that eluded the early seekers (the alchemists) because radium is scarce, because the detection of the disintegration products requires special apparatus, and because the seekers were interested in gold.

Modern transmutations produced by high-energy particles are now almost commonplace. We shall first consider how to generate such particles and then how to detect, identify, and measure the final products of such transmutations.

56.3. Particle Accelerators

I shall describe how two kinds of particle accelerator work—the simple cyclotron, a circular device (with brief mention of some other circular machines), and the linear electron accelerator. The cyclotron gave us our first important breakthrough into the Mev region, and the linear electron accelerator may give us an important breakthrough into the multi-Bev region. The construction of a modern particle accelerator is an engineering feat of large proportions. A modern working accelerator is impossible without a team of scientists and engineers capable of using the most sophisticated mechanical, optical, and electronic devices in existence. An understanding of the basic principles on which an accelerator operates no more ensures the ability to build one and make it work than an understanding of the four-cycle gasoline engine ensures the ability to build a modern automobile, which, although complex, is much less complex than a large accelerator. In seeking the intellectual satisfaction of understanding, in theory, the operation of accelerators, we must not forget to respect the men who actually build them and make them work.

Much of the exciting work in nuclear physics has been done with machines operating in the Mev region of energy. When, for example, an electron and a positron meet, they may disappear completely. Their total rest mass then appears as a pair of gamma-ray photons. (The process is called pair annihilation. Two gammas are needed to conserve momentum.) The reaction may be written as

$$e^+ + e^{-1} \longrightarrow 2\gamma$$

Since the rest mass of an electron is about 0.5 Mev, the energy of the gamma rays must total 1 Mev. To reverse this process and *create* a positron-electron pair requires a gamma-ray photon with an energy of at least 1 Mev.

It now looks, however, as if some of the most revealing experiments of the future might require energies in the Bev region and higher. It is known, for example, that a particle called an antiproton exists. (Its relation to the proton is the same as the relation of the positron to the electron.) To create a proton-antiproton pair (Chap. 59) requires an energy of about 2 Bev, and a particle with an energy of 10^{10} Bev has been recorded in a cosmic-ray shower. The shower was, of course, an uncontrollable event. Cosmic rays arrive with their full complement of energy at the top of the atmosphere, where experimentation is difficult. In order to reproduce in a controllable fashion some of the phenomena that have been observed so far only with cosmic rays, machines able to accelerate particles into the Bev region are needed.

All accelerators operate by subjecting electrically charged particles to the force produced by an electric field. In the circular devices, the particles, kept in a circular or spiral path by powerful magnets, pass many thousands of times through the accelerating electric field, picking up more speed each time.

1. *The Cyclotron*

The cyclotron, capable of accelerating protons to speeds that give them energies in the Mev region without potential differences higher than a few thousand volts, makes very ingenious use of electric and magnetic fields.

Using hindsight, it is easy to invent a cyclotron. How do you accelerate anything? You exert a force on it. Electric and magnetic fields, which can be readily created and controlled, exert forces on charged particles. A particle of mass m and charge q moving with velocity $\mathbf{v}$ in an electric field of intensity $\mathbf{E}$ and a magnetic field of intensity $\mathbf{B}$ experiences (§ 35.1) the force

$$\mathbf{F} = q(\mathbf{E} + \mathbf{v} \times \mathbf{B}) \qquad [56.15$$

A review of § 38.1 will show that, while $q\mathbf{E}$ acts in the direction of $\mathbf{E}$ (§ 4.4), $q(\mathbf{v} \times \mathbf{B})$ acts at right angles to $\mathbf{B}$. In other words, the component $q\mathbf{E}$ can speed up (or slow down) a charged particle, but the component $q(\mathbf{v} \times \mathbf{B})$ can only deflect it without changing its speed (§ 9.6).

All that is needed, apparently, is a strong, homogeneous $\mathbf{E}$ field in which charged particles will readily pick up speed. If e is the magnitude of the electronic charge and V is the potential difference across two electrodes between which there is an electric field, $\mathbf{E}$, the maximum amount of kinetic energy that can be gained by an electron in this field is eV (if e is in coulombs and V is in volts, eV is in joules). Expressed in *electron volts*, the energy is simply V. Now, since for nuclear work we wish to get into the Mev region, V has to be of the order of a million volts. It is not easy to create such a high potential difference in air at atmospheric pressure, but R. J. Van de Graaff, in the United States, built a generator of such voltage (see § 36.5), and John Cockcroft and Ernest Walton, in England, built one of another type (Cockcroft and Walton were awarded the Nobel Prize for Physics in 1951); both machines once played very important roles and in new forms are still being used today.

E. O. Lawrence (who was awarded the Nobel Prize for Physics in 1939) conceived a different method. Instead of applying a constant electric field to a particle moving in a long straight line, he made the particle follow a curved path and gave it momentary tangential kicks to speed it up. His reasoning followed these lines: Suppose you could use a magnetic field to deflect a charged particle (without changing its speed) and an electric field to speed it up during part of its journey. If the push due to the electric field could be repeated many times, the final speed of the particle would equal that of a particle that had been accelerated in a constant field through a very great potential difference.

The electrodes of a cyclotron (Fig. 56.1) are like hollow metal cans (D_1 and D_2) in the shape of the letter D and are therefore called *dees*. If they are charged (Fig. 56.2), one positively and one negatively (A), an electric field, $\mathbf{E}$, will be

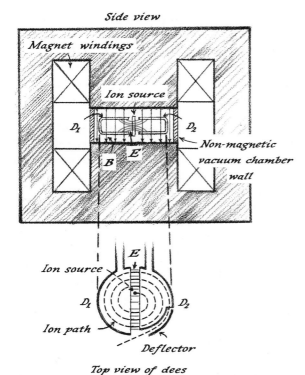

FIG. 56.1. *The dees of a cyclotron placed in the field of a large electromagnet.*

established between them (**B**). A particle at *P*, bearing the positive charge *q* and moving to the right at speed *v*, feels the force *q***E**. Under this influence its speed increases to *v′*, and it enters the second dee, D_2, at *Q*. Within the dee the electric field is practically zero, but the magnetic field, **B**, at right angles to the top and bottom of the dees, causes the particle to move in a circle of radius *R*. The particle arrives at *S* at the same speed but moving to the left. If the polarity of the dees has been reversed while the particle was moving from *Q* to *S*, the electric field between *S* and *T* will produce a new burst of acceleration, and the particle will enter D_1 with increased speed. By equating the centripetal force, mv^2/R, with the magnitude of the magnetic force, $q(\mathbf{v} \times \mathbf{B})$, we get the equation deduced in § 38.6:

$$\frac{v}{R} = \frac{qB}{m} \qquad [56.16$$

If the quantities *m*, *q*, and *B* are constant, *v/R* (the angular velocity) remains constant. Thus an increase in *v*, produced by the force *q***E** as the particle moves from one dee to the other, results in a larger *R* in the second dee, and so on. The particle keeps gaining speed as it spirals, but its

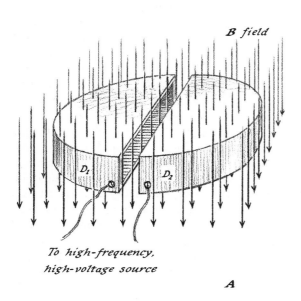

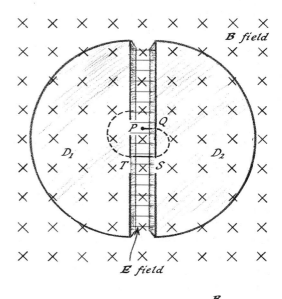

FIG. 56.2. *The* **E** *field increases the speed of the electron as it passes from one dee to the other. The* **B** *field makes it travel in a circular path at constant speed.*

angular velocity, v/R, remains constant as long as qB/m is constant. Connecting the dees to a source of AC potential effects the rapid changes in polarity that are required.

This method works well with protons, deuterons (deuterium nuclei), and other charged particles of similar mass, giving them speeds and kinetic energies that are useful in the collision experiments to be described later. The much less massive electrons can readily be brought up to the same speeds, but their kinetic energies are still not great enough to make them productive bombardment projectiles. Their speeds can be increased until they approach the speed of light, but then their mass also increases, as explained in § 46.3. The increase in mass decreases their angular velocity, according to equation 56.16. The lagging electrons then get out of phase with the AC and drop out of the race. One can diminish this effect, however, either by making B increase with R or by reducing the AC frequency as the acceleration proceeds.

The first cyclotron was built by E. O. Lawrence and M. S. Livingstone in 1931. The diameter of its vacuum chamber was 4.5 inches, and the maximum energy to which it could accelerate protons was 80,000 ev. By contrast, a modern cyclotron with a pole-face diameter of 60 inches has produced deuterons with energies of 20 Mev. The gigantic synchrocyclotron at Berkeley (California), in which the frequency of the accelerating signal is diminished as the mass of the particle increases, has accelerated protons to speeds corresponding to energies of 730 Mev.

In 1956 the only type of accelerator that had entered the Bev (billion electron volts) range was the proton synchrotron (Fig. 56.3), the basic features of which are illustrated by a device, nicknamed the Cosmotron, at Brookhaven National Laboratory on Long Island (New York). It is not a cyclotron, but it is, in a sense, a natural development of the cyclotron idea. The protons are kept in their circular path by a magnetic field produced by a shell built round an orbit of fixed radius, which, in the Cosmotron, is about 30 feet. The acceleration takes place each time the proton passes the radio-frequency accelerating unit. As equation 56.16 indicates, if the speed of the parti-

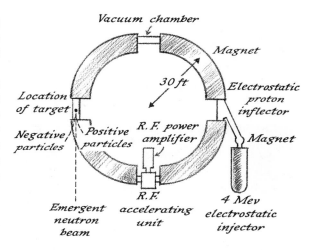

FIG. 56.3. *Schematic diagram of a proton synchrotron.*

cle is increased, the magnetic field must be strengthened correspondingly; and the relativistic increase in mass requires a variation in the frequency of the accelerating voltage. By 1952 the Cosmotron had reached 3 Bev. Similar machines have been built in France, England, Switzerland, and the U.S.S.R. In 1961 an advanced form of proton synchrotron (Brookhaven's alternating-gradient synchrotron) reached an energy of 32 Bev. Preliminary study is under way for a U.S.-U.S.S.R. device, of the same type, that may reach 300 Bev.

2. *The Linear Electron Accelerator*

One disadvantage of having electrons or other charged particles travel in circular paths is that the acceleration involved in their continuous change of direction causes them to lose energy by radiation. (Losses by radiation are relatively greater for electrons, because of their smaller mass, than for protons.) At energies above 10 Bev this loss would probably be prohibitive. A straight path is therefore preferable for electrons. The pipe is a copper tube divided into sections by means of disks, with holes in the center, placed at increasing intervals along the tube (Fig. 56.4). An electromagnetic wave produced by a series of very large Klystron tubes similar to those used in high-powered radar transmitters receives its

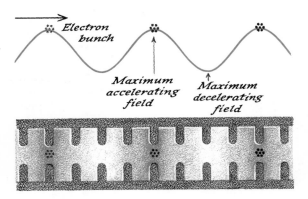

FIG. 56.4. *Wave guide of a linear electron accelerator. The electron bunches are carried along on the crests of the wave.*

energy at intervals along the tube in such a way that the wavelength increases although the frequency is constant. Electrons are injected into one end of the pipe from an electron gun like that in a television picture tube; as they move along the pipe, they are guided by the electric fields of the wave, somewhat as a surfboarder rides an ocean wave. The special characteristics of the wave make the electrons pick up speed as they travel along the tube.

The Congress of the United States, in 1959, authorized the construction of a linear electron accelerator two miles long at Stanford University. Its ultimate energy is expected to be 40 or 45 Bev, and its beam of electrons will be about 5,000 times more intense than the beam of the huge Brookhaven AGS. In principle it will be a direct extension of the machine (the Mark III), built earlier at Stanford, on which Robert Hofstadter performed the experiments that won him half of the Nobel Prize for Physics in 1961. (The other half went to Rudolf Mössbauer for his method of producing and measuring recoil-free gamma rays.) Its estimated cost is $114 million, and it will have taken six years to build. In this machine (Fig. 56.5), the electrons will leave the injecting gun at half the speed of light; by the time their energy reaches 5 Mev, they will be traveling at speed $0.995\ c$; at 20 Bev their mass will be about 40,000 times their rest mass, and their speed will be

$0.9999999997\ c$. In other words, after about the first ten feet of travel the electrons will move through the pipe at almost constant speed, and subsequent gains in energy will appear primarily as gains in mass. For this reason W. W. Hansen, designer of the linear electron accelerator, once said that it should be called a ponderator rather than an accelerator.

Hofstadter and his associates, working with the Mark III, have, by observing the distribution of electrons scattered from nuclei, produced not only some of the most precise measurements to date of the size of atomic nuclei and individual nucleons but also evidence of their inner structure. Their work can be compared to use of the accelerator as a microscope. Since the degree of detail that can be resolved depends on the wavelength associated with the probing particle and thus on the particle's energy, higher electron energies should make it possible to study the structure of individual particles in greater detail. Although there seems to be no upper limit to the energies that can be used in this work, the experiments will become more difficult to perform and the results may become more difficult to interpret as the energy is increased. (See Fig. 56.6 for a comparison of four different microscopes.)

56.4. Detection

We can put the products of nuclear disintegration into two categories: (1) particles with non-zero rest mass and (2) particles, such as photons and neutrinos, with zero rest mass. If the particles are charged, they may ionize atoms with which they collide and thereby be detected. Photons also may induce ionization under the proper circumstances. Neutrons, being uncharged, are hard to detect; but, if allowed to strike hydrogenous material, they eject protons, thus becoming indirectly detectable. So we can say, by oversimplifying a bit, that nuclear events are directly or indirectly detectable through ionization. This is a useful simplification to remember, for the genetic and other biological effects of radiation are also traceable to ionizations.

A systematic survey of detection would be out

of place here. Let us merely consider several of the modern means of detection, especially those that evolved from techniques used when radioactivity was first discovered.

Early investigators used the rate of discharge of a sensitive electroscope as a measure of the strength of ionizing radiations. The electrometer is a direct quantitative descendant of the semiqualitative electroscope: the ions formed within a well-insulated ionization chamber are collected, and their aggregate charge causes a deflection whose magnitude is the measure of the number of collected ions and hence of the radiation that made them. The sensitivity of the best electrometers is about 10^{-18} ampere. A contemporary portable electrometer is the quartz-fiber electroscope, which is used primarily for checking the safety of nuclear laboratories. It is first charged at a source of known potential; ionizing radiation discharges it by calibrated amounts. It depends on insulation of extremely high resistivity to keep from discharging by leakage.

Another early technique that has a modern counterpart is counting scintillations. With dark-adapted eyes, Rutherford was able to see the tiny spots of light produced by the impingement of alpha particles on a fluorescent screen (§ 48.3). The modern scintillation counter utilizes a crystal that fluoresces under the action of gamma rays and other nuclear particles. The tiny flash of light

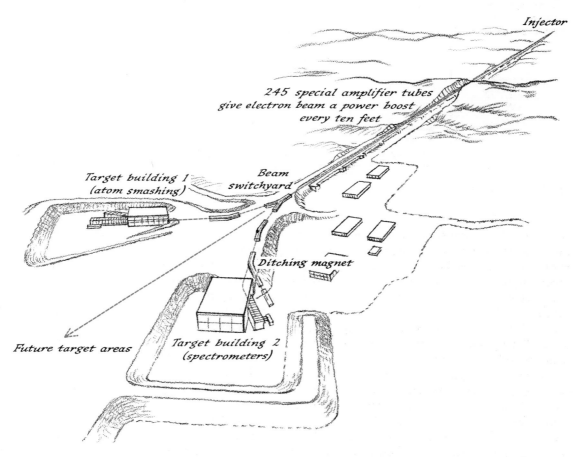

FIG. 56.5. *Schematic diagram of the Stanford two-mile linear electron accelerator. Gigantic electromagnets at the beam switchyard direct the beam into one or the other of two target buildings or split it between them. The ditching magnet can deflect the beam so that it does not enter target building 2. The targets are metallic sheets or containers of liquid hydrogen.*

	OPTICAL MICROSCOPE	ELECTRON MICROSCOPE	STANFORD MARK III ACCELERATOR	PROPOSED 2-MILE ACCELERATOR
PROBE USED	Visible light	Electrons	Electrons	Electrons
WHAT IS SEEN	Image	Image	Diffraction pattern	Diffraction pattern
PARTICLE OR PHOTON ENERGY	2 ev	50,000 ev	700 Mev	40 Bev
WAVELENGTH	10^{-5} cm	10^{-9} cm	10^{-13} cm	10^{-14} to 10^{-15} cm
SMALLEST OBJECT THAT CAN BE SEEN	Millions of atoms	Large molecule (thousands of atoms)	Nuclei. Some details of individual atoms	Details of elementary particles
TYPICAL OBJECTS OF STUDY	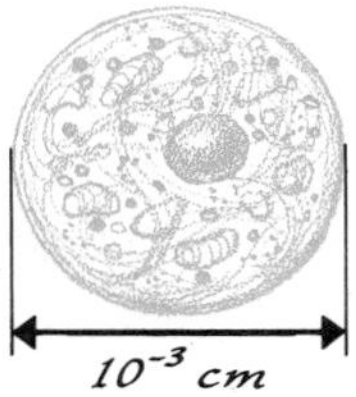 10^{-3} cm Living cell	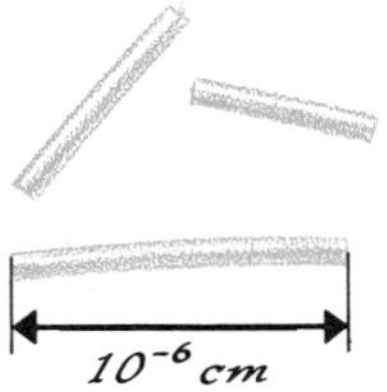 10^{-6} cm Virus	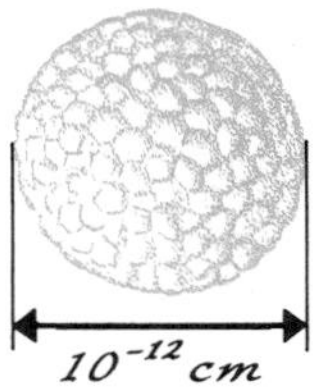 10^{-12} cm Atomic nucleus	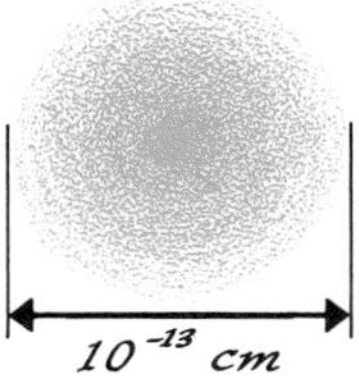 10^{-13} cm Proton

FIG. 56.6. *A comparison of four microscopes.*

is detected by a very sensitive photoelectric tube called a photomultiplier, which has a built-in electron-multiplying factor of about 10^6 even before its signal reaches the outer electronic amplifying circuits. Modern laboratory versions of the device have been able to detect single quanta of visible light. One can reduce the background noise of the photomultiplier by lowering its temperature with liquid nitrogen.

A tremendous gain in the sensitivity of detectors occurred with the invention by Hans Geiger in 1913 and the subsequent development by Wilhelm Müller in 1928 of the counter that now bears their names. It is, in a sense, a descendant of the early ionization chambers. Imagine a fine wire running along the axis of a metal tube and electrically insulated from it. Radiations entering the tube produce ion pairs in the gas that surrounds the wire. An electric field is established between the wire and the tube by a voltage applied across them through an external resistor. As the ions move toward the wire, a surge of current appears as a potential difference across the resistor. This potential difference, electronically amplified, can produce an audible click or operate a mechanical counter, enabling us to count the ionizing particles. Within a certain region of voltage each particle counted gives a surge of constant magnitude across the resistor. If the tube is operated in a different voltage region, high-energy particles can produce pulses of correspondingly greater magnitude, and low-energy particles can produce pulses of smaller magnitude. When operated in this way, the tube is called a **proportional counter,** and its discrimination between energies makes it a form of nuclear spectrometer.

One of the earliest means of detecting x-rays (which are ionizing radiations although not of nuclear origin) and gamma rays utilized their ability to expose photographic film. One modern descendant of this idea is the monitoring badge used for checking the safety of nuclear laboratories. A piece of photographic film, part of which is covered by a strong absorber, such as lead, is put inside a light-tight envelope. The ionizing radiations that penetrate the envelope during a day may leave a dark spot on the developed film. With proper calibration, a rough quantitative check on radiation levels can be made in this way.

A much more sophisticated use of photographic emulsion is the **nuclear plate,** within which nuclear collisions leave their ionizing tracks. This must be examined under a microscope. Painstaking studies by competent observers have led to such startling discoveries (Fig. 56.7) as that of the pi meson (to be discussed in Chap. 59) by C. F. Powell and G. P. S. Occhialini and by C. M. G. Lattes. (Powell won the Nobel Prize for Physics in 1950.)

The most spectacular of the early nuclear detectors was the Wilson cloud chamber, which made the tracks of ionized particles visible. A descendant of this device is the diffusion cloud chamber, in which a thermal gradient between a very cold area (Dry Ice and alcohol will produce it) and a warm room guarantees the existence of the critical temperature and pressure required for the condensation of vapor on an ionized particle. A home-made diffusion cloud chamber built out of a Thermos bottle is shown in Figure 56.8, and tracks made in such a chamber are shown in Figure 56.9. And now we have the modern bubble chamber, with which the exciting picture on page 662 was made.

In this brief review of detectors I have, from lack of space, left out some very important new developments, such as the spark chamber, and no list would be complete without the optical spectroscopes. They are essentially devices for dispersing photon beams. Their range has been extended into the infrared and down into the ultraviolet and x-ray regions. The energy of photons can be determined by them to about one part in 100,000.

It is important to realize that bare nuclei, being

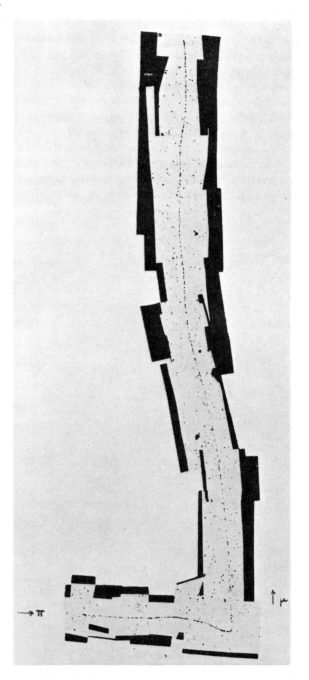

FIG. 56.7. *Nuclear emulsion track showing the transformation of a pi meson into a mu meson. (Reproduced with the permission of C. F. Powell of the University of Bristol, England.)*

positively charged, can readily attract stray electrons and become atoms. The fact that the nucleus deserves to be called the control box of the atom is readily demonstrated. Rutherford collected alpha particles in a glass tube. When he had collected enough of them, he produced an electrical discharge within the tube and was able to obtain the optical spectrum of helium from the glow. Each alpha particle (helium nucleus) had surrounded itself with its proper complement of two orbital electrons and was thereafter identifiable as a helium atom. This demonstration shows how the spectrograph can positively identify some of the products of nuclear reactions by the optical spectra of their corresponding atoms. The Nobel Prize for Chemistry went to G. T. Seaborg and E. M. McMillan in 1951 for their production and identification of transuranium elements produced by nuclear reactions.

And, finally, we have the mass spectrographs (§ 47.5), with which the mass of charged particles can be measured to one part in 10,000.

In considering the detection of particles, I have stressed the measurable characteristics charge, mass, energy, and linear momentum. If we were to include more sophisticated quantities, such as magnetic moment and spin, we should have to extend our list of detectors considerably.

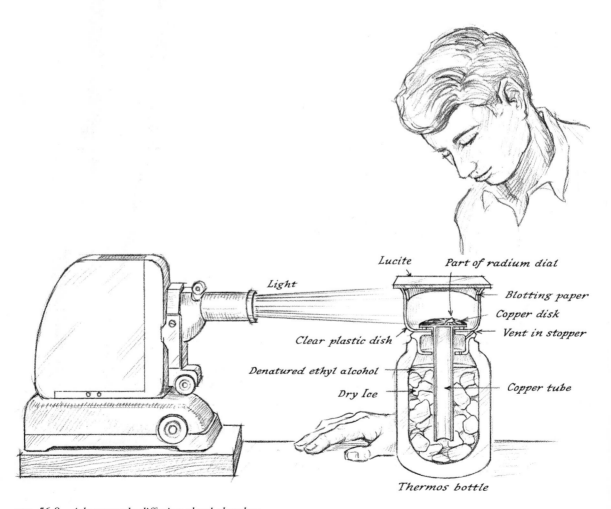

FIG. 56.8. *A homemade diffusion cloud chamber.*

FIG. 56.9. *Tracks made in a homemade diffusion cloud chamber by alpha particles from a watch-dial numeral. (Photograph from Encyclopaedia Britannica Films Inc.)*

56.5. Some Nuclear Reactions

More than a thousand different nuclear reactions have been produced and recorded. I have selected some to illustrate the important developments in this art. They are presented approximately in the order of discovery. A few were chosen for their historical importance. The earliest reactions were brought about with alpha particles from naturally radioactive substances; no accelerator was needed to give such particles the requisite energy. (See § 56.2.) Later the cyclotrons and

their derivatives were able to accelerate the lighter proton and deuteron, and finally the linear accelerator was devised to give even the very light electron enough energy and momentum to be useful in disintegration experiments.

Remember that momentum, p, can be expressed as a non-relativistic approximation in terms of mass, m, and energy, E, as follows:

$$p = \sqrt{2mE} \qquad [56.17$$

One can, in a sense, trade mass for energy: one can reduce the mass by a factor of 2,000 (for example, in going from proton to electron) and keep the same momentum provided the energy is stepped up by a factor of 2,000. Equation 56.17 shows why the relatively massive and energetic alpha particles were among the first to be useful in disintegrations.

1. *Nuclear Reactions Induced by Alpha Particles*

The first man-made disintegration with alpha particles was that performed by Rutherford:

$$_2\text{He}^4 + {}_7\text{N}^{14} \longrightarrow ({}_9\text{F}^{18}) \longrightarrow {}_8\text{O}^{17} + {}_1\text{H}^1 \quad [56.18$$

Another induced reaction was

$$_2\text{He}^4 + {}_9\text{F}^{19} \longrightarrow {}_{10}\text{Ne}^{22} + {}_1\text{H}^1 \quad [56.19$$

The equation that describes Chadwick's discovery of the neutron is

$$_2\text{He}^4 + {}_4\text{Be}^9 \longrightarrow ({}_6\text{C}^{13}) \longrightarrow {}_6\text{C}^{12} + {}_0n^1 \quad [56.20$$

Frédéric and Irène Joliot-Curie were responsible for the following pair of disintegrations, in which both the neutron and the positron figure, and in which artificial radioactivity was first observed:

$$_2\text{He}^5 + {}_{13}\text{Al}^{27} \longrightarrow {}_{15}\text{P}^{30} + {}_0n^1 \quad [56.21$$

The radioactive phosphorus disintegrates into an isotope of silicon according to the equation

$$_{15}\text{P}^{30} \longrightarrow {}_{14}\text{Si}^{30} + {}_{+1}e^0 \quad [56.22$$

The adventurous research that led to identification of each product of these reactions is an interesting bit of history, which I reluctantly leave to other books.

2. *Nuclear Reactions Induced by Protons*

Protons from a Cockcroft-Walton accelerator with an energy of only about 0.3 Mev can disintegrate lithium and produce two alpha particles, each with an energy of about 8.6 Mev, according to the equation

$$_3\text{Li}^7 + {}_1\text{H}^1 \longrightarrow {}_2\text{He}^4 + {}_2\text{He}^4 \quad [56.23$$

which shows that the relatively low-energy proton acts simply as a trigger for the release of nuclear energy. (For simplicity's sake I omit the Q values from these reactions.)

Another disintegration produced by protons is

$$_3\text{Li}^7 + {}_1\text{H}^1 \longrightarrow {}_4\text{Be}^8 + h\nu \quad [56.24$$

Notice that the end products are different from those of reaction 56.23 even though the initial particles are the same. This confirms the idea that the outcome is not certain; different results have different probabilities. Note, for example,

$$_4\text{Be}^9 + {}_1\text{H}^1 \longrightarrow {}_3\text{Li}^6 + {}_2\text{He}^4 \quad [56.25$$

$$_4\text{Be}^9 + {}_1\text{H}^1 \longrightarrow {}_4\text{Be}^8 + {}_1\text{H}^2 \quad [56.26$$

Another proton-induced reaction is

$$_{20}\text{Ca}^{44} + {}_1\text{H}^1 \longrightarrow {}_{21}\text{Sc}^{44} + {}_0n^1 \quad [56.27$$

3. *Nuclear Reactions Induced by Deuterons*

A few of the disintegrations induced by deuterons are

$$_3\text{Li}^6 + {}_1\text{H}^2 \longrightarrow {}_2\text{He}^4 + {}_2\text{He}^4 \quad [56.28$$

$$_6\text{C}^{12} + {}_1\text{H}^2 \longrightarrow {}_6\text{C}^{13} + {}_1\text{H}^1 \quad [56.29$$

$$_{11}\text{Na}^{23} + {}_1\text{H}^2 \longrightarrow {}_{12}\text{Mg}^{24} + {}_0n^1 \quad [56.30$$

$$_{20}\text{Ca}^{40} + {}_1\text{H}^2 \longrightarrow {}_{19}\text{K}^{38} + {}_2\text{He}^4$$
$$\qquad\qquad\qquad \longrightarrow {}_{18}\text{Ar}^{38} + {}_{+1}e^0 \quad [56.31$$

Two interesting points to observe are that heavy elements can be disintegrated by deuterons and that neutrons are a by-product of some disintegrations. The latter point is important because neutrons produced in this way can be used to start still other kinds of reaction.

4. *Nuclear Reactions Induced by Neutrons*

Many more nuclear reactions have been produced with neutrons than with any other particle. The lack of charge permits neutrons to penetrate even heavy, highly charged nuclei. A few typical reactions follow:

$$_1\text{H}^1 + {}_0n^1 \longrightarrow {}_1\text{H}^2 + h\nu \quad [56.32$$

$$_3\text{Li}^6 + {}_0n^1 \longrightarrow {}_1\text{H}^3 + {}_2\text{He}^4$$
$$\qquad\qquad\qquad \longrightarrow {}_2\text{He}^3 + {}_{-1}e^0 \quad [56.33$$

$$_4\text{Be}^9 + {}_0n^1 \longrightarrow {}_2\text{He}^6 + {}_2\text{He}^4$$
$$\qquad\qquad\qquad \longrightarrow {}_3\text{Li}^6 + {}_{-1}e^0 \quad [56.34$$

$$_{13}\text{Al}^{27} + {}_0n^1 \longrightarrow {}_{11}\text{Na}^{24} + {}_2\text{He}^4$$
$$\qquad\qquad\qquad \longrightarrow {}_{12}\text{Mg}^{24} + {}_{-1}e^0 \quad [56.35$$

$$_{79}\text{Au}^{197} + {}_0n^1 \longrightarrow {}_{79}\text{Au}^{198} + h\nu$$
$$\qquad\qquad\qquad \longrightarrow {}_{80}\text{Hg}^{198} + {}_{-1}e^0 \quad [56.36$$

The last equation shows how a radioactive isotope of the heavy element gold is produced by neutron bombardment. The liquid-drop model of the nucleus (§ 55.3) gives a vivid approximate explanation of the reactions involved.

5. *Nuclear Reactions Induced by Photons*

We have seen that light and other electromagnetic radiations, such as gamma rays, have particle-like characteristics. It is not surprising, therefore, that photons also can disintegrate nuclei. Compare equation 56.32 with the following:

$$_1H^2 + h\nu \longrightarrow {}_1H^1 + {}_0n^1 \qquad [56.37$$

This shows that the reaction is reversible, but it is beyond the scope of this book to investigate the experimental conditions under which the two different reactions occur. Reactions such as this are called photo-disintegrations. Another example is

$$_4Be^9 + h\nu \longrightarrow {}_4Be^8 + {}_0n^1 \qquad [56.38$$

56.6. Summary

Nuclear reactions occur when nuclei are converted into other nuclei by an alteration of their nucleons. Some reactions occur spontaneously, but others require an outside source of energy.

Momentum and energy are conserved in nuclear reactions. A complete tally of energy must take mass energy into account. The energy transformed from mass energy to kinetic and other forms is called the disintegration energy. It is commonly of the order of several Mev.

Highly energetic nuclear particles are produced naturally in cosmic rays and in certain radioactive materials, but controlled experiments require particles of known energy, which is imparted to them by accelerators—devices that utilize the effect of electric and magnetic fields on charged particles. Such accelerated particles can be used as bullets to induce certain nuclear reactions.

There are many ways to detect the presence and to measure the energy of the particles produced in nuclear reactions; most of them depend directly or indirectly on the ability of high-speed charged particles to ionize the atoms of the matter they hit.

In the expression for a nuclear reaction the sum of the subscripts and the sum of the superscripts of the reactants equal, respectively, the sum of the subscripts and the sum of the superscripts of the products. The first is a measure of the total charge; the second is a count of the total number of nucleons.

Problems

56.1. 1. The magnetic field in which the dees of a cyclotron are embedded has a magnetic induction of 0.5 weber/m². If it produces deuterons with an energy of 2 Mev, how many times does a deuteron have to cross the gap between the dees if the maximum voltage across them is 50 kilovolts?

2. What is the angular velocity of the deuterons in such a field?

3. How long does it take a deuteron, starting from rest, to achieve this energy?

4. If the mass of the deuteron in a cyclotron increases by 5 percent because of a relativistic speed, can it be kept in orbit in a homogeneous magnetic field by an increase in the frequency of *exactly* 5 percent? Explain.

56.2. 1. Prove the statement that, when an electron achieves a mass of about 40,000 times its rest mass, its speed is 0.9999999997 c. (Hint: $v/c = 1 - 3 \times 10^{-10}$. Refer to Prob. 46.9.)

2. To three significant figures, how long will it take such an electron to travel along the tube of the 2-mi linear electron accelerator?

3. What is the kinetic energy of such an electron in joules? in Bev?

4. What voltage would be required to produce this increase of energy in a homogeneous electric field?

56.3. A linear electron accelerator produces 20-Bev electrons (for which v/c is approximately $1 - 3 \times 10^{-10}$, as in Prob. 56.2).

1. What is the de Broglie wavelength of such electrons?

2. Does it seem reasonable that, using these electrons as a probe, one can distinguish details within a proton? Explain.

56.4. Nuclear reactions go if the thermal energy of the particles is high enough (of the order of Mev). Thermal energy per particle is given by the expression kT (§ 29.5). What temperature does an energy of 1 Mev per particle correspond to?

Radioactivity

IF YOU want to see an event that no one else has ever seen, that you will see once and never again, all you have to do is to look through a magnifier with dark-adapted eyes at the discontinuous flickering of a luminous watch dial of the kind that owes its luminosity to radioactive decay. The flicker of fluorescence you observe announced the explosion of an atom by the ejection of a nuclear particle. If you had planned to observe that particular atomic disintegration, you might have had to wait for thousands of years to see it. But you saw it by chance. It was a random event in a chain of disintegrations that began, in all probability, when the earth was formed. No extremes of heat or pressure, no electric or magnetic fields, could have accelerated it. All the radioactive atoms of the watch dial are normal until they disintegrate. We believe they all have the same probability of disintegrating, but one, by chance, happened to wait until you were looking.

57.1. The Emission of Alpha, Beta, and Gamma Rays

I have already pointed out (§ 47.6) that all nuclei with $Z > 83$ are radioactive (as are also some with $Z \leq 83$); some disintegrate spontaneously by emitting alpha particles (helium nuclei, $_2\text{He}^4$); others disintegrate by emitting beta particles (electrons, $_{-1}e^0$); and still others emit electromagnetic waves of high energy called gamma rays. This activity is called **radioactivity.** Because of the

dual nature of particles and waves, it doesn't matter that the first two, which are particles, are still often called rays and treated as waves, and that the gamma rays are often called photons (although they belong to a part of the electromagnetic spectrum that is invisible). It will be to our advantage to switch back and forth between particle and wave as we try to create a simple theory for the spontaneous disintegration of nuclei.

1. *Alpha Emission*

It is an experimental fact that alpha particles come out of a uranium nucleus with an energy of about 4 Mev. It is also known that the potential-energy curve for alpha particles (Fig. 57.1) rises to a height of about 27 Mev. Classically speaking, an alpha particle with a kinetic energy of 4 Mev could not penetrate into the nucleus, and, similarly, an alpha particle within the nucleus, if it had a total energy of only 4 Mev, could not get out. (For this reason we speak of a **potential barrier**—short for *potential-energy barrier*.) Yet such alpha particles do get out, and their kinetic energy is equal to their total energy minus their potential energy. In 1928, to explain this emission, George Gamow and, independently, E. U. Condon and R. W. Gurney dropped the classical picture of a particle and considered the wave nature of the alpha particle. They said, in effect (Fig. 57.2), that a wave has a finite probability of getting from point A, inside the nucleus, to point B, outside the nucleus. The wave associated with the particle meets a potential barrier.

Part of it is reflected, and part goes through. The amplitude of the transmitted part diminishes as it crosses the barrier.

To illustrate this *barrier penetration*, or *tunneling effect*, with an example from optics, I present Figure 57.3. The upper prism, I, is an ordinary glass prism whose acute angles are each 45°. The lower prism, II, is almost the same, but its upper surface, QTO, is slightly curved. Consider the behavior of three different rays, A, B, and C, entering normally the top face of prism I. There is no difficulty in explaining the behavior of rays A and C; ray A experiences total internal reflection at point R (see § 20.1), and ray C goes right through at T, where there is good contact between the glass surfaces. How about ray B? *When the air gap*, PS, *is only a few wavelengths wide, part of the light energy goes right through;* waves seem to tunnel through. The other part is reflected. Similarly, if a moving alpha particle at A (Fig. 57.2) is conceptually replaced by its de Broglie wave, going to the right, it has a finite probability of emerging on the other side of the boundary. Its amplitude diminishes with the thickness of the barrier, but it may emerge with non-zero ampli-

tude; that is, there is some probability of finding the particle at B, outside the nucleus.

Now let us treat the alpha particle as if it were an entity within the nucleus. (There are serious objections to this crude picture. I have described

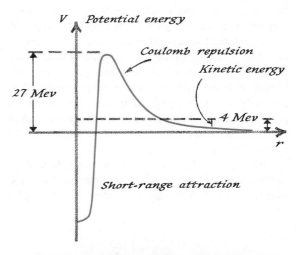

FIG. 57.1. *The potential energy of an alpha particle in the vicinity of a uranium nucleus plotted as a function of the radial distance, r.*

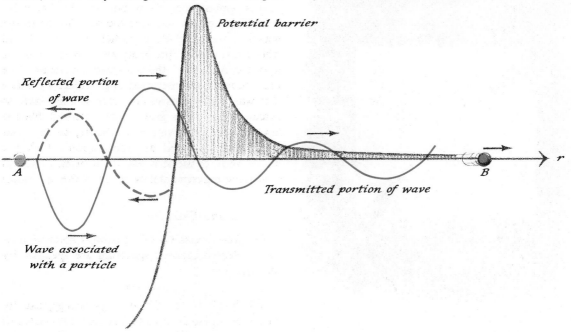

FIG. 57.2. *Penetration of a potential barrier by a wave associated with a particle.*

alpha particles as coming out of nuclei, and other nuclei as being bombarded by alpha particles, but I have not yet treated alpha particles as entities within nuclei. It is better to conceive of the particle as being created as its constituent particles emerge; but let us proceed anyway.) By means of wave mechanics it has been computed that an alpha particle has only 1 chance in 10^{38} to get out; that is, it must make 10^{38} attempts in order to be fairly certain of getting out. Since its speed is about 10^7 m/sec (computed from its kinetic energy) and it bounces within walls that are only 10^{-14} m apart, it makes 10^{21} attempts per second to escape, and it therefore needs $10^{38}/10^{21}$ seconds, or about 3×10^9 years, to be fairly certain of doing so.

Despite the crudity of the picture, this time corresponds, in order of magnitude, to the time experimentally observed as needed for the alpha

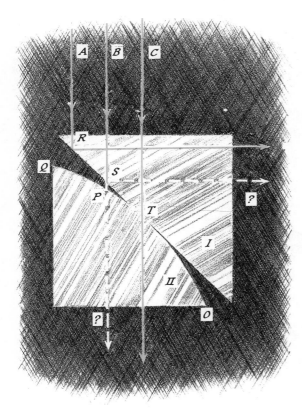

FIG. 57.3. *Optical example of barrier penetration, or tunneling effect.*

emission of uranium to decrease by half. We conclude that both concepts, wave and particle, contribute to an understanding of the observed phenomenon called alpha emission.

2. *Beta Emission*

There are good reasons for believing that electrons cannot reside in a nucleus (see Prob. 57.7). We are therefore forced to conclude that beta rays (electrons) are created when a neutron turns into a proton. This accounts for the conservation of charge, but it is not the whole story. Before beta emission the nucleus was in energy state E_1. After emission the nucleus is in state E_2. Let us use the symbol E to mean $E_1 - E_2$. The kinetic energy of the ejected electron should be $E = m_0c^2$ (m_0 being the rest mass of the electron). Since the experimental conditions under which beta emission is observed lead us to believe that E is a fixed quantity, the ejected beta particles should all have the same kinetic energy. Experiments show, instead, that the particles come out with kinetic energies all the way from zero up to m_0c^2. In beta emission the amount of energy that is converted seems to be variable. The solution of this puzzle required the postulation of the neutrino (see § 59.4), a particle of zero charge whose rest mass is probably zero. Without going into the details of the argument, we may note that theoreticians preferred to postulate a particle that was highly elusive and almost impossible to detect rather than give up the well-established laws of the conservation of charge, energy, and momentum (as well as spin), upon which the whole body of modern physics is built. (There is now some experimental evidence of the neutrino.)

3. *Gamma Emission*

The frequencies (ν) of an atom's spectral lines in the electromagnetic spectrum are specified by the equation

$$\Delta E = h\nu \qquad [57.1$$

in which ΔE is the difference in energy, usually measured in electron volts, between two states of the atom. Nuclei also have excited states, and a nucleus, in going from a state of higher energy to

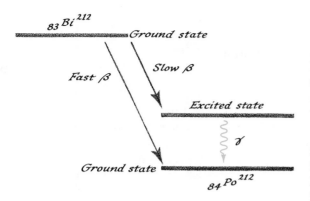

FIG. 57.4. *Gamma emission associated with the transition of a nucleus from an excited state to a ground state.*

one of lower energy, may give off electromagnetic radiation according to equation 57.1. For nuclei, ΔE is usually in Mev, and the corresponding radiations are called gamma rays.

Excitation can take place in different ways—by emission of alpha and beta particles, for example, or by capture of neutrons. Figure 57.4 illustrates excitation by beta particles, which are emitted in the reaction

$$_{83}\text{Bi}^{212} \longrightarrow {}_{-1}e^0 + {}_{84}\text{Po}^{212}$$

The emission of slow beta particles has converted $_{83}\text{Bi}^{212}$ into $_{84}\text{Po}^{212}$. The new nucleus, which is in an excited state, may emit a gamma ray and pass to its ground state. As in the atomic case, each excited state corresponds to a definite energy level, which depends on such factors as spin and magnetic moment. For the time being I wish to stress only that equation 57.1 survives, along with the conservation laws, as one of the fundamental ideas of modern physics. Whenever electromagnetic radiation is associated with a change in energy levels, it obeys this equation.

57.2. Radioactive Decay and Half-life

Consider the following nuclear process:

$$_{19}\text{K}^{39} \longrightarrow {}_{17}\text{Cl}^{35} + {}_2\text{He}^4 \qquad [57.2$$

This looks like a possible reaction. (Charge and total number of nucleons are conserved; look at the subscripts and the superscripts.) But the atomic mass on the left is 38.96371 u, and the sum of atomic masses on the right is 38.97146 u. Energetically, this is not possible; this isotope ($_{19}\text{K}^{39}$) of potassium will not alpha-decay. The alpha decay of bismuth represented by the equation

$$_{83}\text{Bi}^{209} \longrightarrow {}_2\text{He}^4 + {}_{81}\text{Tl}^{205} \qquad [57.3$$

is energetically possible, for the masses, reading from left to right, are 208.98042, 4.00260, and 204.97446 u. What the equation does not tell you, however, is that, if you were watching a single atom of bismuth, you would probably have to wait about 10^{18} years, or even more, before it disintegrated. If you were waiting to see a single polonium atom disintegrate according to the equation

$$_{84}\text{Po}^{212} \longrightarrow {}_2\text{He}^4 + {}_{82}\text{Pb}^{208} \qquad [57.4$$

there is a good chance that you would have to wait only a microsecond. It is remarkable that the time intervals distinguishing the disintegration tendencies of different nuclides range from microseconds to billions of years and that we have the experimental means of determining them. I shall not try to explain the variation, but an illustration may help us to understand it.

One thousand students, each with a coin and all wearing the same kind of hat, board a ship. They have agreed to play the following game. At some time between noon and 1:00 p.m. each student tosses his coin. If it turns up heads, he throws his hat overboard; if it turns up tails, he keeps his hat on. At some time between 1:00 p.m. and 2:00 p.m. each student who still has a hat plays again—throwing his hat overboard if his coin shows heads, keeping it on if his coin shows tails. The game goes on at some time during each hour for those who still have hats.

There is good reason to believe that the graph of the number of students with hats against time will look somewhat like the white curve of Figure 57.5. During each hour, on the average, the number of students with hats is halved.

If, instead of using a coin that had a 50/50 chance of turning up heads, each student had used a die with faces numbered 1, 2, 3, 4, 5, and 6, and if the game had called for tossing his hat

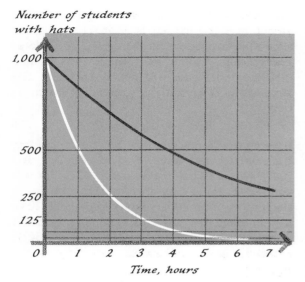

FIG. 57.5. *The number of students with hats plotted against time. The white curve results when the probability of throwing away a hat is determined by a toss of a coin. The black curve results when the probability is determined by the toss of a die.*

overboard only if the die turned up a predetermined number (3, for example), only a sixth of the students, on the average, would lose their hats during the first hour. Repetition of the game once during each hour would produce a graph such as the black curve of Figure 57.5. This time it would take nearly four hours for the number of hatted students to be halved.

Changing the probability of occurrence changes the rate at which the ordinates diminish, but the two curves have a common characteristic. If we start *anywhere* on the white curve, the ordinate one hour later is half of what it was at the start; the ordinate on the black curve is also halved at regular intervals, but the intervals are about 3.75 hours.

The students' game might be extended. A student who had tossed a hat overboard might, for example, be entitled to play a new game, in which chance, determined every hour by a roulette wheel or some such device, would require him to toss a shoe overboard. I shall not pursue this idea further but suggest it as an amusing and instructive extension.

The relevance of the game to radioactive decay is that the emission of an alpha particle is somewhat like the tossing of a hat overboard. The probability of emission per unit of time is somehow fixed by Nature for a given nuclide. What is left after emission is a new kind of nucleus. The new nucleus may emit a beta particle, but the probability of its doing so within a given time is not necessarily the same as the original probability of its emitting an alpha particle.

The hat analogy, like all analogies, has its limitations, but it illustrates the random nature of the toss. If an atom has survived for a long time without tossing out an alpha particle, the probability of its tossing one out within the next hour is the same as it was during the previous hour (if you have tossed ten heads in a row, the probability of tossing tails on the eleventh throw is still 0.5). It is not surprising, therefore, that the curves of radioactive decay are of the same type as the curves of Figure 57.5. The great numbers of atoms usually involved, however, enhance the continuity of the curves.

If, on the average, it takes time T for $N/2$ atoms of a sample containing N atoms to alpha-decay, we say that T is the **half-life** for alpha decay of this particular nuclide. The half-life for other types of decay is defined in a similar way. (By analogy, the half-life for hat-tossing is one hour for the white curve and about 3.75 hours for the black curve of Fig. 57.5.) The half-life of $_{84}Po^{212}$ for alpha decay is 0.304 microsecond, and the half-life of $_{83}Bi^{209}$ for alpha decay is 2×10^{17} years. The half-lives of some other radioactive nuclides are given in Table 57.1.

Since a mole of a substance like helium contains about 6×10^{23} atoms, the number of undecayed atoms left even after ten half-lives have passed is of the order of 10^{21}. That is still a lot of atoms, even though more than a thousand times less than the original number. The process, though discontinuous, still appears continuous.

For any particular nuclide the number, ΔN, of atoms that disintegrate in the time Δt is proportional to the number, N, present at a given time and to the magnitude of Δt; that is,

$$\Delta N = -kN(\Delta t) \qquad [57.5$$

The rate of disintegration is determined by the **decay constant,** k. (This is neither the k of equation 38.6 nor the Boltzmann constant.) Unlike chemical processes, radioactive decay is not speeded up by heat; and, in fact, there seems to be nothing at all that can influence the value of k for a given nuclide. You can't speed up or slow down radioactivity. Equation 57.5 implies that

$$N = N_0 e^{-kt} \qquad [57.6$$

(e being the base of the natural system of logarithms and approximately equal to 2.7) if N_0 is the number of atoms of the nuclide in existence when $t = 0$. The graph of equation 57.6 is similar to those of Figure 57.5. Since the rate, R, of disintegration ($R \cong \Delta N/\Delta t$) is proportional to N, it follows from equation 57.6 that rates obey a similar equation:

$$R = R_0 e^{-kt} \qquad [57.7$$

Thus a counter that can count disintegrations per minute, for example, can be used to determine the constant k. The half-life, T, is related to k as follows:

$$T = \frac{0.693}{k} \qquad [57.8$$

Plutonium 239, a radioactive nuclide that does not occur in nature, has a half-life of 2.41×10^4 years. (Radioactive nuclides produced by artificially accelerated particles are said to be artificially radioactive, but the laws governing their decay are not different from those already described. Hundreds of such nuclides—isotopes of

TABLE 57.1

Half-lives of Some Radioactive Nuclides

Sodium 24	15.0 h	Radium 226	1.62×10^3 y
Potassium 40	1.30×10^9 y	Thorium 232	1.39×10^{10} y
Bromine 87	55.6 s	Uranium 233	1.62×10^5 y
Strontium 90	2.80 y	Uranium 235	7.13×10^8 y
Krypton 92	3.00 s	Uranium 238	4.51×10^9 y
Yttrium 93	10.0 h	Uranium 239	23.5 m
Iodine 131	8.05 d	Neptunium 239	2.33 d
Cesium 137	30.0 y	Plutonium 239	2.44×10^4 y
Polonium 212	3.04×10^{-7} s		

Abbreviations: d = days, h = hours, m = minutes, s = second(s), y = years.

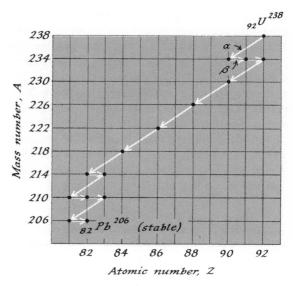

FIG. 57.6. *Possible sequence of events from the uranium series.*

the commoner stable nuclei—have been made.) The age of the earth is thought to be about 3×10^9 years. If some plutonium 239 ($_{94}Pu^{239}$) existed at the time of the earth's origin, by now the number of its half-lives that have elapsed is

$$\frac{3 \times 10^9}{2.41 \times 10^4} \cong 1.3 \times 10^5$$

That is, more than 100,000 half-lives have elapsed. Now look at the white curve of Figure 57.5 to see what the passing of even five half-lives does to the original activity. Small wonder, then, that no $_{94}Pu^{239}$ is found in nature even though it may once have been natural! This example may also suggest how the existence of naturally radioactive thorium 232, with a half-life of 1.39×10^{10} years, gives some clue to the age of the earth.

57.3. Decay Schemes

One of the possible sequences of events starting with uranium $_{92}U^{238}$, which is an alpha emitter with a half-life of 4.50×10^9 years, and ending with lead $_{82}Pb^{206}$, which is stable, is set forth graphically in Figure 57.6. The loss of an alpha particle diminishes the charge by 2 and the mass by 4; the loss of a beta particle increases the charge by 1 (loss of a negative electron) but leaves the mass number unchanged. The uranium series is sometimes called the $4n + 2$ series because the mass number 238 is of the type $4n + 2$ with n equal to 59; that is, $238 = 4 \times 59 + 2$. Three other series exist in nature: the $4n$, or thorium, series; the $4n + 3$, or actinium, series; and the $4n + 1$, or neptunium, series. They have similar characteristics. The rate at which the disintegrations occur in the uranium series is not shown in Figure 57.6, but Table 57.2, a simplified version of the uranium series, gives this in terms of the half-life.

TABLE 57.2

A Possible Sequence from the Uranium Series

Nuclide	Type of Emission	Half-life, T
$_{92}U^{238}$	α	4.51×10^9 y
$_{90}Th^{234}$	β	24.1 d
$_{91}Pa^{234}$	β	1.18 m
$_{92}U^{234}$	α	2.48×10^5 y
$_{90}Th^{230}$	α	8.0×10^4 y
$_{88}Ra^{226}$	α	1.62×10^3 y
$_{86}Em^{222}$	α	3.82 d
$_{84}Po^{218}$	α	3.05 m
$_{82}Pb^{214}$	β	26.8 m
$_{83}Bi^{214}$	α	19.7 m
$_{81}Tl^{210}$	β	1.32 m
$_{82}Pb^{210}$	β	19.4 y
$_{83}Bi^{210}$	α	5.0 d
$_{81}Tl^{206}$	β	4.2 m
$_{82}Pb^{206}$ (stable)		

Abbreviations: d = days, m = minutes, y = years.

Starting with some $_{92}U^{238}$ in a closed and leak-proof container, we should later find a mixture of nuclides. The ratios of their masses could be predicted for any particular time by use of equations 57.6 and 57.8 and some logic. Experimental determinations of some values of the decay constant, k, by means of counting techniques and equation 57.7, have made possible the deduction of others. Even though we have no good theories of the half-lives, the accumulated data have contributed to nuclear engineering and to a clearer understanding of nuclear forces.

57.4. The Uses of Radioactive Isotopes

Radioactive isotopes of all the known atoms have been made by bombardment with neutrons, deuterons, and other particles. Most elements, in fact, have more radioactive than stable isotopes. Sodium, for example, has six radioactive isotopes, cobalt has ten, and iodine has twenty-one. As such isotopes have become available and inexpensive, their uses in scientific research and industry have grown tremendously. In 1960, for example, the International Atomic Energy Agency held a conference on the use of radioactive isotopes in the physical sciences and in industry. Among the topics discussed were radioactive isotopes in geophysics, metallurgy, solid-state physics, nuclear physics, industry, tracer techniques, analytical chemistry, nuclear chemistry, organic chemistry, and physical chemistry. Besides these applications there are, of course, those in biology, biophysics, and medicine.

A simple calculation will give an idea of the effectiveness of the radioactive isotopes. Consider iodine $_{53}I^{131}$, which has a half-life of 8.05 days and a decay constant, k, of 9.96×10^{-7}/sec. Writing equation 57.5 in the form

$$\frac{\Delta N}{\Delta t} = -kN \qquad [57.9$$

we can derive the rate of disintegration, $\Delta N/\Delta t$, if we know the number, N, of radioactive atoms. Suppose that one in every million atoms of a sample of iodine is radioactive $_{53}I^{131}$. Since 127 grams of ordinary iodine contains 6.06×10^{23} atoms, one microgram has

$$\frac{6.06}{127} \times 10^{23} \times 10^{-12} = 4.77 \times 10^9$$

atoms of radioactive $_{53}I^{131}$ in it. Letting N equal 4.8×10^9 and k equal 9.96×10^{-7}/sec in equation 57.9, we get $\Delta N/\Delta t = -4.75 \times 10^3$ per second. If, because of the geometry and the absorption of the counter, we can pick up only 1 percent of the disintegrations, the counter will still register about 48 counts per second. The radioactive atoms thus play the role of tagged atoms. Since their presence is detectable, and since for each of them, on the average, there are a million ordinary atoms of iodine, the flow of ordinary iodine in plants and animals can be traced and its magnitude determined.

Here are a few illustrations of the use of tagged atoms: (1) Iodine taken into the body tends to collect in the thyroid gland. If a patient has cancer of the thyroid, he may be given radioactive iodine. The radioactive atoms lodge where they can destroy the malignant cells. (2) A known fraction of radioactive atoms in an element fed to a plant or an animal will, by means of the Geiger-Müller counter, reveal the element's progress through the organism. Thus, for example, the role of iron in anemia has been studied. It is conceivable that the most powerful tool of the modern biologist and physician, after the microscope, will be the radioactive isotopes. (3) If a known fraction of the carbon atoms used in an automobile tire are radioactive, the amount of rubber left on the road when the car is braked can be estimated through a count of the radioactive atoms.

Hundreds of other examples could be given, but it is sufficient here to recognize that we are dealing with a means of detecting and counting the atoms in micrograms of material. No wonder, then, that the chemical properties of atoms that never existed until they were produced by man could be measured even before the available samples were large enough to be seen under a microscope!

Another interesting use is carbon dating. The radioactive isotope $_6C^{14}$ is about 10^{-6} percent of the $_6C^{12}$ present in living tissue. Now $_6C^{14}$ has a half-life of about 5,600 years, and it would all have disintegrated in the course of geological time if cosmic rays did not keep on replenishing the supply. When plants and animals die and stop breathing and taking in food, their intake of $_6C^{14}$ stops, and the $_6C^{14}$ they have disintegrates without further replenishment. The equilibrium that existed ends with death, and the exponential

decay described by equation 57.6 takes over. The time since the wood of the tree or the bone of the body died can therefore be computed from the concentration of $_6C^{14}$ left in it. The archaeologist and the anthropologist have in carbon dating a clock with which to date past events.

Whereas ordinary clocks, as I pointed out earlier (§ 7.6), depend upon a very precise cyclic process, radioactive clocks depend upon the completely random but statistically predictable behavior of radioactive atoms.

57.5. Summary

Nuclei capable of disintegrating spontaneously and emitting alpha, beta, and gamma rays are said to be radioactive. Some radioactive atoms occur in nature, and many have been produced artificially.

At a given instant the rate of disintegration of a sample of radioactive atoms all of one kind is proportional to the number of atoms present. The constant of proportionality seems to be unaffected by heat or pressure or any other outside influence.

The frequency, ν, of electromagnetic radiation (gamma rays) emitted as a nucleus passes from a higher to a lower state of excitation obeys the equation $\Delta E = h\nu$.

The number of radioactive atoms in a sample of a nuclide diminishes exponentially with time. The time required to reduce the number by a factor of 2 is the half-life of that nuclide. Half-lives ranging from microseconds to billions of years have been measured.

The advent of inexpensive man-made radioactive isotopes has opened up vast new fields of application and research.

Problems

57.1. Using the data of Table 57.2, justify or criticize the following assertion: "If we started with nothing but $_{92}U^{238}$, the only nuclides left after a billion years would be $_{92}U^{238}$ and $_{82}Pb^{206}$."

57.2. Suppose that the students in the hat-tossing illustration associated with Fig. 57.5 had been in-

structed to use a die and to toss if *either* a 3 or a 5 turned up.

1. Graph the number of students with hats against time for a total of seven hours.

2. At what time after zero would the number of students still holding hats be 500?

3. At what time after three hours had passed would the number of such students be half of what it was when two hours had passed?

57.3. The equation $y = 3^{-x}$ has many of the important characteristics of equation 57.6.

1. Plot its graph for $x = 0, 1, 2, 3, 4$.

2. Determine from the graph whether the value of y is cut in half for a fixed value of Δx no matter where the initial y is chosen.

57.4. "The money I earn has a half-life of one day. I receive it one day and when I have finished paying my monthly bills half of it is gone." With the definition of half-life in radioactive decay in mind, criticize this statement.

57.5. If you used $+k$ instead of $-k$ in equation 57.6, you would get exponential growth rather than exponential decay. A snowball rolling on snow and money invested at compound interest are illustrations. The function $y = 3^x$ illustrates exponential growth.

1. Plot $y = 3^x$ for $x = 0, 1, 2, 3$.

2. Starting at any point on the curve, determine the Δx that will double y.

3. Does Δx depend on where you start?

57.6. A counter picking up disintegrations of a radioactive substance with a half-life of 8.05 days registered 48 counts per second. How much later after that instant would the counter register 15 counts per second?

57.7. The order of magnitude of the de Broglie wavelength associated with an electron in a nucleus is 16×10^{-14} m, but the diameter of a nucleus, according to equation 54.1, is more like 10^{-14} m. This makes it improbable that an electron can reside in a nucleus. Compute the de Broglie wavelength of an electron with a kinetic energy of 8 Mev, using the formula $\lambda = h/p$. (For relativistic energies p is approximately E/c. This comes from dividing both sides of the equation $E = mc^2$ by c. The value 8 Mev is the approximate value associated with each nucleon.)

58

Atomic Energy, Controlled and Violent

TO KEEP the average American living happily at the standard to which he is accustomed requires an annual expenditure of energy equivalent to that derived from burning eight tons of coal. In Great Britain the corresponding amount is about five tons; in most of Europe it is about two and a half tons. In the less developed areas of the world the basic need is not to live happily but to stay alive, and that seems to require the energy of about 0.36 ton of coal per person per year. Multiply the lowest of these figures by the total number of people on the earth, and the energy requirements of even a static population are seen to be staggering.

But neither the population nor the supply of energy is static; the former is going up, and the latter is going down. Think for a moment of the great disparity in the utilization of energy between the highly developed countries and the least developed ones, and even with very little imagination you can begin to feel the economic, political, and human drama that these numbers imply. The intangible stuff called energy is necessary for life, and a great quantity of it is needed for the good life.

One reason for considering atomic energy is that it may, at least in part, satisfy mankind's future need of energy. Another is that the story of the nucleus, the storehouse of atomic energy, is dramatic and important in itself.

A single drop of mercury can be broken up into two separate droplets; this illustrates a kind of **fission.** If two separate droplets are brought close together, they will coalesce, or fuse, because of the molecular attraction associated with surface tension; this illustrates a kind of **fusion.** Both processes are, of course, on a macroscopic scale, for one droplet contains about 10^{20} molecules.

In this chapter we shall analyze the fission and the fusion of individual nuclei, but the liquid-drop illustration offers an instructive analogy: It takes work, because of surface tension, to pull a drop apart into droplets; energy may therefore be released in their fusion. If another set of droplets had like charges on them, it would take work to push them together against their electrostatic repulsion; energy might therefore be released in their fission. Nuclei behave somewhat like liquid drops. In a light nucleus the attractive forces between nucleons (analogous to those of surface tension) predominate over electrostatic repulsion, and energy is released in fusion. In a heavy nucleus, some nucleons are far enough away from others so that the electrostatic repulsion between protons predominates, and energy is released in fission.

58.1. Nuclear Fission

The simple argument above might lead one to think that nuclear fission occurs spontaneously. For uranium 238 the masses and energies in-

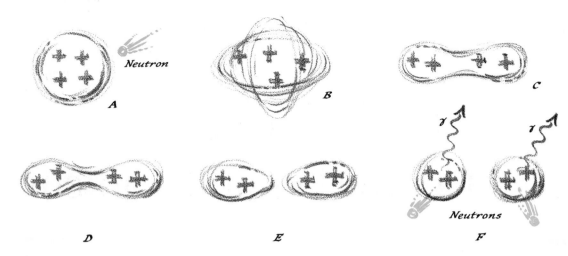

FIG. 58.1. *Neutron-induced nuclear fission described with the aid of the liquid-drop model.*

volved do not prohibit such fission; and, in fact, it has been observed to split spontaneously, but the half-life of the process is of the order of 10^{16} years. Since this is about a million times the age of the earth, the probability of such fission is extremely low; and, indeed, in the ground state the potential barrier preventing fission is extremely high. In an excited state, however, the probability of fission is considerable greater.

One way to produce such excitation is to bombard the uranium with fast neutrons. The liquid-drop model, designed to explain something that has been observed many times, helps us to understand this process. A fast neutron (Fig. 58.1) enters a nucleus (A). The added energy causes the nucleus to oscillate erratically (B). A neck may be formed (C). The electrostatic repulsion forces the two halves apart (D) and finally causes fission (E). The resulting nuclei, being unstable, give off neutrons and perhaps gamma rays (F).

Now let us go back to see how it happened that someone was bombarding uranium with neutrons.

Enrico Fermi (who received the Nobel Prize for Physics in 1938) and his collaborators, in 1934, were bombarding different substances with neutrons to produce artificial radioactivity. In general, the mass number of the product nucleus was 1 greater than that of the original nucleus:

$$_Z X^A + _0 n^1 \longrightarrow _Z X^{A+1} + \text{one or more photons} \quad [58.1$$

The product nucleus was often radioactive, and it beta-decayed according to a scheme such as

$$_Z X^{A+1} \longrightarrow _{Z+1} X^{A+1} + _{-1} e^0 + \text{neutrino} \quad [58.2$$

Other decays usually followed. By bombarding uranium ($_{92} U^{238}$), which was then the last element of the periodic table, Fermi expected to produce, artificially, a transuranium element with Z equal to 93 or more. He probably did, but the experimental evidence was puzzling, for the excited $_{92} U^{238}$ nucleus had split, and the many possible products had shown a perplexing array of different half-lives. Fermi did not, at the time, know just what had happened. The history of the next few decades might have been different if he had realized that he had practically proved the feasibility of the explosive release of nuclear energy. Between 1935 and 1938 the German chemist Otto Hahn (who received the Nobel Prize for this work in 1944) and his colleague Fritz Strassmann studied the same effect and discovered, to their amazement, that the resultant nuclei included that of a much lighter element, barium. This result was so contrary to what physicists had previously observed that they were reluctant to believe it. Finally, Lise Meitner and Otto Frisch, also of Germany, made measurements that helped to explain Hahn's and Strassmann's results as due to fission of the uranium nucleus into two parts of almost equal masses. One of many possible fissions is

$$_{92}U^{235} + _{0}n^{1} \longrightarrow (_{92}U^{236}) \longrightarrow _{40}Zr^{92} + _{59}Pr^{141} + 3_{0}n^{1}$$
[58.3

The importance of this discovery is clear at once if we observe that the binding energy per nucleon is about 1 Mev lower for $_{92}U^{236}$ than for either $_{40}Zr^{92}$ or $_{59}Pr^{141}$ (see Fig. 55.3). This means that the sum of the masses of the two resultant nuclei is less than the mass of the uranium nucleus. Since 236 nucleons are involved, we expect about 236 Mev to be released in this process. The correct figure is closer to 200 Mev. This is a tremendous amount of energy per particle. (The water in a waterfall 450 feet high achieves, at the end of its fall, a kinetic energy of about 0.00025 ev per molecule, and carbon oxidized to carbon dioxide releases 4.0 ev per atom.)

Now we must consider the state of the world at the time these discoveries were made. The possibility of a release of huge energy made the construction of a bomb seem feasible. Scientists in America voluntarily banned publication of results in this field. Hence the theoretical discussion of fission published by Niels Bohr and John Wheeler in the September 1939 issue of the *Physical Review*, which was the first comprehensive article on this topic, was also the last to appear before the curtain of security measures closed down and veiled all such work in secrecy. Although scientists are normally opposed to secrecy, the benefits of open scientific discussion were lost to them until long after World War II. This war brought about the creation of atomic weapons. Eighteen years later we were still testing them.

In these days, when some voices still clamor for a continuation of testing, arguing that some scientific knowledge would be gained through massive explosions, it should be remembered that the great discoveries of Hahn and Strassmann and Meitner and Frisch were made with almost microscopic quantities of material.

58.2. The Chain Reaction

About 99.3 percent of the uranium atoms in nature are $_{92}U^{238}$, and only 0.7 percent are $_{92}U^{235}$. Both can undergo fission, but there is a remark-

able difference between them. Uranium 238 will split only when bombarded by neutrons of very high energy. Medium-energy neutrons are simply captured, forming uranium 239, and low-energy neutrons have no effect at all. Uranium 235 splits readily under bombardment by neutrons even if these are traveling so slowly that they are in thermal equilibrium with the surroundings.

When fission of either U^{238} or U^{235} occurs, one of the fragments usually has an atomic weight of about 90, the other an atomic weight of about 140; but more than a hundred different fragment species have been observed, some very light and some very heavy. A typical balance sheet follows:

$$
\begin{aligned}
_{55}Cs^{133} &= 132.905090 \text{ u} \\
_{44}Ru^{99} &= 98.906080 \text{ u} \\
3 \text{ neutrons @ } 1.008665 \text{ u} &= 3.025995 \text{ u} \\
\hline
\text{Total fragments} &= 234.837165 \text{ u} \\
_{92}U^{235} &= 235.043933 \text{ u} \\
\text{Total fragments} &= 234.837165 \text{ u} \\
\hline
\text{Difference} &= 0.206768 \text{ u}
\end{aligned}
$$

$$0.2068 \text{ u} \times 931.5 \text{ Mev/u} = 192.6 \text{ Mev}$$

Notice that the loss of mass (0.2068 u) is about 0.1 percent of the U^{235} mass. (See Prob. 58.1.)

Since the cesium and ruthenium nuclei, like all nuclei, are positively charged, they repel one another. Their tremendous energy, about 100 Mev each, cannot be utilized to induce further fissions. But an important by-product exists in the approximately 2.5 neutrons per fission that are produced along with the new nuclei. These can bombard other uranium nuclei and induce further fissions. If the number of neutrons produced per fission were 2, and each induced fission, the number of fissions induced after only eighty links in the chain would be 2^{80}, which is about 10^{24}. Since there are only 6.02×10^{23} molecules in a mole, eighty links of such a chain would cause every atom in a mole of uranium to split. There is good reason to believe that it would all happen in about a microsecond or less. The total of 10^{24} fissions, each providing 200 Mev, would yield 2×10^{26} Mev, or 3.2×10^{13} joules, or 8.9×10^{6} kilowatt hours. We have no words to describe such a great transformation in such a short time.

Of the neutrons produced—about 2.5 per fis-

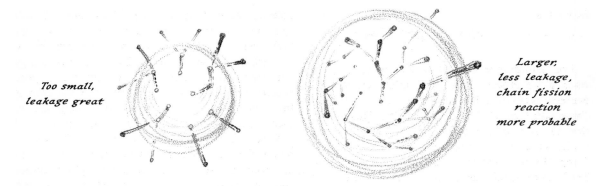

Too small,
leakage great

Larger,
less leakage,
chain fission
reaction
more probable

FIG. 58.2. *Effect of size of sample on probability of chain reaction due to fission.*

sion—not all induce further fissions. Some may simply be absorbed by U^{238} or other nuclei, and some may leak out of the uranium mass. The number of new fissions induced by each fission, on the average, is symbolized by k. If k, because of leakage and other factors, is less than 1, the reaction will stop; if k is greater than 1, an uncontrolled nuclear explosion will take place; if k equals 1, the chain reaction will be sustained, and, if k can be kept from exceeding 1, the chain reaction will be controlled.

Size, obviously, is important. If the mass of uranium is extremely small, most of the neutrons will leak out of it (Fig. 58.2), since they have to travel a certain distance, on the average, before inducing another fission. The mass for which $k = 1$ is called the **critical mass.** For smaller masses a sustained reaction is impossible.

Suppose that you start with a mixture of much U^{238} and a little U^{235}. Despite the unfavorable ratio, you hope, since neutrons of energy as low as 0.1 ev readily cause U^{235} to split, that you can sustain the reaction by slowing down the neutrons until they are likely to be captured by a U^{235} nucleus. Unfortunately, in losing energy through collisions with the U^{238} nuclei, the neutrons pass through the range near 7 ev, where they are very likely to be captured by U^{238} without inducing fission. (There are other such regions.) In order to reduce the neutrons' energy quickly, so that they won't remain long near 7 ev, you introduce another substance as a **moderator,** usually carbon in the form of graphite. Carbon nuclei, because they are light, can absorb much of the energy

of the neutrons. Repeated losses of energy soon bring the neutrons down into the thermal range ($\cong 0.1$ ev), where, since the probability of their capture by U^{235} is high, they induce fission. You can increase the probability of fission either by increasing the ratio of U^{235} to U^{238} (**enrichment**) or by slowing down neutrons so that they reach the thermal range of velocities quickly (**moderation**).

A **nuclear reactor** is a device in which a moderator is used for the slowing-down process and a control rod of absorbing material (often boron or cadmium) is used to reduce, when necessary, the effective value of k to a value less than but controllably close to unity. The first device in which controlled fission took place, called a pile, really *was* a large pile of graphite bricks and small pieces of natural uranium. It was constructed secretly under the grandstand of the University of Chicago stadium. On December 2, 1942, Professor A. H. Compton telephoned President James B. Conant of Harvard, saying: "The Italian navigator has landed. The natives are friendly." This message meant: "Fermi's pile works successfully. The first successful nuclear chain reaction has been achieved." This was, we all now realize, an event of great historic importance.

The following reaction had occurred in the pile:

$$_{92}U^{238} + {}_0n^1 \longrightarrow {}_{92}U^{239} + \gamma \qquad [58.4$$

This first reaction had been followed by others:

$$_{92}U^{239} \longrightarrow {}_{93}Np^{239} + {}_{-1}e^0 \qquad [58.5$$

$$_{93}Np^{239} \longrightarrow {}_{94}Pu^{239} + {}_{-1}e^0 \qquad [58.6$$

It turned out that the by-product plutonium ($_{94}Pu^{239}$) is even more fissile than U^{235}, producing an average of 2.9 neutrons per fission.

When used for the purpose of creating Pu^{239}, a reactor is called a **breeder reactor.** A reactor used mainly to generate large quantities of power is called a **power reactor,** and it requires almost pure U^{235} or Pu^{239}.

Because a reactor has a flux of energetic neutrons, it may be used to make other materials radioactive by neutron bombardment. Cobalt wafers, for example, if bombarded by neutrons in a reactor, become radioactive. They can then be used as powerful sources of radiation for therapeutic work.

If we want to release the tremendous power of a nuclear chain reaction in an extremely short time (that is, if we want an explosion), we use very pure U^{235} or Pu^{239} in the device called an **atomic bomb.** Figure 58.3 shows schematically how the critical mass is exceeded suddenly. Suppose that the sum of masses A, B, and C of U^{235} exceeds, by a little, the critical mass. Explosive fission cannot take place until they are brought together. This is accomplished by simultaneous firing of the gunpowder marked I and II. When the three masses of U^{235} meet, an explosive chain reaction takes place.

The first atomic bomb used for military purposes was exploded over Hiroshima (Japan); the fissile material was U^{235}, and the energy released was equal to that of about 20,000 tons of TNT. The second atomic bomb was exploded over Nagasaki (Japan); it used Pu^{239} and was of about the same strength. The energy liberated in the explosion of one kiloton of TNT equals 5×10^{12} joules or about 10^{12} calories.

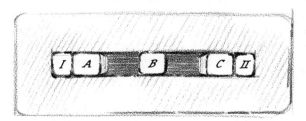

FIG. 58.3. *Schematic diagram of an atomic bomb.*

58.3. Nuclear Fusion

Consider the sun. Its mass is 1.97×10^{30} kg. From measurements taken on the earth it is calculated that the sun is radiating energy at the rate of 3.92×10^{26} J/sec. If it were burning up as coal does, by oxidation, each kilogram would release about 2.8×10^7 joules, and the sun would last, at most,

$$\frac{1.97 \times 10^{30} \text{ kg}}{1.40 \times 10^{19} \text{ kg/sec}} = 1.41 \times 10^{11} \text{ sec} = 4.46 \times 10^3 \text{ yr}$$

Since we have good evidence that the earth and hence the sun are at least 10^9 years old, oxidation is out of the question as an explanation of the sun's energy.

The sun could, conceivably, get energy out of its gravitational field by contracting. It could then live about 3×10^7 years (a period called the Kelvin contraction time). The age of the sun is probably already 100 times as great as this. The sun could live longer if matter were falling into it; but then its mass would change, and there is good geological evidence that the orbit of the earth has not changed appreciably.

If some nuclear process is responsible, we go directly to the formula $E = mc^2$ to account for the 3.92×10^{26} J/sec. (This equation is obeyed, of course, whatever the mechanism of energy conversion.) The sun loses about 4.36×10^9 kg/sec by radiation. At this rate it would take about 1.43×10^{13} years for the sun to be consumed. In 10^9 years it would lose about 1/10,000 of its mass. This sounds more reasonable. (The situation is very complex, however, and George Gamow has calculated that in about 5×10^9 years the sun will be much brighter than it is now.)

Hans Bethe, in 1938, suggested that chains of nuclear reactions would account for the sun's energy. His theory and others boil down to chains in which four hydrogen nuclei combine to form a helium nucleus and two positrons:

$$4_1H^1 \longrightarrow {}_2He^4 + 2_{+1}e^0 + 25.7 \text{ Mev} \qquad [58.7]$$

The energy released, obviously, comes from fusion, not from fission. A more complicated nuclear fusion, in which carbon acts as a catalyst, is important in stars that are more massive than the sun.

This idea spurred the search for ways in which man might induce fusion. The following four fusion reactions, involving heavy isotopes of hydrogen, are now known:

$$_1H^2 + {_1}H^2 \longrightarrow {_2}He^3 + {_0}n^1 + 3.25 \text{ Mev} \qquad [58.8$$

$$_1H^2 + {_1}H^2 \longrightarrow {_1}H^3 + {_1}H^1 + 4 \text{ Mev} \qquad [58.9$$

$$_1H^2 + {_1}H^3 \longrightarrow {_2}He^4 + {_0}n^1 + 17.6 \text{ Mev} \qquad [58.10$$

$$_1H^2 + {_2}He^3 \longrightarrow {_2}He^4 + {_1}H^1 + 18.3 \text{ Mev} \qquad [58.11$$

The energy released per fusion is not as impressive as the 200 Mev per fission of equation 58.3, but deuterium is almost as plentiful as the ocean, and there is little radioactive debris from fusion.

Like certain equations in Chapter 56, equations 58.8–11 tell us nothing about how the reactions are effected. The nuclei on the left side of each equation are positively charged. How do you overcome their electrostatic repulsion and get them close enough together to fuse? The answer is simple: get them moving fast enough toward each other. In other words, heat up the isotopes. You could, for example, heat up the deuterium. This is easier said than done. For a proposed experiment using deuterons it has been calculated that at a temperature of 100 million degrees (and I really mean a kinetic energy corresponding to this figure) the electrons of these atoms, long since stripped from their nuclei, are traveling at 90,000 miles per second, the deuterons at 1,500 miles per second. (Matter broken down in this way, so that it consists of electrically charged nuclei and the electrons stripped from them, is called **plasma**.) All the deuterons react with one another within much less than a second, and their reaction releases energy at a fantastic rate—about 100 million kilowatts; yet the reaction will not be self-sustaining until the temperature of 350 million degrees is reached.

If the objective is a super-explosion, there is a way of achieving such a temperature: by starting the fusion with a fission bomb of U^{238} or Pu^{239}. The fuel is hydrogen, and there is, theoretically, no upper limit to its power. A number of such devices, called hydrogen bombs or thermonuclear bombs, have already been fired, one about 2,000 times more potent than the Hiroshima bomb, with an energy release corresponding to 50 million tons of TNT.

The great need of mankind, however, is not for a destructive energy burst lasting a few microseconds, but for a sustained and controllable fusion reaction releasing energy usefully—a controlled thermonuclear reaction, as it is called. The scientific and engineering problems are formidable, but the stakes are high. The power requirements of the developed countries double about every ten years. It is conceivable that not only coal but the recoverable uranium will be exhausted within another century or so. Fission power also presents the problem of disposing of radioactive waste. By the year 2000, it has been estimated, the radioactive waste, if nuclear fission were being used to supply our energy, would equal that of eight million atomic explosions (of the Hiroshima variety) per year.

If the fusion reaction could be tapped and put to work, it would really solve the problem of energy supply and that of radioactive wastes. The basic fuel, deuterium, is available in practically inexhaustible supply from the oceans, and the radioactive by-products of fusion are not appreciable. No wonder that Richard Post, one of the pioneers of this research, speaks with passion of this work: "Every nation has come to recognize that this research effort may well be the most important in the history of mankind. The ultimate stakes are so high for nations individually and mankind collectively, that a growing sense of urgency and determination is infusing the work of the several nations on the problem."

I shall go no further than to state the requirements of a continuing fusion reaction. They are similar to those required by a chemical reaction: (1) the temperature of the fuel must be raised to the ignition point; (2) there must be enough fuel to sustain a continuing reaction; (3) the energy released must be tapped in a controlled manner. The big difference between fission and fusion has already been mentioned: for the fusion reaction the ignition point is high—hundreds of millions of degrees Celsius. No wonder controlled fusion is difficult to achieve. How would you contain plasma that had reached a temperature of 10^7 degrees Kelvin?

There is some chance that, by the time this book is published, we shall have conclusive proof of man-induced controlled fusion. At the moment of writing we have none.

58.4. Summary

Nuclei behave somewhat like liquid drops. The attractive forces (analogous to those of surface tension) between nucleons of light nuclei predominate over electrostatic repulsion, and energy is released in fusion. Some nucleons of heavy nuclei are far enough away from others so that electrostatic repulsion between protons predominates, and energy is released in fission.

If the fission of a heavy nucleus produces two nuclei in the middle range, the energy released is of the order of 200 Mev because the binding energy per nucleon is about 1 Mev lower for heavy nuclei than for those in the middle range. The energy released in fusion is of the order of a few Mev per fusion. The fuel required is deuterium, and it is available in great quantities.

Some of the energy needs of the future will probably be met by nuclear fission and fusion. Satisfactory methods of producing a controlled reaction have been found for fission and are being sought for fusion. The important equation in both fusion and fission is, of course, $E = mc^2$.

Problems

58.1. In the illustration given in § 58.2 the difference in mass between $_{92}U^{235}$ and the fragments is calculated.

1. Do mass numbers and charges balance? (Hint: Tabulate the total number of protons and neutrons before and after fission.)

2. What kind of decay might explain whatever discrepancy there is?

3. Would such decay appreciably affect the mass balance?

58.2. Consider the least energy required by a human being to be equal to that released in the burning of 0.36 ton of coal per year.

1. Look up the earth's population, and compute the global yearly need in tons of coal that yields 2.54×10^{10} J/ton.

2. Compute the global yearly needs in joules and in Mev.

3. If this total energy were to be obtained from the reaction of equation 58.3, how many $_{92}U^{235}$ nuclei would be involved?

4. What would be the weight, in tons, of these nuclei?

58.3. Someone has said: "There is nothing fundamental in physics to be learned from fission." What do you think he had in mind?

58.4. 1. Compute the total energy available from loss of mass in the reaction

$$_1H^2 + _2He^3 \longrightarrow _2He^4 + _1H^1$$

2. Can you reconcile your result with equation 58.11?

The Particles
and Fields
of Modern Physics

AFTER World War II, physicists, released from their war-time duties, returned to their laboratories with renewed zeal for the study of the fundamental particles of nature. It was clear, of course, that, though the electron, the proton, and the neutron had explained many of the facts of atomic structure, their existence alone would not explain all the mysteries of the nucleus. New and more powerful accelerators were built, and many new particles were discovered. The physicists sought to put their house of particles in order with a suitable theory—the quantum field theory. My intention in this closing chapter is not to develop this theory, which is mathematically complex and still far from complete, but to sketch its characteristics broadly. One of these characteristics is the fact that particles and fields must be considered together. Attempts to consider them separately have always led to dilemmas. Dealing with them together, on the other hand, has yielded a theory that, even in incomplete form, has produced some startling successes. That is the reason for the title of this chapter.

59.1. Source Particles and Field Particles

It is important to distinguish at once between particles as sources of fields and particles as manifestations of fields, and to emphasize the fundamental nature of the field.

I shall start by reviewing the properties of a particle that is quite familiar to you by now—the electron. Associated with the electron is an electric field—the coulombic electrostatic field. This field obeys an inverse-square law of force (§ 36.1); that is, its mathematical form is of the $1/r^2$ type, and, correspondingly, its potential is of the $1/r$ type (§ 51.3). It is reasonable to say that the electron is the source of the electrostatic field. The electron is, then, a **source particle.** If the electron oscillates, its field lines, attached to the electron, carry energy away from it in the form of electromagnetic waves. We know that these waves may be radio waves, light waves, or even gamma rays, according to the frequency of the oscillation. Now another particle, the photon, associated with the electromagnetic wave, makes its appearance. The photon is a **field particle**. I have illustrated, then, a particle (the electron) as the source of a field (the electrostatic field) and a particle (the photon) as the manifestation of a field (the electromagnetic field). It remains to illustrate what I mean by the fundamental nature of the field itself.

In the chapter on electrostatics I dealt with the field of an electron. I did not raise the possibility that an electron might interact with its own field. But the field has energy, which, according to the theory of special relativity, has inertia. The field, in other words, has mass. To accelerate the electron, you have to deal with its inertia and that of the field attached to it. If you calculate the mass of the field alone (this is important—you can calculate the mass of the field, but the mass of the electron is simply inserted into the theory) on the basis of a theory that conforms with the principles of relativity, you are led to an infinite value. This is clearly wrong. It was eventually realized that the difficulty arose from the attempt to consider the mass of the electron and the mass of the field separately. If, as I have already said, you consider the electron alone without considering its interaction with its own field, the calculated mass comes out as infinite. If, on the other hand, you calculate the total mass of the electron, taking into account its interaction with its own field, as predicted by the new theory, it is possible for that mass to be finite. In the development of the theory—and this is the point I wish to stress—it was realized that the concept of field had been elevated in philosophical importance to an equal footing with the concept of particle. This is what I meant when I said that the concept of field is fundamental.

I have used the electron and the photon to illustrate source particle and field particle, respectively, and the interaction of the electron with its own field to illustrate the new importance attached to the field concept, but these ideas are not limited to this particular set of particle and field. The same concepts underlie the modern quantum field theory, which applies to all the fundamental particles of physics. This theory has predicted the discovery of particles that have later been found by experiment. The importance attached to these predictions can be gauged, in part, by the sums—millions of dollars—that have been spent on the production of the huge and powerful particle accelerators that produce, and the sensitive detectors with which we observe, the particles that undergird the particulate structure of matter.

59.2. Annihilation, Creation, and the Conservation Law for Source Particles

The special theory of relativity has a particular bearing on the role of the field. It was invented to take into account the fact that the laws of physics remain the same for two observers moving at constant velocity in relation to each other. The laws of electricity—Maxwell's equations in particular—must remain the same in all inertial frames of reference. Once quantum ideas had been introduced, the next step was to extend electromagnetic theory to the domain of the quantum: what was needed was a quantum electrodynamics. By 1928 theoretical physicists knew that much work remained to be done before quantum mechanics was a complete and logically consistent theory. One of the outstanding problems was to formulate a quantum theory of the electromagnetic field that would be consistent with the special theory of relativity.

In 1928 the English physicist Paul Dirac constructed, for the electron, an equation—analogous to the Schrödinger equation—that conformed strictly with the rules of special relativity. The Dirac equation was notably successful in explaining certain fine details of atomic spectra, but it made, in addition, a curious prediction. It suggested—or demanded, rather, for there was no way to eliminate it from the picture—a new particle, the twin of the electron in every respect except that its charge was positive. This was something different and unprecedented indeed: the prediction, merely by rigid adherence to the principles of quantum mechanics and relativity, of a new, hitherto unsuspected particle in nature.

Before very long, this new particle, named the **positron,** was discovered by C. D. Anderson in the course of a cloud-chamber experiment on cosmic rays (Fig. 59.1). The effect of this discovery on theoretical physics was enormous.

Careful examination of the experiments showed that positrons were actually *created* (in company with electrons) by incoming gamma rays (high-energy photons) in the cosmic radiation. The creation took place in the coulombic field of a nucleus. The presence of the nucleus was required for the conservation of momentum and energy. Later experiments showed that electron-positron pairs can also *annihilate* each other and yield a pair of gamma-ray photons. The reactions are

$$\gamma + \text{coulombic field} \longrightarrow e^+ + e^- \text{ (pair creation)}$$
[59.1

$$e^+ + e^- \longrightarrow \gamma + \gamma \text{ (pair annihilation)} \quad [59.2$$

Note that, in the equations describing creation and annihilation, the coulombic field plays the same role as a gamma ray. This is, of course, not entirely unexpected; both are electromagnetic in nature, and both find their classical description in Maxwell's equations.† What does come as a surprise is the suggestion here of a deeper connection than had been previously supposed between the coulombic field and the source particles (e^+ and e^-) that produce it. It is even possible for the source particles to disappear altogether in annihilation, leaving behind only the electromagnetic field (in the form of two photons). We may not be startled when the grin disappears from the Cheshire Cat, but it does seem strange when the cat disappears and leaves the grin behind.

In short, the relativistic quantum-mechanical description now places the electron and the photon on a practically equal footing. Which shall we now consider to be cause, and which effect?

Perhaps that is not the best way to pose the question, for it turns out that, by considering such basic phenomena as creation and annihila-

† The Dirac equation also predicted a similar situation for the proton; but its positively charged twin, the antiproton, was not discovered until 1955. Only about 1 Mev is required for the production of a positron-electron pair, but the energy required for the production of a proton-antiproton pair is about 2 Bev.

FIG. 59.1. *Discovery of the positron: A charged particle came in from the bottom and followed a circular path because of a strong magnetic field. It was slowed down in traversing 6 mm of lead and came out with a smaller radius of curvature. Knowing the direction of motion of the particle and that of the magnetic field, the investigator, C. D. Anderson, deduced that the particle was positive, and from the magnitude of the change of curvature he was able to show conclusively that it was much lighter than a proton. He concluded that the particle had, in fact, the mass of the electron, and he called it the positron. (Photograph taken in a cloud chamber by C. D. Anderson of the California Institute of Technology.)*

tion, we are led to the view that particles and fields exist simultaneously and must always be considered together.

A conservation law that holds for electrons and positrons arises naturally from Dirac's equation. If n_+ represents the number of positrons and n_- the number of electrons, then, in any closed system in which only electromagnetic interactions are allowed,

$$n_+ - n_- = \text{a constant} \quad [59.3$$

There is no such conservation law for photons. They can be emitted or absorbed without limit. We can create photons in great numbers by lighting a candle. They are absorbed readily by a piece of black cloth.

59.3. Mesons and the Nuclear Force

In 1935 the Japanese physicist Hideki Yukawa considered the force that binds nucleons within a nucleus and attempted to set up a mathematical model based on an analogy with the electromagnetic force. He found it fairly straightforward to prove that the inverse-square ($1/r^2$) dependence of the electromagnetic force on distance is a direct consequence of its having a massless quantum associated with it. (Photons, the field particles of the electromagnetic field, have zero rest mass.) Yukawa reasoned as follows: The electromagnetic field has a particulate manifestation, the photon. Could not something similar also be true of the nuclear force? Is it not conceivable that a field particle is associated with the nuclear force? If so, what about its mass? Would it necessarily be massless?

Then, as now, the nuclear force was incompletely understood, but it was known to be a short-range force, in contrast with the long-range coulombic force. He could incorporate the short range into the theory simply by assigning a rest mass to the field particle. Instead of having the simple form $1/r$, the resulting potential has the form

$$V = \frac{1}{r}\, e^{-\mu r} \qquad [59.4$$

the constant μ being proportional to the mass of the field particle. Observe that, if $\mu = 0$, the potential is simply $1/r$. The range of such a force is measured by the magnitude of $1/\mu$. The more massive the field particle, therefore, the shorter the range. To account for the observed range, Yukawa assigned a mass of about 250 electron masses to this new particle, which came to be called the **meson.**

Experiments on cosmic rays were immediately carried out with the cloud chamber in search of the new particle; and a particle having approximately the right mass was indeed discovered. This particle, however, had the wrong properties to be the field particle of the nuclear force; it interacted only weakly with nucleons, whereas, since the nuclear force is in fact very strong, strong interactions were expected. Yukawa's particle also was

eventually discovered and was called the **pi meson.** It exists in three charge states, positive, neutral, and negative ($+$, 0, $-$). The meson that was discovered first is now called the **mu meson** or the **muon**; it exists only in two charge states, positive and negative. It has properties very similar to those of the electron and is sometimes referred to, in fact, as a heavy electron.

Neither the mu meson nor the pi meson is stable. Except for the neutral pi meson, which can decay directly into two gamma particles, their decays involve a new particle, the neutrino, to which we shall give some attention in succeeding paragraphs. Considerable energy is required for the production of these new particles, owing to their relatively great rest masses. (You cannot produce a pi meson, for example, unless you can convert at least 140 Mev of energy into particle mass.)

With the discovery of the positron and the mesons the family of elementary particles was growing rapidly, and confidence in the new quantum field theory was becoming firmly established.

59.4. The Neutrino

The **neutrino** is such a remarkable particle that it deserves a section to itself. It was postulated as early as 1931 but was not detected until 1956. It interacts so weakly with matter that neutrinos produced at the center of the sun escape from the surface at once. The sun, for all its mass of 10^{30} kilograms, is transparent to neutrinos. Yet the neutrino plays an essential role in nature, and it gives, in many ways, remarkable evidence of its existence.

The beta decay of a nucleus, referred to before, is analogous to the decay of a free neutron: a beta particle (negative or positive) is emitted from the nucleus, the charge of which changes ($\pm$) by one unit. This is equivalent to the decay of a nuclear neutron into a proton (β^- emission) or of a proton into a neutron (β^+ emission). Both are possible within the nucleus.

Now, if a nucleus at rest emits a single particle, the nucleus must recoil so that the total linear momentum is conserved. If M is the mass of the nucleus and m the mass of the electron, and if $\mathbf{v}$ is the velocity of the emitted beta particle and $\mathbf{V}$ the recoil velocity of the nucleus, the equation

$$M\mathbf{V} + m\mathbf{v} = 0 \qquad [59.5$$

must be valid. In addition, energy must be conserved. Let E be the internal energy of the nucleus before beta decay and E' the internal energy after beta decay. Then

$$\tfrac{1}{2}mv^2 + \tfrac{1}{2}MV^2 = E - E' \qquad [59.6$$

These two equations are sufficient to determine $\mathbf{v}$ and $\mathbf{V}$ uniquely if $E - E'$ is fixed. One expects, therefore, that beta particles will be emitted with a single energy from any given nucleus, and that a beta particle's momentum will be in the same line as the recoil momentum. Neither of these things is true.

One finds, instead, that beta particles may be emitted with any energy, from zero up to the maximum of $E - E'$, and that the beta particle's momentum vector is, in general, not on the same line as the recoil-momentum vector.

Immediately upon observation of these curious results, two different suppositions were made. Many physicists chose to argue that momentum and energy were not conserved in beta decay. These conservation laws are, after all, strictly empirical in nature, and, they argued, one must always be prepared to give them up when observations require it.

But another postulate was possible. Wolfgang Pauli suggested, in 1931, that another particle might be emitted simultaneously with the electron in beta decay. Such a particle had to have certain very definite properties: it had to be able to carry both momentum and energy, but, since some of the observed electrons were observed to carry energy roughly equal to $E - E'$, the new particle would have to have a very small rest mass. As experiments were made more and more precise, the upper limit on the mass of the new particle (named the neutrino by Fermi) became lower and lower. Today it is believed that the neutrino, like the photon, has zero rest mass.

Earlier, in 1925, it had been discovered by S. A. Goudsmit and G. E. Uhlenbeck that electrons have still another measurable property—intrinsic-spin angular momentum. In order to conserve spin angular momentum in beta decay, it was necessary to postulate that the neutrino must carry this quantity as well; but, since no trace of the neutrino could be found in cloud chambers or on photographic plates, it had to be electrically neutral.

The existence of the invisible, non-detectable neutrino was either a tantalizing fact or an interesting fiction. Only by direct detection of the neutrino could the issue be resolved, and this was not accomplished until 1956.

A brief description of a current experiment to detect neutrinos from the sun will perhaps illustrate the difficulties. The detector is placed deep in a mine, with several miles of earth above it. It consists of a tank of 100,000 gallons of a compound rich in chlorine (perchlorethylene). At such a depth, almost no particles of the cosmic radiation are left, for even very energetic cosmic-ray particles are filtered out by a mile of rock. The natural radioactivity of the walls of the mine is of low energy, and the detector can be shielded against it with sufficient lead.

If now a neutrino is absorbed by a chlorine nucleus, it induces an inverse beta decay, changing the chlorine to an isotope of argon. Despite the very intense, continuous shower of solar neutrinos presumably taking place, only a few such absorptions occur in a day. Very slight amounts of argon can nevertheless be detected by a sensitive modern chemical technique. In this way it is hoped to make direct observations of neutrinos from the sun. Success could usher in a new period of "neutrino astronomy."

It was discovered in 1964, as a further complication, that there are two different kinds of neutrinos, one associated with electrons (positive or negative), the other with the mu meson, or muon. Thus, in neutron decay,

$$n \longrightarrow p + e + \nu_e \qquad [59.7$$

This neutrino is an **electron neutrino**, given the symbol ν_e. Decay of a pi meson, or pion, involves the **muon neutrino**, given the symbol ν_μ:

$$\pi^+ \longrightarrow \mu^+ + \nu_\mu$$

Both neutrinos are involved in the decay of a muon:

$$\mu^- \longrightarrow e^- + \nu_e + \nu_\mu$$

Although the neutrino saved the conservation laws of energy, linear momentum, and spin, it invalidated a fourth law, that associated with an observable quantity called **parity**. Physicists had long been convinced that no natural phenomenon would show an intrinsic right-handedness or left-handedness, that the image of the world, as viewed, for example, in a mirror, represents another possible state of the world.

We saw earlier that the neutrino has an intrinsic-spin angular momentum. According to quantum mechanics, there are only two possible ways for it to spin, once its direction of motion is known: it can spin (Fig. 59.2) in a clockwise or in a counterclockwise direction when viewed along the direction of motion. It was believed that these two states (which are mirror images of each other) were equally likely, and the term **conservation of parity** was used to describe the maintenance of this symmetry.

In 1956, in order to explain a dilemma related to still another meson called the K meson, two Chinese-American physicists, C. N. Yang and T. D. Lee, suggested that perhaps, in interactions involving the neutrino, conservation of parity was not satisfied. They proposed an experiment on the beta decay of magnetically aligned Co^{60} nuclei, and the experiment was promptly carried out by C. S. Wu and her collaborators at Columbia University. The result was remarkable: parity was not conserved. The conclusion was that neutrinos are intrinsically left-handed; that is, their spin and their linear momentum are related to each other as in Figure 59.2.B.

It is perhaps too early to assess the importance of this result for theoretical physics, but its fundamental nature is not in doubt. Much, in any case, remains to be learned about the elusive neutrino; since the final results are not yet in, we must be content with this brief discussion.

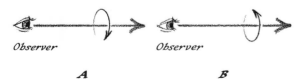

FIG. 59.2. *The two possible orientations of the neutrino's spin.*

59.5. Survey of the Elementary Particles

Many of the elementary particles can be produced by collisions. In low-energy collisions, nuclear particles behave somewhat like impenetrable spheres. Figure 59.3 shows schematically (A) a low-energy collision between two protons and (B) a high-energy collision between two protons, which results in a cascade of nuclear particles. Figure 59.4 is an artist's attempt to picture the effect of a magnetic field on protons with spin. Many nuclear events can be made visible in a bubble chamber. A very sophisticated bubble-chamber experiment using antiprotons as the bombarding particles resulted in the photograph reproduced in Figure 59.5. It is discussed in Problem 59.1. It is apparent, from the wealth of nuclear fragments produced in such collisions, that we have opened the door to a vast field of research whose results may unlock more of the secrets of the nucleus.

The present state of our knowledge of particles is tabulated in Table 59.1. One thing the table does not reveal, however: the intimate relation between particles and fields (not necessarily electromagnetic fields).

I conclude by summarizing the important points made, explicitly or implicitly, so far: (1) Fields and particles always come together, and the field has at least as much importance as the particle; if there is a field, a particle is associated with it. (2) Attempts to consider particles apart from their associated fields have led to dilemmas that we can avoid by considering the particle and the field simultaneously. (3) Experiments have demonstrated the existence of the field particles. (4) The number of source particles (for example, the electron, the proton, and the neutron associated with the meson field) obeys a conservation law; the number of field particles (for example, the photon and those of the meson family) does not obey any such law. (5) The long-range inverse-square law of force implies a massless field particle. The short-range nuclear forces imply field particles with rest mass greater than zero.

A fact I have not stressed enough, perhaps, is that many of the particles are extremely short-lived. (See Table 59.1.) Think for a moment what

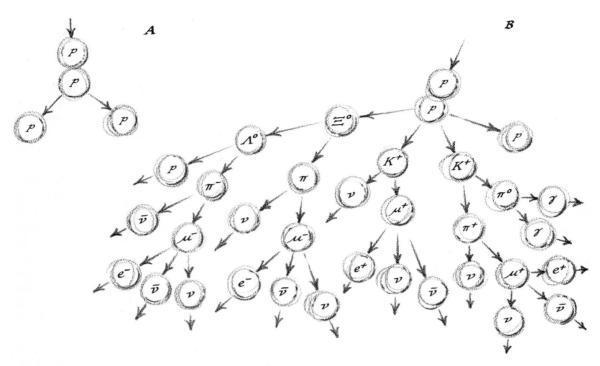

FIG. 59.3. (*A*) *Low-energy collision between two protons, which behave somewhat like elastic spheres.* (*B*) *High-energy collision between two protons; the result is a wealth of nuclear particles (compare Table 59.1), only a few of which are nucleons.*

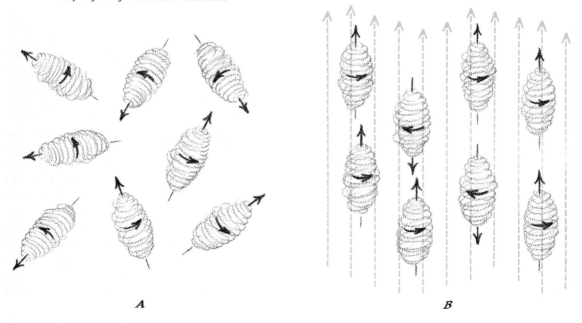

FIG. 59.4. (*A*) *Spinning protons, oriented at random.* (*The event is invisible; this is an artist's conception based upon instructions given to him by a physicist.*) (*B*) *The spinning protons lined up by a steady magnetic field (dashed green lines); those pointing down are in an excited spin state.*

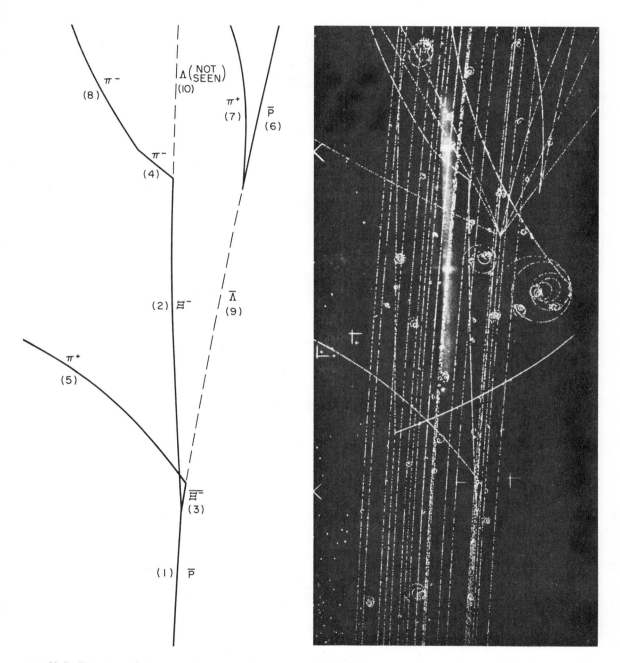

FIG. 59.5. *Event in which an antiproton and a proton yield a Xi-minus particle and an anti-Xi-minus particle. The sketch is labeled according to the most likely mass interpretation of each observed track. [Photograph (taken in the 20-inch liquid-hydrogen bubble chamber) and sketch from the Brookhaven National Laboratory.]*

TABLE 59.1

The Known Elementary Particles

Family	Particle	Symbol	Mass	Spin	Electric Charge	Antiparticle	No. of Distinct Particles	Average Lifetime (seconds)	Typical Mode of Decay
	photon	γ (gamma ray)	0	1	neutral	same particle	1	infinite	—
	graviton	—	0	2	neutral	same particle	1	infinite	—
electron family	electron neutrino	ν_e	0	½	neutral	$\bar{\nu}_e$	2	infinite 10^{21} years	—
	electron	e^-	1	½	negative	e^+ (positron)	2	infinite	—
muon family	muon neutrino	ν_μ	0(?)	½	neutral	$\bar{\nu}_\mu$	2	infinite	—
	muon	μ^-	206.77	½	negative	μ^+	2	2.212×10^{-6}	$\mu^- \longrightarrow e^- + \bar{\nu}_e + \nu_\mu$
mesons	pion	π^+	273.2	0	positive	π^- same as the particles	3	2.55×10^{-8}	$\pi^+ \longrightarrow \mu^+ + \nu_\mu$
		π^-	273.2	0	negative	π^+		2.55×10^{-8}	$\pi^- \longrightarrow \mu^- + \bar{\nu}_\mu$
		π^0	264.2	0	neutral	π^0		1.9×10^{-16}	$\pi^0 \longrightarrow \gamma + \gamma$
	kaon	K^+	966.6	0	positive	$\overline{K^+}$ (negative)	4	1.22×10^{-8}	$K^+ \longrightarrow \pi^+ + \pi^0$
		K^0	974	0	neutral	$\overline{K^0}$		1.00×10^{-10} and^a 6×10^{-8}	$K^0 \longrightarrow \pi^+ + \pi^-$
baryons	nucleon	p (proton)	1,836.12	½	positive	$\bar{p}$ (negative)	4	infinite 10^{28} years	—
		n (neutron)	1,838.65	½	neutral	$\bar{n}$		1,013	$n \longrightarrow p + e^- + \bar{\nu}_e$
	lambda	Λ^0	2,182.8	½	neutral	$\overline{\Lambda^0}$	2	2.51×10^{-10}	$\Lambda^0 \longrightarrow p + \pi^-$
	sigma	Σ^+	2,327.7	½	positive	$\overline{\Sigma^+}$ (negative)	6	8.1×10^{-11}	$\Sigma^+ \longrightarrow n + \pi^+$
		Σ^-	2,340.5	½	negative	$\overline{\Sigma^-}$ (positive)		1.6×10^{-10}	$\Sigma^- \longrightarrow n + \pi^-$
		Σ^0	2,332	½	neutral	$\overline{\Sigma^0}$		about 10^{-20}	$\Sigma^0 \longrightarrow \Lambda^0 + \gamma$
	xi	Ξ^-	2,580	½	negative	$\overline{\Xi^-}$ (positive)	4	1.3×10^{-10}	$\Xi^- \longrightarrow \Lambda^0 + \pi^-$
		Ξ^0	2,570	½	neutral	$\overline{\Xi^0}$		about 10^{-10}	$\Xi^0 \longrightarrow \Lambda^0 + \pi^0$

^{a} The K^0 meson has two different lifetimes. All other particles have only one.

33

10^{-16} second means. To observe these particles at all is a great experimental triumph.

It has recently become apparent that the family of elementary particles can be grouped, according to their properties, into several sub-families.

The **baryons** are, as the Greek word *barys* (meaning heavy) indicates, heavy particles. The proton is the lightest member of the group. All have antiparticles. All obey a conservation law: in any interaction the number of baryons minus the number of antibaryons is constant. All but the proton are, nevertheless, unstable. Conservation of baryons seems to be a fundamental law of physics; no violation of it has yet been observed.

The **mesons**—the pions (pi mesons) and the kaons (*K* mesons)—form a second group. Intermediate in mass, they do not obey a number-conservation law. Their lifetimes are a bit longer than those of the baryons.

The **mu meson** is no longer considered a proper member of the meson family. In much recent literature its name has been shortened, perhaps to emphasize this fact, to **muon**. The muon is very similar to the electron in all but mass. It is possible, in fact, to form a pseudo hydrogen atom with a negative muon in place of the electron. Some interesting experiments have been carried out on this atom, which is called muonium (see Prob. 51.4). The positive muon is the antiparticle of the negative muon. The muon group also includes the muon neutrino.

The electron family consists of the electron and its antiparticle, the positron, and also the electron neutrino. The neutrinos and the positron, whose masses are of the same order as, or of a lesser order than, that of the electron, as well as the electron itself, are sometimes put into the broad class of **leptons** (from the Greek *leptos*, meaning small).

Thirty-three elementary particles are known at this writing. An investigation that began in a rather simple way has burgeoned into something that is, at the moment, quite unmanageable. We are still in the preliminary stage of our understanding of the elementary particles. The theoretical calculations that worked so well in electromagnetic problems turn out to be inappropriate for mesonic problems, for the nuclear force is strong, whereas the electromagnetic force is normally weak, the gravitational force feeble.

We still do not know the answers to the following basic questions: Are there more particles to be discovered? What particles are possible in nature? Are there rules, analogous to those imposed by the laws of relativity, that will enable us to predict the entire family of fundamental particles? What are the mutual relations of the particles within each family, and what is the relation of one family to another?

Is there, in fact, an order underlying these phenomena? The physicist can only hope so. A very considerable effort has been made so far, but the answer is not known at this writing.

Problem

59.1. Fig. 59.5 includes a bubble-chamber photograph showing the short track (3) of an anti-Xi-minus particle after it was produced by a collision of an antiproton (track 1) with a proton (at the vertex near track 3). In the article announcing this discovery the little circles at the right, halfway up the picture, are not mentioned. Using equation 38.20, try to guess their origin.

APPENDIX A

Significant Figures and Powers of Ten

We can learn something about how to write numerical results by analyzing the way the speed of light is printed in the text (§ 1.3):

$$c = (2.997925 \pm 0.000003) \times 10^8 \text{ m/sec}$$

The 0.000003 is a refined measure of precision, which I shall not discuss here. Let us write simply

$$c = 2.997925 \times 10^8 \text{ m/sec}$$

Observe first that the number is followed by a physical unit—m/sec in this case. Almost all numerical results in physics are incorrect if they do not exhibit units. (One exception is specific gravity, which is the ratio of like quantities and hence a pure number.) Notice next the 10 raised to a positive integral power. We can, as we shall see, gain precision as well as economy and convenience in computation by using both positive and negative integral powers of 10. Next, observe that the number is written so that the decimal point falls to the right of the first digit. This is the usual procedure. Seven digits appear in the number, and they are all said to be significant figures. What does that mean?

A significant figure is a digit that is believed to be nearer the actual value than any other. Zeros are significant if any other digit precedes them in the number, otherwise not; there are, for example, three significant figures in 307, 4.50, 100, 5.00, and 0.00790. If, when we measure the length of an object with a rod capable of measuring to a tenth of a millimeter, the result is three meters, twenty-eight centimeters, and no millimeters, this is to be recorded either as 3.2800 m, as 328.00 cm, or as 3,280.0 mm, but not as 3.28 m, 328 cm, or 3,280 mm. Using powers of 10, we should write 3.2800 m as 3.2800×10^2 cm or as 3.2800×10^3 mm.

If we wanted to indicate that a value lies between 2,400 and 2,600 and therefore has two significant figures, we should be wrong in writing it as 2,500, for this, by implying four significant figures, would indicate that the value lies between 2,499 and 2,501. To avoid ambiguity, we should write 2,500 as 2.5×10^3 if it has two significant figures and as 2.50×10^3 if it has three.

You can avoid a great deal of unnecessary calculation by employing the following rules for dropping non-significant, or meaningless, figures.

1. In casting off non-significant figures, if the value of the rejected figures is greater than a half unit in the last place retained, increase the last digit retained by 1; if it is less than half, leave this digit unchanged; if it equals half a unit, increase the digit by 1 half of the time only—for example, when the last retained digit is even. If you round off to three significant figures, for example,

432,678 becomes	4.33×10^5
432,497 "	4.32×10^5
432,500 "	4.33×10^5
435,500 "	4.35×10^5

2. Drop, from sums and differences, every digit that falls under a non-significant digit in any of the quantities to be added or subtracted. The sum of 216.526, 16.5, and 2.054 is 235.1, not 235.080.

3. Retain, in products or quotients, the number of significant figures that appear in the least accurately known quantity involved. The product of 314.428 and 11.0 is 3.46×10^3, not 3,458.7080.

That the method of writing significant figures with powers of 10 can be applied to very small numbers is shown by the charge on the electron, $e = 1.60210 \times 10^{-19}$ coulomb. To illustrate the convenience of using numbers expressed in powers of 10, let us evaluate $N_A e/c$ to slide-rule accuracy. We first write

$$\frac{6.023 \times 10^{23} \times 1.602 \times 10^{-19}}{2.998 \times 10^8} \quad \frac{\text{coul}}{\text{gram-mole} \times \text{m/sec}}$$

Instead of multiplying the two numbers in the numerator first and then dividing by the denominator, we find that it is simpler on the slide rule to divide one of the numbers in the numerator by the denominator and then to multiply this result by the other factor in the numerator. We have carried four digits in each number, but the slide rule is capable of handling, at most, three significant figures for numbers near 9.0 and four for numbers near 1.0. The result is 3.22.

The powers of 10 obey the well-known simple laws:

$$10^p \times 10^q = 10^{p+q}$$
$$10^p \div 10^q = 10^{p-q}$$

Hence

$$10^{23} \times 10^{-19} \div 10^8 = 10^{23} \times 10^{-19} \times 10^{-8}$$
$$= 10^{23} \times 10^{-27} = 10^{-4}$$

The final result is therefore

$$\frac{N_A e}{c} = 3.22 \times 10^{-4} \frac{\text{coul}}{\text{gram-mole} \times \text{m/sec}}$$

Notice that, when numbers are written as indicated, each number, except the powers of 10, lies between 1 and 10, making rapid placement of the decimal point possible. The powers of 10 are handled separately. The units, also handled separately, are treated as algebraic quantities; for example, "per gram-mole" is the equivalent of

$$\text{gram-mole}^{-1}$$

or

$$\frac{1}{\text{gram-mole}}$$

APPENDIX B

How to Use the Front Flyleaf

The relations between units shown on the front flyleaf may be used in the conversion of units from one system to another. There are various systematic procedures for doing this.

To convert 60 miles per hour, for example, to feet per second, we can proceed as follows:

$$1 \frac{\text{mi}}{\text{h}} = 1.467 \frac{\text{ft}}{\text{sec}}$$

We multiply both sides by 60:

$$60 \frac{\text{mi}}{\text{h}} = 60 \times 1.467 \frac{\text{ft}}{\text{sec}}$$
$$= 88.02 \frac{\text{ft}}{\text{sec}}$$

The result is uncertain only in the last digit.

Another method depends upon converting miles to feet and hours to seconds as follows:

$$1 \text{ mi} = 5{,}280 \text{ ft}$$
$$1 \text{ h} = 3{,}600 \text{ sec}$$

Replacing the abbreviation "mi" by "5,280 ft" and the abbreviation "h" by "3,600 sec," we write

$$60 \frac{\text{mi}}{\text{h}} = 60 \frac{5{,}280 \text{ ft}}{3{,}600 \text{ sec}}$$

We may readily perform the indicated multiplications and divisions on a slide rule (after simplifying the expression by cancellation if we wish). The result is

$$60 \frac{\text{mi}}{\text{h}} = 88 \frac{\text{ft}}{\text{sec}}$$

Since the conversion factors were exact, the result is exact.

The table on the flyleaf is, of necessity, condensed. It does not, for example, express 1 gallon in terms of liters. The following procedure illustrates how to evaluate this and similar quantities.

$$1 \text{ liter} = 0.2642 \text{ gal}$$

We divide both sides by 0.2642:

$$\frac{1}{0.2642} \text{ liters} = \frac{0.2642}{0.2642} \text{ gal} = 1 \text{ gal}$$
$$1 \text{ gal} = 3.785 \text{ liters}$$

APPENDIX C

Miscellaneous Terrestrial Data

STP = standard temperature and pressure = 0°C at 1 atm. The value of g given here, the *standard value*, which is used for barometric corrections, legal weights, etc., was adopted by the International Committee on Weights and Measures in 1901; it approximates that determined at sea level at 45° latitude. The solar constant is the mean solar intensity at the surface of the earth.

Acceleration of gravity, g	9.80665 m/sec^2 = 32.1740 ft/sec^2
Density of dry air at STP	1.293 kg/m^3
Equatorial radius of earth	6.378×10^6 m = $3{,}963$ mi
Magnetic dipole moment of earth	6.4×10^{21} amp-m^2
Magnetic induction, B, of earth (at Washington, D.C.)	5.7×10^{-5} weber/m^2
Mass of earth	5.983×10^{24} kg
Mean angular speed of rotation of earth	7.29×10^{-5} rad/sec
Mean density of earth	$5{,}522$ kg/m^3
Mean orbital speed of earth	$29{,}770$ m/sec = 18.50 mi/sec
Mean total solar radiation	3.92×10^{26} W
Polar radius of earth	6.357×10^6 m = $3{,}950$ mi
Solar constant	495 W/m^2 = 0.709 cal/cm^2-min ? 1340
Speed of sound in dry air at STP	331.4 m/sec
Standard atmosphere	1.013×10^5 nt/m^2 = 14.70 lb/in.^{2}
Volume of earth	1.087×10^{21} m^3 = 3.838×10^{22} ft^3

APPENDIX D

Data on the Solar System†

Body	Relative Mass	Distance from Sun km	Distance from Sun miles	Sidereal Period (Days)	Mean Specific Gravity	Diameter km	Diameter miles	Acceleration Due to Gravity at Surface cm/sec²	ft/sec²
Sun	329,390				1.42	1,390,600	864,100	27,440	900.3
Mercury	0.0549	58×10⁶	36.0×10⁶	87.97	5.61	5,140	3,194	392	12.9
Venus	0.8073	108×10⁶	67.1×10⁶	244.70	5.16	12,620	7,842	882	28.9
Earth	1.0000	149×10⁶	92.9×10⁶	365.26	5.52	12,756	7,926	980	32.2
Mars	0.1065	228×10⁶	141.7×10⁶	686.98	3.95	6,860	4,263	392	12.9
Jupiter	314.5	778×10⁶	483.4×10⁶	4,332.59	1.34	143,600	89,229	2,646	86.8
Saturn	94.07	1,426×10⁶	886.1×10⁶	10,759.20	0.69	120,600	74,937	1,176	38.6
Uranus	14.40	2,869×10⁶	1,782.7×10⁶	30,685.93	1.36	53,400	33,181	980	32.2
Neptune	16.72	4,495×10⁶	2,793.1×10⁶	60,187.64	1.30	49,700	30,882	980	32.2
Pluto	1.0 ?	5,900×10⁶	3,666.1×10⁶	90,885					
Moon	0.01228	ᵃ 38×10⁴	ᵃ 23.9×10⁴	27.32	3.36	3,476	2,159.9	167	5.47

ᵃ Distance from earth.

† From the *Handbook of Chemistry and Physics*, Chemical Rubber Publishing Company.

APPENDIX E

Natural Trigonometric Functions

See § 14.3 for definitions of sine and cosine. The tangent function ($\tan \theta = y/x$) obeys the relation $\tan \theta = \sin \theta / \cos \theta$. The cotangent function ($\cot \theta = x/y$) obeys the relation $\cot \theta = \cos \theta / \sin \theta$.

Degrees	Radians	Sine	Tangent	Cotangent	Cosine		
0	.0000	.0000	.0000	———	1.0000	1.5708	90
1	.0175	.0175	.0175	57.290	.9998	1.5533	89
2	.0349	.0349	.0349	28.636	.9994	1.5359	88
3	.0524	.0523	.0524	19.081	.9986	1.5184	87
4	.0698	.0698	.0699	14.301	.9976	1.5010	86
5	.0873	.0872	.0875	11.430	.9962	1.4835	85
6	.1047	.1045	.1051	9.5144	.9945	1.4661	84
7	.1222	.1219	.1228	8.1443	.9925	1.4486	83
8	.1396	.1392	.1405	7.1154	.9903	1.4312	82
9	.1571	.1564	.1584	6.3138	.9877	1.4137	81
10	.1745	.1737	.1763	5.6713	.9848	1.3963	80
11	.1920	.1908	.1944	5.1446	.9816	1.3788	79
12	.2094	.2079	.2126	4.7046	.9781	1.3614	78
13	.2269	.2249	.2309	4.3315	.9744	1.3439	77
14	.2443	.2419	.2493	4.0108	.9703	1.3265	76
15	.2618	.2588	.2679	3.7321	.9659	1.3090	75
16	.2793	.2756	.2867	3.4874	.9613	1.2915	74
17	.2967	.2924	.3057	3.2709	.9563	1.2741	73
18	.3142	.3090	.3249	3.0777	.9511	1.2566	72
19	.3316	.3256	.3443	2.9042	.9455	1.2392	71
20	.3491	.3420	.3640	2.7475	.9397	1.2217	70
21	.3665	.3584	.3839	2.6051	.9336	1.2043	69
22	.3840	.3746	.4040	2.4751	.9272	1.1868	68
23	.4014	.3907	.4245	2.3559	.9205	1.1694	67
24	.4189	.4067	.4452	2.2460	.9135	1.1519	66
25	.4363	.4226	.4663	2.1445	.9063	1.1345	65
26	.4538	.4384	.4877	2.0503	.8988	1.1170	64
27	.4712	.4540	.5095	1.9626	.8910	1.0996	63
28	.4887	.4695	.5317	1.8807	.8829	1.0821	62
29	.5061	.4848	.5543	1.8040	.8746	1.0647	61
30	.5236	.5000	.5774	1.7321	.8660	1.0472	60
31	.5411	.5150	.6009	1.6643	.8572	1.0297	59
32	.5585	.5299	.6249	1.6003	.8481	1.0123	58
33	.5760	.5446	.6494	1.5399	.8387	.9948	57
34	.5934	.5592	.6745	1.4826	.8290	.9774	56
35	.6109	.5736	.7002	1.4281	.8192	.9599	55
36	.6283	.5878	.7265	1.3764	.8090	.9425	54
37	.6458	.6018	.7535	1.3270	.7986	.9250	53
38	.6632	.6157	.7813	1.2799	.7880	.9076	52
39	.6807	.6293	.8098	1.2349	.7771	.8901	51
40	.6981	.6428	.8391	1.1918	.7660	.8727	50
41	.7156	.6561	.8693	1.1504	.7547	.8552	49
42	.7330	.6691	.9004	1.1106	.7431	.8378	48
43	.7505	.6820	.9325	1.0724	.7314	.8203	47
44	.7679	.6947	.9657	1.0355	.7193	.8029	46
45	.7854	.7071	1.0000	1.0000	.7071	.7854	45
		Cosine	Cotangent	Tangent	Sine	Radians	Degrees

APPENDIX F

Table of Relative Atomic Weights (1961)

Based on the Atomic Mass $_6C^{12} = 12$

The atomic weights given here are those of elements found in nature, without artificial alteration of their isotopic composition, and of natural mixtures that do not include radiogenic isotopes.

Name	Symbol	Atomic Number	Atomic Weight	Name	Symbol	Atomic Number	Atomic Weight
Actinium	Ac	89	——	Mercury	Hg	80	200.59
Aluminum	Al	13	26.9815	Molybdenum	Mo	42	95.94
Americium	Am	95	——	Neodymium	Nd	60	144.24
Antimony	Sb	51	121.75	Neon	Ne	10	20.183
Argon	Ar	18	39.948	Neptunium	Np	93	——
Arsenic	As	33	74.9216	Nickel	Ni	28	58.71
Astatine	At	85	——	Niobium	Nb	41	92.906
Barium	Ba	56	137.34	Nitrogen	N	7	14.0067
Berkelium	Bk	97	——	Nobelium	No	102	——
Beryllium	Be	4	9.0122	Osmium	Os	76	190.2
Bismuth	Bi	83	208.980	Oxygen	O	8	15.9994[a]
Boron	B	5	10.811[a]	Palladium	Pd	46	106.4
Bromine	Br	35	79.909[b]	Phosphorus	P	15	30.9738
Cadmium	Cd	48	112.40	Platinum	Pt	78	195.09
Cesium	Cs	55	132.905	Plutonium	Pu	94	——
Calcium	Ca	20	40.08	Polonium	Po	84	——
Californium	Cf	98	——	Potassium	K	19	39.102
Carbon	C	6	12.01115[a]	Praseodymium	Pr	59	140.907
Cerium	Ce	58	140.12	Promethium	Pm	61	——
Chlorine	Cl	17	35.453[b]	Protactinium	Pa	91	——
Chromium	Cr	24	51.996[b]	Radium	Ra	88	——
Cobalt	Co	27	58.9332	Radon	Rn	86	——
Copper	Cu	29	63.54	Rhenium	Re	75	186.2
Curium	Cm	96	——	Rhodium	Rh	45	102.905
Dysprosium	Dy	66	162.50	Rubidium	Rb	37	85.47
Einsteinium	Es	99	——	Ruthenium	Ru	44	101.07
Erbium	Er	68	167.26	Samarium	Sm	62	150.35
Europium	Eu	63	151.96	Scandium	Sc	21	44.956
Fermium	Fm	100	——	Selenium	Se	34	78.96
Fluorine	F	9	18.9984	Silicon	Si	14	28.086[a]
Francium	Fr	87	——	Silver	Ag	47	107.870[b]
Gadolinium	Gd	64	157.25	Sodium	Na	11	22.9898
Gallium	Ga	31	69.72	Strontium	Sr	38	87.62
Germanium	Ge	32	72.59	Sulphur	S	16	32.064[a]
Gold	Au	79	196.967	Tantalum	Ta	73	180.948
Hafnium	Hf	72	178.49	Technetium	Tc	43	——
Helium	He	2	4.0026	Tellurium	Te	52	127.60
Holmium	Ho	67	164.930	Terbium	Tb	65	158.924
Hydrogen	H	1	1.00797[a]	Thallium	Tl	81	204.37
Indium	In	49	114.82	Thorium	Th	90	232.038
Iodine	I	53	126.9044	Thulium	Tm	69	168.934
Iridium	Ir	77	192.2	Tin	Sn	50	118.69
Iron	Fe	26	55.847[b]	Titanium	Ti	22	47.90
Krypton	Kr	36	83.80	Tungsten	W	74	183.85
Lanthanum	La	57	138.91	Uranium	U	92	238.03
Lead	Pb	82	207.19	Vanadium	V	23	50.942
Lithium	Li	3	6.939	Xenon	Xe	54	131.30
Lutetium	Lu	71	174.97	Ytterbium	Yb	70	173.04
Magnesium	Mg	12	24.312	Yttrium	Y	39	88.905
Manganese	Mn	25	54.9380	Zinc	Zn	30	65.37
Mendelevium	Md	101	——	Zirconium	Zr	40	91.22

[a] Known to be variable because of their natural variations in isotopic composition. The ranges observed are:

Boron	±0.003	Oxygen	±0.0001
Carbon	±0.00005	Silicon	±0.001
Hydrogen	±0.00001	Sulphur	±0.003

[b] Believed to have the following experimental uncertainties:

Bromine	±0.002	Iron	±0.003
Chlorine	±0.001	Silver	±0.003
Chromium	±0.001		

APPENDIX G

Physical Quantities: Symbols, Dimensions, and Units

All dimensions and units are in the meter-kilogram-second-coulomb (rationalized) system (called simply the MKS system in the text). You can find the primary units by reading meters for L, kilograms for M, seconds for T, and coulombs for Q. The symbols are those used in the text. See also the list of abbreviations and symbols on pages xvii–xviii.

Quantity	Symbol	Dimensions	Derived Units
Acceleration	**a**	LT^{-2}	meters/second²
Angular acceleration	α	T^{-2}	radians/second²
Angular displacement	θ	——	radian
Angular momentum	**L**	ML^2T^{-1}	kilogram-meters²/second
Angular velocity	ω	T^{-1}	radians/second
Area	A	L^2	meter²
Capacitance	C	$M^{-1}L^{-2}T^2Q^2$	farad
Charge	q	Q	coulomb
Conductivity	σ	$M^{-1}L^{-3}TQ^2$	ohm-meter⁻¹
Current (electrons)	i	$T^{-1}Q$	ampere
Current density	**j**	$L^{-2}T^{-1}Q$	amperes/meter²
Density, mass	ρ	ML^{-3}	kilograms/meter³
Displacement	**r, d**	L	meter
Electric dipole moment	**p**	$L^{-1}Q$	coulomb-meter
Electric field intensity	**E**	$MLT^{-2}Q^{-1}$	volts/meter
Electric flux	Φ_E	$ML^3T^{-2}Q^{-1}$	volt-meter
Electric potential	V	$ML^2T^{-2}Q^{-1}$	volt
Electromotive force	$\mathcal{E}$	$ML^2T^{-2}Q^{-1}$	volt
Energy: heat	Q	ML^2T^{-2}	joule
internal	U	ML^2T^{-2}	joule
kinetic	K	ML^2T^{-2}	joule
potential	U	ML^2T^{-2}	joule
total	E	ML^2T^{-2}	joule
Force	**F**	MLT^{-2}	newton
Frequency	ν	T^{-1}	cycles/second
Gravitational field intensity	γ	LT^{-2}	newtons/kilogram
Inductance	L	ML^2Q^{-2}	henry
Length	L, l	L	meter
Linear momentum	**p**	MLT^{-1}	kilogram-meters/second
Magnetic dipole moment	μ	$L^2T^{-1}Q$	ampere-meter²
Magnetic flux	Φ_B	$ML^2T^{-1}Q^{-1}$	weber
Magnetic induction	**B**	$MT^{-1}Q^{-1}$	webers/meter²
Mass	m	M	kilogram
Period	T	T	second
Power	P	ML^2T^{-3}	watt
Pressure	P	$ML^{-1}T^{-2}$	newtons/meter²
Resistance	R	$ML^2T^{-1}Q^{-2}$	ohm
Resistivity	ρ	$ML^3T^{-1}Q^{-2}$	ohm-meter
Rotational inertia	I	ML^2	kilogram-meter²
Temperature	T	——	degree Kelvin
Time	t	T	second
Torque	τ	ML^2T^{-2}	newton-meter
Velocity	**v**	LT^{-1}	meters/second
Voltage	V	$ML^2T^{-2}Q^{-1}$	volt
Volume	V	L^3	meter³
Wavelength	λ	L	meter
Work	W	ML^2T^{-2}	joule

Index

References are to pages and conform to the following scheme:

245   text of either column or of both columns
245.t   table
245&t   text and table
245.fn   footnote
245&fn   text and footnote
245   term in boldface, accompanied by definition or other explanation

1 BTU, 1.055107 × 10³ joules

1 watt-hour, 3.6 × 10³ joules by def.

1 Horsepower-hour; 2.6845 × 10⁶ joules

1 kilowatt-hour

Energy of 1 ton of TNT; 4.2 × 10⁹ joules

Energy equiv. of 1 gram of matter;
9 × 10¹³ joules

WATT-HOURS

10⁻¹ 10⁰ 10¹ 10² 10³ 10⁴ 10⁵ 10⁶ 10⁷ 10⁸ 10⁹ 10¹⁰ 10¹¹ 10¹² 10¹³ 10¹⁴ 10¹⁵ 10¹⁶ 10¹⁷ 10¹⁸ 10¹⁹ 10²⁰

10² 10³ 10⁴ 10⁵ 10⁶ 10⁷ 10⁸ 10⁹ 10¹⁰ 10¹¹ 10¹² 10¹³ 10¹⁴ 10¹⁵ 10¹⁶ 10¹⁷ 10¹⁸ 10¹⁹ 10²⁰ 10²¹ 10²² 10²³ 10²⁴ 10²⁵ 10²⁶ 10²⁷ 10²⁸ 10²⁹ 10³⁰ 10³¹ 10³² 10³³ 10³⁴ 10³⁵

WEIGHT OF TNT EXPLODED

Megatons — Kilotons — Tons

10⁻⁶ 10⁻⁵ 10⁻⁴ 10⁻³ 10⁻² 10⁻¹ 10⁰ 10¹ 10² 10³ 10⁴ 10⁵ 10⁶ 10⁷ 10⁸ 10⁹

MASS OF MATTER CONVERTED

Metric tons — Grams

10⁻⁶ 10⁻⁵ 10⁻⁴ 10⁻³ 10⁻² 10⁻¹ 10⁰ 10¹ 10² 10³ 10⁴ 10⁵ 10⁶ 10⁷ 10⁸ 10⁹ 10¹⁰ 10¹¹ 10¹² 10¹³ 10¹⁴ 10¹⁵

Muzzle energy of cartridges, ball
(30 cal., M2 – 151 gm bullet, 2800 fps, 2626 ft-lb.)

Energy released in complete
fission of 1 kg of U-235;
approx. 20 kt of TNT

Burning 7,000 tons of coal

Solar energy per day on 2 sq miles

Daily output of Hoover Dam

Moderate rain (¼") over Wash., D.C.

World use of energy in 1950;
10²⁰ joules. Energy of
a strong earthquake

Earth's daily receipt of solar
energy; 1.49 × 10²² joules

Moon's kinetic energy of
translation in its orbit;
3.63 × 10²⁸ joules

Sun's daily output of energy;
3 × 10³² joules

Earth's kinetic energy of
translation in its orbit,
2.57 × 10³⁴ joules